NATURAL PRODUCTS
Related to
PHENANTHRENE

by
LOUIS F. FIESER and MARY FIESER
Department of Chemistry
Harvard University

THIRD EDITION
of the Monograph Previously Entitled
CHEMISTRY OF NATURAL PRODUCTS
RELATED TO PHENANTHRENE
By L. F. Fieser

REINHOLD PUBLISHING CORPORATION
430 Park Avenue, New York 22, N.Y.
1949

Copyright 1949 by

REINHOLD PUBLISHING CORPORATION

———

Second Printing, 1952
Third Printing, 1955

Lithoprinted in U.S.A.
EDWARDS BROTHERS, INC.
ANN ARBOR, MICHIGAN

GENERAL INTRODUCTION

American Chemical Society's Series of
Chemical Monographs

By arrangement with the Interallied Conference of Pure and Applied Chemistry, which met in London and Brussels in July, 1919, the American Chemical Society was to undertake the production and publication of Scientific and Technologic Monographs on chemical subjects. At the same time it was agreed that the National Research Council, in cooperation with the American Chemical Society and the American Physical Society, should undertake the production and publication of Critical Tables of Chemical and Physical Constants. The American Chemical Society and the National Research Council mutually agreed to care for these two fields of chemical progress. The American Chemical Society named as Trustees, to make the necessary arrangements of the publication of the Monographs, Charles L. Parsons, secretary of the Society, Washington, D. C.; the late John E. Teeple, then treasurer of the Society, New York; and the late Professor Gellert Alleman of Swarthmore College. The Trustees arranged for the publication of the ACS Series of (a) Scientific and (b) Technological Monographs by the Chemical Catalog Company, Inc. (Reinhold Publishing Corporation, successor) of New York.

The Council of the American Chemical Society, acting through its Committee on National Policy, appointed editors (the present list of whom appears at the close of this sketch) to select authors of competent authority in their respective fields and to consider critically the manuscripts submitted.

The first Monograph of the Series appeared in 1921. After twenty-three years of experience certain modifications of general policy were indicated. In the beginning there still remained from the preceding five decades a distinct though arbitrary differentiation between so-called "pure science" publications and technologic or applied science literature. By 1944 this differentiation was fast becoming nebulous. Research in private enterprise had grown apace and not a little of it was pursued on the frontiers of knowledge. Furthermore, most workers in the sciences were coming to see the artificiality of the separation. The methods of both groups of workers are the same. They employ the same instrumentalities, and frankly recognize that their objectives are common, namely, the

iii

search for new knowledge for the service of man. The officers of the Society therefore combined the two editorial Boards in a single Board of twelve representative members.

Also in the beginning of the Series, it seemed expedient to construe rather broadly the definition of a Monograph. Needs of workers had to be recognized. Consequently among the first hundred Monographs appeared works in the form of treatises covering in some instances rather broad areas. Because such necessary works do not now want for publishers, it is considered advisable to hew more strictly to the line of the Monograph character, which means more complete and critical treatment of relatively restricted areas, and, where a broader field needs coverage, to subdivide it into logical subareas. The prodigious expansion of new knowledge makes such a change desirable.

These Monographs are intended to serve two principal purposes: first, to make available to chemists a thorough treatment of a selected area in form usable by persons working in more or less unrelated fields to the end that they may correlate their own work with a larger area of physical science discipline; second, to stimulate further research in the specific field treated. To implement this purpose the authors of Monographs are expected to give extended references to the literature. Where the literature is of such volume that a complete bibliography is impracticable, the authors are expected to append a list of references critically selected on the basis of their relative importance and significance.

PREFACE

Since the publication of the first and second editions of this book in 1936 and 1937, vast strides have been made in the development of the chemistry of naturally occurring phenanthrene derivatives, particularly the steroids. By 1937 most of the important physiologically active steroid hormones and vitamins had been isolated and their structures established, but very little was known of the stereochemical configurations. Extensive studies of the stereochemistry of the steroids have culminated only in recent years and months in the complete solution of all the major problems concerned. This, therefore, is a particularly appropriate time to present a revision in which we hope we have accurately interpreted a highly confused and voluminous literature in the light of present-day stereochemical evidence that seems secure. We are greatly indebted to Dr. Richard B. Turner for contributing a chapter devoted to a critical survey of the stereochemical evidence.

The advances of the past decade have been so generally extensive that the present edition represents a complete overhauling of the original book, with retention merely of a few of the sections describing events in the history of the science that have become classic. There is so much new material that some of the earlier chapters and sections have been omitted: chemistry of phenanthrene (not pertinent to the chemistry of hydrophenanthrene derivatives), carcinogenic hydrocarbons (not now indicated to be of probable natural occurrence), triterpenoid sapogenins (related to picene rather than to phenanthrene, problem of structure still unsettled). Even so, the book is twice as long as before.

Achievements in partial and total synthesis have been prominent in recent researches in the field, and we have endeavored to review all synthetic work that has afforded actual natural products or close relatives. In accordance with a further trend, considerable prominence has been given to the use of spectrographic and optical rotational data in the determination of structure or configuration. Unfortunately the empirical importance and possible future theoretical significance of accurately determined optical constants are only now gaining general recognition, and some of the current reports of constants are regrettably incomplete. It is now apparent that determination of the specific rotations of a parent compound and several of its derivatives under comparable conditions should be as obligatory as determination of the melting points, and that absorption characteristics should be reported in terms of the numerical values of the maxima and extinction coefficients rather than in a graph that cannot be interpreted with ease or accuracy. Failure to state the solvent used in the determination is a source of confusion, since a change from one common solvent to another may shift the absorption maximum of an α,β-unsaturated ketone by as much as 11 mμ. The effect of solvent on the absorption characteristics of steroid polyenes awaits investigation.

The preparation of this book has involved consideration of the merits and general applicability of various alternate schemes of steroid nomenclature. In making a choice of names, not only for use in this book but for presentation as a studied recommendation for general adoption, we have followed the principle of seeking maximum simplicity and systematization with minimum departure from current usage. Our proposals are as follows:

(1) Configurations at nuclear centers of asymmetry relative to the molecule as a whole are designated β if the orientation of the hydrogen atom or a substituent corresponds to that of the two angular methyl groups and the side chain (written above the plane of the ring system; full line), α if the reverse (below the plane; dotted line). The Greek letters are written without parentheses. A purely arbitrary trivial index is written with quotation marks.

(2) The configuration at C_{20} relative to that at C_{17} and the whole ring system is designated α or β according to the convention given on page 412.

(3) Arbitrary, non-relative configurations in the side chain are designated a and b. Cholesterol and the bile acids are described as compounds of 20b-orientation and ergosterol and stigmasterol as 20b,24b-compounds. Campesterol can be described as 24a-methylcholesterol. The substance arbitrarily named pregnane-3α,20α-diol by Marker is called pregnane-3α,20a-diol. The arbitrary, non-relative designations provisionally applied in one series imply no correspondence to those in another.

(4) Where a substance can be regarded as derived from either of two natural or typical compounds, the choice should be guided by the consideration of practical chemical relationship.

Examples. The products of the Oppenauer oxidation of cholesterol and of the dehydrohalogenation of cholestene hydrochloride are called cholestenone and Δ^4-cholestene, not coprostenone and coprostene as suggested by Rosenheim and King. The two oxides of cholesterol are described adequately by their trivial names; thus cholesterol β-oxide is preferred to 5β,6β-oxidocoprostanol-3β. The classical name coprosterol violates the spirit of the principle and can be replaced by coprostanol.

(5) A substance differing from a natural or typical steroid in the configuration at an asymmetric center other than C_5 but similarly involving the orientation of a carbon-carbon or carbon-hydrogen linkage is ordinarily described as an iso compound.

Examples. 17-Isoallopregnane,17-iso-R diacetate, 5-isoandrosterone (instead of the cumbersome 3α-hydroxyetiocholanone-17), 8-isoestradiol (not 8-epiestradiol), 8-isoestrone (not 8-epiestrone), d-14-isoequilenin (d-isoequilenin), 17-isoetioallocholanic acid, 14-iso-17-isoetioallocholanic acid.

Exceptions. Where convenient descriptive trivial names are available, these are preferred: lumisterol, lumiestrone.

(6) The configuration at C_5 in most instances is indicated by classical names: cholestane, allocholanic acid, allopregnane, androstane; coprostane, cholanic acid, pregnane, etiocholane or 5-isoandrostane. The prefix allo is reserved for indication of the configuration at C_5. The name allocholesterol is discarded and replaced by Δ^4-cholestenol-3β.

(7) The configuration of the carbon skeleton should be indicated by the basic name and not merely implied by the orientation of hydroxyl groups.

Example. The compound listed in the literature as allopregnanetriol-3β,17β,20β is actually a 17-isoallopregnanetriol and should, we think, be so named.

(8) A substance differing from a natural or typical steroid with respect to the steric orientation of a hydroxyl group is ordinarily described as an epi compound.

Examples. Epicholestanol, epitestosterone, 11-epicorticosterone, epiestradiol (the natural hormone can now be called estradiol-17β), 16-epiestriol (not isoestriol-A), 17-epiestriol (third isomer), 12-epietiodesoxycholic acid, epiandrosterone (for isoandrosterone), dehydroepiandrosterone (for dehydroisoandrosterone).

(9) Where the basic name indicates the orientation of one of two groups at C_{17}, an index defining the orientation of the other group is unnecessary. However, the inclusion of the second index may be desirable in instances where an index has recently been reversed, for emphasis, or in order to avoid the implication that the orientation of one of several hydroxyl groups is unknown.

Examples. 17α-Hydroxyprogesterone (natural), 17β-hydroxy-17-isoprogesterone (synthetic series), 17α-ethinyltestosterone (OH in testosterone is β-oriented), 17α-vinyltestosterone (the trivial name is both more convenient and more informative than 17-iso-$\Delta^{4,20}$-pregnandiene-17β-ol-3-one), estradiol-17β, cholestane-3β,5α,6β-triol.

(10) The position of a double bond, or of a pair of formerly unsaturated carbon atoms, is indicated by a number that locates the first atom of the pair. The number of the second atom is also given if it is not the next higher number. Alternate methods of writing the numbers are given in the examples.

Examples. $\Delta^{7,14}$-Cholestadiene, or cholestadiene-(7,14); $\Delta^{7,9(11)}$-cholestadiene, or cholestadiene-(7,9:11); $\Delta^{8(14)}$-cholestenol-3β, or cholestene-

(8:14)-ol-3β; 22-dihydroergosterol; 5-dihydroergosterol ("α"-dihydroergosterol); 7-dehydrocholesterol; 6-dehydroestrone (Δ⁶-isoequilin); 9-anhydrocorticosterone; 9-dehydroprogesterone.

We have aimed to present in this book reasonably complete topical discussions of a selection of the main points of interest in the chemistry of the phenanthrene derivatives, and to survey more briefly the biochemistry and pharmacology of the compounds. A few papers, even recent ones, have been omitted because the material does not fall within the framework of the present arrangement of topics. The literature coverage extends to journals received to November 1, 1948, and some later ones. In view of the current congestion of some of the chemical journals, we are particularly grateful to several colleagues in this country and in England and Switzerland for their courtesy in sending us advance copies of manuscripts, some of which are still in press.

We are greatly indebted to several American colleagues for critical comments on parts of the book, and we wish to acknowledge the very full and helpful cooperation in this respect extended by Dr. C. W. Shoppee and Dr. D. H. R. Barton in England. Dr. Turner, in addition to his own contribution, has given us constant guidance in the interpretation of the literature. Our collaborators Dr. Minlon-Huang and Dr. S. Rajagopalan kindly read and checked the entire manuscript. We are indebted to Eleanore Blaisdell for the drawing of our Siamese cat Georgie and to Dr. Frederic C. Chang for the Chinese seals.

Louis F. Fieser
Mary Fieser

Cambridge, Massachusetts
November 17, 1948

Contents

CHAPTER I

CHAPTER II

CHAPTER III

CHAPTER V

CHAPTER VI

CHAPTER VII

Chapter I
Quinones; Morphine and Related Alkaloids

Of the many phenanthrene and hydrophenanthrene derivatives that occur in nature, the majority are steroids or diterpenes. These substances have ring systems that are either exclusively or predominantly alicyclic and they contain angular methyl groups that prevent full aromatization under conditions short of drastic degradations that expel the obstructing groups. The compounds included in the present chapter all contain at least one benzenoid ring and they are easily convertible into fully aromatic products.

QUINONE PIGMENTS

Thelephoric Acid. Zopf[1] in 1889 isolated from a fungus of the species *Thelephora* the pigment thelephoric acid, which forms beautiful crystals closely resembling potassium permanganate in color and luster. The pigment was not analyzed or characterized until 1930, when Kögl and coworkers[2] collected 1.5 g. of the substance and by application of ingenious methods of micromanipulation conducted degradations that completely elucidated the structure. The pigment is very sparingly soluble in the usual solvents but can be extracted readily with hot pyridine. Analyses and tests established that the substance is a quinone having three hydroxyl and two carboxyl groups. Zinc-dust distillation of 125 mg. of the triacetate in 8 – 10 mg. portions gave 12 mg. of a hydrocarbon $C_{18}H_{14}$ (II); 9.8 mg. of this substance on permanganate oxidation consumed 9.3 atoms of oxygen and afforded 4 mg. of an acid that yielded phenanthrene on decarboxylation and proved to be identical with 2-phenanthroic acid (III). The intermediate hydrocarbon must, therefore, have a butadiene side chain (calculated oxygen consumption, 10 atoms). The point of attachment of the side chain and the position of the carboxyl group were revealed by the results of oxidation of the hexahydro derivative IV with alkaline hydrogen peroxide, for one product was identified as adipic acid (VI). A second acid, also obtained by a similar oxidation of thelephoric acid, was identified as 5-hydroxytrimellitic acid (V); the identification of this degradation product establishes the structure of one of the terminal rings. The location of the two hydroxyl groups in the ring carrying the side chain was deter-

[1] Zopf, *Bot. Zeitung*, 69 (1889).
[2] Kögl, Erxleben and Jänecke, *Ann.*, **482**, 105 (1930).

mined in another degradation. The hydroxyl groups were protected by acetylation, and chromic acid oxidation then opened the quinone grouping

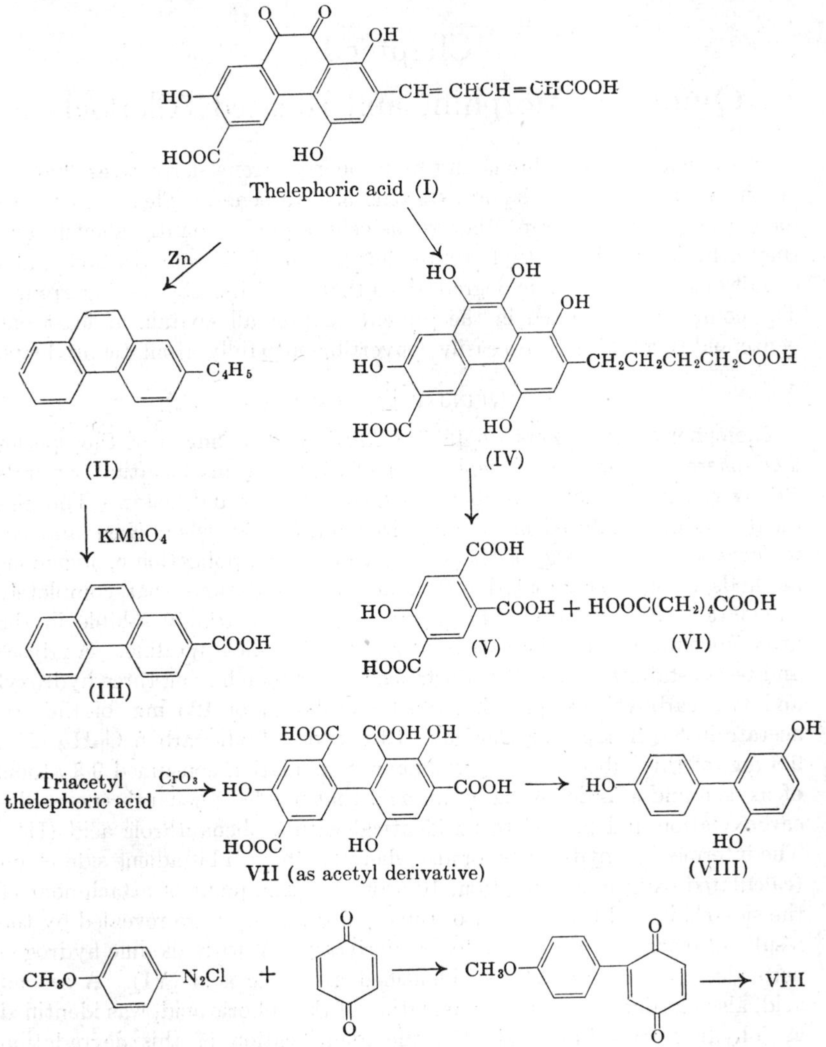
OH
HO
HOOC
HO
-CH= CHCH=CHCOOH
Thelephoric acid (I)
Zn
C_4H_5
(II)
$KMnO_4$
COOH
(III)
HO
OH
OH
$CH_2CH_2CH_2CH_2COOH$
HOOC
HO
(IV)
COOH
HO
COOH + $HOOC(CH_2)_4COOH$
HOOC
(V)
(VI)
Triacetyl thelephoric acid
CrO_3
HOOC
COOH OH
COOH
VII (as acetyl derivative)
(VIII)
CH_3O
N_2Cl
O
VIII

to give a diphenic acid derivative (VII). This on decarboxylation afforded a trihydroxydiphenyl identified as having the structure VIII by synthesis: benzoquinone was arylated with *p*-methoxybenzenediazonium chloride and the product reduced and demethylated.

A pigment identical with thelephoric acid was isolated by Asahina[3] from *Lobaria retigera* Trév.

Tanshinones. From the Chinese purgative drug tanshen derived from the root of *Salvia miltiorrhiza*, Nakao and Fukushima[1] isolated the following pigments:

> Tanshinone I, $C_{18}H_{12}O_3$, m.p. 231°, H_2SO_4-blue
> Tanshinone II, $C_{19}H_{18}O_3$, m.p. 216°, H_2SO_4-green
> Tanshinone III, $C_{19}H_{20}O_3$, m.p. 182°, H_2SO_4-brown

The first pigment was characterized as an *o*-quinone by the preparation of a quinoxaline derivative and by reductive acetylation to a hydroquinone diacetate. v. Wessely[2] confirmed the empirical formula assigned by the Japanese investigators and characterized further a degradation product resulting from oxidation of the pigment with potassium permanganate,[1] chromic acid,[2] or hydrogen peroxide.[3] The product was identified by synthesis as 1-methylnaphthalene-5,6-dicarboxylic acid (or anhydride). One of two C-methyl groups found present by Kuhn-Roth analysis was thereby identified; the other must be present in a methylfurano side ring (one of the three oxygens is inert). The evidence presented by v. Wessely indicates that the pigment must have one of four possible structures, of which IX is one. A second structure is that in which the furano ring is inverted;

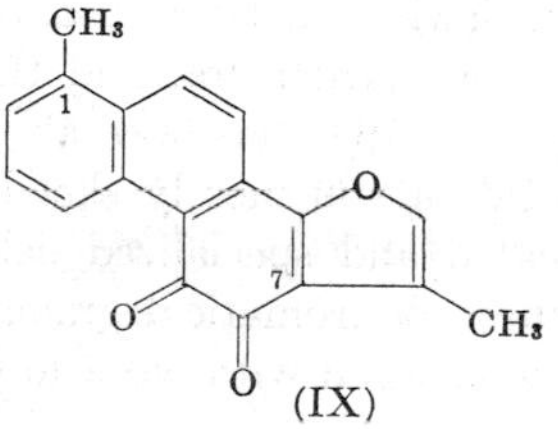

(IX) 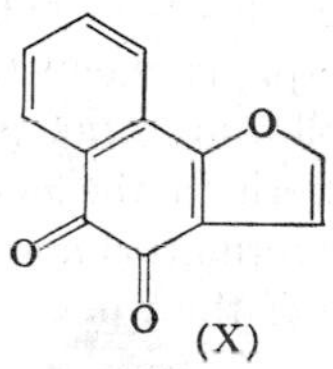   (X)

in the third and fourth formulas the positions of the quinone oxygens and the side ring are reversed. Tanshinone II has been less extensively characterized,[3] but appears to contain the same β-methylfuranoquinone grouping. Todd[4] has commented that formula IX for tanshinone I is the most attractive possibility because the carbon skeleton corresponds to that of a number of diterpenoid resin acids and derived products, for example retene (1-methyl-7-isopropylphenanthrene; Chapter II). Further arguments are

[3] Asahina and Shibata, *Ber.*, **72**, 1531 (1939).

[1] Nakao and Fukushima, *J. Pharm. Soc. Japan*, **54**, 844 (1934) [*Chem. Zentr.*, I, 580 (1935)].

[2] v. Wessely and Wang, *Ber.*, **73**, 19 (1940); v. Wessely and Bauer, *ibid.*, **75**, 617 (1942).

[3] v. Wessely and Lauterbach, *Ber.*, **75**, 958 (1942).

[4] Todd, *Ann. Repts.*, **38**, 209 (1941).

that the structure IX resembles the structures of the natural naphtho-
quinone pigments lapachol and lomatiol and that the color reactions of
tanshinone I and tanshinone II in concentrated sulfuric acid resemble those
of Hooker's synthetic furano-1,2-naphthoquinone X:[5] green, turning to
blue on absorption of moisture from the air.

Xylindein, $C_{34}H_{26}O_{11}$. The green coloration that frequently appears on
rotting branches of beech, oak, and birch is due to the pigment xylindein
of the fungus *Peziza aeruginosa.*[6] Kögl and co-workers[7] isolated the green
pigment in a pure condition by extraction with warm phenol; they characterized the substance extensively but did not elucidate the structure.
The substance contains two hydroxyl and two carboxyl groups and appears
to be a quinone but not an *o*-quinone. Phenanthrene was identified as a
product of the zinc dust distillation of an acetyl ester derivative.

OPIUM ALKALOIDS

Some of the known alkaloids that contain a hydrophenanthrene nucleus
are related to sterols or to diterpenes and will be surveyed in a later chapter.
Several others—the alkaloids of the morphine group, companion alkaloids
of opium, and structurally related alkaloids from other sources—constitute
a separate group having certain distinctive structural characteristics, and
these are the subject of the present review. The larger part of the chemical
investigations in this field belong to an earlier era, and the voluminous
literature of morphine chemistry prior to 1932 has been ably surveyed by
Small.[1] The following brief presentation will merely sketch the outlines
of the earlier work in the complicated and specialized field, with some
emphasis on the formation and synthesis of aromatic degradation products,
since this phase of the work has a connection with work in other fields to
be considered.

The Morphine Group. Most prominent among the opium alkaloids are
morphine (Gr. *Morpheus*), codeine (Gr. *kodeia*, poppy head) and thebaine
(from a kind of Egyptian opium produced at Thebes). On account of the
analgesic, hypnotic, and calmative properties of the alkaloids or their
conversion products, these drugs have become indispensable in modern
medical practice in spite of their dangerous habit-forming character, and
the chemistry of the three related compounds has been the subject of active

[5] Hooker and Steyermark, *J. Am. Chem. Soc.*, **58**, 1202 (1936).

[6] Rommier, *Compt. rend.*, **66**, 108 (1868); Liebermann, *Ber.*, **7**, 1102 (1874).

[7] Kögl and Taeuffenbach, *Ann.*, **445**, 170 (1925); Kögl and Erxleben, *ibid.*, **484**, 65 (1930).

[1] L. F. Small, "Chemistry of the Opium Alkaloids," U. S. Treasury Department, Supplement No. 103 to the Public Health Reports (1932).

investigation since the discovery of morphine by Sertürner in 1803.   Nearly twenty different morphine formulas have received consideration and, on account of the peculiarly intricate nature of the problem, rigid proof of the structure of the alkaloid is still incomplete and the synthesis is a problem of the future.   The formula of Gulland and Robinson,[2] however, although not proved beyond all question, is generally accepted as the true structure of morphine.   This formula, I, which is conveniently abbreviated as in Ia,

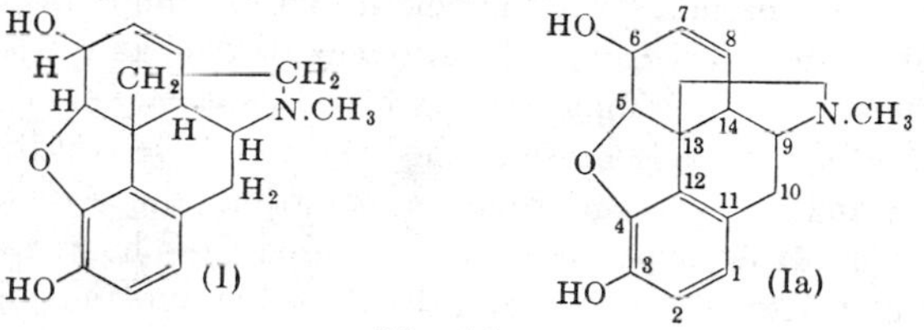

Morphine

represents the alkaloid as a hexahydrophenanthrene derivative having a phenolic hydroxyl group (C_3), a secondary alcoholic group (C_6), an oxide bridge between positions 4 and 5, and an ethanamine chain, —$CH_2CH_2N(CH_3)$—, inserted between positions 9 and 13 and constituting a part of a six-membered heterocyclic ring.

Codeine is the phenolic methyl ether of morphine and can be prepared from this substance by methylation, best with phenyltrimethylammonium

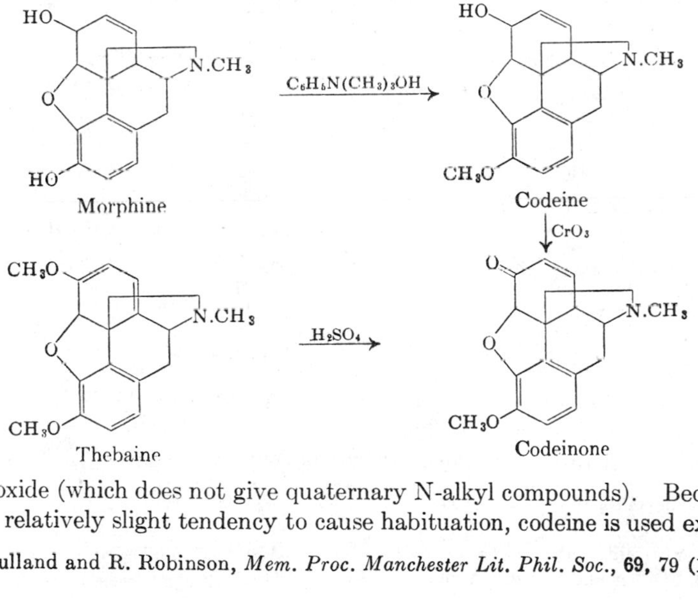

Morphine   Codeine

Thebaine   Codeinone

hydroxide (which does not give quaternary N-alkyl compounds).   Because of its relatively slight tendency to cause habituation, codeine is used exten-

[2] Gulland and R. Robinson, *Mem. Proc. Manchester Lit. Phil. Soc.*, **69**, 79 (1925).

sively in medical practice, and since it is present in opium in smaller amounts (0.2 – 0.8%) than morphine (7 – 15%), the methylation process is one of considerable importance.   Since codeine is a secondary alcohol, it can be oxidized to the ketone codeinone, which forms a connecting link to thebaine.   This alkaloid is the methyl ether of the enolic form of codeinone.   On hydrolysis of the enol ether group with dilute acids, thebaine is transformed into codeinone.   Thebaine contains a reactive diene system and forms addition products with maleic anhydride and with quinones.[3]

Morphol Cleavage.   The formation of phenanthrene as a product of the zinc-dust distillation of morphine was observed as early as 1881,[1] but the use of gentler methods made possible the isolation of substituted phenanthrenes that provided more information regarding the structure of the alkaloid.   When, for example, morphine methiodide is heated with acetic anhydride, the nitrogen is cleaved from the molecule and the chief product is the diacetyl derivative of 3,4-dihydroxyphenanthrene, or morphol.[2] The changes occurring are illustrated by an example of a stepwise Hofmann degradation.   The quaternary base obtained in solution by the action of

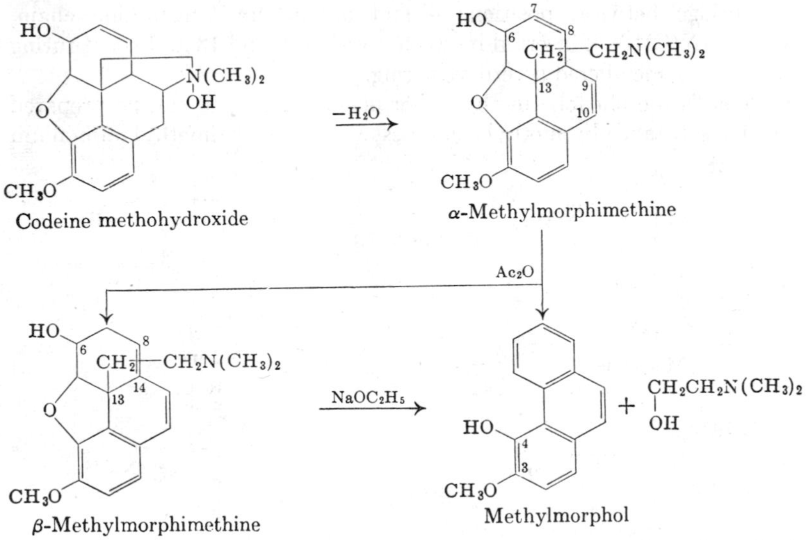

Codeine methohydroxide

$-H_2O \longrightarrow$

α-Methylmorphimethine

Ac$_2$O

NaOC$_2$H$_5$ $\longrightarrow$

β-Methylmorphimethine

Methylmorphol

alkali on codeine methiodide loses the elements of water when the solution is heated and yields α-methylmorphimethine; a double bond is introduced at $C_9 - C_{10}$ on rupture of the nitrogen-containing bridge ring. α-Methyl-

[3] Sandermann, *Ber.*, **71**, 648 (1938); Schöpf, v. Gottberg and Petri, *Ann.*, **536**, 216 (1938).

[1] Vongerichten and Schrötter, *Ann.*, **210**, 396 (1881).

[2] O. Fischer and Vongerichten, *Ber.*, **19**, 792 (1886).

morphimethine on acetolysis yields the cleavage products methylmorphol (the 3-methyl ether of morphol) and ethanoldimethylamine as the acetyl derivatives. A part of the material escapes acetolysis by conversion into the more stable isomeride, β-methylmorphimethine, through the migration of the double bond from $C_7 - C_8$ to $C_8 - C_{14}$. The β-methine can be converted into methylmorphol by vigorous treatment with sodium ethoxide.

The degradations of the methines involve elimination of the angular ethanamine chain with the allylic hydroxyl group and the opening of the oxidic bridge; the complex changes occur easily under the driving force of aromatization. The migration of the isolated double bond of α-methylmorphimethine (λ_{max} 273 mμ, log ϵ 3.9) to a position of conjugation in β-methylmorphimethine (λ_{max} 320 mμ, log ϵ 4.0) is attended not only by a marked displacement of the absorption maximum to the region of longer wave length but also by a change from levo- to dextrorotation amounting to no less than 650°. Whereas dienes of the diterpene and sterol series are reducible by metal combinations only if the two double bonds are contained in a single ring, β-methylmorphimethine can be reduced to a dihydride by sodium and alcohol[3] or by sodium amalgam[4] (70 – 80% yield); the difference is probably attributable to conjugation with the aromatic ring.

When α- or β-methylmorphimethine is submitted to a second Hofmann degradation the oxide ring is retained in the final product. Thus exhaustive methylation of the α-isomer and thermal decomposition of the quaternary base gives methylmorphenol. Normal decomposition with loss of tri-

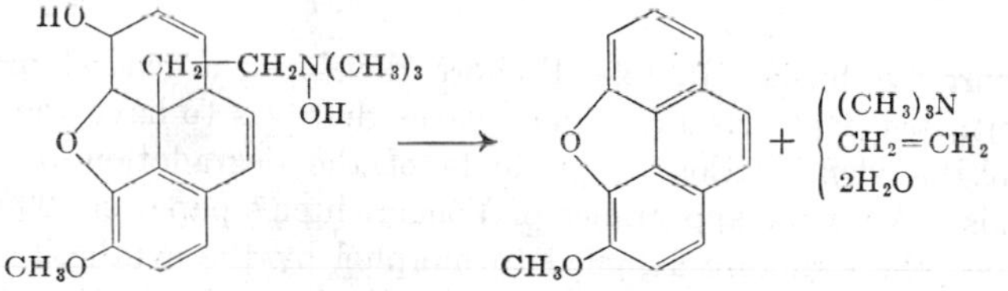

α-Methylmorphimethine methohydroxide   Methylmorphenol

methylamine would give a vinylhydrophenanthrene derivative, but the reaction proceeds beyond this stage and gives a fully aromatic product in which the entire side chain has been eliminated. A procedure for the large-scale preparation of methylmorphenol has been described in which the overall yield from morphine is 65 percent.[5] A minor by-product[6] is a cyclic ether derived from a migration of the transient vinyl group to the

[3] Vongerichten, *Ber.*, **34**, 2722 (1901).

[4] Mosettig, *J. Org. Chem.*, **5**, 401 (1940).

[5] Mosettig and Meitzner, *J. Am. Chem. Soc.*, **56**, 2738 (1934).

[6] Small, *J. Org. Chem.*, **7**, 158 (1942).

5-position; the substance yields pyrene on zinc-dust distillation. The oxide ring of methylmorphenol is more resistant to hydrolysis than the methoxyl group, for methylmorphenol can be hydrolyzed to morphenol by the action of hydrobromic-acetic acid in 50 – 60 percent yield.[4]

Morphol and morphenol, in the form of acetyl derivatives or ethers, were isolated as degradation products by Vongerichten in 1881–1882, but the chemistry of phenanthrene had been so little explored that nearly twenty years elapsed before tentative structures could be suggested.[1, 2, 7] Vongerichten found that diacetylmorphol can be oxidized to a 9,10-phenanthrenequinone and that the product of hydrolysis, morpholquinone (3,4-dihydroxy-9,10-phenanthrenequinone), has affinity for mordanted fabrics resembling that of alizarin; he concluded that the hydroxyl groups of morphol cannot be situated at C_9 or C_{10} and probably occupy ortho positions. Vongerichten then found that morphenol is cleaved by alkaline fusion to a trihydroxyphenanthrene(3,4,5) and can be reduced with sodium and

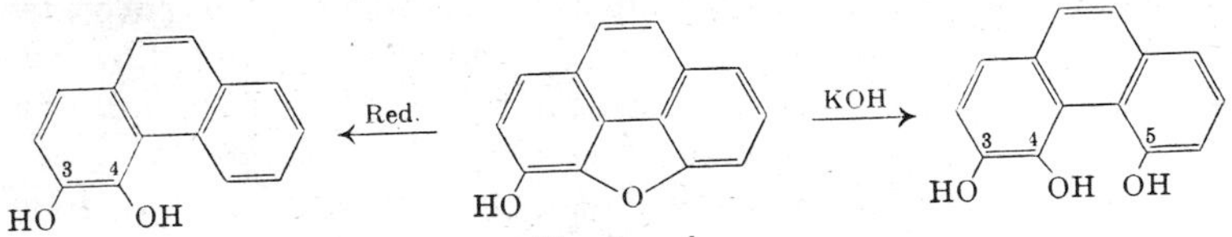

Morphenol

alcohol to morphol. Since the oxide bridge must extend between positions 4 and 5, one of the hydroxyl groups of morphol is at C_4 and the other is probably at C_5.

Pschorr Synthesis. In 1896 Pschorr[1] developed a general method for the syntheses of phenanthrene derivatives that was to have wide application in the identification of products of the degradation of morphine alkaloids. After the appearance of Vongerichten's paper of 1900, Pschorr confirmed the structure assigned to morphol by the synthesis of the dimethyl ether.[2] vic-o-Nitrovanillin methyl ether was condensed with sodium phenylacetate and the resulting α-phenyl-o-nitrocinnamic acid converted through the amine into the diazonium salt, which under catalysis by copper powder loses nitrogen and hydrogen chloride and yields a phenanthrene-9-carboxylic acid. The product of decarboxylation proved to be identical with morphol dimethyl ether. The Pschorr synthesis was further applied[3] to the proof of the structures of methylmorphol and of

[7] Vongerichten and Schrötter, *Ber.*, **15**, 1484 (1882); Vongerichten, *ibid.*, **31**, 2924, 3198 (1898); **33**, 352, 1824 (1900).

[1] Pschorr, *Ber.*, **29**, 496 (1896); Pschorr, Wolfes and Buckow, *ibid.*, **33**, 162 (1900); Pschorr, *ibid.*, **33**, 176 (1900).

[2] Pschorr and Sumuleanu, *Ber.*, **33**, 1810 (1900).

[3] Pschorr and co-workers, *Ber.*, **33**, 1826, 1829 (1900); **34**, 3998 (1901); **35**, 4400, 4412 (1902); **39**, 3106 (1906).

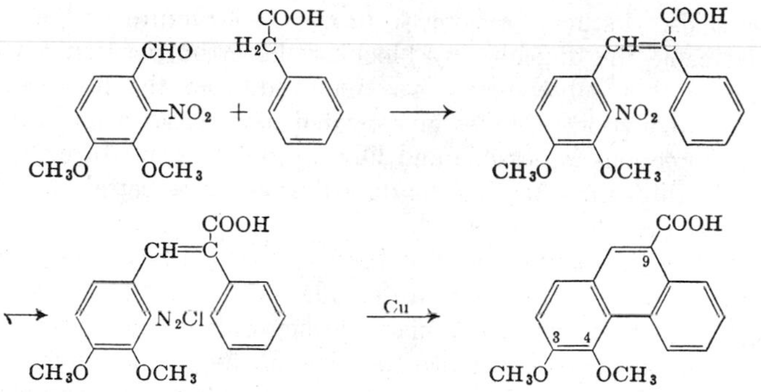

thebaol, a degradation product obtained in the form of the acetyl derivative on acetolysis of thebaine.

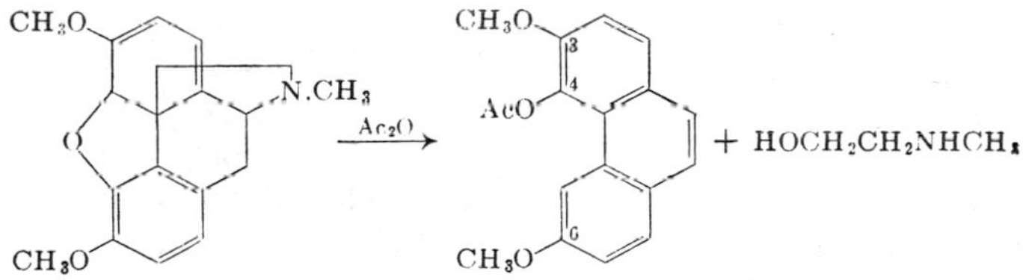

Thebaine   Acetyl thebaol

The *o*-nitroaldehyde component can carry substituents at any of the available positions, and derivatives of phenylacetic acid substituted at the ortho or para position can be employed. With a meta derivative, for

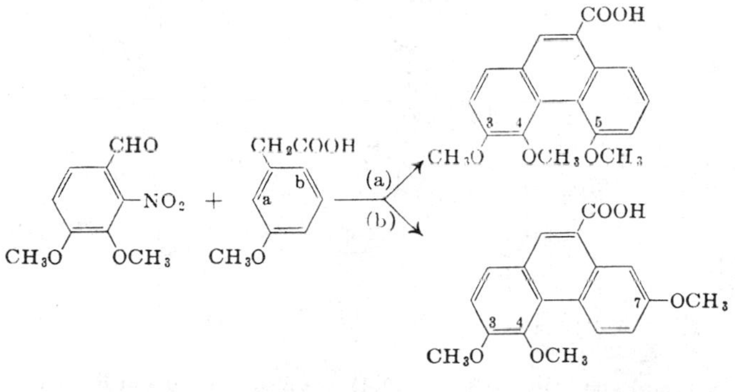

example *m*-methoxyphenylacetic acid, ring closure can and does take place at both ortho positions (*a* and *b*);[4] the components shown in the formulas yielded a mixture of 3,4,5- and 3,4,7-trimethoxyphenanthrene-9-

[4] Pschorr, *Ann.*, **391**, 40 (1912).

carboxylic acids.   Pschorr,[4] seeking to prove the structure of the 3,4,5-isomer, overcame the difficulty by blocking the ortho position *b* with a bromine atom that subsequently was removed from the phenanthrene derivative by reduction.   Mayer investigated other cases where ring closure in two directions is possible and likewise obtained mixtures;[5] he encountered difficulties in effecting the decarboxylation of certain alkylated 9-phenanthroic acids.[6]

A modification introduced by Windaus[7] in the synthesis of 9-methylphenanthrene for comparison with a degradation product from colchicine consisted in employing oxindole in place of phenylacetic acid as the active-methylene component; oxindole also contains, in the position ortho to the side chain, a latent amino group that later is available for the ring closure:

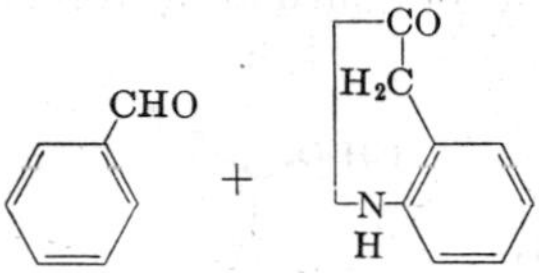

CHO   +   CO H₂C N H

One advantage of the method is that ketones can be employed in the condensation as well as aldehydes and hence that 9-alkylphenanthrenes can be synthesized.   The desired 9-methyl derivative was obtained from the starting materials acetophenone and oxindole.   The condensation product (I) was hydrogenated, and the amine (III) obtained on the hydrolysis of the cyclic amide was converted into the methyldihydrophenanthrene-

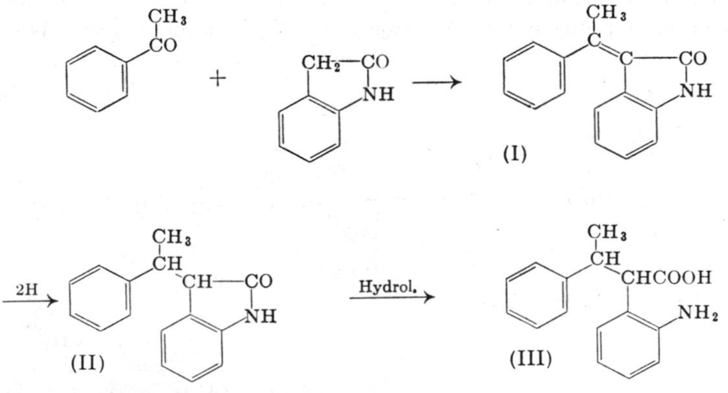

CH₃ CO   +   CH₂—CO NH   →   CH₃ C=C—CO NH   (I)

2H→   CH₃ CH CH—CO NH   (II)   Hydrol.→   CH₃ CH CHCOOH NH₂   (III)

⁵ F. Mayer and Balle, *Ann.*, **403**, 167 (1914); see also Rapson and R. Robinson, *J. Chem. Soc.*, 1533 (1935).
⁶ F. Mayer and English, *Ann.*, **417**, 60 (1918).
⁷ Windaus and Eickel, *Ber.*, **57**, 1871 (1924); Windaus, H. Jensen and A. Schramme, *ibid.*, **57**, 1875 (1924).

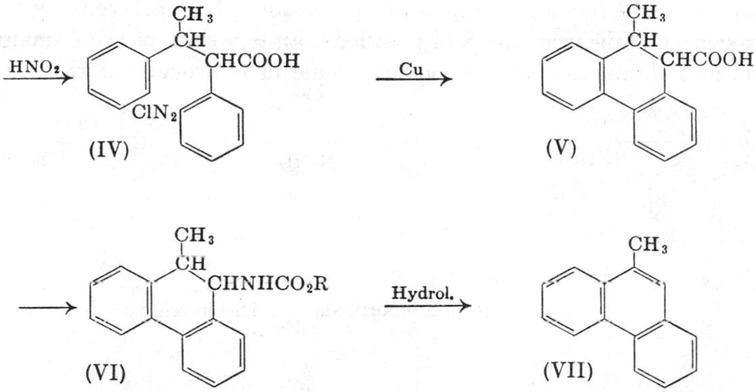

(IV) → (V)

(VI) → (VII)

carboxylic acid V through the diazonium salt (IV). The ester of the acid was converted into the urethan VI, and this was subjected to hydrolysis. An aminodihydrophenanthrene, which would be expected as the primary product, was not observed, for it apparently loses the elements of ammonia at once and gives the hydrocarbon (VII) directly.

Work of Ruggli[8] indicates that one function of the carboxyl group in the ordinary Pschorr synthesis is to control the condensation in such a way that the stilbene derivative has a configuration suitable for subsequent ring closure. Pure o-amino-trans-stilbene gave no phenanthrene on reaction of the diazonium salt with copper, whereas the hydrocarbon was produced in 80 percent yield from o-amino-cis-stilbene. Improvements in the procedure of the Pschorr synthesis and in the preparation of the required arylacetic acids are reported in papers describing the synthesis of alkyl-, alkoxyl-, and bromo-substituted phenanthrenes.[9]

Apomorphine. The Pschorr synthesis not only provided evidence for the positions of the three oxygen atoms and of the methoxyl groups in morphine, codeine, and thebaine, but was of assistance in the elucidation of some of the remarkable rearrangements exhibited by these alkaloids. One is the rearrangement of morphine on acid dehydration into apomorphine (levorotatory). In this reaction water is eliminated, the oxide ring is opened, and the ethanamine chain is displaced from C_{13} to C_8. Small[1] has reported that β-chloromorphide and dichlorodihydrodesoxymorphine (see formulas) can be isolated in early stages of the reaction and has suggested that the trans-

[8] Ruggli and Staub, *Helv. Chim. Acta*, **19**, 1288 (1936); **20**, 37 (1937).

[9] Akin, Stamatoff and Bogert, *J. Am. Chem. Soc.*, **59**, 1268 (1937); Cassaday and Bogert, *ibid.*, **61**, 2461 (1939); Small and Turnbull, *ibid.*, **59**, 1541 (1937); P. Hill and Short, *J. Chem. Soc.*, 260 (1937); Higginbottom, P. Hill and W. F. Short, *ibid.*, 263 (1937).

[1] Small, Faris and Mallonee, *J. Org. Chem.*, **5**, 334 (1940).

formation of the dichloro compound into apomorphine proceeds by loss of hydrogen chloride from the 8,14-positions, an α,γ-shift of the ethanamine chain, and elimination of a second molecule of hydrogen chloride.

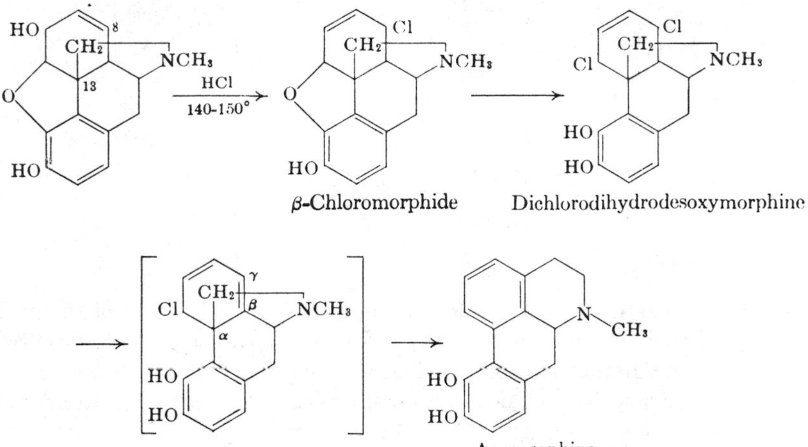

β-Chloromorphide   Dichlorodihydrodesoxymorphine

Apomorphine

Pschorr established the structure of apomorphine as follows.[2] Two Hofmann degradations eliminated nitrogen from the molecule and left a residual vinyl group. For establishment of the position of this group, and hence the new point of attachment of the ethanamine chain, the vinyl compound (I) was oxidized to an acid (II) and this was converted by the Curtius

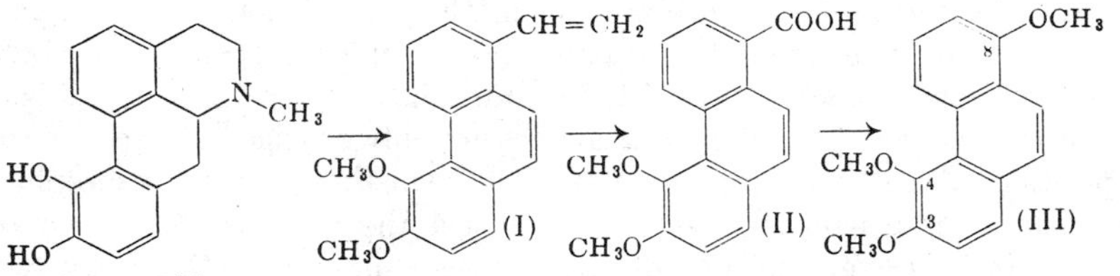

Apomorphine

method through the azide into the urethan and the corresponding amine. Hydrolysis of the diazonium salt and methylation gave an ether identified by synthesis as 3,4,8-trimethoxyphenanthrene (III).

The structure inferred from the degradation was confirmed by a synthesis of *dl*-apomorphine achieved by Späth and Hromatka.[3] 2-Nitrohomoveratroyl chloride was condensed with β-phenylethylamine and the amide IV was cyclized with phosphorus pentoxide in boiling xylene solution

[2] Pschorr and co-workers, *Ber.*, **35**, 4377 (1902); **39**, 3124 (1906); **40**, 1984, 1995, 1998, 2001 (1907).

[3] Späth and Hromatka, *Ber.*, **62**, 325 (1929).

(Bischler-Napieralski reaction) to the dihydroisoquinoline derivative V. This was converted through the methiodide into the methochloride VI, which on treatment with tin and hydrochloride was reduced to a tetra-

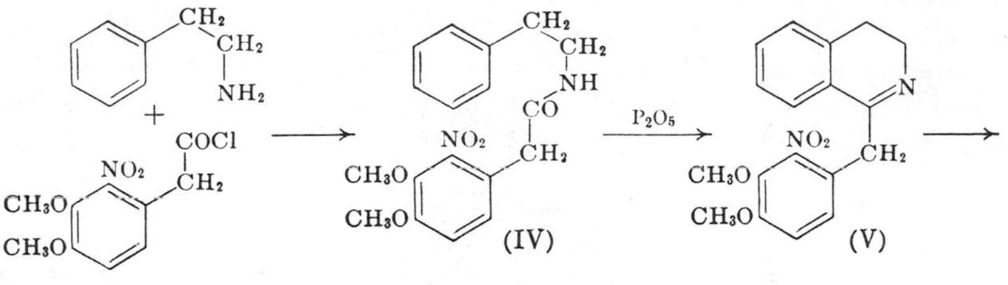

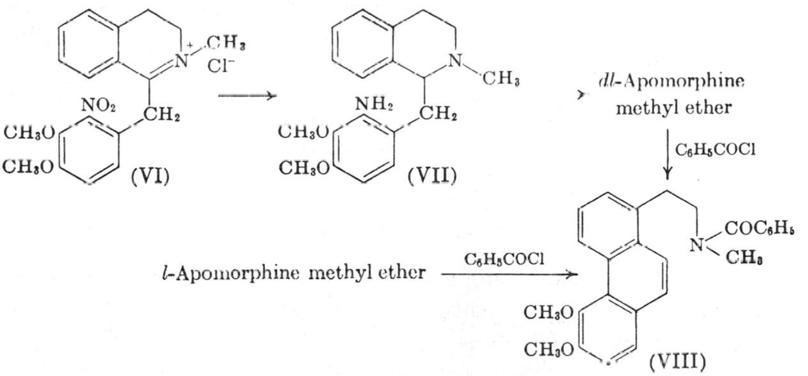

CH₂ CH₂ NH₂ + COCl NO₂ CH₂ CH₃O CH₃O → CH₂ CH₂ NH CO NO₂ CH₂ CH₃O CH₃O (IV) → P₂O₅ → N NO₂ CH₂ CH₃O (V) →

N⁺ CH₃ Cl⁻ NO₂ CH₂ CH₃O CH₃O (VI) → N CH₃ NH₂ CH₂ CH₃O CH₃O (VII) → *dl*-Apomorphine methyl ether ↓ C₆H₅COCl

l-Apomorphine methyl ether → C₆H₅COCl → N COC₆H₅ CH₃ CH₃O CH₃O (VIII)

hydroisoquinoline with simultaneous reduction of the nitro group (VII). The final phase of the synthesis consisted in diazotization and cyclization with copper powder, as in the Pschorr synthesis. Attempts to prepare a sample for comparison with the *dl*-product of synthesis by racemization of the ether from levorotatory apomorphine were unsuccessful, but benzoylation of the *dl*- and *l*-bases opened the heterocyclic ring with destruction of the center of asymmetry and afforded an identical reaction product, VIII. An alternate synthesis claimed by Avenarius and Pschorr[4] must be discounted in the light of evidence presented by Gulland and Virden.[5]

Structure of Morphine. The above investigations had been actively pursued in the belief that knowledge of the structure of apomorphine would clarify the structure of morphine, for the fact of rearrangement was not at the time recognized. A morphine formula corresponding to that eventually

[4] H. Avenarius and Pschorr, *Ber.*, **62**, 321 (1929).

[5] Gulland and Virden, *J. Chem. Soc.*, 1791 (1929); see also Gulland, *Chemistry and Industry*, **16**, 774 (1938).

established for apomorphine was proposed by Pschorr in 1902 but was not long sustained. In apomorphine the terminal carbon atom of the ethan-amine chain is joined to the nucleus at C_8, but in 1907 Knorr and Hörlein[1] discovered evidence that excludes this position as the point of attachment in codeine and hence in morphine. Treatment of codeine with thionyl chloride, phosphorus tri- or pentachloride affords α-chlorocodide, which when heated above the melting point or in an indifferent solvent rearranges to β-chlorocodide by an allylic shift. Each chloride on hydrolysis with

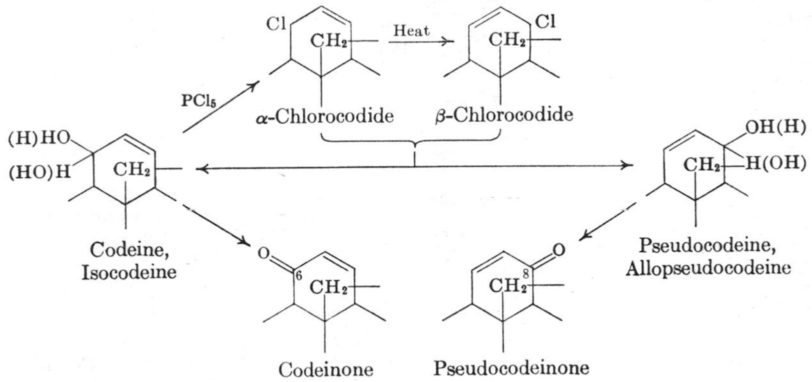

dilute acid yields mixtures containing some or all of four isomeric alcohols. One of these, isocodeine, is identified as the epimer of codeine because it yields codeinone on oxidation. Pseudocodeine and allopseudocodeine con-stitute a further pair of epimers because they are converted by oxidation into a second ketone, pseudocodeinone. The configurational relationships of the four alcohols and the two chlorides have not been clarified. Knorr and Hörlein established that codeinone and pseudocodeinone have carbonyl groups at the 6- and 8-positions, respectively, by degradations to 3,4,6- and 3,4,8-trimethoxyphenanthrene. The 8-position therefore is not avail-able as a seat of attachment for the ethanamine chain as pictured by Pschorr. Knorr and Hörlein proposed an alternate formula in which the chain is joined to the nucleus at C_5, but this did not adequately account for the codeine-pseudocodeine change. Gulland and Robinson[2] and Wieland and Koralek[3] independently interpreted the structural change as involving rearrangement in an allylic system. Wieland later suggested a modified formulation in which the double bond is moved from $C_8 - C_{14}$ to $C_7 - C_8$, whereas Gulland and Robinson proposed a formula differing from that of

[1] Knorr and Hörlein, *Ber.*, **40**, 3341 (1907).
[2] Gulland and R. Robinson, *J. Chem. Soc.*, **123**, 980 (1923).
[3] Wieland and Koralek, *Ann.*, **433**, 267 (1923).

Wieland only in that the ethanamine chain was transposed to the 13-position.

The Wieland and Gulland-Robinson formulas are the only representations admissible on the basis of the evidence briefly surveyed above. The

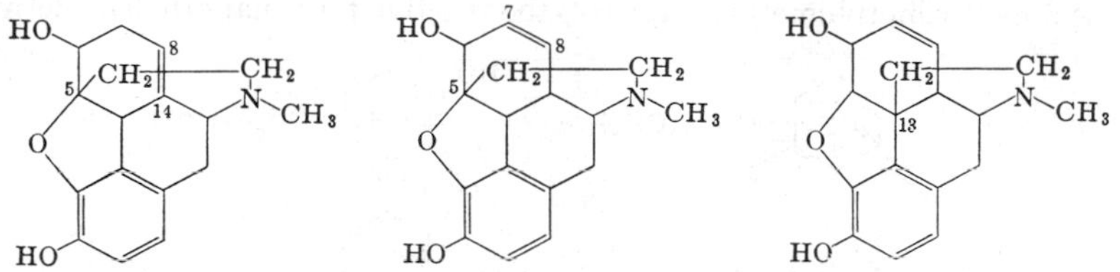

Knorr-Hörlein (1907)   Wieland (1925)   Gulland-Robinson (1925)

positions of the three oxygen atoms are fixed by the degradations to phe⁻ nanthrene derivatives; the attachment of the nitrogen atom at C_9 is estab⁻ lished by the relationship to apomorphine; and the double bond is located at $C_7 - C_8$ by the allylic rearrangement to the 8-ketone. The ethanamine chain cannot be rooted at C_{14}, because this carbon atom is capable of becoming unsaturated (thebaine, β-methylmorphimethine), and the only positions available are C_5 and C_{13}. The facile extrusion of the side chain with aromatization of the unsaturated ring finds a ready explanation in the formula of Gulland and Robinson, but not in that of Wieland. The same

TABLE I. Properties of Morphine and Related Alkaloids

COMPOUND	BASE		HYDROCHLORIDE $[\alpha]_D^{H_2O}$
	M.p.	$[\alpha]_D^{alc}$	
Morphine	254°	− 131°	− 98°
Diacetylmorphine (Heroin)	173°	− 166°	− 151°
α-Methylmorphimethine	119°	− 212°	
β-Methylmorphimethine	135°	+ 438°	
Apomorphine			− 49°
Codeine	155°	− 136°	− 107.5°
Dihydrocodeine	65°	− 198°	
Dihydrodesoxycodeine	107°	− 82.5°	
Codeinone	186°	− 205°	
Dihydrocodeinone (Dicodide)	198°		
Isocodeine	172°	− 151°	
Pseudocodeine	182°	− 97°	
Allopseudocodeine	117°	− 235°	
α-Chlorocodide	153°	− 380°	
β-Chlorocodide	157°	− 10°	
Thebaine	196°	− 219°	− 157°
Neopine	128°	0°	+ 19°
Sinomenine	182°	− 71°	

is true of the isomerization of α-methylmorphimethine to β-methylmorphimethine, which is known to involve the migration of a double bond to a
position of conjugation.   If the Wieland formula were correct the double
bond should migrate into the central ring to give a naphthalene derivative,
but β-methylmorphimethine appears too reactive for a naphthalene deriva-

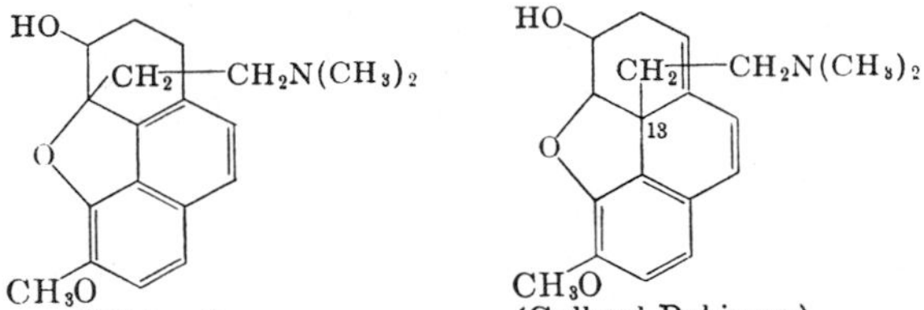

(Wieland)   (Gulland-Robinson)

β-Methylmorphimethine

tive and the absorption spectrum does not correspond to such a substance.
The Wieland formula also fails to account for the labile character of the
oxide bridge in 6,7-unsaturated ethers and for the course of the Grignard
reactions of such substances (next section).   The Gulland-Robinson formula alone fits all the known facts, but an unequivocal proof of the position
of the ethanamine chain is still lacking.

Grignard Reaction.   The carbonyl group of 6-keto alkaloids of the
morphine series has long been recognized as inert to the action of Grignard
reagents, and the same is true of the one saturated 8-ketone investigated.
Under ordinary conditions of reaction with RMgX in ether, codeinone[1] (I),
dihydropseudocodeinone[2] (II), and dihydrocodeinone[2] (III) are recovered
unchanged.   On the other hand, dihydrocodeinone reacts readily with

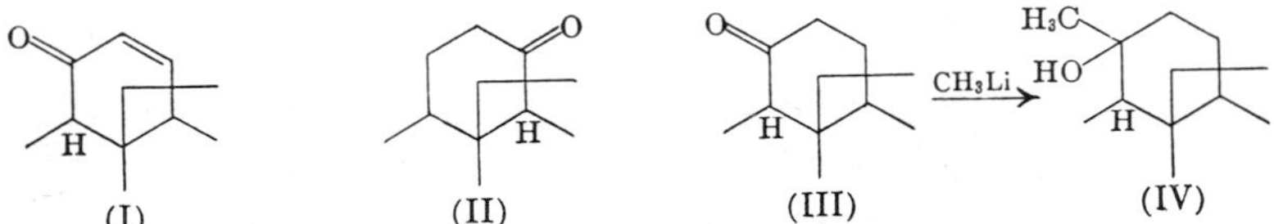

Inert to RMgX

methyllithium to give 6-methyldihydrocodeine[3] (IV), and the failure of
this substance and of the other ketones to add Grignard reagents may be
due merely to a prior enolic shift of a tertiary hydrogen atom, available in
each instance at an adjacent position.

Paradoxically, a number of nonketonic morphine derivatives readily

---

[1] Schneider, *Dissertation*, Jena, 1906.
[2] Lutz and Small, *J. Am. Chem. Soc.*, **57**, 2651 (1935).
[3] Small and Rapoport, *J. Org. Chem.*, **12**, 284 (1947).

yield Grignard addition products. The first instance of such a reaction was reported in 1905 by Freund,[4] who found that phenylmagnesium bromide reacts with thebaine to give a product, phenyldihydrothebaine, in which the elements of benzene appeared to have added to the doubly unsaturated enol ether system. The early work afforded no inkling of the nature of the reaction, and later investigations by Small at first introduced added mystery to the problem but eventually led to a dramatic denouement by Robinson. The interesting development and novel disclosures of the research will be described presently, but first an account will be given of simpler Grignard additions to compounds having but one double bond at the 6,7-position. Such a compound is dihydrothebaine (V), obtainable

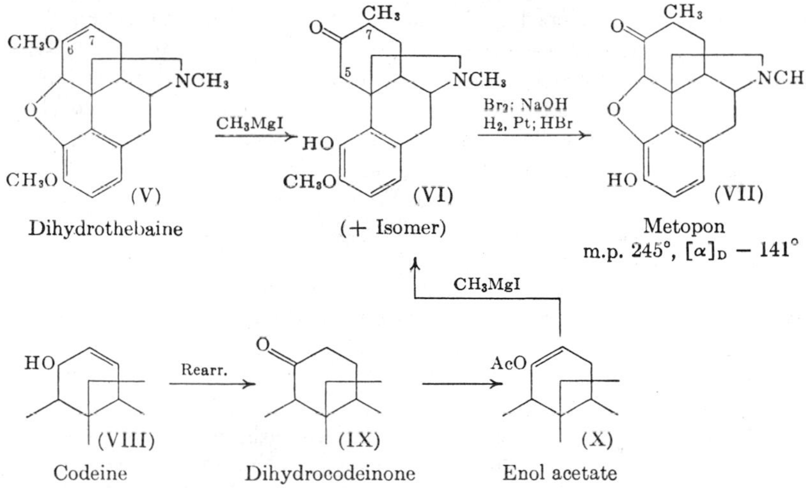

(V)	(VI)	(VII)
Dihydrothebaine	(+ Isomer)	Metopon
		m.p. 245°, $[\alpha]_D - 141°$

(VIII)	(IX)	(X)
Codeine	Dihydrocodeinone	Enol acetate

by selective hydrogenation of thebaine; the structure was established by the observation[6] that the substance is easily hydrolyzed to dihydrocodeinone and by the results of ozonization experiments.[6] Small[7] found that dihydrothebaine reacts with methylmagnesium iodide and he utilized this reaction as a step in the first synthesis of the compound now known as metopon and regarded as a promising morphine substitute. The reaction involves opening of the oxide bridge with liberation of a phenolic hydroxyl group and cleavage of the enol ether with formation of a keto group. Schöpf[8] had observed a tendency of the allylic oxide bridge to undergo

[4] M. Freund, *Ber.*, **38**, 3234 (1905); see also M. Freund and Speyer, *ibid.*, **49**, 1287 (1916).

[5] M. Freund, Speyer and Guttmann, *Ber.*, **53**, 2250 (1920).

[6] Wieland and Small, *Ann.*, **467**, 17 (1928).

[7] Small, Fitch and W. E. Smith, *J. Am. Chem. Soc.*, **58**, 1457 (1936).

[8] Schöpf, *Ann.*, **452**, 237 (1927).

reductive fission, and Small interpreted the Grignard reaction as a 1,4-addition to the conjugated system comprising the oxide bridge and the 6,7-double bond. A minor companion substance was regarded as the 5-methyl isomer formed by 1,2-addition. The two isomeric methyldihydrocodeinones form nonidentical enol acetates and hence are not stereoisomers, but the location of the methyl groups has not been established. The principal product, formulated as VI, affords a dibromide in which one bromine probably is in the phenolic ring and the other at C_5, since alkali removed the latter bromine with closure of the oxide ring and hydrogenation removed the former; demethylation then afforded metopon (VII). A more practical preparative route utilizing codeine rather than the rare and costly thebaine was later developed.[9] Codeine was converted by catalytic rearrangement in strongly acid solution (Pd, 100°) into dihydrocodeinone (IX), and this was transformed by reaction with acetic anhydride and sodium acetate into the enol acetate X, which was found to react very vigorously with methylmagnesium iodide to give VI and the isomer. The enol ether or acetate group is not essential to this novel type of Grignard addition, for desoxycodeine-C, which differs from V only in the absence of the methoxyl group at position 6, reacts with alkyl and aryl Grignard reagents to form addition products.[10]

Freund[4] investigated the action of phenylmagnesium bromide on thebaine in the hope that the results would cast light on the nature of the oxygen atom now known to form the oxide bridge. Far from lending itself to a solution of this problem, the phenolic reaction product, phenyldihydrothebaine, was found to present many anomalies. The peculiarities, which were adequately interpreted only some forty years later, are as follows.[4] The two double bonds originally present are so resistant to hydrogenation that they remain unaffected during reductive opening of the nitrogen-containing ring by hydrogenolysis (Pd, HOAc). One of the two methoxyl groups (Zeisel) has lost the original character of an enol ether group, for phenyldihydrothebaine is stable to boiling 36 percent hydrochloric acid. Complete demethylation can be accomplished by still more vigorous treatment and gives a product that fails to react with ketonic reagents and behaves like a triphenol; it reacts with diazomethane to give a product identical with phenyldihydrothebaine methyl ether. A further peculiarity is that double Hofmann degradation affords a product that retains a vinyl group, whereas this is ordinarily eliminated in (ring) unhydrogenated morphine derivatives.

Small and Fry[11] sought an elucidation of the chemistry of the unusual

[9] Small, Turnbull and Fitch, *J. Org. Chem.*, **3**, 204 (1938).

[10] Small and Yuen, *J. Am. Chem. Soc.*, **58**, 192 (1936).

[11] Small and Fry, *J. Org. Chem.*, **3**, 509 (1939).

substance through an investigation of the reaction of thebaine with methyl-magnesium iodide, and they isolated two phenolic isomers, each of which could be partially isomerized to a further new compound by the action of heat. The four isomeric methyldihydrothebaines all exhibited the same anomalous properties as Freund's substance, and the reaction thus appeared wholly unlike that of dihydrothebaine, where the enol ether was so sensitive to hydrolysis that it could not be isolated. Small, Sargent, and Bralley[12] then made a careful and extensive reinvestigation of Freund's phenyldi-hydrothebaine and found that it is a mixture of two isomers, II and III (formulated below), each of which could be partially transformed by heat treatment to further isomers: II → I and III → IV. Extensive chemical and physical characterization of the four phenyldihydrothebaines and of numerous derivatives and degradation products established beyond question that I is the antipode of III, and II the antipode of IV. The molecule must have two seats of asymmetry, and only two, for a paired thermal epimerization at two centers is hardly conceivable. Small found further that when the ring containing nitrogen is opened by hydrogenolysis one center of asymmetry is destroyed: isomers I and IV yield the same dextro-rotatory base and isomers II and III yield its enantiomer. The carbon atom involved in this ring fission is therefore asymmetric and must have the opposite configurations in the two products of the Grignard reaction, II and III. The same conclusion was reached from the results of successive Hofmann degradations. Small[11, 12] considered a number of formulations but found none that fitted the stereochemical requirements and accounted for the chemical peculiarities. In particular, the possibility that the enol ether ring had become aromatic was discounted because the absorption spectrum gave no evidence of the presence of a diphenyl system and because such a structure could have only one asymmetric carbon atom. Finding no explanation for the perplexing set of facts on the basis of the accepted structures, Small considered that the results cast doubt upon the Gulland-Robinson formula for morphine.

Robinson[13] studied the problem in the light of the elegant experimental elaboration by Small and concluded that the original enol ether ring must be aromatic; the resistance to hydrogenation, the resistance of the originally labile methoxyl group to hydrolysis, and the phenolic character of the demethylated product (reaction with diazomethane) all pointed in this direction. If the phenyldihydrothebaines are indeed derivatives of diphenyl, they can contain only one asymmetric carbon atom, and the nitrogen-free products resulting from two Hofmann degradations, although optically active, can contain no asymmetric carbon atoms. The optical

[12] Small, Sargent and Bralley, *J. Org. Chem.*, **12**, 839 (1947).
[13] R. Robinson, *Nature*, **160**, 815 (1947); *Proc. Roy. Soc.*, **B135**, 14 (1947).

Chart 1.
Phenyldihydrothebaines
(I-IV)

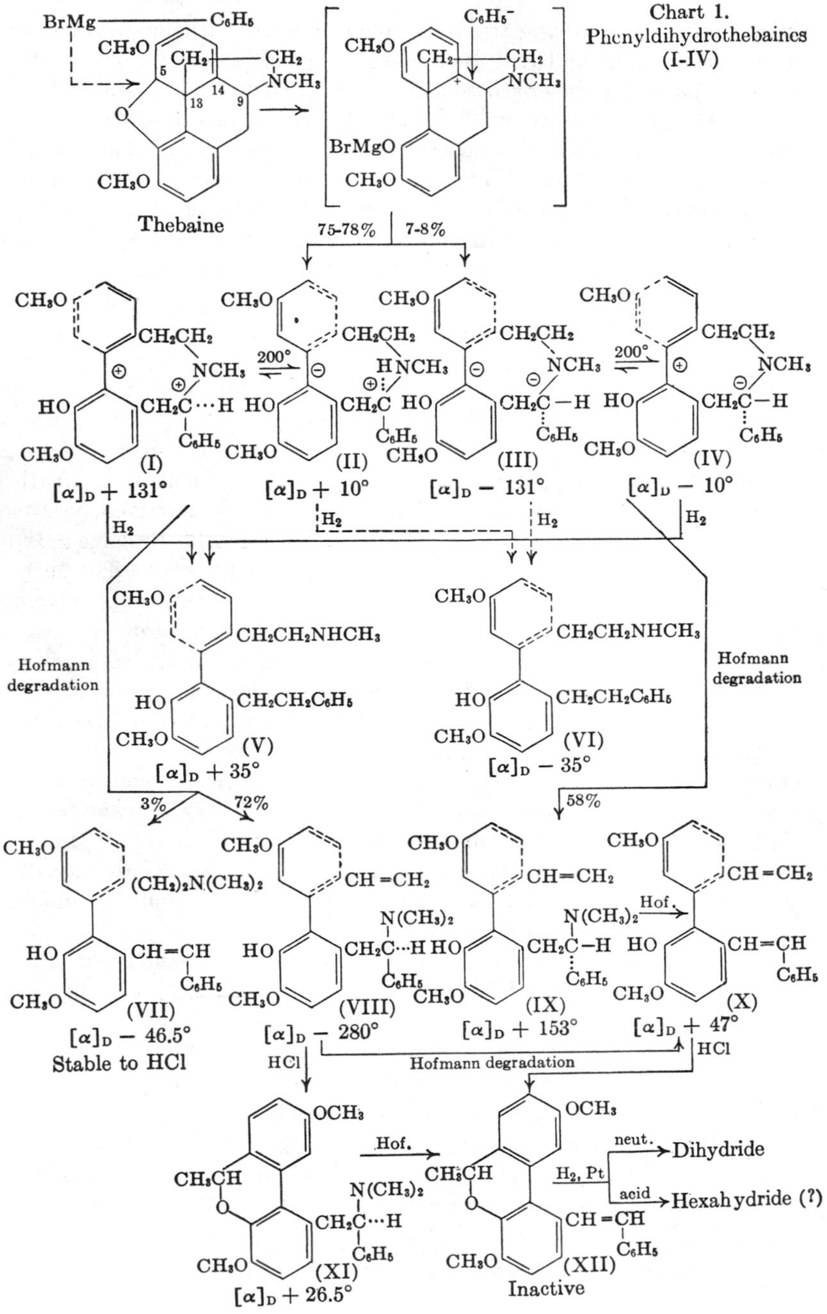

Thebaine

75-78%   7-8%

(I)
$[\alpha]_D + 131°$

(II)
$[\alpha]_D + 10°$

(III)
$[\alpha]_D - 131°$

(IV)
$[\alpha]_D - 10°$

H_2 H_2 H_2 H_2

Hofmann
degradation

Hofmann
degradation

(V)
$[\alpha]_D + 35°$

(VI)
$[\alpha]_D - 35°$

3%   72%   58%

(VII)
$[\alpha]_D - 46.5°$
Stable to HCl

(VIII)
$[\alpha]_D - 280°$
HCl

(IX)
$[\alpha]_D + 153°$

Hof.

(X)
$[\alpha]_D + 47°$
HCl

Hofmann degradation

Hof.

H_2, Pt

neut. → Dihydride

acid → Hexahydride (?)

(XI)
$[\alpha]_D + 26.5°$

(XII)
Inactive

activity, Robinson reasoned, must therefore arise from molecular asymmetry due to restricted rotation of the two aromatic rings of diphenyl, with resulting noncoplanarity. If the two benzene rings do not lie in a plane, normal resonance is not possible and the absorption spectrum should correspond to that of isolated, rather than conjugated, benzene nuclei; this assumption corresponds to Small's findings. The isomerism of the phenyldihydrothebaines thus arises from the novel combination of molecular and atomic dissymmetry. Robinson then found a formulation consistent with these theoretical requirements in a structure having a diphenyl system bridged at the 2, 2′-positions by a nitrogen-containing nine-membered ring, and he and Bentley proved this to be correct by permanganate oxidation of a phenyldihydrothebaine to 4-methoxyphthalic acid and of a product of two Hofmann degradations (probably the methyl ether of X, Chart 1) to a trimethoxydiphenic acid.

In the absence of further details, we have interpreted the isomerism and the transformations with the formulations shown in Chart 1. The dotted lines indicate the inclination of a ring, atom, or group in the direction below the plane of the paper, and the full lines indicate the reverse; the orientations are purely arbitrary and merely represent relative relationships. The unusual rearrangement reaction induced by the Grignard addition can be interpreted by various mechanistic schemes. In that formulated the initial attack is at the allylic ether linkage, as in the 6,7-monounsaturated enol ethers investigated by Small; the now activated 9,14-linkage is then cleaved by attack of the phenyl anion and the ethanamine chain migrates from C_{13} to C_{14} under the driving force of aromatization. The two isomeric phenyldihydrothebaines produced, II and III, must differ in the configuration at the asymmetric carbon center rather than in the orientation of the diphenyl system because on destruction of atomic asymmetry by hydrogenolysis they yield the same product, VI. The partial thermal isomerizations then must involve rotation about the diphenyl link.

Hofmann degradation of II proceeded with ring fission in both possible directions to give the methine VII and the isomethine VIII. The isomethine predominated, and in degradations of the isomers I and III the isomethine was the sole product isolated. We see no explanation for the preferential splitting of the link to nitrogen that is not under activation by the phenyl group. The methine is stable to boiling hydrochloric acid, but the isomethine is readily isomerized by acid to a cyclic ether (XI). The ether is optically active, for it still retains the asymmetric carbon center, but when this is destroyed by a further Hofmann degradation to XII the optical activity disappears. The molecular asymmetry due to the diphenyl system is thus abolished in the formation of the cyclic ether XI. Small noted that the nitrogen-free cyclic ether XII, which was prepared also through the intermediate X, absorbs two moles of hydrogen in a neutral solvent but in acid solution is further hydrogenated to a product described as a hexahydride. The analysis does not distinguish between a hexa- and an octahydride, and undoubtedly one of the benzene rings has been saturated. Small stressed the contrasting behavior of the isomethine VIII, which under forcing conditions could be hydrogenated only in the vinyl group; a likely explanation is that the coplanar molecule XII can lie flat on the catalyst surface and the noncoplanar VIII cannot.

Inferences concerning the relative contributions of the two seats of asymmetry to the rotatory power of the molecule are indicated in formulas I – IV by the encircled signs. It appears probable that the asymmetric carbon atom is the more powerful rotophore. Substances VII and X possess only molecular asymmetry and they exhibit low rotations of opposite signs. The methine VII is probably the more representative of the phenyldihydrothebaines and hence diphenyl isomerism in the sense represented in VII and in II is assumed to make a levo contribution of a low order. The strong dextrorotation of I, then, is due to the combination of two positive rotophores, one powerful and the other weak. The predominating product of the Grignard reaction is the weakly rotatory l,d'-isomer (II); the equilibria in the thermal isomerizations favor the l,d'- and d,l'-forms. The Hofmann degradations that proceed with retention of both seats of asymmetry, II → VIII and III → IX, are attended with marked reversals in optical activity. Since Walden inversions can hardly occur, the asymmetric carbon atom of the isomethine VIII seems to contribute in the opposite sense to that of the ring carbon of the same orientation. The low positive rotation of XI illustrates the marked effect of ring formation on the rotatory contribution of an asymmetric center that is not a member of the ring concerned.

A Grignard addition product probably analogous in structure to the phenyldihydrothebaines was prepared by Lutz and Small[14] from pseudo-codeinone (XIII). The substance was found to be phenolic, resistant to

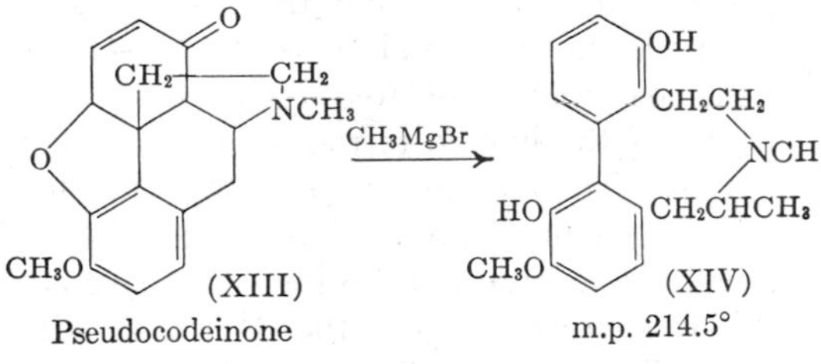

$$CH_3MgBr \longrightarrow$$

(XIII)
Pseudocodeinone

(XIV)
m.p. 214.5°

reduction with sodium and cyclohexanol or to hydrogenation in acetic acid solution, and unreactive to carbonyl reagents. The unsaturated ketone

[14] Lutz and Small, *J. Am. Chem. Soc.*, **57**, 2651 (1935).

probably reacts in the enolic form in the manner shown in Chart 1 to give XIV.

Configuration of Morphine. Inferences deduced by Schöpf in interpreting some of his extensive investigations in the field seem to us to afford the basis for a reasonably secure conception of the orientation in space of the entire morphine molecule. In developing this theme we shall employ the method of representation introduced in the field of the sterols. An atom or group postulated to project above the plane of the paper is described as a β-oriented group and is represented by a full-line bond; the opposite or α-orientation is indicated by a dotted line. Thus in the partial formula for thebaine (I) the hydrogen atoms at C_5 and C_9 have the β- and

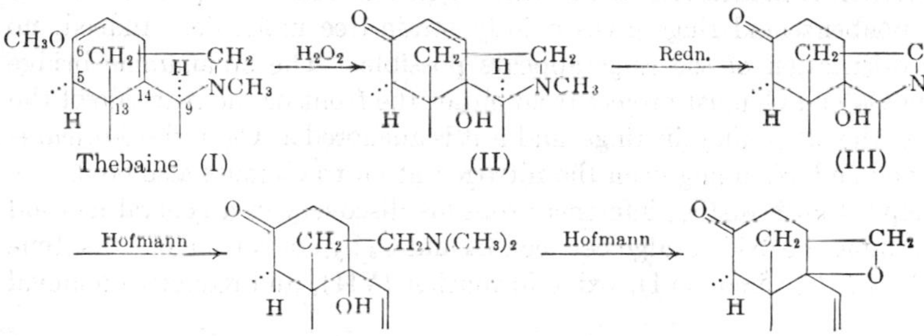

Thebaine (I)   (II)   (III)

(IV)   (V)

α-orientations, respectively, and the ethanamine bridge projects from the front side of the molecule. Freund and Speyer[1] found that thebaine reacts with hydrogen peroxide in acetic acid to give hydroxycodeinone (II), a monounsaturated keto alcohol with an acylable hydroxyl group. Gulland and Robinson[2] inferred that the hydroxyl group is at C_{14} and that the substance arises by 1,4-hydroxylation of the diene system with consequent elimination of methanol from the enol ether grouping. The hydroxy compound is resistant to the usual dehydrative aromatization reactions; for example, it is stable to 20 percent hydrochloric acid at 120°. The structure II accounts for this peculiarity, for neither position in the unsaturated ring adjacent to the hydroxyl group carries a hydrogen atom. An allylic alcohol grouping is present, and this may account for the ready acetylation of the tertiary alcoholic group, but allylic rearrangement, like dehydration, is blocked. The double bond is very reactive and can be reduced with sodium hydrosulfite[3] as well as by hydrogenation.[1] Schöpf[4] extended the evidence by investigating the nitrogen-free product resulting from two

[1] M. Freund and Speyer, *J. prakt. Chem.*, **94**, 135 (1916).
[2] Gulland and R. Robinson, *J. Chem. Soc.*, **123**, 980 (1923).
[3] M. Freund and Speyer, U. S. patent 1,479,293 (1924).
[4] Schöpf, *Ann.*, **452**, 211 (1927).

Hofmann degradations of the dihydride III. The substance was characterized as an ether (V) presumably arising by cyclization of an initially formed vinyl group at C_{13} with the hydroxyl group at C_{14}. The observation confirms the location of the hydroxyl group and shows that this group and the ethanamine bridge must be cis to each other, as represented in the formulas by like orientations (arbitrarily defined as β). No rigid proof is available to show that the 14-hydrogen atom of morphine and codeine has the same orientation as the 14-hydroxyl group in the compounds just described; but Schöpf considered such correspondence highly probable because hydrogenations of 8,14-unsaturated compounds, like the hydroxylation of thebaine, proceed exclusively in one steric sense, and because examination of models shows that this particular manner of juncture of the three nonbenzenoid rings gives a fully strain-free molecule. Indeed, no other orientation of the rings appears possible. The ethanamine bridge linking C_{13} and C_9 must project from either the front or the rear side of the plane of the other alicyclic rings, and if it is anchored at C_{13} in the β-orientation the bond extending from the nitrogen atom to C_9 must also be β.

Schöpf[5] drew a further inference from his discovery of a general method of reforming the oxide bridge between C_4 and C_5 by conversion of a 6-ketone into the 1,5-dibromide (VI), oxide formation (VII), and reductive removal

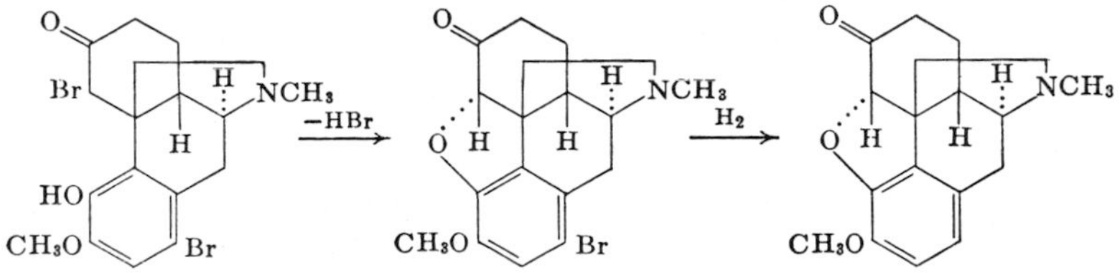

     (VI)   (VII)   (VIII)

of the 1-bromine atom (VIII). The ring closures invariably proceed easily in a single steric direction to give products of the morphine series and not their epimers, and Schöpf noted that the model of VI has a rigid structure in which the rear 5α-position is close in space to the 4-hydroxyl group but the front (β) position is not. He inferred that the oxide bridge is oriented at C_5 trans to the ethanamine bridge.

In extension of Schöpf's deductions, we suggest that the course of the hydrogenation of a 6-ketone (or of an 8-ketone) can be predicted with reasonable assurance from a consideration of hindrance effects. Such hydrogenations often give structural isomers, but the opening of the carbonyl group always proceeds in a single steric sense and gives an alcohol having the orientation at C_6 of morphine. In the model of formula IX

---

[5] Schöpf and T. Pfeifer, *Ann.*, **483**, 157 (1930).

the ketonic ring, which forms part of a cis decalin system, is folded sharply to the rear along the axis of C_5 and C_{14} and approaches a plane at right angles to that of the aromatic ring. The ketonic ring and the oxide ring thus form a cage, and the rear bond of the 6-keto groups (dotted line) is

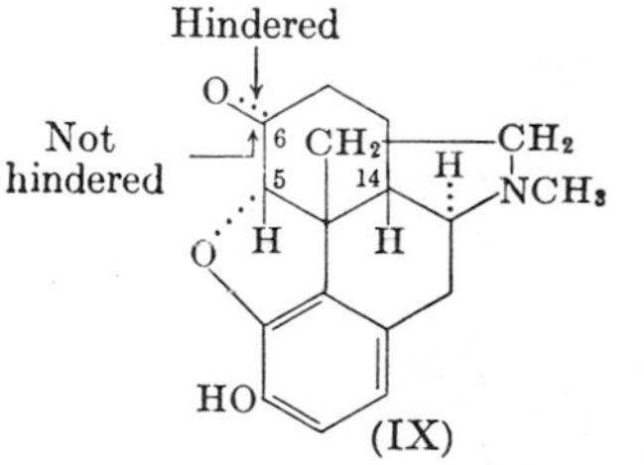

Morphine

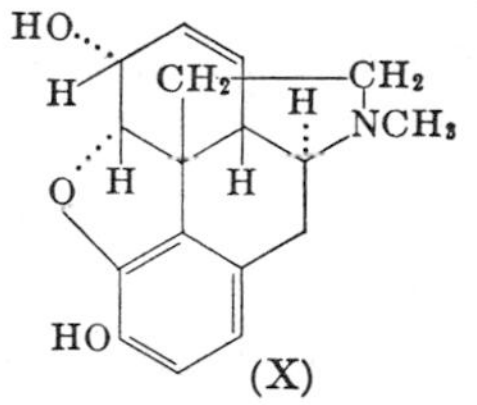

within this cage and should be subject to considerable hindrance; the front bond (full line) is unhindered. The situation resembles that of the 11-keto-steroids, which are hydrogenated exclusively through the opening of the less hindered linkage. The hydrogenation of a 6-ketone of the morphine series thus should result in the opening of the less hindered frontal bond and give an alcohol of 6α-orientation. Morphine, therefore, probably has the configuration shown in formula X. The 6α-hydroxyl groups in morphine and in dihydromorphine, although hindered, are capable of being acetylated; the 6β-epimers are also acylable. Differences in the rates of acetylation and hydrolysis of 6- and 8-epimers should reveal the orientations.

From a speculative analysis of molecular rotations, particularly those of the amine hydrochlorides in aqueous solution, Emde[6] deduced the signs of rotation at the five asymmetric centers in the morphine molecule as follows: C_6, C_5, and C_9 levorotatory; C_{13} and C_{14} dextrorotatory. The evidence will not be presented here in full, but the nature of the reasoning can be indicated by a few examples. The optical activity of apomorphine is due to the lone center of asymmetry at C_9, and the negative sign of rotation of the hydrochloride in aqueous solution, $[M]_D^{HCl} - 149°$, shows that this center is levorotatory. Carbon atom 6 in morphine must be levorotatory, Emde reasoned, because an increase in the dissymmetry at C_6 as the result of acetylation of the alcoholic group produces a marked enhancement of the original levorotation of the alkaloid. The change from an acetyl to a propionyl group represents a minor increase compared with the change from hydrogen to acetyl, and the following comparisons show that the effect on the molecular rotation is relatively small.

[6] Emde, *Helv. Chim. Acta*, **13**, 1035 (1930).

$$[M]_D^{HCl}$$

Morphine. . . . . $-370°$
6-Acetylmorphine. . . . . $-593°$
Diacetylmorphine. . . . . $-619°$
Dipropionylmorphine. . . . . $-671°$

The rotatory moments at the other three centers were inferred from inter-comparisons of compounds possessing symmetry and asymmetry at these centers. In making such comparisons allowance must be made for a

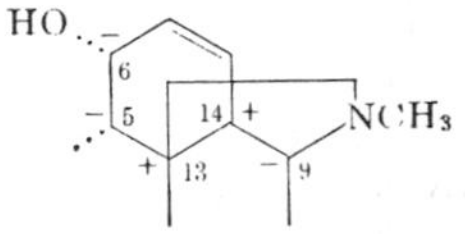

marked optical exaltation produced by a double bond adjacent to an asymmetric carbon atom. Emde noted that morphine resembles the cyclic forms of the aldohexoses in containing a chain of five adjacent asymmetric centers in the sequence: $--++-$.

Sinomenine. This alkaloid, isolated in 1920 by Ishiwari from a woody vine of Eastern Asia (*Sinomenium acutum*), was the subject of a series of masterly investigations by Kondo[1] and by Goto[2] that led to a remarkable disclosure. By degradations to phenanthrene and apomorphine derivatives that were identified by synthesis, sinomenine was shown to have a phenolic hydroxyl group at C_4, a keto group at C_6, a double bond in conjugation at $C_7 - C_8$, and methoxyl groups at C_3 and C_7. The alkaloid in short was proved to have the structure of a 7-methoxy derivative of thebainone, an unsaturated ketone resulting from the action of stannous chloride on either thebaine or codeinone. On converting sinomenine into derivatives corresponding in structure to known compounds of the morphine series, the

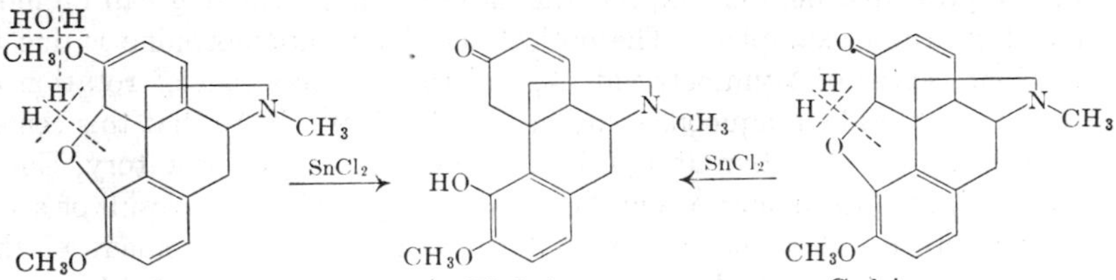

Thebaine   Thebainone   Codeinone

---

[1] Kondo and Ochiai, *Ann.*, **470**, 224 (1929); *Ber.*, **63**, 646 (1930).

[2] Goto, Inaba and Shishido, *Ann.*, **485**, 247 (1931); Goto, Takubo and Mitsui, *ibid.*, **489**, 86 (1931); Goto, Inaba and Nozaki, *ibid.*, **530**, 142 (1937); Goto and Shishido, *ibid.*, **539**, 262 (1939); Goto and Arai, *ibid.*, **547**, 194 (1941); Goto and co-workers, *C. A.*, **41**, 4502, 4504 (1947).

Japanese investigators made the surprising discovery that the sinomenine derivatives are the optical antipodes of the morphine derivatives and form racemates when crystallized with these substances in equal proportions. According to the convention employed above, sinomenine has the structure and configuration shown in formula I. Schöpf[3] confirmed the fundamental

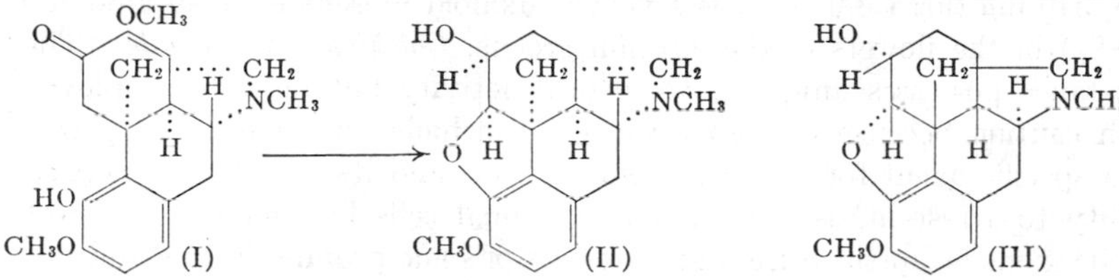

Sinomenine (I)

(II)
$[\alpha]_D + 146.4°$

(−)-Dihydrocodeine (III)
$[\alpha]_D - 146.7°$

Racemate

discovery of the Japanese investigators and elucidated the nature of the reaction of the alkaloid with bromine, which he showed involves the closing of an oxide ring and bromination at C_1 (VI → VIII in preceding section). By a sequence of reactions that utilized the Schöpf ring closure in one step and employed as the last step the catalytic hydrogenation of a 6-ketone in pyridine solution (90% yield), Goto later prepared the sinomenine derivative II, which has five centers of asymmetry. The substance proved to be the dextrorotatory optical opposite of the isomer resulting from the reduction of codeine. As expected, the steric effects controlling the direction of the closing of the oxide ring and the mode of opening of the carbonyl double bond operate in the reverse sense in the sinomenine and morphine series.

Neopine,[4] isolated in small amounts from opium, differs from codeine only in the position of the double bond, for on hydrogenation it yields dihydrocodeine.[5, 6] The location of the double bond at $C_8 - C_{14}$ was estab-

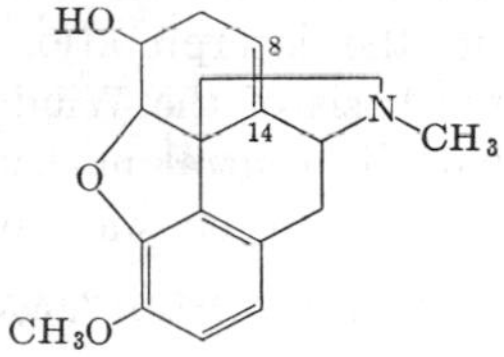

Neopine

[3] Schöpf and T. Pfeifer, *Ann.*, **483**, 157 (1930).

[4] L. F. Small, "Chemistry of the Opium Alkaloids," p. 205; Homeyer and Shilling, *J. Org. Chem.*, **12**, 356 (1947).

[5] Van Duin, R. Robinson and J. C. Smith, *J. Chem. Soc.*, 903 (1926).

[6] Confirmed by Small, *J. Org. Chem.*, **12**, 359 (1947).

lished by the observation[5, 6] that decomposition of the methohydroxide affords β-methylmorphimethine rather than the α-isomer. The hydrogenation reaction is another instance of the preferential formation of a product of the natural morphine configuration.

Colchicine. Colchicine, $C_{22}H_{25}O_6N$, m.p. 155°, $[\alpha]_D - 121°$, $\lambda_{max}^{CHCl_3}$ 245, 340 mμ (log ε 3.9, 1.9), is a yellow alkaloid present in small amounts (0.8%) in the flowers of the autumn crocus, *Colchicum autumnale*. The substance possesses unique physiological activity but must be employed with caution because of high toxicity. Colchicine has long been prized as a specific agent for the treatment of gout, and its recently recognized ability to arrest mitosis of plant and animal cells has led to important applications in horticulture and to results of some promise in the study of cancer.

One of four methoxyl groups present in the alkaloid has the character of an enol ether group and is readily eliminated on acid hydrolysis to the desmethyl derivative colchiceine. The relationship of colchicine to colchiceine was established in a careful analytical study by Zeisel,[1] who not only established the empirical formulas by numerous analyses of highly purified samples[2] but also isolated the volatile product of hydrolysis (methanol) by distillation and characterized it by conversion to methyl iodide. The combination and simplification of these reactions, initially carried out with large (33-g.) samples of a costly alkaloid, eventually led to the development of the valuable Zeisel method of methoxyl determination.

The structure of the alkaloid was investigated extensively by Windaus, whose researches culminated in the suggestion of the tentative formula I;[3] this was deduced in part from the identification of 3,4,5-trimethoxyphthalic acid as a product of oxidation and of 9-methylphenanthrene as the end product of a series of degradative steps. Some of the subsequent work supported formula I and extended the evidence,[4, 5] but Cook[6] discovered an inconsistency in the interpretation of the degradation to 9-methylphenanthrene on the basis of the Windaus formula. Cook[7] adduced evidence showing that the central nucleus (B) must be a seven-membered ring (II), and the conclusion was confirmed by independent

[1] Zeisel and co-workers, *Monatsh.*, **4**, 162 (1883); **7**, 557 (1886); **9**, 1, 865 (1888); **34**, 1181, 1327, 1339 (1913).

[2] Purification of colchicine by chromatography: Ashley and J. O. Harris, *J. Chem. Soc.*, 677 (1944).

[3] Windaus, *Ann.*, **439**, 59 (1924).

[4] Grewe, *Ber.*, **71**, 907 (1938); see also *Naturwiss.*, **33**, 187 (1946).

[5] Bursian, *Ber.*, **71**, 245 (1938).

[6] Buchanan, J. W. Cook and Loudon, *J. Chem. Soc.*, 325 (1944).

[7] J. W. Cook, Dickson and Loudon, *J. Chem. Soc.*, 746 (1947).

evidence presented by Tarbell and co-workers.[8]   Dewar[9] suggested that ring C may also be seven-membered (III), and evidence that this is indeed the case has been presented by Tarbell.[10]   Since the problem of structure

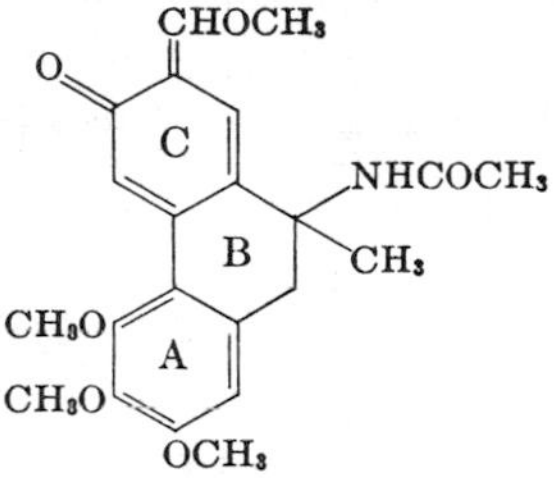

(I) 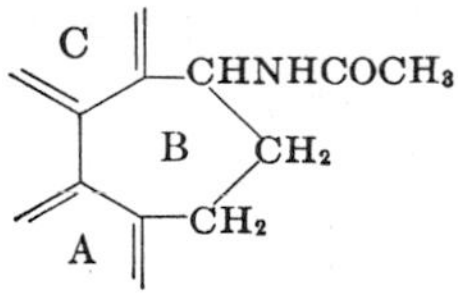   (II) 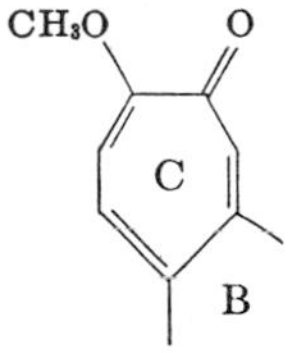   (III)

is not yet solved, and since colchicine does not now appear to be a true phenanthrene derivative, the investigations cited will not be reviewed in detail.

The Aporphine Group.   Apomorphine, the product of rearrangement of morphine, provides a connecting link between bases of the morphine series and a number of phenanthrene alkaloids derived from the parent substance aporphine, of which apomorphine is the 3,4-dihydroxy derivative.   Apor-

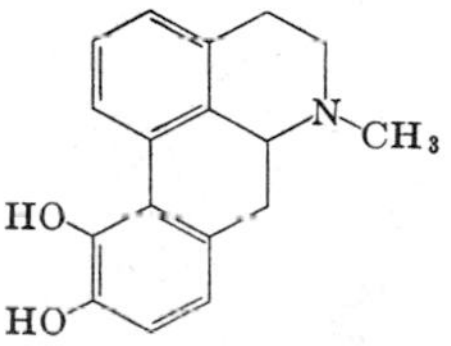

Apomorphine 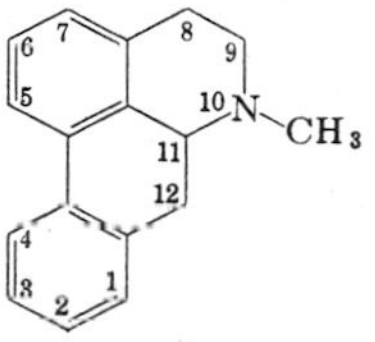   Aporphine

phine does not occur in nature but has been synthesized by Gadamer[1] from o-nitrotoluene and the pseudo base (I) of N-methylisoquinolinium

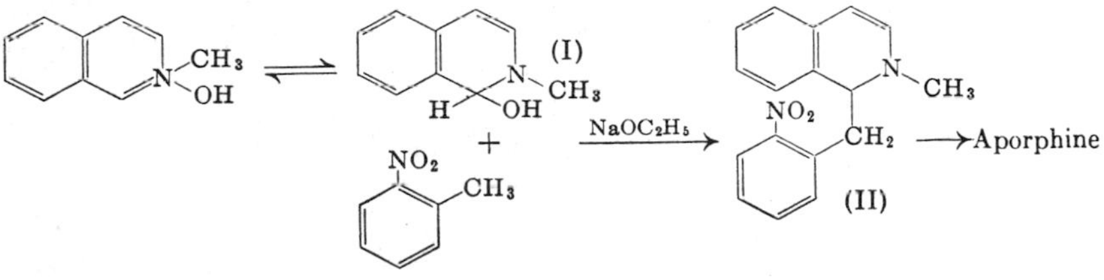

---

[8] Tarbell, H. R. Frank and Fanta, *J. Am. Chem. Soc.*, **68**, 502 (1946).

[9] Dewar, *Nature*, **155**, 141 (1945).

[10] Arnstein, Tarbell, H. T. Huang and G. H. Scott, *J. Am. Chem. Soc.*, **70**, 1669 (1948).

[1] Gadamer, Oberlin and Schoeler, *Arch. Pharm.*, **263**, 81 (1925).

hydroxide. After reduction of the nitro group of II and saturation of the double bond, the ring was closed by the Pschorr method.

The alkaloids of the aporphine series are all very similar to one another and the majority are more or less highly etherified derivatives of either 2,3,5,6- or 3,4,5,6-tetrahydroxyaporphine. Boldine, glaucine, and dicentrine belong in the former class and are related not only in structure

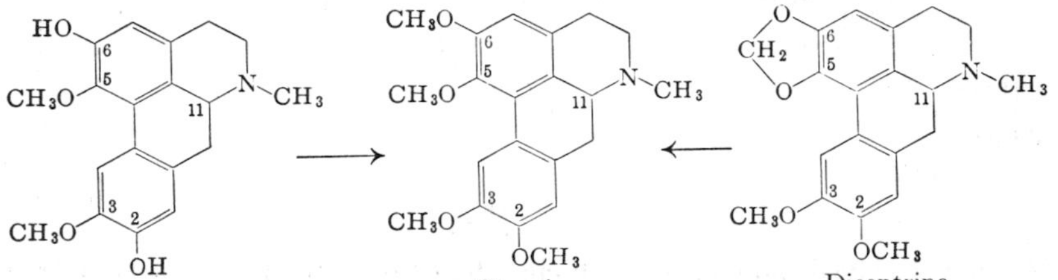

Boldine   Glaucine   Dicentrine

but in the configuration at the asymmetric center C_{11}. Boldine on methylation yields a product identical with natural glaucine,[2] and the same substance has been obtained from dicentrine by hydrolysis of the methylenedioxy group and methylation of the resulting 2,3-dimethoxy-5,6-dihydroxy compound.[3] The cleavage of the methylene ether linkages without disturbance of the methoxyl groups is accomplished by warming the compound with dilute sulfuric acid and phloroglucinol.[4] The formaldehyde split from the one molecule forms a red condensation product with phloroglucinol. The structure of glaucine, the key substance of the group, was established

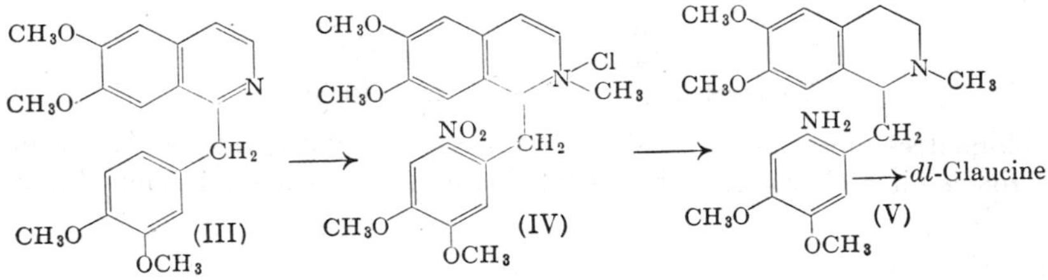

Papaverine

by Gadamer's synthesis[5] of the alkaloid from papaverine, a method suggested by the hypothesis that this represents the course of the phytosynthesis. The process already had been carried nearly to completion by Pschorr.[6] The essential steps consist in the nitration of papaverine (III),

[2] Warnat, Ber., 58, 2768 (1925); 59, 85 (1926).
[3] Osada, J. Pharm. Soc. Japan, 48, 85 (3928) [Chem. Zentr., II, 672 (1928)].
[4] Späth and Quietensky, Ber., 60, 1882 (1927).
[5] Gadamer, Arch. Pharm., 249, 680 (1911).
[6] Pschorr, Stählin and Silberbach, Ber., 37, 1926 (1904).

reduction of nitropapaverine methochloride (IV) to aminotetrahydro-N-methylpapaverine (*dl*-aminolaudanosine, V), and ring closure through the diazonium salt.

dl-Dicentrine has been synthesized by a similar method and the naturally occurring *d*-base obtained by resolution.[7] The structure of boldine was established by the application of standard methods developed for the investigation of partially alkylated members of the series. Having established the positions of the oxygen atoms by the conversion to glaucine, Warnat[2] sought to locate the methoxyl groups by oxidation. If the two protected groups had been in the same ring they might have appeared in a benzene di- or tricarboxylic acid, but apparently both of the terminal rings were destroyed in the process, for only oxalic acid was obtained. Warnat's conclusion that each nucleus contains a phenolic group was later confirmed by Schlittler,[8] who oxidized boldine diethyl ether (VI) and obtained the methyl ethyl ether of nor-*m*-hemipinic acid (VII). On account of the

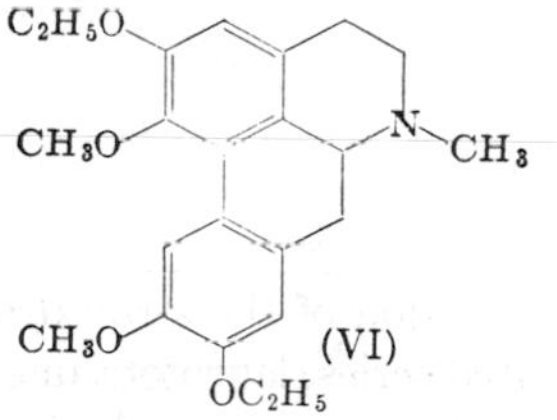

C_2H_5O — CH_3O — N—CH_3 — CH_3O — OC_2H_5 (VI)

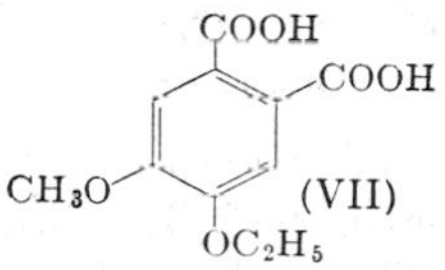

COOH — COOH — CH_3O — OC_2H_5 (VII)

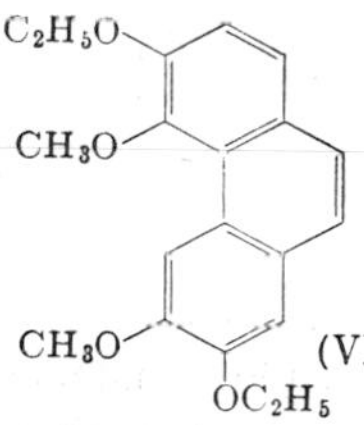

C_2H_5O — CH_3O — CH_3O — OC_2H_5 (VIII)

symmetry of the acid VII, this observation was not sufficient to establish the positions of the groups in the ring in question, for the same acid would result if the methoxyl and ethoxyl groups were interchanged.

To complete the evidence Schlittler chose the synthetic approach, whereas Späth and Tharrer[9] independently and at the same time undertook the Hofmann degradation of the diethyl ether VI. This ether, which is prepared with the use of diazoethane, was converted in succession to a methine base, to an alkoxyvinylphenanthrene, to an alkoxyphenanthroic acid, and finally to the dimethoxydiethoxyphenanthrene VIII, which was identified by synthesis according to the Pschorr method. Schlittler's synthesis, employing the amide IX, involved a Bischler-Napieralski isoquinoline ring closure, N-methylation, and a phenanthrene ring closure. The final product, X, was a racemic mixture and a comparison with boldine diethyl ether was made by the convenient method introduced by Gadamer.[10]

[7] R. D. Haworth, W. H. Perkin Jr. and J. Rankin, *J. Chem. Soc.*, 2018 (1925); 29 (1926).

[8] Schlittler, *Ber.*, **66**, 988 (1933).

[9] Späth and Tharrer, *Ber.*, **66**, 904 (1933).

[10] Gadamer and Knoch, *Arch. Pharm.*, **259**, 135 (1921).

On reaction with ethyl chlorocarbonate the nitrogen ring is cleaved and the center of asymmetry destroyed. The ester XI proved to be identical with the material prepared from the natural alkaloid.

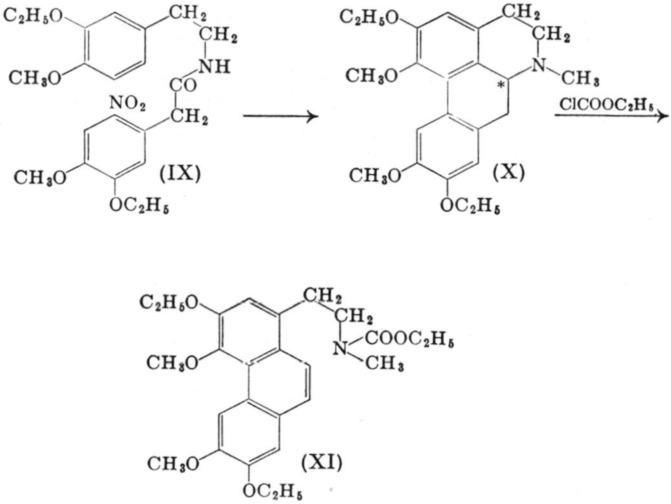

Similar methods of investigation led to the elucidation of the structures of two additional members of the 2,3,5,6-substituted series, laurotetanine[11] and actinodaphnine.[12] These alkaloids are secondary bases, and since they lack the N-methyl group characteristic of aporphine they are derivatives of noraporphine. The following alkaloids of corydalis are ethers of

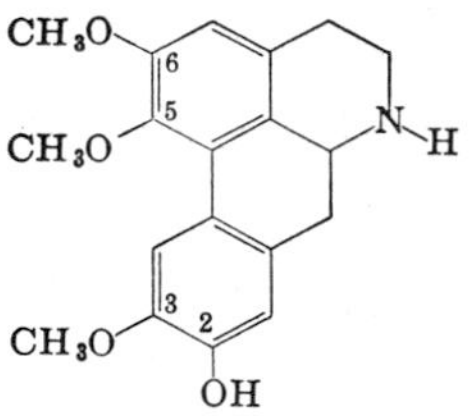

Laurotetanine

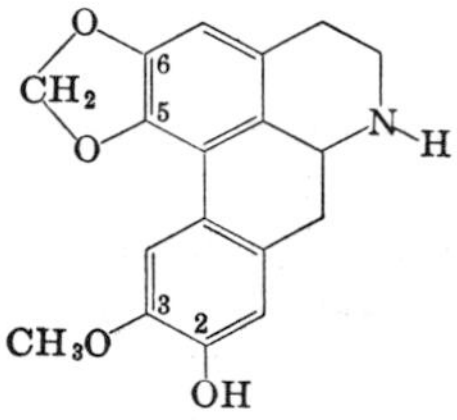

Actinodaphnine

3,4,5,6-tetrahydroxyaporphine of the structures shown in the formulas: corytuberine,[13] corydine,[13] isocorydine,[13] bulbocapnine.[14]

[11] Structure: Späth and Strauhal, *Ber.*, **61**, 2395 (1928); Späth and Tharrer, *ibid.*, **66**, 583 (1933); Barger and Silberschmidt, *J. Chem. Soc.*, 2919 (1928); Barger, J. Eisenbrand, L. Eisenbrand and Schlittler, *Ber.*, **66**, 450 (1933).

[12] Structure: Ghose, Krishna and Schlittler, *Helv. Chim. Acta*, **17**, 919 (1934).

[13] Structure: Späth and Berger, *Ber.*, **64**, 2038 (1931). Synthesis of corytuberine dimethyl ether: Späth and Hromatka, *ibid.*, **61**, 1692 (1928).

[14] Structure: Gadamer, *Arch. Pharm.*, **249**, 498, 503 (1911); Gadamer and Kuntze,

Some members of the aporphine group contain but three oxygen functions;[15] for example, pukateine[16] is 4-hydroxy-5,6-methylenedioxyaporphine and laureline[17] is 3-methoxy-5,6-methylenedioxyaporphine.

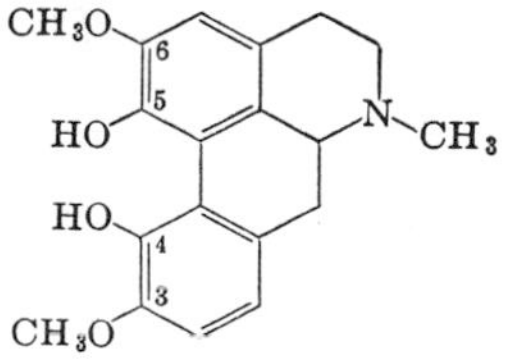

Corytuberine

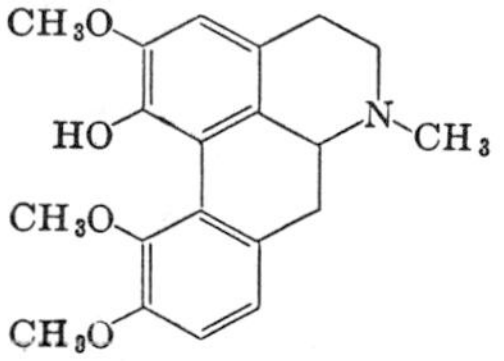

Corydine

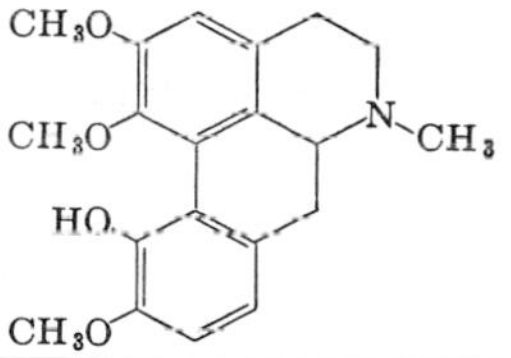

Isocorydine

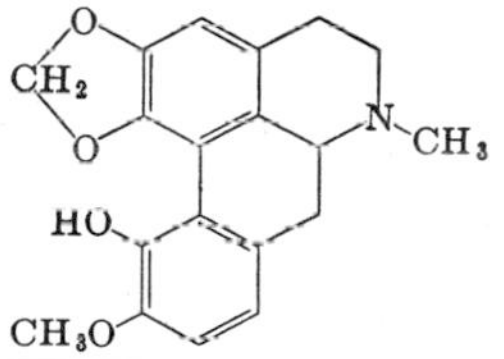

Bulbocapnine

The synthesis of aporphines having free phenolic groups can be accomplished[18] by protecting the phenolic functions by benzylation, for the benzyl groups can be subsequently removed under such mild conditions of hydrolysis (36% hydrochloric acid at 50°) that methoxyl groups in the molecule remain intact.

Biogenetic Relationships. A striking outcome of the investigations of the phenanthrene alkaloids is the recognition of close structural relationships both within the different series and from series to series. The benzylisoquinoline alkaloids papaverine, laudanine, laudanosine, and narcotine occur in opium, and their structural relationship to the aporphine alkaloids is illustrated by the synthesis of glaucine from papaverine.

A still closer relationship is evident from the formulas of isocorydine, laudanine, and laurotetanine. If the two aromatic nuclei of laudanine were linked by dehydrogenation at positions *a* and *b*, the product would have

ibid., **249**, 598 (1911). Synthesis of the methyl ether: Gulland and R. D. Haworth, *J. Chem. Soc.*, 1132 (1928).

[15] Barger and Girardet, *Helv. Chim. Acta*, **14**, 481 (1931). See also Goto, *Ann.*, **521**, 175 (1935).

[16] Synthesis of *l*-pukateine methyl ether: Barger and Schlittler, *Helv. Chim. Acta*, **15**, 381 (1932).

[17] Synthesis: Schlittler, *Helv. Chim. Acta*, **15**, 394 (1932).

[18] Kondo and Ishiwata, *Ber.*, **64**, 1533 (1931); Gulland, Ross and Smellie, *J. Chem. Soc.*, 2885 (1931); Douglas and Gulland, *ibid.*, 2893 (1931).

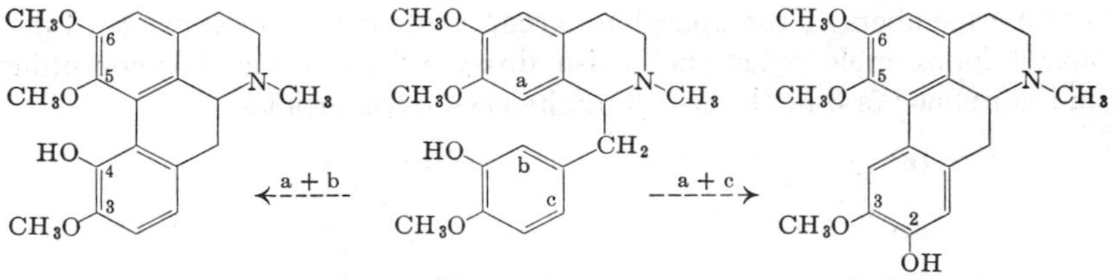

| Isocorydine | Laudanine | (unknown) |

the structure of isocorydine. The ortho position c is also available (rotation of the lower ring), and a ring closure between positions a and c would lead to a 2,3,5,6-substituted aporphine, N-methyllaurotetanine (or 2-demethylglaucine). The exact correspondence in the location of the methyl groups in the first case may be a coincidence, but the relationship undoubtedly accounts for the preponderance of aporphine alkaloids with substituents at either the 2,3,5,6- or the 3,4,5,6-positions.

The benzylisoquinoline alkaloids theoretically can undergo intramolecular cyclization in a different direction, as suggested by the following formulas:[1]

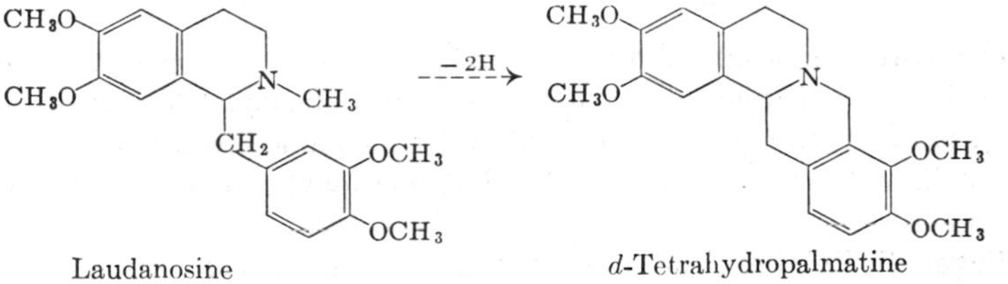

| Laudanosine | *d*-Tetrahydropalmatine |

The ring system of *d*-tetrahydropalmatine is characteristic of corydaline, the principal alkaloid of corydalis plants, and of berberine, an important constituent of plants of the genus *Berberis*.

Of some twenty-three alkaloids isolated from opium, five belong to the morphine group and the remainder are benzylisoquinolines or simpler substances that appear to be building units or by-products of the phytosynthesis of these substances. Morphine is chemically related to the benzylisoquinoline alkaloids through apomorphine and the aporphines, but the possibility of a direct biogenetic relationship was suggested by Gulland and Robinson[2] and by Schöpf:[3] the benzylisoquinoline alkaloids may be the natural precursors of the morphine compounds. Laudanosine, for example, might suffer reduction in the isoquinoline nucleus and O-de-

[1] See syntheses by Späth and Kruta, *Ber.*, **62**, 1024 (1929); Hahn and Kley, *ibid.*, **70**, 685 (1937).
[2] Gulland and Robinson, *Mem. Proc. Manchester Lit. Phil. Soc.*, **69**, 79 (1925).
[3] Schöpf, *Ann.*, **452**, 211 (1927).

methylation to I. If, in the hypothetical formula I, ring A is revolved through an angle of 180° about the axis of the dotted line, the formula can be written as in Ia. Ring closure is imagined as taking place at the carbon atom (*a*) of an original bridge head and this consequently is the point of attachment (C_{13}) of an ethanamine chain in the final product. In this way it is possible to conceive the phytosynthesis of the complex ring system of morphine from benzylisoquinoline alkaloids or their progenitors by a process involving no readjustment of the carbon skeleton.

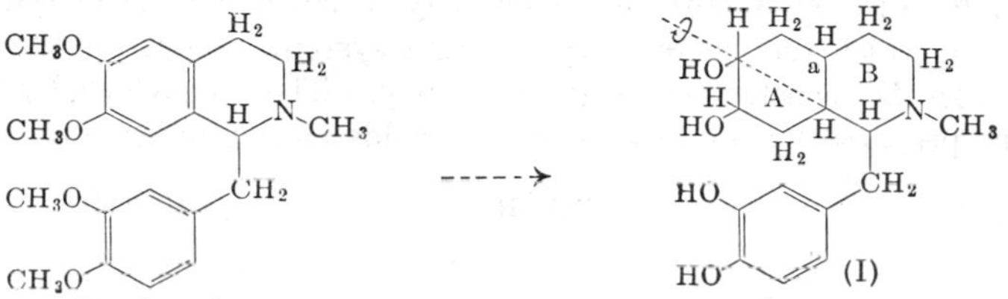

Laudanosine   →   (I)

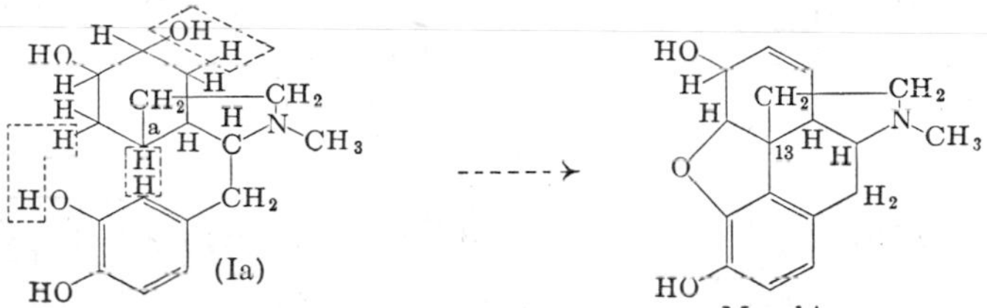

(Ia)   →   Morphine

Synthetic Experiments. Although the morphine molecule contains five asymmetric carbon atoms, the spatial arrangement in the network of the four rings appears to be such that only one combination of orientations at the four asymmetric sites of ring juncture (or the mirror image arrangement) would give a strain-free structure. The synthetic construction of a ring system of the correct structure therefore would probably afford a product of the morphine-sinomenine orientation at all ring junctures. Furthermore, the closing of the oxide bridge and the reduction of the 6-keto group affords exclusively products of the natural orientation at C_5 and C_6. Although the synthesis would appear to be simplified by these considerations, the problem still awaits solution. The postulated biogenetic relation to benzylisoquinolines led to a few attempts to oxidize the suspected precursors, but the early experiments were without promise.

Work has only recently been started on the development of methods applicable to total synthesis. Fieser and Holmes[1] effected the synthesis

[1] Fieser and Holmes, *J. Am. Chem. Soc.*, **58**, 2319 (1936); **60**, 2548 (1938); see extensions by Holmes and Trevoy, *Can. J. Res.*, **22B**, 56, 109 (1944); Holmes and Mann, *J. Am. Chem. Soc.*, **69**, 2000 (1947).

of 3,4-dimethoxy-13-carboxyoctahydrophenanthrene by a method employing a Diels-Alder addition (18% yield); Ghosh and Robinson[2] synthesized the corresponding ethyl derivative from a substituted β-tetralone through a Mannich base; and Gates and Newhall[3] have developed an efficient diene synthesis of 13-cyanomethyl-9,10-diketo-5,8,9,10,13,14-hexahydrophenanthrene; but these experiments were directed to the preparation of substances for comparison with possible products of alkaloid degradation. Early exploratory experiments by Koelsch[4] and by Grewe[5] were without immediate issue, but Grewe[6] more recently discovered a novel synthetic method by which the entire morphine ring system, except for the oxide bridge, can be constructed with efficiency. The benzylhexahydroisoquinoline prepared by the process shown yields an octahydride on hydro-

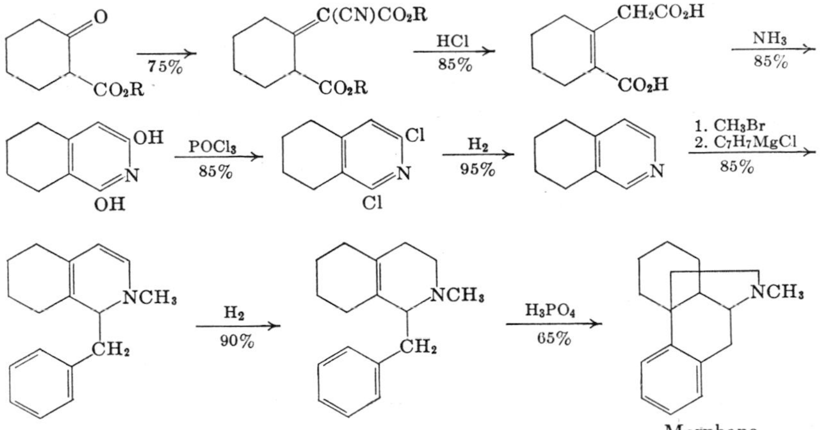

Morphane

genation that undergoes smooth cyclization with phosphoric acid in the manner postulated for the morphine biogenesis to a product designated morphane (m.p. 62°).[7] The substance was degraded through a des-base to a dihydro-des-base of established[5] structure.

Morphine Substitutes. Morphine has long been held in high value in medicine because of its outstanding analgesic action, or ability to alleviate excruciating pain. This beneficial action on the central nervous system unfortunately is accompanied by the insidious property of producing drug

[2] Ghosh and Robinson, *J. Chem. Soc.*, 506 (1944).

[3] Gates and Newhall, *J. Am. Chem. Soc.*, **70**, 2261 (1948).

[4] Koelsch, *J. Am. Chem. Soc.*, **67**, 569 (1945).

[5] Grewe, *Ber.*, **72**, 426, 785, 1314 (1939); **76**, 1072, 1076 (1943).

[6] Grewe, *Naturwiss.*, **11**, 333 (1946).

[7] For other syntheses of tetrahydroisoquinoline, see Schlittler and Merian, *Helv. Chim. Acta*, **30**, 1339 (1947); Witkop, *J. Am. Chem. Soc.*, **70**, 2617 (1948).

addiction. Morphine not only relieves pain and restlessness, but also, for a time, produces a pleasurable feeling of well-being, or euphoria, which invites continued use that may soon lead to physical and mental dependence upon the drug. Morphine addicts develop an amazingly high demand for and tolerance of morphine, much of which is excreted in unchanged form in the urine,[1] and withdrawal of drug from a tolerant individual is attended with extremely distressing symptoms. The likewise habit-forming narcotic drug cocaine has been largely replaced by the synthetic substance novocaine, an effective local anesthetic free from addiction properties. Considerable effort has been expended in the search for addiction-free analgesic agents to replace morphine, and several substances are at present under consideration for this purpose. The toxicity and relative analgesic activity in test animals are easily determined, but the systemic effects and the habituation characteristics of a given compound can only be evaluated from the results of extended clinical studies. Present indications are that most or all of the proposed substitutes are addictive. Some may nevertheless prove to be preferable because of a decreased tendency to cause habituation or because they can be administered orally; morphine is not tolerated by mouth and produces severe nausea and vomiting.

In an extensive program of research initiated in 1929 at the Universities of Virginia and Michigan under the auspices of the National Research Council, hundreds of morphine derivatives and synthetic substances of related structure were prepared and documented.[2] The most interesting substances developed by Small, Mosettig and associates in the course of this work are dihydrodesoxymorphine-D and metopon.[3] Dihydrodesoxymorphine-D is by far the most potent analgesic known but suffers from briefness of action and rapid development of tolerance.[4] Metopon has no

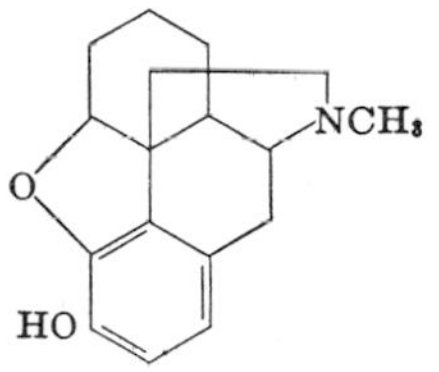

Dihydrodesoxymorphine-D 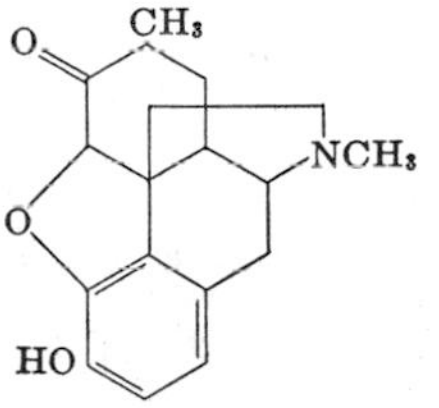   Metopon

[1] Oberst, *J. Pharmacol.*, **73**, 401 (1941); **74**, 37 (1942).

[2] Small, Eddy, Mosettig and Himmelsbach, "Studies in Drug Addiction," U. S. Treasury Department, Supplement No. 138 to the Public Health Reports (1938).

[3] See Announcement, *J. Am. Med. Assoc.*, **134**, 291 (1947); Eddy, *J. Am. Pharm. Assoc.*, **VIII**, No. 9 (1947).

[4] Pharmacology: Stöckli and Fromherz, *Helv. Physiol. Pharmacol. Acta*, **3**, 335 (1945) [*C. A.*, **40**, 948 (1946)].

particular advantage in general analgesia work (acute brief pain), and it is prepared from morphine at a cost probably several times that of the natural alkaloid, but it is a very promising drug for chronic pain relief in terminal cancer cases. The analgesic effectiveness is at least twice that of morphine; the duration of action and the addiction liability are about the same; and tolerance appears to develop more slowly to metopon than to morphine. The great advantage is that metopon can be administered orally without causing nausea and vomiting and gives adequate pain relief with very little mental dulling.

A series of simpler and more readily available synthetic analgesic agents were developed by chemists of the I. G. Farbenindustrie. The first (1939) was the substance known as dolantin in Germany and as demerol (or meperidine) in the United States.[5] According to present reports, demerol

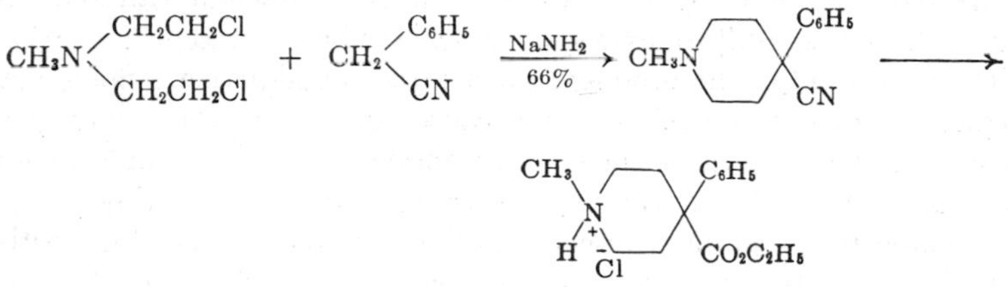

$$CH_3N\begin{cases}CH_2CH_2Cl \\ CH_2CH_2Cl\end{cases} + CH_2\begin{cases}C_6H_5 \\ CN\end{cases} \xrightarrow[66\%]{NaNH_2} CH_3N\underset{CN}{\overset{C_6H_5}{\bigcirc}} \longrightarrow$$

Demerol

is distinctly less powerful in analgesic action than morphine but is also less toxic. It has addiction properties, but the liability is probably less than for morphine. Demerol, like atropine, is spasmolytic (relaxes smooth muscle); it is said to be useful in the alleviation of pain associated with

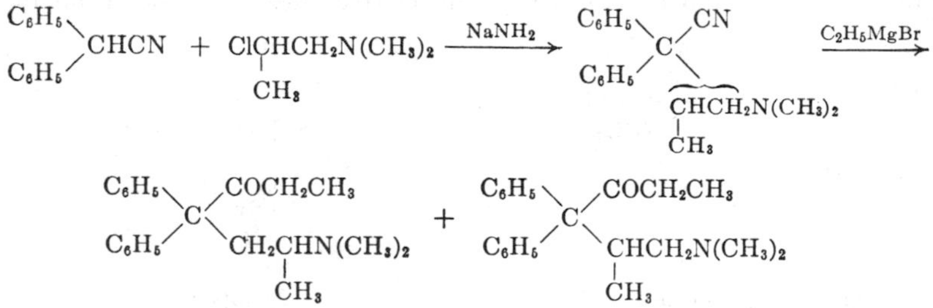

$$\begin{matrix}C_6H_5 \\ C_6H_5\end{matrix}CHCN + ClCHCH_2N(CH_3)_2 \xrightarrow{NaNH_2} \begin{matrix}C_6H_5 \\ C_6H_5\end{matrix}C\begin{matrix}CN \\ CHCH_2N(CH_3)_2\end{matrix} \xrightarrow{C_2H_5MgBr}$$
$$\underset{CH_3}{} \qquad \underset{CH_3}{}$$

$$\begin{matrix}C_6H_5 \\ C_6H_5\end{matrix}C\begin{matrix}COCH_2CH_3 \\ CH_2CHN(CH_3)_2\end{matrix} + \begin{matrix}C_6H_5 \\ C_6H_5\end{matrix}C\begin{matrix}COCH_2CH_3 \\ CHCH_2N(CH_3)_2\end{matrix}$$
$$\underset{CH_3}{} \qquad \underset{CH_3}{}$$

Amidone   Isoamidone

muscular spasm. The drugs amidone and isoamidone developed more recently in Germany are many times more potent than demerol and are

[5] Eisleb and Schaumann, *Deut. mediz. Wochschr.*, **65**, 967 (1939). Synthesis: Eisleb, *Ber.*, **74**, 1433 (1941); Bergel, Morrison and Rinderknecht, *J. Chem. Soc.*, 265 (1944); Walton and Green, *ibid.*, 315 (1945).

comparable to morphine in analgesic activity[6]; one or the other drug probably will replace morphine in many of its applications. The original synthesis affords amidone as the chief product through a rearrangement.[7] A new synthesis of amidone from diphenylacetonitrile and propylene oxide has been described.[8] Although the structural formulas of demerol, amidone, and isoamidone can be written in ways that simulate the morphine structure, any implication of a true correlation of physiological activity with structure seems to us unfounded.

[6] Report 981, Office of the Publication Board, Department of Commerce.

[7] E. M. Schultz, Robb and Sprague, *J. Am. Chem. Soc.*, **69**, 188 (1947); Easton, J. H. Gardner and J. R. Stevens, *ibid.*, **69**, 976 (1947).

[8] Easton, J. H. Gardner and J. R. Stevens, *J. Am. Chem. Soc.*, **69**, 2941 (1947).

Chapter II
Resin Acids

The limpid oleoresin that exudes from incisions cut in the bark of living pine trees is separated by steam distillation into a steam-volatile fraction, gum turpentine (1 part), and a nonvolatile residue which when cold sets to a yellow or brown glass known as rosin or colophony (4 parts). The two products are known as "naval stores" because of the long-established use of rosin for calking the hulls of ships and for weatherproofing of ropes. In the United States the supply of naval stores from Southern long-leaf pine forests has been supplemented by the recovery of turpentine and rosin from stumps remaining from lumbering operations by solvent extraction. Turpentine oils contain α-pinene (chief constituent), β-pinene, monocyclic terpenes, and terpene alcohols. Rosin is composed largely of diterpene acids of the formula $C_{19}H_{29}COOH$ in various stages of isomerization. The chief useful product obtainable from American pine rosin is the relatively stable substance abietic acid (L. *abies*, fir tree). This acid is a minor constituent of the original fresh oleoresin but is formed by isomerization of labile resin acids. One of these, the principal primary acid from American pines, is levopimaric acid, a labile bond-isomer that is transformed into abietic acid by mineral acid in the cold, by hot acetic acid, or by mild heat treatment. The structures of these and other acids known to be constituents of the gum oleoresin of *Pinus palustris* are shown in Chart 1; the relative proportions indicated are those found by G. C. Harris.[1] Fresh pine resin is found to contain less levopimaric acid when collected in the summer than in the winter, probably because of a greater acidity of the summer sap. *d*-Pimaric acid, a minor constituent of the resins from certain species of pine, is stable to heat and is not subject to acid isomerization. The names originally given to the two pimaric acids implied that they are stereoisomers; they are now known to be structural isomers and the trivial name levopimaric acid is applied to one and the name *d*-pimaric acid to the other as an indication of lack of correspondence in structure. The 7-epimer of *d*-pimaric acid was recently isolated by Harris.

Some of the resin acids are sensitive not only to acids and heat but also to air and light. Abietic acid, although it can be formed by heat treatment

[1] G. C. Harris, *J. Am. Chem. Soc.*, **70**, 3671 (1948).

and is the end product of acid isomerization, is partially isomerized to neoabietic acid on moderate heat treatment and at higher temperatures suffers
disproportionation to give mixtures of dehydroabietic acid and di- and
tetrahydroabietic acids.   Abietic acid is also very sensitive to autoxidation
even when highly purified.   Fresh oleoresin is subject to ready air oxidation
and rapidly becomes discolored on exposure; the oxidation is believed
to be catalyzed by a neutral, vaguely characterized companion substance

Chart 1.   ACIDS OF *Pinus palustris**

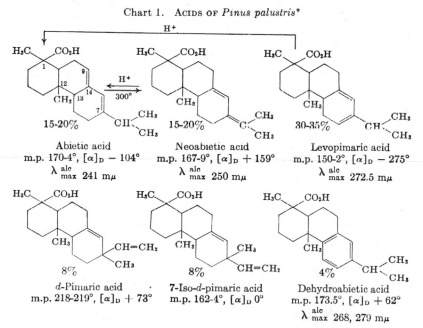

* A dihydroabietic acid also has been isolated as the lactone.

("resene").[2]   Thus extensive changes can occur during the collection and
storage of oleoresins and in the process of separation of turpentine by steam
distillation.   The copal and kauri copal of various tropical trees are found
largely as fossil resins after the plant has decayed.   In the process of aging
the more volatile oils evaporate and the acidic constituents, modified by
isomerization and oxidation, form a viscous gum or a hard, glasslike resin.
The investigation of primary acid constituents is subject to considerable
uncertainty because of the ease with which changes occur.   The isolation
of acids, however, can be accomplished without separation of the terpenes

[2] Kesler, Lowy and Faragher, *J. Am. Chem. Soc.*, **49**, 2898 (1927).

by steam distillation. When a fresh oleoresin is allowed to stand at a low temperature, preferably under nitrogen, the acidic components partly separate in a crystalline state, and centrifugation affords a cake of crystalline mixed acids known as a galipot. The processing of galipots of various sources has led to the isolation of a number of supposedly homogeneous acids. However, the characterization and identification of the often labile primary resin acids presents considerable difficulty, particularly since the isomeric acids have similar solubilities and tend to form isomorphous crystals. Even the purest samples of abietic acid and of levopimaric acid melt over a considerable range, and the melting point thus does not provide a reliable criterion of purity or identity. Constancy of rotation also cannot be relied upon as an index of purity, for some mixtures of acids show no change in composition on repeated crystallization. Thus many of the preparations described in the literature as new primary resin acids are very probably mixtures derived from the seven true components listed in Chart 1.

Abietic Acid from Rosin. Crude abietic acid prepared from rosin by the action of acids or heat is one of the cheapest and most abundantly available of higher organic acids. The rosin production in the United States in the year ending March 31, 1948 was 1,990,831 drums (520-lb.); about 60 percent of the production is normally exported. Rosin is used in low-grade soaps, in paper sizes and varnishes, and in the plastics industry. A disadvantage is the sensitivity to air oxidation with attending discoloration, but stabilization can be effected by hydrogenation or by disproportionation (see Dehydroabietic Acid).

The most satisfactory laboratory procedures for the preparation of abietic acid of high quality involve an initial mild isomerization by acids. In a convenient method described by Steele,[1] rosin of good quality (not oxidized) is dissolved in 98 percent acetic acid and the solution is refluxed for two hours, filtered, and cooled; the crystalline product that separates is recrystallized once and affords partially purified abietic acid, m.p. 159 – 161°, $[\alpha]_D - 77°$, in about 40 percent yield. Isomerized rosin of comparable quality can be prepared by refluxing rosin (250 g.) in 95 percent alcohol (740 cc.) containing 36 percent hydrochloric acid (42 cc.) for one and one-half hours.[2,3] Further purification of the Steele acid was accomplished by Palkin[2] by repeated crystallization of the quarter-salt:[4] $C_{19}H_{29}CO_2Na \cdot 3C_{19}H_{29}CO_2H$, m.p. 175°. This acid salt is much less soluble than the normal salt and crystallizes well from alcohol; after crystallization

[1] Steele, *J. Am. Chem. Soc.*, **44**, 1333 (1922).
[2] Palkin and T. H. Harris, *J. Am. Chem. Soc.*, **55**, 3677 (1933); **56**, 1935 (1934).
[3] G. C. Harris and Sanderson, *J. Am. Chem. Soc.*, **70**, 334 (1948).
[4] Dupont, *Compt. rend.*, **172**, 1373 (1921).

to constant melting point it is converted into the more soluble abietic acid by acidification of an alcoholic solution and dilution with water. Palkin's purest abietic acid is characterized by high levorotation, $[\alpha]_D - 104°$. The colorless crystals of the pure acid became yellowish and tacky on exposure to the air for a few hours, and the acid is best stored in the form of the quarter-salt, which is completely stable to air. Palkin prepared the crude quarter-salt by refluxing rosin in alcoholic solution containing hydrochloric acid and then adding the proper amount of sodium hydroxide. Another method[5] of purifying acid-isomerized material involves crystallization of the l-bornylamine salt (m.p. 162°, $[\alpha]_D - 43°$); the abietic acid recovered from the salt is reported to melt at $174 - 175°$; $[\alpha]_D - 116°$. A practical method described by Harris and Sanderson[3] consists in crystallization of the di-amylamine salt and acidification with acetic acid; the yield of abietic acid, m.p. $172 - 175°$, $[\alpha]_D - 106°$, was 40 percent of isomerized rosin.

Ruzicka conducted extensive studies of structure with material prepared by distillation of rosin at $200 - 210°/1$ mm. (yield 90%) and crystallization of the glassy distillate from alcohol.[6] The resulting partially purified material had about the same melting point and optical rotation as the Steele acid but may have contained different contaminants.

Relationship of Abietic Acid to Retene. Chemical investigations of the acids of rosin were undertaken in the early part of the nineteenth century. The name abietic acid was first applied by Baup[1] in 1826 to a product obtained from *Pinus abies*. Much of the early work dealt with the isolation of acids from different sources, and many substances of doubtful individuality were described and named. Attention was directed particularly to the abundant and relatively stable abietic acid. The occurrence of the acid in conjunction with terpenes suggested a relationship to these substances, but a still more enlightening relationship was that established between abietic acid and the aromatic hydrocarbon retene, $C_{18}H_{18}$.

A hydrocarbon preparation that apparently was essentially retene in an impure condition was described as early as 1837 by Trommsdorff,[2] who studied a substance found by Fikentscher in fossilized pine wood from a peat bed, along with fichtelite (see below). The hydrocarbon was obtained in a purer form in 1858 by Knauss from the pine tar oil resulting from the destructive distillation of pine wood or of rosin. This material was studied and described by Fehling[3] and by Fritzsche.[4] Pure retene (Gr. *rhetine*,

[5] Bardyshev, *J. Gen. Chem.* (U.S.S.R.), **11**, 996 (1941) [*C. A.*, **39**, 4616 (1945)].

[6] Ruzicka and J. Meyer, *Helv. Chim. Acta*, **5**, 315 (1922).

[1] Baup. *Ann. chim. phys.*, [2], **31**, 108 (1826).

[2] Trommsdorff, *Ann.*, **21**, 126 (1837).

[3] Fehling, *Ann.*, **106**, 388 (1858).

[4] Fritzsche, *J. prakt. Chem.*, **75**, 281 (1858); **82**, 321 (1861).

pine tree) is a colorless, crystalline substance melting at 98 – 99°. Only small amounts of retene were obtained from the technical oils produced industrially by the high-temperature distillation of resins and oleoresins, but in 1887 patents were assigned for a method of increasing the yield of retene by heating the oils with sulfur until no further hydrogen sulfide is evolved, followed by distillation of the residue.[5] The pine tar oils probably contain various products of the pyrolysis of abietic acid. In 1903 Vesterberg[6] submitted abietic acid ($C_{19}H_{29}COOH$) to reaction with sulfur and obtained retene ($C_{18}H_{18}$) as the principal product. This reaction is the first instance of the dehydrogenation of a hydroaromatic compound to a completely aromatic type. The method of dehydrogenation introduced by Vesterberg has been of the greatest importance in the investigation of other natural products, and in the case of abietic acid Vesterberg's observation provided a valuable clue to the structure of the substance. Retene contains all but two of the original carbon atoms of the resin acid and the structure of the hydrocarbon was in large part already known at the time when it became a matter of importance in resin acid chemistry.

Structure of Retene. Comprehensive studies of retene and its derivatives were carried out by Wahlforss[1] in Finland in 1869 and by Ekstrand[2] in Sweden in 1877, but neither investigator was able to arrive at a very clear conception of the structure. Bamberger[3] started work on the problem in the Munich laboratory in 1884 and characterized an orange oxidation product, first prepared by Wahlforss, as an ortho quinone closely resembling phenanthrenequinone. The colored retenequinone could be reduced to a colorless hydroquinone, it yielded a quinoxaline derivative, and it could be oxidized to a dicarboxylic acid resembling diphenic acid. The quinone presented a perplexing problem, however, for although it could be obtained from retene under the conditions employed for the preparation of phenanthrenequinone, and although retene could be regenerated on zinc dust distillation, the analytical figures available did not indicate that the quinone and the hydrocarbon are related to each another in the normal manner. There were other apparent contradictions in the early work and although a number of derivatives and degradation products of retene had been prepared in a pure condition the relationship between them remained obscure until special attention was given to the problem of analysis in the investigations of Bamberger and Hooker.[4] Hooker, a young Englishman who

[5] See for example, *Ber.*, **21R**, 553 (1888).
[6] Vesterberg, *Ber.*, **36**, 4200 (1903).
[1] Wahlforss, *Chem. Zentr.*, **40**, 479 (1869).
[2] Ekstrand, *Ann.*, **185**, 75 (1877).
[3] Bamberger, *Ber.*, **17**, 453 (1884); **18**, 81 (1885).
[4] Bamberger and Hooker, *Ber.*, **18**, 1024, 1030, 1750 (1885); *Ann.*, **229**, 102 (1885).

took up the problem where other of Bamberger's students had left off, discovered that many of the compounds of the retene group burn with great difficulty and that macrocombustions conducted in the ordinary way with a copper oxide filling often lead to erroneous results. By using a very small sample, mixing it with lead chromate, and conducting the combustion in a tube packed with lead chromate, Hooker was able to obtain accurate analytical results. Several of the empirical formulas previously assigned were found to require revision, and the new formulas made possible a rational interpretation and extension of accumulated earlier results. In a very short time Bamberger and Hooker were able to untangle the accumulated observations in the field and to carry the determination of structure nearly to completion.

One series of degradations established that retene is an alkyl derivative of phenanthrene and that the central ring is the one involved in the formation of the quinone. The oxidation of retenequinone (I) with alkaline

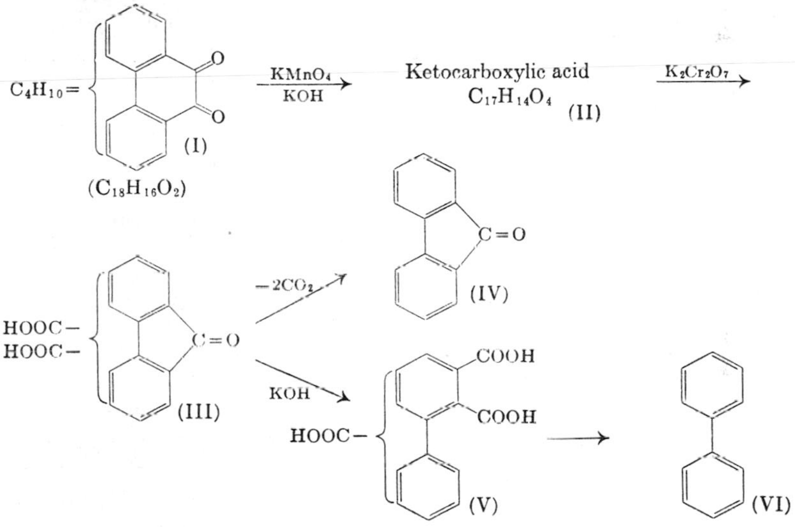

permanganate proceeds by way of a benzilic acid rearrangement and results in the elimination of one carbonyl group from the quinonoid ring. The character of the oxidation product II will be discussed below. The product of further oxidation, III, was shown to be a fluorenonedicarboxylic acid by its conversion to fluorenone (IV) and diphenyl (VI). The presence of two carboxyl groups in the fluorenone derivative III shows that the C_4H_{10}-residue of the quinone (I) must be distributed between two alkyl groups. The location of one of these groups can be inferred from the fact that the tricarboxylic acid V easily forms an anhydride whereas the dibasic acid III does not do so. One carboxyl group must be in the ortho position to the carbonyl group of III and to the carboxyl group which is liberated in the fusion with alkali. It follows that an alkyl group of the original quinone is situated at C_1, adjacent to a quinonoid carbonyl group.

According to this evidence retenequinone is either a diethyl- or a methyl-propyl-phenanthrenequinone, and the character of the keto acid (II, above) obtained as the first oxidation product distinguishes between the two possibilities. Since the carbon atom lost in the formation of this keto acid is known to come from the quinonoid nucleus, the four carbon atoms of the original alkyl groups are still intact. The carboxyl group of the oxidation product (II) could not have come from an ethyl or propyl group without the loss of carbon and it must have arisen from a methyl group. The second alkyl radical therefore is a propyl group, and a choice between the normal and the branched-chain structure can be made from the fact that the keto acid II contains one oxygen atom not accounted for in the carbonyl and carboxyl groups. Since the *n*-propyl group is not susceptible to partial oxidation, whereas an isopropyl group can be hydroxylated by alkaline permanganate, the degradation product can be assigned structure VII.

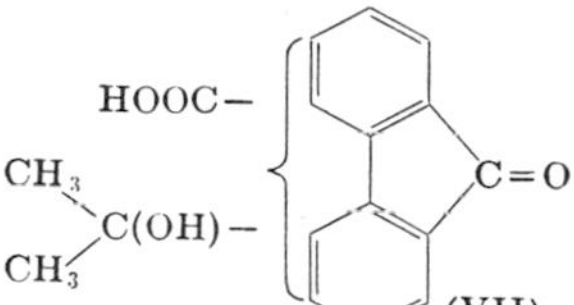

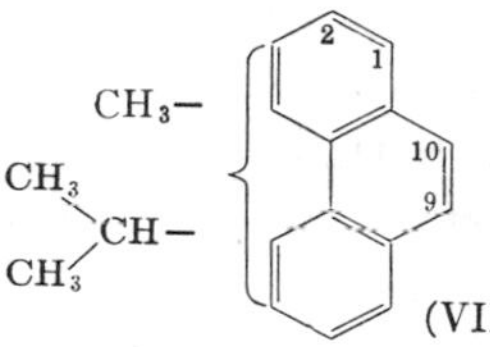

Retene is a methylisopropylphenanthrene, in which one of the alkyl groups is located at C_1 and the other is at some position other than C_2, C_9, or C_{10}.

This much of the structure of retene was established by Bamberger and Hooker in 1885. The problem of locating the alkyl groups completely remained unsolved for twenty-five years, although isolated observations[5] indicated that the methyl and the isopropyl groups probably are situated at C_1 and C_7 or at C_7 and C_1. Finally in 1910 Bucher[6] at Brown University achieved a complete proof of structure in a series of brilliantly executed oxidations. By the action of potassium permanganate on retenequinone in pyridine solution, Bucher obtained a tribasic hydroxy acid (IX) in which the carboxyl groups at C_2 and C_2' obviously come from the opening of the

---

[5] Fortner, *Monatsh.*, **25**, 443 (1904); Lux, *ibid.*, **29**, 763 (1908); Schultze, *Ann.*, **359**, 129 (1908).

[6] Bucher, *J. Am. Chem. Soc.*, **32**, 374 (1910).

quinonoid ring. Whereas diphenic acid itself sublimes unchanged, although it can be converted into an anhydride by the action of acetyl chloride, the degradation product (IX) forms an anhydride when heated at the melting

(IX)

(X)

Hemimellitic acid

Trimellitic acid

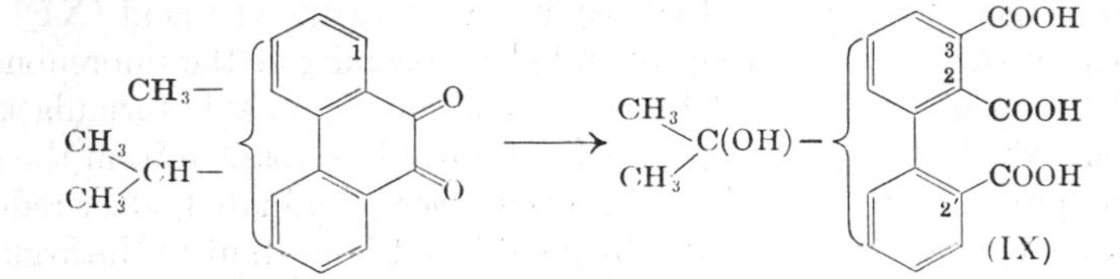

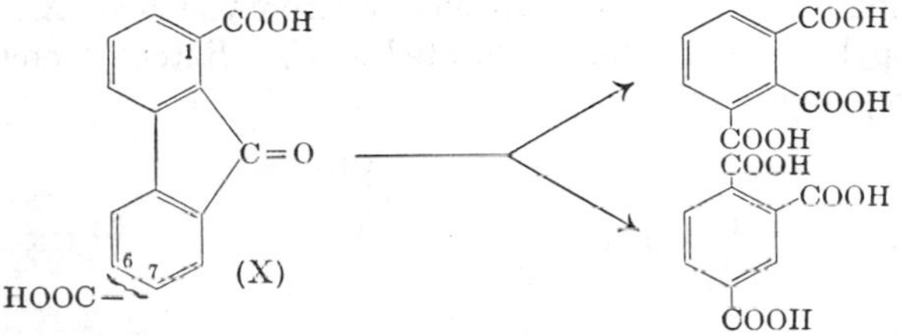

point. The third carboxyl group therefore is ortho to one of the other groups and can be placed at C_3, corresponding to C_1 in retene. The alkyl group originally occupying this position could not be the isopropyl group, for the C_3-residue is still retained in the product in a hydroxylated condition. The carboxyl group appearing at C_3 in the oxidation product comes from a methyl group at C_1 in retene and retenequinone.

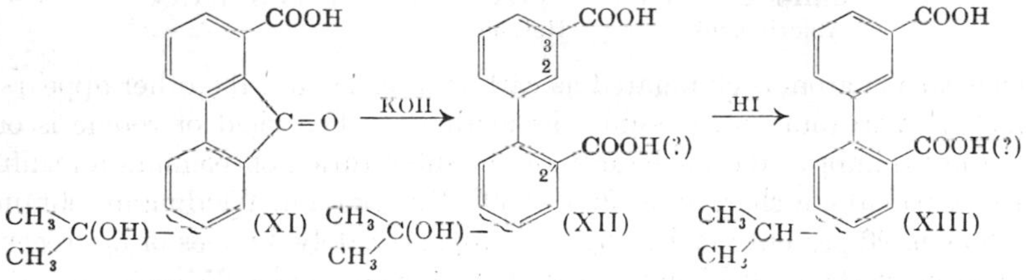

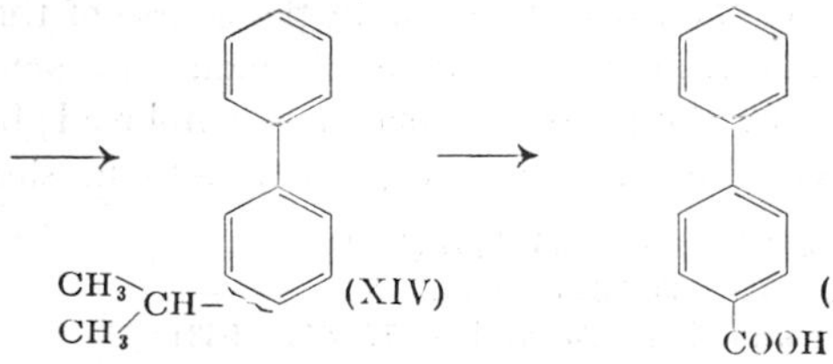

Some indication of the position of the isopropyl group was furnished by Bucher's observation that the fluorenonedicarboxylic acid (X) of Bamberger and Hooker yields hemimellitic acid and trimellitic acid on oxidation

(XI) (XII) (XIII)

(XIV) (XV)

with potassium permanganate, which shows that the unlocated carboxyl group in the dibasic acid (X) is in the ring not occupied by the first group and is at either C_6 or C_7. A final decision was obtained by the degradation of Bamberger and Hooker's hydroxyfluorenonecarboxylic acid (XI). The position of the carboxyl group liberated on opening of the fluorenone ring of XI by alkali fusion is not known. The more probable formula is that (XII) in which the new group is as far removed as possible from the group already present. Since both of the groups were eliminated, after reduction of the alcoholic hydroxyl group, the point is not important to the argument. The final oxidation gave the known diphenyl-4-carboxylic acid (XV), and hence the isopropyl group of retene is located at C_7. Retene therefore is 1-methyl-7-isopropylphenanthrene.

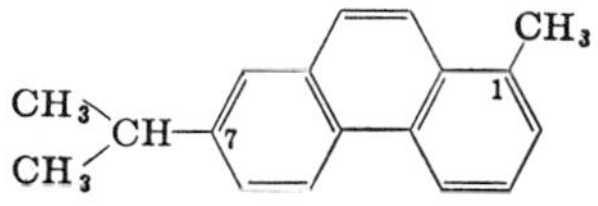

Retene

When retene is refluxed with Fuller's earth the isopropyl group is eliminated as propylene, and 1-methylphenanthrene is obtained in 29 percent yield.[7]

Structure of Abietic Acid. The identification of the aromatic hydrocarbon resulting from the dehydrogenation of abietic acid with sulfur establishes the arrangement of eighteen of the twenty carbon atoms of the resin acid. The main reaction probably is that represented by the equation:

$$C_{19}H_{29}COOH + 5S \rightarrow C_{18}H_{18} + 4H_2S + CH_3SH + CO_2$$
Abietic acid   Retene

One carbon atom is eliminated as carbon dioxide, and the other appears as methyl mercaptan or, possibly, as methane. The yield of retene is only fair but is improved considerably by the substitution of selenium for sulfur.[1] Using palladium charcoal at $300-330°$, Ruzicka and Waldmann[2] obtained retene in 90 percent yield along with approximately 4 moles of hydrogen, 1 mole of methane, 0.75 mole of carbon dioxide, and 0.25 mole of carbon monoxide. The loss of the carboxyl group in the course of these reactions provides no reliable indication of its manner of linkage, for acids of various kinds are unstable under the pyrolytic conditions employed; but the elimination of a methyl group as methyl mercaptan or methane shows that this

[7] Hasselstrom, *J. Am. Chem. Soc.*, **63**, 1164 (1941).
[1] Diels and Karstens, *Ber.*, **60**, 2323 (1927).
[2] Ruzicka and Waldmann, *Helv. Chim. Acta*, **16**, 842 (1933).

group must occupy some special situation in the abietic acid molecule. Since the methyl and isopropyl groups which survive the reaction appear as substituents in the aromatic rings of retene, the group eliminated must have occupied a position not available for substitution in the dehydrogenation product. A methyl group thus must be situated in an angular position between two rings:

$$\longrightarrow \qquad + CH_4 + 2H_2$$

Such a substituent, whether it is an alkyl, carboxyl, or hydroxyl group, will be referred to as a tertiarily bound group, for it is situated on a (quaternary) carbon atom which is joined to three other carbon residues.

Abietic acid appears from this evidence to be a 1-methyl-7-isopropyl-perhydrophenanthrene with a methyl group at any of the positions: 1, 11, 12, 13, or 14, and with an unlocated carboxyl group. In the formula the

nuclear hydrogen atoms are omitted for convenience and the three rings are numbered in the same sequence as the carbon atoms. Since the number of carbon atoms in the resin acid is an even multiple of the C_5-isoprene unit, and since the acid occurs along with various terpenes, all of which are known to be constructed of condensed isoprene groups, it was early suspected that abietic acid is a diterpene acid, and the hypothesis that the carbon skeleton is resolvable into four isoprene residues served as a useful guide to probable formulations. More evidence was required, however, to limit the number of possibilities in terms of the isoprene rule.

The composition of abietic acid indicates the presence of either two double bonds or two additional rings. The acid is unsaturated[3] to permanganate and to halogens, and extensive studies of various addition reactions have clearly indicated the presence of two ethylenic linkages. The addition of two molecules of hydrogen bromide was accomplished by Levy,[4] who also succeeded in obtaining a tetrahydroxyabietic acid[5] by oxidation with per-

---

[3] It gives the Liebermann-Burchard test (Chapter III) characteristic of unsaturated sterols, La Lande, *J. Am. Chem. Soc.*, **55**, 1536 (1933).

[4] P. Levy, *Ber.*, **40**, 3658 (1907); *Z. anorg. Chem.*, **81**, 145 (1913).

[5] P. Levy, *Ber.*, **42**, 4305 (1909); **59**, 1302 (1926); **61**, 616 (1928).

manganate under controlled conditions. Ruzicka and Meyer[6] isolated a dihydroxy acid under similar conditions. In the presence of platinum catalyst, abietic acid readily absorbs one mole of hydrogen, and a tetrahydro derivative is formed more slowly.[7] The molecular refraction of the esters of abietic acid[7] and the behavior of the acid toward perbenzoic acid[8] also point to the presence of two double bonds. The action of ozone is anomalous, for abietic acid forms a triozonide, perhaps as the result of a dehydrogenating action of the reagent.[7] The nature of two products of the oxidation of abietic acid suggested that one or both double bonds is associated with the ring (II) carrying the isopropyl group. Oxidation with nitric acid gives trimellitic acid as one degradation product.[9] The $1,2,4$-acid cannot come from ring I or ring III and must arise from the ring (II) having an alkyl group in a β-position. A second oxidation product is isobutyric acid;[10,11] the formation of this acid indicates the presence of a double bond at either the $6,7$- or $7,8$-position.

By energetic oxidation of abietic acid with potassium permanganate Ruzicka[11,12] isolated a C_{12}-acid and a C_{11}-acid identified as containing the original ring I by the presence of the nuclear methyl group characteristic of both abietic acid and retene. The yields were very poor, for only $22 - 24$ g. of each acid was obtained from 3 kg. of starting material, but the acids were isolated in both permanganate and nitric acid[13] oxidations. It will be shown presently that the acids can be represented by the formulas (b) and (c); the former probably is the precursor of the latter. The sepa-

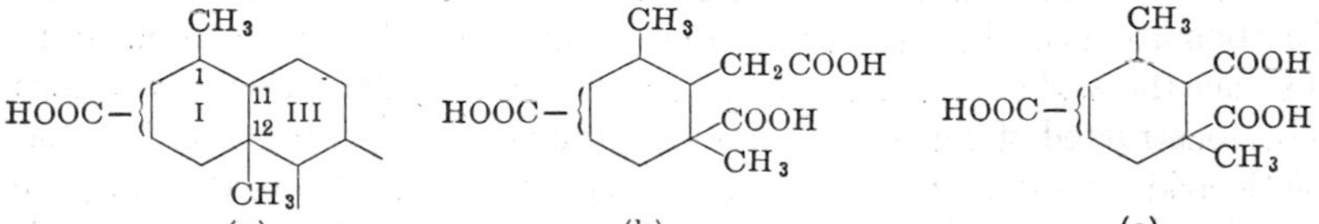

(a)	(b)	(c)
Abietic acid	$C_{12}H_{18}O_6$	$C_{11}H_{16}O_6$

ration of the acids is accomplished either by partial esterification or by partial hydrolysis of the ester mixture; the C_{12}-acid reacts more rapidly or completely in each case. Two of the carboxyl groups represent remnants of ring III, whereas the third must correspond to the original carboxyl

[6] Ruzicka and J. Meyer, *Helv. Chim. Acta*, **6**, 1097 (1923).

[7] Ruzicka and J. Meyer, *Helv. Chim. Acta*, **5**, 315 (1922).

[8] Ruzicka, Huyser and Seidel, *Rec. trav. chim.*, **47**, 363 (1928).

[9] Ruzicka and Pfeiffer, *Helv. Chim. Acta*, **8**, 632 (1925).

[10] P. Levy, *Ber.*, **42**, 4305 (1909).

[11] Ruzicka, J. Meyer and Pfeiffer, *Helv. Chim. Acta*, **8**, 637 (1925).

[12] Ruzicka, Goldberg, Huyser and Seidel, *Helv. Chim. Acta*, **14**, 545 (1931).

[13] P. Levy, *Ber.*, **62**, 2497 (1929).

group of abietic acid. Of the two methyl groups, one is that originally located at C_1 and the other is the tertiarily bound group eliminated in the conversion of abietic acid into retene. The latter group must be at C_{11} or at C_{12}, and Ruzicka[12] was able to distinguish between the two possibilities by dehydrogenation (and decarboxylation) of the C_{12}- and C_{11}-acids with selenium. The first acid gave 1,2,3-trimethylbenzene; the second, m-xylene. The tertiary methyl group and the nuclear methyl group at C_1 therefore bear a 1:3 relationship to one another, and the only possible location for the former group is at C_{12}. In confirmation of this point Ruzicka and Waldmann[2] isolated 1,3-dimethylcyclohexanone-2 in small yield in another oxidation.

The most perplexing point in the determination of the complete structure was the location of the carboxyl group of the resin acid. To early workers it seemed significant that abietic acid is esterified only with difficulty. Prolonged boiling with alcohol containing about 20 percent of sulfuric acid is necessary for complete conversion into the ethyl ester,[14] and the other esters are more conveniently prepared by methods that are not subject to steric hindrance, for example, by the action of alkyl sulfates or alkyl p-toluenesulfonates on the silver or sodium salt of the acid. Fahrion[15] suggested in 1901 that the carboxyl group probably is tertiarily bound, as for example at C_1 or C_{11} in the above partial formula. Such a location would account for the observed loss of the carboxylate group on dehydrogenation of methyl abietate with sulfur,[16] but the information available at the time did not exclude the possibility that sulfur would eliminate an ester group regardless of its location. Consequently Ruzicka and Meyer[16] undertook to reduce the carboxyl group completely and to determine if the corresponding alkyl group is eliminated on dehydrogenation. Ethyl abietate ($RCOOC_2H_5$) was reduced by the Bouveault method (sodium and alcohol) to abietinol (RCH_2OH), and the primary alcohol on dehydration with phosphorus pentachloride gave the triply unsaturated hydrocarbon "methylabietin" ($C_{20}H_{30}$). On reaction with sulfur this yielded not retene but its homolog, "methylretene," $C_{19}H_{20}$. Ruzicka assumed that the extra methyl group that survives the aromatization is joined to the phenanthrene nucleus, and that the original carboxyl group occupies a corresponding position in ring I and is not bound by a tertiary linkage.

By 1932 abietic acid was thus regarded as having the structure I or II, both of which conform with the isoprene rule. In that year, however, independent observations in three laboratories indicated that this conclusion is not valid and that abietic acid does not have the carbon framework

[14] Ruzicka, Schinz and J. Meyer, Helv. Chim. Acta, **6**, 1077 (1923).

[15] Fahrion, Z. angew. Chem., **14**, 1197 (1901).

[16] Ruzicka and J. Meyer, Helv. Chim. Acta, **5**, 581 (1922).

of either I or II.   Vocke[17] at Munich was the first to suggest a revision, but his results were not entirely conclusive.   An attempted oxidative degradation of the diphenylcarbinol obtained from the methyl ester of tetrahydro-

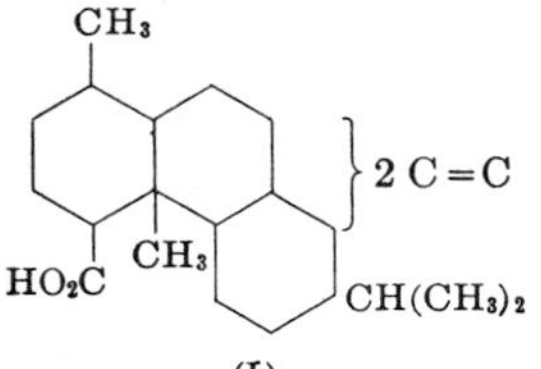

CH₃ ... 2 C = C ... (I) ... CH₃ ... HO₂C ... 2 C = C ... (II)

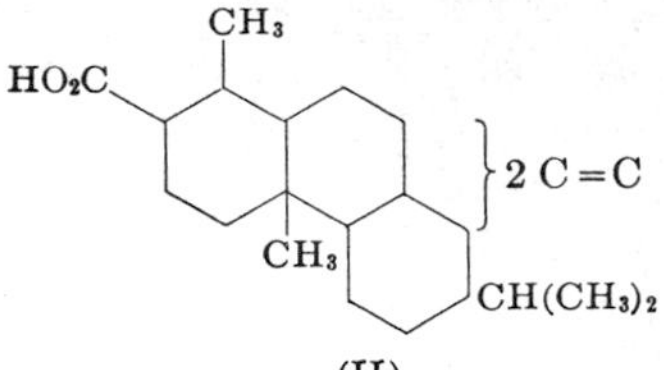

abietic acid and phenylmagnesium bromide was unsuccessful; the oxygen-containing group was so resistant to attack as to suggest a tertiary attachment.   Since, according to Bistrzycki,[18] secondarily bound carboxyl groups are rather stable to concentrated sulfuric acid whereas acids with tertiary groups often lose carbon monoxide on warming, Vocke applied this diagnostic test to tetrahydroabietic acid and to Ruzicka's tribasic C_{11}-acid. The results were inconclusive, but again suggestive of the presence of a tertiarily bound carboxyl group, for these acids lose some carbon monoxide on being heated with sulfuric acid.   Vocke then carried out a degradation of the C_{11}-acid and concluded that the results were best interpreted on the basis of formula III for this oxidation product.[19]   Energetic treatment with

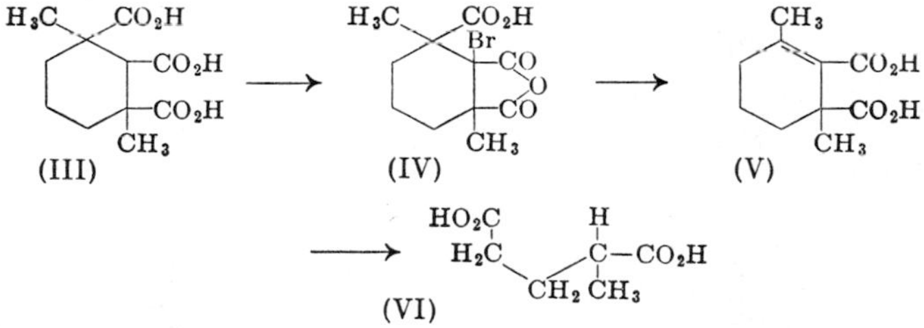

bromine and red phosphorus gave an α-bromoanhydride acid (IV) together with the corresponding acid bromide.   The —COBr group of the latter compound is highly resistant to hydrolysis.   The elimination of hydrogen bromide from IV by means of alkali was accompanied by the loss of carbon dioxide and formation of a dibasic acid of properties consistent with formula

[17] Vocke, *Ann.*, **497**, 247 (1932).

[18] Bistrzycki and v. Siemiradzki, *Ber.*, **39**, 51 (1906); **41**, 1665 (1908); Bistrzycki and Reintke, *ibid.*, **38**, 839 (1905); Ruzicka and Mauron, *ibid.*, **40**, 4370 (1907).

[19] Arbusov and Schapschinskaja, *Ber.*, **68**, 437 (1935), attempted the synthesis of an acid of this structure but did not obtain a crystalline product, possibly because of the presence of several stereoisomerides.

V.[20] The product of ozonization was not isolated but it gave a positive iodoform reaction, an indication of an original —C(CH₃)= group. Further oxidation of the ozonide gave methylglutaric acid (VI). As expected for a β,γ-unsaturated acid, V was converted by dilute sulfuric acid into a stable lactone. Vocke recognized that, although the degradation supported the formulation III for Ruzicka's acid, a possible, but not very satisfactory, explanation of the transformations can be given on the basis of the alternate formulas VII and VIII for the C_{11}-acid and the dibasic acid obtained from it.

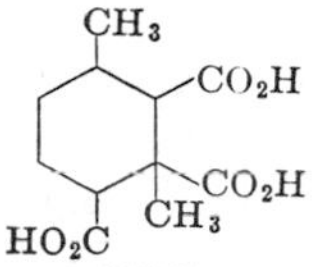

HO₂C   (VII)   HO₂C   (VIII)

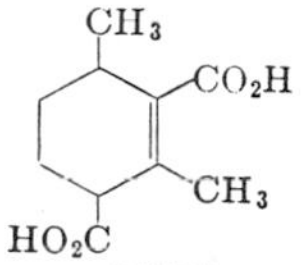

Shortly after the appearance of Vocke's paper, Ruzicka[21] reported the results of an investigation of the problem from a different point of view. Ruzicka undertook to distinguish between what he had regarded as the two most probable formulas for abietic acid (I and II above) by the degradation of "methylretene." The extra methyl group might be identified as a carboxyl group in a suitable oxidation product. In his work on *d*-pimaric acid (see below) Ruzicka had found that alkylphenanthrenes can be oxidized to phenanthrenecarboxylic acids by means of alkaline potassium ferricyanide,[22] a reagent employed by Weissgerber and Kruber[23] in the naphthalene series. Retene yields phenanthrene-1,7-dicarboxylic acid, along with diphenyl-2,3,2',4'-tetracarboxylic acid, a product of further oxidation. From "methylretene," Ruzicka, de Graaff and Müller[21] obtained, instead of the expected tribasic acid, a dibasic acid identical with the 1,7-derivative from retene. The additional methyl group is not in the phenanthrene nucleus! The only position possible is in a side chain, and indeed the extra carbon atom must be combined with the original methyl group at C_1 in the form of an ethyl group. The supposed "methylretene" is in fact 1-ethyl-7-isopropylphenanthrene.

This conclusion was reached independently and at practically the same time by R. D. Haworth[24] at the University of Durham. With the object of identifying the hydrocarbons resulting from the dehydrogenation of the

---

[20] This structure was later proved to be correct by syntheses, Rydon, *J. Chem. Soc.*, 257 (1937).

[21] Ruzicka, de Graaff and H. J. Müller, *Helv. Chim. Acta*, **15**, 1300 (1932).

[22] Ruzicka, de Graaff and Hosking, *Helv. Chim. Acta*, **14**, 233 (1931).

[23] Weissgerber and Kruber, *Ber.*, **52**, 346 (1919).

[24] R. D. Haworth, *J. Chem. Soc.*, 2717 (1932).

resin acids and their derivatives, Haworth had perfected methods for the synthesis of a wide variety of alkylphenanthrenes. This work will be described in a special section, and it is sufficient at present to state that after synthesizing the 4-methyl derivative of retene and finding that it is not identical with "methylretene," Haworth was led to suspect that the latter hydrocarbon contains an ethyl group. In the work cited, Haworth established the identity of the hydrocarbon by comparison with a sample of 1-ethyl-7-isopropylphenanthrene obtained by synthesis.

The facts could be explained on the assumption of the grouping —CH_2COOH at position C_1 in abietic acid, but a primary linkage of the carboxyl group is inconsistent with the hindrance evident in the esterification reaction. A more probable interpretation, suggested by both Ruzicka and Haworth, is that the carboxyl group is located at C_1, along with the methyl group, and that a rearrangement of the Wagner-Meerwein type occurs in the dehydration of abietinol:

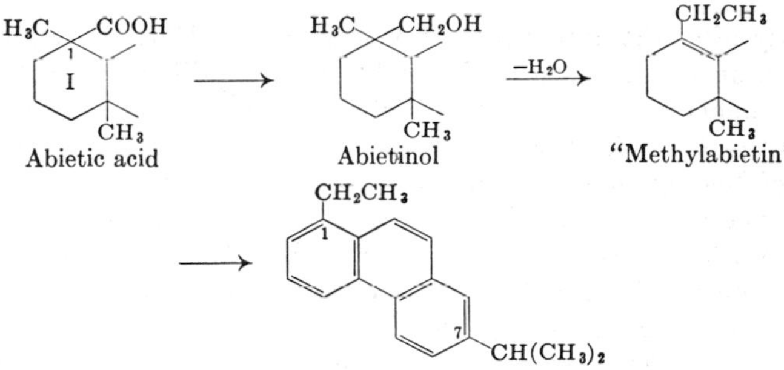

"Methylretene" (Homoretene)

If the structures are as pictured, abietinol is an alcohol of a type susceptible to dehydration only by virtue of a molecular rearrangement, for it contains a tertiarily bound primary alcoholic group. This view of the reaction series was later substantiated by the results of a degradation which involved no dehydration. Ruzicka and co-workers[25] converted abietinol into the corresponding aldehyde and reduced the carbonyl group of this substance by the Wolff-Kishner method (semicarbazone heated with sodium ethoxide). The resulting hydrocarbon gave retene, rather than its homolog, on dehydrogenation:

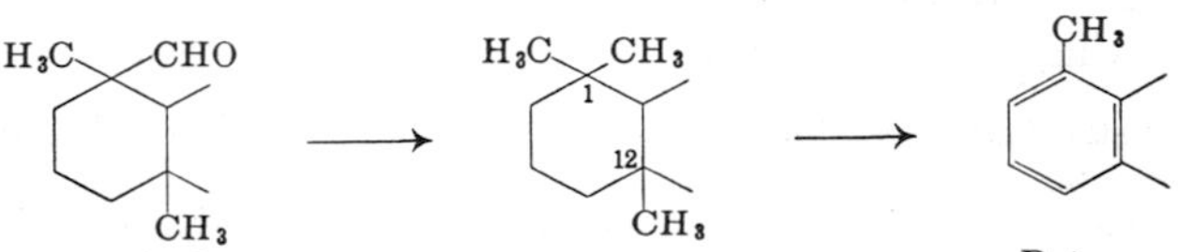

[25] Ruzicka, Waldmann, Meier and Hösli, *Helv. Chim. Acta*, **16**, 169 (1933).

One of the methyl groups at C_1, like that at C_{12}, is eliminated in the course of the aromatization of the ring in question because it is tertiarily bound. It can be inferred that the same factor is responsible for the ready elimination of the original carboxyl or carbethoxyl group in the dehydrogenation of abietic acid or its ester.[26]

The only problem remaining was that of the disposition of the two unsaturated linkages. Abietic acid was found to add maleic anhydride at temperatures above 100°,[27] and this fact was originally taken as evidence of conjugation. Ruzicka later[28] found that the same addition product (m.p. 227°) is formed from levopimaric acid at room temperature. The isomerization of levopimaric acid to abietic acid therefore is reversible and abietic acid reacts with maleic anhydride only by virtue of an isomerization to levopimaric acid at the elevated temperature required for addition. The observation was confirmed independently by Wienhaus and Sandermann,[29] who found that levopimaric acid, but not abietic acid, reacts at room temperature with quinone and with α-naphthoquinone to give crystalline yellow products. Levopimaric acid also forms an addition product with β-naphthoquinone.[30] Since levopimaric acid apparently is the only constituent of oleoresins that reacts with dienophilic reagents under mild conditions, the reaction has been useful in the investigation of primary resin acids.

The absorption spectrum[31] of abietic acid, however, furnishes conclusive evidence of the presence of a conjugated system. Supplementary chemical evidence[32] is that abietic acid couples rapidly with *p*-nitrobenzenediazonium chloride; the reaction is characteristic of open-chain[33] and cyclic[32] dienes. It was pointed out in the second edition of this book that the absorption maximum at 241 mμ found for abietic acid is indicative of the presence of

[26] From the work of Darzens [*Compt. rend.*, **183**, 748 (1926) and later papers] it appears that a secondarily bound carboxyl group similar to that indicated in Ruzicka's early formulas for abietic acid normally withstands dehydrogenation with sulfur, for example, the carboxyl group of 4-methyl-1,2,3,4-tetrahydronaphthalene-2-carboxylic acid. That 4-methyl-1,2,3,4-tetrahydronaphthalene-1-carboxylic acid loses carbon dioxide on dehydrogenation with sulfur or selenium [Darzens and A. Lévy, *ibid.*, **199**, 1131 (1934)] can be attributed to the influence of the unsaturated aromatic ring adjacent to the carboxyl group.

[27] Ruzicka, Ankersmit and B. Frank, *Helv. Chim. Acta*, **15**, 1289 (1932); Arbusov, *J. Gen. Chem.* (U. S. S. R.), **2**, 806 (1932).

[28] Bacon and Ruzicka, *Chemistry and Industry*, **55**, 546 (1936).

[29] Wienhaus and Sandermann, *Ber.*, **69**, 2202 (1936).

[30] Arbusov, *J. Gen. Chem.* (U.S.S.R.), **12**, 343 (1942) [*C. A.*, **37**, 3099 (1943)].

[31] Kraft, *Ann.*, **520**, 133 (1935); Sandermann, *Ber.*, **74**, 154 (1941); G. C. Harris and Sanderson, *J. Am. Chem. Soc.*, **70**, 334 (1948).

[32] Fieser and Campbell, *J. Am. Chem. Soc.*, **60**, 159 (1938).

[33] K. H. Meyer, *Ber.*, **52**, 1468 (1919).

a conjugated system distributed between two rings, as in formulas IX, X, and XI. Formulas IX and X would account for the formation of Ruzicka's

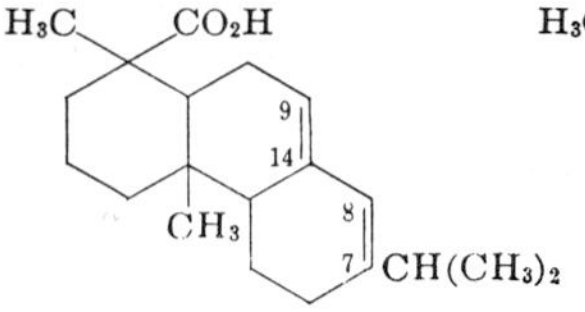

C_{12}-acid, which has a methylene group corresponding to that at the 10-position, whereas a substance of formula XI could not give rise to the C_{12}-acid and would be expected to lactonize on vigorous treatment with hydrochloric and acetic acid, which is not true of abietic acid.[7] A distinction between formulas IX and X is provided by the formation of isobutyric acid as a product of oxidation. The isolation[10] and identification[11] of this acid was later confirmed[32] with the use of abietic acid purified according to Palkin, and hence abietic acid must have the structure IX. This formula is supported by the results of various transformations of dihydroxy- and tetrahydroxyabietic acid, obtained by mild permanganate oxidation.[34]

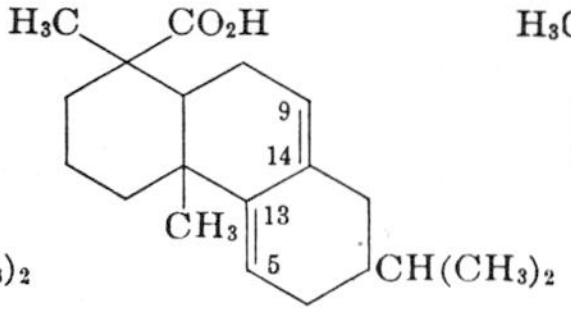

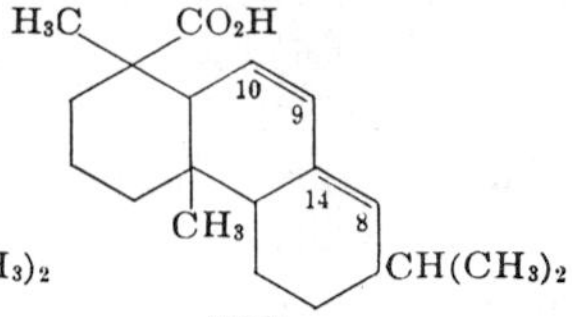

The recently expanded knowledge of the ultraviolet absorption characteristics of various types of dienic systems in the sterol series is surveyed in Chapter III, Part 2. This includes a scheme of calculation that can be applied in the present instance; the calculated maxima for formulas IX, X, and XI are: 239, 244, and 234 mμ. The observed value of 241 mμ agrees best with that calculated for IX.

Levopimaric Acid. Supplies of this labile isomer of abietic acid for investigations of structure have been obtained chiefly from the galipots of *Pinus maritima* (French) and of *Pinus palustris* (American longleaf pine).[1] Early methods of isolation[2,3] were improved and extended by Palkin and T. H. Harris,[4] who describe a process for the separation of both levopimaric acid and *d*-pimaric acid from *Pinus palustris* galipot. The crude crystallizate from the oleoresin is drained from the sirupy gum turpentine, crystallized from alcohol, and converted into the crystalline sodium salt, which contains about 70 percent levopimaric acid and 30 percent *d*-pimaric acid. The former is most easily isolated by addition of an amount of acid calcu-

[34] Ruzicka and Sternbach, *Helv. Chim. Acta*, **21**, 565 (1938); **23**, 333, 341, 355 (1940); **24**, 492 (1941); Ruzicka, Sternbach and Jeger, *ibid.*, **24**, 504 (1941).

[1] For references to the occurrence of the acid, see Elsevier's Encyclopedia, Vol. 13, 960 (1946).

[2] Dupont and Dubourg, *Bull. soc. chim.*, **39**, 1029 (1926).

[3] Ruzicka, Balas and Vilim, *Helv. Chim. Acta*, **7**, 458 (1924).

[4] Palkin and T. H. Harris, *J. Am. Chem. Soc.*, **55**, 3677 (1933).

lated from the value of the optical rotation to suffice for liberation of the levopimaric acid present and recrystallization of the free acid that separates; *d*-pimaric acid can be isolated by fractional crystallization of the mixed sodium salts. A more convenient and efficient method for the isolation of levopimaric acid from the galipot of *P. palustris* described by G. C. Harris[5] consists in crystallization of the butanolamine salt from acetone and liberation of the free acid by shaking the purified salt with ether and boric acid solution. Crystallization from dilute alcohol then gives pure levopimaric acid, $[\alpha]_D - 276°$, amounting to 20 percent of the galipot. The acid was also isolated from the whole oleoresin by precipitation of the cyclohexylamine salt from gasoline and purification through the butanolamine salt (yield about 15% of the total acids present, or nearly half the actual content of levopimaric acid).

The isomerization of levopimaric acid and its ready reaction with maleic anhydride and with quinones have been mentioned. The substance is isomerized to a dextrorotatory isomer by ultraviolet light.[6] Ozonization of levopimaric acid affords isobutyric acid[7] but no formaldehyde;[8] and retene is produced on dehydrogenation with sulfur.[3] On hydrogenation in a neutral medium in the presence of platinum or palladium catalyst, levopimaric acid absorbs one mole of hydrogen and gives a mixture of dihydro acids.[3,4,9] In acetic acid solution a second mole of hydrogen is absorbed, and from the resulting mixture a tetrahydro derivative has been isolated (m.p. 197°, $[\alpha]_D + 7°$); this gives no coloration with tetranitromethane.[9] The presence of two double bonds is indicated also by the results of titration with perbenzoic acid.[8] Although more reactive in most respects than abietic acid, pure crystalline levopimaric acid remains unchanged on storage without protection from atmospheric oxygen, whereas abietic acid rapidly deteriorates.

Levopimaric acid enters into diazo coupling,[10] and the absorption maximum at 272.5 mμ[5,6] indicates that the conjugated diene system is contained in a single ring. The formation of isobutyric acid as a product of ozonization shows that the unsaturated system is in the ring carrying the isopropyl group. Further inferences regarding the location of the double bonds deduced from the characterization of Diels-Alder addition products can be regarded as fully valid because the addition reactions proceed under such mild conditions (20 – 25°) as to preclude rearrangement. Ozonization of

[5] G. C. Harris and Sanderson, *J. Am. Chem. Soc.*, **70**, 334 (1948).
[6] Kraft, *Ann.*, **520**, 133 (1935).
[7] Ruzicka, Bacon, Lukes and J. D. Rose, *Helv. Chim. Acta*, **21**, 583 (1938).
[8] Kraft, *Ann.*, **524**, 1 (1936).
[9] Ruzicka and Bacon, *Helv. Chim. Acta*, **20**, 1542 (1937).
[10] Fieser and Campbell, *J. Am. Chem. Soc.*, **60**, 159 (1938).

the maleic anhydride addition product as the methyl ester (III, Chart 2) affords among other products a keto ester acid $C_{25}H_{34}O_8$[11, 12, 13] for which formula IV is one of several possible formulations.   More specific but still incomplete information concerning the location of the diene system was

Chart 2.   STRUCTURE OF LEVOPIMARIC ACID
(MALEIC ANHYDRIDE = MA)

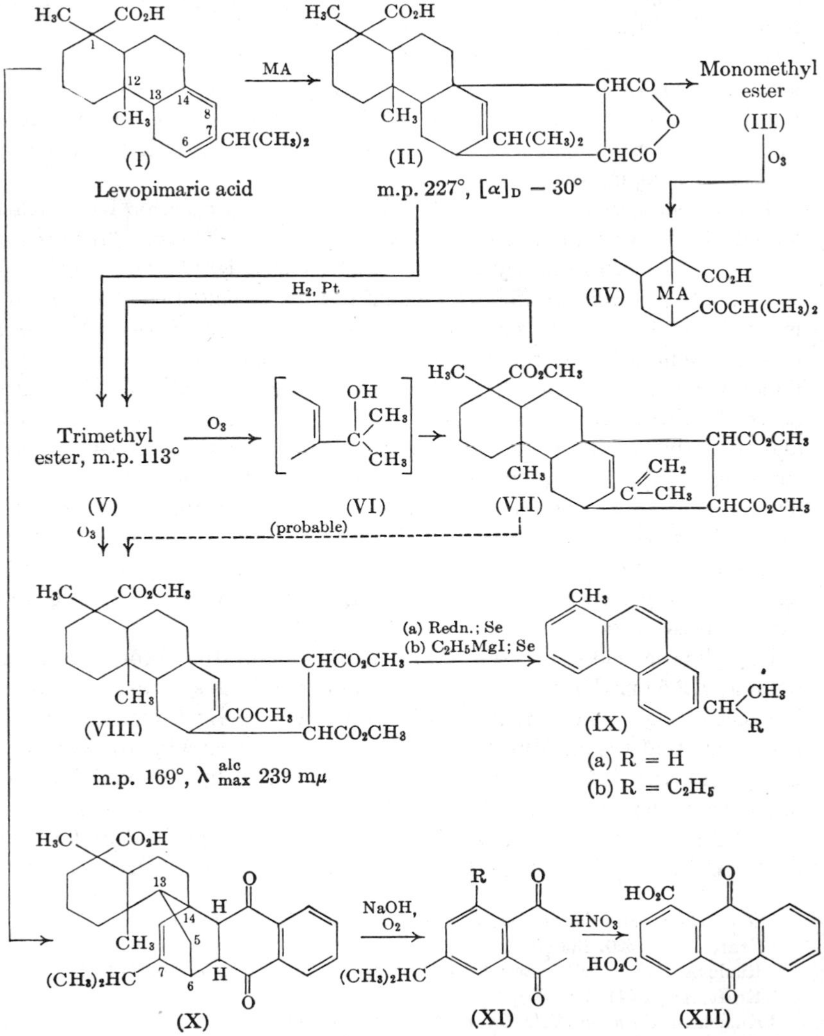

obtained by Ruzicka from a study of the trimethyl ester (V).[14] The double bond in this ester is inert to hydrogenation but is recognizable from a distinct yellow coloration with tetranitromethane. This double bond is also resistant to treatment with ozone in acetic acid, which affords two abnormal products very probably arising from allylic hydroxylation of the isopropyl group (VI). One is a doubly unsaturated ester (VII) probably resulting from the dehydration of the alcohol; it is reconvertible into the mono-unsaturated ester V by hydrogenation, and hence the original double bond has not migrated. The second product (VIII) has the absorption spectrum of an α,β-unsaturated ketone (calcd. λ_{max}^{alc} 237 mμ) and on hypobromite oxidation it afforded bromoform and an α,β-unsaturated tetra acid mono ester (λ_{max}^{alc} 227 mμ). The aceto group was shown to be at the 7-position by degradation to the 1,7-dialkylphenanthrenes IX. The evidence of conjugation proves that the aceto group is attached to one of the unsaturated carbon atoms of the ring and hence that the double bond in the Diels-Alder adduct is either at the 7,8-position as shown or at position 6,7. Arbusov[15] achieved another degradation that confirmed the above conclusion and settled the remaining point at issue. The addition product X from levopimaric acid and α-naphthoquinone was converted into an anthraquinone (XI) by isomerization with alkali and air oxidation; in this process of aromatization the saturated endocyclic bridge rather than the unsaturated one evidently suffers cleavage. Oxidation of XI afforded anthraquinone-1,3-dicarboxylic acid (XII), a product that could arise only from an adduct with the double bond at the 7,8-position. The double bonds in levopimaric acid therefore are at positions 6,7 and 8,14. An early argument against this formulation is now recognized as invalid. Fieser and Campbell[10] could isolate no isobutyric acid from the permanganate oxidation of the maleic anhydride addition product and took this as evidence that the double bond is not located at the site of the isopropyl group. Probably permanganate oxidation follows the same abnormal course as ozonization (VI).

The absorption maximum (λ_{max}^{alc} 272.5 mμ) is slightly lower than the value expected in analogy with comparable dienes of the sterol series (calcd. 278 mμ). The chemical relationship between levopimaric acid and abietic acid corresponds exactly to that between the similarly constituted pair: $\Delta^{2,4}$-cholestadiene (homoannular diene) and $\Delta^{3,5}$-cholestadiene (heteroannular

[11] Ruzicka, Waldmann, Meier and Hösli, *Helv. Chim. Acta*, **16**, 169 (1933); Ruzicka, Bacon, Lukes and J. D. Rose, *ibid.*, **21**, 583 (1938).

[12] Wienhaus and Sandermann, *Ber.*, **69**, 2202 (1936).

[13] Ruzicka and La Lande, *Helv. Chim. Acta*, **23**, 1357 (1940).

[14] Ruzicka and St. Kaufmann, *Helv. Chim. Acta*, **23**, 1346 (1940).

[15] Arbusov, *Chem. Zentr.*, II, 892, 893 (1942).

diene).   The 2,4- diene is isomerized by acids to the 3,5-diene; it is reducible
by sodium and amyl alcohol and adds maleic anhydride readily, whereas
the 3,5-isomer is not reducible and reacts with maleic anhydride only at a
high temperature.   Methyl abietate is reduced by sodium and amyl alcohol
only to abietinol, in which the diene system is still intact.[16]

Lactonization of Dihydro Acids.   Various dihydro acids of unknown
structure are described in the literature: dihydroabietic acids of melting
points ranging from 141 to 218° and $[\alpha]_D$ from $- 23°$ to $+ 108°$; dihydrolevopimaric acids of melting points from 135 to 144° and $[\alpha]_D$ from $+ 24°$ to
$+ 35°$.   Ruzicka[1] found that a dihydroabietic acid (m.p. 168°, $[\alpha]_D - 12°$)
is converted by strong mineral acid into a saturated lactone.   Fleck and
Palkin[2] found that the same lactone can be obtained from another dihydroabietic acid, $[\alpha]_D + 108°$, and from a dihydrolevopimaric acid, $[\alpha]_D + 35°$;
the lactone has been encountered as a product of the treatment of various
mixtures with acid,[3,4] and can be obtained readily by the action of cold
sulfuric acid on commercial hydrogenated rosin.[5]   The corresponding
hydroxytetrahydroabietic acid melts at 163° with reformation of the lactone.   Since the hydroxy acid is resistant to oxidation, even by permanganate in alkali solution,[2] the hydroxyl group must be tertiary.   For this
reason, and because of the stability and ease of formation, Fleck and Palkin[2]
suggested that the lactone ring extends to position 13, as in I.   Recently

Lactone of hydroxytetrahydroabietic
acid m.p. 131° $[\alpha]_D - 3°$

Barton[6] has noted that structure I is improbable because the juncture between the first two rings is known to be trans (see below); he has suggested
that lactonization is attended with migration of the methyl group from C_{12}

[16] Ruzicka and J. Meyer, *Helv. Chim. Acta*, **5**, 581 (1922).
[1] Ruzicka and J. Meyer, *Helv. Chim. Acta*, **5**, 315 (1922); Ruzicka, Waldmann, Meier and Hösli, *ibid.*, **16**, 169 (1933).
[2] Fleck and Palkin, *J. Am. Chem. Soc.*, **61**, 3197 (1939).
[3] Hasselstrom, Brennan and McPherson, *J. Am. Chem. Soc.*, **60**, 1267 (1938).
[4] Fleck and Palkin, *J. Am. Chem. Soc.*, **60**, 2621 (1938).
[5] Fleck and Palkin, *J. Am. Chem. Soc.*, **61**, 1230 (1939).
[6] Barton, *Chemistry and Industry*, 638 (1948).

to C_{13} and establishment of a lactone bridge at C_{12} is in II (see Westphalen's Diol). Cox[7] found that the lactone reacts abnormally with methylmagnesium iodide to give two dihydroabietic acids different from any of the acids prepared by hydrogenation: m.p. 186°, $[\alpha]_D - 36°$; and m.p. 148°, $[\alpha]_D + 68°$. Both acids on lactonization yield the original lactone.

d-Pimaric Acid. This acid- and heat-stable isomer was isolated from French galipot of *Pinus maritima* by Cailliot[1] in 1874. A procedure for isolation of the acid by crystallization of the sparingly soluble sodium salt was reported by Vesterberg[2] in 1887; an improved procedure of isolation from *Pinus palustris* worked out by Palkin and T. II. Harris is described above (Levopimaric acid). Recently G. C. Harris[3] has described a simpler and more efficient method of isolation based upon the observation that *d*-pimaric acid is more volatile than the companion acids. Rosin is distilled slowly at 136 – 200°/1 mm. until about 12 percent of distillate has collected. The acidic fraction is extracted and neutralized with butanolamine; the amine salt of *d*-pimaric acid is easily purified by crystallization and affords pure *d*-pimaric acid amounting to 4 percent of the rosin.

d-Pimaric acid can be identified[4] readily by catalytic hydrogenation to a sparingly soluble dihydro derivative (IV, Chart 3) formed by saturation of the vinyl group that constitutes a distinguishing feature of the resin acid. The characteristic dihydride is formed under various conditions of hydrogenation,[5,6,7] including hydrogenation of an aqueous solution of the sodium salt in the presence of Raney nickel at room temperature.[8] Abietic and levopimaric acid are not hydrogenated as readily as this vinyl derivative, and the selective hydrogenation of *d*-pimaric acid has been used for the analysis of the mixtures of acids present in galipots.[8] *d*-Pimaric acid, on the other hand, is inert to maleic anhydride or quinone and can be isolated from French galipot after precipitation of the alcohol-insoluble adduct of levopimaric acid with quinone.[9,10] The fact that *d*-pimaric acid is not isomerized by acids provides a basis for a method for the determination of

[7] R. F. B. Cox, *J. Am. Chem. Soc.*, **66**, 865 (1944).

[1] Cailliot, *Bull. soc. chim.*, [2], **21**, 387 (1874).

[2] Vesterberg, *Ber.*, **20**, 3248 (1887).

[3] G. C. Harris and Sanderson, *J. Am. Chem. Soc.*, **70**, 2079 (1948).

[4] Hasselstrom and Bogert, *J. Am. Chem. Soc.*, **57**, 2118 (1935).

[5] Tschugaeff and Teearu, *Ber.*, **46**, 1769 (1913).

[6] Ruzicka and co-workers, *Helv. Chim. Acta*, **6**, 677 (1923); **7**, 875 (1924); **14**, 233 (1931); **15**, 915, 1289, 1300 (1932); *Ann.*, **460**, 202 (1928); *Rec. trav. chim.*, **47**, 363 (1928).

[7] Palkin and T. H. Harris, *J. Am. Chem. Soc.*, **55**, 3677 (1933).

[8] Lombard, *Bull. soc. chim.*, **11**, 201 (1944).

[9] Sandermann, *Ber.*, **75**, 174 (1942).

[10] Lombard, *Bull. soc. chim.*, **9**, 698 (1942).

this component of fresh oleoresins;[9,10] the content of *d*-pimaric acid is calculated from determinations of the optical rotation before and after isomerization of the other constituents with hydrochloric acid. Neither analytical method allowed for the presence of the subsequently discovered neoabietic acid and 7-iso-*d*-pimaric acid.

The main outlines of the structure of *d*-pimaric acid were established by degradations conducted by Ruzicka and co-workers[6] (Chart 3). On dehydrogenation with sulfur, *d*-pimaric acid yields pimanthrene (II), identified as 1,7-dimethylphenanthrene by oxidation to III (Ruzicka) and by synthesis (Haworth). Bouveault reduction of the ester of *d*-pimaric acid

Chart 3. *d*-PIMARIC ACID

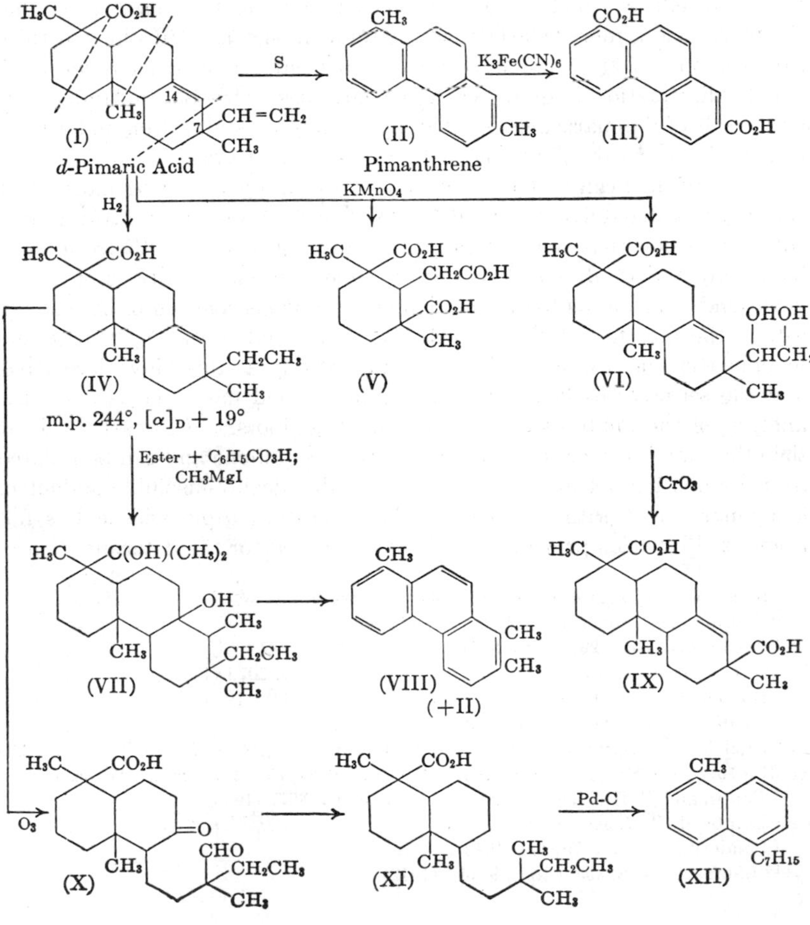

followed by dehydration and dehydrogenation proceeds as with abietic acid and affords 1-ethyl-7-methylphenanthrene, as established by oxidation to III and by synthesis. The formation of the same C_{12}-acid (V) from *d*-pimaric acid as from abietic acid establishes the structure of ring I. The presence of a vinyl group is indicated by the isolation of formaldehyde as a product of ozonization and by the conversion of the resin acid through the glycol VI to the dibasic nor acid IX. The vinyl group is eliminated on dehydrogenation and therefore must be at one of the quaternary positions: 7, 13, or 14. Ruzicka[11] considered the 14-position the most likely site on the ground that the 13-vinyl formulation would not conform to the isoprene rule and that if the vinyl group were at the 7-position dehydrogenation might be expected to yield both pimanthrene and 1-methyl-7-ethylphenanthrene, whereas pimanthrene is the sole product isolated. The latter argument is invalidated by the observation of Barker and Clemo[12] that the dehydrogenation of gem-methylethyl compounds proceeds with loss of the ethyl group. Fleck and Palkin[13] observed that *d*-pimaric acid is converted by sulfuric acid at 25° in about 50 percent yield into a saturated hydroxylactone (m.p. 182°, $[\alpha]_D - 4°$) that has an unacylable hydroxyl group and that distils unchanged at 250°/1 mm. The hydroxylactone required treatment with potassium hydroxide in butanol for hydrolysis and hence resembled the lactone from dihydroabietic and dihydrolevopimaric acid. Fleck and Palkin inferred that the lactone ring closure proceeds through a 13,14-unsaturated intermediate and hence that the vinyl group is not at C_{14} but at C_7; *d*-pimaric acid therefore has the structure I. They noted that this formula accounts just as satisfactorily as that proposed by Ruzicka for a further degradation[11] proceeding through a Grignard reaction on the oxide of dihydro-*d*-pimaric acid followed by dehydrogenation (VII, VIII). The structure of the hydroxylactone from *d*-pimaric acid has not been elucidated; possibly hydration of the vinyl group produces a secondary alcoholic group that rearranges to give a 7-hydroxy-7-isopropyl derivative.

The structure suggested by Fleck and Palkin has been established unequivocally by Harris and Sanderson,[14] who ozonized dihydro-*d*-pimaric acid and isolated a ketoaldehyde (X) that on Wolff-Kishner reduction and dehydrogenation yielded a C_{18}-hydrocarbon characterized by spectroscopy as a 1,5-dialkylnaphthalene (XII). If the vinyl group were at one of the alternate positions (13 or 14), the degradation could afford naphthalene derivatives having 13 or 14 carbon atoms but not a C_{18}-hydrocarbon. The

[11] Ruzicka and Sternbach, *Helv. Chim. Acta*, **23**, 124 (1940).
[12] Barker and Clemo, *J. Chem. Soc.*, 1277 (1940).
[13] Fleck and Palkin, *J. Am. Chem. Soc.*, **62**, 2044 (1940).
[14] G. C. Harris and Sanderson, *J. Am. Chem. Soc.*, **70**, 2081 (1948).

structure I is therefore correct; this is divisible into isoprene units as shown by the dotted lines.

7-Iso-*d*-pimaric Acid. This acid was isolated by Harris and Sanderson[1] from *P. palustris* gum oleoresin as follows. The total resin acid fraction was separated through the cyclohexylamine salt and refluxed for two 48-hour periods with maleic anhydride in benzene saturated with hydrogen chloride, when all acids of the abietic-levopimaric type were converted into the common adduct. A solution of the resulting mixture in dilute alkali was then acidified to pH 6.2, whereupon the unreacted *d*-pimaric type acids precipitated and the tribasic acid derived from the adduct was retained in solution. The precipitated acids (24%) proved to be a mixture of *d*-pimaric

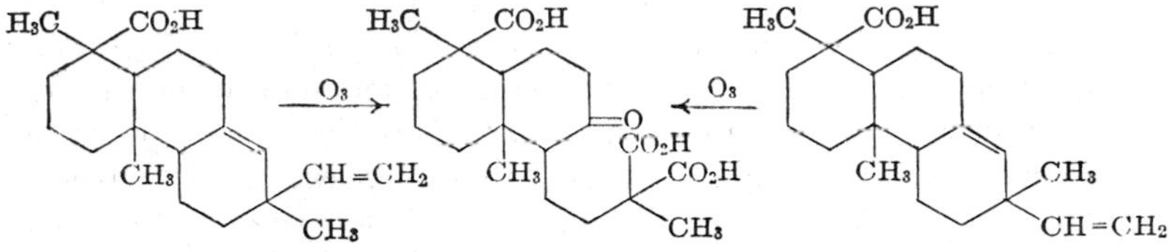

d-Pimaric Acid   7-Iso-*d*-pimaric acid

acid and 7-iso-*d*-pimaric acid, and on treatment with butanolamine the former acid formed a soluble salt and the latter a sparingly soluble salt that was easily isolated in a pure form. The solubility relationship is the reverse of that of the sodium salts; the sodium salt of 7-iso-*d*-pimaric acid is very soluble. The new acid yielded formaldehyde on ozonization and piman-threne on dehydrogenation, and was thus characterized as an acid of the *d*-pimaric type. Degradation[2] by ozonization of the dihydro derivative, Wolff-Kishner reduction, and dehydrogenation gave a C_{18}-naphthalene derivative identical with that from *d*-pimaric acid (XII, Chart 3). The precursor XI could not be caused to crystallize, but a method for the selective elimination of the asymmetry at C_7 was found in the ozonization of the doubly unsaturated acids, when both gave an identical, crystalline, ketotricarboxylic acid. The acids therefore are C_7-epimers.

Neoabietic Acid. That abietic acid is converted in part to dextrorotatory material was suggested by observations of Ruzicka.[3] Harris and Sanderson[4] heated abietic acid at 300° for twenty minutes, separated unreacted abietic acid (76%) as the insoluble diamylamine salt, and from the residue isolated by crystallization of the butanolamine salt a new, strongly dextro-

[1] G. C. Harris and Sanderson, *J. Am. Chem. Soc.*, **70**, 2079 (1948).
[2] G. C. Harris and Sanderson, *J. Am. Chem. Soc.*, **70**, 2081 (1948).
[3] Ruzicka and J. Meyer, *Helv. Chim. Acta*, 5, 338, 342 (1922).
[4] G. C. Harris and Sanderson, *J. Am. Chem. Soc.*, **70**, 334 (1948).

rotatory acid, neoabietic acid, $[\alpha]_D$ + 159°.   The same acid was then isolated from the resin acids of gum oleoresin by alternate crystallization of
the diethylamine and butanolamine salts.   Neoabietic acid is readily isomerized by a trace of mineral acid to abietic acid, and it affords retene on
dehydrogenation.   The structure predicted from the absorption maximum

Neoabietic acid
$\lambda \frac{alc}{max}$ 250 mμ

$\lambda \frac{alc}{max}$ 242 mμ

(calculated value 249 mμ) was established[5] by ozonization experiments.
Mild ozonization afforded acetone and a β,β-disubstituted α,β-unsaturated
ketone (calcd. λ_{max} 244 mμ); exhaustive ozonization followed by dehydrogenation afforded a hydrocarbon identified as 1-methyl-5-*n*-propylnaphtha-
lene by synthesis.

Composition of the Acid Fraction of *Pinus palustris.*   The relative proportions indicated in Chart 1 for the seven primary acids of gum oleoresin
were established by Harris as follows.   The starting material was a large
batch of oleoresin from longleaf pine stored at 0° in the dark in the absence
of air.   The total acid fraction was separated through the cyclohexylamine
salt and treated in *n*-pentane-acetone with acid-free maleic anhydride at
room temperature for two hours for removal of the levopimaric acid (not
precipitated on acidification of an alkaline solution to pH 6.2).   Spectrographic analysis of the unreacted fraction established the presence and
relative amounts of abietic acid and neoabietic acid, which are distinguished
by absorption bands at 241 and 250 mμ.[1]   Analysis of the acids not convertible into abietic acid was conducted with the acid mixture remaining
after treatment of the total acid fraction with maleic anhydride in benzene
saturated with hydrogen chloride as described above.   The presence and
amount of dehydroabietic acid were established from the ultraviolet absorption spectrum.   7-Iso-*d*-pimaric acid was isolated as the butanolamine
salt; Fleck and Palkin's value for the amount of dihydroabietic acid present,
based upon the yield of lactone, was taken as an estimate of this component,
and the *d*-pimaric acid content was assumed by difference.

[5] G. C. Harris and Sanderson, *J. Am. Chem. Soc.*, **70**, 339 (1948).
[1] Wienhaus, Ritter and Sandermann, *Ber.*, **69**, 2198 (1936), isolated abietic acid by
repeated crystallization of an unisomerized resin acid mixture from methanol.

66   *RESIN ACIDS*

A number of supposed primary resin acids have been shown to be mixtures;[2,3] for example, Harris[4] succeeded in establishing the presence in Kraft's "proabietic acid"[5] of the following acids: abietic, levopimaric, neoabietic, and 7-iso-*d*-pimaric acid.

7-Iso-*d*-pimarinal, $C_{20}H_{30}O$, m.p. 52°, isolated by Sörensen and Bruun[6] from Scots fir (*P. silvestris* L.) and by Harris[7] from commercial rosins of longleaf (*P. palustris*) and slash pines (*P. caribaea*), was shown by Harris to be the aldehyde corresponding to 7-iso-*d*-pimaric acid by chromic acid oxidation to this acid.

Dehydroabietic Acid. Pure dehydroabietic acid was prepared for the first time by Fieser and Campbell[1] by oxidation of abietic acid with selenium dioxide to the 6-hydroxy derivative and dehydration of this by short boiling with acetic acid[2] to a substance characterized by the absorption spectrum as having one aromatic ring. The observation that dehydroabietic acid gives a dinitro derivative identical with one previously prepared[3] from inadvertently heat-treated abietic acid or from supposedly homogeneous "pyroabietic acids" suggested that the action of heat on abietic acid results in part in a disproportionation to mixtures of hydro and dehydro derivatives. Fleck and Palkin, who had developed a convenient method[4] of preparing a "pyroabietic acid" in 92 percent yield by heating Steele-abietic

[2] Dupont, *Bull. soc. chim.*, **29**, 718 (1921).
[3] Ruzicka, Balas and Vilim, *Helv. Chim. Acta*, **7**, 458 (1924).
[4] G. C. Harris and Sparks, *J. Am. Chem. Soc.*, **70**, 3674 (1948).
[5] Kraft, *Ann.*, **524**, 1 (1936).
[6] N. A. Sörensen and Bruun, *Acta Chem. Scand.*, (1), **1**, 112 (1947).
[7] G. C. Harris and Sanderson, *J. Am. Chem. Soc.*, (in press).
[1] Fieser and Campbell, *J. Am. Chem. Soc.*, **60**, 159 (1938).
[2] Pyrolysis of 6-hydroxyabietic acid at 200° gave a substance designated anhydroabietic acid, m.p. 167.5-169.5°, $[\alpha]_D + 21°$, λ_{max}^{alc} 238 mμ, tentatively regarded as having the dienic system of abietic acid and a bridge bond extending between positions 6 and 13 (compare the i-steroids). Sandermann and Höhn, *Ber.*, **76**, 1257 (1943), and Sandermann, *Ber.*, **76**, 1261 (1943), describe (without analyses) a substance of very similar properties which Sandermann characterized with a high degree of probability as 13-isoabietic acid (m.p. 172°, $[\alpha]_D + 21°$, λ_{max} 238 mμ); the diglycol gave no acetone on glycol cleavage with lead tetraacetate but gave acetone on chromic acid oxidation; energetic permanganate oxidation gave isobutyric acid; oxidation with nitric acid, the $C_{12}H_{18}O_6$ acid. The Sandermann acid was obtained by thermal decomposition of the maleic-anhydride addition product and by the action of alcoholic potassium hydroxide on abietic acid dihydrobromide; Hasselstrom and McPherson, *J. Am. Chem. Soc.*, **61**, 2247 (1939), by a similar procedure converted the dihydrochloride into an isomer of abietic acid, m.p. 143°, $[\alpha]_D + 20°$. The implication that anhydroabietic acid and 13-isoabietic acid are identical is contrary to the evidence; the analyses of the former acid and its methyl ester agree accurately with the requirements of the formula $C_{20}H_{28}O_2$ but not $C_{20}H_{30}O_2$.
[3] Johansson, *Arkiv. Kemi. Min. Geol.*, **6**, No. 19 (1917).
[4] Fleck and Palkin, *J. Am. Chem. Soc.*, **59**, 1593 (1937).

acid with palladium charcoal at 245° for one hour, established the fact of disproportionation by the isolation[5,6] from this material of pure dehydroabietic acid, a tetrahydro acid (m.p. 184°, $[\alpha]_D$ + 6°), the known lactone (m.p. 131°, $[\alpha]_D$ − 3°) of hydroxytetrahydroabietic acid, and a dihydroabietic acid (m.p. 176°, $[\alpha]_D$ + 108°). Pyro acids produced by heat treat-

Chart 4. DEHYDROABIETIC ACID

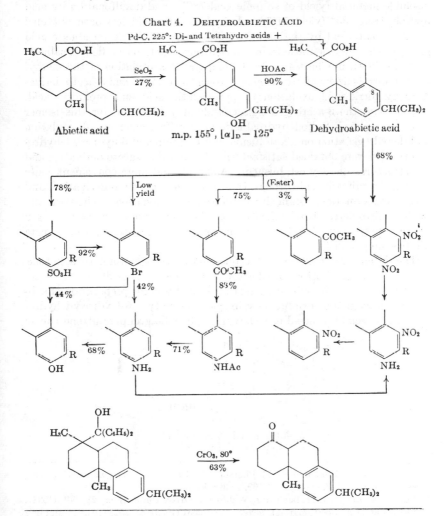

[5] Fleck and Palkin, *J. Am. Chem. Soc.*, **60**, 921, 2621 (1938).
[6] See also Littmann, *J. Am. Chem. Soc.*, **60**, 1419 (1938).

ment have also been shown to contain dehydroabietic acid,[7,8] the above lactone,[7] and a dihydro acid,[8] m.p. 194°, $[\alpha]_D + 9°$.

A convenient process[9] for the preparation of pure dehydroabietic acid consists in sulfonation of pyro acid prepared according to Palkin and Fleck, separation of the crystalline sulfonic acid of the dehydro acid from water-insoluble material (yield of sulfonic acid 78%), and desulfonation by acid hydrolysis at 135° (yield 71%). Dehydroabietic acid has been obtained in 32 percent yield by the action of N-bromosuccinimide on abietic acid methyl ester.[10] Orientations in substitution reactions of dehydroabietic acid are shown in Chart 4. Friedel and Crafts acetylation of the methyl ester in nitrobenzene affords isomers shown to be the 6- and 8-aceto derivatives by nitric acid oxidation to pyromellitic acid and prehnitic acid, respectively; the 8-aceto group is considerably hindered, for this isomer forms no oxime. Sulfodehydroabietic acid suffers extensive degradation and dehydrogenation on alkali fusion, but 6-amino and 6-hydroxydehydroabietic acid were obtained satisfactorily through the 6-aceto derivative and the structures thereby established. A shorter and more convenient route is from the sulfonic acid through the corresponding bromo derivative, and these transformations establish the position of sulfonation. The structure of the dinitro derivative is inferred from the transformations indicated and by the observation that the substance has the characteristics of a meta dinitro compound.

The interesting oxidation of diphenyl-*t*-dehydroabietinol to a ketone, formulated at the bottom of Chart 4, is reported by Zeiss.[11]

An objective of the substitution studies cited was the preparation of substances that might exhibit physiological activity. 6-Hydroxydehydroabietinol[9] resembles estradiol in having a phenolic grouping at one end of

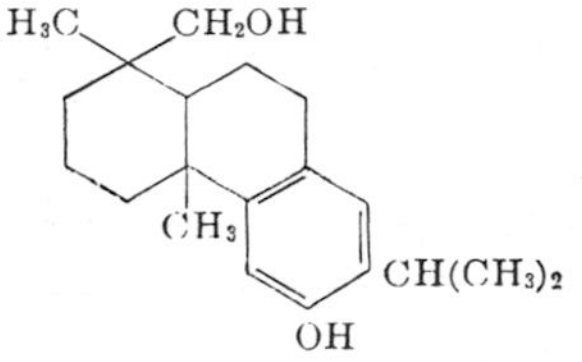

6-Hydroxydehydroabietinol
m.p. 181.5°, $[\alpha]_D + 72°$

---

[7] Hasselstrom, Brennan and McPherson, *J. Am. Chem. Soc.*, **60**, 1267 (1938); Hasselstrom and McPherson, *ibid.*, **60**, 2340 (1938).

[8] Ruzicka, Bacon, Sternbach and Waldmann, *Helv. Chim. Acta*, **21**, 591 (1938).

[9] Fieser and Campbell, *J. Am. Chem. Soc.*, **60**, 2631 (1938); **61**, 2528 (1939); Campbell and Morgana, *ibid.*, **63**, 1838 (1941).

[10] Jeger, Dürst and Büchi, *Helv. Chim. Acta*, **30**, 1853 (1947).

[11] Zeiss, *J. Am. Chem. Soc.*, **70**, 858 (1948).

the molecule and an alcoholic group at the other, and the substance possesses estrogenic activity about comparable to that of estrone. The substance was prepared by hydrogenolysis of methyl 6-aminodehydroabietate and hydrolysis of the diazonium salt.

Podocarpic Acid. Podocarpic acid, $C_{17}H_{22}O_3$, the chief acidic constituent of the resin of the Javanese *Podocarpus cupressinus* and of the New Zealand kahikatea resin (*Podocarpus dacrydioides*) and rimu resin (*Dacrydium cupressinum*), was first isolated by Oudemans.[1] Degradation of the acid by zinc-dust distillation,[1] or in better yield by selenium dehydrogenation, affords a hydrocarbon[1,2] and a phenol,[2] which Short and co-workers found identical with synthetic 1-methylphenanthrene[2] and 6-hydroxy-1-methylphenanthrene,[3] respectively. Sherwood and Short[4] established the presence of a benzenoid ring carrying a phenolic hydroxyl group (methyl ester, λ_{max} 282 mμ; ready nitration and sulfonation but not hydrogenation; diazo coupling) and noted that the carboxyl group is more strongly hindered than that of abietic acid (Fischer esterification negative; ester unaffected by boiling 0.5 N alcoholic potassium hydroxide).

A suggestion[5] that podocarpic acid might be the des-isopropyl derivative of 6-hydroxydehydroabietic acid was investigated by Campbell and Todd[6] with the following results (Chart 5). An isopropyl group was introduced into podocarpic acid (I) by Friedel-Crafts acetylation of the methyl ether methyl ester, reaction with methylmagnesium chloride, dehydration of the carbinol, and hydrogenation to II. A substance of the same composition (VII) was prepared for comparison from methyl 6-hydroxydehydroabietate (VI) by methylation of the strongly hindered 6-hydroxyl group by the action of dimethyl sulfate on the magnesio-chloride derivative. The esters II and VII proved to be nonidentical, but on demethylation and dehydrogenation they both yielded 6-retenol (IV). The esters therefore correspond in the positions of the isopropyl and hydroxyl groups and must differ in the nature or orientation of the substituents at C_1 or C_{12}. Campbell and Todd then transformed the carboxylate group of each ester to methyl by conversion to the acid chloride and the aldehyde, followed by Wolff-Kishner reduction, whereupon the esters II and VII yielded the same product, which proved to be identical with the diterpene resinol ferruginol, which was thereby characterized as having the structure V. Ferruginol had been

[1] Oudemans, *Ber.*, **6**, 1122 (1873); *Ann.*, **170**, 213 (1873); *J. prakt. Chem.*, **9**, 385 (1874).
[2] Radcliffe, Sherwood and Short, *J. Chem. Soc.*, 2293 (1931); P. Hill, Short and Higginbottom, *ibid.*, 317 (1936).
[3] Plimmer, Short and P. Hill, *J. Chem. Soc.*, 694 (1938).
[4] Sherwood and Short, *J. Chem. Soc.*, 1006 (1938).
[5] Fieser and Campbell, *J. Am. Chem. Soc.*, **61**, 2528 (1939).
[6] Campbell and Todd, *J. Am. Chem. Soc.*, **62**, 1287 (1940); **64**, 928 (1942).

isolated by Brandt and Neubauer[7] from the resin of the miro tree of New Zealand (*Podocarpus ferrugineus*) in 70 percent yield and characterized by selenium dehydrogenation to an unidentified retenol and a small amount of pimanthrene. The work of Campbell and Todd also further elucidated the structure of a dihydroxy resinol hinokiol (III), isolated from the

Chart 5. Podocarpic Acid

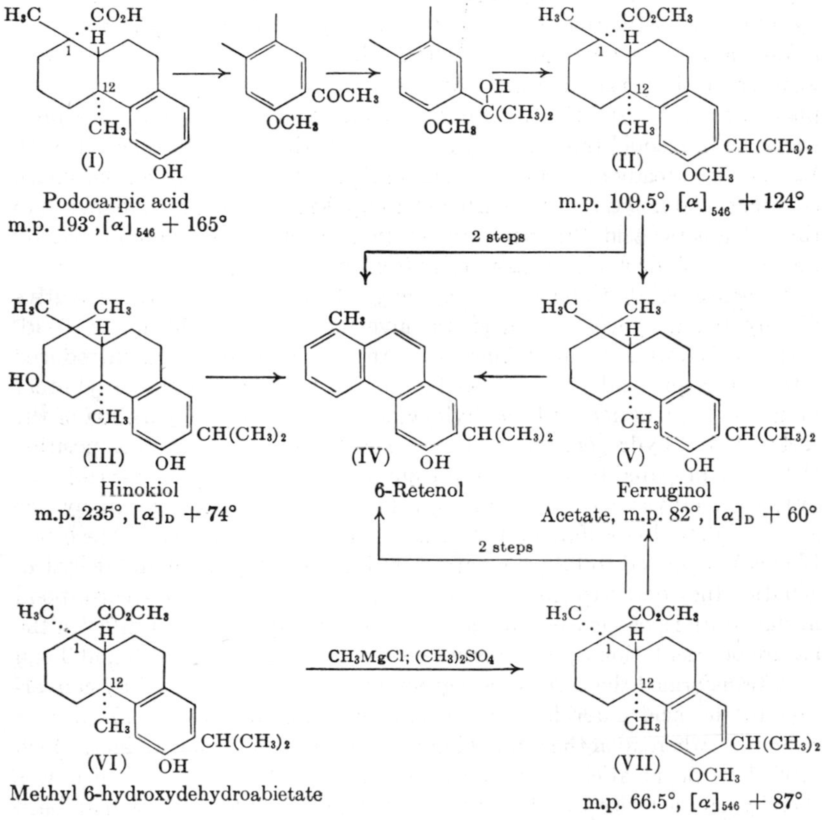

(I) Podocarpic acid
m.p. 193°, [α]$_{546}$ + 165°

(II) m.p. 109.5°, [α]$_{546}$ + 124°

2 steps

(III) Hinokiol
m.p. 235°, [α]$_D$ + 74°

(IV) 6-Retenol

(V) Ferruginol
Acetate, m.p. 82°, [α]$_D$ + 60°

2 steps

(VI) Methyl 6-hydroxydehydroabietate

CH_3MgCl; $(CH_3)_2SO_4$

(VII) m.p. 66.5°, [α]$_{546}$ + 87°

Japanese hinoki wood *Chamaecyparis obtusa*,[8] for this substance on dehydrogenation[9] had afforded retene, a retenol identical[7] with that from ferruginol, and a dihydroxyretene (m.p. 235°) characterized by conversion to a number of derivatives, including a diacetoxy-9,10-retenequinone.

[7] Brandt and Neubauer, *J. Chem. Soc.*, 1031 (1939).
[8] Yoshiki and Ishiguro, *Chem. Zentr.*, I, 3201 (1933).
[9] Keimatsu and Ishiguro, *Chem. Zentr.*, II, 3663 (1935).

Hinokiol has a secondary alcoholic group[10] and can be dehydrogenated to the corresponding ketone, hinokione (m.p. 189°, $[\alpha]_D + 103°$, λ_{max} 286 mμ), also isolated from the wood resin. The alcoholic group cannot be at position 9 or 10 because it is not eliminated on conversion to the 9,10-quinone, and the 2 and 4 positions are unlikely because hinokiol and hinokione readily form hydroxyl and carbonyl derivatives and show no evidence of hindrance. Thus the nonphenolic oxygen function is probably at position 3 (III).

The formation of ferruginol from the esters II and VII could mean either that these esters differ in the configuration at C_1, as shown in the formulas, or that in the ester from podocarpic acid the carboxylate group is at C_{12} and both methyl groups are at C_1. The latter possibility was ruled out by the degradation of podocarpic acid methyl ether methyl ester by reduction of the carboxylate group, dehydration, and dehydrogenation to 6-methoxy-1-ethylphenanthrene. Podocarpic acid therefore differs from 6-hydroxy-dehydroabietic acid both in the absence of a 7-isopropyl group and in the orientation at position 1. Ruzicka[11] had observed that the tribasic acid $C_{11}H_{16}O_6$ isolated as a product of the oxidation of abietic acid is optically inactive and inferred that the two similar asymmetric carbon atoms substituted by methyl and carboxyl groups must be oriented in the manner shown for the two possible meso isomers VIII and IX.

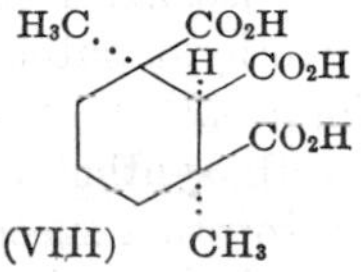

(VIII) CH₃   (IX) CH₃

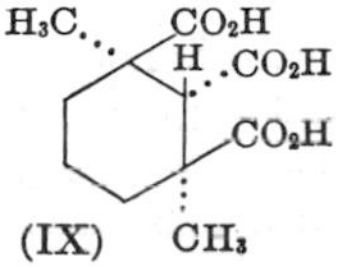

cis   trans

Ring-juncture in abietic acid

For the representation of configurational relationships in the resin acid series a convention will be employed similar to that applied to the sterols. The angular methyl group at C_{12} is taken as the point of reference and is arbitrarily defined as having the α-orientation and represented as projecting below the plane of the paper (dotted line), or the back side of the molecule; in formula I the carboxyl group is α-oriented and the C_1-methyl group is β-oriented (full line; front side of the molecule) with respect to the asymmetric center at C_{12}. The convention is arbitrary, and the actual configurations may correspond to the mirror images of those indicated. From a consideration of hindrance effects estimated from molecular models, Camp-

[10] Fukui and Chikamori, *Chem. Zentr.*, II, 1494 (1939).
[11] Ruzicka and Sternbach, *Helv. Chim. Acta*, **21**, 565 (1938).

bell and Todd suggested that the C_{11}-acid has the configuration IX, corresponding to a trans ring juncture in both abietic acid and the more hindered podocarpic acid derivatives. With trans fusion of the two alicyclic rings, the 1β-carboxyl group of abietic acid should be less hindered than the 1α-carboxyl group of podocarpic acid, for this would be close in space to the 12α-methyl group. This inference appears to us sound, but the proposition that the hindrance effects would be reversed if the ring juncture were cis seems questionable; Ruzicka[12] made the opposite deduction from an examination of models. Barton,[13] however, has reinvestigated the configuration of the C_{11}-acid and has established that the ring fusion is actually trans. The configurations inferred by Campbell and Todd on a speculative basis (Chart 5) thus appear to be correct.

Podocarpinol, prepared by Rosenmund reduction of podocarpic acid chloride acetate and hydrogenation of the aldehyde over copper chromite catalyst,[14] and also obtained more conveniently in 56 percent yield by reduction of podocarpic acid with lithium aluminum hydride,[15] is reported to possess estrogenic activity.[14]

Agathic Acid. Agathic acid, isolated from Manila or kauri copal,[1] is a bicyclic diterpene, but it is readily isomerized by formic acid to isoagathic acid,[2] characterized as a tricyclic dicarboxylic acid. The structures of the acids were established by Ruzicka and co-workers[3] as follows (Chart 6). On dehydrogenation with sulfur or selenium isoagathic acid yields pimanthrene, and agathic acid yields 1,2,5-trimethylnaphthalene, a trace of pimanthrene, and a hydrocarbon $C_{17}H_{20}$ (m.p. 42°; picrate, m.p. 139°).[2,4] The latter hydrocarbon is not identical with synthetic 3,6-dimethyl-1-isopropylacenaphthene[5] but has a similar absorption spectrum; the structure 2,2,8-trimethyl-1,2,3,4-tetrahydrophenanthrene is suggested as another possibility. One of the two carboxyl groups of agathic acid and of isoagathic acid is readily lost on heating, with the formation of noragathic acid and isonoragathic acid, and is therefore located on an unsaturated carbon atom; the absorption spectrum of agathic acid also is indicative of an α,β-unsaturated acid.

The positions of the two double bonds in agathic acid were established

[12] Ruzicka and Bernold, *Helv. Chim. Acta*, **24**, 931 (1941).
[13] Barton and Schmeidler, *J. Chem. Soc.* 1197 (1948).
[14] Brandt and D. J. Ross, *Nature*, **161**, 892 (1948).
[15] Zeiss, Slimowicz and Pasternak, *J. Am. Chem. Soc.*, **70**, 1981 (1948).
[1] Ruzicka and Hosking, *Ann.*, **469**, 147 (1929).
[2] Ruzicka and Hosking, *Helv. Chim. Acta*, **13**, 1402 (1930).
[3] Ruzicka, Bernold and Tallichet, *Helv. Chim. Acta*, **24**, 223 (1941).
[4] Ruzicka and Hosking, *Helv. Chim. Acta*, **14**, 203 (1931).
[5] Ruzicka and Rey, *Helv. Chim. Acta*, **26**, 2136 (1943).

Chart 6. AGATHIC ACID

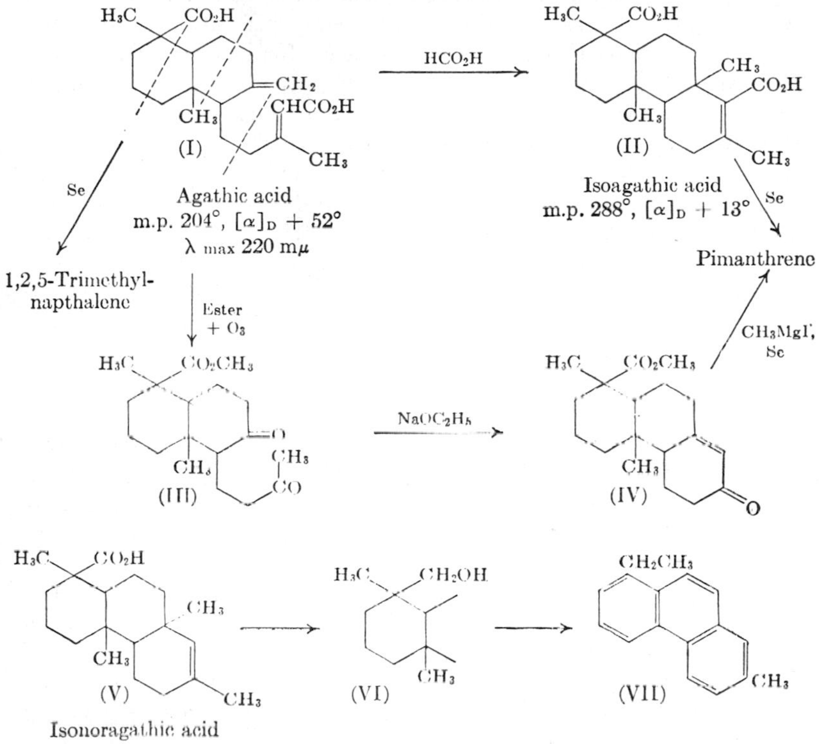
H3C
CO2H
=CH2
CHCO2H
CH3
(I)
CH3
Agathic acid
m.p. 204°, [α]D + 52°
λ max 220 mμ
HCO2H
H3C
CO2H
CH3
CO2H
CH3
(II)
CH3
Isoagathic acid
m.p. 288°, [α]D + 13°
Se
Pimanthrene
Se
1,2,5-Trimethyl-
napthalene
Ester
+ O3
H3C
CO2CH3
=O
CH3
CH3
CO
(III)
NaOC2H5
H3C
CO2CH3
CH3MgI,
Se
CH3
(IV)
O
H3C
CO2H
CH3
CH3
(V)
CH3
Isonoragathic acid
H3C
CH2OH
CH3
(VI)
CH2CH3
(VII)
CH3

by ozonization of the diester, which afforded formaldehyde (methylene group), oxalic acid (unsaturated acid grouping), and the diketo ester III, the structure of which was established by cyclization to IV, Grignard reaction, and dehydrogenation to pimanthrene.[3] One of the carboxyl groups of agathic acid is strongly hindered; on hydrolysis of the diester a mono ester is obtained readily and the second ester group is cleaved only with difficulty. The hindered group is identified as that attached to the nucleus and not the labile group by the fact that the monoester of the nor acid is also saponified only with difficulty. Although the labile carboxyl group of agathic acid is not hindered, it becomes so after cyclization to isoagathic acid. Ruzicka initially suspected that the hindered nuclear group might be located at C_{12}, but a degradation[6] of isonoragathic acid by reduction of the ester to the carbinol (VI), dehydration, and dehydrogenation afforded

[6] Ruzicka and H. Jacobs, *Rec. trav. chim.*, **57**, 509 (1938).

1-ethyl-7-methylphenanthrene (VII) and thus established that the carboxyl group is at position 1 as in abietic acid. The configuration in this ring, however, is different from that of abietic acid, for agathic acid on permanganate oxidation gives a dextrorotatory C_{11}-tricarboxylic acid[7] and not the meso acid derived from abietic acid (IX, preceding section).

Stereochemical and Rotational Relationships. The results of the investigations described above permit some tentative inferences concerning the individual rotatory contributions of the various centers of asymmetry in the resin acids. The epimeric esters II and VII, Chart 5, derived from podocarpic acid and from abietic acid, respectively, correspond in the configurations at C_{11} and C_{12} and have the opposite configurations at C_1. These 1-epimers differ considerably in molecular rotation, defined as follows:

$$M_D = \frac{[\alpha]_D \times \text{Mol. Wt.}}{100}$$

The C_1 α-carboxy podocarpic derivative II (M_D + 346) is more dextrorotatory than the C_1 β-carboxy abietic derivative VII (M_D + 243) by 103 units, and hence the rotational contributions are: $C_1\alpha = +51.5$, $C_1\beta = -51.5$. In derived or related compounds known to correspond in configuration to either of these esters, the sign of the rotational contribution at C_1 must be the same as in II or VII, but the magnitude of the effect is subject to influence of structural changes, and exaltational effects can be anticipated whenever a double bond or other unsaturated group is adjacent to a center of asymmetry. In the meso tribasic acid $C_{11}H_{16}O_6$ derived from abietic acid (Podocarpic Acid, formula IX), the carbon atom corresponding to the original position 1β must be levorotatory and that corresponding to 12α must be dextrorotatory to the same extent. In the resin acids $C_{12}\alpha$ must also be dextrorotatory, although the magnitude of the contribution cannot be evaluated from the evidence cited. In ferruginol (V, Chart 5) asymmetry at C_1 is abolished and the remaining asymmetric centers at C_{11} and C_{12} give rise to strong dextrorotation (acetate, M_D + 197). In dehydroabietic acid (M_D + 186) the contribution of $C_1\beta$ can be assumed to be close to − 51.5 and hence the combined contribution of $C_{11}\beta$ and $C_{12}\alpha$ is about +138.5 units. In podocarpic acid (M_D + 366) a contribution at $C_1\alpha$ of +51.5 would mean that the net rotation of $C_{11}\beta$ and $C_{12}\alpha$ is +314.5. The combined effect is in each of the three instances so great as to suggest that $C_{11}\beta$ is either dextrorotatory, like $C_{12}\alpha$, or weakly levorotatory.

Abietic acid (M_D − 314) and levopimaric acid (M_D − 831) contain an additional asymmetric center at C_{13}, and the pronounced shifts to levorotation, as compared with the rotation of dehydroabietic acid, must mean that

[7] Ruzicka and Bernold, *Helv. Chim. Acta*, **24**, 931 (1941).

this center is levorotatory in both acids. Neoabietic acid ($M_D + 480$) is also asymmetric at C_{13}, but the contrasting strong dextrorotation suggests that the process of bond migration that occurs to some extent when abietic acid is heated is attended with an inversion and that C_{13} in this acid is dextrorotatory. *d*-Pimaric acid ($M_D + 220$) and 7-iso-*d*-pimaric acid ($M_D \pm 0$) are known to correspond to abietic and levopimaric acid in the configurations at C_1, C_{11}, and C_{13}, because the former yields the meso C_{12}-acid, and the relatively more dextrorotatory character of both epimers suggests that C_{13} is dextrorotatory in these acids.

The tentative inferences concerning levopimaric and abietic acid are indicated in formulas that are written in such a way as to bring out the striking analogy to $\Delta^{2,4}$- and $\Delta^{3,5}$-cholestadiene. The orientation of the hydrogen

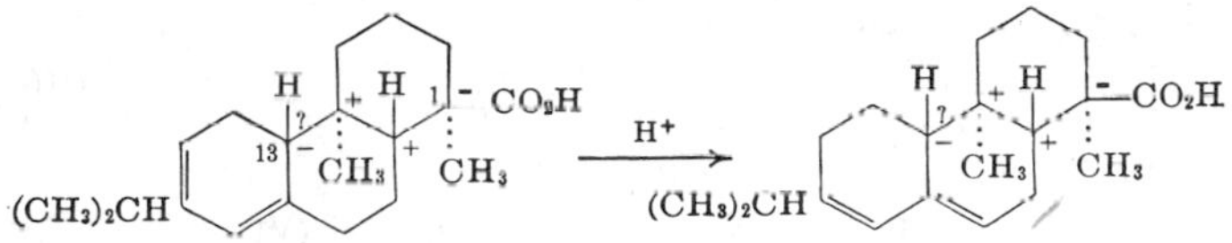

Levopimaric acid
$M_D - 831$

Abietic acid
$M_D - 314$

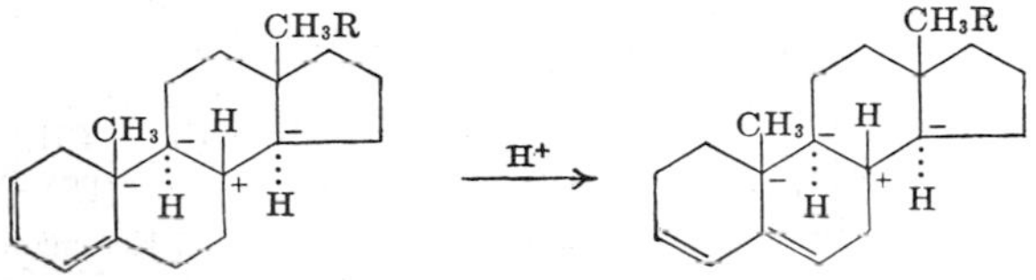

$\Delta^{2,4}$-Cholestadiene
$M_D + 627$

$\Delta^{3,5}$-Cholestadiene
$M_D - 458$

atom at C_{13} is not known but is represented as probably β, like the methyl group in the corresponding position of the cholestadienes; in the sterol series a trans ring juncture at this point represents a condition of greater stability than a cis juncture. The hydroxyl group of the easily lactonized hydroxytetrahydroabietic acid, which according to present indications is probably at position 12 (p. 60), evidently has the same β-orientation as the carboxyl group at C_1. Acid isomerization of levopimaric acid is attended with a marked shift to greater dextrorotation, whereas acid isomerization of $\Delta^{2,4}$-cholestadiene involves a striking levorotatory shift. That the rotatory change is in the opposite direction in the two series may mean that the true orientation in one series or the other is the mirror image of that represented in the arbitrary conventional formulations.

Resin Alcohols and Oxides. Four neutral resin components that have been interrelated are formulated in Chart 7. The diterpene alcohol

Chart 7. SCLAREOL-MANOOL GROUP

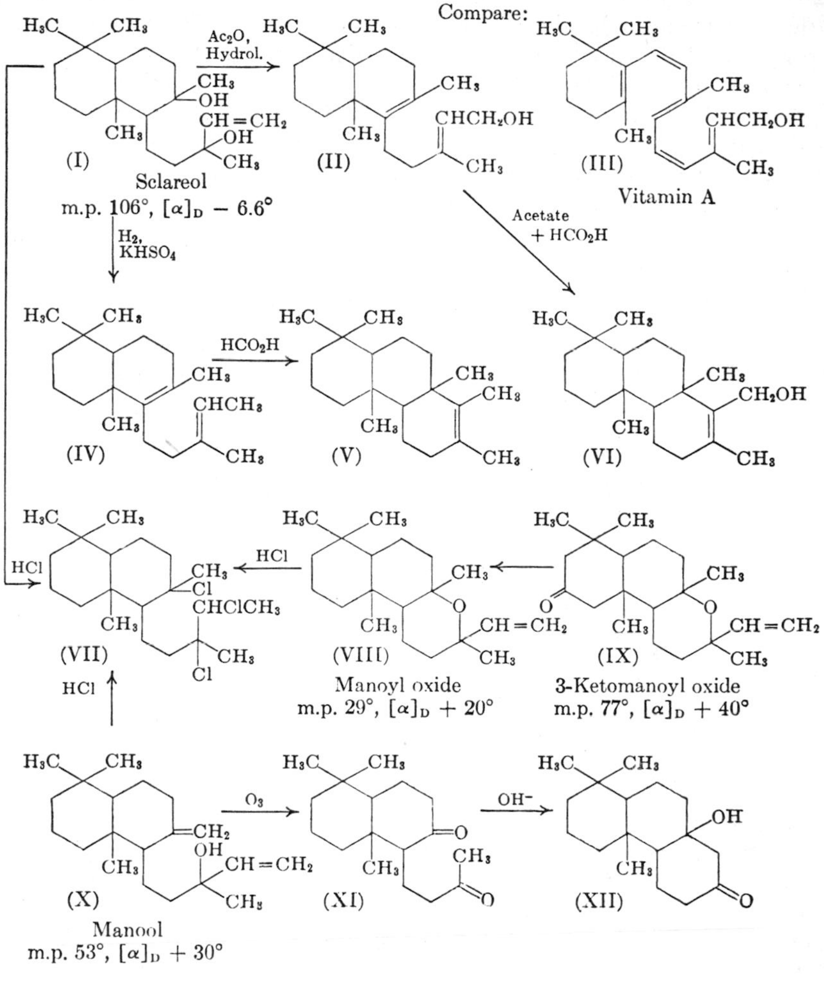
Compare:
Ac₂O, Hydrol.
(I)
Sclareol
m.p. 106°, [α]D − 6.6°
(II)
(III)
Vitamin A
Acetate + HCO₂H
H₂, KHSO₄
HCO₂H
(IV)
(V)
(VI)
HCl
(VII)
(VIII)
Manoyl oxide
m.p. 29°, [α]D + 20°
(IX)
3-Ketomanoyl oxide
m.p. 77°, [α]D + 40°
O₃
OH⁻
(X)
Manool
m.p. 53°, [α]D + 30°
(XI)
(XII)

sclareol (I) extracted from the essential oil of *Salvia sclarea* has been investigated by Ruzicka and by Janot.[1] It contains one double bond (dihydrosclareol, m.p. 114 – 115°) and yields formaldehyde on ozonization. The two oxygen atoms apparently are present as tertiary alcoholic groups,

[1] Ruzicka and Janot, *Helv. Chim. Acta*, **14**, 645 (1931); Janot, *Ann. Chim.*, **17**, 5 (1932); Ruzicka, L. L. Engel and W. H. Fischer, *Helv. Chim. Acta*, **21**, 364 (1938); Ruzicka, Seidel and L. L. Engel, *ibid.*, **25**, 621 (1942).

for they are easily eliminated on treatment with dehydrating agents with the formation of the triply unsaturated hydrocarbon sclarene (oil). On selenium dehydrogenation sclareol yields 1,2,5-trimethylnaphthalene, a degradation product of agathic acid. Like agathic acid, sclareol can be converted into tricyclic derivatives; thus the dihydride on treatment with potassium bisulfate and then with formic acid afforded a hydrocarbon oil (V) that on dehydrogenation yielded pimanthrene, 1,2,8-trimethylphenanthrene, and a hydrocarbon $C_{18}H_{18}$. The formulation IV represents a possible intermediate step, but the product of dehydration, an oil, probably was already largely cyclized. Treatment of sclareol with acetic anhydride appears to effect dehydration and allylic rearrangement to a substance formulated as II (oil); the proposed structure is similar to that of vitamin A (III). The rearrangement product can be cyclized (VI) by the action of formic acid on the acetate.

A group of related diterpenes have been isolated and characterized by Hosking and Brandt.[2] The neutral resin of the New Zealand silver pine (*Dacrydium colensoi*) was found to contain manoyl oxide ($C_{20}H_{34}O$), 3-keto-manoyl oxide, and a monounsaturated trihydroxy diterpene oxide ($C_{20}H_{22}O_4$). Manool ($C_{20}H_{34}O$) was isolated from the wood of the pink pine (*Dacrydium biforme*). Manoyl oxide on selenium dehydrogenation yielded 1,2,5-trimethylnaphthalene and 1,2,8-trimethylphenanthrene, and the phenanthrene derivative was the main product of dehydrogenation of the hydrocarbon isomanoene ($C_{20}H_{32}$) resulting from treatment of manoyl oxide with formic acid (elimination of oxide bridge and cyclization). The oxygen function was indicated as an oxide linkage from the negative results of tests for active hydrogen, carbonyl, or alkoxyl groups. Both manoyl oxide (VIII) and manool (X) react with dry hydrogen chloride in ether to give a crystalline trichloro derivative identical with a product obtained from sclareol on similar treatment. These observations establish the skeletal structures and the relationship of the alcohol to the oxide. The double bond of manoyl oxide was shown to be present in the vinyl group by permanganate oxidation to a carboxylic acid having one less carbon atom. The second double bond present in manool is less reactive than that of the vinyl group (selective hydrogenation). The position of the less reactive linkage, and hence the position of the tertiary hydroxyl group of sclareol and of manool and the point of attachment of the oxide bridge to the carbocyclic ring, was established by ozonization to a diketone (XI) that undergoes ready cyclization to a crystalline saturated hydroxyketone (XII). The carbonyl group of XII was shown to be at position 6 by addition of

[2] Hosking and Brandt, *Ber.*, **67**, 1173 (1934); **68**, 37, 286, 1311 (1935); Hosking, *Ber.*, **69**, 780 (1936).

methyl Grignard reagent, dehydration, and dehydrogenation to piman-threne. 3-Ketomanoyl oxide is converted into manoyl oxide by Wolff-Kishner reduction, and the position of the carbonyl group was established by Grignard methylation and degradation to 1,3,5,6-tetramethylnaphtha-lene and a tetramethylphenanthrene (probably 1,3,7,8-).

The diketone XI has been prepared also by osmium tetroxide hydroxyl-ation of manool and cleavage of the pentaol with lead tetraacetate.[3] By the addition of isopropylmagnesium bromide to the hydroxyketone XII, dehydration, and treatment of the resulting diene with N-bromosuccini-mide, Jeger, Dürst and Büchi[3] obtained a hydrocarbon identical with dehydroabietane (m.p. 44°), prepared from dehydroabietic acid by Rosen-mund reduction of the acid chloride and Wolff-Kishner reduction. The substances of the sclareol-manool group thus correspond to abietic acid in the configuration at C_{11} and C_{12}.

Fichtelite. Certain fossil resins contain, along with varying proportions of retene, a completely saturated hydrocarbon resembling paraffin in both chemical and physical properties and known as fichtelite (Ger. *Fichte*, pine). The hydrocarbon, m.p. 46.5°, $[\alpha]_D + 18°$, was first isolated by Bromeis[1] from material obtained by Fikentscher from remnants of pine trunks in a peat bed of the Fichtelgebirge region of Bavaria. From the same material Trommsdorff previously had obtained retene, probably admixed with some fichtelite. The material has the appearance of dried pine wood and the hydrocarbons are present in a crystalline condition and are found mostly between the annual rings of the fossilized wood. Fichtelite and retene have been found in other peat beds and lignite beds from pine forests and the substances undoubtedly come from the resin acids originally present in the live trees.

Fichtelite is very resistant to attack by chemical agents. On the basis of early analyses and its occurrence with retene, the hydrocarbon was at first regarded as a perhydro derivative of retene of the formula $C_{18}H_{18}$.[2] A definite relationship was established by the observation that the hydrocar-bon yields retene on dehydrogenation with sulfur.[3] Recognizing that ordinary analyses do not distinguish between the formulas $C_{18}H_{32}$ and $C_{19}H_{34}$, Ruzicka and Waldmann[4] undertook to settle this point by following quantitatively the dehydrogenation of fichtelite with palladium charcoal

---

[3] Jeger, Dürst and Büchi, *Helv. Chim. Acta*, **30**, 1853 (1947).

[1] Bromeis, *Ann.*, **37**, 304 (1841).

[2] Hell, *Ber.*, **22**, 498 (1889); Liebermann and Spiegel, *ibid.*, **22**, 779 (1889); Spiegel, *ibid.*, **22**, 3369, (1889); Bamberger, *ibid.*, **22**, 635 (1889); Bamberger and Strasser, *ibid.*, **22**, 3361 (1889).

[3] Ruzicka, Balas and Schinz, *Helv. Chim. Acta*, **6**, 692 (1923).

[4] Ruzicka and Waldmann, *Helv. Chim. Acta*, **18**, 611 (1935).

at 330 – 370°. If the hydrocarbon has the same number of carbon atoms as retene, the gas should consist solely of hydrogen. Analysis of the gas, which was obtained in 90 percent yield, indicated the presence of methane, and the ratio corresponded approximately with that required by the equation:

$$C_{19}H_{34} \rightarrow C_{18}H_{18} + 6\,H_2 + CH_4$$

This result indicated the presence of an additional methyl group in tertiary linkage. Since fichtelite probably arises from abietic acid in the process of decay, Ruzicka and Waldmann suggested that it has a corresponding

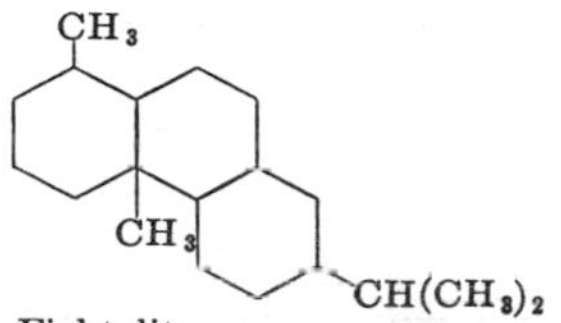

Fichtelite

structure. An analysis[5] of fichtelite by the precision technique of G. P. Baxter distinguishes unambiguously between the above formulas:

	% H
Calculated for $C_{18}H_{32}$:	12.981
Calculated for $C_{19}H_{34}$:	13.056
Found:	13.062

Determination of the molecular weight by the X-ray method[6] is also decisive: found, 264 ± 4; calcd. for $C_{19}H_{34}$, 262.

Kahweol and Cafestol. The substances kahweol[1] ($C_{20}H_{26}O_3$,[2] $[\alpha]_D$ – 204.5°, acetate – 234°, λ_{max} 287 mμ, log ϵ 3.96) and cafestol,[3] formerly "cafesterol"[3] ($C_{20}H_{28}O_3$, $[\alpha]_D$ – 114°, acetate – 89°, λ_{max} 226 mμ) from the unsaponifiable fraction of coffee bean oil were at first thought to be steroids related to the sex hormones, because of mistaken early indications of estrogenic activity. Later investigators were unable to verify the reported physiological activity, and present evidence indicates that the two substances are probably related to the diterpenoid resinols.[4-7] Kahweol contains three double bonds and cafestol two (hydrogenation), and kahweol has been transformed into cafestol by reduction with sodium and ethanol. Both substances are extremely sensitive to oxygen and to acids. The

[5] Fieser and Jacobsen, *J. Am. Chem. Soc.*, **58**, 943 (1936).
[6] Crowfoot, *J. Chem. Soc.*, 1241 (1938).
[1] Bengis and R. J. Anderson, *J. Biol. Chem.*, **97**, 99 (1932).
[2] Wettstein and Miescher, *Helv. Chim. Acta*, **26**, 631 (1943).
[3] Slotta and Neisser, *Ber.*, **71**, 1991, 2342 (1938).

separation is difficult and, since mixtures show no depression in melting point, homogeneity is best determined from the rotation and extinction coefficient.   A preparation described as cafestol yielded a maleic anhydride addition product, but similar samples later were shown to contain kahweol and hence this may have been the actual reactant.

Kahweol and cafestol both contain one acylable hydroxyl group and they appear to contain a tertiary hydroxyl group arranged as in I in a glycol group regarded as present in a five-membered ring.   Slotta[3] found

$$\begin{array}{ccc} | & & | \\ -CH_2C(OH)CH_2OH & \longrightarrow & -CH_2CHCHO \\ (I) & & (II) \end{array}$$

$$\downarrow HIO_4$$

$$\begin{array}{ccccc} | & & & & \\ -CH_2CO & \xrightarrow{I_2,\ KOH} & Diacid & \longrightarrow & Anhydride \\ (III) & & (IV). & & (V) \end{array}$$

that sublimation of cafestol from zinc dust results in dehydration to an aldehyde (II).   The reaction proceeds better when the acetate is used, and tetrahydrocafestol acetate undergoes the same reaction.   The glycol group of tetrahydrocafestol is cleaved by periodic acid to a ketone (III), and the diacid resulting on opening of the ketonic ring on reaction with acetic anhydride in pyridine forms an anhydride (indication that the original ring is five-membered).   One of the carboxyl groups of the diacid is markedly hindered and hence is probably on a quaternary carbon atom.

The third oxygen atom has not been characterized and is regarded as present in enol ether linkage.   The facts cited, particularly the absorption spectra, seem to us to suggest the possibility that the third oxygen atom is present in a lactone ring that includes also the oxygen atom previously assumed to be present in a tertiary hydroxyl group.   Kahweol possibly is an α, β; γ, δ-diunsaturated lactone with a further double bond in a position of cross conjugation; and cafestol an α,β-unsaturated lactone with an additional nonconjugated double bond.

[4] Wettstein, Fritzsche, Hunziker and Miescher, *Helv. Chim. Acta*, **24**, 332E (1941); Wettstein and Miescher, *ibid.*, **26**, 788 (1943); Wettstein, Hunziker and Miescher, *ibid.*, **26**, 1197 (1943); Wettstein, Spillman and Miescher, *ibid.*, **28**, 1004 (1945).

[5] H. Hauptmann and França, *Z. physiol. Chem.*, **259**, 245 (1939); *J. Am. Chem. Soc.*, **65**, 81 (1943); Hauptmann, França and Bruck-Lacerda, *ibid.*, **65**, 993 (1943).

[6] França, *Bol. faculdade filosifia, cienc. letras, Univ. São Paulo*, **14**, 141 (1942) [*C. A.*, **40**, 1528 (1946)].

[7] P. N. Chakravorty, Wesner and R. H. Levin, *J. Am. Chem. Soc.*, **65**, 929 (1943); the "isocafestrol" described by Chakravorty, Levin, Wesner and G. Reed, *ibid.*, **65**, 1325 (1943), is probably pure cafestol containing no kahweol (Wettstein, 1945).

TABLE I. Diterpene Derivatives of Unknown Structure

NAME, FORMULA	M.p., $[\alpha]_D$	SOURCE	CHARACTERIZATION
Marrubiin,[a] $C_{20}H_{28}O_4$	160°, $+46°$	Horehound, *Marrubium vulgare*	Lactone (hydrol. to marrubic acid, $C_{20}H_{30}O_5$); one tert-OH; 2 double bonds; Se→1,2,5-trimethylnaphthalene; stable to HCl
Miropinic acid,[b,c] $C_{20}H_{30}O_2$	160°, $-3.6°$	Miro tree, *Podocarpus ferrugineus*	Two double bonds; Se→pimanthrene; tetrahydride different from tetrahydro-*d*-pimaric acids;[d] HCl→isomiropinic acid
Isomiropinic acid[b]	284°, $+21.2°$	Miro tree	
Cryptopimaric acid,[e] $C_{20}H_{30}O_2$	161°, $-19°$	*Cryptomeria japonica*	Se→pimanthrene
Sugiol,[f] $C_{20}H_{28}O_2$	284°, $+34°$	*C. japonica*	Unsaturated to $C(NO_2)_4$ but resists hydrog.; Se→6-retenol; resembles hinokione in spectrum
Rubiabietic acid,[g] $C_{20}H_{30}O_2$	162°, levorot.		
Rubenic acid,[g] $C_{20}H_{30}O_3$	88°, inactive	*Ceroplastes rubens* Mask	Two double bonds; Se→retene
Rubenol,[g] $C_{20}H_{32}O_2$	Liq., inactive		
Vouacapenic acid,[h] $C_{20}H_{28}O_3$	269°, $+108°$	*Vouacapoua Americana*	Two double bonds; COOH group hindered; one inert oxygen
Cativic acid,[i] $C_{20}H_{34}O_2$	Liq.		Readily esterified; KMnO₄→dihydroxy acid m.p. 158°
Rimuic acid,[j] $C_{16}H_{20}O_3$	193°, $-159°$	*Dacrydium cupressinum*	Identical with podocarpic acid. Sherwood and Short. *J. Chem. Soc.*, 1006 (1938).
Abienol hydrate,[k] $C_{17}H_{30}O_2$	62°, $+19°$	*Abies pectinata*	One double bond; O₃→CH₂O; tert. alcohol; KMnO₄→acid $C_{15}H_{26}O_3$, m.p. 122°

TABLE I.—*Concluded*

NAME, FORMULA	M.p., $[\alpha]_D$	SOURCE	CHARACTERIZATION
Totarol,[1] $C_{20}H_{30}O$	132°, + 41°	*Podocarpus totara*	Three double bonds; inert to maleic anhyd.; Se→7-hydroxy-1-methylphenanthrene; Pd-C→ $C_{18}H_{18}$, m.p. 102°, picrate, m.p. 142.5°, quinone m.p. 161.5°

[a] Lawson and Eustice, *J. Chem. Soc.*, 587 (1939); Hollis, Richards and A. Robertson, *Nature*, **143**, 604 (1939).

[b] Brandt and Neubauer, *J. Chem. Soc.*, 683 (1940).

[c] Probably identical with an acid isolated from *Dacrydium biforme* and from *D. Kirkü*: Hosking and Brandt, *Ber.*, **68**, 1311 (1935); Hosking, *N. Z. J. Sci. Tech.*, **19**, 206 (1937).

[d] Ruzicka, Huyser and Seidel, *Rec. trav. chim.*, **47**, 363 (1928).

[e] Keimatsu, Ishiguro and Fukui, *J. Pharm. Soc. Japan*, **57**, 92 (1937) [*Chem. Zentr.*, II, 596 (1937)].

[f] Huzii and Tikamori, *C. A.*, **33**, 4592 (1939).

[g] Kono and Moruyama, *C. A.*, **31**, 5805 (1937); **32**, 6253 (1938).

[h] Spoelstra, *Rec. trav. chim.*, **49**, 226 (1930).

[i] Kalman, *J. Am. Chem. Soc.*, **60**, 1423 (1938).

[j] Easterfield and Aston, *Proc. Chem. Soc.*, **19**, 190 (1903).

[k] Wienhaus and Mucke, *Ber.*, **75**, 1830 (1942).

[l] Short and Stromberg, *J. Chem. Soc.*, 516 (1937).

TABLE II. Hydrocarbons of Unknown Structure

NAME, FORMULA	M.p., $[\alpha]_D$	SOURCE	CHARACTERIZATION
Rimuene,[a] Totarene,[g] $C_{20}H_{32}$	55°, + 45°	*Daceydium cupressinum, Podocarpus totara*	Se→pimanthrene; O_3→CH_2O; H_2→ dihydride (satn. of vinyl group; O_3→no CH_2O); 2 H_2→tetrahydride
Phyllocladene,[b] $C_{20}H_{32}$	98°, + 16°	Several	Se→pimanthrene, retene; O_3→ CH_2O, HCO_2H, ketone ($C_{19}H_{30}O$); probably tetracyclic with one double bond
Isophyllocladene,[c] $C_{20}H_{32}$	112°, + 24°		From phyllocladene or rimuene with HCO_2H; O_3→keto acid $C_{20}H_{30}O_3$
Mirene,[d] $C_{20}H_{32}$	112°, − 24.5°	*Podocarpus ferrugineus*	May be *l*-isophyllocladene
Kaurene,[e] $C_{20}H_{30}$	60°, − 1.1°	*Agathis australis*	Se→pimanthrene; yields saturated dihydride

TABLE II.—*Concluded*

Cupressene,[c] $C_{20}H_{32}$	75°, $+ 59°$	*Cupressus macrocarpa*	Tetrahydride
Podocarprenes:[f]			
α;	51°, $- 112°$	*P. macrophylla,*	The three isomers yield an identical hydrochloride, m.p. 115°
β;	liq., $- 16°$	*Sciadopitys verticillata*	
γ;	65°, $- 27°$		
$C_{20}H_{32}$			

[a] McDowell and Finlay, *J. Soc. Chem. Ind.*, **44**, 42T (1925); Beath, *ibid.*, **52**, 338T (1933); Hosking and McFadyen, *ibid.*, **53**, 195T (1934); Brandt, *N. Z. J. Sci. Tech.*, **20**, 8B (1938) [*C. A.* **33**, 551 (1939); *Chem. Zentr.*, II, 856 (1939)].

[b] Identical with dacrene and sciadopitene, Briggs, *J. Chem. Soc.*, 79 (1937).

[c] Briggs and Sutherland, *J. Org. Chem.*, **7**, 397 (1942).

[d] Hosking and Short, *Rec. trav. chim.*, **47**, 834 (1928); Kawamura, *C. A.*, **26**, 4679 (1932).

[e] Hosking, *Rec. trav. chim.*, **49**, 1036 (1930).

[f] Nishida and Uoda, *C. A.*, **25**, 4547 (1931); Kawamura, *C. A.*, **26**, 4679 (1932).

[g] Aitken, *J. Soc. Chem. Ind.*, **48**, 344T (1929).

SYNTHESIS OF ALKYLPHENANTHRENES

The Pschorr synthesis provided a successful means for the identification of methoxylated phenanthrene derivatives resulting from the degradation of morphine alkaloids but proved of only limited use for the synthesis of products of the dehydrogenation of resin acids. New synthetic methods developed in 1932 for the specific purpose of identifying the supposed "methylretene" and "methylpimanthrene" not only accomplished the objective in view but paved the way to the subsequent synthesis of compounds related to natural products other than the resin acids.

Haworth's Synthesis. The general method used by Haworth and co-workers[1] consists in the synthesis and cyclization of a γ-arylbutyric acid, followed by the aromatization of the new six-membered ring. This method of obtaining polynuclear types had been employed to a limited extent for the production of hydro derivatives[2] and for the synthesis of 4-methylphenanthrene.[3]

[1] R. D. Haworth and co-workers, *J. Chem. Soc.*, 1125, 1784, 2248, 2717, 2720 (1932); 454 (1934).

[2] Schroeter, *Ber.*, **57**, 2003, 2025 (1924); Schroeter, H. Müller and Huang, *ibid.*, **62**, 645 (1929).

[3] Radcliffe, Sherwood and W. F. Short, *J. Chem. Soc.*, 2293 (1931). See also the later synthesis of acephenanthrene, Fieser and M. Peters, *J. Am. Chem. Soc.*, **54**, 4373 (1932).

For the synthesis of a phenanthrene derivative, a γ-naphthylbutyric acid is required. One preparative method is Friedel and Crafts reaction of succinic anhydride with a suitable naphthalene derivative, followed by reduction of the resulting β-aroylpropionic acid. With naphthalene itself and in most other cases the reaction proceeds best in nitrobenzene solution at a low temperature.[4] Aluminum chloride dissolves in nitrobenzene and combines with the solvent to form a molecular compound[5] that is less reactive than the halide itself and less destructive of the sensitive naphthalene compounds. Mixtures of the 1- and 2-derivatives ordinarily are obtained,

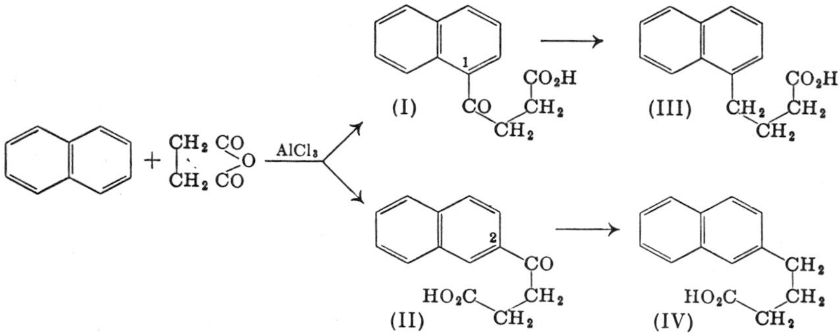

but a separation usually is possible. In the case of naphthalene itself the pure keto acids I and II can be prepared in yields as high as 36 percent and 47 percent, respectively.[6] The 2-acid invariably is the higher-melting and less soluble isomer and can be obtained pure by crystallization; the 1-acid is conveniently purified by the distillation of the methyl ester. In some cases the 2-acid forms a nicely crystalline sodium salt and separation is easy. A procedure for separation of the naphthoylpropionic acids by partial extraction with alkali has been described.[7] β-Aroylpropionic acids also can be obtained from the reaction of succinic anhydride with one mole of an aryl Grignard reagent, but the yields are poor.[8] For the reduction of the keto acids the Clemmensen method usually is satisfactory, although with a high-melting or sparingly soluble acid it often is necessary to add an organic solvent such as alcohol, acetic acid, or dioxane, or to use the lower-melting esters. In any case the results usually are considerably improved

[4] German Patent 376,635 (1923); French Patent 636,065 (1928); Swiss Patent 131,959 (1929); U. S. Patent 1,759,111 (1930).

[5] Kohler, *Am. Chem. J.*, **24**, 385 (1900); **27**, 241 (1902).

[6] Fieser and M. Peters, *J. Am. Chem. Soc.*, **54**, 4347 (1932).

[7] Drake and McVey, *J. Org. Chem.*, **4**, 464 (1939).

[8] Komppa and Rohrmann, *Ann.*, **509**, 259 (1934); Weizmann, Blum-Bergmann and F. Bergmann, *J. Chem. Soc.*, 1370 (1935).

by providing a layer of toluene, for this keeps the carbonyl compound out of contact with the metal and inhibits dimolecular reduction.[9] In some instances superior results are obtained by the simplified Wolff-Kishner procedure of Huang-Minlon.[10]

Haworth converted the acids III and IV into 1-keto-1,2,3,4-tetrahydrophenanthrene (V) and the isomeric 4-ketone (VI) by treatment with 85 percent sulfuric acid. Cyclization can also be effected by treating the

(V)   (VI)

acid chloride in a solvent with aluminum chloride or, in the case of compounds having a particularly reactive and sensitive aromatic nucleus, with the milder condensing agent stannic chloride. Ring closure can be accomplished efficiently with liquid anhydrous hydrogen fluoride[11] or with acetic anhydride and a catalyst ($ZnCl_2$, HCl).[12] The ketones V and VI serve as starting materials for the synthesis of 1- and 4-substituted phenanthrenes. For example, with methylmagnesium iodide they are converted into carbinols, which on distillation yield methyldihydrophenanthrenes. These hydrocarbons on dehydrogenation afford 1- and 4-methylphenanthrene.

One variation in the synthesis consists in the reaction of the esters of keto acids with one mole of Grignard reagent (inverse). In this way an alkyl group can be introduced in a position corresponding to that of the carbonyl group (formulas VII–IX). On attempting to prepare 4-methyl-

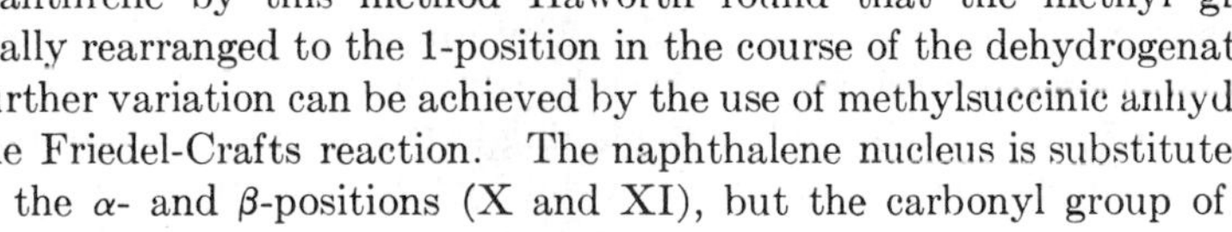

(VII)   (VIII)   (IX)

phenanthrene by this method Haworth found that the methyl group partially rearranged to the 1-position in the course of the dehydrogenation.

Further variation can be achieved by the use of methylsuccinic anhydride in the Friedel-Crafts reaction. The naphthalene nucleus is substituted in both the α- and β-positions (X and XI), but the carbonyl group of the

[9] E. L. Martin, *J. Am. Chem. Soc.*, **58**, 1438 (1936).

[10] Huang-Minlon, *J. Am. Chem. Soc.*, **68**, 2487 (1946).

[11] Fieser and Hershberg, *J. Am. Chem. Soc.*, **61**, 1272 (1939).

[12] Fieser and Hershberg, *J. Am. Chem. Soc.*, **59**, 1028 (1937); **60**, 1893 (1938); Scholl and K. Meyer, *Ber.*, **65**, 1398 (1932).

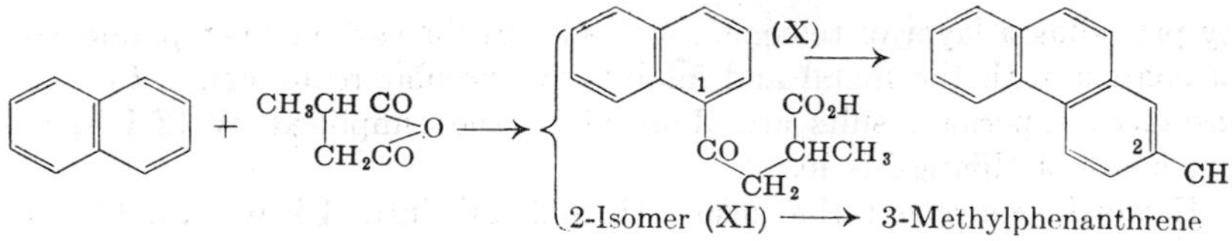

$$\text{2-Isomer (XI)} \longrightarrow \text{3-Methylphenanthrene}$$

anhydride which is farthest removed from the methyl group invariably is
the one to become joined to the aromatic ring. The condensation of an α-
bromo ketone with malonic ester affords another means for the introduction
of alkyl groups, for example: XII $\rightarrow$ XIII. The starting materials are
obtained by bromination of the ketones prepared by the Friedel and Crafts
reaction.

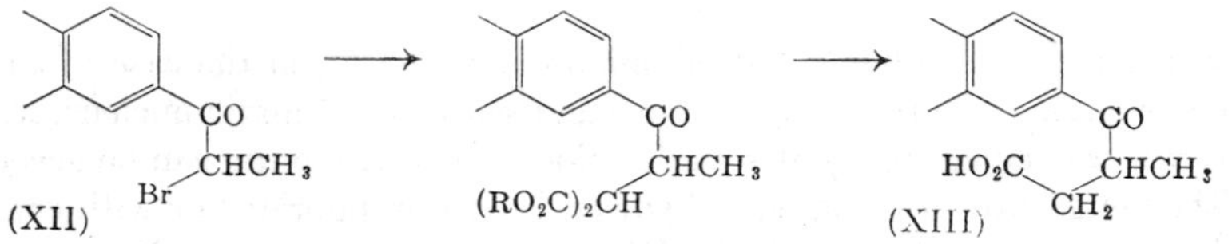

By suitable combination of these methods groups can be introduced at
will at the positions C_1, C_2, C_3, and C_4, but substitution in the second
terminal ring of phenanthrene is not subject to so much variation. With
α- or β-methylnaphthalene as the starting material it is necessary to effect
a substitution and cyclization in the unmethylated ring, as indicated by the
dotted lines in formula XIV. In the case of α-methylnaphthalene, how-

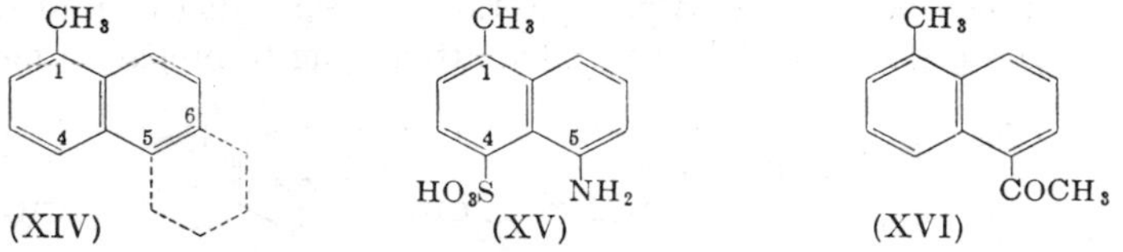

ever, the reactions with succinic anhydride and with acyl halides yield
exclusively the 4-derivatives. Haworth employed as starting material
the aminomethylnaphthalenesulfonic acid XV. After hydrolysis of the
acid group, the group at C_5 was replaced by a nitrile group, and a Grignard
reaction then afforded 5-acetyl-1-methylnaphthalene (XVI). With this
substance it was possible to build on a ring in the desired 5,6-position and
to introduce alkyl groups into the new ring by the above methods.

With β-methylnaphthalene the situation is more favorable than might
have been anticipated from the fact that the hydrocarbon is nitrated and
brominated almost exclusively in the 1-position. Sulfonation, however,
under conditions favoring β-substitution (high temperature) yields the
6-sulfonic acid as the chief product. The 1-acid would not be stable at the

reaction temperature and the sulfonic acid group probably avoids the β-position C_3 partly because this is no true ortho position[13] and partly because of the steric factor. The Friedel and Crafts reaction is also subject to steric influences, and the course of substitution is often dependent upon the temperature, the nature of the carbonyl reagent, and the character of the solvent. Although acyl halides condense with β-methylnaphthalene in carbon disulfide solution almost exclusively in the 1-position, Haworth found that with succinic anhydride in nitrobenzene solution at a low temperature it was possible to obtain the 6-substituted derivative in yields as high as 79 percent. On studying the action of acetyl chloride on naphthalene in nitrobenzene and in benzene, Rivkin[14] obtained chiefly the β-isomer in the former case and a mixture of equal parts of the α- and β-compounds in the latter instance. A possible explanation is that the bulky molecular compound from aluminum chloride, nitrobenzene, and the carbonyl component finds better spatial accommodation in the β-position than in the α-position. Possibly only a slight contributory influence of the solvent or of the carbonyl reagent is sufficient to alter greatly the course of substitution. Even with phthalic anhydride in tetrachloroethane solution, β-methylnaphthalene and 2,3-dimethylnaphthalene yield some products of heteronuclear substitution.[15]

Making use of the above discovery, Haworth succeeded in synthesizing retene through the series of reactions: XVII → XXI. It is necessary to hydrogenate the unsaturated acid corresponding to XVIII prior to ring

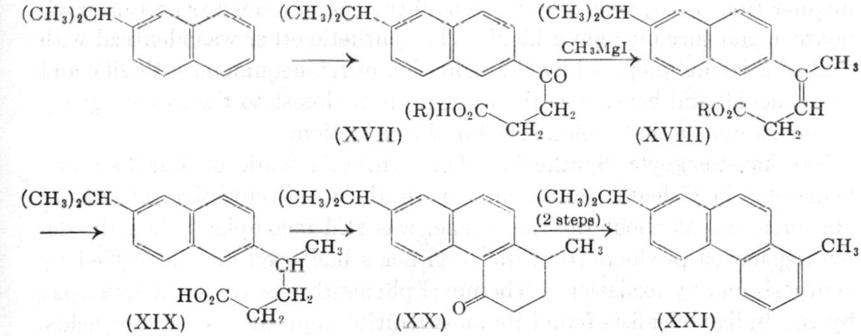

closure, as the unsaturated compound is not suitable for such a reaction. The ketone is not converted directly into the aromatic hydrocarbon but is reduced by the Clemmensen method and the resulting hydrocarbon is dehydrogenated with selenium. In another series Haworth substituted

[13] Fieser and Lothrop, *J. Am. Chem. Soc.*, **57**, 1459 (1935).
[14] Rivkin, *J. Gen. Chem.* (U. S. S. R.), **5**, 277 (1935).
[15] Fieser and M. Peters, *J. Am. Chem. Soc.*, **55**, 3342 (1933).

ethyl for methyl Grignard reagent in the reaction with the ester of the keto acid XVII and obtained 1-ethyl-7-isopropylphenanthrene, identical with "methylretene." Pimanthrene and "methylpimanthrene" were synthesized similarly from β-methylnaphthalene. Ruzicka and Waldmann[16] synthesized pimanthrenequinone by similar methods. A methoxyl group was introduced in order to direct the succinic acid residue into the para position in the unmethylated ring of XXII.

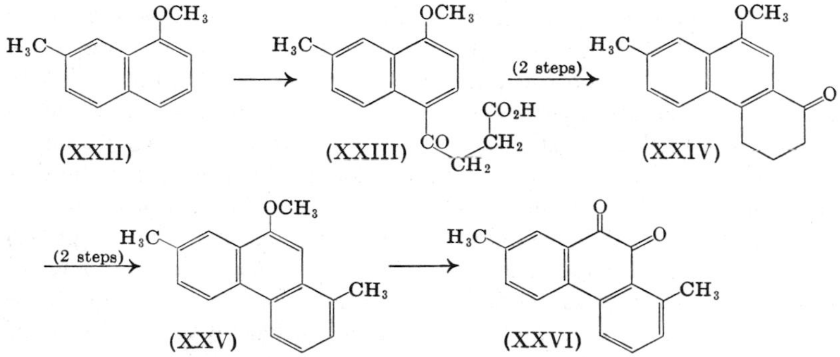

The keto acid XXIII was converted into the phenanthrene derivative XXV as above, and the methoxyl group was eliminated on oxidation to the quinone, XXVI. 9-Methoxyretene has been synthesized in a similar manner from 7-isopropyl-1-methoxynaphthalene, obtained from isopropylbenzene and succinic anhydride.[17] The synthetic ether was identical with that of a retenol prepared by the reduction of retenequinone with zinc and acetic acid,[18] and hence it is the oxygen atom closest to the methyl group in retenequinone that is eliminated in the reduction.

Bardhan-Sengupta Synthesis. The synthetic work of Bardhan and Sengupta[1] in Calcutta, undertaken with the same objective as that of Haworth and at about the same time, was still incomplete when the dehydrogenation products from the resin acids had been fully identified by synthesis and by oxidation. The novel phenanthrene synthesis developed by the Indian chemists found its most fruitful applications in other fields. In the simplest example of the Bardhan-Sengupta synthesis β-phenylethyl bromide is first condensed with the potassium derivative of cyclohexanone-2-carboxylic acid ester. The sodium derivative of the β-keto ester is not suitable for the alkylation. The alkaline hydrolysis of the substituted

[16] Ruzicka and Waldmann, *Helv. Chim. Acta*, **15**, 907 (1932).
[17] Keimatsu, Ishiguro and Sumi, *J. Pharm. Soc. Japan*, **56**, 119 (1936).
[18] Fieser and M. N. Young, *J. Am. Chem. Soc.*, **53**, 4120 (1931).
[1] Bardhan and Sengupta, *J. Chem. Soc.*, 2520, 2798 (1932).

β-keto ester (I) is accompanied by decarboxylation to the ketone II. This is reduced with sodium in moist ether and the alcohol (III) is heated in vacuum with phosphorus pentoxide to effect dehydration and cyclization to octahydrophenanthrene (IV). Bardhan and Sengupta assumed that the ring is closed as the result of a direct elimination of water between the hydroxyl group and the benzene nucleus, but other observations indicate that an unsaturated hydrocarbon formed by dehydration of the alcohol enters into the cyclization. The synthesis is completed by dehydrogenation with selenium. The structure of the octahydrophenanthrene (IV) was established by the following interesting synthesis, which constitutes an

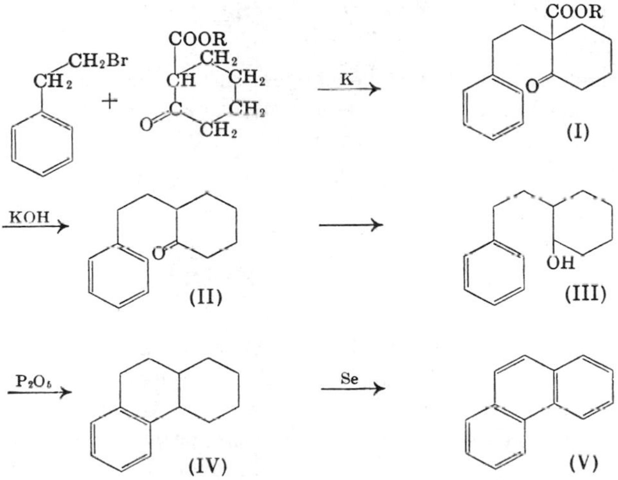

independent route to phenanthrene. Rabe[2] had submitted 3,4-dihydronaphthoic acid ester (VI) to the Michael reaction with acetoacetic ester

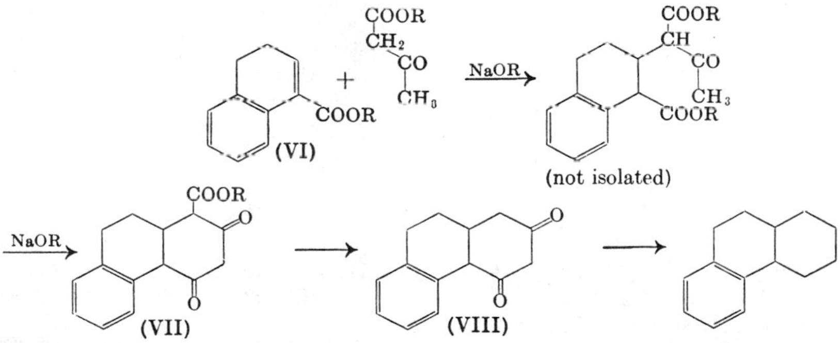

---

[2] Rabe, *Ber.*, **31**, 1896 (1898).

and had found that the addition is followed by an ester condensation, with closure of a new ring (VII). Hydrolysis of the ester gave a 1,3-diketone (VIII), and the Indian investigators found that on reduction by the Clemmensen method this yielded a hydrocarbon identical with their octahydride.

The Bardhan-Sengupta synthesis is capable of wide variation. Substitution products of both of the reagents required for the initial condensation are readily available. Keto esters such as IX are conveniently prepared

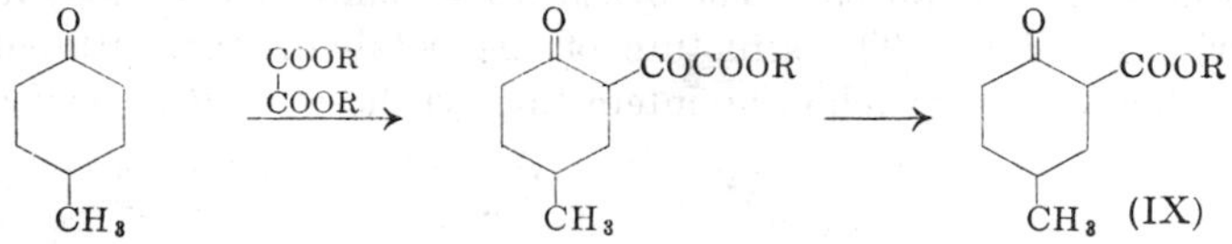

by the condensation of cyclohexanones with oxalic ester. Both retene (X) and pimanthrene were synthesized by the method, in the first case from the reagents indicated in the formulas.

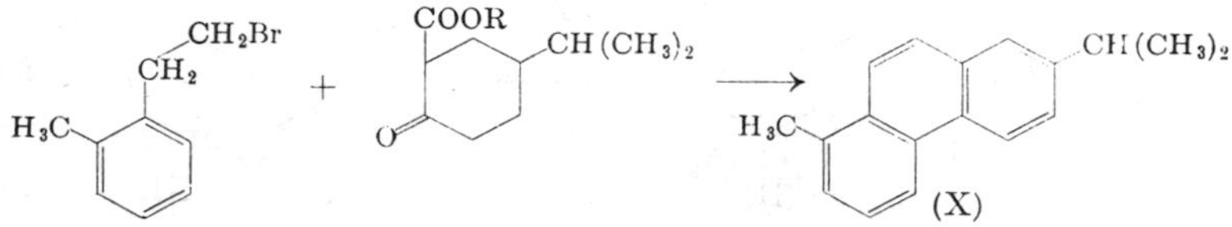

Bogert-Cook Synthesis. A simpler route to phenanthrene involving some of the same steps of the Bardhan and Sengupta method was discovered independently by Perlman, Davidson, and Bogert[1] and by Cook and Hewett.[2] The first step in the synthesis consists in the Grignard condensation of β-phenylethylmagnesium bromide with cyclohexanone to

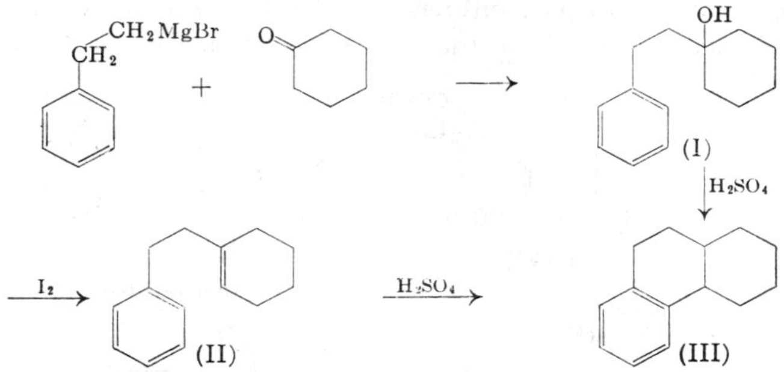

[1] Bogert, *Science*, **77**, 289 (1933); Perlman, Davidson and Bogert, *J. Org. Chem.*, **1**, 288, 300 (1936); Bogert and co-workers, *Rec. trav. chim.*, **52**, 584 (1933); *J. Am. Chem. Soc.*, **56**, 185, 959 (1934); **57**, 151 (1935).

[2] Cook and Hewett, *Chemistry and Industry*, **52**, 451 (1933); Cook, *ibid.*, **52**, 603 (1933); *J. Chem. Soc.*, 1098 (1933).

the tertiary alcohol I. Under the influence of concentrated sulfuric acid this undergoes cyclodehydration with the formation of octahydrophenanthrene (III), as in the Bardhan-Sengupta synthesis. A small amount of an isomeric cyclization product[3,4] has been identified[1] as the spiran. The cyclization of I cannot result directly from the elimination of the elements of water, and the reaction was found to proceed in two steps. The unsaturated hydrocarbon II was prepared by brief treatment of the alcohol with 50 percent sulfuric acid or by catalytic dehydration with iodine, and it was found to undergo cyclization to III under the influence of concentrated sulfuric acid (also with aluminum chloride). The same unsaturated hydrocarbon undoubtedly is an intermediate in the Bardhan-Sengupta synthesis. The Bogert-Cook synthesis is more general in application and provides a simpler means of obtaining the same type of intermediate for the cyclization. Haworth has employed the Bogert-Cook method for the synthesis of optically inactive substances corresponding in structure to dehydroabietic acid[5] and to podocarpic acid.[6] Sterling and Bogert[7] synthesized a liquid hydrocarbon of the structure assigned to fichtelite.

[3] van de Kamp and Mosettig, *J. Am. Chem. Soc.*, **58**, 1062 (1936).
[4] Cook, Hewett and Lawrence, *J. Chem. Soc.*, 71 (1936).
[5] R. D. Haworth and R. L. Barker, *J. Chem. Soc.*, 1299 (1939).
[6] R. D. Haworth and B. P. Moore, *J. Chem. Soc.*, 633 (1946).
[7] Sterling and Bogert, *J. Org. Chem.*, **4**, 20 (1939).

Chapter III
Sterols and Bile Acids

Part 1. Structure

Sterols are crystalline alcohols (Gr. *stereos*, solid) isolated from the unsaponified residues of lipids derived from animals and plants. Most of them are C_{27}–C_{29} compounds having one secondary alcoholic group; some are completely saturated substances, others contain one, two, or three double bonds. Typical bile acids, isolated by the saponification and processing of biles of various animals, are C_{24}-substances having one carboxyl group and one, two, or three secondary alcoholic groups. Chemical investigations initiated over a century ago on each of the two series of physiologically important substances eventually met on common ground and established a correlation between the sterols and bile acids. The information acquired in arduous researches extending for many years finally led, in the period 1932–1934, to the complete elucidation of the structures of key compounds in both series, as illustrated by the accompanying formulas for cholesterol and cholic acid. The two compounds are very similar: they both have the

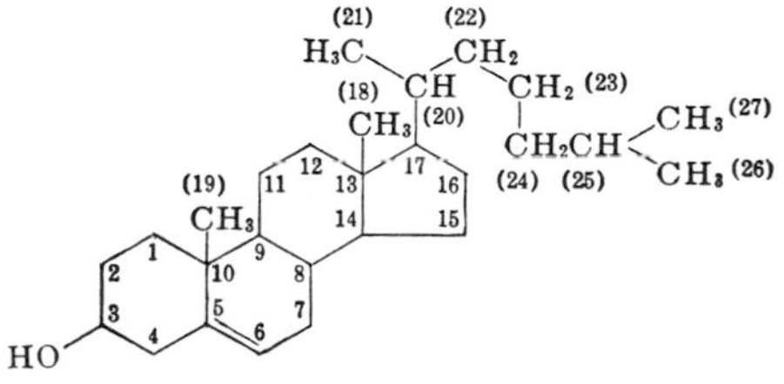

Cholesterol 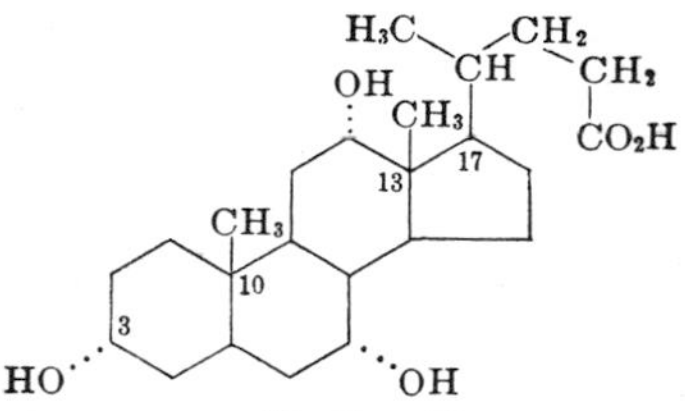   Cholic acid

perhydro-1,2-cyclopentenophenanthrene ring system and possess characteristic tertiarily bound or angular methyl groups at C_{10} and C_{13}, the secondary hydroxyl group of cholesterol occupies a position (C_3) corresponding to one of three groups in cholic acid, and the side chains at C_{17} differ only in length and in the nature of the terminal group, isopropyl or carboxyl. That the established system of numbering is not fully rational is because it incorporates some parts of a provisional system employed at a time when the structures were not fully elucidated.

Cholesterol contains eight asymmetric carbon atoms and cholic acid eleven, but each substance as isolated from natural sources is sterically pure and free from contamination with any of the numerous possible optical isomers. Although the determination of the configurations of these complicated molecules presented a particularly difficult problem, investigations culminating in 1947 established beyond reasonable doubt the relative configurations at all asymmetric centers of the nucleus in key compounds of both series (see Chapter X). The convention for the indication of configurations in formulas is to employ a full-line bond for a group assumed to project above the plane of the ring system and a dotted line for a group extending below this plane; the former arrangement is designated β and the latter α. The conventional designations arose from an early, arbitrary use of the name β-cholestanol for the normal product of hydrogenation of cholesterol, otherwise known as dihydrocholesterol; the reduced sterol and its precursor are now described as 3β-hydroxy compounds. Any hydroxyl

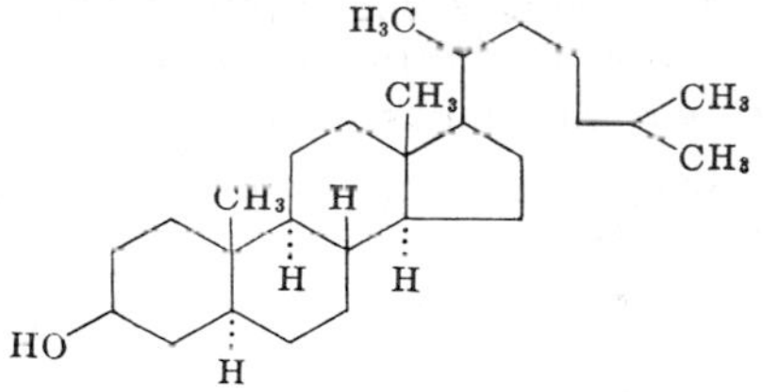

Cholestanol

group, angular methyl group, C_{17} side chain, or tertiary hydrogen that lies on the same side of the ring plane as the C_3-hydroxyl group of cholesterol is described as β-oriented, and the carbon atom to which the group is joined by definition has the β-configuration. The opposite orientations and configurations are designated α. The full configuration established for β-cholestanol, now named simply cholestanol, is shown in the formula. The two angular methyl groups and the C_{17}-side chain, like the 3-hydroxyl group, all have the β-orientation. All three ring junctures are trans.

It should be noted that the conventional representation arbitrarily assumes one of two possible absolute configurations and that a differentiation cannot yet be made between the formula of cholestanol as written and its mirror image.

Members of the sterol series that are fully saturated, like cholestanol, are conveniently described as stanols; those that contain one double bond are stenols. Cholesterol is thus a stenol and affords a stanol on hydrogenation. A C_5-epimer of cholestanol that is excreted in the feces and was originally called coprosterol will be designated coprostanol in this book. The term sterol thus embraces both saturated and unsaturated members of the series. The generic term steroid is employed to indicate all those substances that are structurally related to the sterols and bile acids to the extent of possessing the characteristic perhydrocyclopentenophenanthrene ring system.

DESCRIPTION

Sterols. Along with phosphatides, sterols are regular constituents of animal and plant fats and oils. They are neutral, stable, crystalline alcoholic substances that occur partly in the free condition and partly esterified with higher fatty acids. Isolation is accomplished by hydrolysis of the neutral fatty fraction with alcoholic alkali and extraction of the unsaponifiable matter with ether or petroleum ether. The extracted material often crystallizes readily from alcohol, but material purified merely by a few crystallizations is seldom homogeneous and is liable to be a mixture of related sterols of comparable solubilities from which fully pure individuals can be isolated only by laborious special processing. This is particularly true of sterols of vegetable origin, the phytosterols, which occur in small amounts in all parts of plants and are found in relatively great abundance

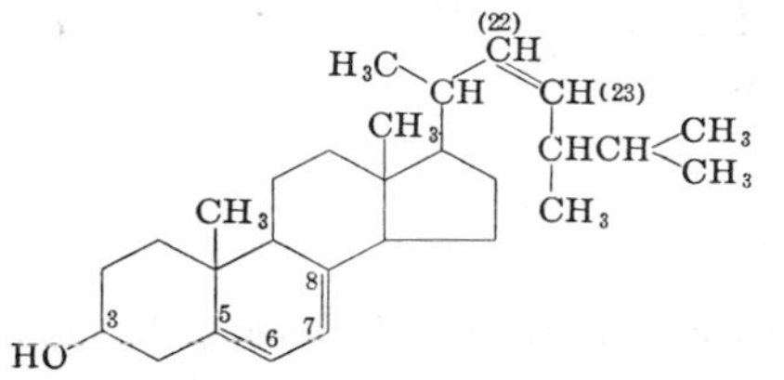

Ergosterol 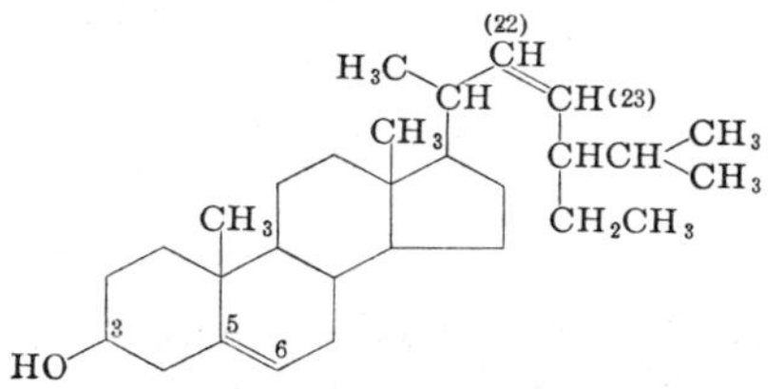   Stigmasterol

in seeds and pollen. Ordinary preparations of sitosterol (Gr. *sito-*, grain), the most widely distributed sterol of plants, have been found to consist of mixtures of several stereoisomers and dihydro derivatives. Ergosterol, a long known and important sterol isolated from yeast, is accompanied by an array of other sterols; stigmasterol occurs in the Calabar bean and soybean along with sitosterols. Ergosterol (see formula) differs from cholesterol in having an additional methyl group in the side chain (C_{24}) and two additional double bonds (C_7–C_8, C_{22}–C_{23}). Stigmasterol has an ethyl group at C_{24} and an external double bond at C_{22}–C_{23} in addition to the double bond at C_5–C_6.

Cholesterol (Gr. *chole*, bile + *stereos*, solid) has been known since the eighteenth century as the chief constituent of human gall stones. It is the characteristic sterol of higher animals and is present in all cells of the animal organism, in largest amounts in the brain and nerve tissue, in the suprarenal glands, and in egg yolk. The solid matter of the human brain contains as much as 17 percent of the substance. The cholesterol of brain tissue and of gall stones is present almost exclusively in the free condition,

TABLE I. Properties of Typical Sterols and Derivatives

NAME	FORMULA	DOUBLE BONDS	M.p.	$[\alpha]_D$ Chf	SOURCE
Cholesterol	$C_{27}H_{46}O$	1	149°	− 39°	All animal cells
Cholestanol	$C_{27}H_{48}O$	0	142°	+ 24°	Companion of cholesterol
Epicholestanol	$C_{27}H_{48}O$	0	182°	+ 28°	See Chart 2
Cholestanone	$C_{27}H_{46}O$	0	129°	+ 41°	CrO_3 oxid. of cholestanol
Coprostanol	$C_{27}H_{48}O$	0	101°	+ 28°	Feces
Epicoprostanol	$C_{27}H_{48}O$	0	118°	+ 32°	See Chart 2
Coprostanone	$C_{27}H_{46}O$	0	63°	+ 36°	CrO_3 oxid. of coprostanol
Ergosterol	$C_{28}H_{44}O$	3	165°	− 130°	Ergot, yeast
Stigmasterol	$C_{29}H_{48}O$	2	170°	− 49°	Calabar bean, soybean

Chf = Chloroform

but the material found in most organs of the body occurs partly in the form of fatty acid esters. Sperry[1] found that the blood serum of several individuals contained 0.15–0.25 g. of total cholesterol per 100 cc. and that the average amount of uncombined cholesterol was 26.9 ± 1.4 percent. The cholesterol of commerce is prepared from the spinal cord of cattle by solvent extraction (*e.g.* CH_2Cl_2), with or without saponification (saponification increases the amount of material available but produces troublesome emulsions). A reported laboratory method for the preparation of cholesterol consists in freezing brain tissue in liquid air, grinding it, and extracting the powder with acetone; a yield of 83 percent of the total cholesterol present is claimed.[2] Schoenheimer[3] found that cholesterol preparations derived from various organs and tissues contain 1–2 percent of the dihydro derivative cholestanol. Cholesterol preparations may also contain traces of more highly unsaturated products. Purification is best accomplished by recrystallization of the sparingly soluble 5,6-dibromide,[4] from which the unsaturated alcohol is regenerated by debromination with zinc dust and acetic acid or, more satisfactorily, with sodium iodide.[5]

Stereoisomerism of Sterols. Coprostanol (Gr. *kopra*, dung) differs from cholestanol only in having the epimeric configuration at C_5. The spatial arrangement of the hydroxyl at C_3 is the same as that of cholestanol and of cholesterol ($C_3\beta$), and the isomeric relationship is maintained in the saturated hydrocarbons cholestane and coprostane, which were first recog-

[1] Sperry, *J. Biol. Chem.*, **114**, 125 (1936).

[2] Remesow and Lewaschowa, *Z. physiol. Chem.*, **241**, 81 (1936).

[3] Schoenheimer, v. Behring, Hummel and Schindel, *Z. physiol. Chem.*, **192**, 73 (1930); Schoenheimer, v. Behring and Hummel, *ibid.*, **192**, 93 (1930).

[4] Windaus, *Ber.*, **39**, 518 (1906); Windaus and Hauth, *ibid.*, **39**, 4378 (1906); R. J. Anderson, *J. Biol. Chem.*, **71**, 407 (1927).

[5] Schoenheimer, *Z. physiol. Chem.*, **192**, 86 (1930); *J. Biol. Chem.*, **110**, 461 (1935).

nized by Windaus[1] as differing from each other in the nature of the union between rings A and B. In cholestane the juncture between rings A and B corresponds to that of trans decalin (two "chair" rings), whereas coprostane corresponds to cis decalin (two "bed" rings). The isomerism is dependent upon the configuration at the asymmetric center C_5; the C_5-hydrogen atom has the β-orientation in coprostane and the α-orientation in cholestane.

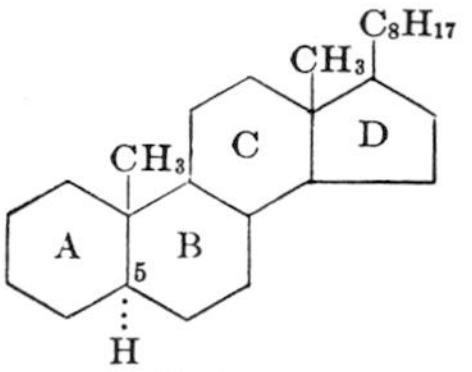

Cholestane
(A/B: trans decalin type)
Allo-series

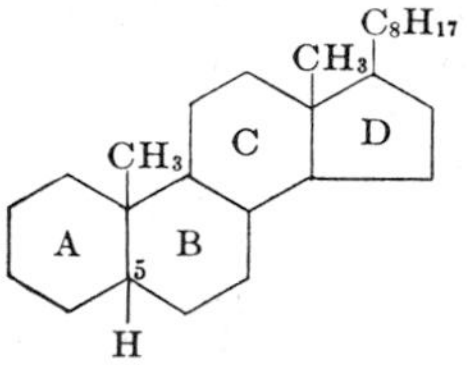

Coprostane
(A/B: cis decalin type)
Normal series

Coprostane and coprostanol are classified as normal sterols because they correspond in configuration at C_5 to the natural bile acids. Cholestane and other substances of the C_5-configuration are members of the allo-series.

A second important type of stereoisomerism involves the configuration of the C_3-carbon atom, which in all known sterols of natural occurrence is the site of the lone hydroxyl group. As stated above, the natural $C_3\beta$-arrangement of cholesterol and cholestanol (I) is taken as a reference standard. The epimeric configuration is illustrated in the partial formula for epicholestanol (II). In I the hydroxyl group is trans to the hydrogen atom at C_5, and in II the groups are cis.[2]

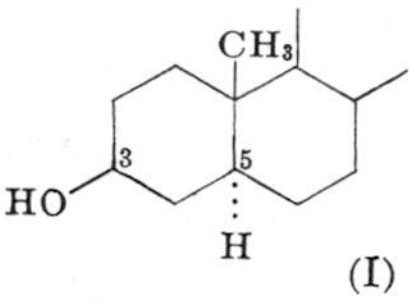

Cholestanol (I)

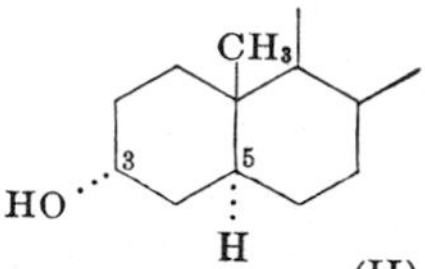

Epicholestanol (II)

[1] Windaus, *Ann.*, **447**, 233 (1926).

[2] A system of nomenclature based upon this relationship was proposed by Ruzicka, Brüngger, Eichenberger and J. Meyer, *Helv. Chim. Acta*, **17**, 1407 (1934): cholestanol and epicholestanol were termed "3-trans" and "3-cis" compounds, respectively. Schoenheimer and Evans, *J. Biol. Chem.*, **114**, 567 (1936), criticized the system and proposed an alternate one in which the steric arrangement of the C_3-hydroxyl is described in terms of its relationship to the C_{10}-methyl group: cholestanol is "3-cis." Shortcomings and disadvantages of both systems were reviewed in the second edition of this book, and the "α-β" convention based on cholestanol was proposed as an alternate system. This has been accepted by most workers in the field and is hence employed exclusively in the present edition.

The conversion of cholesterol into substances of both the coprostane series and the $C_3\alpha$-type was studied most extensively in the course of investigations in the field of the sex hormones, but the methods will be described at this point in order to illustrate the stereochemical relationships. The sole product of the hydrogenation of cholesterol in the presence of platinum catalyst is cholestanol,[3] but three stereoisomers can be prepared through the ketones cholestanone and cholestenone. The saturated ketone is obtained by chromic acid oxidation of the readily available cholestanol, and the α,β-unsaturated cholestenone can be prepared from cholesterol by various methods (Chart 1). The first process employed consisted in the

Chart 1. PREPARATION OF CHOLESTENONE

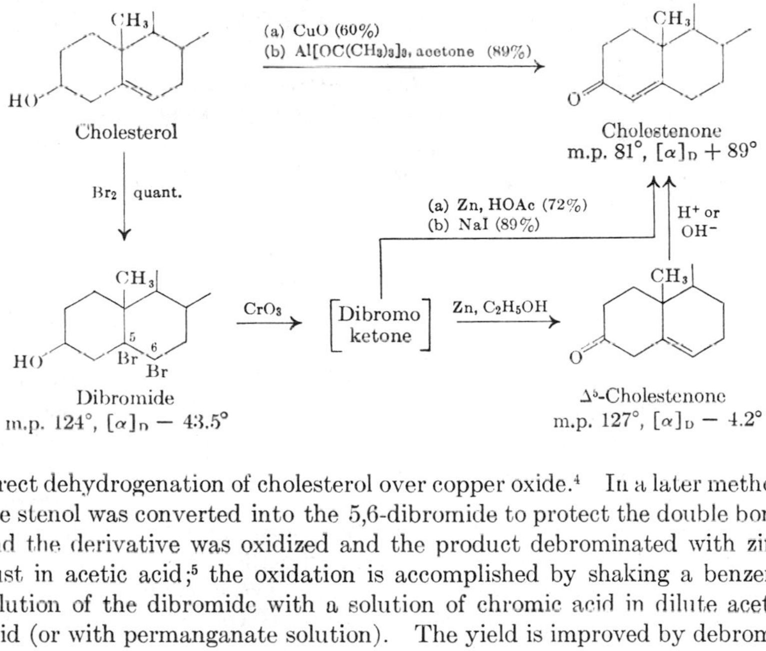

(a) CuO (60%)
(b) Al[OC(CH₃)₃]₃, acetone (89%)

Cholesterol

Cholestenone
m.p. 81°, $[\alpha]_D + 89°$

Br₂ | quant.

(a) Zn, HOAc (72%)
(b) NaI (89%)

H⁺ or OH⁻

Dibromide
m.p. 124°, $[\alpha]_D - 43.5°$

CrO₃ → [Dibromo ketone] → Zn, C₂H₅OH

Δ⁵-Cholestenone
m.p. 127°, $[\alpha]_D - 4.2°$

direct dehydrogenation of cholesterol over copper oxide.[4] In a later method the stenol was converted into the 5,6-dibromide to protect the double bond and the derivative was oxidized and the product debrominated with zinc dust in acetic acid;[5] the oxidation is accomplished by shaking a benzene solution of the dibromide with a solution of chromic acid in dilute acetic acid (or with permanganate solution). The yield is improved by debromination in benzene with a solution of sodium iodide in absolute alcohol.[6] The double bond migrates from the 5,6-position to a position of conjugation

[3] Willstätter and E. W. Mayer, *Ber.*, **41**, 2199 (1908).

[4] Diels and Abderhalden, *Ber.*, **37**, 3099 (1904); Diels, Gädke and Körding, *Ann.*, **459**, 21 (1927).

[5] Windaus, *Ber.*, **39**, 518 (1906); Ruzicka, Brüngger, Eichenberger and J. Meyer, *Helv. Chim. Acta*, **17**, 1407 (1934).

[6] Schoenheimer, *J. Biol. Chem.*, **110**, 461 (1935).

in either instance, but if the dibromide is treated with zinc dust in neutral alcoholic solution the intermediate Δ^5-cholestenone can be isolated;[7] the substance easily isomerizes to the more stable isomer in the presence of either acid or base. None of the above methods of preparing cholestenone is as generally satisfactory as Oppenauer's method of oxidation with aluminum t-butoxide and acetone in benzene solution;[8] this smoothly proceeding reaction has been the preferred method for the preparation of Δ^4-stenones. Recently Kleiderer and Kornfeld[9] have described the preparation of cholestenone in 80 percent yield by refluxing cholesterol in toluene with Raney nickel in the presence of cyclohexanone as hydrogen acceptor.

The methods for the conversion of cholestanone and cholestenone into the four isomeric stanols are indicated in Chart 2. When cholestanone is hydrogenated in a neutral medium, or when it is reduced with sodium and amyl alcohol, the chief product is cholestanol,[10] but Vavon and Jakubowicz[11] discovered that in the presence of a small amount of hydrochloric acid the catalytic hydrogenation takes a different stereochemical course and gives epicholestanol as almost the exclusive product. Previously epicholestanol had been obtained in small amounts by the epimerization of cholestanol with sodium ethoxide, but the reaction reaches a point of equilibrium when only about 10 percent of the material has been isomerized.[12] No satisfactory route to compounds of the coprostane series was available until Grasshof[13] discovered that coprostanone can be obtained in good yield by the partial hydrogenation of cholestenone. The C_4–C_5 double bond theoretically can open in two ways, with the establishment of either of the alternate configurations at C_5, and the course of the reduction evidently is dependent upon the conditions, for Diels and Abderhalden[10] obtained cholestanol from cholestenone by reduction with sodium and amyl alcohol. With coprostanone readily available, Grasshof[14] found that coprostanol can be obtained by hydrogenation of the ketone in an acidic medium (glacial acetic acid), and Ruzicka and co-workers (see Ref. 5) found that in ethereal solution the chief product of hydrogenation is epicoprostanol. The interconversion of the epimers had been observed earlier by Windaus.[15]

The stereochemical arrangement of the C_3-hydroxyl group of cholestanol with respect to the C_5-hydrogen atom (OH/H:trans) was inferred by

[7] Butenandt and Schmidt-Thomé, *Ber.*, **69**, 882 (1936).

[8] Oppenauer, *Rec. trav. chim.*, **56**, 137 (1937).

[9] Kleiderer and Kornfeld, *J. Org. Chem.*, **13**, 455 (1948).

[10] Diels and Abderhalden, *Ber.*, **39**, 884 (1906).

[11] Vavon and Jakubowicz, *Bull. soc. chim.*, **53**, 584 (1933).

[12] Windaus and Uibrig, *Ber.*, **47**, 2384 (1914).

[13] Grasshof, *Z. physiol. Chem.*, **223**, 249 (1934).

[14] Grasshof, *Z. physiol. Chem.*, **225**, 197 (1934).

[15] Windaus and Uibrig, *Ber.*, **48**, 857 (1915); Windaus, *ibid.*, **49**, 1724 (1916).

Ruzicka[5] on the basis of the Auwers-Skita rule that catalytic hydrogenation in an acidic medium usually gives cis forms, whereas trans isomers are produced in a neutral or alkaline medium; the configurations indicated in

Chart 2. EPIMERIC STANOLS

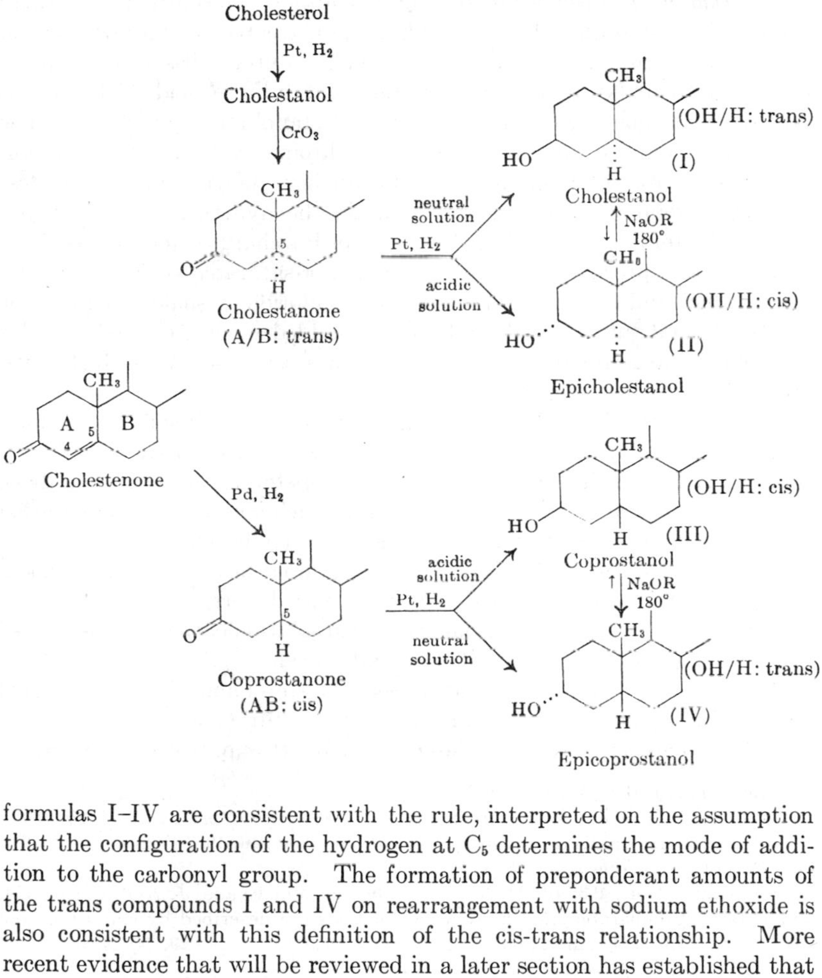

formulas I–IV are consistent with the rule, interpreted on the assumption that the configuration of the hydrogen at C_5 determines the mode of addition to the carbonyl group. The formation of preponderant amounts of the trans compounds I and IV on rearrangement with sodium ethoxide is also consistent with this definition of the cis-trans relationship. More recent evidence that will be reviewed in a later section has established that this early inference is correct and that the arbitrarily assumed configurations correspond to actuality.

Color Reactions. When treated with strong acids under dehydrating conditions, colorless sterols often give rise to beautiful and varied displays of colors. Usually there is a period of induction followed by the gradual development of a succession of colors. These and other phenomena form the basis of a number of color tests that are of value in the qualitative and quantitative determination of specific steroids and in the diagnosis of structure.

Liebermann[1] *or Liebermann-Burchard*[2] *reaction.* A solution of a small crystal of the sterol in cold acetic anhydride is treated with a few drops of concentrated sulfuric acid (Liebermann), or the sterol is dissolved in chloroform and treated with acetic anhydride and sulfuric acid. The test is positive with cholesterol, negative with cholestanol and coprostanol. The transient colors are probably due to halochromic salts of either the unsaturated sterol or a product of its further dehydration. The test affords a useful index of the end point in the hydrogenation of an unsaturated sterol. A modified Liebermann-Burchard reaction has been employed in a procedure for the purification of saturated sterols.[3] A solution of the crude material in carbon tetrachloride is shaken with acetic anhydride and sulfuric acid, and water is added until a colored complex containing unsaturated steroid contaminants separates as a thick layer from the clarified solution.

Rosenheim reaction.[4] The substance to be tested is dissolved in chloroform and a few drops of an aqueous solution of trichloroacetic acid are added. A Rosenheim color is characteristic of sterols that contain a diene system (ergosterol) or are capable of forming such a system by dehydration under the influence of trichloroacetic acid (Δ^4-cholestenol).[5]

Salkowski reaction.[6] A solution of the material in chloroform is shaken with concentrated sulfuric acid (colors in both layers).

Tschugaeff reaction.[7] A glacial acetic acid solution of the sterol is treated with zinc chloride and acetyl chloride and boiled.

Lifschütz reaction.[8] Small quantities of the sterol and of perbenzoic acid are heated in glacial acetic acid solution and sulfuric acid is added.

Elaborations of these tests are described by Whitby[9] and by Schoenheimer.[10]

[1] Liebermann, *Ber.*, **18**, 1803 (1885).

[2] Burchard, *Inaugural Dissertation*, Rostock (1889), see *Chem. Zentr.*, I, 25 (1890).

[3] R. J. Anderson and Nabenhauer, *J. Am. Chem. Soc.*, **46**, 1957 (1924).

[4] Rosenheim, *Biochem. J.*, **23**, 47 (1929).

[5] Windaus, *Ann.*, **453**, 101 (1927); Schoenheimer and Evans, *J. Biol. Chem.*, **114**, 567 (1936). Comparable and improved color tests are described by Christiani and Anger, *Ber.*, **72**, 1124 (1939), and by Miescher, *Helv. Chim. Acta*, **29**, 743 (1946).

[6] Salkowski, *Z. physiol. Chem.*, **57**, 523 (1908).

[7] Tschugaeff, *Chem. Z.*, **24**, 542 (1900).

[8] Lifschütz, *Ber.*, **41**, 252 (1908).

[9] Whitby, *Biochem. J.*, **17**, 5 (1923).

[10] Schoenheimer, Dam and v. Gottberg, *J. Biol. Chem.*, **110**, 659 (1935); Schoenheimer, *Z. physiol. Chem.*, **192**, 77 (1930).

The *Tortelli-Jaffé test*[11] is conducted by pouring a layer of a 2 percent solution of bromine in chloroform onto a solution of the sterol in acetic acid; a green coloration appears at the interface. The reaction is specific for compounds that contain a ditertiary double bond between bridgeheads (exceptions: ergosterol and dehydroergosterol are positive) or that are easily isomerized to such substances.

Another group of color reactions involve a condensation at a reactive methylene group adjacent to a carbonyl group.

Zimmermann reaction.[12] An alcoholic solution of a ketosteroid is treated with m-dinitrobenzene and potassium hydroxide. In a positive reaction a transient violet coloration appears and reaches maximum intensity in about eighty minutes. The reaction is used extensively for the quantitative determination of 17-ketosteroids, for example androsterone and estrone. The absorption maximum of the colored complex varies with the position and nature of the carbonyl group, and hence the test has diagnostic value. The 17-ketosteroids show maxima at about 520 mμ, and Δ^4-unsaturated 3-ketosteroids have a band of comparable intensity at 380 mμ.[13] A 20-ketosteroid gives a color only about one-fifth as intense (at 520 mμ) as that from a 17-ketosteroid.[14] Although a quantitative comparison is lacking, an intense violet Zimmermann color is characteristic also of saturated sterols and bile acids containing a 3-keto group.[15] The test is negative when the keto group is in the 6-, 7-, or 12-position.

Other tests depend upon the development of an interfacial color when a solution of a sterol containing *furfural*,[16] *benzaldehyde*,[17] or *mercuric acetate*[18] is underlayered with concentrated sulfuric acid.

A *diazo coupling test* is useful for the characterization of nonketonic steroids containing a conjugated system of double bonds either contained in the same ring or distributed between two rings.[19] An orange color develops (at varying rates) on addition of p-nitrobenzenediazonium chloride to a solution of the sterol in acetic acid or acetic acid-dioxane.

[11] Tortelli-Jaffé, *Chem. Z.*, **39**, 14 (1915); Heilbron and Spring, *Biochem. J.*, **24**, 133 (1930); Häussler and Brauchli, *Helv. Chim. Acta*, **12**, 187 (1929); U. Westphal, *Ber.*, **72**, 1243 (1939).

[12] Zimmermann, *Z. physiol. Chem.*, **233**, 257 (1935); **245**, 47 (1936); *Vitamine und Hormone*, **5**, 1 (1944).

[13] Langstroth and Talbot, *J. Biol. Chem.*, **128**, 759 (1939).

[14] L. P. Hansen, Cantarow, Rakoff and Paschkis, *Endocrinology*, **33**, 282 (1943).

[15] Kaziro and Shimada, *Z. physiol. Chem.*, **249**, 220 (1937).

[16] Pettenkofer, *Ann.*, **52**, 90 (1844); Kerr and Hoehn, *Archiv. Biochem.*, **4**, 155 (1944); Woker and Antener, *Helv. Chim. Acta*, **22**, 47, 511, 666, 1309 (1939).

[17] Scherrer, *Helv. Chim. Acta*, **22**, 1329 (1939).

[18] Nath, *Ann. Biochem. Exptl. Med.*, **2**, 83 (1942); Nath and M. K. Chakraborty, *ibid.*, **2**, 73 (1942).

[19] L. F. Fieser and Campbell, *J. Am. Chem. Soc.*, **60**, 159 (1938).

Precipitation with Digitonin. Many applications have been made of the important discovery by Windaus[1] that cholesterol forms a remarkably stable and sparingly soluble molecular compound with digitonin, a glycosidic saponin of the composition $C_{56}H_{92}O_{29}$. The compound, called cholesterol digitonide, is made up of one molecule each of cholesterol and digitonin. The substance has no definite melting point, but it separates from solutions in a characteristically crystalline form. The solubility is so slight (0.014 g. in 100 cc. of 95 percent alcohol at 18°) that the compound is easily freed from foreign materials. Dissociation into the components occurs in alcoholic solution to a definite, but very slight, extent. The precipitation of cholesterol from an alcoholic solution by digitonin affords a sensitive qualitative test for the presence of the sterol, for a reaction is observable at a dilution of 1:10,000. Use is also made of the precipitation of cholesterol and other sterols by digitonin in separation of sterols from mixtures. Special methods are required for the recovery of the sterols and of the costly digitonin, for the molecular compounds are so stable that they are not decomposed, for example, by continued extraction with ether. Boiling with xylene for several hours extracts the sterol portion, but certain sterols are too sensitive for such treatment. One method of cleavage depends upon the fact that the acetyl derivatives of cholesterol and some other sterols do not combine with digitonin: after treatment of cholesterol digitonide with acetic anhydride the cholesteryl acetate can be extracted with ether (Windaus[2]). An improved method consists in dissolving the molecular compound in cold pyridine, in which dissociation is apparently complete, and precipitating the digitonin with ether.[3] The sterol remains in solution. This method of cleavage is of value for the isolation of such substances as Δ^4-cholestenol, which easily loses a molecule of water. Dissociation into the components also can be brought about by boiling a solution of cholesterol digitonide with alcoholic sodium acetate solution and adding ether; digitonin and sodium acetate are precipitated and the cholesterol remains in solution.[4] Another method of scission consists in heating cholesterol digitonide at 240° in high vacuum; cholesterol distils in good yield and the residual digitonin suffers only slight decomposition.[5]

The presence in cholesterol of the free hydroxyl group is essential to the formation of the molecular compounds, since cholesteryl acetate (or the *i*-butyrate or palmitate) is not precipitated by digitonin; the same is true

[1] Windaus, *Ber.*, **42**, 238 (1909).
[2] Windaus, *Z. physiol. Chem.*, **65**, 110 (1910).
[3] Schoenheimer and Dam, *Z. physiol. Chem.*, **215**, 59 (1933).
[4] Lifschütz, *Biochem. Z.*, **282**, 441 (1935).
[5] Christiani and Pailer, *Microchim. Acta*, **1**, 26 (1937).

of the C_3-halogen compounds and ketones. The configuration of the carbon atom carrying the hydroxyl group must, however, correspond to that of cholesterol. Cholestanol combines with digitonin but epicholestanol is not precipitated by the reagent. On the other hand, the manner of linkage between rings A and B is not a factor of importance, for coprostanol (but not epicoprostanol) forms a molecular compound as well as cholestanol. Digitonin also combines with the phytosterols stigmasterol, sitosterol, ergosterol, and fucosterol, and it is known from degradations and interconversions that all these compounds are of the 3β-type corresponding to cholestanol.

The remarkable space specificity of the digitonin reaction is of great value in stereochemical studies in the sterol series. It is also very useful in preparative work for the removal from indifferent material of traces of substances capable of combining with the reagent. For example in the preparation of epicoprostanol by the hydrogenation of coprostanone in ethereal solution a completely pure product is easily obtained by precipitation of traces of coprostanol with digitonin. For the separation of saturated sterols (of the β-type) from cholesterol or other unsaturated sterols, Schoenheimer[6] developed a method based on the observation that the sterol dibromides are not precipitable with digitonin. The mixture is treated with bromine to convert the cholesterol present into the dibromide, and digitonin then precipitates only the saturated sterols.

Although precipitability with digitonin is characteristic of most sterols that contain a free 3β-hydroxyl group, a few exceptions to the rule have been encountered. An acyloxy group at the 4- or 7-position prevents the precipitation of a complex.[7] An inversion at some center of asymmetry other than C_3, for example at C_{10}, may interfere with digitonin precipitation (see lumisterol). Noller[8] determined the solubility products of several steroid sapogenins and found that in this series digitonin precipitation can be used as a guide to the configuration at C_3 only if the behavior of both C_3-epimers can be compared; sometimes even the invariably less soluble 3β-epimers form digitonides no more than barely less soluble than digitonin itself and of the same order of solubility as the digitonide of epicholestanol. Fortunately the ready precipitability of the 3β-sterols is characteristic also of most steroids with shortened side chains or with a ketonic or alcoholic group at C_{17}. Among the many hormones and companion steroids originating in the gonads or in the adrenal cortex, those that contain a 3β-

[6] See C. E. Bills, "Physiology of the Sterols, including Vitamin D," *Physiol. Rev.*, **15**, 1 (1935).

[7] Spring and Swain, *J. Chem. Soc.*, 1356 (1939); Wintersteiner and Ruigh, *J. Am. Chem. Soc.*, **64**, 1177 (1942); see also W. Stoll, *Z. physiol. Chem.*, 246, 1, (1937).

[8] Noller, *J. Am. Chem. Soc.*, **61**, 2717 (1939).

hydroxyl group invariably are precipitated and those that lack this configurational feature are not. Effective use is made of the reaction in the separation of urinary steroid mixtures into 3α- and 3β-fractions.

Microdetermination of Cholesterol. Windaus[1] introduced the use of the digitonin reaction for the macrogravimetric determination of cholesterol; the digitonide was merely collected and weighed.[2] The introduction of colorimetry for the determination of the cholesterol content of the precipitate led to the development of rapid and accurate methods of microdetermination. A widely used procedure applicable to the determination of both free and total cholesterol in a 0.2-cc. sample of blood serum is that of Schoenheimer and Sperry.[3, 4] The sample is extracted with acetone-alcohol and the free cholesterol is precipitated from a portion of the solution with digitonin. Total cholesterol is precipitated similarly from another portion of the extract after alkaline hydrolysis of the cholesteryl esters, and the cholesterol content of the two precipitates is determined by application of a color reaction with acetic anhydride and sulfuric acid with use of a sensitive photometer. The results deviate slightly from those of the macrogravimetric procedure because any saturated sterols are precipitated by digitonin but do not give the color reaction. Utilizing this procedure, Sperry[5] found that the blood serum of a number of normal individuals contained 0.15–0.25 g. of total cholesterol per 100 cc. and that the average proportion of unesterified cholesterol was 26.9 percent, with a standard deviation of only ±1.4 percent. In another micromethod[6] the cholesterol present in saponified and unsaponified extracts is precipitated as pyridine cholesterol sulfate, the precipitate is freed from cholesteryl esters and other lipids by extraction with petroleum ether, and the cholesterol content determined by the Liebermann-Burchard reaction. The method gives values for the total cholesterol content of blood serum comparable to those obtained by the Schoenheimer-Sperry procedure, but the amount of free cholesterol found is lower (6–10 percent) than the average value determined by Sperry[5] and substantiated by other work.[7]

[1] Windaus, *Z. physiol. Chem.*, **65**, 110 (1910).

[2] Improved procedure: Gardner, Gainsborough and R. Murray, *Biochem. J.*, **32**, 15 (1938).

[3] Schoenheimer and Sperry, *J. Biol. Chem.*, **106**, 745 (1934); Sperry, *Am. J. Clin. Path. Tech. Suppl.*, **2**, 91 (1938).

[4] For improvements and modifications, see Fitz, *J. Biol. Chem.*, **109**, 523 (1935); C. Riegel and H. J. Rose, *J. Biol. Chem.*, **113**, 117 (1936); Begg, *Can. J. Med. Tech.*, **2**, 137 (1940); Kaucher, Button and H. H. Williams, *J. Lab. Clin. Med.*, **27**, 1349 (1942); Sobel and A. M. Mayer, *J. Biol. Chem.*, **157**, 255 (1945).

[5] Sperry, *J. Biol. Chem.*, **114**, 125 (1936).

[6] Sobel, Drekter and Natelson, *J. Biol. Chem.*, **115**, 381, 391 (1936); Kaye, *J. Lab. Clin. Med.*, **25**, 996 (1940).

[7] R. M. Smith and Marble, *J. Biol. Chem.*, **117**, 673 (1937).

Methods based upon direct application of colorimetry without saponification do not afford a reliable index of the total cholesterol content because cholesteryl esters give rise to higher Liebermann-Burchard color densities than free cholesterol does.[8] Extracts thus must be saponified, best with sodium ethoxide,[9] before application of procedures of direct colorimetry.[10, 11, 12]

A biochemical method of assay with a sensitivity of less than 1γ of cholesterol is based upon the hemolysis of erythrocytes with a standard solution of digitonin and the inhibition of the process by cholesterol.[13]

Bile Acids. Human bile is a golden brown liquid having an alkaline reaction (pH 7.8–8.6) and containing inorganic salts, bile salts (sodium salts of conjugated bile acids), and small amounts of cholesterol, lecithin, and bile pigments. The principal pigment is bilirubin, an oxidation product of hemin. Bile is produced in the liver, stored in the gall bladder, and secreted in small amounts into the intestines, and its chief function is to promote the resorption of fats in the intestinal tract. The bile salts, which are the chief constituents of the solid matter of bile, have the specific power of keeping water-insoluble substances in solution or dispersion.

Saponification of bile affords an acidic fraction consisting of a mixture of bile acids. That from ox bile is composed chiefly of cholic acid and desoxycholic acid, with smaller amounts of chenodesoxycholic and lithocholic acid. The structures and configurations of these four bile acids are indicated on page 106. The ring system is that characteristic of the sterols. The configuration at C_5 corresponds to that of coprostanol (A/B-cis), and the configurations at the other ring junctures are the same as in the series of natural sterols. When any one of the acids is heated in vacuum and slowly distilled, water is eliminated and an unsaturated acid is produced. Cholic acid yields a cholatrienic acid mixture, desoxycholic and chenodesoxycholic acid yield choladienic acids, and lithocholic acid gives a cholenic acid. All these unsaturated acids afford on hydrogenation the same saturated compound, cholanic acid. The four acids isolated from ox bile are thus 3-hydroxy-, 3,7- and 3,12-dihydroxy-, and 3,7,12-trihydroxy-cholanic acids. The alcoholic groups have all been shown to have the α-orientation, and these 3α-hydroxysteroids are not precipitated by digitonin.

The acids occur in bile as the water-soluble sodium salts of peptide con-

[8] Noyons, *Biochem. Z.*, **298**, 391 (1938).
[9] Noyons and Polano, *Biochem. Z.*, **303**, 415 (1940).
[10] Bloor, *J. Biol. Chem.*, **77**, 53 (1928).
[11] Drekter, *Bull. N. Y. Med. Coll.*, **6**, 138 (1943).
[12] Sperry and Brand, *J. Biol. Chem.*, **150**, 315 (1943).
[13] Schmidt-Thomé and Augustin, *Z. physiol. Chem.*, **275**, 190 (1942).

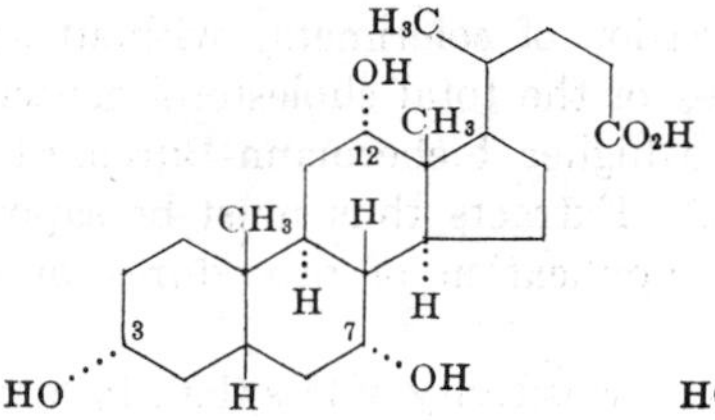

Cholic acid

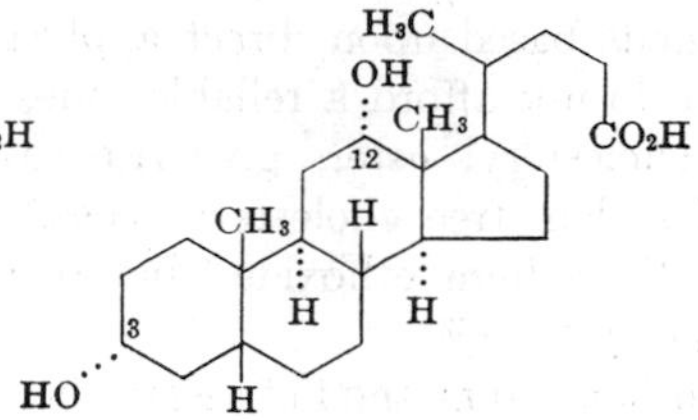

Desoxycholic acid

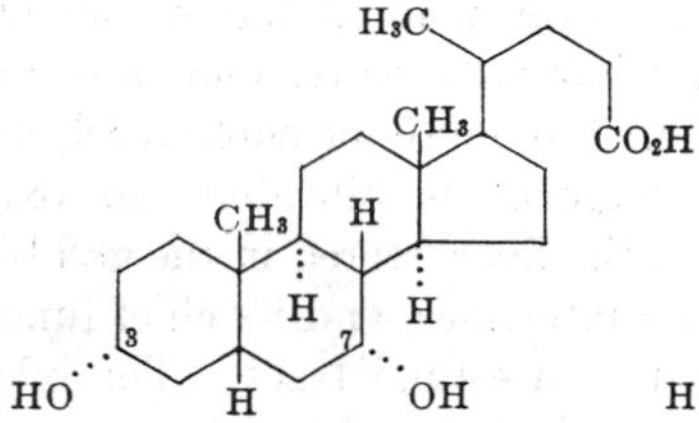

Chenodesoxycholic acid

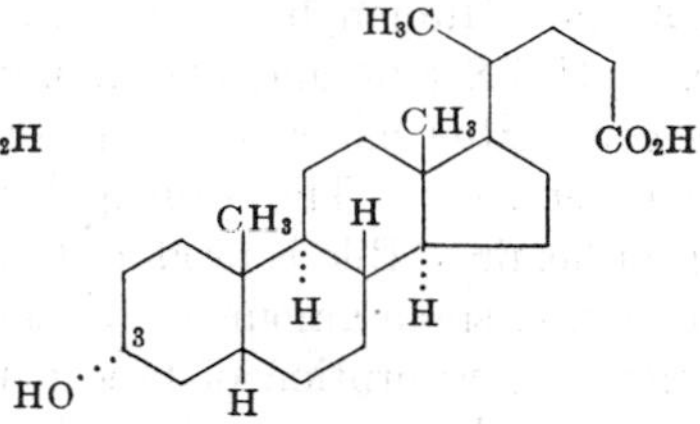

Lithocholic acid

jugates of glycine or taurine. The hydrolysis of the most abundant conjugated acids of ox bile proceeds as follows:

$$C_{23}H_{36}(OH)_3CONHCH_2COOH \xrightarrow{NaOH} C_{23}H_{36}(OH)_3COOH + CH_2(NH_2)COOH$$

Glycocholic acid   Cholic acid   Glycine

$$C_{23}H_{36}(OH)_3CONHCH_2CH_2SO_3H \xrightarrow{NaOH} C_{23}H_{36}(OH)_3COOH + CH_2(NH_2)CH_2SO_3H$$

Taurocholic acid   Cholic acid   Taurine

Glyco- and taurodesoxycholic acid also have been isolated, and the other bile acids are known to occur in conjugation with the same amino acids. The glyco-acids are somewhat more abundant constituents of human bile and ox bile than the tauro-compounds, but there are variations from species to species. Hog bile contains principally glyco-acids, whereas codfish bile is particularly rich in tauro-bile acids. The conjugated acids are somewhat more strongly acidic than the free acids. The isolation of the conjugated acids from bile is a troublesome and uncertain procedure, and the pure acids required for experimentation are best prepared by synthetic conjugation of the components. Bondi and Müller[1] effected conjugation by converting a bile acid through the ester and hydrazide into the azide, which was then coupled with the appropriate amino acid in an alkaline medium. Cortese and co-workers developed an alternate synthesis in which the bile acid is formylated for protection of the hydroxyl groups and the formyl

[1] Bondi and E. Müller, Z. physiol. Chem., **47**, 499 (1906); see also Wieland and Stender, ibid., **106**, 181 (1919).

ester is converted into the acid chloride and this is coupled with the amino acid in the presence of alkali, which removes the formyl groups.[2,3] Cortese[4] more recently has described improvements in the Bondi-Müller synthesis that render it more convenient than the alternate process.

Bile salts—the sodium salts of the amino acid conjugates of the hydroxycholanic acids present in bile—serve the important function of promoting the passage of lipids through the intestinal mucosa. Water-insoluble, nonester substances such as β-carotene and vitamin K_1 are absorbed into the animal organism from the intestinal tract under the emulsifying influence of bile salts, which are comparable in structural character and molecular weight to effective modern synthetic surface-active agents. Persons suffering from obstructive jaundice, which impedes the normal flow of bile into the intestines, develop a hemorrhagic condition because of faulty absorption of the antihemorrhagic vitamin K_1 in the absence of bile salts. The absorption of natural fats—glycerides—probably is due in part to the emulsifying action of the surface-active bile salts and in part to a process of enzymatic hydrolysis and resynthesis of fats absorbed in the intestinal mucosa. The enzymatic esterification of colloidal cholesterol[5] with higher fatty acids under the influence of pancreatic lipase has been observed to occur in the presence of bile salts but not in their absence.[6]

Isolation and Synthetic Preparation. Investigations of the constituents of the bile of various animals have resulted in the isolation and characterization of a number of mono-, di-, and trihydroxy acids, and additional steric and structural isomers have been produced by chemical transformations or synthetic (partial) methods. The accompanying table includes known acids of both types and records the properties, sources, and known or probable configurations of the hydroxylated carbon atoms. The majority of the substances listed are hydroxylated cholanic acids. In most of the natural bile acids one hydroxyl group is at C_3 and any others are distributed between positions 7 and 12.

Cholic acid is the most abundant of the acids obtainable from ox bile and

[2] F. Cortese and Bauman, *J. Am. Chem. Soc.*, **57**, 1393 (1935); *J. Biol. Chem.*, **113**, 779 (1936); F. Cortese and Bashour, *ibid.*, **119**, 177 (1937).

[3] R. H. Levin and co-workers [*J. Am. Chem. Soc.*, **70**, 511, 1907 (1948); *Science*, **108**, 82 (1948)] have reported several instances in the sterol and bile acid series where the formyl ester of a 3-hydroxysteroid can be deformylated quantitatively by chromatography (alumina); under the same conditions other esters suffer no appreciable hydrolysis.

[4] F. Cortese, *J. Am. Chem. Soc.*, **59**, 2532 (1937).

[5] Prepared by pouring an acetone solution of the sterol into water and evaporating the acetone: Porges and Neubauer, *Biochem. Z.*, **7**, 152 (1908).

[6] Nedswedski, *Z. physiol. Chem.*, **236**, 69 (1935); **239**, 165 (1936); *Biokhimiya*, **2**, 758 (1937).

TABLE II. Bile Acids

NAME	HYDROXYL GROUPS	M.p.	$[\alpha]_D$	SOURCE
Lithocholic acid[1]	3α	184–186°	+ 32°	Man, ox, rabbit
3β-Hydroxycholanic acid	3β	176–177°	+ 26°	Synth.[2]
6α-Hydroxycholanic acid	6α	221–222°	+ 8.5°	Synth.[3]
7α-Hydroxycholanic acid	7α	96–102°		Synth.[4]
11β-Hydroxycholanic acid	11β			Synth.[5]
Methyl ester		85–86°	+ 50°	
12α-Hydroxycholanic acid	12α	90–95°	+ 43.5°	Synth.[6]
12β-Hydroxycholanic acid	12β	110–116°	+ 38°	Synth.[7]
$3\alpha,6\beta$-Dihydroxy-cholanic acid	$3\alpha,6\beta$	205°	+ 37°	Synth.[8]
"α"-Hyodesoxy-cholic acid[9]	$3\alpha,6\alpha$	196–197°	+ 8°	Hog, boar
"β"-Hyodesoxy-cholic acid[10]	$3\beta,6\alpha$	189–190°	+ 5°	Hog
$3\beta,6\beta$-Dihydroxy-cholanic acid	$3\beta,6\beta$	250°		Synth.[10a]
Chenodesoxycholic acid[11]	$3\alpha,7\alpha$	140°	+ 11°	Man, ox, goose, hen, bear, guinea pig

[1] Isolation: H. Fischer, Z. physiol. Chem., **73**, 234 (1911). Characterization: Wieland and Weyland, ibid., **110**, 123 (1920).

[2] Reindel and Niederländer, Ber., **68**, 1243 (1935); Fernholz, Z. physiol. Chem., **232**, 97 (1935).

[3] Hoehn, Linsk and Moffett, J. Am. Chem. Soc., **68**, 1855 (1946).

[4] Wieland and Dane, Z. physiol. Chem., **210**, 268 (1932); Wieland and Kapitel, ibid., **212**, 269 (1932).

[5] Reich and Reichstein, Helv. Chim. Acta, **26**, 562 (1943).

[6] Wieland and Schlichting, Z. physiol. Chem., **150**, 267 (1925); Barnett and Reichstein, Helv. Chim. Acta, **21**, 926 (1938); Hoehn and Linsk, J. Am. Chem. Soc., **67**, 312 (1945).

[7] Sorkin and Reichstein, Helv. Chim. Acta, **26**, 2097 (1943).

[8] Tukamoto, J. Biochem. (Japan), **32**, 451 (1940); Hoehn, Linsk and Moffett, J. Am. Chem. Soc., **68**, 1855 (1946); Moffett and Hoehn, ibid., **69**, 1995 (1947).

[9] Structure: Windaus and Bohne, Ann., **433**, 278 (1923); Windaus, ibid., **447**, 233 (1926); Z. angew. Chem., **36**, 309 (1923); Wieland and Dane, Z. physiol. Chem., **212**, 41 (1932). Improved isolation procedure: Wieland and Gumlich, ibid., **215**, 18 (1933). Configuration: Moffett and Hoehn, J. Am. Chem. Soc., **69**, 1995 (1947).

[10] Kimura, Z. physiol. Chem., **248**, 280 (1937).

[10a] Moffatt, J. Chem. Soc., 812 (1947).

[11] Isolation: Windaus, Bohne and Schwarzkopf, Z. physiol. Chem., **140**, 177 (1924);

TABLE II.—*Continued*

NAME	HYDROXYL GROUPS	M.p.	$[\alpha]_D$	SOURCE
Ursodesoxycholic acid[12]	$3\alpha,7\beta$	203°	+ 57°	Bear
$3\alpha,11\alpha$-Dihydroxycholanic acid	$3\alpha,11\alpha$	147°	+ 22°	Synth.[13]
$3\alpha,11\beta$-Dihydroxycholanic acid	$3\alpha,11\beta$	201°	+ 55°	Synth.[14]
Methyl ester of 3-acetate		146–148°	+ 71°	
$3\beta,11\beta$-Dihydroxycholanic acid	$3\beta,11\beta$			Synth.[15]
Methyl ester of 3-acetate		139–140°	+ 50°	
Desoxycholic acid[16, 17, 17a]	$3\alpha,12\alpha$	176–177°	+ 53°	Man, ox, deer, dog, sheep, goat, antelope, rabbit
12-Epidesoxycholic acid	$3\alpha,12\beta$	186°	+ 38°	Synth.[18]
Isodesoxycholic acid	$7\alpha,12\alpha$	210–211°	+ 27°	Synth.[19]

Wieland and Reverey, *ibid.*, **140**, 186 (1924).

[12] Isolation: Shoda, *J. Biochem.* (*Japan*), **7**, 505 (1927). Structure: Koozoo Kaziro, *Z. physiol. Chem.*, **185**, 151 (1929); **197**, 206 (1931); Iwasaki, *ibid.*, **244**, 181 (1936).

[13] Long and Gallagher, *J. Biol. Chem.*, **162**, 511 (1946); Gallagher and Long, *ibid.*, **162**, 521 (1946).

[14] Lardon and Reichstein, *Helv. Chim. Acta*, **26**, 586 (1943); Ott and Reichstein, *ibid.*, **26**, 1799 (1943); R. B. Turner, Mattox, Engel, McKenzie and Kendall, *J. Biol. Chem.*, **166**, 345 (1946).

[15] Press, Grandjean and Reichstein, *Helv. Chim. Acta*, **26**, 598 (1943).

[16] Large-scale isolation: Wieland and Weyland, *Z. physiol. Chem.*, **110**, 123 (1920). For other references see Elsevier's *Encyclopedia of Organic Chemistry*, Vol. 14, Series III (1940). Simplified procedures for the isolation of cholic acid and desoxycholic acid are described in Gattermann-Wieland, "Laboratory Methods of Organic Chemistry," pp. 411–417, Macmillan Company, New York, 1937.

[17] The physical constants are those reported by Reichstein and Sorkin [*Helv. Chim. Acta*, **25**, 797 (1942)]; Charonnat and Gauthier [*Compt. rend.*, **223**, 1009 (1946)] report a melting point of 190–190.5° and a specific rotation of + 49° (methyl ethyl ketone).

[17a] Separation from cholic acid by chromatography of the colored esters prepared by reaction of the sodium salts with ω-bromo-p-methylazobenzene, Silberman and Silberman-Martyncewa, *J. Biol. Chem.*, **165**, 359 (1946).

[18] Koechlin and Reichstein, *Helv. Chim. Acta*, **25**, 918 (1942).

[19] Borsche and Feske, *Z. physiol. Chem.*, **176**, 109 (1928); Wieland and Dane, *ibid.*, **210**, 268 (1932); Haslewood, *Biochem. J.*, **38**, 108 (1944); Grand and Reichstein, *Helv. Chim. Acta*, **28**, 344 (1945); Kuwada and Morimoto, *Bull. Chem. Soc.* (*Japan*), **17**, 147 (1942) [*C. A.*, **41**, 4504 (1947)].

TABLE II.—*Concluded*

NAME	HYDROXYL GROUPS	M.p.	$[\alpha]_D$	SOURCE
7,12-Dihydroxy-cholanic acid.......		226–227°		Synth.[20]
11,12-Dihydroxy-cholanic acid.......	$11\alpha,12\alpha^{21}$	211–214°	+ 3.2°	Synth.[22]
11,12-Dihydroxy-cholanic acid.......	$11\beta,12\beta^{21}$	170.5–174.5°		Synth.[23]
Methyl ester			+ 56°	
Bufodesoxycholic acid[24]...............				Toad
"α"-Lagodesoxycholic acid[25].............		156–157°	+ 80°	Rabbit
"β"-Lagodesoxycholic acid[25].............		213°	+ 37°	Rabbit
Cholic acid[16].........	$3\alpha,7\alpha,12\alpha$	196–198°	+ 37°	Man, ox, goat, sheep, antelope
$3\alpha,11\alpha,12\alpha$-Trihy-droxycholanic acid.	$3\alpha,11\alpha,12\alpha$	173–175°	+ 31°	Synth.[26]
$3\alpha,11\alpha,12\beta$-Trihy-droxycholanic acid.	$3\alpha,11\alpha,12\beta$	164–166°	+ 45°	Synth.[26]
$3\alpha,11\beta,12\alpha$-Trihy-droxycholanic acid.	$3\alpha,11\beta,12\alpha$	145–147°	+ 54°	Synth.[26]
$3\alpha,11\beta,12\beta$-Trihy-droxycholanic acid.	$3\alpha,11\beta,12\beta$	177°	+ 43°	Synth.[27]
"β"-Phocaecholic acid[28, 29]............	3,7,23	222–223°	+ 27°	Walrus, seal
Nutriacholic acid[30]...		198°		Beaver

is easily isolated. Desoxycholic acid can be prepared fairly readily from the same source, but the isolation of the other acids of ox bile is difficult. According to Wieland and Weyland 100 kg. of ox bile yields 5–6 kg. of cholic

[20] Wieland, Honold and Pascual-Vila, *Z. physiol. Chem.*, **130**, 326 (1923).

[21] Configuration on the basis of cis-addition of oxidation reagent and on the basis of the optical rotation.

[22] Alther and Reichstein, *Helv. Chim. Acta*, **25**, 805 (1942). This acid may be identical with a dihydroxycholanic acid, m.p. 204–208°, prepared by Marker, Shabica, E. M. Jones, Crooks and Wittbecker, *J. Am. Chem. Soc.*, **64**, 1228 (1942).

[23] Reich, *Helv. Chim. Acta*, **29**, 581 (1946).

[24] Isolation and characterization of the noncrystalline product: Okamura, *Chem. Zentr.*, I, 2624 (1928); I, 1113 (1929); I, 1310 (1930).

[25] Kishi, *Z. physiol. Chem.*, **238**, 210 (1936).

[26] Gallagher, *J. Biol. Chem.*, **162**, 539 (1946).

[27] Wintersteiner, Moore and Reinhardt, *J. Biol. Chem.*, **162**, 707 (1946).

[28] Isolation: Hammarsten, *Z. physiol. Chem.*, **61**, 454 (1909); *ibid.*, **68**, 109 (1910).

[29] Windaus and van Schoor, *Z. physiol. Chem.*, **173**, 312 (1928).

[30] Brigl and Benedict, *Z. physiol. Chem.*, **220**, 106 (1933).

acid, 600–800 g. of desoxycholic acid, and about 2 g. of lithocholic acid. Chenodesoxycholic acid appears to be present in even smaller amounts than lithocholic acid. Lithocholic acid (Gr. *lithos*, stone) was obtained for the first time not from bile but from gall stones. H. Fischer discovered this rare acid in 1911 in an investigation of the bile pigment bilirubin that initiated the brilliant series of investigations of the blood pigments from which bilirubin arises as an oxidation product. The bilirubin was extracted from the gall stones and lithocholic acid appeared as an incidental product in the course of the separations. The first 3,7-dihydroxycholanic acid was isolated simultaneously by Wieland from human bile (anthropodesoxycholic acid, Gr. *anthropo*, man) and by Windaus from goose bile (chenodesoxycholic acid, Gr. *cheno*, goose); the prefix cheno- had been applied by earlier workers to a partially purified acid from goose bile and is now accepted. Bile from cadavers contains nearly as much cheno-acid as desoxycholic acid. Ursodesoxycholic acid (L. *ursus*, bear) is the C_7-epimer of chenodesoxycholic acid. "*α*"-Hyodesoxycholic acid (Gr. *hyo-*, swine) is unique in having one of the two hydroxyls at the 6-position (3,6-dihydroxy). The acid is readily isolated from hog bile and has been of value in studies of structure and configuration because production of a carbonyl group at C_6 permits epimerization at C_5. The isomeric "*β*"-hyodesoxycholic acid is the only known natural bile acid having a 3β-hydroxyl group.

Nearly all the bile acids have been submitted to dehydration followed by hydrogenation, or converted by other methods into the hydroxyl-free acids. Cholic acid, desoxy-, chenodesoxy-, lithocholic, and ursodesoxycholic acid all yield the same substance, cholanic acid, but this is not true of any of the other compounds investigated. Although "*α*"-hyodesoxycholic acid be-

TABLE III. Cholanic Acids

	M.p.	$[\alpha]_D$	SOURCES
Cholanic acid[31]	164°	+ 21.7°	Coprostane, cholic acid, desoxy-, chenodesoxy-, and lithocholic acid
Allocholanic acid[32]	170°	+ 22.5°	Cholestane, hyodesoxycholic acid, scillaridin A
Bufocholanic acid[33]	236°	− 20.3°	Bufodesoxycholic acid
Isobufocholanic acid[34]	179°	+ 50.5°	Bufotalin

[31] Wieland and Weil, *Z. physiol. Chem.*, **80**, 287 (1912); Wieland and Boersch, *ibid.*, **106**, 193 (1919); Windaus and Neukirchen, *Ber.* **52**, 1915 (1919).

[32] Windaus and Neukirchen, *Ber.*, **52**, 1915 (1919); Windaus and Bohne, *Ann.*, **433**, 284 (1923).

[33] T. Okamura, *J. Biochem.* (*Jap.*), **10**, 5 (1928); **11**, 103 (1929).

[34] Wieland, Hesse and H. Meyer, *Ann.*, **493**, 272 (1932).

longs to the stereochemical series of cholanic acid (and coprostane), a stereochemical inversion occurs in the course of the degradation, for the saturated acid has the epimeric configuration at C_5 and is allocholanic acid (A/B: trans). The configuration of the other cholanic acids (see table) is unknown.

Other Compounds from Bile. The continued search for new bile acids and companion substances has been stimulated by the prospect of the establishment of the physiological relationship of the bile acids to other steroids. A knowledge of the structures of intermediate products of metabolism may cast light on the origin and fate of the acids of the bile.

A few **keto bile acids** have been isolated, for example 3α-hydroxy-12-ketocholanic acid (ox bile),[1] 3α-hydroxy-7-ketocholanic acid (guinea pig),[2] and 3-hydroxy-6-ketoallocholanic acid (hog).[3] The last compound may not be a primary constituent but may well arise in the course of the saponification by C_5-allomerization of the corresponding acid of the cholanic acid series, which is known to be susceptible to such change in the presence of alkali.[4] Minute amounts of 3,12-dihydroxy-7-ketocholanic acid and 7,12-dihydroxy-3-ketocholanic acid have been isolated from cow bile.[5] The biological reduction of keto bile acids has been demonstrated.[6] 3,7,12-Triketocholanic acid (dehydrocholic acid) injected subcutaneously into toads is reduced at the 3-position; incubation of the same acid with *B. coli* results in reduction at the 7-position.

Scymnol, a substance related to the bile acids, has been isolated from the bile of various sharks and rays.[7] In place of bile acids of the usual type and apparently fulfilling similar functions, shark bile contains the sulfate ester of scymnol, a neutral tetrahydric alcohol $C_{27}H_{46}O_5$. The results of still incomplete investigations[8] of the structure have been expressed in the provisional formula shown. Scymnol contains three secondary hydroxyl groups and one primary group, for it yields on chromic acid oxidation a C_{27}-triketomonocarboxylic acid. The fifth, nonhydroxylic oxygen atom probably is present in an oxide ring, for scymnol on reaction with hydrogen

[1] Wieland and Kishi, *Z. physiol. Chem.*, **214,** 47 (1933).

[2] Imai, *Z. physiol. Chem.*, **248,** 65 (1937).

[3] Fernholz, *Z. physiol. Chem.*, **232,** 202 (1935); Sugiyania, *J. Biochem. (Japan),* **25,** 157 (1937).

[4] Wieland and Dane, *Z. physiol. Chem.*, **212,** 41 (1932).

[5] Haslewood, *Biochem. J.*, **40,** 52 (1946).

[6] Yamasaki and Kyogoku, *Z. physiol. Chem.*, **233,** 29 (1935); **235,** 43 (1935); Fukui, *J. Biochem. (Japan),* **25,** 61 (1937).

[7] Hammarsten, *Z. physiol. Chem.*, **24,** 322 (1898); J. W. Cook, *Nature,* **147,** 388 (1941).

[8] Windaus, W. Bergmann and G. König, *Z. physiol. Chem.*, **189,** 148 (1930); Tschesche, *ibid.*, **203,** 263 (1931); Asikari, *J. Biochem. (Japan)*, **29,** 319 (1939) [*Chem. Zentr.*, **110,** II, 2666 (1939)]; W. Bergmann and Pace, *J. Am. Chem. Soc.*, **65,** 477 (1943).

chloride forms a chlorohydrin from which the oxide can be regenerated. The observation that further oxidation of the C_{27}-acid mentioned above affords dehydrocholic acid establishes the structure and configuration of the ring system and the location of the three nuclear hydroxyl groups and further indicates that one linkage of the oxide bridge must extend to

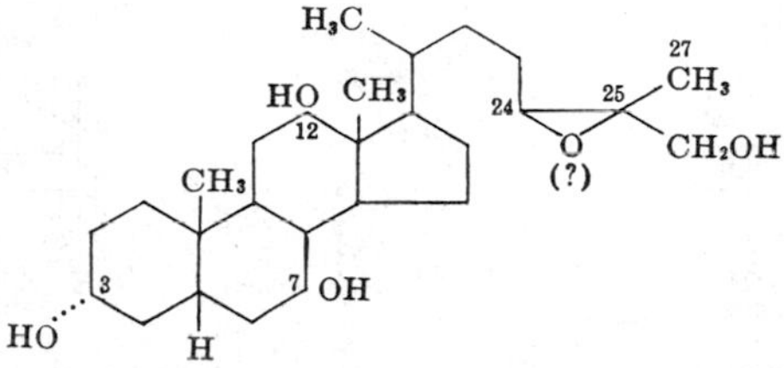

Scymnol, m.p. 187°

position 24. In the provisional formula the second point of linkage is assumed to be C_{25}, but from evidence cited in Part 2 it appears unlikely that an ethylene oxide grouping would remain untouched in the process of oxidation of the primary and secondary alcoholic groups. Possibly scymnol is a trimethylene oxide with the bridge extending from C_{24} to C_{27}.

An acid $C_{27}H_{46}O_6$ found along with cholic acid in the bile of the gigi fish is named **tetrahydroxynorsterocholanic acid**[9] because the number of carbon atoms is one less than in a C_{28}-phytosterol. Mild oxidation with permanganate leads to an unknown trihydroxycholanic acid (m.p. 208°;

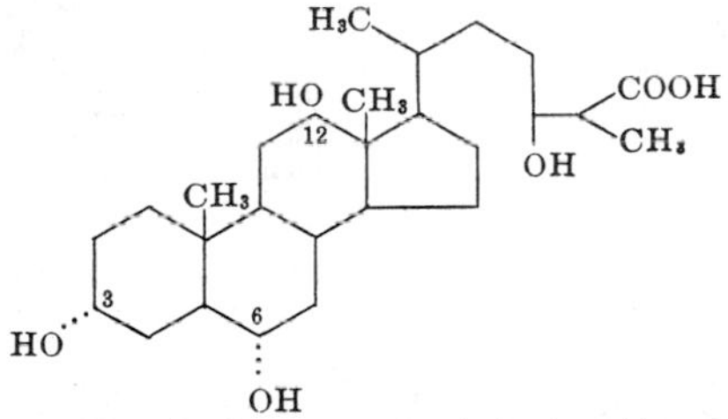

Tetrahydroxynorsterocholanic acid
m.p. 212-214°; $[\alpha]_D$ + 27°

3,6,12-acid ?); chromic acid oxidation leads to a triketocholanic acid that on Clemmensen reduction yields allocholanic acid. A tentative formula suggested by Ohta[9] is supported by transformations[10] of the substance into "α"-hyodesoxycholic acid (oxidation of 3,6-diacetate, Wolff-Kishner reduction) and into 12-ketocholanic acid (pyrolysis of the keto diacetate and hydrogenation.

[9] Ohta, *Z. physiol. Chem.*, **259**, 53 (1939).
[10] Isaka, *Z. physiol. Chem.*, **266**, 117 (1940).

A series of C_{27}- and C_{28}-**substances** have been isolated from the winter bile of the hibernating toad and may be transitional products of arrested metabolism. Two of these are found in the neutral fraction, along with cholesterol: pentahydroxybufostane,[11] $C_{28}H_{50}O_5$ (9 g. from 4 kg. bile), and tetrahydroxynorbufostane,[12] $C_{27}H_{48}O_4$ (1.3 g. from 800 cc. bile). These

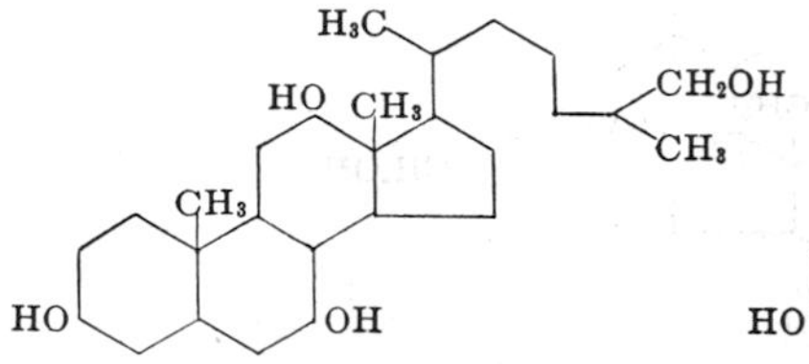

Tctrahydroxynorbufostane (?)   Pentahydroxybufostane (?)
m.p. 230°, $[\alpha]_D + 37.5°$ m.p. 172°, $[\alpha]_D + 33.5°$

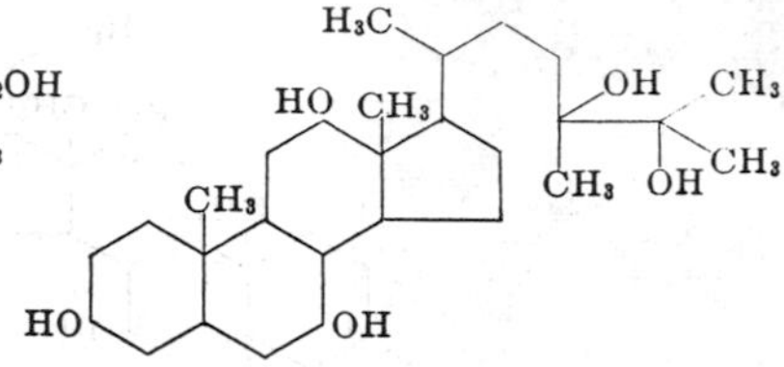

neutral, fully saturated substances exhibit color reactions of bile acids but correspond in carbon content to sterols. The tetrahydroxy compound contains one primary and three secondary alcoholic groups. The pentahydroxy compound has hydroxyl groups at positions 3, 7, and 12 since the triacetate yields the triacetate of cholic acid on chromic acid oxidation; the other two hydroxyl groups occupy adjacent positions in the side chains. Tentative formulas are shown.

One of two isomeric acids of the formula $C_{28}H_{46}O_5$ isolated from toad bile is trihydroxybufosterocholenic acid[13] (0.1 percent yield from bile). Since the substance on ozonization gives bisnorcholic acid,[14] the hydroxyl groups

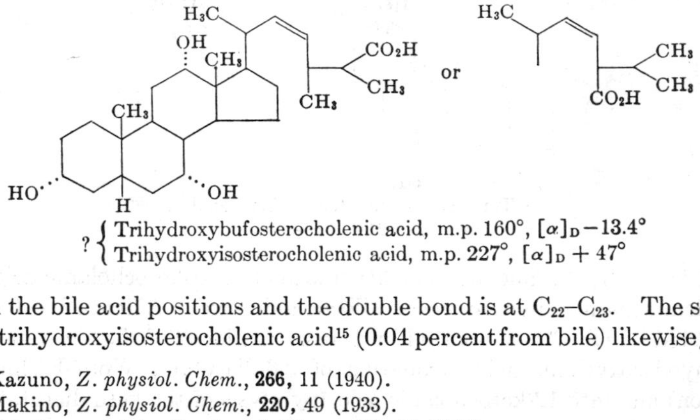

? { Trihydroxybufosterocholenic acid, m.p. 160°, $[\alpha]_D -13.4°$
?   Trihydroxyisosterocholenic acid, m.p. 227°, $[\alpha]_D + 47°$

are in the bile acid positions and the double bond is at C_{22}–C_{23}. The second acid, trihydroxyisosterocholenic acid[15] (0.04 percent from bile) likewise yields

---

[11] Kazuno, *Z. physiol. Chem.*, **266**, 11 (1940).

[12] Makino, *Z. physiol. Chem.*, **220**, 49 (1933).

[13] Shimizu and Oda, *Z. physiol. Chem.*, **227**, 74 (1934).

[14] Shimizu and Kazuno, *Z. physiol. Chem.*, **239**, 74 (1936); **244**, 167 (1936).

[15] Shimizu and Kazuno, *Z. physiol. Chem.*, **239**, 67 (1936).

bisnorcholic acid[16] and therefore differs from the isomer in the as yet unestablished structure of the terminal part of the side chain.

Choleic Acids. Cholic acid is a colorless, crystalline solid of high melting point and slight solubility in water. It separates from solutions in alcohol or in aqueous acetic acid with one molecule of alcohol or water of crystallization, and the solvent is held very tenaciously and can be removed completely only after prolonged heating at reduced pressure.

In desoxycholic acid the property of formation of stable molecular compounds is magnified to a high degree. The unique character of the 3,12-dihydroxy acid was discovered by Wieland and Sorge[1] in an important investigation that originated in an interesting manner. A substance known as "choleic acid" had been isolated from bile many years earlier and was commonly regarded as a true bile acid, probably isomeric with desoxycholic acid. Wieland and Sorge subjected this substance to dehydration by vacuum distillation in the expectation of obtaining an unsaturated acid similar to that resulting from the dehydration of desoxycholic acid. The substance, however, was not an isomer of the choladienic acid but identical with it. There was also formed a small amount of fatty acid (palmitic or stearic acid), and this was shown not to arise through a pyrolytic rupture of the original ring structure but to be present in "cholcic acid" in molecular combination with desoxycholic acid. The supposed bile acid is a coordinative compound containing one molecule of the fatty acid and no less than eight molecules of desoxycholic acid. The complex dissolves in alkali without change and the stearic acid is so firmly bound that it can be split off only with difficulty, as by transformation of the bile acid into products of dehydration or oxidation. A substance identical with "choleic acid" crystallizes from an alcoholic solution of desoxycholic acid on the addition of stearic acid. The melting point is fairly sharp (186°) and appreciably higher than that of desoxycholic acid. So small is the proportion of the fatty acid that its presence is not easily apparent from the analytical figures.

After this discovery, Wieland and Sorge and later workers found that desoxycholic acid forms remarkably stable molecular compounds not only with the higher fatty acids but with simple acids, esters, alcohols, ethers, phenols, and hydrocarbons. Stable additive compounds are formed with cholesterol and with aromatic hydrocarbons and alkaloids. These unique substances, which are known in a wide variety of types, are now referred to as choleic acids. Compounds that combine with desoxycholic acid have been called acholic constituents of choleic acids.[2]

[16] Shimizu and Kazuno, *J. Biochem.* (*Japan*), **25**, 245 (1937) [*Chem. Zentr.*, **110**, I, 674 (1939)].
[1] Wieland and Sorge, *Z. physiol. Chem.*, **97**, 1 (1916).
[2] Sobotka and A. Goldberg, *Biochem. J.*, **26**, 555 (1932).

From a systematic study of the choleic acids from fatty acids and esters, Rheinboldt[3] concluded that the ability to combine with desoxycholic acid is dependent upon the size and character of the hydrocarbon part of the acid or ester. In the series of monobasic fatty acids, formic acid alone fails to form a compound. The other acids combine with the bile acid in varying but definite molecular proportions to produce well-defined, crystalline choleic acids. The choleic acid of acetic acid contains the components in equimolecular proportion, whereas propionic acid forms a 1:3 compound with desoxycholic acid. The normal acids having 3–7 carbon atoms in the hydrocarbon radical form 1:4 compounds, those having 8–13 carbon atoms combine with 6 molecules of the bile acid, and with the higher acids the ratio is 1:8. Rheinboldt noted that the number of molecules of desoxycholic acid found in combination with the acholic constituent conforms to the coordination principle and can be regarded as a coordination number: 1, 2, 3, 4, 6, 8. As with other coordination compounds, the space requirements apparently are not satisfied by a cluster of 5 or 7 surrounding molecules. Branching the chain of the acids tends to reduce the coordination number, and with such compounds the coordination number is that of the longest straight chain in the molecule.[4] The cis-trans isomers oleic and elaidic acid have the same coordination number (8) as stearic acid.[5] Acids containing alicyclic rings have the same coordination numbers as open-chain acids of the same carbon content.[6]

Desoxycholic acid has the power to bind even normal paraffin hydrocarbons;[7, 8] higher members of the series (C_{35}, C_{43}) all combine in the ratio 1:8.[8] Branching interferes with complex formation, for hexamethylethane forms no choleic acid in alcoholic solution.[7]

The choleic acids differ greatly in their solubility in organic solvents and in the degree of association of the components in the solutions. Ethyl alcohol is commonly used for crystallizing desoxycholic acid because it forms a rather labile complex from which the acid can be recovered by prolonged drying in vacuum. Xylene displaces alcohol from the complex even in an alcoholic solution and xylene-choleic acid separates in a crystalline condition. By crystallization from glacial acetic acid the xylene can be displaced by this reagent. Precipitation of the ether complex affords a convenient

[3] Rheinboldt, *Ann.*, **451**, 256 (1926); *Z. physiol. Chem.*, **180**, 180 (1929); Rheinboldt, O. König and Otten, *Ann.*, **473**, 249 (1929).

[4] Sobotka and A. Goldberg, *Biochem. J.*, **26**, 566 (1932); Chargaff and G. Abel, *ibid.* **28**, 1901 (1934).

[5] Marx and Sobotka, *J. Org. Chem.*, **1**, 275 (1936).

[6] Buu-Hoi, *Z. physiol. Chem.*, **278**, 230 (1943).

[7] Fieser and Newman, *J. Am. Chem. Soc.*, **57**, 1602 (1935).

[8] Rheinboldt, P. Braun, Flume, O. König and Lauber, *J. prakt. Chem.*, **153**, 313 (1939).

method for purification of the bile acid.[2] Naphthalene and some of the higher aromatic hydrocarbons form choleic acids in alcoholic solution; for example acenaphthene, phenanthrene, and methylcholanthrene form crystalline complexes of coordination numbers 2, 3, and 4, respectively.[7] In each case the melting point is higher than that of either component. Other hydrocarbons (*e.g.* anthracene, chrysene, 3,4-benzpyrene) crystallize in the free state from alcoholic solutions of desoxycholic acid. The formation or nonformation of a choleic acid under these conditions is dependent merely upon the relative solubilities of the components and of the complex and upon the degree of association of the coordinate compound. Thus anthracene tetracholeic acid has been prepared from a solution of the components in alcohol-benzene.[5] A dilute solution of methylcholanthrene-choleic acid gives the spectrum of the pure hydrocarbon, which indicates that the molecular compound is completely dissociated.

Kratky and Giacomello[9] investigated the X-ray diagrams of the choleic acid complexes of acids ranging from propionic to cerotic acid and found that they showed identical interference and intensity patterns. A suggested orientation of fatty acid molecules in canals formed by a surrounding network of desoxycholic acid molecules does not explain why acids, paraffins, and aralkyl derivatives show coordination numbers no higher than 8,[6] or why polynuclear aromatic hydrocarbons have relatively low coordination numbers.

The choleic acids dissolve in aqueous alkali without dissociation into the components; water-insoluble fats and hydrocarbons can be brought into aqueous solution in the form of the sodium salts of the choleic acids. Wieland and Sorge suggested that the dissolving power of bile may be associated with this phenomena, but the evidence does not support the hypothesis. Desoxycholic acid is merely a minor constituent of most biles, and the other bile acids do not share the ability to form choleic acid complexes. Furthermore desoxycholic acid is present in bile not in the free form but conjugated with glycine and taurine, and pure synthetic glycodesoxycholic acid does not form coordinative complexes with fatty acids.[10] Desoxycholic acid also loses its power to form choleic acids when the hydroxyl groups are formylated or when the acid is esterified.[10] Advantage can be taken of the solubilizing effect of unconjugated desoxycholic acid in promoting the absorption of orally administered drugs; thus camphor-choleic acid is employed as a pharmaceutical preparation (Codechol).

Substances acquire considerably modified properties when present in coordinate combination with desoxycholic acid, for example benzaldehyde-choleic acid is not subject to autoxidation. Sobotka found that choleic

[9] Kratky and Giacomello, *Monatsh.*, **69**, 427 (1936).
[10] F. Cortese and Bauman, *J. Biol. Chem.*, **113**, 779 (1936).

acid formation favors the enolization of ketones;[11] he suggested the possibility of resolving chemically inert compounds by crystallization of salts of the choleic acids.[12]

Apocholic Acid. Although no other natural bile acid is capable of forming choleic acid complexes, the special property of desoxycholic acid is shared by an unsaturated derivative, apocholic acid, discovered by Boedecker.[1] Mild dehydrating agents effect the elimination of the 7-hydroxyl group of cholic acid and produce mixtures of the monounsaturated acids I and II[1] and an unidentified "isodihydroxycholenic acid"[2] (m.p. 198°, $[\alpha]_D$ + 5.9°). The reaction of cholic acid with anhydrous zinc chloride in acetone solution affords apocholic acid (II) in 75 percent yield;[3] the yield is only 24–49 percent when acetic acid is used as the solvent.[4] The loca-

Chart 3. DIHYDROXYCHOLENIC ACIDS

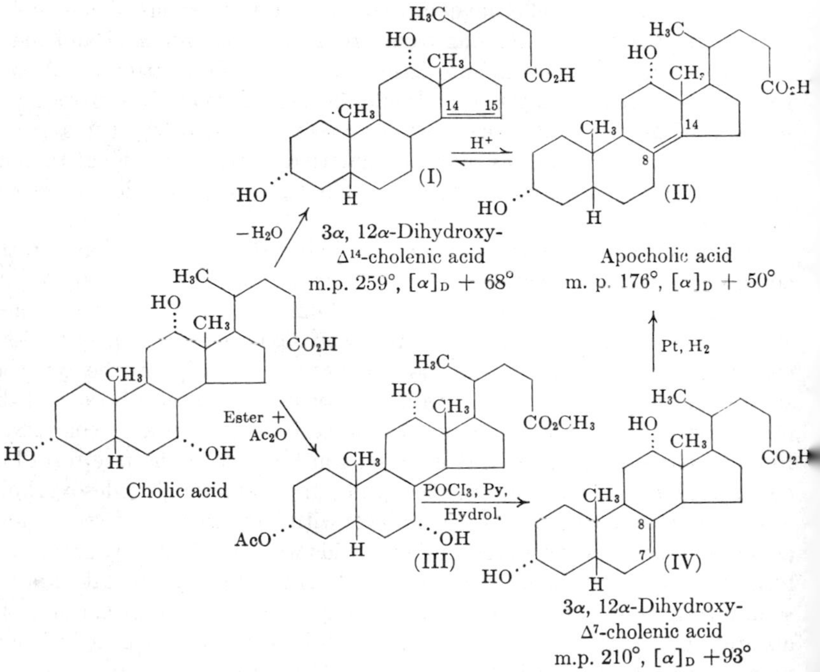

(I)
3α, 12α-Dihydroxy-Δ14-cholenic acid
m.p. 259°, $[\alpha]_D$ + 68°

(II)
Apocholic acid
m. p. 176°, $[\alpha]_D$ + 50°

Cholic acid

(III)

(IV)
3α, 12α-Dihydroxy-Δ7-cholenic acid
m.p. 210°, $[\alpha]_D$ +93°

[11] Sobotka and Kahn, *Biochem. J.*, **26**, 898 (1932); *Ber.*, **65**, 227 (1932).
[12] Sobotka and A. Goldberg, *Biochem. J.*, **26**, 905 (1932).
[1] Boedecker, *Ber.*, **53**, 1852 (1920); Boedecker and Volk, *ibid.*, **54**, 2489 (1921).
[2] Yamasaki, *Z. physiol. Chem.*, **220**, 42 (1933); **233**, 10 (1935).
[3] Devor and Marlow, *J. Am. Chem. Soc.*, **68**, 2101 (1946).
[4] Plattner, Ruzicka and Holtermann, *Helv. Chim. Acta*, **28**, 1660 (1945).

tion of the double bond at the 14,15- and 8,14-position in acids I and II was inferred by Callow[5] and has been substantiated by an accumulation of evidence.[6,7] The isomer IV, with a double bond at the 7,8-position, was obtained[7] by the dehydration of cholic acid 3-acetate methyl ester (III) with phosphorus oxychloride in pyridine at room temperature. The relationship of the three monounsaturated acids to one another is the same as in the more extensively characterized series of stenols to be discussed later. The Δ^{14}-isomer I is readily hydrogenated to desoxycholic acid,[8] whereas when the Δ^7-acid is shaken with hydrogen and platinum catalyst the double bond migrates to the 8,14-position and resists attack. Apocholic acid, with a ditertiary double bond between the bridgehead positions 8 and 14, is completely inert to catalytic hydrogenation. Apocholic acid has been converted[5] into two isomeric products of dehydrogenation, one of which on hydrogenation affords a substance with an inert double bond isomeric with apocholic acid and called "β"-apocholic acid. This probably also

Apocholic acid $\xrightarrow[\text{SeO}_2]{\text{C}_6\text{H}_5\text{CO}_3\text{H}}$ α-Dihydroxycholadienic acid
m.p. 248°, $[\alpha]_D - 60°$; diacetate, λ max 242 mμ

β-Apocholic acid $\xleftarrow{\text{H}_2,\ \text{Pd}}$ β-Dihydroxycholadienic acid
m.p. 165°, $[\alpha]_D + 79°$ m.p. 251°, $[\alpha]_D + 72°$; diacetate, λ max 244 mμ

has the double bond at the 8,14-position and differs from apocholic acid in the configuration at C_9 (Callow[5]); the structures of the dienic acids are still in question.[4, 5, 6]

Both apocholic acid and "β"-apocholic acid form stable coordinative complexes of the choleic acid type. They are both derivatives of desoxycholic acid differing from this substance only in having an unreactive double bond.

Investigations of Structure[1]

Nature of the Problem. The investigations directed to the elucidation of the structures of the sterols and bile acids were beset by a conspiracy of adverse factors. The structural formulas eventually assigned show that

[5] R. K. Callow, *J. Chem. Soc.*, 462 (1936).

[6] Barton, *J. Chem. Soc.*, 1116 (1946).

[7] Berner, Lardon and Reichstein, *Helv. Chim. Acta*, **30**, 1542 (1947).

[8] Wieland and Dane, *Z. physiol. Chem.*, **212**, 263 (1932); Wieland, Dietz and Ottawa, *ibid.*, **244**, 194 (1936).

[1] For review papers see Windaus, *Z. physiol. Chem.*, **213**, 147 (1933); Wieland, *Ber.*, **67A**, 27 (1934); Dane, *Z. angew. Chem.*, **47**, 351 (1934); Windaus, *Ann. Rev. Biochem.*, **1**, 109 (1932); Rosenheim and King, *ibid.*, **3**, 87 (1934); Sobotka, *Chem. Revs.*, **15**, 311 (1934).

the problem was inherently difficult, for the substances are of a complicated type with no previous parallel. Hydrogenated polynuclear compounds were not available by synthesis for comparison studies. Since cholic acid contains no less than eleven asymmetric carbon atoms the possibility for stereoisomerism is enormous. The natural products often crystallize well when they are perfectly pure, but crystallization can be thrown completely out of gear by the presence of small amounts of foreign bodies. Since the large molecules offer particular opportunity for the occurrence of side reactions, transformation products usually must be separated from mixtures by repeated, slow crystallizations. The yields are often very poor, and the difficulty experienced in obtaining a certain bile acid degradation product in quantity sufficient for characterization led Pregl to undertake the development of his classical methods of microanalysis. These methods proved to be of inestimable service in the subsequent investigations in this and other fields. Another source of difficulty and delay in working with the bile acids is associated with the tendency of these substances to form molecular compounds and to retain solvents. The long and arduous study of a succession of compounds of much the same crystalline character was at no point either assisted or enlivened by the appearance of colored substances.

Early Observations. Three phases may be distinguished in the investigations of the sterols and bile acids, in the first of which attention was directed chiefly to the isolation, analysis, and characterization of the compounds. Accurate analyses of cholesterol were carried out by Chevreul in 1823, and in 1859 his results were recalculated to the modern basis by Berthelot, who suggested the formula $C_{26}H_{44}O$, for which the theoretical composition is: C, 83.80; H, 11.91. This is remarkably close to the correct formula $C_{27}H_{46}O$ (C, 83.86; H, 11.99) established by Reinitzer in 1888 from the analysis of halogen derivatives, which offer a better means of discrimination. Early work on the nature of the constituents of bile and of gall stones was reported from the laboratories of Gmelin, Thénard, Berzelius, and Liebig, but the first isolation of pure substances was reported in 1848 by Strecker, who obtained the conjugated acids glycocholic acid and taurocholic acid. In 1886 Mylius isolated desoxycholic acid from hydrolyzed bile and Hammarsten soon obtained taurodesoxycholic acid. "Choleic acid," the supposed isomer of desoxycholic acid, was isolated by Latschinoff in 1885.

Of the earlier findings regarding the nature of the functional groups, only a few of the more significant observations will be outlined. In the case of cholesterol the presence of the hydroxyl group was established by Berthelot (1859) by the preparation of acyl derivatives, and Diels and Abderhalden[2]

---

[2] Diels and Abderhalden, *Ber.*, **36**, 3177 (1903); **37**, 3092 (1904).

in 1903 showed this to be a secondary alcoholic group by the dehydrogenation of cholesterol to cholestenone. Wislicenus and Moldenhauer[3] (1868) established the presence of the double bond by the formation of a dibromide, and the parent hydrocarbon, cholestane, was obtained by Mauthner and by Diels (1907–1909).[4] One route to the saturated hydrocarbon is by way of the chloride of cholesterol, as shown in the formulas (a). The stereoisomer

(a)

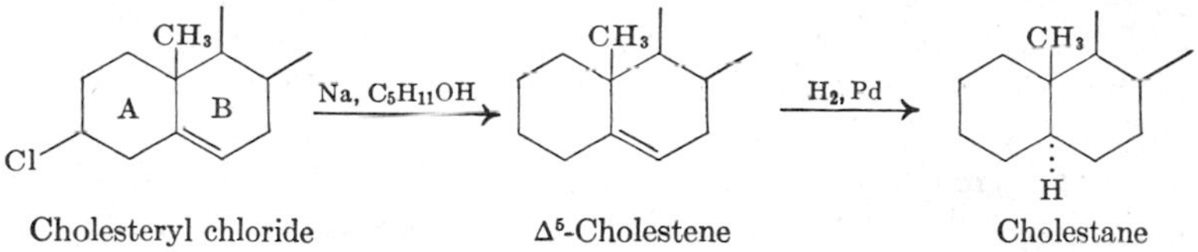

Cholesteryl chloride Δ^5-Cholestene   Cholestane

(b)

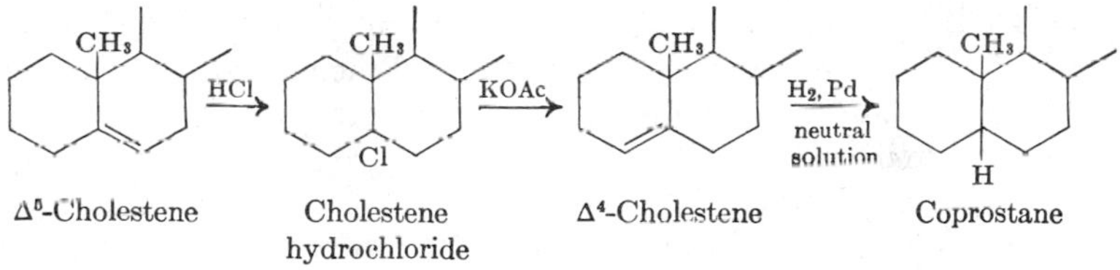

Δ^5-Cholestene   Cholestene hydrochloride Δ^4-Cholestene   Coprostane

coprostane was prepared from an isomerization product of Δ^5-cholestene (b). Whereas the hydrogenation of Δ^4-cholestene (pseudocholestene) in neutral solution yields principally coprostane, cholestane is the exclusive product when an acidic medium is employed. Coprostane can be obtained also by the reduction of coprostanyl chloride with sodium and amyl alcohol.[5]

Since cholestane and coprostane are saturated compounds, the empirical formula $C_{27}H_{48}$, in comparison with that for an open chain paraffin hydrocarbon ($C_{27}H_{56}$), indicated the presence of four rings in the cholesterol molecule. The same inference was drawn in the case of the bile acids. The functional groups of these substances were characterized by orthodox methods and the parent substance cholanic acid was obtained in the manner already described.

Method of Attack. In the second phase of the study an insight into the structures of the complicated molecules was sought through an examination of various products of oxidation, and the most important contributions to this part of the work are associated with the names of Borsche, Diels, Mauthner, Schenck, Wieland, and Windaus. Of outstanding brilliance was the work of Windaus on cholesterol dating from 1903[6] and that ini-

[3] Wislicenus and Moldenhauer, *Ann.*, **146**, 175 (1868).

[4] Mauthner, *Monatsh.*, **28**, 1113 (1907); **30**, 635 (1909). Diels and Linn, *Ber.*, **41**, 544 (1908).

[5] Windaus and Uibrig, *Ber.*, **48**, 857 (1915).

[6] Windaus, *Ber.*, **36**, 3752 (1903).

tiated by Wieland[7] in 1912 in the field of the bile acids. The long series of investigations at Göttingen and at the Freiburg and Munich laboratories followed for a time parallel but independent paths and the method of attack in each case was by degradation. To attempt to approach the problem by the synthesis of substances related to the complicated natural products was out of the question, not so much because adequate synthetic methods would have to be developed, but because there was no characteristic property to serve as a guide. H. Fischer was able to investigate the blood pigments from the synthetic side because the highly distinctive absorption spectra of the porphyrins made it possible to determine when the synthetic attempts were leading in the right direction. Such a method was excluded in the case of the colorless, and for the most part saturated, bile acids and sterols. Conversion to an aromatic substance by dehydrogenation probably was tried many times with negative results, for the dehydrogenation presents unusual experimental difficulties. When eventually success was achieved in 1927 the results formed an important link in the chain of evidence (see below).

Attempts to determine the character of the ring systems were made at an early date in the studies of oxidative degradation, but this proved to be the most difficult part of the problem. The elaboration of the character of the side chains was not simple, but this part of the work was the first to be carried to a sure conclusion and it affords the more convenient starting point for a description of some of the advances made by the German investigators.

Characterization of the Side Chain. The ready oxidation of both the sterols and the bile acids had invited early attempts to characterize a host of oxidation products obtainable under various conditions. It had been observed as early as 1872 that a pleasant smelling substance appears in the course of the oxidation of cholesterol and its derivatives. Various investigators had commented on the odor and Diels in 1908 noted a resemblance to that of methyl hexyl ketone. Finally Windaus in 1913,[1] using in all 500 g. of material, succeeded in isolating the odoriferous substance as the semicarbazone and in identifying it as methyl isohexyl ketone:

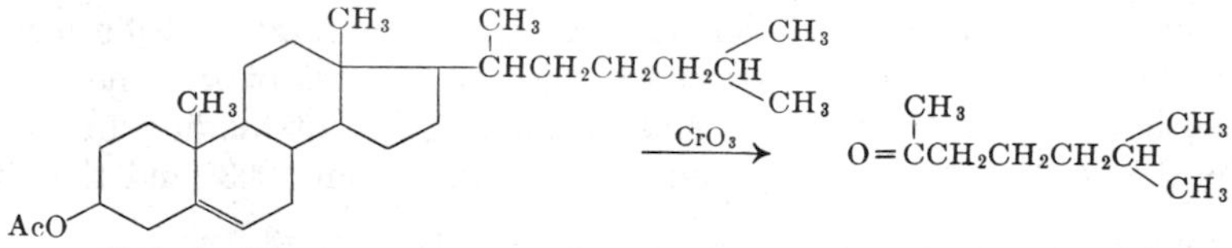

Cholesteryl acetate   Methyl isohexyl ketone

---

[7] Wieland and F. J. Weil, *Z. physiol. Chem.*, **80,** 287 (1912).
[1] Windaus and Resau, *Ber.*, **46,** 1246 (1913).

Although the fate of the ring system was not established and although the yield was poor, subsequent findings confirmed this evidence.

The establishment of a relationship to the bile acids would fix the nature of the side chain in this case as well. The investigations of the sterols on the one hand and of the bile acids on the other hand had been undertaken as independent problems, but a relationship had been suspected at least as early as 1908,[2] for the two types occur together, they resemble one another in composition and molecular complexity, and they both give certain characteristic color reactions. No real evidence was forthcoming, however, until Windaus[3] in 1919 succeeded in establishing a connection between the two series. The method was suggested by the observation that acetone usually is formed in the oxidation of cholesterol derivatives (C_{27}) but not of the bile acids (C_{24}), an indication that the carbon systems may differ by an isopropyl group. In order to retain the carbocyclic system Windaus oxidized the saturated hydrocarbon cholestane and obtained an acid having the composition of cholanic acid, the parent substance of the bile acid group, which had been prepared and characterized by Wieland and Weil.[4] The two acids were not identical, but the general similarity in properties suggested that they might be stereoisomers. The oxidation of coprostane was next investigated and the acid obtained was in every respect identical with Wieland's cholanic acid. The evidence that the

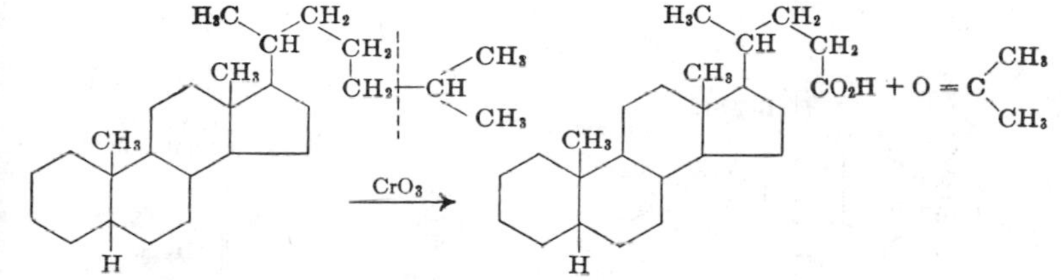

Coprostane   Cholanic acid

carbon skeleton of the bile acids is identical with that of a large part of the cholesterol molecule was later confirmed by the resynthesis of coprostane from cholanic acid.[5] The two separate problems were in this way brought together and evidence adduced in the one series could be applied in the other.

The Hydroxycholanic Acids. In the characterization of the four carbocyclic rings, the secondary alcoholic groups served as indispensable handles

[2] Windaus, *Arch. Pharm.*, **246**, 117 (1908).
[3] Windaus and Neukirchen, *Ber.*, **52**, 1915 (1919).
[4] Wieland and F. J. Weil, *Z. physiol. Chem.*, **80**, 287 (1912).
[5] Wieland and R. Jacobi, *Ber.*, **59**, 2064 (1926).

with which to manipulate the complicated structures. A ring containing such a group could be opened by oxidation at the vulnerable point and its character investigated. In the case of the bile acids several natural substances were available for experimentation and as the work unfolded methods were discovered for conversion of cholic acid into naturally occurring mono- and dihydroxycholanic acids and for proof that the location of the hydroxyl groups in these acids is largely limited to three positions. It also became possible to obtain for use in oxidative degradations certain other hydroxy acids or the corresponding keto acids, and the following examples illustrate the methods of transformation.

The hydroxycholanic acids can be converted smoothly into the corresponding keto (dehydro) acids by oxidation with chromic oxide in acetic acid solution at room temperature. The three carbonyl groups of dehydrocholic acid (I) differ sufficiently in reactivity to permit selective partial reduction. Borsche[1] found that mild Clemmensen reduction attacks the 3-keto group preferentially and affords the 7,12-diketo acid (II); he also

Chart 4. RELATIVE REACTIVITY OF CARBONYL GROUPS

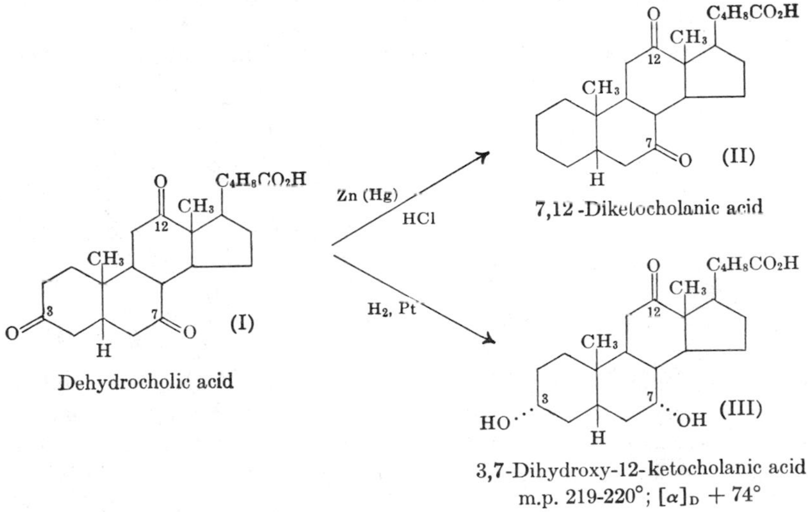

(II) 7,12-Diketocholanic acid

(I) Dehydrocholic acid

(III) 3,7-Dihydroxy-12-ketocholanic acid
m.p. 219-220°; $[\alpha]_D + 74°$

found[2] that reduction with sodium amalgam gives 3-hydroxy-7,12-diketocholanic acid (which on Wolff-Kishner reduction affords lithocholic acid in very low overall yield). An analogy to the first reaction is the reduction

[1] Borsche, *Ber.*, **52**, 1363 (1919).
[2] Borsche and Hallwass, *Ber.*, **55**, 3318 (1922).

of dehydrodesoxycholic acid to 12-ketocholanic acid with unamalgamated zinc and acid.[3] A distinction between the reactivities at the 7- and 12-positions is given by the observation that partial hydrogenation of dehydrocholic acid affords the 3,7-dihydroxy-12-keto acid (III).[4] The order of reactivity of the carbonyl groups is thus $C_3 > C_7 > C_{12}$. The relationship is probably attributable to steric effects. The 12-position is the most hindered because it is adjacent to a bridgehead carrying an angular methyl group; the 7-position is adjacent to a bridgehead; a group at C_3 occupies a β-position in the ring and is the least hindered.

That the same order of reactivity holds for acylation and hydrolysis reactions is demonstrated by the series of transformations illustrated in Chart 5.[5] Cholic acid was converted by partial acetylation into the 3,7-diacetate (IV), which gave the ketone V on oxidation. By partial hy-

Chart 5. Removal of Hydroxyl Groups

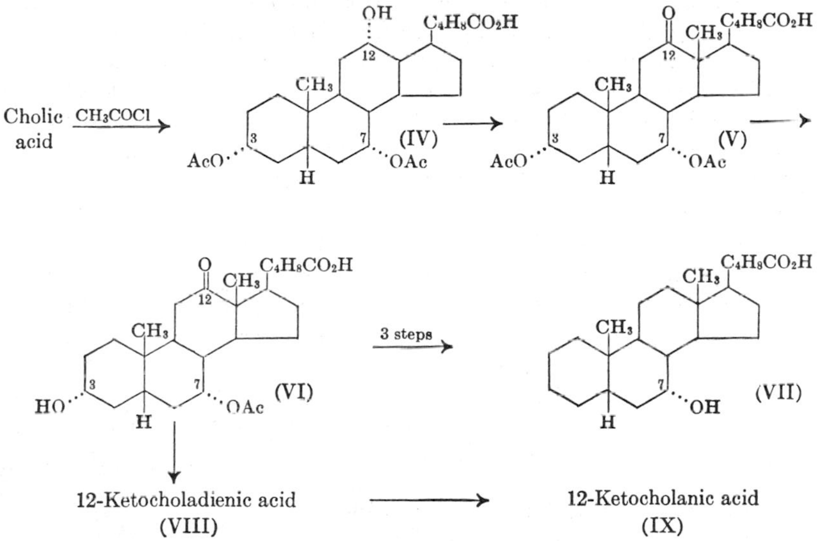

Cholic acid $\xrightarrow{CH_3COCl}$ (IV) $\longrightarrow$ (V) $\longrightarrow$

(VI) $\xrightarrow{\text{3 steps}}$ (VII)

12-Ketocholadienic acid (VIII) $\longrightarrow$ 12-Ketocholanic acid (IX)

drolysis the acetyl group at the more reactive 3-position could be eliminated, and oxidation of the product VI gave the 3,12-diketo-7-acetate, which was converted by Wolff-Kishner reduction and hydrolysis into 7-hydroxycholanic acid, VII. 12-Ketocholanic acid (IX) was obtained by pyrolysis of VI to a ketodienic acid and hydrogenation.

[3] Wieland and Schlichting, *Z. physiol. Chem.*, **150**, 273 (1925).
[4] Borsche and Feske, *Z. physiol. Chem.*, **176**, 109 (1928); Kawai, *ibid.*, **214**, 71 (1933).
[5] Wieland and Kapitel, *Z. physiol. Chem.*, **212**, 269 (1932).

No explanation has been advanced for the curious fact that the order of reactivity in oxidations is not the same as in the reactions of reduction, hydrogenation, acylation, and hydrolysis. The order is $C_7 > C_{12} > C_3$, and it is known further that a hydroxyl group at C_6 is attacked more readily than one at C_3. Evidence for these statements is provided by the following partial oxidations (chromic acid):

7,12-Dihydroxycholanic acid	→ 7-Keto-12-hydroxy acid[6]
Chenodesoxycholic acid ⎫	
Ursodesoxycholic acid ⎬	→ 3-Hydroxy-7-keto acid[7]
Desoxycholic acid	→ 3-Hydroxy-12-keto acid[8]
Hyodesoxycholic acid	→ 3-Hydroxy-6-keto acid[9]

The above transformations provide routes to the 3-, 7-, and 12-hydroxy or ketocholanic acids from cholic acid, but more practical routes to the 3- and 12-derivatives are shown in Chart 6. 12-Hydroxycholanic acid and lithocholic acid are both obtainable from desoxycholic acid by efficient processes (a[10] and b[11]) involving selective acylation of the 3-hydroxyl group, and the high yields show that tosylation and succinoylation proceed practically exclusively in the direction desired. Acetylation is less specific, for in earlier work lithocholic acid had been prepared through desoxycholic acid 3-acetate and the yield of 3-hydroxy-12-ketocholanic acid was only 44 percent.[12] A process[13, 14] for the preparation of lithocholic acid from the cheaper cholic acid by selective acetylation of the 3-hydroxyl group, oxidation, and reduction of the diketo acetate also suffered from a low yield in the acylation (31%). This process likewise is greatly improved by the use of the 3-succinate (c), and the reactions formulated in the chart have been conducted on a large scale without isolation of intermediates with overall yield of 88 percent.[15]

The reduction of the two carbonyl groups of 3-hydroxy-7,12-diketocholanic acid has been accomplished by the preparation of the diethylenemercaptal derivative (77 percent yield) and desulfuration with Raney

---

[6] Wieland and Dane, Z. physiol. Chem., **210**, 279 (1932).

[7] Iwasaki, Z. physiol. Chem., **244**, 186 (1936).

[8] Kaziro and Shimada, Z. physiol. Chem., **249**, 223 (1937).

[9] Wieland and Dane, Z. physiol. Chem., **212**, 44 (1932).

[10] Barnett and Reichstein, Helv. Chim. Acta, **21**, 926 (1938).

[11] Schwenk, B. Riegel, Moffett and Stahl, J. Am. Chem. Soc., **65**, 549 (1943); see also Ref. 13.

[12] Wieland, Dane and Scholz, Z. physiol. Chem., **211**, 266 (1932); Marker and Lawson, J. Am. Chem. Soc., **60**, 1334 (1938).

[13] Grand and Reichstein, Helv. Chim. Acta, **28**, 344 (1945).

[14] Meystre and Miescher, Helv. Chim. Acta, **29**, 33 (1946).

[15] Heusser and Wuthier, Helv. Chim. Acta, **30**, 2165 (1947).

Chart 6. PREPARATION OF 12-HYDROXYCHOLANIC ACID AND LITHOCHOLIC ACID

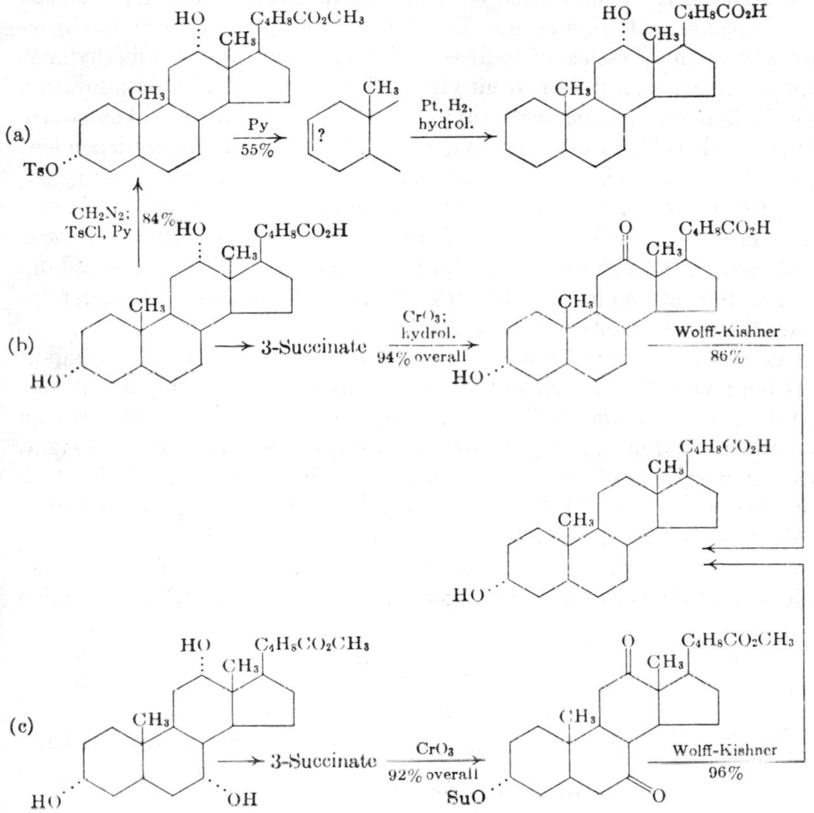

nickel catalyst (60 percent yield).[16] The yield is not so good as in the Wolff-Kishner reaction but the method of reduction has other useful applications (see Cholestenes). Hauptmann[16] found that all three keto groups of dehydrocholic acid ethyl ester react with ethanedithiol in the presence

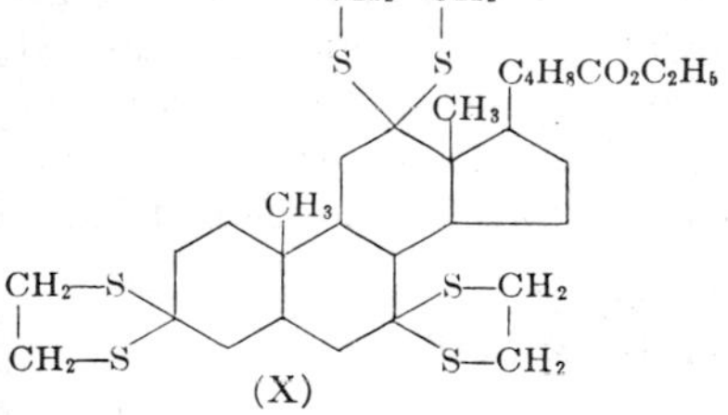

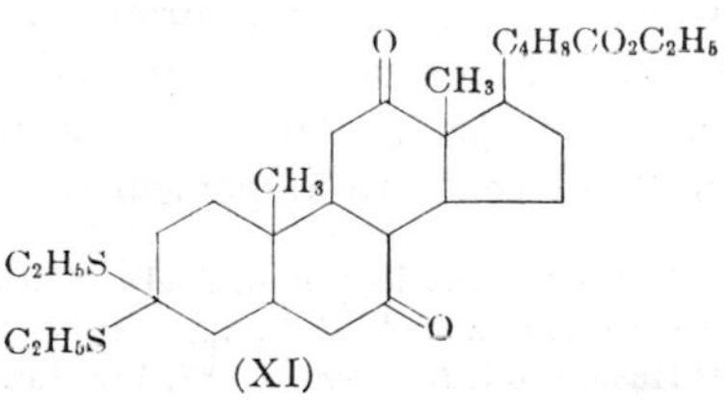

[16] Hauptmann, *J. Am. Chem. Soc.*, **69**, 562 (1947).

of gaseous hydrogen chloride to produce the triethylenemercaptal X in 77 percent yield; desulfuration of X in dioxane-alcohol with Raney nickel gave cholanic acid ethyl ester.   Ethyl mercaptan proved to be less reactive and in the presence of hydrogen chloride afforded the 3-diethylmercaptal derivative XI in 54 percent yield; XI was converted by desulfuration into 7,12-diketocholanic acid ethyl ester (91 percent yield).   The course of the reaction of ketosteroids with mercaptans seems to be highly dependent upon the experimental conditions and the nature of the mercaptan. Hauptmann[16] obtained cyclic mercaptal derivatives of steroids with carbonyl groups at the 3,7,12, and 17-positions.   Ethyl mercaptan has been condensed with 3-ketosteroids in the presence of zinc chloride and sodium sulfate, but attempted condensations with 7-keto and 12-ketosteroids under the same conditions were unsuccessful.[17]

Desoxycholic acid is the starting point for the partial synthesis of important hormones, but the amount obtainable from ox bile is only about one-eighth as great as the cholic acid isolated in the same process; hence an efficient method of converting cholic to desoxycholic acid has been sought. The conversion was first accomplished by the hydrogenation of the 3,12-dihydroxycholenic acid formed as a product of dehydration (see apocholic acid), but the yield is very low.   The present best procedures all involve the selective oxidation of cholic acid at the 7-position and Wolff-Kishner reduction of the keto acid.   Gallagher and Long[18] conducted the oxidation

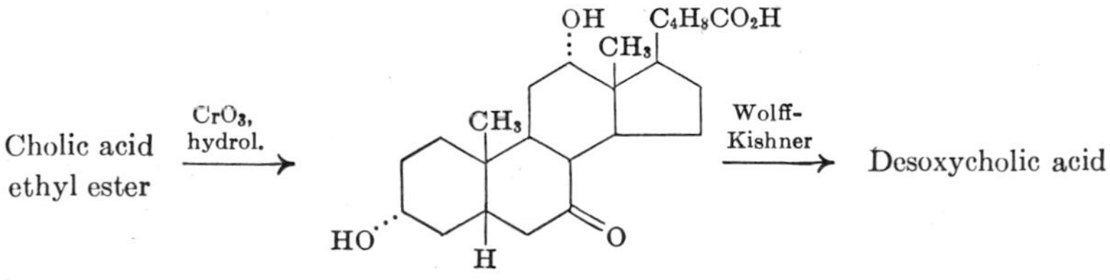

Cholic acid ethyl ester $\xrightarrow{\text{CrO}_3, \text{ hydrol.}}$ ... $\xrightarrow{\text{Wolff-Kishner}}$ Desoxycholic acid

3,12-Dihydroxy-7-ketocholanic acid
m.p. 199-200°, $[\alpha]_D + 1.5°$

of the ethyl ester at -7 to $0°$ in acetic acid-water and isolated the monoketo acid by chromatographic adsorption in 40 percent yield; the residue contained 3-hydroxy-7,12-diketocholanic acid[8] and dehydrocholic acid.   Haslewood[19] used potassium chromate in highly purified acetic acid buffered with sodium acetate and reported an overall yield of 40–50 percent of desoxycholic acid.   The yield in the Wolff-Kishner reduction is raised from 24 percent[18] to 57 percent by the modification of the method intro-

[17] Bernstein and Dorfman, *J. Am. Chem. Soc.*, **68**, 1152 (1946).
[18] Gallagher and W. P. Long, *J. Biol. Chem.*, **147**, 131 (1943).
[19] Haslewood, *Biochem. J.*, **37**, 109 (1943).

duced by Huang.[20] Two procedures for the large-scale oxidation of cholic acid were worked out by Hoehn and Linsk.[21] In one cholic acid is oxidized in aqueous alkali-bicarbonate with bromine at 0° (40 percent yield); the other consists in the chromic acid oxidation of the ethyl ester (33 percent yield). 3,12-Dihydroxy-7-ketocholanic acid can be converted into 12-hydroxycholanic acid by partial acid hydrolysis of the diacetate, chromic acid oxidation, and Wolff-Kishner reduction of the diketone.[21] A longer route to 3,7-diketo-12-hydroxycholanic acid is described by Haslewood.[22]

Hoehn, Schmidt and Hughes[23] investigated the oxidation of cholic acid by the bacillus *Alcaligenes faecalis* and found that microbiological oxidation follows the same path as chemical oxidation and affords the 3,12-dihydroxy-7-keto acid, the 3-hydroxy-7,12-diketo acid, and finally dehydrocholic acid.

Characterization of Ring A. Having available for experimentation many interrelated hydroxyl derivatives of cholanic acid, the investigators in the field were able to open the complicated ring structure by oxidation at various different points and so effect degradations that furnished information about both the ring system and the location of the alcoholic groups. The work in this direction was so profuse that the following account merely illustrates the nature of the experimental methods and summarizes the more important conclusions.

The hydroxycholanic acids or stanols can be converted by mild oxidation into the corresponding keto compounds and on further oxidation, usually with either concentrated nitric acid or potassium permanganate, the ring containing the carbonyl group is opened with the production of two new carboxyl groups. In the bile acid series the tricarboxylic acid obtained by the opening of a single ring is called a bilianic acid and a prefix (desoxy-, litho-, cheno-, etc.) is used to indicate the series in question. In the oxidation of the diketo acid (I) from desoxycholic acid the reactive

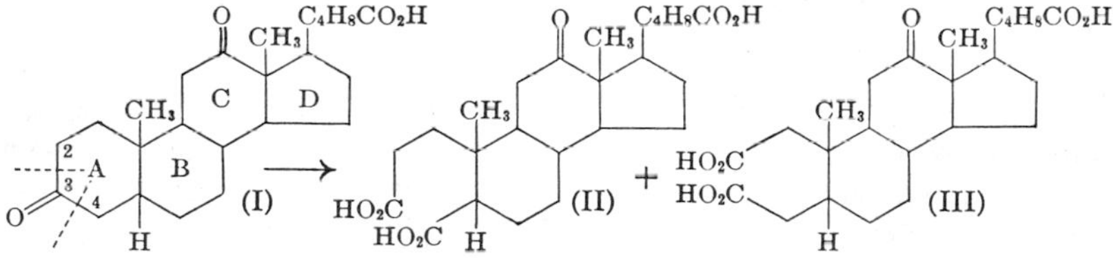

Dehydrodesoxycholic acid	Desoxybilianic acid	Isodesoxybilianic acid

---

[20] Communication from Dr. Huang, see *J. Am. Chem. Soc.*, **68**, 2487 (1946).

[21] Hoehn and Linsk, *J. Am. Chem. Soc.*, **67**, 312 (1945); see also Schneider and Hoehn, *ibid.*, **65**, 485 (1943).

[22] Haslewood, *Biochem. J.*, **38**, 108 (1944).

[23] Hoehn, L. H. Schmidt and Hughes, *J. Biol. Chem.*, **152**, 59 (1944).

group at C_3 forms the first point of attack and the ring is cleaved both between positions 3 and 4 (chief product, normal series) and between positions 2 and 3 (iso series), with formation of two acids (II and III).[1] The formation of tribasic acids as the main products reveals the presence of a methylene group adjacent to the carbonyl group in the ring attacked (-CH$_2$$\vdots$CO-), and the isolation of an isomer, shown by independent evidence not to arise from the opening of ring C and not to be a stereoisomeride, indicates that the reactive group is flanked on each side by methylene groups (-CH$_2$$\vdots$CO$\vdots$CH$_2$-).   This evidence identifies the ring in question (A) as being at the end of the molecule, for a ring situated in the manner of either B or C could open in only one way.   The evidence also locates the carbonyl group at a β-position in ring A, namely at C_2 or C_3.

The size of ring A was inferred from a further transformation of the desoxybilianic acids, namely cyclization by distillation.   From regularities observed among simple dibasic acids, Blanc[2] had formulated a rule which Windaus[3] first applied to this type of oxidation product in 1919 and which has since occupied a position of prominence in the study of structure.   The Blanc rule states that if the two carboxyl groups occupy the 1,3-, 1,4- or 1,5-positions in the chain the acid on treatment with acetic anhydride (or on distillation) is converted into an anhydride, whereas 1,6- and higher

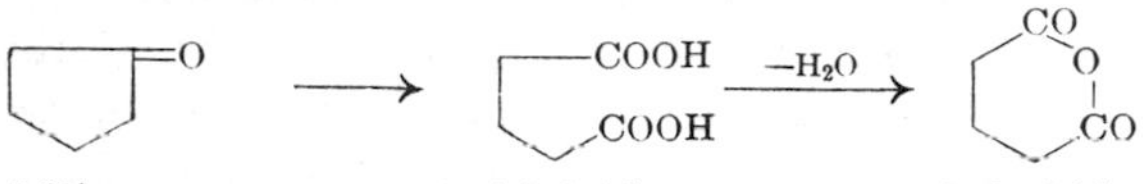

5-Ring   1,5-Acid   Anhydride

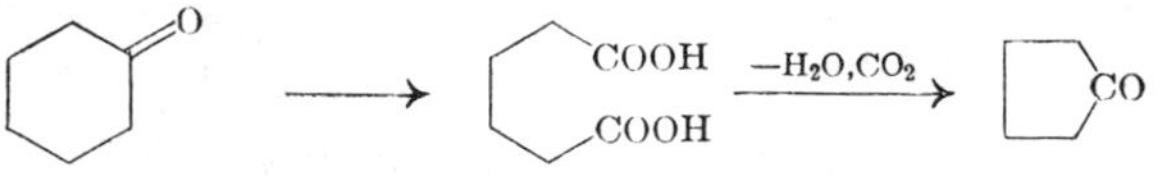

6-Ring   1,6-Acid   Ketone

diacids yield cyclic ketones.   The most pertinent applications to the present problem are in the cases of the acids resulting from the opening of five- and six-membered rings.   Both desoxybilianic acid and its isomer on distillation lose carbon dioxide and water and form ketones; hence ring A of the original bile acid is a six-membered ring.

In the sterol series the same conclusion was reached[3] regarding the ring (A) containing the lone alcoholic group, and the evidence was carried a step further.   The acid resulting from the oxidation of cholestanol yields

[1] Wieland and Kulenkampff, *Z. physiol. Chem.*, **108**, 295 (1920).
[2] Blanc, *Compt. rend.*, **144**, 1356 (1907).
[3] Windaus and Dalmer, *Ber.*, **52**, 162 (1919).

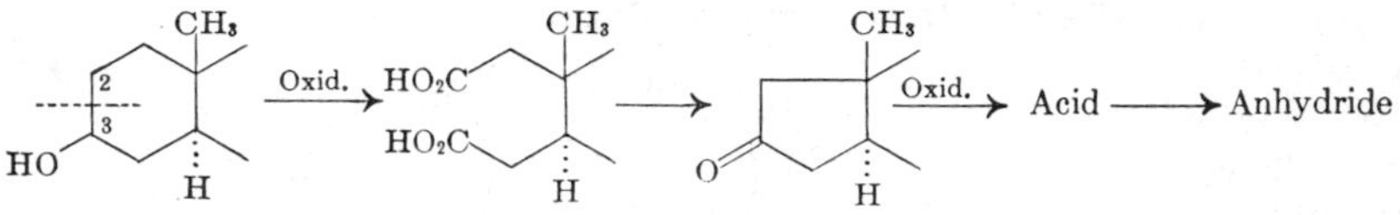

a ketone on pyrolysis, whereas the acid from the pyroketone gives an anhydride. According to the Blanc rule both observations indicate an original six ring.

That ring A of cholestanol is opened largely between positions 2 and 3 was established by later evidence (Windaus[4]). The oxidation follows a course different from that observed in the case of the bile acids, where cleavage occurs chiefly at $C_3 - C_4$. The difference appears to be connected with the fact that rings A and B of the bile acids have the cis configuration whereas cholesterol belongs to the trans (allo) series. Coprostanol (A/B:cis) is attacked chiefly at the 3,4-position.

Evidence Regarding Ring B. The rule of Blanc was not at first employed in a similarly direct manner to the investigation of the size of ring B of the bile acids because various other observations furnishing information on this point became available before methods suitable for the selective opening of ring B had been developed. One piece of evidence emerged from a study of the further degradation of desoxycholic acid, a complete account of which is given in Chart 7. When desoxybilianic acid (II) is oxidized ring C is cleaved adjacent to the keto group at C_{12} and on pyrolysis of the reaction product, choloidanic acid (III), cyclization with loss of carbon dioxide takes place in the part of the molecule corresponding to the original ring A, with formation of IV (in the form of the anhydride). The new ketonic ring is cleaved on oxidation of the pyroacid and, since the bond severed makes connection to a tertiary carbon atom rather than to a methylene group, the acid V has only one new carboxyl group and is a keto acid. Prosolannelic acid (V) forms the starting point for the opening of ring B, which originally carried no hydroxyl groups, and the Blanc reaction can be applied to the oxidation product VI which, since only one of the original rings (D) is still intact, is called solannelic acid (L. *solus anulus*). Since carbon dioxide is lost in the formation of the ketonic pyroacid VII, it was concluded that B is a six-membered ring.

A careful analysis of the series of degradations furnishes still further information. The evidence given above located the hydroxyl group of ring A at either C_2 or C_3 and in the formulas it has been placed at C_3. The alternate location would require a modification in the structures in such a way that prosolannelic acid (V) would acquire formula IX. This structure is inadmissible, however, because prosolannelic acid does not have the

[4] Windaus, *Z. physiol. Chem.*, **213**, 147 (1932).

Chart 7. DEGRADATION TO BILOIDANIC ACID

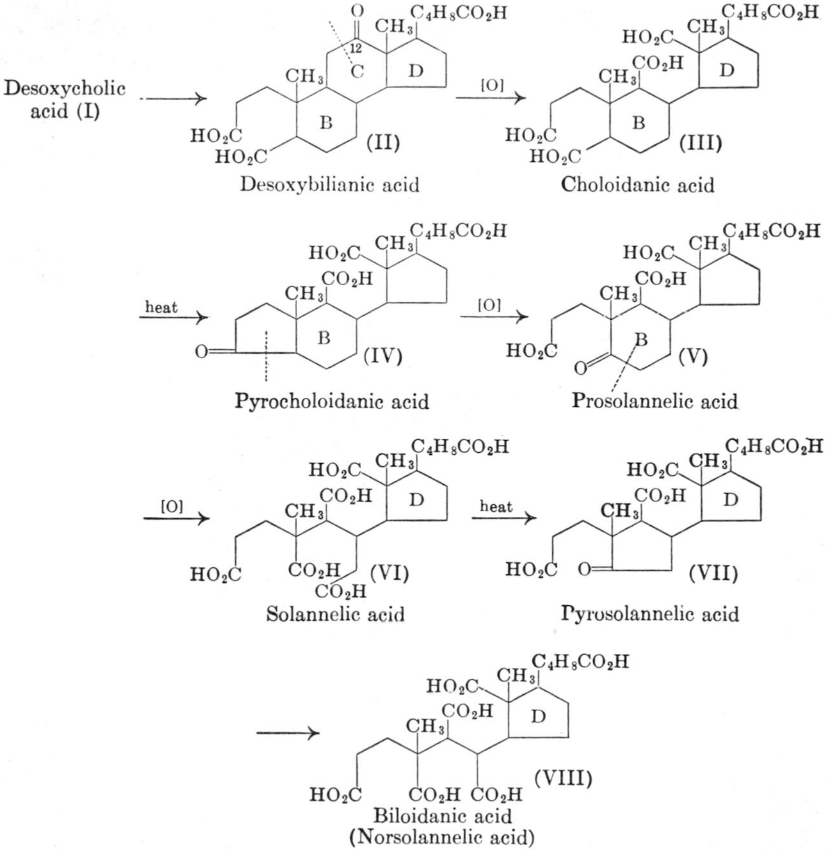

Desoxycholic acid (I)

Desoxybilianic acid (II)

Choloidanic acid (III)

heat →

Pyrocholoidanic acid (IV)

Prosolannelic acid (V)

[O] →

Solannelic acid (VI)

heat →

Pyrosolannelic acid (VII)

→

Biloidanic acid (Norsolannelic acid) (VIII)

properties of a β-keto acid as demanded by the formula.[1] This observation rules out other structures for the original desoxycholic acid. If one hy-

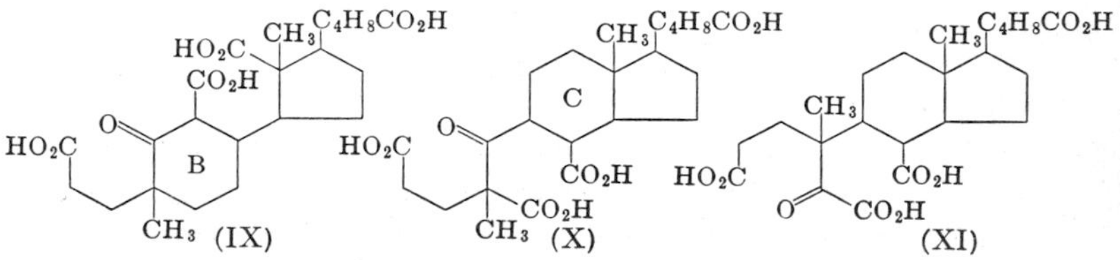

(IX)

(X)

(XI)

---

[1] Wieland and Schulenburg, *Z. physiol. Chem.*, **114**, 167 (1921).

droxyl group were at C_2 or at C_3 and if the second were located in ring B, prosolannelic acid would have the structure X, of a β-keto acid, or the equally inadmissible structure XI, of an α-keto acid. The location of the hydroxyl groups at C_2 and C_{12} (or at C_2 and C_{11}) is excluded on similar grounds, and the degradations indeed furnish evidence that B is a six-membered ring, that one hydroxyl group is at C_3, and that the second one is attached to ring C. Corroborative evidence is not lacking to establish the order in which the rings open. For example desoxybilianic acid and isodesoxybilianic acid can be reduced by the Wolff-Kishner method to the carbonyl-free acids, which are identical with lithobilianic acid and isolithobilianic acid, respectively.[2] Since the conversion of lithocholic acid into these isomeric acids can only be the result of the opening of the terminal ring, this proves that ring A is cleaved in the formation of the desoxybilianic acids.

Another line of evidence regarding the nature of ring B was developed by Borsche.[3] A number of investigators had studied the oxidation of dehydrocholic acid; Pregl[4], for example, obtained bilianic acid (XII) and isobilianic acid in yields of 44 percent and 2 percent, respectively. Lassar-Cohn[5] had obtained from bilianic acid with alkaline permanganate another oxidation product called cilianic acid, and this substance had been investigated extensively by Wieland and Schlichting,[6] who cleared up many points but failed to arrive at the true interpretation of the formation and degradation of cilianic acid. According to Borsche the first step in the oxidation consists in the formation of the unstable triketo acid XIII, which undergoes the benzilic acid rearrangement in the alkaline solution (Chart 8). The presence of the various functional groups was established by orthodox methods and their arrangement was inferred largely from the behavior of the oxidation product, ciloidanic acid (XV), when warmed with concentrated sulfuric acid. Carbon monoxide and water are eliminated from the α-hydroxy acid group:

$$> C < ^{OH}_{COOH} \longrightarrow > C{=}O + CO + H_2O$$

and the resulting β-keto acid then easily becomes decarboxylated to XVI. The last oxidation product (XVII) was found identical with biloidanic acid, obtained as described above from desoxycholic acid. If B is a six ring, as pictured in the formulas, the transformation of this into a five-membered

[2] Borsche and Hallwass, *Ber.*, **55**, 3318, 3324 (1922); Borsche and Behr, *Nachr. Ges. Wiss. Göttingen*, **188**, (1920).

[3] Borsche and R. Frank, *Ber.*, **60**, 723 (1927).

[4] Pregl, *Monatsh.*, **24**, 19 (1903).

[5] Lassar-Cohn, *Ber.*, **32**, 683 (1899).

[6] Wieland and Schlichting, *Z. physiol. Chem.*, **120**, 227 (1922); **123**, 213 (1922).

ring by way of a benzilic acid rearrangement is readily understandable, but it would not be admissible to assume that the new ring formed in this

Chart 8. REARRANGEMENT TO CILIANIC ACID

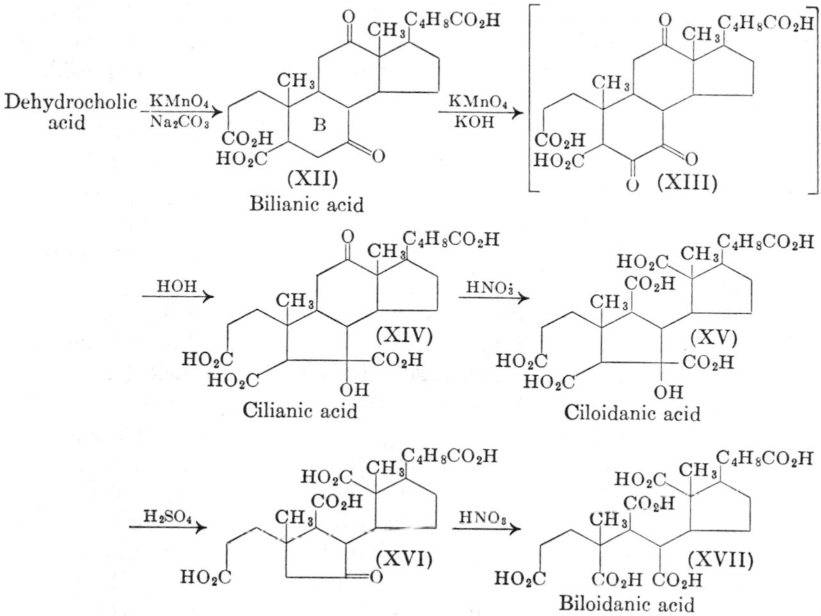

Dehydrocholic acid $\xrightarrow[\text{Na}_2\text{CO}_3]{\text{KMnO}_4}$ (XII) Bilianic acid $\xrightarrow[\text{KOH}]{\text{KMnO}_4}$ (XIII)

$\xrightarrow{\text{HOH}}$ (XIV) Cilianic acid $\xrightarrow{\text{HNO}_3}$ (XV) Ciloidanic acid

$\xrightarrow{\text{H}_2\text{SO}_4}$ (XVI) $\xrightarrow{\text{HNO}_3}$ (XVII) Biloidanic acid

facile manner contains only four carbon atoms and hence that it comes from an original five-membered ring. The degradations lend further support to the structure attributed to the second ring of cilianic acid, and the observations taken as a whole provide reliable evidence that ring B in the bile acids is a cyclohexane ring. In this case an inference based upon the Blanc rule was checked by independent evidence.

Failure of the Blanc Rule. The evidence available from the early work concerning ring C was limited to a single observation by Wieland[1] in 1920 regarding choloidanic acid, and this unfortunately led to a conclusion that was later found to be erroneous. Choloidanic acid, the oxidation product of desoxycholic acid in which both rings A and C have been opened, yields on pyrolysis an acid containing two new rings, a ketonic ring coming from the residue of A and an anhydride ring formed from the carboxyl groups originating from the cleavage of C. In accordance with the Blanc rule, Wieland took this to mean that rings A and C contain six and five carbon

[1] Wieland, *Z. physiol. Chem.*, **108**, 306 (1920).

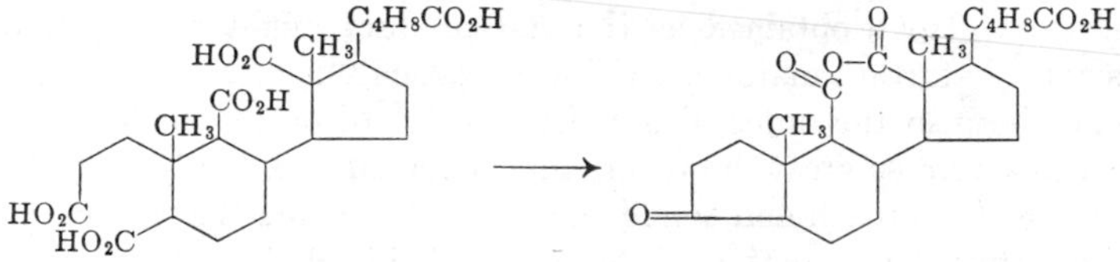

Choloidanic acid → Pyrocholoidanic acid anhydride

atoms, respectively. Although the assumption was plausible enough at the time, it is now known that C is a six-membered ring. As will be shown later the Blanc rule does not hold for ring C because both carboxyl groups are attached to rings. Because of the apparent success in the application of the method of diagnosis in other cases, the validity of the Blanc rule was not at first questioned and the erroneous conclusion remained uncontested for a number of years. The manner in which the mistake was discovered will be described later.

Character of Ring D. The investigation of the fourth ring, D, presented special difficulties because no bile acid or sterol having an oxidizable group in this part of the molecule had been discovered. One plan of attack pursued for a time by Wieland was to destroy all the other rings by oxidation in the search for a degradation product suitable for characterization of the remaining ring. The closest approach to the realization of this project was the degradation of pyrodesoxybilianic acid[2] (Chart 9).

Chart 9. DEGRADATION OF PYRODESOXYBILIANIC ACID

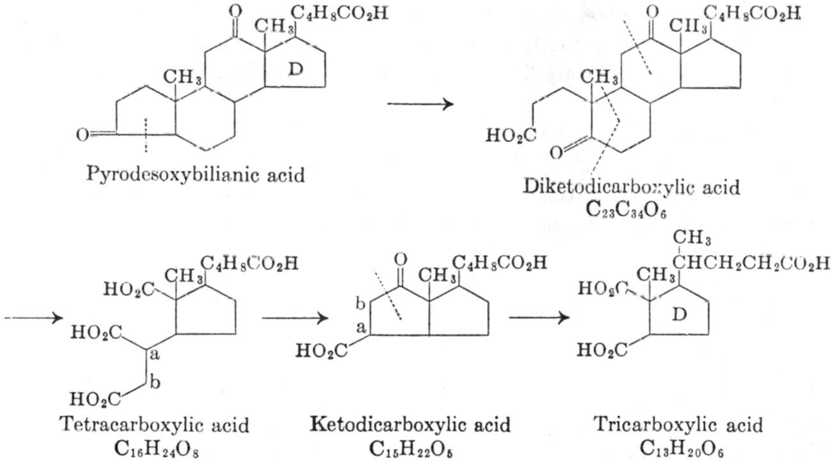

Pyrodesoxybilianic acid →

Diketodicarboxylic acid
$C_{23}C_{34}O_6$

Tetracarboxylic acid
$C_{16}H_{24}O_8$
→
Ketodicarboxylic acid
$C_{15}H_{22}O_5$
→
Tricarboxylic acid
$C_{13}H_{20}O_6$

---

[2] Wieland and Schlichting, *Z. physiol. Chem.*, **134**, 276 (1924).

The acid $C_{13}H_{20}O_6$ obtained as the end product might have served as a satisfactory starting material for the investigation of ring D if the yield had not been in the order of 5 g. from 1 kg. of desoxycholic acid. The difficulties were so great, however, that Wieland eventually turned to another line of approach and sought a means of opening the ring in question by the stepwise degradation of the bile acid side chain. A number of the known methods of degradation were found to be quite useless when applied to the complex bile acid molecule, but the objective was finally achieved by Wieland, Schlichting and Jacobi[3] in 1926 by application of a general method described earlier by Barbier[4] and now known as the Barbier-Wieland degradation. The method involves the successive oxidation of the carbinols obtained by the Grignard reaction from the esters of cholanic acid and its lower homologs, as follows:

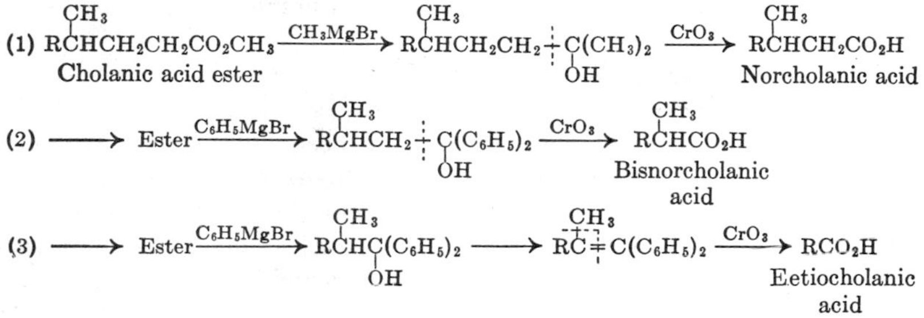

$$
\begin{array}{l}
\text{(1)}\ \underset{\text{Cholanic acid ester}}{\overset{CH_3}{RCHCH_2CH_2CO_2CH_3}} \xrightarrow{CH_3MgBr} \overset{CH_3}{RCHCH_2CH_2} \!+\! \underset{OH}{C(CH_3)_2} \xrightarrow{CrO_2} \underset{\text{Norcholanic acid}}{\overset{CH_3}{RCHCH_2CO_2H}}
\end{array}
$$

$$
\begin{array}{l}
\text{(2)}\ \longrightarrow \text{Ester} \xrightarrow{C_6H_5MgBr} \overset{CH_3}{RCHCH_2} \!+\! \underset{OH}{C(C_6H_5)_2} \xrightarrow{CrO_3} \underset{\substack{\text{Bisnorcholanic}\\\text{acid}}}{\overset{CH_3}{RCHCO_2H}}
\end{array}
$$

$$
\begin{array}{l}
\text{(3)}\ \longrightarrow \text{Ester} \xrightarrow{C_6H_5MgBr} \underset{OH}{\overset{CH_3}{RCHC(C_6H_5)_2}} \longrightarrow \overset{CH_3}{RC}\!\doteq\!C(C_6H_5)_2 \xrightarrow{CrO_2} \underset{\substack{\text{Eetiocholanic}\\\text{acid}}}{RCO_2H}
\end{array}
$$

This work incidentally confirmed the structure already assigned to the side chain, for the loss of a single carbon atom in steps (1) and (2) proves the presence of two methylene groups next to the acid group, and the branching methyl group is revealed by the elimination of two carbon atoms in (3).

It was evident that the base of the chain had been reached in the formation of etiocholanic acid (Gr. *aitio-*, fundamental), for on further oxidation this was converted into a dibasic acid, etiobilianic acid, which could only arise from the opening of the ring carrying the acid group. The opening

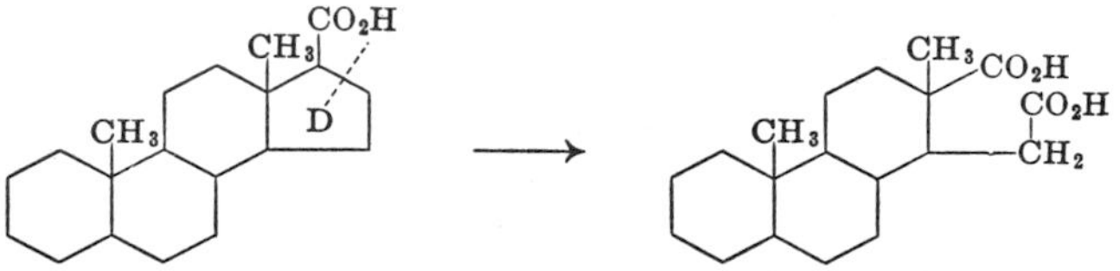

Etiocholanic acid   Etiobilianic acid

---

[3] Wieland, Schlichting and R. Jacobi, *Z. physiol. Chem.*, **161**, 80 (1926).
[4] Barbier and Locquin, *Compt. rend.*, **156**, 1443 (1913).

of ring D was in this way realized and although etiobilianic acid was obtained in extremely low overall yield it could be characterized by the Blanc reaction. The acid lost no carbon dioxide on distillation but formed an anhydride, from which it was correctly concluded that the ring in question contains five carbon atoms. The conclusion was at the time quite unexpected.

The "Old" Formulas. By 1928 the work had reached a point where the structural problem appeared to be settled in all the most essential points, and the award of the Nobel Prize of that year to Wieland and to Windaus was a fitting tribute to the brilliant success in the arduous investigations in a difficult field. The formulas suggested in 1928 hardly reflect the real progress that had been made, for they were unduly distorted by the errors that had crept into the train of evidence. One error arose from the

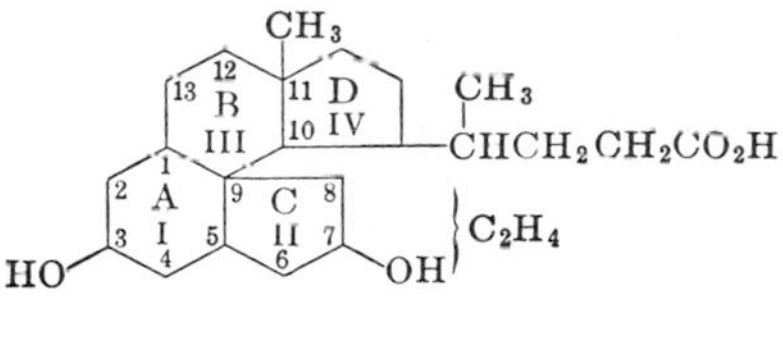

Desoxycholic acid
(Wieland, 1928)

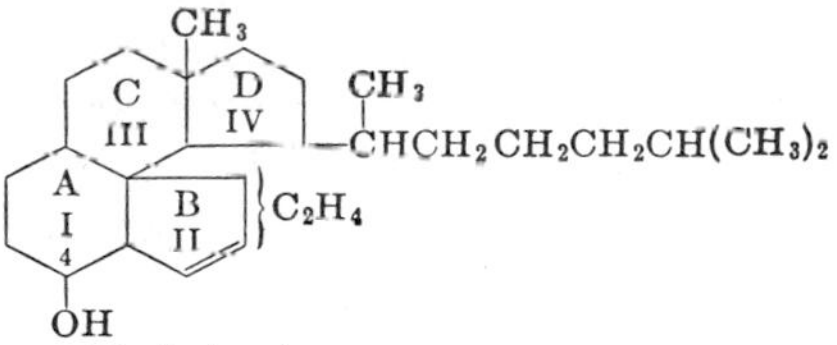

Cholesterol
(1928)

failure of the Blanc rule when the carboxyl groups concerned are located between two ring systems. Another was in the inference from certain of the degradations[1] that the supposedly five-membered ring C, which carries the second hydroxyl group of desoxycholic acid, is attached to ring A and shares two carbon atoms in common with this ring. It is unfortunate that this assumption remained for many years unchallenged, for it really could not be justified on the basis of the experimental evidence available. That ring B is directly joined to ring A, as in the formulas now accepted, had been established quite definitely. The oxidation of pro-solannelic acid to solannelic acid, for example, proves that the oxygen-free ring (B) of desoxycholic acid is attached to the ring (A) that is opened first in the oxidation of the bile acid.

The combination of the correct and the mistaken evidence led to the construction of a curious formula[2] in which the three rings in question were pictured as being directly united. In the older literature the four rings were indicated by Roman numerals in the manner shown; the identity of the rings in terms of the modern structure is indicated by the letters. The numbering of the positions is such that, whereas C_3 is identical in the

---

[1] Wieland, *Z. physiol. Chem.*, **108**, 306 (1920).
[2] Wieland, *Z. angew. Chem.*, **42**, 421 (1929).

old and the new formulas, the C_7 position is now called C_{12}, and vice versa. Desoxycholic acid, known in the early literature as "3,7"-dihydroxycholanic acid is now the 3,12-acid. The tentative formula for cholesterol was based in large part upon that assigned to the bile acids, for the latter offered more points of attack by oxidative degradation. The old ring II that contains the double bond was supposed to be identical with the old ring II of the bile acids because both rings showed the same behavior in the pyro-reaction.[1] Both rings were regarded as five-membered because anhydrides were produced, but in each case the results are contrary to the predictions of the Blanc rule and the rings are now known to be different (B and C). In both the old and the new formulas for cholesterol the double bond is placed in the β,γ-position with respect to the hydroxyl group, but the latter has been shifted from C_4 to C_3 in the light of recent evidence.

The placing of a methyl group at C_{11} in the old formula was not without some experimental foundation, but this left two "homeless" carbon atoms for which no satisfactory account could be given. Wieland's tentative hypothesis that an ethyl group is located at C_{10} (old formula) was later found to be inadmissible[3] and the suggested insertion[4] of the grouping —$CH(CH_3)$— between C_1 and C_9 or between C_{11} and C_{12} could not be supported for long and it proved to be impossible to place the "homeless" carbon atoms anywhere in the ring system.

Problem of Revision. With the realization of these difficulties in adding the finishing touches to a picture that in 1928 had appeared to be practically complete, the way was thrown open to a consideration of a modified formulation for the bile acid ring skeleton, and at this point the investigations can be said to have entered a third phase, that of revision. The first indication of the direction this revision would have to take came from an unexpected source. Bernal[1] at the Mineralogical Museums, Cambridge, made an X-ray crystallographic examination of ergosterol and its irradiation products in 1932 with the primary object of defining the position in the series of vitamin D; he made the incidental observation that ergosterol molecules form double layers similar to those of long-chain alcohols and that the molecular dimensions do not fit at all well with the values calculated from the Wieland-Windaus sterol formula. This represents three rings as meeting at a single point (C_9), and the molecule would necessarily be rather thick; but Bernal's evidence pointed to a long, thin molecule. Bernal's conclusion that the results were difficult to reconcile with the accepted structure had the support of a previous but less specific observa-

[3] Wieland and Vocke, *Z. physiol. Chem.*, **191**, 69 (1930).
[4] Wieland and Dane, *Z. physiol. Chem.*, **206**, 243 (1932).
[1] Bernal, *Nature*, **129**, 277 (1932).

tion of Adam and Rosenheim,[2] who had investigated the surface films formed by certain of the sterols.

In speculating on the matter of the molecular dimensions and seeking some new formulation that would accord better with the X-ray measurements, Rosenheim and King,[3] at the National Institute for Medical Research, London, took a clue from an important but little-considered observation reported by Diels in 1927.[4] Diels had discovered that the sterols and bile acids can be dehydrogenated by the action of palladium charcoal at a high temperature (*ca.* 500°) or, better, by prolonged heating of the substances with selenium at a more moderate temperature (360°), and he had isolated from some of the resulting mixtures small amounts of three aromatic hydrocarbons. Two of these had not been identified in 1932, but the third substance had been recognized as chrysene. The formation of this hydrocarbon from cholesterol represents the loss of no less than nine carbon atoms, and it seemed by no means unlikely that a deep-seated rearrangement in the ring system also occurs under the rather brutal conditions of the reaction. The Wieland-Windaus conception of the cholane skeleton appeared at the time to be so firmly established that Diels, Wieland, and most other investigators were inclined to the view that chrysene arises as the result of a drastic rearrangement, rather than that the reaction affords any reliable indication of the nature of the original ring system. When the old formulation became subject to serious doubt as the result of the X-ray studies, it occurred to Rosenheim and King that chrysene might be a normal degradation product, and on this basis they constructed an entirely novel cholane formula, which is illustrated for desoxycholic acid. Ring III was moved to the other side of ring II and the two "homeless" carbon atoms were accommodated by enlarging rings II and IV to six-membered rings. The agreement with the X-ray data was now quite satisfactory, as shown by the following comparisons reported by Bernal.[5]

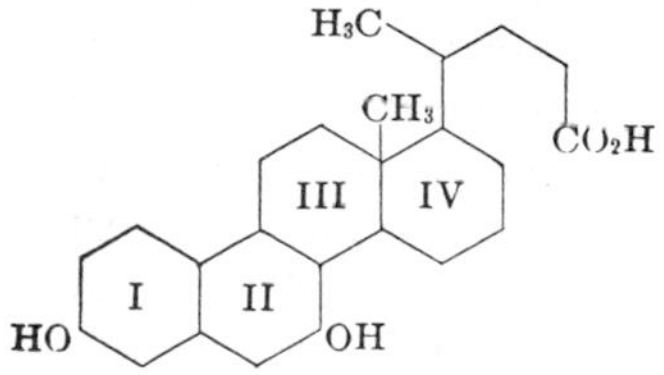

Rosenheim and King (May, 1932) 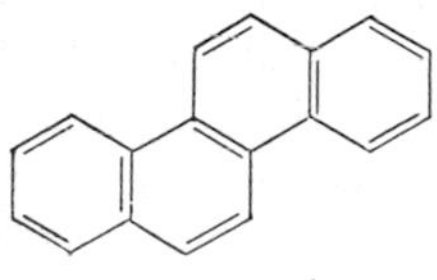   Chrysene

[2] Adam and Rosenheim, *Proc. Roy. Soc.* (*London*), **A126**, 25 (1929).

[3] Rosenheim and King, *Chemistry and Industry,* **51**, 464 (1932).

[4] Diels and Gädke, *Ber.*, **60**, 140 (1927); Diels, Gädke and Körding, *Ann.*, **459**, 1 (1927).

[5] Bernal, *Chemistry and Industry*, **51**, 466 (1932).

Ergosterol dimensions $\begin{cases} \text{Found:} \\ \text{Wieland-Windaus formula:} \\ \text{Rosenheim and King formula:} \end{cases}$ $\begin{matrix} 7.2 \times 5 \times 17\text{--}20 \text{ Å} \\ 8.5 \times 7 \times 18 \text{ Å} \\ 7.5 \times 4.5 \times 20 \text{ Å} \end{matrix}$

In an investigation completed two months after the appearance of Rosenheim and King's paper, Wieland and Dane[6] made an observation that revealed for the first time the uncertainty in the determination of the size of a ring by the Blanc method. It already was known[7] that lithobilianic acid, in which ring A has been opened, yields a ketone on pyrolysis and that an isomeric acid, formed by oxidization of 12-hydroxycholanic acid and thus cleavage of ring C, gives an anhydride, in conformity with the then accepted view that rings A and C contain six and five atoms, respectively. On investigating the third isomer, called thilobilianic acid (transposition of "litho") to indicate the relationship to the litho compounds, Wieland and Dane were surprised to find that the pyrolysis product is an anhydride.

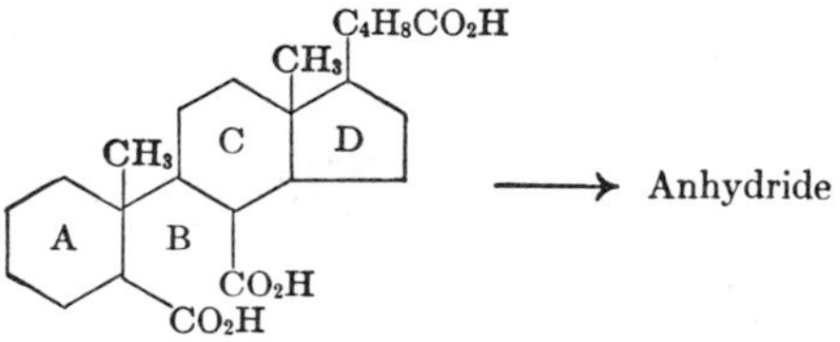

Thilobilianic acid   ⟶ Anhydride

According to the Blanc rule this would imply that ring B is a five-membered ring, but convincing evidence was already on record characterizing this as a six ring, in particular that furnished by Borsche's work on cilianic acid. Indeed the evidence regarding ring B from the behavior of thilobilianic acid is directly contradictory to that furnished by the pyrolysis of solannelic acid, for an anhydride is formed in one case and a ketonic ring is produced in the other. It is evident that the Blanc rule is not always a reliable guide, and from the information now available it appears that although the rule is probably valid for open-chain acids and most other acids, it is not applicable to compounds such as thilobilianic acid (or allothilobilianic acid) in which the carbon chain linking the two carboxyl groups also connects two ring systems. It appears that acids of this type can yield either anhydrides or ketones according to special, and as yet unrecognized, features of their structures. In contrast with thilobilianic acid and "isolithobilianic" acid, which easily form anhydrides, Vocke[8] found that two stereoisomeric perhydrodiphenic acids show little tendency to form anhydrides on pyrolysis

[6] Wieland and Dane, *Z. physiol. Chem.*, **210**, 268 (1932).

[7] Wieland and Weyland, *Z. physiol. Chem.*, **110**, 123 (1920).

[8] Vocke, *Ann.*, **508**, 1 (1934).

but very slowly lose carbon dioxide and are converted into ketones. That the Blanc rule failed to give accurate information regarding ring B destroyed all the previous evidence that C is a five-membered ring, for this was derived from the behavior of acids of the same type as thilobilianic acid. The observation, on the other hand, did not of necessity invalidate the previous characterization of rings A and D. Although the chrysene structure of Rosenheim and King represented an important advance, it was in some respects contradicted by reliable evidence and required modification. It failed to show the connection known to exist between rings I(A) and III(B), but this was easily remedied by transposing these two rings (shown for desoxycholic acid).[6, 9] Wieland and Dane also preferred to

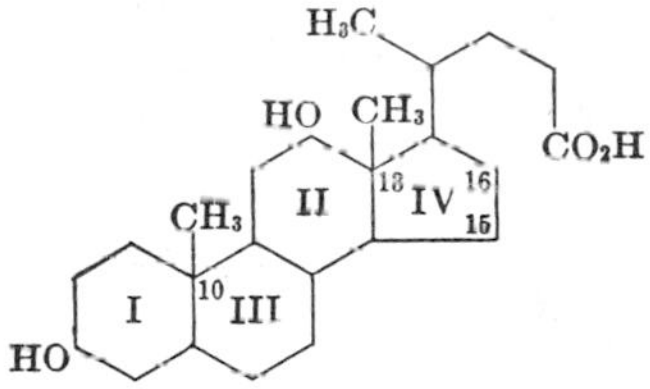

Wieland and Dane (September, 1932)
Rosenheim and King (August, November, 1932)

retain the cyclopentane structure for ring IV and to include a tertiarily bound methyl group between I and III. The formation of chrysene in the dehydrogenation might result from pyrolytic rupture of ring IV and closure of a new six-ring by inclusion of the angular methyl group at C_{13}.

The development of the modified formula was followed by active inquiry from different quarters into the validity of the new assumptions. Particular attention was concentrated on the identification of the aromatic hydrocarbons obtainable from various sterols and bile acids by the method of Diels. Complementary data obtained by oxidations will be discussed first.

Positions of the Methyl Groups. If the ring system is assumed to be that of perhydrocyclopentenophenanthrene, only a limited number of positions are available as possible locations for the two methyl groups. The various oxidations exclude the positions adjacent to those occupied by the three hydroxyl groups of cholic acid and also positions 15 and 16. This leaves only C_1 and the carbon atoms shared in common by two rings. Position 1 was eliminated by the work of Tschesche[1] at Göttingen on a keto acid that Windaus[2] had prepared from cholestenone. Cholesterol is a

[9] Rosenheim and King, *Nature*, **130**, 315 (1932); *Chemistry and Industry*, **51**, 954 (1932).

[1] Tschesche, *Ann.*, **498**, 185 (1933).

[2] Windaus, *Ber.*, **39**, 2008 (1906).

β,γ-unsaturated alcohol and cholestenone (I) is an α,β-unsaturated ketone. The latter structure was established by Menschick, Page and Bossert[3] from a study of the absorption spectrum; the double bond moves into a position of conjugation in the course of the dehydrogenation. The conversion of the unsaturated ketone into Windaus' keto acid (II) by oxidation with either sodium hypobromite or ozone was interpreted by Dane as follows:

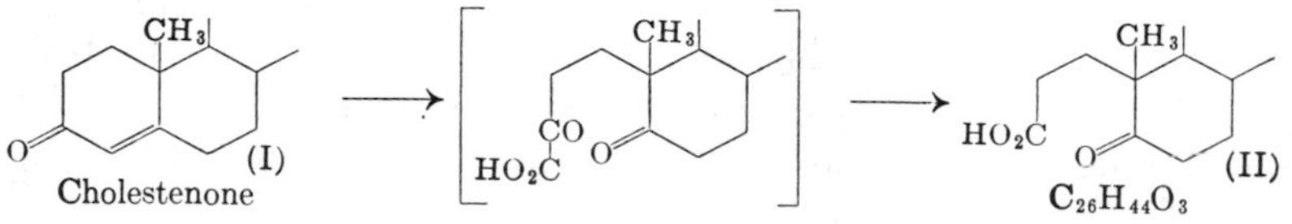

Tschesche reduced the keto acid by the Clemmensen method and subjected the product (III) to stepwise Grignard degradation. The ester of III gave

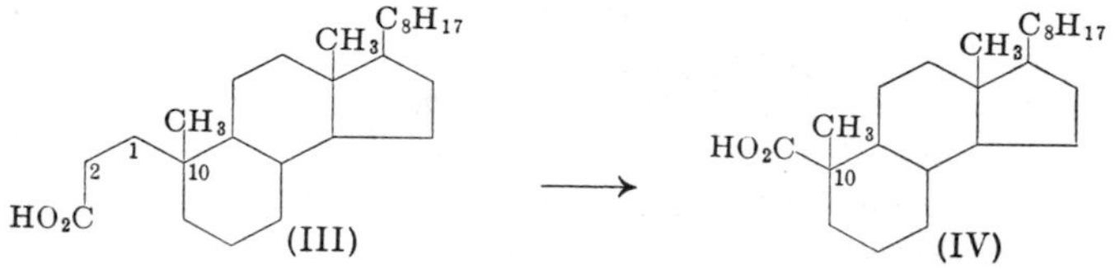

with phenyl Grignard reagent an unsaturated hydrocarbon, and this on oxidation with ozone yielded the nor-derivative of III. This established the presence of a methylene group at the original C_2-position, and a repetition of the degradation indicated a similar group at C_1 and gave the bisnor-acid IV. The methyl group obviously cannot be at C_1 and evidence for the location at C_{10} was found in the observation that the acid IV, like other tertiary carboxylic acids and unlike substances such as III, is esterified with considerable difficulty and loses carbon monoxide readily when warmed with concentrated sulfuric acid.

The location of a methyl group at the 10-position accords with an earlier observation of Wieland and Vocke,[4] who isolated α-methylglutaric-α-

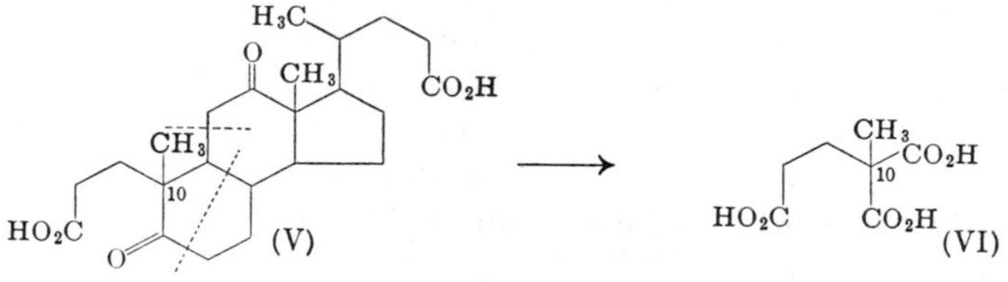

---

[3] Menschick, Page and Bossert, *Ann.*, **495**, 225 (1932).
[4] Wieland and Vocke, *Z. physiol. Chem.*, **177**, 68 (1928).

carboxylic acid (VI) as one of the oxidation products of the keto acid V $(C_{23}H_{34}O_6)$ from pyrodesoxybilianic acid.

That the second methyl group is not situated at either of the bridge heads C_8 or C_9 is shown by Wieland's degradation of 12-ketocholanic acid (VII).[5] Bromination at C_{11} and hydrolysis gave the 11-hydroxy-12-keto

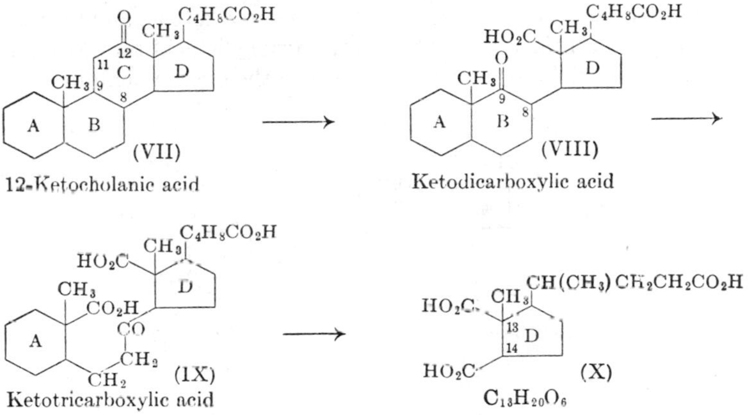

(VII)
12-Ketocholanic acid

(VIII)
Ketodicarboxylic acid

(IX)
Ketotricarboxylic acid

(X)
$C_{13}H_{20}O_6$

acid, and on oxidation this yielded the ketodicarboxylic acid, VIII. On bromination at C_8, followed again by hydrolysis and oxidation, ring B was opened at a hitherto inaccessible point with the formation of the acid IX, in which the original rings A and D are connected by remnants of the other rings originally present. This demonstrates the relationship between rings B and C and shows that the second methyl group must be associated with D, the only ring remaining.

Further oxidation of the ketotricarboxylic acid (IX) gave the tricarboxylic acid (X), which already had been obtained by the degradation of pyrodesoxybilianic acid. The observation[4] that one of the three carboxyl groups of this acid can be esterified with diazomethane but not by the Fischer method is evidence that it is attached to a quaternary carbon atom, and this locates the methyl group at either C_{13} or C_{14}. A more specific but involved argument presented by Wieland and Dane[6] from the stereochemical properties of the acid and its precursors places the methyl group at C_{13}, but a clearer decision between these two possibilities was achieved by the method of dehydrogenation, which also provided evidence of the position of attachment of the bile acid side chain. These points will be

[5] Wieland and Posternak, *Z. physiol. Chem.*, **197**, 17 (1931); Wieland and Dane, *ibid.*, **216**, 91 (1933).

[6] Wieland and Dane, *Z. physiol. Chem.*, **216**, 91 (1933). See also Laucht, *ibid.*, **237**, 236 (1935).

discussed below.   In the work cited Wieland and Dane made the observa̧-
tion that the acid X forms an anhydride only as the result of a rearrangement (to the cis acid), and consequently that the linkage between the
original rings C and D is trans.

Structure of Cholesterol. The relationship between the different rings
of the bile acids and the sterols was established by the stepwise degradation
of lithocholic acid (I) by oxidation, pyrolysis to a ketone, and ring cleavage[1]
to a product, III, identical with a tetracarboxylic acid that Windaus[2] had
obtained from cholesterol by the cleavage of the oxygen-containing ring (A)

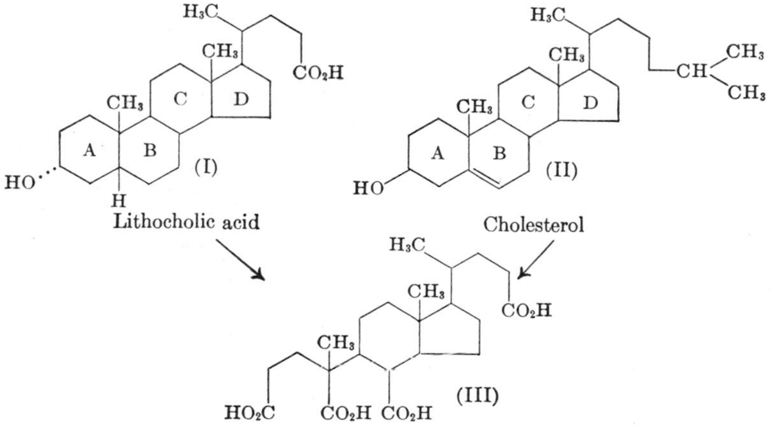

(I) Lithocholic acid

(II) Cholesterol

(III)

$C_{22}H_{34}O_8$

with hypobromite, followed by the opening of the ring (B) containing the
ethylenic linkage.   The identity of the products correlates these rings with
rings A and B of the bile acids.

A correlation of the sterols and bile acids with respect to the position of
the oxygen function in ring A presented the difficulty that the saturated
compounds differ in the configuration of the ring system.   Windaus' work
on hyodesoxycholic acid[3] from hog bile established the nature of the stereoisomerism and provided a means of passing from one series to the other.
Hyodesoxycholic acid (IV) was shown to be a 3,6-dihydroxycholanic acid
of the normal series.   The diketo acid (V) obtained on careful oxidation
also belongs to the normal series, but the substance readily rearranges on
treatment with acids or bases to a more stable stereoisomeride of the allo
series.   The change is due to an inversion at the asymmetric center (C_5)

---

[1] Wieland, Dane and Scholz, *Z. physiol. Chem.*, **211**, 261 (1932).   A further demonstration of the point was made by Stange, *ibid.*, **220**, 34 (1933).

[2] Windaus, *Ber.*, **42**, 3770 (1909).

[3] Windaus, *Ann.*, **447**, 233 (1926).

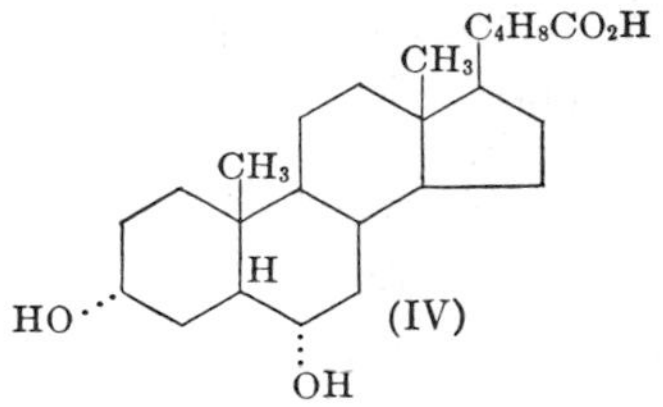

Hyodesoxycholic acid (IV)

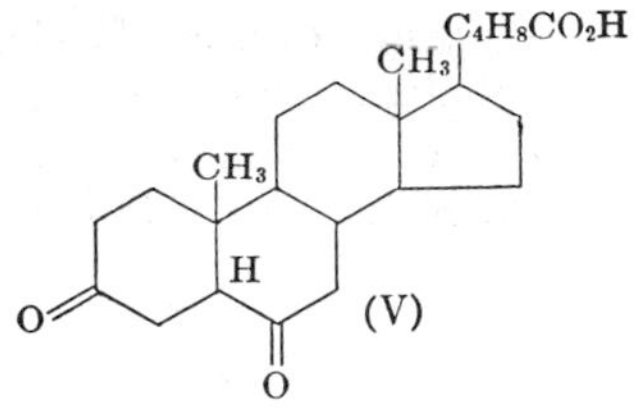

Dehydrohyodesoxycholic acid (V)

adjacent to the C_6-carbonyl group, for keto acids lacking this feature of structure show no tendency to isomerize. By selection of reactions and conditions, Windaus was able to convert hyodesoxycholic acid into derivatives of both the normal and the allo series, and from the behavior of these substances he was able to show that the cholanic acid compounds have the configuration in rings A and B of cis decalin whereas the allo compounds are of the trans type, as might be expected from the greater stability of dehydrohyodesoxyallocholic acid, as compared with the isomer. The proof is as follows. Since lithobilianic acid (VI) and allolithobilianic acid (VIII) both yield the same keto acid (VII) on pyrolysis, one or the other of these acids must suffer a rearrangement in the process through an inversion at the position (C_5) adjacent to the carboxyl group. The pyroacid VII must have the more easily formed cis configuration, and the desoxoacid (XI) obtained on reduction can be regarded as a cis compound. Isolithobilianic acid (IX) and its allo stereoisomeride (Staden's acid) are not of the type susceptible to partial racemization (no α-C*), and they yield stereoisomeric pyroacids in which the original configurations are retained. The pyroacid from isolithobilianic acid (IX) was found to give the cis desoxyacid (XI) on reduction, and, since the lithobilianic acids are of the normal cholanic acid series, cholanic acid is a cis compound. Allocholanic acid and dihydrocholesterol are of the trans decalin type.

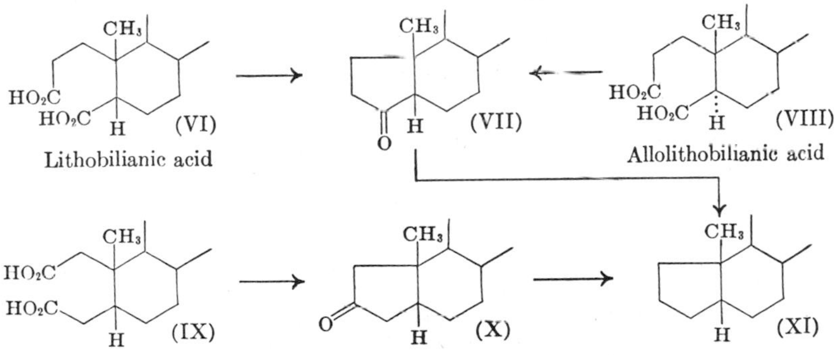

Lithobilianic acid (VI) (VII) Allolithobilianic acid (VIII)

Isolithobilianic acid (IX) (X) (XI)

After these discoveries, Wieland and Dane[4] were able to correlate a 3-hydroxycholanic acid with cholesterol as follows. Hyodesoxycholic acid was converted by partial oxidation into 3-hydroxy-6-ketocholanic acid (XII). On reduction by the Wolff-Kishner method this suffered partial

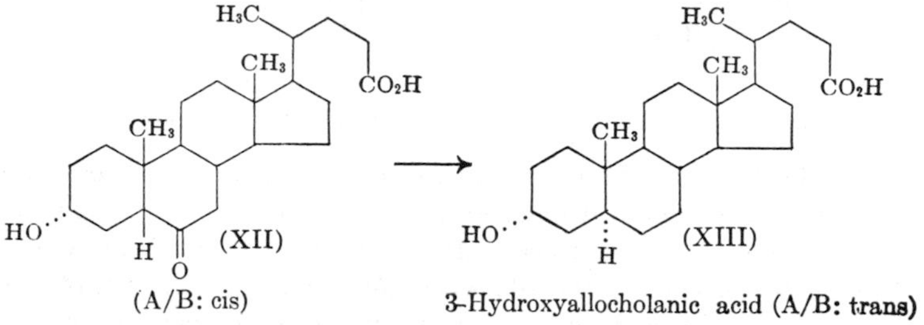

(A/B: cis)   3-Hydroxyallocholanic acid (A/B: trans)

allomerization, and 3-hydroxyallocholanic acid (XIII) was isolated from the reaction mixture. The substance is isomeric with lithocholic acid, and it was found to be identical with a substance obtained previously by Windaus[5] from cholesterol by protecting the hydroxyl group, saturating the double bond, and shortening the side chain by oxidation, as follows: cholesterol → cholesteryl chloride → cholestanyl chloride → 3-chloroallocholanic acid → 3-hydroxyallocholanic acid. The identity of the products proved that the hydroxyl group of cholesterol occupies the characteristic 3-position.

To complete the evidence it is necessary to show that the double bond of cholesterol is in the β,γ-position with respect to the hydroxyl group rather than in the α,β-position, as in the case of cholestenone. Evidence is found in the following series of transformations, starting with cholesterol (XIV). This substance can be converted into a triol (XVI) through the oxide (XV).[6]

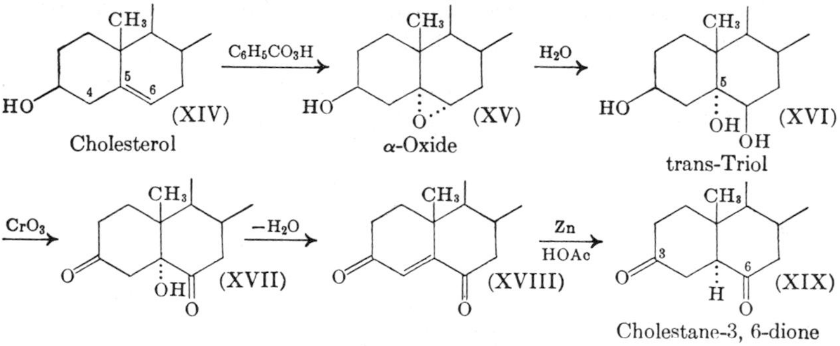

Cholesterol α-Oxide   trans-Triol

Cholestane-3, 6-dione

---

[4] Wieland and Dane, *Z. physiol. Chem.*, **212**, 41 (1932).

[5] Windaus and Hossfeld, *Z. physiol. Chem.*, **145**, 177 (1925).

[6] Westphalen, *Ber.*, **48**, 1064 (1915); see Oxides, below.

Oxidation of the triol (XVI) attacks only two of the alcoholic groups, and hence the remaining group is in a tertiary location, as at C_5. This hydroxyl is easily eliminated from the dione-ol (XVII) and the unsaturated linkage of XVIII can be reduced chemically to give the saturated diketone (XIX). This substance does not have the properties of a 1,2- or 1,3-diketone and hence the second carbonyl group must be in ring B at position 6. The reaction of the cholestanedione with hydrazine to form a pyridazine derivative[7] was formerly regarded as evidence of the 3,6-dione grouping, but Noller[8] has shown that the substance is not a simple ring compound but is polymeric.

Dehydrogenation. Although the method of dehydrogenation with selenium discovered by Diels eventually became a valuable tool for the investigation of various natural products, several complications were initially encountered in the interpretation of evidence from this source. The dehydrogenation of a steroid usually gives a difficultly separable mixture of several higher aromatic hydrocarbons, and the nature of the mixture can vary with the temperature of the reaction. Diels[1] had reported the formation of chrysene (and two unidentified hydrocarbons) in the selenium dehydrogenation of cholic acid at 360°, and the identification was confirmed by others.[2] Ruzicka[3] initially was unable to detect chrysene in mixtures obtained under supposedly identical conditions, but later[4] traced the failure to a difference in temperature. On dehydrogenating cholic acid or cholatrienic acid at 420° he obtained both chrysene and picene, but reported that at 360° the presence of chrysene may be obscured by the formation of

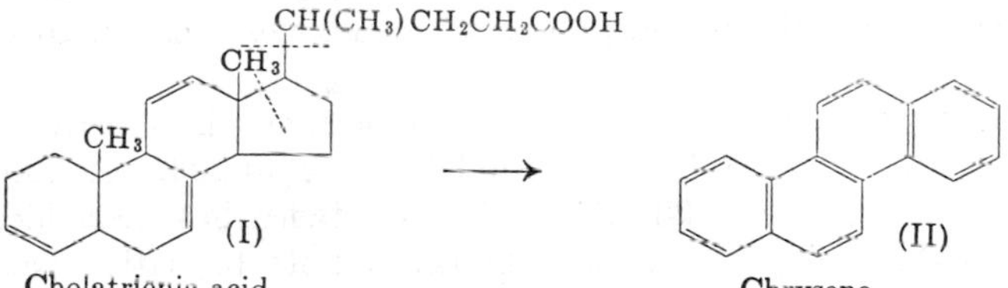

CH(CH₃) CH₂CH₂COOH

$$\text{CH(CH}_3\text{) CH}_2\text{CH}_2\text{COOH}$$

(I)
Cholatrienic acid

(II)
Chrysene

[7] Windaus, *Ber.*, **39**, 2256 (1906); Fernholz, *Ann.*, **508**, 215 (1934); Windaus, Inhoffen and v. Reichel, *ibid.*, **510**, 254 (1934).

[8] Noller, *J. Am. Chem. Soc.*, **61**, 2976 (1939).

[1] Diels, Gädke and Körding, *Ann.*, **459**, 1 (1927); Diels and Karstens, *ibid.*, **478**, 129 (1930); Diels, *Ber.*, **66**, 487, 1122 (1933).

[2] Raudnitz, Petrů and Stadler, *Ber.*, **66**, 879 (1933); Cook and Hewett, *J. Chem. Soc.*, 1098 (1933).

[3] Ruzicka and Thomann, *Helv. Chim. Acta*, **16**, 216 (1933); Ruzicka, Goldberg and Thomann, *ibid.*, **16**, 812 (1933).

[4] Ruzicka, Thomann, Brandenberger, Furter and Goldberg, *Helv. Chim. Acta*, **17**, 200 (1934).

another hydrocarbon (m.p. 276°) that is not stable at the higher temperature. The formation of chrysene appears to result from severance of the bond holding the side chain, rupture of ring D, and incorporation of the angular methyl group at C_{13} into a new six-membered ring (see I → II). Picene (III) may result from a similar enlargement of ring D, closure of a new five-membered ring, and rearrangement of the methylcyclopenteno ring to an aromatic six ring.

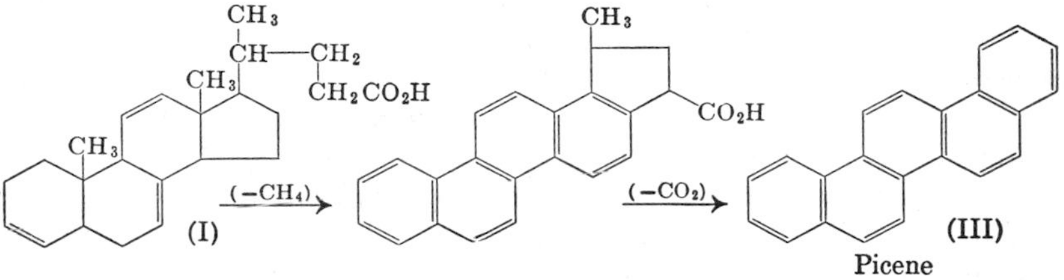

Picene

Ruzicka and Peyer[5] found that aromatization of an alkylated five ring often occurs when alkylhydrindenes are heated with selenium or with palladium charcoal at 450°. They found that indenes when similarly treated at 350° are partly destroyed and partly converted into hydrindenes. Nenitzescu and Cioranescu[6] isolated small amounts of naphthalene on passing 1-methylhydrindene or its hexahydride over palladium charcoal at only 310–350°. A hydrogenating and isomerizing action of selenium was observed by Dorée and Petrow,[7] who found that at 230° cholesterol is converted in part into cholestanone, and in smaller amounts into cholestanol and cholestenone. Model compounds having cyclohexane rings containing obstructing tertiarily bound groups are sometimes resistant to aromatization by selenium at 360°.[8]

Diels Hydrocarbon. Of particular importance is a dehydrogenation product isolated by Diels, Gädke and Körding[1] in 1927: the Diels hydrocarbon, $C_{18}H_{16}$, m.p. 126–127°. The substance has been identified as 3'-methyl-1,2-cyclopentenophenanthrene, and its formation from cholesterol is interpreted as involving the migration of the C_{13}-methyl group to the position vacated in the pyrolytic cleavage of the branched side chain. Cook and Hewett[9] suggested that the methyl migration is a Wagner-Meerwein type rearrangement that is concomitant with the elimination of

[5] Ruzicka and Peyer, *Helv. Chim. Acta*, **18**, 676 (1935).

[6] Nenitzescu and Cioranescu, *Ber.*, **69**, 1040 (1936).

[7] Dorée and Petrow, *J. Chem. Soc.*, 1391 (1935). See also Yokoyama and Kotake, *Bull. Chem. Soc. Japan*, **10**, 138 (1935).

[8] Clemo and Dickenson, *J. Chem. Soc.*, 735 (1935); 255 (1937).

[9] Cohen, Cook and Hewett, *J. Chem. Soc.*, 445 (1935). See also E. Bergmann, *Chemistry and Industry*, **54**, 175 (1935).

the side chain. An experiment by E. Bergmann and F. Bergmann[10] indicates that methyl migration is not dependent upon the process of dehydrogenation: the pyrolysis of cholesteryl chloride at 300° gave a C_8-fraction

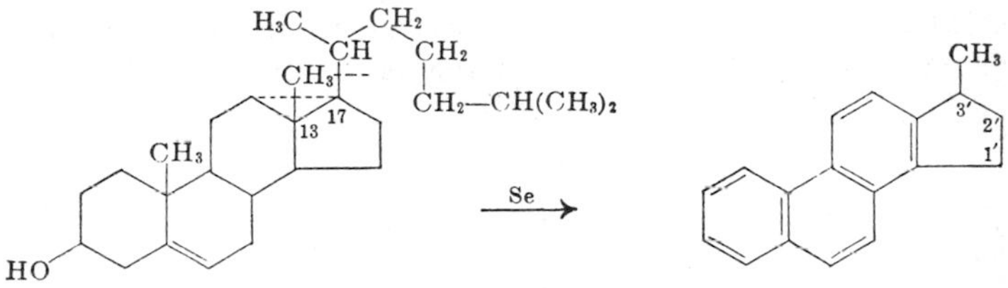

Cholesterol   Diels Hydrocarbon

consisting largely of octane and a monounsaturated hydrocarbon $C_{19}H_{30}$ that probably has the methyl group at C_{17}. The Bergmanns interpret the reaction as involving cleavage of the side chain as octane with production of a C_{17}-diradical that undergoes retropinacol rearrangement with the appearance of methyl at C_{17} and a double bond at C_{13}–C_{17}. Kon and Woolman[11] isolated both 7-methyl- and 3',7-dimethyl-1,2-cyclopentenophenanthrene as products of the selenium dehydrogenation of 3-methylcholestene; the formation of the first hydrocarbon, which has no methyl group at the position corresponding to C_{17}, demonstrates that the elimination of the side chain is not invariably accompanied by methyl migration. In terms of the Bergmann postulate, this means that the diradical can stabilize itself either by rearrangement or by the acquisition of hydrogen.

The structure of the Diels hydrocarbon was not easily established. Diels initially interpreted analyses of the hydrocarbon and of a characteristic nitroso derivative ($C_{18}H_{13}O_2N$, m.p. 239°) in terms of the formula $C_{18}H_{16}$, which ultimately was established as correct. Diels and Karstens[1] obtained the same hydrocarbon from ergosterol, and Ruzicka[3] from cholic acid; Ruzicka pointed out that the analyses do not distinguish between $C_{18}H_{16}$ and $C_{17}H_{14}$. From a study of the absorption spectrum Rosenheim and King[12] (1933) tentatively suggested the structure that eventually was found to be correct, but the data would apply to 1,2-cyclopentenophenanthrene just as well as to the 3'-methyl derivative. Since new methods for the synthesis of phenanthrene derivatives had just been developed in the investigation of degradation products of the resin acids, experiments were initiated in several laboratories to settle the structure of the Diels hydrocarbon by synthesis. Ruzicka soon reported the synthesis of 1,2-cyclo-

[10] E. Bergmann and F. Bergmann, *Chemistry and Industry*, **55**, 272 (1936); *J. Chem. Soc.*, 1019 (1939).

[11] Kon and Woolman, *J. Chem. Soc.*, 794 (1939).

[12] Rosenheim and King, *Chemistry and Industry*, **52**, 299 (1933).

pentenophenanthrene and its 1'- and 2'-methyl derivatives by the method of Bardhan and Sengupta[13], and Kon[14] synthesized the first hydrocarbon by the same method. β-(1-Naphthyl)-ethyl bromide condensed fairly well (65% yield) with ethyl cyclopentanone-2-carboxylate to give the β-keto ester I, but the decarboxylation of this substance proceeded so poorly that the ketone III was best obtained by way of the dibasic acid II. Kon did

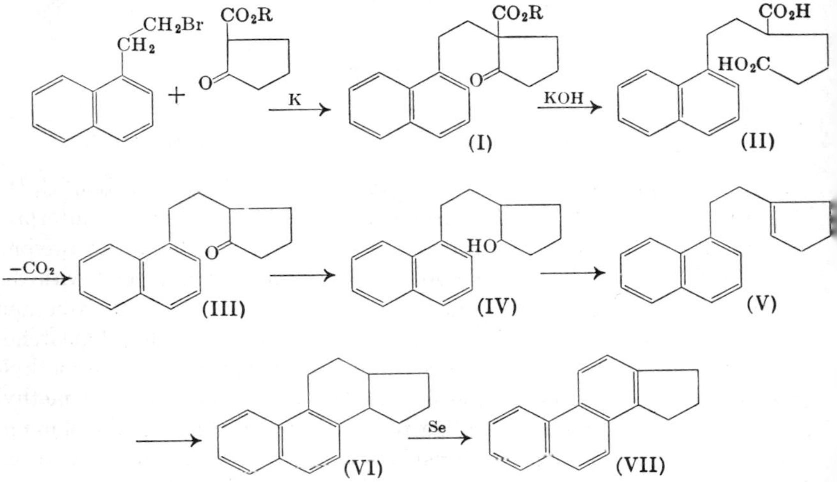

(I)   (II)

(III)   (IV)   (V)

(VI)   Se→   (VII)

not isolate the unsaturated hydrocarbon V, but heated the carbinol IV with phosphorus pentoxide and obtained VI directly; treatment with selenium gave the desired hydrocarbon VII. Ruzicka found that the keto ester I is converted directly into the final hydrocarbon VII on being heated with strong sulfuric acid.

Cook and Hewett[15] synthesized 1,2-cyclopentenophenanthrene by the Bogert-Cook method starting with the condensation of β-(1-naphthyl)-ethylmagnesium chloride with cyclopentanone. The unsaturated hydrocarbon V is an intermediate in both syntheses, for it can be obtained by the controlled dehydration of both the carbinols IV and VIII. In the prepara-

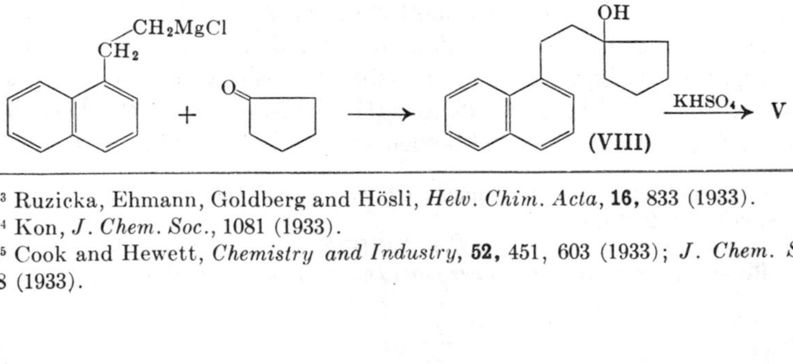

(VIII)

[13] Ruzicka, Ehmann, Goldberg and Hösli, *Helv. Chim. Acta*, **16**, 833 (1933).
[14] Kon, *J. Chem. Soc.*, 1081 (1933).
[15] Cook and Hewett, *Chemistry and Industry*, **52**, 451, 603 (1933); *J. Chem. Soc.*, 1098 (1933).

tion of 1,2-cyclopentenophenanthrene (VII), Cook and Hewett found the isolation of intermediate hydrocarbons unnecessary, for when the carbinol VIII is heated with a mixture of sulfuric and acetic acids it yields the aromatic hydrocarbon VII directly; dehydration and cyclization are followed by dehydrogenation at the expense of the sulfuric acid.

The cyclization of the unsaturated hydrocarbon V with aluminum chloride or stannic chloride was studied more extensively by Cook and Hewett in a later investigation,[16] and they were able to establish the nature of two by-products that accompany the hydrocarbon VI. In addition to the normal intramolecular condensation between positions C_2 and $C_{2'}$, condensation also appears to take place between positions C_1 and $C_{2'}$, which leads to the spiran IX, and between C_1 and $C_{8'}$, with the formation of X. On

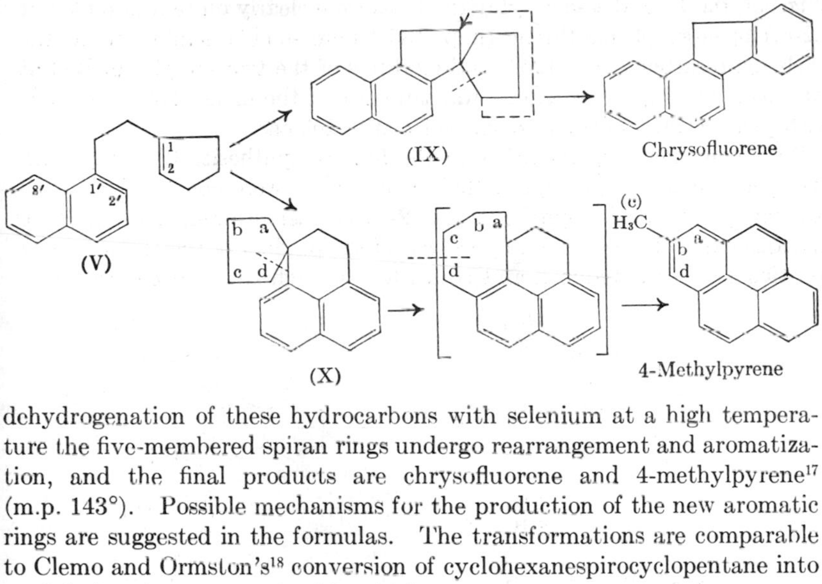

(IX)

Chrysofluorene

(V)

(X)

4-Methylpyrene

dehydrogenation of these hydrocarbons with selenium at a high temperature the five-membered spiran rings undergo rearrangement and aromatization, and the final products are chrysofluorene and 4-methylpyrene[17] (m.p. 143°). Possible mechanisms for the production of the new aromatic rings are suggested in the formulas. The transformations are comparable to Clemo and Ormston's[18] conversion of cyclohexanespirocyclopentane into naphthalene by treatment with selenium.

The formation of spirans materially diminishes the yield of the desired product, but later work showed that the tendency to form spirans is greatly diminished if a methyl group is introduced on the second carbon atom (C_2) of the ethylenic linkage. In the synthesis of chrysene,[19] for example, the

[16] Cook and Hewett, *J. Chem. Soc.*, 365 (1934). See also A. Cohen, Cook and Hewett, *ibid.*, 1633 (1935).

[17] Identified by the synthesis of Vollmann, Becker, Corell and Streeck, *Ann.*, **531**, 1 (1937); a companion substance was shown to be 3-methylpyrene, m.p. 71°.

[18] Clemo and Ormston, *J. Chem. Soc.*, 352 (1933).

[19] Cook and co-workers, *J. Chem. Soc.*, 653, 1727 (1934); 667 (1935).

unsaturated hydrocarbon XI yields chiefly spirans on cyclization, but the methyl derivative XII is converted in good yield into methyloctahydro-

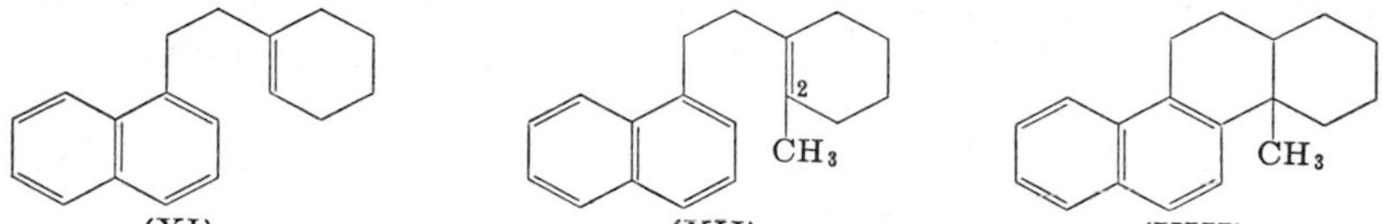

(XI)   (XII)   (XIII)

chrysene (XIII), from which chrysene can be obtained by dehydrogenation with selenium (but not with platinum black).

Opinions at first differed about the relationship of the Diels hydrocarbon to the synthetic preparations. Of the three hydrocarbons synthesized by Ruzicka, the 1'- and 2'-methyl derivatives were clearly quite different, but 1,2-cyclopentenophenanthrene (m.p. 135°) bore some resemblance to the Diels hydrocarbon (m.p. 125°) and mixtures of the two samples melted at intermediate temperatures; this was true also of the molecular compounds with picric acid, trinitrobenzene, and trinitrotoluene.

Bergmann and Hillemann[20] were the first to synthesize 3'-methyl-1,2-cyclopentenophenanthrene, but their comparisons were not decisive. The starting point for the synthesis was 2-acetylphenanthrene (XIV). The unsaturated acid obtained on hydrolysis of the product of the Reformatsky reaction (XV) was reduced and converted through the acid chloride into

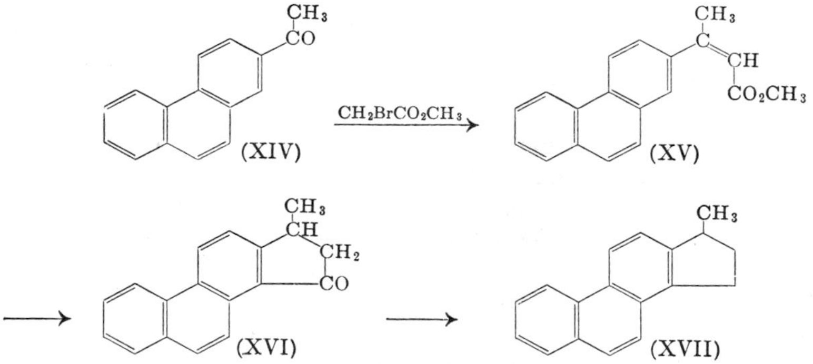

the cyclic ketone, from which the final product (XVII) was obtained by the Clemmensen method. Another synthesis of 3'-methyl-1,2-cyclopentenophenanthrene was carried out in 1934 by Harper, Kon and F. C. J. Ruzicka[21] by the Bogert-Cook method. The carbinol (XVIII) from β-(1-

---

[20] E. Bergmann and Hillemann, *Ber.*, **66**, 1302 (1933).

[21] Harper, Kon and F. C. J. Ruzicka, *J. Chem. Soc.*, 124 (1934). Kon and Narracott, *ibid.*, 672 (1938) later found that carbinol XVIII undergoes cyclization without

naphthyl)-ethylmagnesium bromide and 2-methylcyclopentanone proved to be of no value for the purpose at hand because the double bond introduced on dehydration appeared at the 1,2- rather than the 1,5-position,

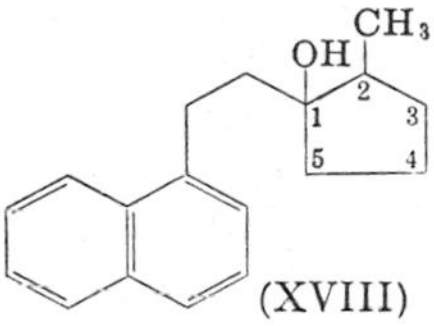

CH_3
OH
(XVIII)

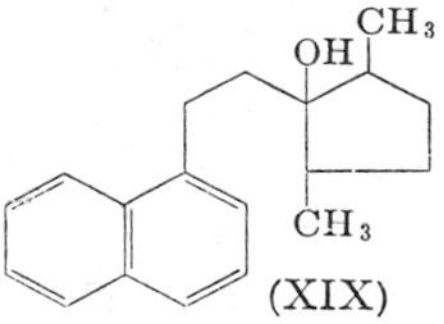

CH_3
OH
CH_3
(XIX)

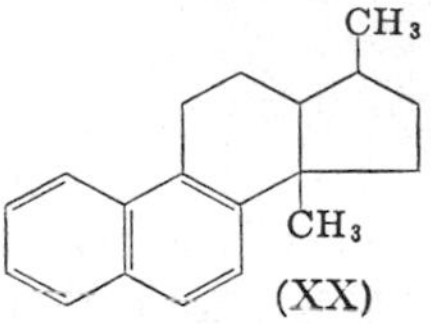

CH_3
CH_3
(XX)

and the methyl group at C_1 in the hydrophenanthrene was eliminated in the final dehydrogenation. 2,5-Dimethylcyclopentanone was then employed as the starting material and the carbinol XIX subjected to cyclodehydration (with phosphorus pentoxide at 140°); the hydrocarbon XX was obtained in good yield, and on treatment with selenium the tertiarily bound methyl group was eliminated and 3'-methyl-1,2-cyclopentenophenanthrene was isolated in a pure condition (m.p. 125 – 126°) by crystallization of the trinitrobenzene derivative. The melting point was identical with that of a sample of the Diels hydrocarbon and there was no depression in the melting points of mixtures. However, mixed melting point determinations cannot be relied upon in this series of compounds. No depression was noted by the above investigators with mixtures of 1,2-cyclopentenophenanthrene and its 3'-methyl derivative, and a similar observation has been reported by Jacobs and Fleck[22] for mixtures of the Diels hydrocarbon with a substance having the composition of a dimethylphenanthrene. Bernal made X-ray and crystallographic comparisons of the substances prepared by various investigators and expressed the opinion[23] that the Diels hydrocarbon is identical with the samples of 3'-methyl-1,2-cyclopentenophenanthrene prepared by Bergmann and Hillemann and by Harper, Kon, and F. C. J. Ruzicka, but not with the unmethylated hydrocarbon.

The chemical characterization of the Diels hydrocarbon presented more difficulties than anticipated. All attempts to oxidize the hydrocarbon to the phenanthrenequinone have been unsuccessful, probably because the first point of attack is in the five-membered ring. Butenandt[24] found that 1,2-cyclopentenophenanthrene is oxidized by chromic acid to a ketone

---

rearrangement to give the C_1-methylhydrophenanthrene whereas the isomeric carbinol in which the positions of the methyl and hydroxyl groups are reversed undergoes retropinacol rearrangement on cyclodehydration and yields the identical C_1-methylhydrophenanthrene.

[22] Jacobs and Fleck, *J. Biol. Chem.*, **97**, 59 (1932).

[23] See Bernal and Crowfoot, *J. Chem. Soc.*, 93 (1935).

[24] Butenandt, Dannenberg and von Dresler, *Z. Naturforsch.*, **1**, 222 (1946).

corresponding in melting point to synthetic 1'-keto-1,2-cyclopenteno-phenanthrene,[25] but succeeded in preparing 1,2-cyclopenteno-9,10-phenanthrenequinone (m.p. 213°) by hydroxylation of the 9,10-double bond with osmium tetroxide in pyridine-benzene and oxidation of the glycol (CrO_3). In his original paper of 1927 Diels had recommended identification of the "sterol-$C_{18}H_{16}$" by conversion to the characteristic nitroso compound, and he later noted[26] that a sample of 1,2-cyclopentenophenanthrene from Cook and Hewett did not react similarly with oxides of nitrogen. Synthetic samples of 3'-methyl-1,2-cyclopentenophenanthrene were not tested in this way until Hillemann[27] repeated the earlier synthesis with Bergmann and showed that the synthetic hydrocarbon and "sterol-$C_{18}H_{16}$" had the same melting point and mixed melting point and that both yielded the characteristic nitroso compound. Hillemann also oxidized the synthetic hydrocarbon to prehnitic acid and thereby proved that the cyclopenteno ring is indeed attached at the 1,2-position and carries the methyl substituent. Diels and Rickert[28] discovered another characteristic derivative in a tribromo compound, dec. 235°, and found samples prepared from hydrocarbons derived by dehydrogenation and by synthesis to be identical.[29] The structure of the Diels hydrocarbon is thereby firmly established. Although the yield usually is very low, the isolation of the hydrocarbon is reliable evidence of the presence of the characteristic steroid ring system.

Companion Hydrocarbons. The formula of the hydrocarbon m.p. 276° isolated by Ruzicka[4] as one product of the low-temperature dehydrogenation of cholic acid was revised from $C_{21}H_{16}$ to $C_{22}H_{16}$ on the basis of spectrographic[30] and X-ray crystallographic[23] evidence. The substance was then identified by synthesis (Bogert-Cook method) as 5-methyl-2',1'-naphtho-1,2-fluorene[31] (II). A new six ring is closed between the terminal carbon

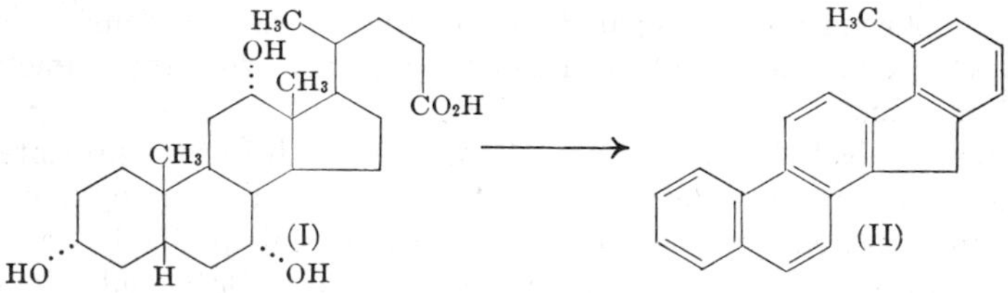

Cholic acid $C_{22}H_{16}$, m.p. 276°

[25] Bachmann, *J. Am. Chem. Soc.*, **57**, 1381 (1935).

[26] Diels and Klare, *Ber.*, **67**, 113 (1934).

[27] Hillemann, *Ber.*, **68**, 102 (1935); **69**, 2610 (1936).

[28] Diels and Rickert, *Ber.*, **68**, 267, 325 (1935).

[29] Confirmed by Gamble, Kon and Saunders, *J. Chem. Soc.*, 644 (1935).

[30] Cook, Dansi, Hewett, Iball, Mayneord and Roe, *J. Chem. Soc.*, 1319 (1935).

[31] Bachmann, Cook, Hewett and Iball, *J. Chem. Soc.*, 54 (1936).

of the bile acid side chain and position 16, and both angular methyl groups are eliminated.

A **second Diels hydrocarbon** (m.p. 225 – 226°) from cholesterol or cholesteryl chloride, originally regarded as $C_{25}H_{24}$, has not yet been conclusively identified. Diels[1] had found that the hydrocarbon yields a ketone (m.p. 194°) on oxidation, and Cook[32] noted that the formulas $C_{25}H_{22}$ and $C_{26}H_{24}$ corresponding to an alkylated naphthofluorene are admissible. Rosenheim and King[12] had speculated that the substance may arise through the transformation I → II, but Cook[33] synthesized the methylisopropylnaphthofluorene II and found it different from the second Diels hydrocarbon. A

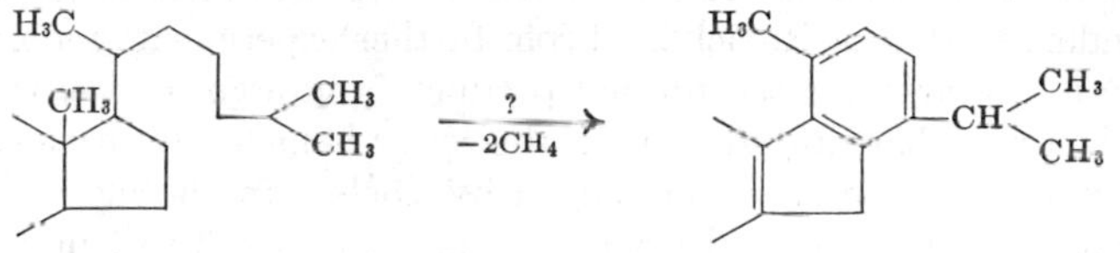

Cholesterol (I) $C_{25}H_{22}$ (II)

close correspondence in the absorption spectra, however, demonstrates that the dehydrogenation product is a 2′,1′-naphtho-1,2-fluorene.[33]

E. Bergmann[34] has advanced a plausible interpretation of the structures of this and related hydrocarbons based upon the assumption that the angular methyl group at C_{13} becomes incorporated into a new five ring that replaces the original ring D (III→V), just as this group is incorporated into a new six ring in the formation of chrysene from cholic acid. The structure

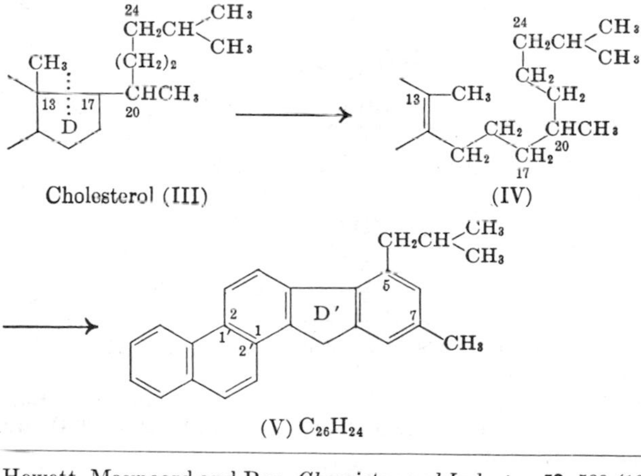

Cholesterol (III)   (IV)

(V) $C_{26}H_{24}$

[32] Cook, Hewett, Mayneord and Roe, *Chemistry and Industry*, **53,** 569 (1934).

[33] Cook, Hewett, Mayneord and Roe, *J. Chem. Soc.*, 1727 (1934).

[34] E. Bergmann, *J. Am. Chem. Soc.*, **60,** 2306 (1938).

V proposed for the second Diels hydrocarbon, 7-methyl-5-isobutyl-2′,1′-naphtho-1,2-fluorene, is consistent with the analysis, spectrum, and molecular weight[23] (327 ±7) deduced from crystallographic dimensions and density. Diels[35] repeatedly affirmed that ergosterol on selenium dehydrogenation yields the same hydrocarbon (m.p. 226°, ketone m.p. 194°) as cholesterol, whereas Ruzicka[36] contended that the hydrocarbon from ergosterol is the next higher homolog (m.p. 215°, ketone m.p. 175°). The apparent difference has now been resolved. In a reinvestigation of the dehydrogenation of ergosterol conducted by careful control of the temperature in boiling acetanilide, Diels[37] confirmed his previous finding of the hydrocarbon (m.p. 226°) but isolated also a second hydrocarbon (m.p. 214°, ketone m.p. 175°) corresponding to that of Ruzicka. From further experiments reported by Ruzicka[38] it appears that the normal product from ergosterol is the 215° hydrocarbon and that degradation to the lower homolog from cholesterol occurred under the conditions employed by Diels. In the light of Bergmann's postulate,[34] the normal product from ergosterol (215°) probably is $C_{27}H_{26}$ and that from a phytosterol mixture[38] (206°, ketone m.p. 204°) is $C_{28}H_{28}$ and the substances are homologs of V substituted at the α-position of the isobutyl group by a methyl or ethyl group, respectively, corresponding to the original substituent at position C_{24} in the sterol side chain.

Hydroxyl Group of Cholesterol. A direct proof that the oxygen atom of cholesterol is at the 3-position was adduced by Kon[39] by dehydrogenation of the methylcarbinol derivative I and identification of the products II and III by synthesis.

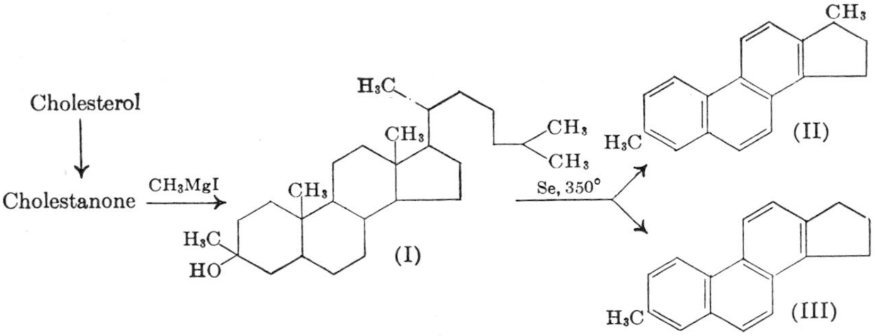

---

[35] Diels and Karstens, *Ann.*, **478**, 129 (1930); Diels, *Ber.*, **66**, 1122 (1933); Diels and Klare, *ibid.*, **67**, 113 (1934).

[36] Ruzicka, Goldberg and Thomann, *Helv. Chim. Acta*, **16**, 812 (1933); Ruzicka, Thomann, Brandenberger, Furter and Goldberg, *ibid.*, **17**, 200 (1934); Ruzicka and Goldberg, *ibid.*, **18**, 434 (1935).

[37] Diels and H. J. Stephan, *Ann.*, **527**, 279 (1937).

[38] Ruzicka and Goldberg, *Helv. Chim. Acta*, **20**, 1245 (1937).

[39] Farmer and Kon, *J. Chem. Soc.*, 414 (1937); Kon and Woolman, *J. Chem. Soc.*, 794 (1939).

Position of the Side Chain. A particularly interesting product is the carcinogenic hydrocarbon methylcholanthrene, which Wieland and Dane[1] obtained as a product of the degradation of desoxycholic acid. 12-Ketocholanic acid, prepared by the partial Clemmensen reduction of dehydrodesoxycholic acid, when heated for several hours at 330° undergoes a Perkin-type intramolecular condensation and decarboxylation and yields the colorless, crystalline hydrocarbon dehydronorcholene.[2] That no molec-

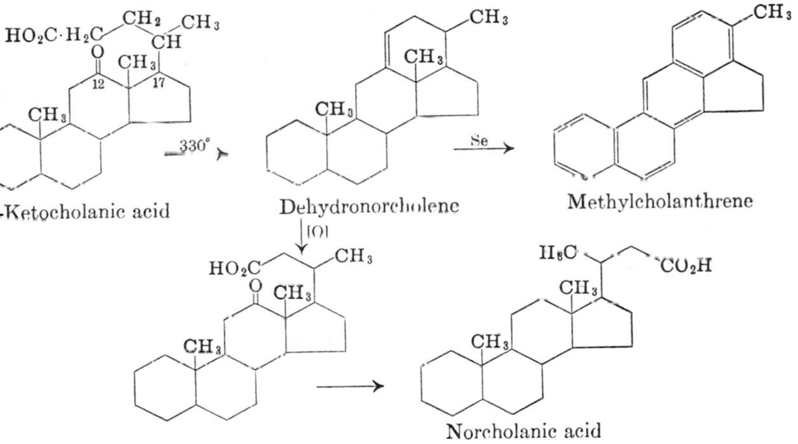

12-Ketocholanic acid   Dehydronorcholene   Methylcholanthrene

Norcholanic acid

ular rearrangement occurs in the course of the pyrolysis was established by the observation that dehydronorcholene can be oxidized to a keto acid[2] that on Wolff-Kishner reduction[3] yields a product identical with norcholanic acid. Wieland and Dane[1] found that the monounsaturated hydrocarbon on selenium dehydrogenation is converted into the yellow aromatic hydrocarbon methylcholanthrene (20-methylcholanthrene, according to a convention that utilizes the sterol numbering system[4]). Kennaway and Cook[5] had seen the possibility of cyclizing the bile acid side chain to a structure closely related to the synthetic carcinogens that they had recently discovered, and Cook and Haslewood[3] independently prepared methylcholanthrene from dehydronorcholene and established the structure by converting the hydrocarbon by oxidation and decarboxylation into a dimethylbenzanthraquinone that was identified by synthesis. The struc-

[1] Wieland and Dane, *Z. physiol. Chem.*, **219**, 240 (1933).

[2] Wieland, Schlichting and Wiedersheim, *Z. physiol. Chem.*, **150**, 273 (1925); Wieland and Wiedersheim, *ibid.*, **186**, 229 (1930).

[3] Cook and Haslewood, *J. Chem. Soc.*, 428 (1934).

[4] Fieser and Seligman, *J. Am. Chem. Soc.*, **57**, 1377 (1935).

[5] Kennaway and Cook, *Chemistry and Industry*, **51**, 521 (1932).

ture was soon confirmed by a synthesis of methylcholanthrene itself;[6] an improved synthesis[7] that constitutes the best practical method for preparation of the hydrocarbon is shown in Chart 10.

Chart 10. METHYLCHOLANTHRENE; STRUCTURE AND SYNTHESIS

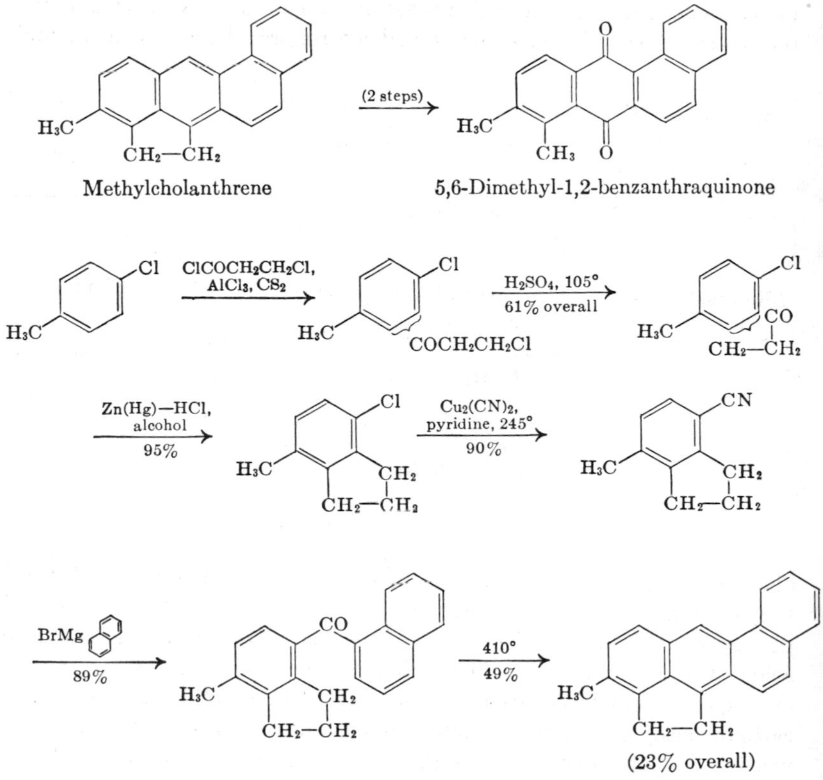

Methylcholanthrene   5,6-Dimethyl-1,2-benzanthraquinone

(23% overall)

The degradation of desoxycholic acid constitutes a proof that the bile acid side chain is attached to ring D at the 17-position, since only such a location would account for the closing at C_{12} of a new ring capable of becoming aromatic.

Methylcholanthrene has been isolated as a degradation product of the more abundant cholic acid through dehydrocholic acid and 3,7-dihydroxy-12-ketocholanic acid, which was pyrolyzed and submitted to selenium

[6] Fieser and Seligman, *J. Am. Chem. Soc.*, **57**, 228, 942 (1935).
[7] Fieser and Seligman, *J. Am. Chem. Soc.*, **58**, 2482 (1936).

dehydrogenation;[8] the overall yield is 5.4 percent, as compared with a yield of 4.3 percent from desoxycholic acid. The hydrocarbon has also been obtained by an anomalous degradation of cholesterol:[9] a product of the condensation of cholestanone with phenylhydrazine of the formula $C_{33}H_{49}N$ affords methylcholanthrene in about 1 percent yield on selenium dehydrogenation.

Methylcholanthrene was indeed found capable of initiating malignant growth in test animals,[3] and it is now recognized as probably the most potent known carcinogen in overall activity in the production of tumors of various types. If the hydrocarbon can be produced in the laboratory by chemical transformations of normal constituents of the human organism, it is possible that the substance may arise in the body through a process of abnormal metabolism and initiate cancer. The degradations of desoxycholic acid, cholic acid, and cholesterol all involve low-yield pyrolytic reactions and have not been effected under anything approaching physiological conditions, and careful processing of cancerous tissues and urines has failed to establish the presence of methylcholanthrene. There is thus no evidence that this or other hydrocarbon carcinogen plays any role in the etiology of human cancer. On the other hand, present evidence does not exclude such a possibility. A very minute amount of methylcholanthrene could produce a few malignant cells, which by cell-division and without further stimulation from the initiating agent could lead to a palpable cancerous proliferation after an induction period during which the initiating agent may have been eliminated from the system.

STRUCTURES OF STIGMASTEROL AND ERGOSTEROL

Stigmasterol. This sterol, first isolated from the phytosterol mixture of the Calabar bean[1] (*Physostigma venenosum*), is best obtained from soybean oil. The amount present is small, but stigmasterol can be separated easily from the sterol mixture as the sparingly soluble acetate tetrabromide. The empirical formula[2] ($C_{29}H_{48}O$) indicated that the sterol contains two carbon atoms more than cholesterol, and the isolation of ethylisopropylacetaldehyde,[3] $(CH_3)_2CHCH(C_2H_5)CHO$, as a product of ozonization established the presence of an ethyl group at C_{24} and a double bond at C_{22}–C_{23}. A relationship to cholesterol was first proved in a further investigation at Göttingen that was later of importance in the work on steroid hormones.

---

[8] Fieser and Newman, *J. Am. Chem. Soc.*, **57**, 961 (1935).

[9] Rossner, *Z. physiol. Chem.*, **249**, 267 (1937).

[1] Windaus and Hauth, *Ber.*, **39**, 4378 (1906).

[2] Sandqvist and Gorton, *Ber.*, **63**, 1935 (1930); Windaus, v. Werder and Gschaider, *ibid.*, **65**, 1006 (1932).

[3] Guiteras, *Z. physiol. Chem.*, **214**, 89 (1933).

Fernholz[4] found that the nuclear double bond is more reactive than the one in the side chain and that the sterol acetate (I) reacts with one mole of bromine to give the 5,6-dibromide (II). Ozonization of II and dehalo-

Chart 11. STIGMASTEROL; STRUCTURE OF THE SIDE CHAIN

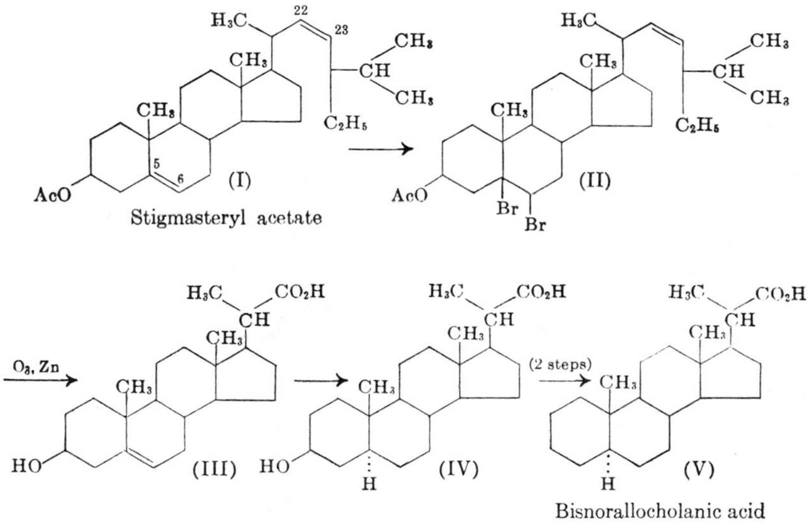

Stigmasteryl acetate

Bisnorallocholanic acid

genation with zinc gave an unsaturated acid (III) that was converted by hydrogenation, oxidation to the saturated keto acid, and Clemmensen reduction into a substance identical with a sample of bisnorallocholanic acid (V) prepared by Barbier-Wieland degradation of allocholanic acid.

The position of the hydroxyl group was established as follows.[5] Stigmasterol was hydrogenated and the stanol acetate (VI) was oxidized with chromic acid, when a small amount of an acid (VII) was isolated in which the ring system and the acetoxy group are intact but a six-carbon fragment has been eliminated from the side chain. A comparison acid of structure VII was obtained by a similar oxidation of acetyl cholestanol followed by Barbier-Wieland shortening of the side chain. The hydroxyl group thus corresponds to that of cholesterol in both position and orientation (β; precipitated by digitonin). The position of the nuclear double bond was inferred[6] from the conversion of stigmasterol through the oxide acetate and

[4] Fernholz, *Ann.*, **507**, 128 (1933).

[5] Fernholz and P. N. Chakravorty, *Ber.*, **67**, 2021 (1934).

[6] Fernholz, *Ann.*, **508**, 215 (1934).

Chart 12. STIGMASTEROL; POSITION OF THE HYDROXYL GROUP

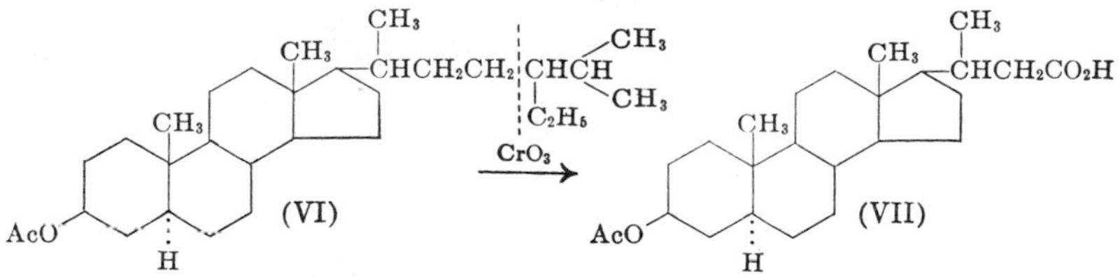

(VI)
Acetyl stigmastanol

(VII)
Acetyl 3β-hydroxynorallocholanic acid

Grignard degradation

Acetyl cholestanol
(VIII)

Acetyl 3β-hydroxyallocholanic acid
(IX)

triol into a 3,6-diketone analogous to that in the cholesterol series. Further evidence is the relationship of stigmasterol to stigmastenone;[7,8] it is of interest that reduction of stigmastenone with sodium and amyl alcohol does not affect the double bond in the side chain and yields 5,6-dihydrostigmasterol.[7]

Ergosterol. This sterol, which was investigated particularly extensively because of its relationship to the vitamin D problem, was first isolated from ergot and is now prepared in considerable quantity from yeast. After establishment of the empirical formula $C_{28}H_{44}O$ by Windaus[1] in 1932, rapid progress in the characterization of ergosterol was made by various workers at the Göttingen laboratory. The isolation of methylisopropylacetaldehyde as a product of ozonization[2,3] (Chart 13) was evidence of the presence of a double bond at C_{22}–C_{23} and a methyl group at C_{24}. Oxidation of the parent saturated hydrocarbon ergostane to norallocholanic acid[4] correlated the ring system and the first four carbon atoms of the side chain with cholesterol. The isolation[5] of an acid oxidation product from acetyl ergostanol identical with that obtained directly from stigmastanol and indirectly

[7] Marker and Wittle, *J. Am. Chem. Soc.*, **59**, 2704 (1937).

[8] Marker and Rohrmann, *J. Am. Chem. Soc.*, **60**, 1073 (1938).

[1] Windaus and Lüttringhaus, *Nachr. Ges. Wiss., Göttingen*, 4 (1932).

[2] Reindel and Kipphan, *Ann.*, **493**, 181 (1932).

[3] Guiteras, *Ann.*, **494**, 116 (1932).

[4] Chuang, *Ann.*, **500**, 270 (1933).

[5] Fernholz and P. N. Chakravorty, *Ber.*, **67**, 2021 (1934).

from cholesterol proved that the hydroxyl group is at C_3 and has the β-orientation. The location of the two nuclear double bonds presented initial difficulties. A suggestion that they may both be contained in the same ring was afforded

Chart 13. DEGRADATION OF ERGOSTEROL

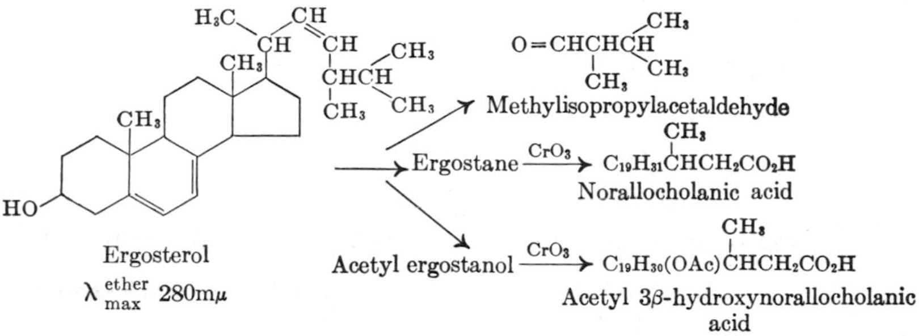

by the observation that ergosterol on oxidation with nitric acid yields an aromatic acid[6] (compare the oxidation of abietic acid to trimellitic acid). The reaction is abnormal, however, for the oxidation product is a methyl-benzenetetracarboxylic acid evidently formed in a reaction involving a methyl migration.

That one of the nuclear double bonds is at the "cholesterol" position C_5-C_6 was established by Windaus, Inhoffen, and v. Reichel.[7] Ergosterol reacts with perbenzoic acid, apparently by addition to one of three double bonds, to give the monobenzoate of a triol, I; this on hydrolysis yields ergostadienetriol-II,[8] so called to distinguish it from an isomer to be described below (the configurations are not certain). Since the triol forms a diacetyl derivative, one of the new hydroxyl groups is secondary and the other is tertiary. The remaining ethylenic linkage of the ring system can be saturated by hydrogenation of the diacetate[9] and the substance converted into the saturated triol III. This compound closely parallels cholestane-3,5,6-triol in its reactions,[7] for it yields in succession a dione-ol (IV), an ergostenedione (V), and an ergostadione (VI) that reacts with hydrazine in the same way that cholestane-3,6-dione does. The reaction with perbenzoic acid therefore consists in an addition to a double bond at C_5-C_6. Additional evidence of this location of one double bond was pre-

[6] Inhoffen, Ann., 494, 122 (1932); see also Reindel and Niederländer, ibid., 482, 264 (1930).
[7] Windaus, Inhoffen and v. Reichel, Ann., 510, 248 (1934).
[8] Windaus and Lüttringhaus, Ann., 481, 127 (1930).
[9] Heilbron, Morrison and J. C. E. Simpson, J. Chem. Soc., 302 (1933).

Chart 14. ERGOSTEROL; NUCLEAR DOUBLE BONDS AND THE HYDROXYL GROUP

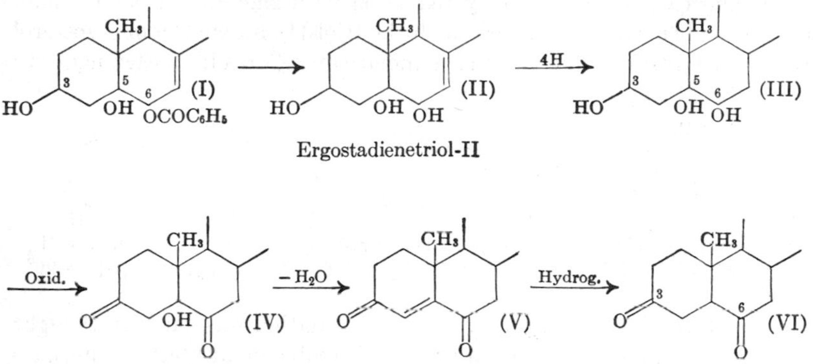

Ergostadienetriol-II

sented in a further study by Heilbron.[10]   An interesting reaction observed by Burawoy[11] is the oxidation of ergosterol with chromic acid to an ergostadiene-3,6-dione-5-ol identical with that obtained[9,10] by oxidation of ergostadienetriol-II (or of the triol-I, see below).

Windaus inferred that the second nuclear double bond is likewise in ring B and conjugated with the first one, namely at C_7–C_8. The absorption maximum at 281 mμ (log ϵ 4.0)[12] and the fact that ergosterol can be reduced with sodium and amyl alcohol[13] bear evidence to the presence of two conjugated double bonds in the same ring.   Further evidence is that ergosterol reacts with maleic anhydride at a moderate temperature (135°) to give an addition product[14] from which ergosterol can be regenerated almost quantitatively and in a pure state by heating the adduct in vacuum at 250°.[16] Degradation studies[15,16] of the addition product support the interpretation of the reaction as a 1,4-addition to a diene system extending from C_5 to C_8.

Ergosterol Peroxide and Dehydroergosterol.   When an alcoholic solution of ergosterol is aerated and exposed to visible light in the presence of a sensitizing dye such as eosin, the sterol is converted into a crystalline peroxide;[1] the peroxide has been isolated from the mycelium of the mold

[10] Dunn, Heilbron, Phipers, Samant and Spring, *J. Chem. Soc.*, 1576 (1934).
[11] Burawoy, *J. Chem. Soc.*, 409 (1937).
[12] Heilbron, R. A. Morton and Sexton, *J. Chem. Soc.*, 47 (1928), observed secondary peaks at 270 and 293.5 mμ.
[13] Windaus and Brunken, *Ann.*, **460**, 225 (1928).
[14] Windaus and Lüttringhaus, *Ber.*, **64**, 850 (1931).
[15] Inhoffen, *Ann.*, **508**, 81 (1934).
[16] Windaus and Inhoffen, *Ann.*, **510**, 260 (1934); Inhoffen, *Ber.*, **68**, 973 (1935).
[1] Windaus and Brunken, *Ann.*, **460**, 225 (1928).

Aspergillus fumigatus.[2] Ergosterol peroxide is sensitive to acids but not to alkalis, and can be converted by reduction with zinc and alcoholic alkali into ergostadienetriol-I,[3] isomeric with the triol-II obtained from ergosterol oxide. The triol-I, which forms a monoacetate,[4] readily rearranges[4] to

Ergosterol peroxide m.p. 178°, $[\alpha]_D - 36°$	Ergostadienetriol-I m.p. 227°, $[\alpha]_D - 13°$	Ergostadienetriol-II m.p. 242°, $[\alpha]_D + 29°$

triol-II, which gives a diacetate. The peroxidation was initially thought to involve the addition of oxygen to the 5,6-double bond,[5] but an alternate interpretation was suggested in the first edition of this book. Ergosterol peroxide differs from known 1,2-peroxides[6] in being stable to alkaline reagents, and it has more the character of a transannular peroxide formed by a 1,4-addition to the diene system. This formulation accords with the fact that the triol-I formed on reduction has but one acylable hydroxyl group. The conversion into the more stable triol-II, which forms a diacetate, is interpreted as an allylic rearrangement. The transannular formulation has been substantiated by the work of W. Bergmann, who presented convincing evidence that certain cholestadienes add oxygen under similar conditions to form comparable transannular peroxides (see below).

Ergostadienetriol-I on distillation loses two molecules of water, corresponding to the two tertiary hydroxyl groups, and gives the tetraunsaturated substance dehydroergosterol,[7] also obtained by oxidation of ergosterol acetate with mercuric acetate (43% yield[8]). Ergostadienetriol-II is more stable and can be distilled unchanged, but it can be converted into dehydroergosterol by pyrolysis of the monobenzoate or the diacetate.[4] The absorption spectrum of dehydroergosterol is indicative of the presence of a conjugated triene system, and Müller[5] suggested a formula differing from that of ergosterol only in the presence of an additional conjugated double

[2] P. Wieland and Prelog, *Helv. Chim. Acta*, **30**, 1028 (1937). Ergosterol itself is the sole sterol isolated from three molds of the family Fusarium: Fiore, *Arch. Biochem.*, **16**, 161 (1948).

[3] Windaus and Linsert, *Ann.*, **465**, 148 (1928); Windaus, W. Bergmann and Lüttringhaus, *ibid.*, **472**, 195 (1929).

[4] Achtermann, *Z. physiol. Chem.*, **217**, 281 (1933).

[5] M. Müller, *Z. physiol. Chem.*, **231**, 75 (1935).

[6] Kohler, *Am. Chem. J.*, **36**, 177 (1906).

[7] Windaus and Linsert, *Ann.*, **465**, 148 (1928).

[8] W. Bergmann and Stevens, *J. Org. Chem.*, **13**, 10 (1948).

bond in ring C. The formula accounts for the formation of a peroxide that shows no absorption above 230 mμ, and evidence for the presence of a diene system extending from C_5 to C_8 is furnished by Honigmann's observation[9]

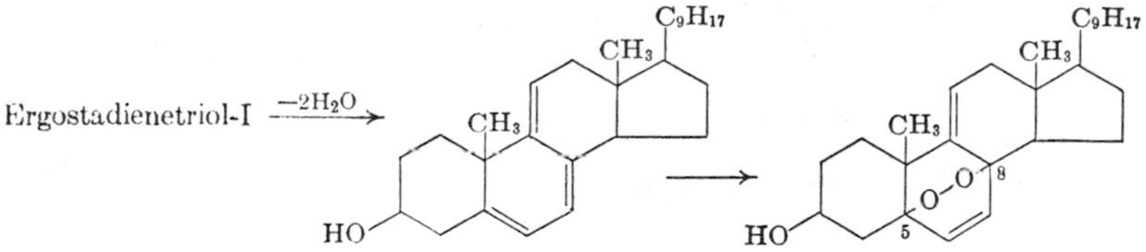

Ergostadienetriol-I $\xrightarrow{-2H_2O}$

Dehydroergosterol
m.p. 146°, $[\alpha]_D + 149°$,
λ_{max}^{ether} 320 mμ

Dehydroergosterol
peroxide
m.p. 155°

that the maleic anhydride addition products from ergosterol and from dehydroergosterol are converted into identical substances on absorption of two and three moles of hydrogen, respectively. The driving force in the formation of dehydroergosterol by the reactions of dehydration and dehydrogenation indicated seems attributable to the tendency to form a system of extended conjugation.

Neoergosterol. Whereas ergosterol forms a peroxide when an alcoholic solution containing eosin is exposed to visible light in the presence of oxygen, an entirely different reaction occurs in the absence of oxygen.[1] The sterol undergoes dehydrogenation, with decoloration of the dye, and affords a sparingly soluble substance originally called "ergopinacol" but better designated[2] bisergostadienol (Chart 15).

$$3C_{28}H_{44}O \xrightarrow[40\%]{} C_{56}H_{86}O_2 + H_2$$

The structure shown in formula I was advanced by Inhoffen[3] and is supported by evidence summarized and extended by Windaus.[4] When bisergostadienol is distilled at reduced pressure or heated with acetic anhydride at 170°, methane is liberated and neoergosterol (II) can be isolated from the reaction mixture in 30 percent yield. The bonds severed in the pyrolysis — that extending to the angular methyl group at C_{10} and the $C_7 - C_7'$ linkage — are both under the activating influence of at least two double bonds. Neoergosterol (II) gives no sterol color reactions and contains only one

[9] Honigmann, *Ann.*, **508**, 89 (1934).
[1] Windaus and Borgeaud, *Ann.*, **460**, 235 (1928); Windaus and Linsert, *ibid.*, **465**, 148 (1928); Inhoffen, *ibid.*, **497**, 130 (1932).
[2] Jacobsen and Nawrocki, *J. Am. Chem. Soc.*, **62**, 2612 (1940), proposed biergostadienol.
[3] Inhoffen, *Naturwissenschaften*, **25**, 125 (1937).
[4] Windaus and Roosen-Runge, *Ber.*, **73**, 321 (1940).

reactive double bond;[5] this was shown to be at $C_{22} - C_{23}$ in the side chain by the isolation of methylisopropylacetaldehyde as a product of ozonization (Inhoffen[1]).   That the three additional (inert) double bonds indicated by

Chart 15. BISERGOSTADIENOL

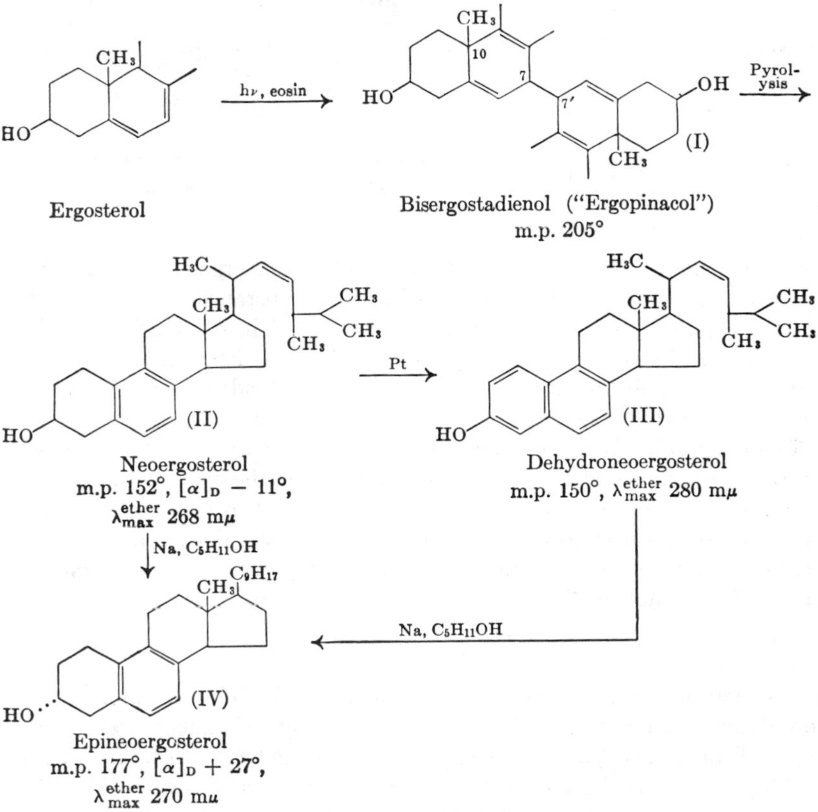

Ergosterol

Bisergostadienol ("Ergopinacol")
m.p. 205°

Neoergosterol
m.p. 152°, $[\alpha]_D - 11°$,
λ_{max}^{ether} 268 mμ

Dehydroneoergosterol
m.p. 150°, λ_{max}^{ether} 280 mμ

Epineoergosterol
m.p. 177°, $[\alpha]_D + 27°$,
λ_{max}^{ether} 270 mμ

the analysis are present in a benzenoid ring was inferred from the absorption spectrum and from the fact that neoergosterol yields prehnitic acid (1,2,3,4-) on oxidation with nitric acid (Inhoffen[1]).   Prehnitic acid could arise as a fragment from ring B or C, but the latter possibility was eliminated by the observation[6] that neoergosterol can be dehydrogenated smoothly and without elimination of methane into a substance (III) having the properties of a naphthol derivative, dehydroneoergosterol ("tetra-

[5] Bonstedt, *Z. physiol. Chem.*, **185,** 165 (1929).
[6] Honigmann, *Ann.*, **511,** 292 (1934).

dehydroneoergosterol"). Windaus[7] found that when dehydroneoergosterol is treated with sodium and amyl alcohol ring A is reduced and the C_3-hydroxyl group is epimerized. The product, epineoergosterol (IV), can also be obtained directly from neoergosterol.

VITAMIN D

Rickets, a disease of infancy or early childhood characterized by faulty ossification due to defective deposit of calcium phosphate at the growing ends of the bones, has long been known to respond favorably to treatment either with sunlight or with cod liver oil and other fish oils added to the diet. Studies of experimental rickets in rats led to the recognition that the disease is due primarily to a nutritional deficiency, and the remedial quality of cod liver oil was traced to the presence of a fat-soluble principle now known as vitamin D. The antirachitic properties were at first incorrectly attributed to vitamin A, which also concentrates in the fat-soluble, unsaponifiable fraction of cod liver oil. The special activity of the fraction is retained, however, after removal of vitamin A, most conveniently by means of its addition product with maleic anhydride.[1] Vitamin D is more closely related in properties to the sterols, although it is not precipitated by digitonin. The alcoholic nature of the substance was demonstrated by Ender,[2] who found that vitamin D reacts readily with phthalic anhydride to form an acid ester. These observations were the basis for the preparation of D-concentrates from tuna liver oil (Ender) and cod liver oil[3] representing a 20,000-fold enrichment, but the preparations were still so crude that inferences drawn regarding the properties of the vitamin were largely erroneous.

A second line of attack was prompted by knowledge of the beneficial effects of exposure to sunlight or ultraviolet light in the treatment of rickets. In 1924 Hess and Steenbock independently discovered that a vitamin deficiency in the diet can be remedied by irradiation of foodstuffs rather than of the patient. In this way inert oils can be endowed with antirachitic activity similar to that naturally possessed by fish liver oils. Since the activated material was found in the unsaponifiable sterol fraction, the provitamin apparently present both in foodstuffs and in the skin and convertible into the vitamin by irradiation must be a sterol. The irradiation of cholesterol was investigated, and some of the early results suggested that this widely occurring substance is the provitamin. However, although

[7] Windaus and Deppe, *Ber.*, **70**, 76 (1937).
[1] Dalmer, v. Werder and Moll, *Z. physiol. Chem.*, **224**, 86 (1934).
[2] Ender, *Z. Vitaminforsch.*, **2**, 241 (1933).
[3] Rygh, *Nature*, **136**, 396 (1935).

some samples of purified cholesterol could be activated by irradiation, the results were irregular, and in 1926 proof was presented from three laboratories that the provitamin is not cholesterol but a persistent companion substance.[4] Cholesterol that is not activatable can be obtained by extensive purification through the dibromide, by treatment with oxidizing agents, or by adsorption of impurities on activated charcoal. The nature of the methods suited to destruction or removal suggested that the provitamin is more reactive than cholesterol, and comparison of the absorption spectra of activatable and nonactivatable cholesterol indicated that the former contained a substance more unsaturated than cholesterol. Ergosterol seemed a likely possibility, and irradiation of this sterol was found to give material of far greater antirachitic potency than that from any of the crude cholesterol samples. Ergosterol also corresponded in chemical properties and in absorption spectrum to the vitamin precursor, and in 1926 it was regarded as very probably identical with the provitamin.[5] Although, nearly a decade later, this inference was proved definitely to be incorrect, the intensive investigations at once initiated on the chemistry of the irradiation products of ergosterol ultimately led to the identification of the true vitamin and provitamin.

Irradiation of Ergosterol. The isolation of the antirachitic irradiation product of ergosterol in a pure form presented unusual difficulties, for under the influence of ultraviolet light the sterol is transformed not into a single substance but into a mixture of several isomers.[1] The first crystalline substances isolated,[2] suprasterol I and II, proved to be physiologically inactive products of over-irradiation. The isolation of crystalline preparations of antirachitic potency was announced in 1930 – 31 in both England[3] and Germany,[4] and the products were called calciferol and vitamin D_1, respectively. In each case the crystallizate was later found to be nonhomogeneous, but the isolation of a completely pure preparation of established high biological potency was reported in October 1931 by the research team at the National Institute for Medical Research in London;[5a] a few weeks

[4] Pohl, *Nachr. Ges. Wiss., Göttingen,* 142 (1926); Heilbron, E. D. Kamm, and R. A. Morton, *Chemistry and Industry,* **45,** 932 (1926); Rosenheim and Webster, *ibid.,* **45,** 932 (1926).
[5] Pohl, *Nachr. Ges. Wiss., Göttingen,* 185 (1926); Windaus and Hess, *ibid.,* 175 (1926); Rosenheim and Webster, *Biochem. J.,* **21,** 389 (1927).
[1] Windaus, *Nachr. Ges. Wiss., Göttingen,* 36 (1930).
[2] Windaus, Gaede, Köser and Stein, *Ann.,* **483,** 17 (1930).
[3] Askew, Bourdillon, Bruce, Jenkins and Webster, *Proc. Roy. Soc. (London),* **B107,** 76 (1930); Angus, Askew, Bourdillon, Bruce, R. K. Callow, Fischmann, Philpot and Webster, *ibid.,* **B108,** 340 (1931).
[4] Windaus, Lüttringhaus and Deppe, *Ann.,* **489,** 252 (1931).
[5] (a) Askew, Bruce, R. K. Callow, Philpot and Webster, *Nature,* **128,** 758 (1931);

earlier the Göttingen group had announced the isolation of the pure vitamin,[6] but they did not at the time have evidence of its high potency. The pure substance was fully described in 1932 by both groups of investigators.[5b,7] The English group retained the name calciferol for the new preparation; Windaus and co-workers named the pure product vitamin D_2. The earlier preparation, vitamin D_1, was found to be a molecular compound of vitamin D_2 and the isomer lumisterol.[8] A fifth isomer, a very sensitive substance known only in the form of derivatives, was called tachysterol[9] (Gr. *tachys*, swift) because of the rapidity with which it forms an addition compound with citraconic anhydride. Four further isomers are produced by thermal treatment alone or followed by irradiation. Of the nine isomeric transformation products derived from ergosterol, only vitamin D_2 (calciferol) possesses antirachitic activity. This substance, or carefully standardized preparations containing it, was soon introduced into medicine and has given valuable service in human therapy.

The properties of the isomeric products of irradiation or pyrolysis are recorded in the accompanying table, which includes results of some of the

TABLE IV. Isomeric Transformation Products of Ergosterol

	M.p.	$[\alpha]_D$	DOUBLE BONDS	RINGS	DEHYDROG. PRODUCTS	OXIDN. TO $CH_3C_6H(CO_2H)_4$	λ_{max}
Ergosterol...	165°	− 130° Chf	3	4	$C_{18}H_{16}$	Positive	280 (ether)
Lumisterol..	118°	+ 191° An	3	4	$C_{18}H_{16}$	Positive	280
Tachysterol.		− 70° Lig	4	3		Negative	280
Vitamin D_2..	116°	+ 33° Lig	4	3	None	Negative	265 (hexane)
Suprasterol I.........	104°	− 76° Chf	3	4	None		None
Suprasterol II........	110°	+ 63° Chf	3	4	None		None
Isopyrocalciferol.....	115°	+ 332° Chf	3	4	$C_{18}H_{16}$	Positive	280
Pyrocalciferol	95°	+ 502° Al	3	4	$C_{18}H_{16}$	Positive	274, 294
Photoisopyrocalciferol	80°	− 60° Chf	3	4		Negative	None
Photopyrocalciferol..	105°	+ 50° Chf	3	4		Negative	None

(b) Askew, Bourdillon, Bruce, R. K. Callow, Philpot and Webster, *Proc. Roy. Soc. (London)*, **B109**, 488 (1932).

[6] Windaus and Linsert, *Ann.*, **489**, 269 (1931); footnote added to proof in September.

[7] Windaus, Linsert, Lüttringhaus and Weidlich, *ibid.*, **492**, 226 (1932).

[8] Windaus, Dithmar and Fernholz, *Ann.*, **493**, 259 (1932).

[9] Windaus, v. Werder and Lüttringhaus, *Ann.*, **499**, 188 (1932).

characterizations. Unlike ergosterol, none of the irradiation products is precipitated by digitonin, and isopyrocalciferol is precipitated only incompletely. The double linkage at $C_{22} - C_{23}$ is not involved in the transformations, for the first five compounds all yield methylisopropylacetaldehyde on ozonization.[10] The degree of unsaturation of the different compounds was established by microhydrogenation experiments or perbenzoic acid titrations. The estimates of the number of rings from the degree of unsaturation and from the analyses were confirmed by the results of dehydrogenation experiments. Lumisterol was found like ergosterol to contain three double bonds and hence four rings, and it afforded the Diels hydrocarbon on dehydrogenation with selenium; the substance is therefore a stereoisomer of ergosterol. Tachysterol and vitamin D_2 contain one double bond more than ergosterol, and hence one of the four original rings must have opened in the course of the photoisomerization; confirmatory evidence is that in repeated dehydrogenation experiments by different investigators neither substance has yielded a crystalline hydrocarbon. Suprasterol I contains a four-ring system, but this evidently is different from that of ergosterol. The two pyro compounds, on the other hand, yield the Diels hydrocarbon and therefore contain the perhydrocyclopentenophenanthrene ring system.

Although the oxidation of ergosterol with nitric acid to a methylbenzene-tetracarboxylic acid involves an unexplained rearrangement, the reaction as applied to the isomers appears to be indicative of an accumulation of double bonds in ring B. The acid was isolated as an oxidation product of those isomers that yielded the Diels hydrocarbon and in which ring B was therefore intact. The observation that lumisterol yields the methylbenzene-tetracarboxylic acid, whereas tachysterol does not, indicated that the change lumisterol → tachysterol involves the opening of ring B.[11,12] Lettré[11] suggested that the key reaction leading to tachysterol and vitamin D_2 consists in rupture of the 9,10-bond.

Structure of Vitamin D_2. The structure of vitamin D_2 (calciferol) was ultimately established in a series of degradations conducted by Windaus[1] and by Heilbron,[2] the main results of which are summarized in Chart 16. That the 9,10-ring linkage is actually severed was established by careful chemical oxidation of D_2 and isolation of an aldehyde $C_{21}H_{34}O$ (IV), characterized as being α,β-unsaturated from the absorption spectrum of the

[10] Guiteras, *Ann.*, **494**, 116 (1932).

[11] Lettré, *Ann.*, **511**, 280 (1934).

[12] M. Müller, *Z. physiol. Chem.*, **233**, 223 (1935).

[1] Windaus and W. Thiele, *Ann.*, **521**, 160 (1936); Windaus and Grundmann, *ibid.*, **524**, 295 (1936).

[2] Heilbron, Samant and Spring, *Nature*, **135**, 1072 (1935); Heilbron and Spring, *Chemistry and Industry*, **54**, 795 (1935); Heilbron, R. N. Jones, Samant and Spring, *J. Chem. Soc.*, 905 (1936).

semicarbazone. Because of the carbon content and the absence of a hydroxyl group, the aldehyde can only arise from the cleavage of a double bond in the original 5,6-position in a structure with ring B open. A ketone $C_{19}H_{32}O$, V, was also isolated. Like the aldehyde, this retains the double bond in the side chain; its isolation confirms the evidence of a double bond

Chart 16. DEGRADATION OF VITAMIN D₂

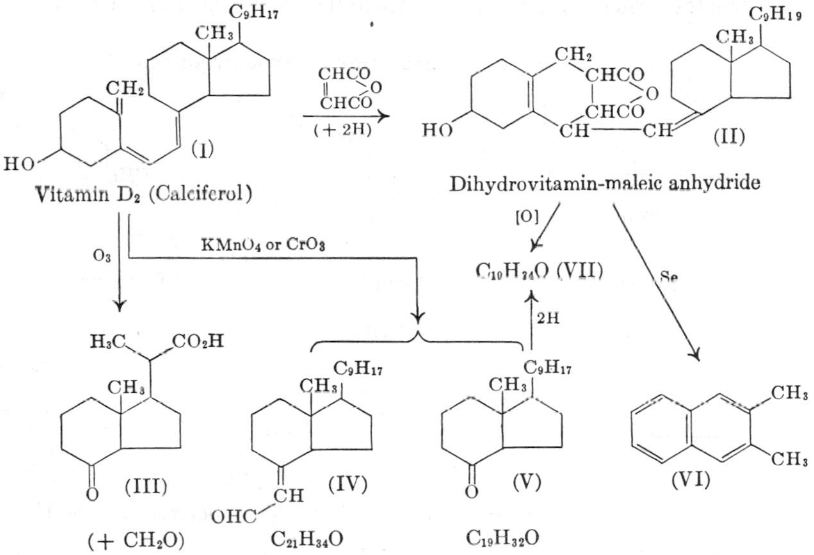

Vitamin D₂ (Calciferol)

Dihydrovitamin-maleic anhydride

(+ CH₂O) $C_{21}H_{34}O$ $C_{19}H_{32}O$

at $C_7 - C_8$. Ozonization of vitamin D₂ gave a keto acid $C_{13}H_{20}O_3$ (III), also derived from rings C and D, and afforded formaldehyde, isolated as the dimedon derivative in 30 percent of the amount calculated for formula I. Permanganate oxidation gave 20 percent of the theoretical amount of formic acid, but since ergosterol under similar conditions gave a few percent of formic acid and a trace of formaldehyde, Windaus regarded the isolation of the other oxidation products as the most secure indication of the structure.

Further evidence resulted from a study of two isomeric (stereoisomeric ?) maleic anhydride addition products of vitamin D₂ and the dihydro derivatives obtained by saturation of the double bond in the side chain. Windaus formulated the addition as occurring to the diene system extending from C_6 to C_{19}, as in II. Ozonization of both dihydro addition products gave a saturated C_{19}-ketone (VII), and an identical product was obtained by the hydrogenation of V. More interesting is the result of selenium dehydrogenation, for the product was identified as 2,3-dimethylnaphthalene (VI).

The reduction of anhydride carbonyl groups to methyl groups appeared surprising, but Thiele and Trautmann[3] found that such a reaction can be realized with simpler hydroaromatic anhydrides or with a mixture of an aromatic anhydride and a hydrogen donor. Thus 2,3-dimethylnaphthalene was produced by heating naphthalene-2,3-dicarboxylic anhydride with selenium and *p*-cyclohexylphenol.

Nature of the D_2 Isomers. The transformations leading to and following the formation of vitamin D_2 are indicated in Chart 17. Under activa-

Chart 17. IRRADIATION OF ERGOSTEROL

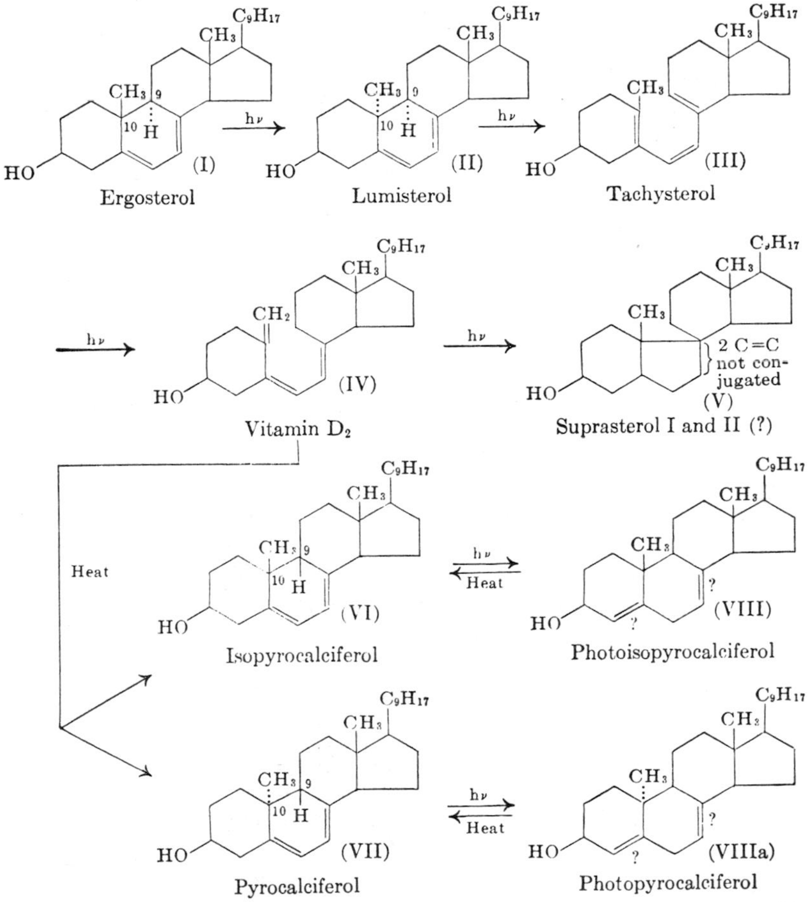

[3] W. Thiele and Trautmann, *Ber.*, **68**, 2245 (1935).

tion by light ergosterol first suffers epimerization at C_{10}, adjacent to one end of the absorbing system, and yields lumisterol (II), in which the angular methyl group is in the inverted position; the failure to precipitate with digitonin can be attributed to this configurational change and not, as once supposed, to epimerization at C_3. The next change is rupture of the C_9 – C_{10} bond, which is under the activating influence of both ends of the absorbing diene system. The resulting triene system in tachysterol (III) then migrates to a new position in vitamin D_2 (IV). Overirradiation results in ring closure in some manner other than reformation of the original tetracyclic system (V). Heat treatment of D_2 does result in closure of the perhydrocyclopentenophenanthrene ring system, but not in the original steric sense. Both pyro compounds, VI and VII, have the β- rather than α-configuration at C_9; the first has the normal β-configuration at C_{10} and the other belongs to the C_{10}-α series. When the pyro compounds are irradiated the bonds migrate out of positions of conjugation to unknown positions; the photoisomerism of isopyrocalciferol is twenty times as fast as that of pyrocalciferol. Heat treatment (190°) reconverts the photo isomers into the original pyro compounds.

The principal evidence on which the formulation is based is as follows. Lumisterol has an absorption spectrum comparable to that of ergosterol and on dehydrogenation with mercuric acetate yields a substance, dehydro lumisterol[1] (X, Chart 18), closely analogous in spectrum[2] to dehydroergosterol but isomeric with this substance. In analogy to ergosterol, lumisterol is convertible through the peroxide into two lumistadienetriols[1,2] that on oxidation afford the same diketone (lumistadiene-3,6-dione-5-ol)[3] isomeric with the product from ergosterol; this points to the presence of a diene system extending from C_5 to C_8 and characterizes lumisterol as a steroisomer of ergosterol inverted at some center other than C_3. A clue to the nature of the isomerism was discovered by Dimroth,[2] who found that dehydrolumisterol yields a perhydro derivative (XI) different from lumistanol (XII), the hydrogenation product of lumisterol. Since in the transformation through the dehydro compound the originally asymmetric center C_9 becomes unsaturated and available for steric inversion, lumistanol and perhydrodehydrolumisterol must be C_9-epimers. Dimroth then discovered that perhydrodehydrolumisterol is identical with the perhydro derivative of pyrocalciferol (XIII), and Windaus and Dimroth[4] found further that pyrocalciferol yields a dehydro derivative identical with dehydrolumisterol

[1] Heilbron, Spring and P. A. Stewart, *J. Chem. Soc.*, 1221 (1935).

[2] K. Dimroth, *Ber.*, **69**, 1123 (1936).

[3] Heilbron, Moffet and Spring, *J. Chem. Soc.*, 411 (1937). See also Heilbron, Kennedy, Spring and Swain, *ibid.*, 869 (1938).

[4] Windaus and K. Dimroth, *Ber.*, **70**, 376 (1937).

Chart 18. CORRELATION OF ISOMERS

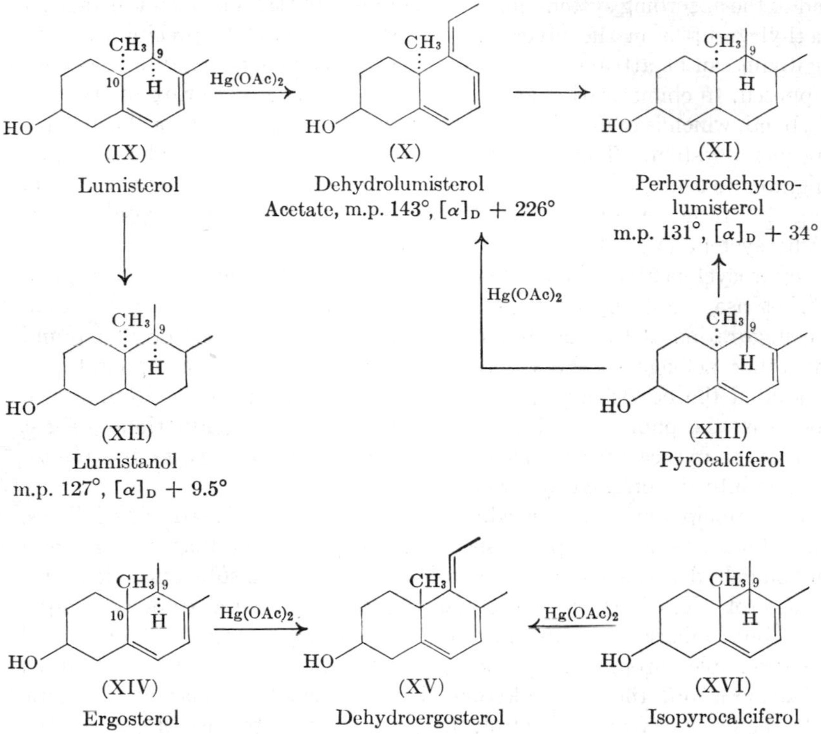

(IX)
Lumisterol

Dehydrolumisterol
Acetate, m.p. 143°, $[\alpha]_D + 226°$
(X)

Perhydrodehydro-
lumisterol
m.p. 131°, $[\alpha]_D + 34°$
(XI)

(XII)
Lumistanol
m.p. 127°, $[\alpha]_D + 9.5°$

Pyrocalciferol
(XIII)

(XIV)
Ergosterol

Dehydroergosterol
(XV)

Isopyrocalciferol
(XVI)

(X). Lumisterol and pyrocalciferol are therefore C_9-epimers, and the configuration at C_{10} must be opposite to that of ergosterol. Windaus and Dimroth then converted isopyrocalciferol (XVI) with either mercuric acetate or perbenzoic acid into a dehydro derivative identical with dehydroergosterol (XV), which proves that isopyrocalciferol differs from ergosterol only in the configuration at C_9, the center of asymmetry destroyed in the course of the dehydrogenation, and therefore is the C_9-epimer of the natural sterol.

The above evidence contains no proof that lumisterol and pyrocalciferol are $C_9\alpha$- and $C_9\beta$-compounds, respectively, and not the reverse. The reverse configurations seem unlikely, for then the photoisomerism of ergosterol would involve inversion at two centers rather than one (with no intermediates) and the thermal ring closure of D_2 would involve the formation of only two of four possible stereoisomers. The more probable configurations are supported by the observation of Kennedy and Spring that pyrocalciferol on irradiation with eosin in the absence of oxygen yields a dimolecular dehydrogenation product analogous to bisergostadienol (ergopinacol), whereas lumisterol and isopyrocalciferol do not react.[5] Since dehydrolumisterol gives a "pinacol,"[2] an inversion at C_{10} does not interfere with the reaction, and Kennedy and Spring conclude that the important factor is the steric relation of the methyl at C_{10} and the hydrogen at C_9: according to the formulations given, these are trans in the two isomers that yield "pinacols" (XIV and XIII) and cis in the two that do not (IX and XVI). An interesting analogy to the inversion of ergosterol at C_{10} on irradiation has been discovered in the cholesterol series.[6] Isodehydrocholesterol, which is a $C_5\alpha$-compound with a diene system extending from the adjacent position C_6 to C_9, is isomerized by light to the 5β-epimer.

Since all natural sterols with a 5,6-double bond are strongly levorotatory (ergosterol, $[\alpha]_D - 130°$), it is interesting to note the marked change to dextrorotation attending inversion at the following centers: C_{10}: lumisterol, $[\alpha]_D + 191°$; C_9: isopyrocalciferol, $[\alpha]_D + 332°$; C_9 and C_{10}: pyrocalciferol, $[\alpha]_D + 502°$. The only one of the three isomers of unnatural configuration that is precipitated by digitonin (partially) is isopyrocalciferol, in which the C_{10}-methyl group is oriented in the normal manner.

Tachysterol is very sensitive to air oxidation and has not been obtained in crystalline form, although highly pure samples have been prepared by thermal decomposition of the crystalline citraconic anhydride addition product and by hydrolysis of the 3,5-dinitro-4-methylbenzoate.[7] The ready reaction with dienophils and the characteristic ultraviolet absorption spectrum show that the three nuclear double bonds[8] are conjugated. The bond structure shown in Chart 17 and in the partial formula XVII (Chart 19) is based in part on the observation[9] that tachysterol on ozonization yields neither formaldehyde nor the C_{19}-ketone resulting from the fission of the $C_7 - C_8$ double bond of vitamin D_2. Further evidence was found in the characterization of two products resulting from the reduction of tachysterol (as ester) with sodium and propyl alcohol.[10] One is identical with dihydrovitamin D_2 (XVIII), the chief product of the reduction of D_2 by the same method, and the other is the isomeric dihydrotachysterol (XIX). The spectrum of dihydrotachysterol is indicative of the presence of a conjugated diene system, and the fact that the substance does not add maleic anhydride may be because both ends of the system are disubstituted. Formula XIX

[5] Kennedy and Spring, *J. Chem. Soc.*, 250 (1939).
[6] Windaus and Zühlsdorff, *Ann.*, **536**, 204 (1938).
[7] Windaus, v. Werder and Lüttringhaus, *Ann.*, **499**, 188 (1932).
[8] Lettré, *Ann.*, **511**, 280 (1934).
[9] Grundmann, *Z. physiol. Chem.*, **252**, 151 (1938).
[10] v. Werder, *Z. physiol. Chem.*, **260**, 119 (1939).

Chart 19. DIHYDRO DERIVATIVES

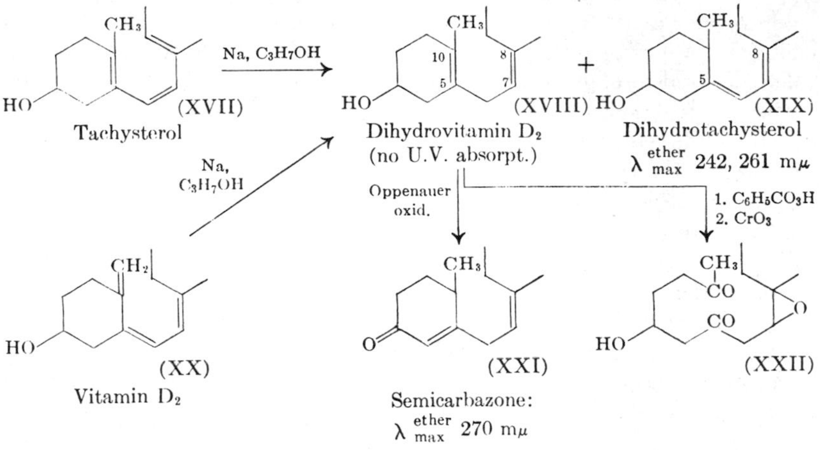

(XVII) Tachysterol

Na, C_3H_7OH

(XVIII) Dihydrovitamin D_2 (no U.V. absorpt.)

Oppenauer oxid.

+

(XIX) Dihydrotachysterol
λ_{max}^{ether} 242, 261 mμ

1. $C_6H_5CO_3H$
2. CrO_3

(XX) Vitamin D_2

(XXI) Semicarbazone:
λ_{max}^{ether} 270 mμ

(XXII)

is supported by chromic acid oxidation of dihydrotachysterol to the ketone $C_{19}H_{32}O$ obtained from vitamin D_2, for this degradation locates a double bond at $C_7 - C_8$. Dihydrovitamin $D_2{}^{10,11}$ contains two nuclear double bonds that are not conjugated. In an investigation of an analogous dihydro derivative[12] (from vitamin D_3) one of the double bonds was located at $C_7 - C_8$ by isolation as an oxidation product of a ketone analogous to the $C_{19}H_{32}O$ ketone. A suggestion that the second double bond is at $C_5 - C_{10}$ was furnished by the isolation of a methyl ketone of the probable partial formula XXII by mild chromic acid oxidation of the trioxide;[13] more secure evidence is the Oppenauer oxidation of dihydrovitamin D_2 to a substance characterized as an α,β-unsaturated ketonic derivative by the absorption spectrum.[14]

These observations establish the structures of the two dihydro derivatives and of tachysterol. The reduction of vitamin D_2 involves a 1,4-addition to a portion of the triene system; the reduction of tachysterol proceeds by 1,4- and 1,6-additions.

Dihydrotachysterol is devoid of antirachitic activity but markedly increases the serum calcium and is used for the treatment of idiopathic and hypoparathyroid tetany. It was introduced in 1934 by the German firm of E. Merck under the trade name A.T. 10 (antitetany compound 10).[15]

[11] Windaus, Linsert, Lüttringhaus and Weidlich, *Ann.*, **492**, 226 (1932).
[12] Windaus, Deppe and Wunderlich, *Ann.*, **533**, 118 (1938).
[13] v. Reichel and Deppe, *Z. physiol. Chem.*, **239**, 143 (1936).
[14] Windaus and Roosen-Runge, *Z. physiol. Chem.*, **260**, 181 (1939).
[15] German Patent 624,231; clinical use: McLean, "Activated Sterols in the Treat-

The photoisomers[16] of isopyrocalciferol and pyrocalciferol, VIII and VIIIa (above), revert to the pyro isomers on heat treatment. The two nuclear bonds have not been located, but the absence of selective absorption between 248 and 320 mμ shows that they are not conjugated. The suprasterols have been characterized only to the extent of the data given in the table above. The spirocyclopentano formulation (V) suggested by Müller[17] is not consistent with crystallographic data,[18] which indicate that the substance is of the normal sterol type. An alternate formulation has been suggested by Rosenheim and King.[19]

A recent X-ray analysis of the 4-iodo-5-nitrobenzoate of calciferol by Crowfoot and Dunitz[20] provides unambiguous confirmation of the Windaus formula and shows that the molecule has an extended orientation and not a steroid-like structure. The analysis also affords evidence of the C/D-trans ring fusion and of the β-orientation of the hydroxyl group and the side chain in calciferol.

Natural Vitamin D. At an early stage in the investigations of the irradiation of ergosterol, Windaus discovered that antirachitic activity is not specific to the ergosterol series. 22-Dihydroergosterol, prepared by blocking the nuclear conjugated system with maleic anhydride, hydrogenating the $C_{22} - C_{23}$ double linkage, and eliminating maleic anhydride, yielded an active product on irradiation.[1] In another investigation[2] cholesterol was converted by reactions to be discussed below into 7-dehydrocholesterol (I),

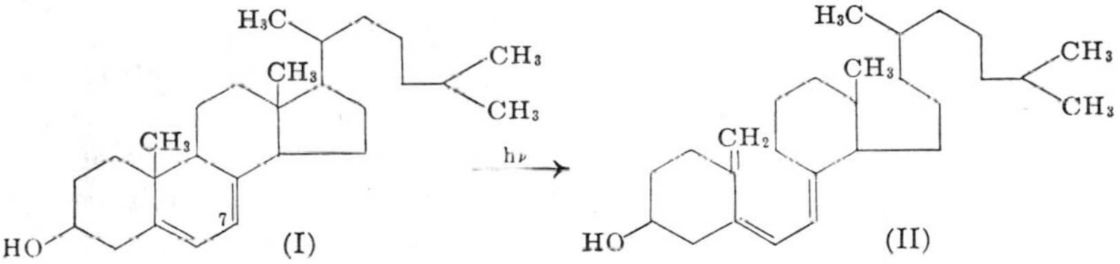

(I)	(II)
7-Dehydrocholesterol	Vitamin D_3
m.p. 150°, $[\alpha]_D - 114°$,	m.p. 82-84°, $[\alpha]_D + 83°$
λ_{max}^{ether} 280 mμ	3,5-dinitrobenzoate, m.p. 129°,
	λ_{max}^{hexane} 265 mμ

ment of Parathyroid Insufficiency," *Glandular Physiology and Therapy*, Am. Med. Assoc., Chicago (1942).

[16] K. Dimroth, *Ber.*, **70**, 1631 (1937).

[17] M. Müller, *Z. physiol. Chem.*, **233**, 223 (1935).

[18] Bernal and Crowfoot, *Chemistry and Industry*, **54**, 701 (1935); Bernal, Crowfoot and Fankuchen, *Trans. Roy. Soc. London*, **A239**, 135 (1940).

[19] Rosenheim and King, *Chemistry and Industry*, **54**, 699 (1935).

[20] Crowfoot and J. D. Dunitz, *Nature* (in press).

[1] Windaus and Langer, *Ann.*, **508**, 105 (1934).

[2] Windaus, Lettré and Fr. Schenck, *Ann.*, **520**, 98 (1935).

178   STEROLS AND BILE ACIDS

which has the same nuclear bond structure as ergosterol.   Irradiation of
7-dehydrocholesterol gave a crude product of antirachitic potency comparable to that of vitamin D_2.   The active component, designated vitamin
D_3, was later isolated in the form of the 3,5-dinitrobenzoate and allophan-
ate[3] and finally in a crystalline condition.[4]

The demonstration that two substances differing from vitamin D_2 in only
minor features of the side chain structure possess comparable biological
activity destroyed the basis of the early supposition that the active irradiation product of ergosterol is identical with the natural vitamin D of fish
liver oils.   In the meantime evidence was accumulating from the results of
differential bioassays that pointed to the nonidentity of the two substances.
In 1930 Massengale and Nussmeier[5] found that, on the same rat-unit basis,
irradiated ergosterol has much less antirachitic activity in chicks than cod
liver oil.   Studies of the chemical activation of cholesterol had been initiated by an observation by Bills[6] that cholesterol that has been heated with
the fuller's earth floridin acquires weak antirachitic activity on irradiation, and many other procedures for activation were subsequently reported.[7]
In 1934 – 36 several comparisons indicated that irradiated crude or heat-
treated cholesterol is more effective in preventing rickets in chicks than an
equivalent number of rat units of irradiated ergosterol.[8]   The biological
studies had reached a stage where the true provitamin seemed less likely to
be ergosterol than a transformation product of cholesterol, when the problem was solved, in 1936, by the isolation of the pure antirachitic principle
of tuna liver oil by Brockmann at the Göttingen laboratory.[9]

Brockmann designed a successful procedure for the isolation of natural
vitamin D on the basis of trial experiments with vitamin D_2 and the assumption of a fair correspondence in the solubilities and adsorbabilities of this
substance with those of D_2.   The process of enrichment was followed in
part by a colorimetric assay of D_2 (or D) based upon measurement of the
intensity of an absorption band at 500 mμ of an antimony chloride complex;[10] the vitamin A complex has a maximum at 620 mμ and does not inter-

[3] Windaus, Fr. Schenck and v. Werder, Z. physiol. Chem., 241, 100 (1936).
[4] Fr. Schenck, Naturwissenschaften, 25, 159 (1937).
[5] Massengale and Nussmeier, J. Biol. Chem., 87, 423 (1930);   confirmed by Steenbock, Kletzien and Halpin, ibid., 97, 249 (1932).
[6] Bills, J. Biol. Chem., 67, 753 (1926).
[7] See Yoder, J. Biol. Chem., 116, 71 (1936).
[8] Waddell, J. Biol. Chem., 105, 711 (1934); Dols, Z. Vitaminforsch., 5, 161 (1936);
Hathaway and Lobb, J. Biol. Chem., 113, 105 (1936); Haman and Steenbock, ibid,
114, 505 (1936).
[9] Brockmann, Z. physiol. Chem., 241, 104 (1936).
[10] Brockmann and Y. H. Chen, Z. physiol. Chem., 241, 129 (1936); F. A. Robinson
and F. E. Young, Chemistry and Industry, 55, 835 (1936).

fere. The starting material was the unsaponifiable fraction from tuna liver oil and contained 0.32 percent of vitamin D by assay. On distribution between 90 percent methanol and ligroin the bulk of the vitamin A was retained in the methanol, and the D collected in the ligroin. Extraction of the ligroin solution with 95 percent methanol removed the vitamin D and left inactive material in the ligroin. Further enrichment by chromatographic adsorption on aluminum hydroxide was guided by the use of a dye of the same degree of adsorbability as vitamin D_2 to reveal the adsorption zone. Finally, the dye was removed with alkali, cholesterol was precipitated with digitonin, and the active principle was esterified with 3,5-dinitrobenzoyl chloride. Purification by chromatography gave a crystalline 3,5-dinitrobenzoate melting at 128 – 129°; the sterol resulting from hydrolysis of the pure ester was noncrystalline but corresponded in absorption spectrum to vitamin D_2 (max. 265 mμ) and had antirachitic activity of the same order of magnitude. The crystalline ester differed from the ester of vitamin D_2 in melting point and composition but proved to be identical with the 3,5-dinitrobenzoate of vitamin D_3, the active product of the irradiation of 7-dehydrocholesterol that Windaus, Fr. Schenck and v. Werder[3] had just characterized by the preparation of crystalline derivatives. Natural vitamin D is identical with vitamin D_3 of the structure II, above. 7-Dehydrocholesterol, not ergosterol, is the true provitamin of the fish liver oil.

In rats vitamin D_3 is slightly more potent than D_2.[11] Vitamin D_3 also exhibits high antirachitic activity in chicks, whereas vitamin D_2 has only 1–3 percent the activity in chicks that it does in rats.[11] The relative potency of the two substances in man closely resembles that in the rat. Some clinical reports indicate that D_2 and D_3 are equally effective in the treatment of rickets in children;[12] others[13] indicate that D_3 is better absorbed from the intestines than D_2 and is about twice as effective; the therapeutic dose is about 0.02 mg. per kg. per day. The vitamin is not properly absorbed unless bile is present in the chyme.[14] Irradiated ergosterol served as a satisfactory substitute for D_3 in human therapy but proved of no value for the poultry industry, which requires large amounts of either fish oil concentrates or of vitamin D_3 prepared by irradiation of 7-dehydrocholesterol.

7-Dehydrocholesterol. The first method (a) of preparing this important intermediate formulated in Chart 20 includes improvements over the orig-

---

[11] Grab, *Z. physiol. Chem.*, **243**, 63 (1936).

[12] Folberth, *Z. Kinderheilk.*, **59**, 329 (1937); G. Jacoby, *Klin. Wochschr.*, **17**, 1173 (1938); N. Morris and M. M. Stevenson , *Lancet*, II, 876 (1939).

[13] Herbert Brockmann, *Klin Wochschr.*, **16**, 1383 (1937); Hartenstein, *Deut. med, Wochschr.*, **66**, 143 (1940); E. W. McChesney, *J. Nutrition*, **26**, 487 (1943).

[14] W. Heymann, *J. Biol. Chem.*, **122**, 249 (1937).

Chart 20.   PREPARATION OF 7-DEHYDROCHOLESTEROL (V)

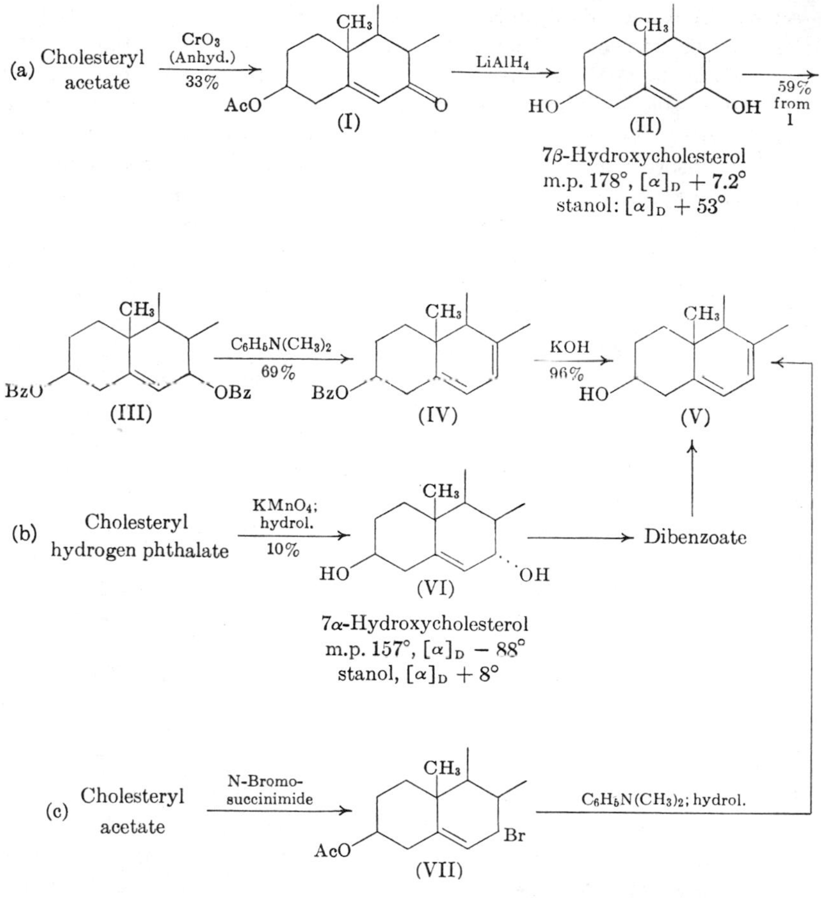

(a) Cholesteryl acetate $\xrightarrow[\substack{\text{(Anhyd.)}\\33\%}]{\text{CrO}_3}$ (I) $\xrightarrow{\text{LiAlH}_4}$ (II)

7β-Hydroxycholesterol
m.p. 178°, $[\alpha]_D + 7.2°$
stanol: $[\alpha]_D + 53°$

$\xrightarrow[\text{from}]{59\%}$ 1

(III) $\xrightarrow[69\%]{\text{C}_6\text{H}_5\text{N(CH}_3)_2}$ (IV) $\xrightarrow[96\%]{\text{KOH}}$ (V)

(b) Cholesteryl hydrogen phthalate $\xrightarrow[10\%]{\substack{\text{KMnO}_4;\\ \text{hydrol.}}}$ (VI) $\longrightarrow$ Dibenzoate

7α-Hydroxycholesterol
m.p. 157°, $[\alpha]_D - 88°$
stanol, $[\alpha]_D + 8°$

(c) Cholesteryl acetate $\xrightarrow[\text{succinimide}]{\text{N-Bromo-}}$ (VII) $\xrightarrow{\text{C}_6\text{H}_5\text{N(CH}_3)_2; \text{ hydrol.}}$

inal process developed by Windaus[1] and recently reinvestigated by Buser,[2] in which cholesteryl acetate was first oxidized in acetic acid with aqueous chromic acid to the known[3] 7-keto derivative I in yield of 26[2] – 28[1] percent. Reduction of the keto acetate by the Meerwein-Ponndorf reaction afforded a crude cholestenediol mixture from which the 3β,7β-diol dibenzoate III was isolated in 20[2] – 29[1] percent yield. These two steps have been improved with the results shown in the chart by conducting the oxidation

[1] Windaus, Lettré and Fr. Schenck, *Ann.*, **520,** 98 (1935).

[2] Buser, *Helv. Chim. Acta*, **30,** 1385 (1947).

[3] Mauthner and Suida, *Monatsh.*, **17,** 579 (1896).

under anhydrous conditions (solid chromic anhydride is added to a stirred solution of the acetate in glacial acetic acid at 55°) and effecting reduction with lithium aluminum hydride[4]; the reduction is rapid and clean and proceeds predominately in one steric direction, although 5 percent of the 3β,7α-diol dibenzoate was isolated. The conversion of the dibenzoate III to 7-dehydrocholesterol benzoate IV was originally[1] effected by pyrolysis, but the yield of the dehydro compound V was only 48 percent. In the preparation of the bile acid analog of V, 3α-hydroxy-Δ[5,7]-choladienic acid, by the same sequence of reactions, Haslewood[5] found that the pyrolysis of the dibenzoate proceeded poorly but that the elimination of benzoic acid could be conducted satisfactorily by refluxing the dibenzoate in dimethylaniline solution. Buser[2] applied this method to the preparation of V with the favorable results shown in the chart; these results have been confirmed.[4] An alternate procedure[6] in which the dibenzoate is converted by sodium methoxide in methanol into the 7-monobenzoate (81%) and this is refluxed with dimethylaniline (65%) appears to offer little advantage over the original process.

A second route (b) to 7-dehydrocholesterol described by Heilbron and co-workers[7] consists in the oxidation of cholesteryl acid phthalate with alkaline permanganate, which results in part in the introduction of a hydroxyl group at the 7-position. The diol VI resulting on hydrolysis is convertible into 7-dehydrocholesterol through the dibenzoate, but it is only one of three oxidation products isolated (along with a tetrahydroxycholestane and a hydroxy keto acid) and the yield is very low. The diol VI obtained by hydroxylation is the C7-epimer of the diol II isolated by reduction of the 7-ketone. Wintersteiner found that the crystalline reduction product actually contains both epimers,[8] which he isolated and characterized as such and as the corresponding stanols.[9] Both Heilbron and Wintersteiner employed the arbitrary designations "7α" and "7β" for diols II and VI, respectively. Plattner and Heusser[10] suggested that analogy to 7α- and 7β-hydroxycholanic acids of known configuration indicates that the true configurations are the opposite of those corresponding to the arbitrary designations. It will be shown in Part 2 that an analogy between the A/B-cis and A/B-trans series is not necessarily valid but that the configurations assigned by Plattner and Heusser are actually supported by chemical

[4] Fieser, Fieser and R. N. Chakravarti, publication in press.
[5] Haslewood, *J. Chem. Soc.*, 224 (1938).
[6] Wintersteiner and Ruigh, *J. Am. Chem. Soc.*, **64**, 1177 (1942).
[7] Barr, Heilbron, Parry and Spring, *J. Chem. Soc.*, 1437 (1936).
[8] Wintersteiner and Ruigh, *J. Am. Chem. Soc.*, **64**, 2453 (1942).
[9] Wintersteiner and M. Moore, *J. Am. Chem. Soc.*, **65**, 1503 (1943).
[10] Plattner and Heusser, *Helv. Chim. Acta.*, **27**, 748 (1944).

evidence.   Thus in this book the slightly dextrorotatory diol II is named 7β-hydroxycholesterol and the levorotatory diol VI is named 7α.   If the diacetate of either diol is refluxed in acetic acid, epimerization occurs and the final equilibrium mixture contains about $\frac{2}{3}$ of the 7β-diacetate and $\frac{1}{3}$ of the 7α-diacetate.[11]   The ready interconversion is undoubtedly associated with the presence of an allylic system.

A third method for preparation of 7-dehydrocholesterol (c) is allylic bromination of cholesteryl acetate according to Ziegler and dehydrohalogenation with dimethylaniline;[12,13] the overall yield calculated from the spectrographic analysis of the digitonin-precipitated reaction mixture is given as 23 percent.[13]

Other Natural Vitamins and Provitamins.   Brockmann's isolation of vitamin D_3 as the 3,5-dinitrobenzoate from tuna liver oil has been confirmed by others.[1]   Brockmann and Busse[2] later isolated crystalline D_3 from the same source.   The natural vitamin D of the liver oils of the halibut[3] and of the blue fin tuna[4] was isolated and likewise identified as D_3.   From a reinvestigation of the vitamin isolated from tuna fish liver,[5] Brockmann concluded that small differences in melting point and other properties of the natural vitamin and pure D_3 are indicative of the presence of about 10 percent of D_2.

Although no antirachitic principle other than D_3 has been isolated from fish oils, Hickman[6] has conducted molecular distillations of fish oils by a technique employing pilot dyes and has separated several fractions which according to distillation data and differential bioassays[7] probably consist in a series of vitamins D of different length of side chain.

7-Dehydrocholesterol has been isolated and identified as the provitamin of pig skin[8] (4% of provitamin present), commercial cholesterol,[9] and the

[11] Ruzicka, Prelog and Tagmann, *Helv. Chim. Acta*, **27**, 1149 (1944).

[12] Henbest, E. R. H. Jones, Bide, Peevers and Wilkinson, *Nature*, **158**, 169 (1946).

[13] Buisman, W. Stevens and Vliet, *Rec. trav. chim.*, **66**, 83 (1947); Redel and Gauthier, *Bull. soc. chim.*, **15**, 607 (1948).

[1] Simons and T. Zucker, *J. Am. Chem. Soc.*, **58**, 2655 (1936); Zucker, Simons, Colman and Demarest, *Naturwissenschaften*, **26**, 11 (1938).

[2] Brockmann and Busse, *Naturwissenschaften*, **26**, 122 (1938).

[3] Brockmann, *Z. physiol. Chem.*, **245**, 96 (1937).

[4] Brockmann and Busse, *Z. physiol. Chem.*, **249**, 176 (1937).

[5] Brockmann and Busse, *Z. physiol. Chem.*, **256**, 252 (1938).

[6] Hickman and Gray, *Ind. Eng. Chem.*, **30**, 796 (1938); Hickman, *ibid.*, **32**, 1451 (1940).

[7] Bills, Massengale, Hickman and Gray, *J. Biol. Chem.*, **126**, 241 (1938).

[8] Windaus and Bock, *Z. physiol. Chem.*, **245**, 168 (1937).

[9] Boer, Reerink, van Wijk and van Niekerk, *Proc. Acad. Sci. Amsterdam*, **39**, 622 (1936).

snail *Buccinum undatum* (27% provitamin).[10] Ergosterol is the provitamin present in hen yolk cholesterol,[11] cottonseed oil,[12] scopolia root,[12] wheat germ oil,[13] the snail *Arion empiricorium*.[10] In higher animals the provitamin D content of the skin is much higher (4% of total sterol) than that of inner organs (0.1 – 0.5%). The subcutaneous injection of 7-dehydrocholesterol, 7-hydroxy- or 7-ketocholesterol into D-deficient rats has been found to prevent rickets if the animals are irradiated.[14]

Structure and Antirachitic Activity. The specificity of the nuclear part of the molecule and arrangement of the triene system is well demonstrated by the fact that vitamin D_2 is the only one of the many irradiation products and other isomers that possesses antirachitic activity. The same is true of the analogous series of isomers derived from cholesterol.[1] Some variations can be made in the side chain without great loss in antirachitic activity in the rat, but the feeble activity of vitamin D_2 in chicks as compared to D_3 shows that the cholesterol side chain is very much more favorable for chick activity than that of ergosterol. Results of comparative rat assays[2] are as follows: vitamin D_4[3] (m.p. 108°, $[\alpha]_D$ | 89°), from the irradiation of 22-dihydroergosterol, is more potent than D_2 and nearly as active as D_3. Irradiated 7-dehydrositosterol[4] has high antirachitic activity, but irradiated 7-dehydrostigmasterol[5,6] is only feebly active. The irradiation product of 7-dehydroepicholesterol[7] is only $1/20$ as active as D_3. The noncrystalline ketonic derivative of vitamin D_2[8] is almost completely devoid of activity. Irradiation products analogous to D_2 and D_3 but having at C_{17} the bile acid side chain[6] or an alcoholic group[9] are feebly active and inactive, respectively.

[10] Bock and Wetter, *Z. physiol. Chem.*, **256**, 33 (1938).

[11] Windaus and Stange, *Z. physiol. Chem.*, **244**, 218 (1936).

[12] Windaus and Bock, *Z. physiol. Chem.*, **250**, 258 (1937).

[13] Windaus and Bock, *Z. physiol. Chem.*, **256**, 47 (1938).

[14] Geiger and Lassen, *Proc. Soc. Exp. Biol. Med.*, **52**, 11 (1943).

[1] Windaus, Deppe and Wunderlich, *Ann.*, **533**, 118 (1938); Windaus, Deppe and Roosen-Runge, *ibid.*, **537**, 1 (1939). The properties of the three tetracyclic isomers of 7-dehydrocholesterol are as follows: lumisterol₃, m.p. 88° and 64°, $[\alpha]_D$ + 197°; pyrovitamin D_3, 3,5-dinitrobenzoate, m.p. 142°, $[\alpha]_D$ + 221°; isopyrovitamin D_3, 3,5-dinitrobenzoate, m.p. 170°, $[\alpha]_D$ + 318°.

[2] Grab, *Z. physiol. Chem.*, **243**, 63 (1936); McDonald, *J. Biol. Chem.*, **114**, Proc. lxv (1936).

[3] Windaus and Trautmann, *Z. physiol. Chem.*, **247**, 185 (1937); Windaus and Güntzel, *Ann.*, **538**, 120 (1939).

[4] Wunderlich, *Z. physiol. Chem.*, **241**, 116 (1933).

[5] Linsert, *Z. physiol. Chem.*, **241**, 125 (1936).

[6] Haslewood, *Biochem. J.*, **33**, 454 (1939).

[7] Windaus and Naggatz, *Ann.*, **542**, 204 (1939).

[8] Windaus and Buchholz, *Z. physiol. Chem.*, **256**, 273 (1938).

[9] K. Dimroth and Paland, *Ber.*, **72**, 187 (1939).

Part 2.   Properties and Reactions

ULTRAVIOLET ABSORPTION SPECTRA

The characteristic ultraviolet absorption spectra of steroids containing conjugated unsaturated groupings are of considerable value as a guide to structure.   Both the position of the principal absorption maxima (λ_{max}) and the intensity of absorption at these maxima, as expressed either by the value of the molecular extinction coefficient ϵ or by the function log ϵ, can often be correlated with specific features of structure.   The extinction coefficient is sometimes the best available guide to the purity of a sample.   In the case of α,β-unsaturated ketones, the position of the absorption bands is influenced to a significant extent by the nature of the solvent used in the determination; the effect on the extinction coefficient is negligible.   Determinations recorded in the literature were conducted in various solvents; and unfortunately in some instances the solvent used is not specified.   The present preferred practice is to conduct the determinations in absolute ethanol (abbrev.: alc) and to report the results numerically ($\lambda_{max}^{solvent}$; log ϵ) rather than graphically, since curves that are greatly reduced in reproduction cannot be read with accuracy.   Comparison of spectrographic data for α,β-unsaturated ketosteroids determined in different solvents can be made with reasonable assurance by application of the correction factors listed in Table I based upon comparative determinations of the Δ^4-3-ketosteroid testosterone recorded in a monograph by Dannenberg,[1] who carefully documented and correlated a large body of spectrographic data for steroids.

TABLE I.   Absorption Maxima of Testosterone in Various Solvents; (log ϵ 4.18–4.20)

SOLVENT	λ_{max}, mμ	FACTOR FOR CORRECTION TO ETHANOL
Hexane	230	+ 11
Ether	234	+ 7
Dioxane	236	+ 5
Chloroform	240	+ 1
Ethanol (alc)	241	0

Solvents exert little effect on the absorption characteristics of dienes and polyenes containing no polar groups, and no correction factor is necessary for the comparison of hydrocarbons.   In the more often encountered case of a steroid that contains both a conjugated system of double bonds and nonconjugated hydroxyl or carbonyl groups, a solvent effect is to be anticipated but has not as yet been evaluated; comparisons referred to different solvents are subject to some uncertainty.

[1] Dannenberg, *Abhandl. preuss. Akad. Wiss.*, **21**, 3 (1939).

Diene and Polyene Systems. Compounds containing an isolated ethylenic linkage have absorption maxima in the region 185 – 200 mμ; ϵ max is about 10,000 (log ϵ = 4.0). Since measurements in this region are difficult, the constants have been of little value for purposes of characterization. A compound containing two nonconjugated double bonds absorbs light in the same region, but the extinction coefficient is approximately doubled. It is generally true that the intensity of absorption of a substance containing two nonconjugated chromophoric systems is approximately equal to the sum of the molecular extinction coefficients of the two separate chromophores. The introduction of a second double bond into a position of conjugation shifts the absorption maximum toward the red (230 – 290 mμ) and increases slightly the value of log ϵ. It was noted in the second edition of this book that cyclic dienes fall into two broad groups depending upon whether the two double bonds are in the same ring or in different rings. Those of the first type (homoannular dienes) absorb in the region 265 – 285 mμ as exemplified by ergosterol: λ_{max}^{ether} 280 mμ, log ϵ 4.1; those of the second type (heteroannular dienes) have maxima in the region 230 – 250 mμ, as exemplified by $\Delta^{3,5}$-cholestadiene: λ_{max}^{ether} 234 mμ, log ϵ 4.3. Both Dannenberg[1] and Gillam[2] observed further that an exocyclic location of one or both double bonds results in a small displacement of the absorption band toward the red, as compared with a system having only endocyclic double bonds. The effect is attributed to the introduction of strain into the chromophore with resulting labilization of the electronic system;[3] thus a compound with a double bond exocyclic to a six-membered ring is thermodynamically unstable with respect to the endocyclic isomer.[4]

Woodward[5] analyzed the spectroscopic data for alicyclic dienes and for those cyclic dienes in which the double bonds are distributed between two rings and showed that the results in both series can be correlated on the basis of the following simple empirical rules:

(1) Each alkyl substituent or ring residue linked to the diene chromophore shifts λ_{max} 5 mμ in the direction of longer wave length.

(2) Each exocyclic double bond produces a similar bathochromic effect of 5 mμ; the effect is twice as great if the same bond is exocyclic to two rings. Woodward's calculations of predicted values were based upon the absorption maximum of butadiene in hexane: λ_{max}^{hexane} 217 mμ. Thus the value calculated for the diene No. 1, Table II, is: 217 + [3 × 5](substitution factor) + 5 (one exocyclic double bond) = 237 mμ. The value calculated

[2] Brooker, L. K. Evans and Gillam, *J. Chem. Soc.*, 1453 (1940).
[3] Lewis and Calvin, *Chem. Rev.*, **25**, 273 (1939).
[4] Hückel, "Theoretische Grundlagen d. organischen Chemie," 2nd ed., Vol. I, 72, 1934.
[5] Woodward, *J. Am. Chem. Soc.*, **64, 72** (1942).

TABLE II. Polyene Systems

Absorption Maxima (and log ε Values)

1. 234 mμ* λ_{max}^{ether} 234 mμ (4.3) $\Delta^{3,5}$-Cholestadiene	2. 234 mμ* λ_{max} 235 mμ (4.2) $\Delta^{4,6}$-Cholestadiene	3. 244 mμ* λ_{max}^{ether} 245 mμ (4.5) $\Delta^{6,8(14)}$-Cholesta-diene-3,9-diol 3-acet.	4. 244 mμ* λ_{max}^{ether} 245 mμ (4.1) $\Delta^{7,9,(11)}$-Cholesta-diene-3-ol acet.
5. 244 mμ* $\lambda_{max}^{CHCl_3}$ 242 mμ (4.0) Ergosterol-B_3	6. 244 mμ* λ_{max}^{alc} 249 mμ (4.2) Ergosterol-B_1	7. 239 mμ* λ_{max} 236 mμ (4.3) 7-Methylene-cholesterol	8. 273 mμ* λ_{max}^{alc} 275 mμ (3.8) $\Delta^{2,4}$-Cholestadiene
9. 283 mμ* λ_{max}^{ether} 280 mμ (4.1) Ergosterol	10. 273 mμ* λ_{max}^{ether} 275 mμ (3.7) Isodehydro-cholesterol	11. 303 mμ* λ_{max}^{alc} 304 mμ (4.2) $\Delta^{4,6,22}$-Ergostatriene-3-one enol acet.	12. 313 mμ* λ_{max}^{alc} 316 mμ (4.3) $\Delta^{3,5,7,22}$-Ergosta-tetraene
13. 323 mμ* λ_{max}^{ether} 320 mμ (4.0) Dehydroergosterol	14. λ_{max}^{ether} 284 mμ (3.9) $\Delta^{6,8(14),9(11)}$-Choles-tatriene-3-ol acet.	15. 353 mμ* λ_{max}^{alc} 356 mμ (4.2) $\Delta^{5,7,9(11),22}$-Ergostatet-raene-3-one enol acet.	16. λ_{max}^{ether} 355 mμ (4.1) $\Delta^{4,6,8,11}$-Cholesta-tetraene-3-ol

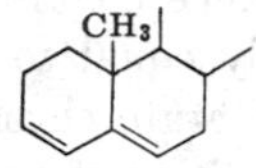

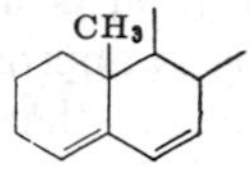

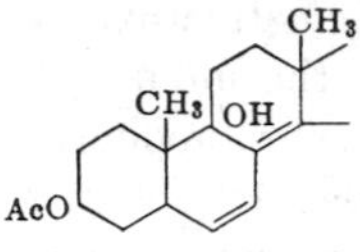

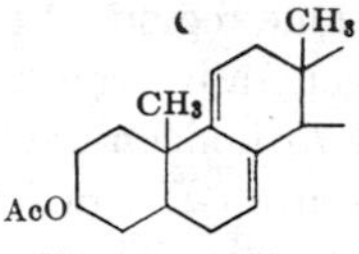

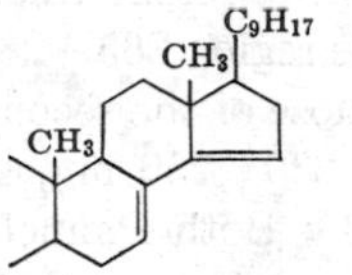

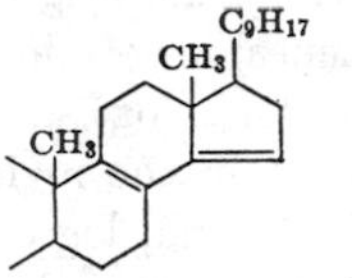

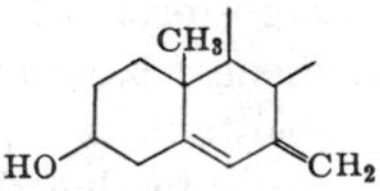

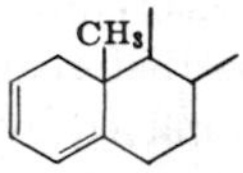

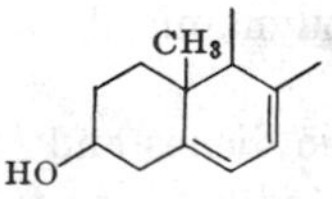

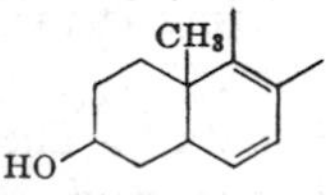

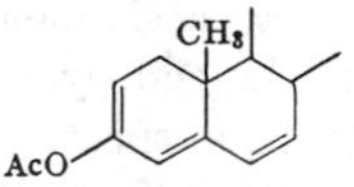

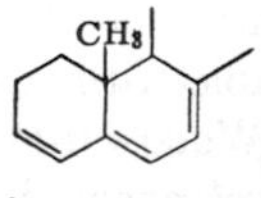

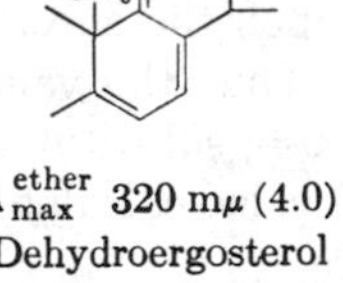

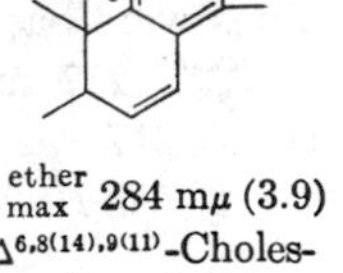

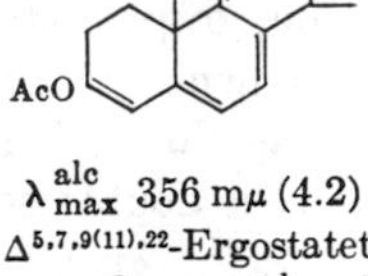

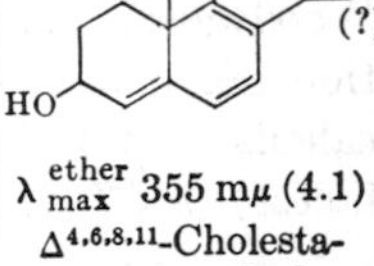

* Calculated λ_{max}

for No. 7 is: 217 + [3 × 5] + [2 × 5] = 242. In these and other instances the calculated maxima are sufficiently close to the values observed to substantiate Woodward's postulates.

For the specific purpose of correlation of data in the sterol field, some refinement can be made by basing the calculations not on a single value reported for a much simpler model compound but rather on an average value for a hypothetical parent steroid diene derived from the results for the first seven steroids listed in Table II,[6,7] with the application of the Woodward factors (1) and (2). The average found is λ_{max} 214 mμ, and recalculated values based on this empirical constant are included in the table (starred figures); the agreement is in all cases close.

An extension of the same scheme of analysis to homoannular dienes and to at least some trienes and tetraenes is as follows. Calculations from the maxima observed for the dienes Nos. 8, 9, and 10 with application of the Woodward factors indicate for the hypothetical parent homoannular diene with no substituents or exocyclic double bonds the average value λ_{max} 253 mμ. A third double bond that extends a homoannular system (Nos. 11, 12, 13), and that does not introduce cross conjugation as in No. 14, produces an average bathochromic shift of 30 mμ. Thus the calculated maximum for the triene No. 13 is: 253 (parent homoannular diene) + 25 (5 substituents) + 15 (3 exocyclic bonds) + 30 = 323 mμ (found 320). The value calculated for the tetraene No. 15 on the same basis is 353 mμ (found 356). The triene No. 14 contains a cross-conjugated system and the wave length of the absorption band is somewhat less than that calculated for the more active chromophoric diene system in ring C (293 mμ); the cross-conjugated linkage in ring B thus has some damping influence. The maximum calculated as above for the tetraene No. 16 is 343 mμ, whereas the value observed is 355 mμ; probably the combination of two homoannular dienic systems in rings B and C has some bathochromic influence not allowed for in the calculation.

The scheme of calculation and the constants defined are summarized in Table III. The calculation is always based upon the most active chromophoric system present in the molecule; thus a compound having both homo-

---

[6] Data for compounds 1–15 are taken from Dannenberg's monograph, Ref. 1; the value for No. 10 is given in the original paper as 270–280 mμ, and comparison with $\Delta^{6,8}$-coprostadienol-3 (not $\Delta^{4,6}$ as listed by Dannenberg) indicates that the position of the peak is at 275 mμ. The value for No. 16 is reported by Windaus, Riemann and Zühlsdorff, *Ann.*, **552**, 142 (1942).

[7] A superscript to the symbol Δ indicates the first of the two carbon atoms comprising the double bond, counted in the usual order of sterol numbering. The number of the second unsaturated carbon atom of the same pair is given only when it is not the next higher number, and in this case the number is inclosed in parentheses and precedes the comma (see No. 3, 14).

TABLE III.   Dienes and Polyenes; Calculation of Absorption Maxima

	$m\mu$
Heteroannular diene:	
Parent system..	214
Increment for each $\left\{\begin{array}{l}\text{C—Substituent}\ldots\ldots\ldots\ldots\ldots\ldots\ldots \\ \text{Exocyclic} > \text{C} = \ldots\ldots\ldots\ldots\ldots\ldots\ldots\end{array}\right.$	5 5
	$\lambda_{\text{max}} = $ Total
Homoannular diene or polyene:	
Parent homoannular diene system........................	253
Increment for each $\left\{\begin{array}{l}\text{C—Substituent}\ldots\ldots\ldots\ldots\ldots\ldots \\ \text{Exocyclic} > \text{C}=\ldots\ldots\ldots\ldots\ldots\ldots \\ \text{C}=\text{C extending conjugation}\ldots\ldots\ldots\ldots\end{array}\right.$	5 5 30
	$\lambda_{\text{max}} = $ Total

and heteroannular dienic systems is treated as a homoannular diene.

Enol Acetates. Absorption spectroscopy has been an invaluable guide in the investigations of the various isomers of ergosterol and of the cholestadienes (see later sections). Another useful application is in the study of enol acetate and ether derivatives of unsaturated ketones. For example, two structures, II and III, are possible for the enol acetate of cholestenone.

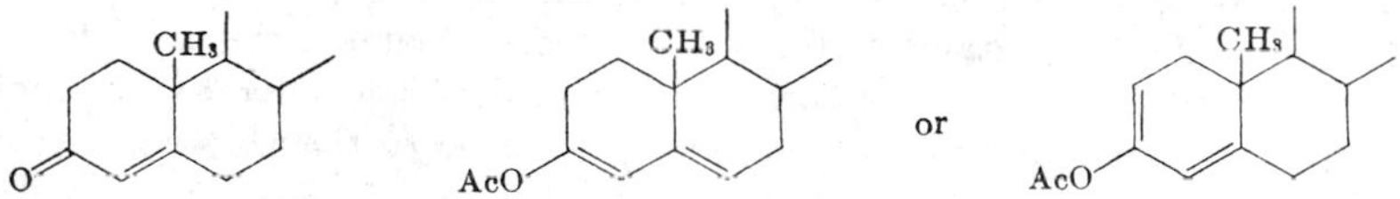

(I)   (II)   (III)

In analogy with the corresponding dienes, II would be expected to exhibit absorption at about 234 mμ and III at about 273 mμ. The observed value, $\lambda_{\text{max}}^{\text{CHCl}_3}$ 238 (log ϵ 4.2), enabled Westphal[1] to decide in favor of structure II; this structure evidently possesses greater stability than III. The structure of the enol acetate of $\Delta^{4,6,22}$-ergostatriene-3-one (No. 11) was likewise deduced from spectrographic evidence (calcd. for alternate structure: λ_{max} 313 mμ). In these and other instances an acetoxyl group attached to the unsaturated system has little effect on the position of the absorption band. Dannenberg observed that a bromine or chlorine substituent produces a bathochromic shift of about 4 mμ, or nearly as great as that of an alkyl group.

Some of the examples cited in Table II to illustrate the properties of polyene systems are enol acetates of unsaturated 3-ketosteroids; the structures were largely inferred from the absorption spectra. Oppenauer

[1] U. Westphal, *Ber.*, **70**, 2128 (1937).

oxidation of ergosterol affords chiefly the ergostatrienone IV,[2] in which only one double bond has shifted into conjugation with the carbonyl group, along with a trace of the isomer V.[3,4]   The ketones yield the isomeric enol acetates

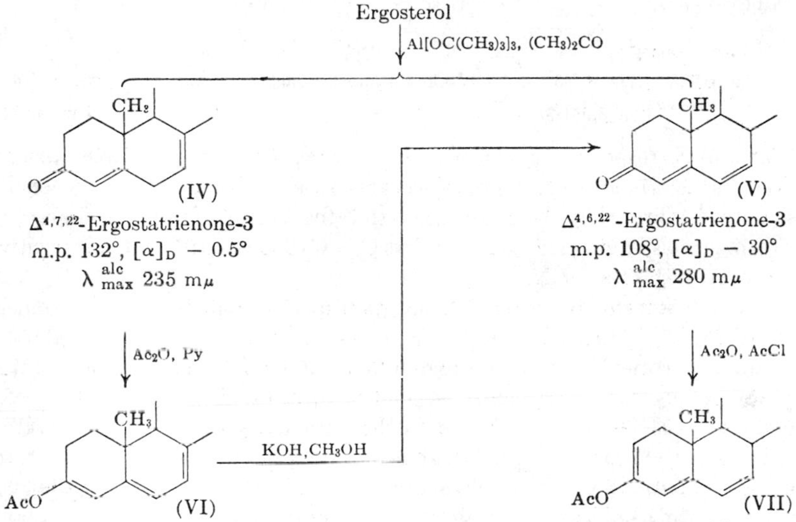

Ergosterol

$$\downarrow \text{Al[OC(CH}_3)_3]_3, \text{ (CH}_3)_2\text{CO}$$

(IV)

$\Delta^{4,7,22}$-Ergostatrienone-3
m.p. 132°, $[\alpha]_D$ − 0.5°
λ_{max}^{alc} 235 mμ

(V)

$\Delta^{4,6,22}$-Ergostatrienone-3
m.p. 108°, $[\alpha]_D$ − 30°
λ_{max}^{alc} 280 mμ

$\downarrow$ Ac₂O, Py

$\downarrow$ Ac₂O, AcCl

(VI)

KOH,CH₃OH

Enol acetate
m.p. 146°, $[\alpha]_D$ − 143.5°
λ_{max}^{alc} 316.5 mμ

(VII)

Enol acetate (No. 11)
m.p. 137°, $[\alpha]_D$ − 85°
λ_{max}^{alc} 304 mμ

VI and VII;[4] the triene system of the former contains one more carbon substituent and one more exocyclic double bond than the latter, and hence the displacement of the absorption maximum 12.5 mμ to the red is close to the expected shift (10 mμ). Eckhardt[5] attributed a structure analogous to that of the enol acetate VI to a product of the pyrolysis of 7-aminocholesterol phosphate: "$\Delta^{3,5,7}$-cholestratriene," m.p. 69°, $[\alpha]_D$ ± 0°, λ_{max}^{ether} 302 mμ. The absorption maximum is much too low for such a structure and the hydrocarbon does not exhibit the strong levorotation associated with the presence of a double bond at the 5,6-position (see VI); hence the structure suggested appears to be incorrect.

Ross[6] found that Δ^4-cholestene-3,6-dione (IX) can be converted into either of two enol dibenzoates by operating under different conditions. The high-melting and low-melting isomers were assigned the structures

[2] Oppenauer, Rec. trav. chim., 56, 137 (1937).
[3] Wetter and K. Dimroth, Ber., 70, 1665 (1937).
[4] Heilbron, Kennedy, Spring and Swain, J. Chem. Soc., 869 (1938).
[5] Eckhardt, Ber., 71, 461 (1938).
[6] Ross, J. Chem. Soc., 737 (1946).

(VIII)

m.p. 208°, $[\alpha]_D$ − 85°

$\lambda \ ^{CHCl_3\text{-alc}}_{max}$ 316 mμ (4.3)

(IX)

Δ^4-Cholestene-3,6-dione

(X)

m.p. 180°, $[\alpha]_D$ − 32°

$\lambda \ ^{CHCl_3\text{-alc}}_{max}$ 307 mμ (4.3)

VIII and X, respectively, because of the concordance in ultraviolet absorption characteristics with the enol acetates VI and VII above.   The conclusion was confirmed by the observation that the Tortelli-Jaffé test, characteristic of sterols having a double bond at $C_7 - C_8$ but not at $C_6 - C_7$, is positive for VIII, negative for X.

α,β-Unsaturated Ketones.   Absorption spectroscopy has been extremely useful for the characterization of α,β-unsaturated ketones, which show a strong absorption band in the region 230 − 260 mμ (in alcohol) attributed to the conjugated system and a second band of low intensity with a maximum at 315 − 320 mμ attributed to the carbonyl group.   This characteristic absorption provides good evidence of the presence of such a structural grouping, particularly if supplemented by the further observation that the corresponding semicarbazone shows a maximum of high intensity at about 267 − 275 mμ.[1]   Woodward[2] noted that ring residues joined to the α- and β-positions exert regular bathochromic substitutional effects, and Evans and Gillam[1,3] observed that the effect increased with increasing distance of the substituent from the carbonyl group.   Woodward noted further that an exocyclic location of the ethylenic bond results in the same bathochromic shift (5 mμ) as in the diene series and presented a general scheme for the calculation of predicted absorption maxima for α,β-monounsaturated ketones based upon the definition of a series of chromophoric systems in terms of the location of the substituents (α or β) and the endo- or exocyclic character of the ethylenic linkage.

A modified scheme of calculation similar to that applied above to the polyenes is based on the analysis of the data recorded in Table IV for eleven α,β-unsaturated ketones (with exclusion of No. 21, see below) with application of solvent corrections according to Table I and on the assumption of the following bathochromic effects: 10 mμ for an α-substituent; 12 mμ for a β-substituent; 5 mμ for each double linkage exocyclic to a ring.   The average value found for a hypothetical parent chromophoric system with

[1] L. K. Evans and Gillam, *J. Chem. Soc.*, 815 (1941); 565 (1943).

[2] Woodward, *J. Am. Chem. Soc.*, **63**, 1123 (1941); **64**, 76 (1942).

[3] L. K. Evans and Gillam, *J. Chem. Soc.*, 432 (1945).

TABLE IV. α,β-Unsaturated Ketones

Absorption Maxima (and log ϵ Values)

17.[a] 227 mμ*	18.[a] 244 mμ*	19.[a] 242 mμ*	20.[a] 242 mμ*
λ max^{alc} 230 mμ (4.0) Δ^1-Cholestenone-3	λ max^{ether} 234 mμ (4.2) Δ^4-Cholestenone-3	λ max^{CHCl_3} 240 mμ (3.5) Δ^5-Androstene-17β-ol-4-one	λ max^{alc} 239 mμ (3.8) Δ^4-Cholestene-3β-ol-6-one
21.[a] 244 mμ*	22.[a] 244 mμ*	23.[b] 249 mμ*	24.[a] 259 mμ*
λ max^{CHCl_3} 252 mμ (4.1) Δ^7-Ergostene-3,6-dione-5-ol	λ max^{ether} 234 mμ (4.1) 7-Ketocholesteryl acetate	λ max^{alc} 252 mμ (4.0) Δ^8-Ergostene-3-ol-7-one acetate	λ max^{ether} 254 mμ (4.0) $\Delta^{8(14)}$-Ergostene-3,7-dione-5-ol
25.[b] 259 mμ*	26.[a] 237 mμ*	27.[c] 244 mμ*	28.[a] 254 mμ*
λ max^{alc} 259 mμ (4.1) $\Delta^{8(14)}$-Ergostene-3β-ol-15-one acetate	λ max^{alc} 239 mμ (4.0) Δ^{16}-Pregnene-3,20-dione	λ max^{alc} 243 mμ (4.1) 3,12-Diketo-$\Delta^{9(11)}$-cholenic acid	λ max^{ether} 245 mμ (4.1)

* Calculated λ_{max}^{alc}.

[a] Dannenberg, Monograph.

[b] Stavely and Bollenback, *J. Am. Chem. Soc.*, **65**, 1285, 1290 (1943).

[c] Sarett, *J. Biol. Chem.*, **162**, 591 (1946). Barnett and Reichstein, *Helv. Chim. Acta*, **21**, 926 (1938), report the concordant value λ_{max}^{hexane} 234 mμ for 12-keto-$\Delta^{9(11)}$-cholenic acid methyl ester.

no substituents or exocyclic double bonds is $\lambda_{max}^{alc} = 215$ mμ, a figure close to that found for the corresponding parent diene (214 mμ). The maxima for the eleven compounds recalculated from this average (starred figures in Table IV) agree with the values found (corrected for solvent effect) with an average deviation of ± 2 mμ. The deviation of 9 mμ in the case of No. 21 is beyond the limit of error in the measurement or in the solvent correction, and the abnormally high value of λ_{max} remains unexplained.[4] The magnitude of cumulative substitutional and positional effects is well illustrated by the contrast in the calculated maxima for the β-substituted endocyclic ketone No. 17 (227 mμ) and the α,β,β-substituted di-exocyclic ketones No. 24 and 25 (259 mμ).

Although relatively few results for steroid dienones are available for analysis, the above scheme of calculation seems capable of extension to such systems with use of the additional constants listed in Table V. This

TABLE V. α,β-Unsaturated Ketones and Dienones; Calculation of Absorption Maxima

$$\begin{array}{c}\beta\quad\alpha\quad 0\qquad\qquad\delta\quad\gamma\quad\beta\quad\alpha\quad 0\\ |\quad|\quad\|\qquad\qquad|\quad|\quad|\quad|\quad\|\\ \beta-C{=}C-C-R\ \text{and}\ \delta-C{=}C-C{=}C-C-R\end{array}$$

Parent system..	215 mμ
Increment for C-substituents $\begin{cases}\alpha\\ \beta\\ \gamma\\ \delta\end{cases}$	
α...	10 mμ
β...	12 mμ
γ...	18 mμ
δ...	18 mμ
Increment for each exocyclic $> C =$...............................	5 mμ
Increment for each C=C extending conjugation........................	30 mμ

$$\lambda_{max}^{alc} = \text{Total}$$

table also summarizes the method of calculation defined for the mono-unsaturated ketones.   Table VI records representative absorption maxima for six types of dienones; maxima calculated for alcoholic solutions according to Table V are given as starred figures.   The $\Delta^{1,4}$-diene-3-one No. 29 is cross-conjugated and the figure 244 mμ (for alcohol; equivalent to 237 mμ for ether) is that calculated for the more active of the two monounsaturated ketonic systems present. . Compounds 30 and 31 are both β,δ-disubstituted dienones with one exocyclic linkage and the calculated values are the same; the agreement with the observed maxima is excellent.   Compound 32 differs in being γ,δ-disubstituted, which results in a bathochromic shift of 6 mμ.   The position of the double bonds in No. 33 is not known with certainty (see Spinasterols).   In the structure shown, if the basic chromophore consists of the carbonyl group and the 8,14-double bond, shifts to the red would be expected from the double bond linked at the α-position, from substituents that probably are to be regarded as β,β,β,γ, and from

[4] Reactions affording No. 21 are discussed in the section on Chromic Acid Oxidation.   The possibility that the oxygen atom at C_5 exerts a bathochromic effect because it is in conjugation with the unsaturated system [Burawoy, *J. Chem. Soc.*, 1177 (1939)] seems discounted by the normal character of the similarly constituted allylic alcohol No. 20.

TABLE VI. Dienones and Diketones

Absorption Maxima (and log ε Values)

29.[a]	244 mμ*	30.[b]	280 mμ*	31.[d]	280 mμ*	32.[e]	286 mμ*
λ_{max}^{ether} 236 mμ (4.2) $\Delta^{1,4}$-Cholestadiene-3-one		λ_{max}^{alc} 283 mμ (4.3) 6-Dehydrocorticosterone		λ_{max}^{alc} 280 mμ (4.4) $\Delta^{3,5}$-Cholestadiene-7-one		λ_{max} 290 mμ $\Delta^{3,5}$-Cholestadiene-2-one	
33.[f]		34[f]		35.[g]	244 mμ*	36.[f]	259 mμ*
(?)		(?)					
λ_{max}^{alc} 298 mμ (3.7) $\Delta^{9(11),8(14)}$-Ergostadiene-3β-ol-7-one acet.		λ_{max}^{alc} 307 mμ (4.0) $\Delta^{9(11),8(14)}$-Ergostadiene-3β-ol-15-one acet.		$\lambda_{max}^{CHCl_3}$ 252 mμ (4.0) Δ^4-Cholestene-3,6-dione		λ_{max}^{alc} 253 mμ (3.7) $\Delta^{8(14)}$-Ergostene-7,15-dione-3β-ol acet.	

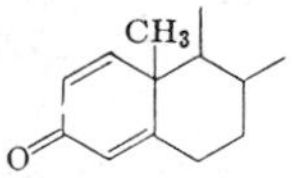

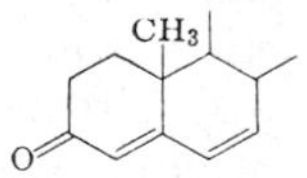

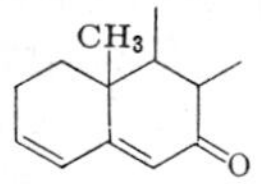

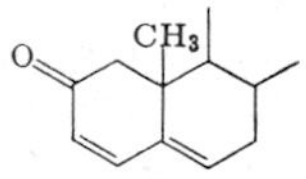

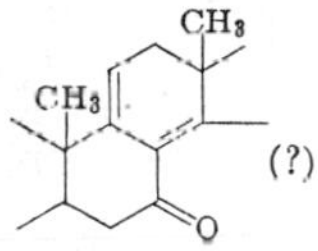

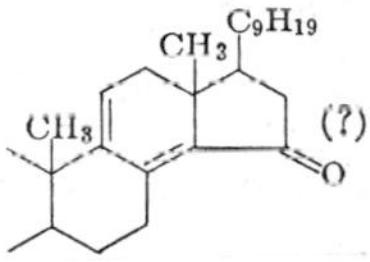

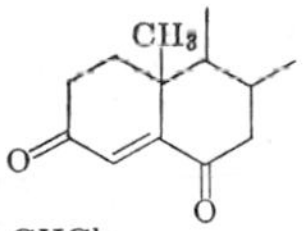

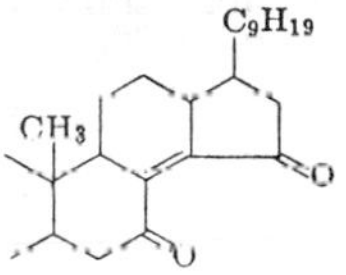

* Calculated λ_{max}^{alc}.

[a] Dannenberg, Monograph.

[b] The maximum coincides with the average for six $\Delta^{4,6}$-diene-3-ones.[a, e]

[c] L. K. Evans and Gillam, *J. Chem. Soc.*, 432 (1945).

[d] Same as average for three compounds.[a, c]

[e] Ruzicka, Plattner and Furrer, *Helv. Chim. Acta*, **27**, 525 (1944); solvent not specified.

[f] Stavely and Bollenback, *J. Am. Chem. Soc.*, **65**, 1285, 1290 (1943).

[g] Close to average for five compounds.[a]

three exocyclic linkages, whereas the cross-conjugation would result in some damping; but no exact calculation can be made. The alternate structure of a $\Delta^{8(14),15}$-diene-7-one (Woodward, footnote in Ref. f) is consistent with the chemical evidence and the calculated maximum (λ_{max}^{alc} 295 mμ) is close to that found. Both the structure and the homogeneity of the dienone No. 34 are subject to uncertainty; the observed maximum (307 mμ) is midway between values calculated for the $\Delta^{8(14),9(11)}$-diene-15-one (318 mμ) and for the $\Delta^{6,8(14)}$-diene-15-one (295 mμ).

Maxima for the unsaturated diketones 35 and 36 are calculated on the basis of the more actively chromophoric of the alternate unsaturated monoketonic groupings. In the case of No. 36 the two alternative structures are

of identical types (corresponding to Nos. 24 and 25 in Table IV) of calculated maxima 6 mμ higher than that found for No. 36. The calculated
maximum for the Δ^4-3,6-dione No. 35, on the other hand, is 9 mμ lower than
the observed value. It seems odd that the less highly substituted unsaturated system with only one exocyclic linkage (No. 35) absorbs at as long a
wave length as No. 36. The examples perhaps show merely that a second
carbonyl at the end of an α,β-unsaturated ketonic system produces no
bathochromic shift comparable to that of an ethylenic bond in the same
location. This is because in such a diketone the resonance effects are
opposed; the polarization of the second carbonyl group is in the direction
opposite to that of the first.

The dienone No. 37,[5] not included in the table, is perhaps a special case.
The maximum calculated in the usual way is 296 mμ (alcohol), whereas the

$\Delta^{14,16}$-Allopregnane-3β-ol-20-one acetate
λ max 239, 308 mμ (3.7, 3.9)

principal absorption band observed is at 308 mμ (solvent not specified). A
likely explanation of the discrepancy is that the incorporation of two double
bonds in a five-membered ring is attended with strain, with consequent
bathochromic displacement.

A comprehensive study of the absorption spectra of α,β-unsaturated
ketonic systems conjugated with an aromatic nucleus has been made by
Wilds and co-workers.[6] An interesting finding is that a benzene ring in
conjugation with a carbonyl group or with an enone system has approximately the same bathochromic effect as an α,β-disubstituted double bond.

α-Diketones and Enols. Only a few authentic steroid α-diketones are
known; some substances listed in the literature as α-diketones are actually
enolic. True α-diketones exhibit two distinct absorption bands, both of
which are very much less intense than the bands characteristic of dienes
and α,β-unsaturated ketones, as illustrated by compounds I[1] and II[2]. The

[5] Plattner, Ruzicka, Heusser and Angliker, *Helv. Chim. Acta*, **30**, 385 (1947).
[6] Wilds and co-workers, *J. Am. Chem. Soc.*, **69**, 1985 (1947).
[1] Barnett and Reichstein, *Helv. Chim. Acta*, **21**, 926 (1938).
[2] Mattox, R. B. Turner, Engel, McKenzie, McGuckin and Kendall, *J. Biol. Chem.*,
164, 569 (1946).

chromophoric system bears some resemblance to that of a homoannular diene with two substituents and two exocyclic double bonds, but the α-

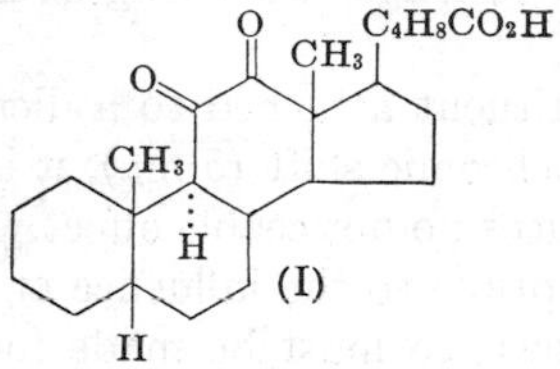

11,12-Diketocholanic acid
λ_{max}^{hexane} 279 mμ (1.94); 347 mμ (1.67)

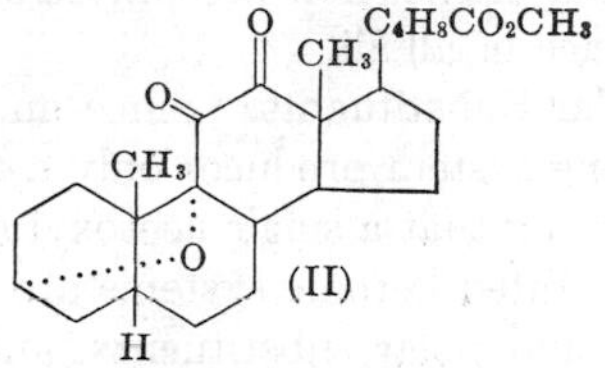

3,9-Oxido-11,12-diketocholanic acid methyl ester
λ_{max}^{alc} 295 mμ (2.02); 376 mμ (1.59)

diketonic absorption band of lower wave length and slightly higher intensity (λ_{max}^{alc} about 290 mμ) is displaced somewhat to the red as compared to such a system (λ_{max}^{alc} 273 mμ).

Monoenols derived from α-diketones exhibit a distinct red-displacement of the absorption maximum. Thus the enolic form[1] of 11,12-diketocholanic acid, for which no structure other than III is possible, has an absorption maximum 38 mμ higher than that of the related $\Delta^{9(11)}$-12-one (No. 27, Table

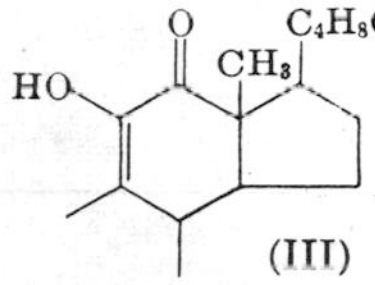

Enol of I
λ_{max}^{alc} 281 mμ (3.9)

Enols of Cholestane-2,3-dione
λ_{max}^{alc} 272 mμ
Acet., λ_{max}^{alc} 238 mμ

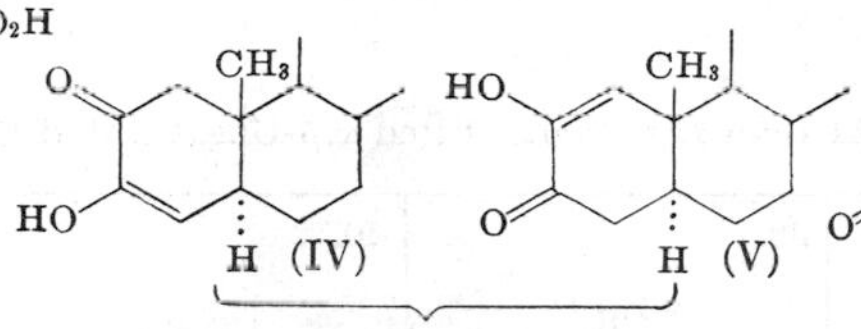

λ_{max}^{alc} 270 mμ
Acet., λ_{max}^{alc} 237 mμ

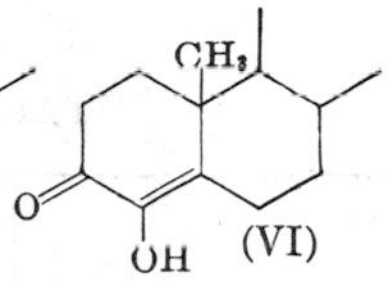

Enol of cholestane-3,4-dione
$\lambda_{max}^{CHCl_3}$ 280 mμ (4.2)
Acet., $\lambda_{max}^{CHCl_3}$ 248 mμ

IV). The enols IV and V similarly absorb at wave lengths 45 and 40 mμ higher than calculated or observed for the hydroxyl-free systems (see Table IV, page 191, for unsaturated ketones). An enol[3] derived from cholestane-3,4-dione very probably has the structure VI rather than the alternate Δ^2-4-keto structure because the displacement calculated for the former structure (37 mμ) alone is consistent with the effects observed in the other cased noted. In two other instances cited in later sections bathochromic displacements of 31 and 23 mμ are recorded, and hence the average of six rather divergent estimations of the displacement effect for enols is 35 mμ. The effect probably is due to ionization[4] and disappears on acetylation; the

[3] Butenandt, Schramm, A. Wolff and Kudszus, *Ber.*, **69**, 2779 (1936).
[4] Blout, Eager and Silverman, *J. Am. Chem.Soc.*, **68**, 566 (1946).

monoacetates of IV and V have absorption maxima only 7 – 11 mμ higher than expected for the parent systems (see next section). The absorption maxima of the enols are shifted about 50 mμ to longer wave lengths in the presence of alkali.

Polar Substituents. Since an alkyl substituent attached to a diene or polyene system produces only a small bathochromic shift (5 mμ), it is not surprising that a single acetoxyl group produces no noticeable effect. The unsaturated ketonic systems are more susceptible to the influence of both alkyl and polar substituents, and some allowance must be made for the latter as well as the former effect in the calculation of predicted maxima for enol acetates, enol ethers, and halogen-substituted systems. The data available are not very extensive but the results suggest that a fair approximation can be made by attributing to acetoxy, alkoxy, and halogen substituents, according to their position with respect to the carbonyl group, the same bathochromic effects as given in Table V for alkyl substituents. The typical examples of Table VII show that in most cases values calculated on this basis are in reasonably good agreement with the observed maxima. The calculation for No. 38 is: 215 + 12 (β-alkyl) + 18 (γ-OC$_2$H$_5$) + 18 (δ-alkyl) + 5 (exo-bond) + 30 (double bond) − 7 (solvent cor-

TABLE VII.[a]   Substituted α,β-Unsaturated Ketones

38.	39.	40.	41.
OC$_2$H$_5$	OAc		AcO
λ max, mμ: 295 (ether)	248 (CHCl$_3$)	237 (alc)	238 (alc)
calcd: 291	253	237	237

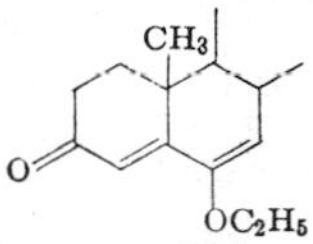

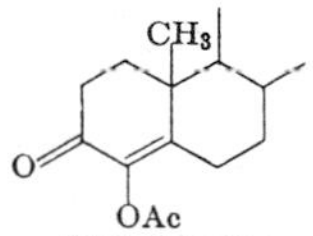

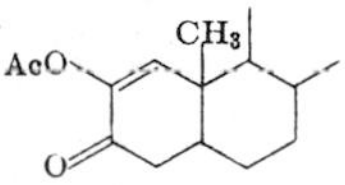

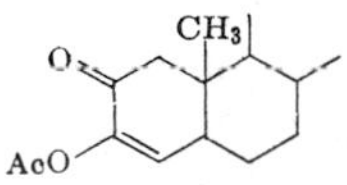

42.[b]	43.	44.[c]	45.[c]
λ max, mμ: 243 (alc)	250, 248 (ether)	298 (CHCl$_3$)	313 (CHCl$_3$)
calcd: 254	247	307	325

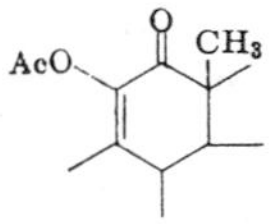

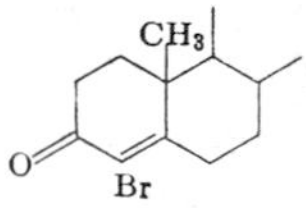

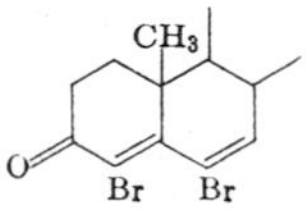

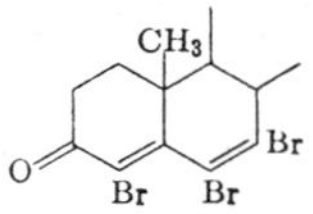

[a] Where no references are given, the data are to be found in the Dannenberg monograph or elsewhere in this section.

[b] Wintersteiner, M. Moore and Reinhardt, *J. Biol. Chem.*, **162**, 725 (1946).

[c] Butenandt, Schramm and Kudszus, *Ann.*, **531**, 176 (1937).

rection) = 291 mμ. The calculated values for the enol acetates 39 – 41 agree well with the values found; that for No. 42 is divergent. The maxima found for two compounds of the structural type No. 43 are listed. The results for Nos. 44 and 45 show that in polybromo compounds the effect of the substituents is actually less than expected for a strictly additive function; since the sum of the various bathochromic effects involved in the calculations amounts to a shift of some 100 mμ, the calculations even so represent reasonably good approximations.

A series of ketones resulting from the action of collidine on 2,2-dibromo-3-ketosteroids are listed in the literature as 2-bromo-Δ^1-3-ketones[5] but have absorption maxima (λ_{max}^{alc} 255 mμ) considerably higher than expected for such a structure (calcd. 237 mμ). No explanation of the anomaly has been suggested.

Benzenoid Systems. Steroids containing a benzenoid nucleus (Table VIII) are characterized by an absorption band in the same region as for homoannular dienes (260 – 280 mμ) but of distinctly lower intensity (log ϵ about 1 unit less). The fine structure characteristic of the spectrum of

TABLE VIII.[a] Aromatic Systems; Absorption Maxima (and log ϵ Values)

46.	47.	48.	49
λ_{max}^{ether} 280 mμ (3.3)	λ_{max}^{alc} 280 mμ (3.4)	λ_{max}^{ether} 268 mμ (2.7)	λ_{max}^{ether} 268 mμ (4.1)
Phenol	Estrone	Neoergosterol	Ergostapentaene

50.	51.	52.
λ_{max}^{alc} 272 mμ (4.2)	λ_{max}^{alc} 263 mμ (3.9)	λ_{max} 280, 342 mμ (3.7, 3.4)
Isoequilin-A	6-Dehydroestrone	Equilenin

[a] Data from Dannenberg, Monograph.

benzene itself is lacking in the spectra of the large steroid molecules. A double bond conjugated with a benzenoid ring does not displace the absorption band but greatly increases the intensity of absorption (Nos.

[5] Inhoffen and Zühlsdorff, *Ber.*, **76**, 233 (1943); Djerassi and Scholz, *J. Am. Chem. Soc.*, **69**, 2404 (1947).

49, 50, 51). A naphthalenoid system (No. 52) is characterized by an absorption spectrum showing more detail, with prominent bands at about 280 and 340 mμ. From the meager data available, it would appear that substitutional effects of alkyl and hydroxyl groups are of relatively minor importance; comparison of compounds 47 and 48, with allowance for possible solvent correction, suggests that the effect of a hydroxyl group on a benzenoid ring is to increase the intensity of absorption without appreciable shift of the wave length of absorption. John[6] observed a characteristic relationship between a free phenol and its acetate: acetylation results in a displacement of the absorption band of 15 – 20 mμ to shorter wave lengths and produces a marked depression in the extinction coefficient. Thus for estrone acetate John found λ_{max}^{alc} 265 mμ (log ϵ 3.0). Salt formation results in a bathochromic shift; estrone anion shows an absorption band at 300 mμ.

Infrared Spectroscopy

The absorption of ultraviolet light by specific unsaturated systems, which in the sterol series results in characteristic spectra with one or two principal absorption bands, is associated with the nature and lability of the orbital systems of electrons of the chromophoric centers. Absorption of light in the infrared region is associated not with electronic systems but with vibrations of atomic groupings, both longitudinal and transverse. A longitudinal vibration of a carbonyl group can be described as the result of a stretching of the double bond, comparable to the stretching of an elastic element, and the ensuing oscillation between the condition of extension and relaxation. Such a vibration in response to excitation by light of a specific wave length produces an infrared absorption band characteristic of the carbonyl group in question. The same carbonyl group may give rise to a low-intensity absorption band in the ultraviolet region. However, saturated groupings that are completely indifferent to ultraviolet light vibrate under excitation by infrared radiation and may also cause selective absorption. Thus absorption bands appear in the infrared spectrum associated with the longitudinal oscillation or stretching of specific carbon-hydrogen and oxygen-hydrogen bonds. The various atomic groups in the molecule also can participate in bending motions that give rise to bands appearing for the most part at longer wave length than the bands associated with stretching motions of the same groups. In a complicated steroid molecule the longitudinal and transverse vibrations associated with the many hydrogen atoms, with methyl groups, and with any hydroxyl and carbonyl groups present, as well as complicated interactions between

---

[6] John, *Z. physiol. chem.*, **250**, 18 (1937).

different vibrating systems, can give rise to a highly elaborate infrared spectrum that contains much intricate detail. Thus the spectrum of a typical steroid is made up of some 30 – 60 bands of varying intensity and constitutes an identifying pattern comparable to a fingerprint. Even minor differences in structure or configuration are reflected in significant changes in the spectrum, and every steroid thus far investigated exhibits an infrared spectrum that is completely unique to that individual compound.

Infrared spectrometry thus provides a means of identification that is free from any ambiguity. If the spectra of two substances correspond precisely in the positions and relative intensities of some fifty absorption bands, the substances most certainly are identical. The sample required is small (2 mg.), and the material is unchanged in the analysis and can be recovered. The time required to prepare the sample and record the most significant region of the spectrum in permanent form is less than ten minutes. Examination can be made of noncrystalline substances or of unisolated substances in solution. In their work on the fractionation of steroids from individual urines, Dobriner and co-workers[1] found that chromatographic eluates derived from one individual urine or from different urines could be safely pooled on the basis of identical spectral characteristics. If the principal constituent of one of a consecutive series of fractions has been isolated and identified, spectrometric analysis of the other fractions will reveal which of them contain a predominant amount of the same component.

Technique of Determination.[2] The available instruments all employ electronic methods of amplification and yield automatic records of the spectra. Those manufactured by Perkin-Elmer Corporation and by National Technical Laboratories are of the single-beam type and the spectrographic records are converted to percentage transmission by calculation; for the purpose of empirical identification, the instrumental records can be compared directly. The Baird and the Hilger instruments are of double-beam type and yield percentage transmission curves directly.

Most of the common solvents themselves absorb infrared radiation to an extent that renders them valueless for spectrometric determinations. Carbon bisulfide, carbon tetrachloride and chloroform are transparent in considerable regions of the spectrum and are the usual solvents employed.[3] These liquids unfortunately have little solvent power for hydroxylic com-

[1] Dobriner, Lieberman, Rhoads, R. N. Jones, V. Z. Williams and Barnes, *J. Biol. Chem.*, **172**, 297 (1948).

[2] Barnes, Gore, Liddel and V. Z. Williams, "Infrared Spectroscopy, Industrial Applications and Bibliography", Reinhold Publishing Corporation, New York, 1944.

[3] For the spectrographic characterization of various solvents see Torkington and H. W. Thompson, *Trans. Faraday Soc.*, **41**, 184 (1945).

pounds, for example, steroid diols. However, even a completely insoluble substance can be prepared for analysis by milling it with Nujol (micro mortar and pestel). Another technique, applied by Furchgott, Rosenkrantz and Shorr[4] to the study of steroids, consists in the spectrometric examination of a thin film of powder of the crystalline solid deposited on a rock salt plate. Solutions usually are measured in cells of 1 – 3 mm. path length; a 1-mm. cell holds 0.2 cc. of solution, and since a convenient concentration is about 10 mg./cc. a 2-mg. sample is sufficient for analysis.

Wave Length (λ) vs. Wave Number (ν). The position of an absorption band can be indicated by citation of either the wave length (in μ) or the wave number (in cm.$^{-1}$). The wave number is the reciprocal of the wave length in centimeters:

$$\lambda \text{ (in } \mu) = \frac{1 \times 10^4}{\nu \text{ (in cm.}^{-1})}$$

Since infrared absorption is associated with vibrational effects in the molecule, physical computations usually are made in terms of the frequency (wave number). In practical organic chemistry the use of wave lengths to indicate the positions of absorption bands in the infrared would seem the logical extension of the standard practice with respect to the ultraviolet region. Since the general application of infrared spectroscopy to organic research is still in a formative stage, we shall cite both wave lengths and wave numbers in order that a comparison can be made. In any case we urge investigators to report incidental spectrographic constants in the experimental part of the paper along with melting points, rotations and refractions, and to indicate the solvent or technique of measurement in some unambiguous and concise form, for example: $\lambda_{max}^{CS_2}$, ν_{max}^{Nujol}, λ_{max}^{cryst}.

Present instrumental errors are such that absolute intensities of infrared absorption are not sufficiently reproducible to be of much significance. Even relative intensities are not accurately reproducible from instrument to instrument. Furthermore, the relative intensities of different bands vary with the concentration.

Correlation with Structure. The region of absorption of significance in the study of steroids is that portion of the near infrared spectrum from 2.5 to 16.7 μ (4000 to 600 cm.$^{-1}$), and this region can be further subdivided into two parts, as illustrated by the typical spectrum shown in Figure 1;[5] the gaps in the spectrum represent regions of absorption by the solvent. The region of longer wave length (7 – 13 μ) or lower frequency (1400–770 cm.$^{-1}$) consists of a complex series of as yet unidentified bands probably associated

---

[4] Furchgott, Rosenkrantz and Shorr, *J. Biol. Chem.*, **163**, 375 (1946); **164**, 621 (1946); **167**, 627 (1947).

[5] Reproduced through the courtesy of Dr. R. N. Jones and Dr. K. Dobriner.

with vibrational effects in the molecule as a whole. The pattern in this region is highly sensitive to slight changes in structure and configuration and constitutes an identifying characteristic unique to each individual compound. The region of shorter wave length (2.5 – 6 μ) contains only a few

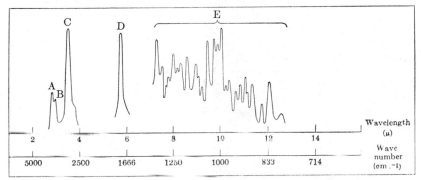

Fig. 1. INFRARED ABSORPTION SPECTRUM OF ANDROSTERONE IN CARBON BISULFIDE
A, hydroxyl group; B, overtone of D; C, C—H bonds; D, carbonyl group; E, region of unidentified bands, useful for empirical identification.

bands, and these have been correlated with specific structural groupings. In the case of androsterone (Figure 1) the low-intensity band A is identified as associated with the longitudinal vibration or stretching of the oxygen-hydrogen bond of the hydroxyl group; band C is associated with one or more carbon–hydrogen bonds; and band D with the carbon–oxygen bond of the carbonyl group.[6] The minor band B, which might be mistaken for that characteristic of the hydroxyl group, is the result of an overtone of the vibration responsible for band D.

The problem of correlating infrared absorption characteristics with specific features of steroid structure has been investigated extensively by R. N. Jones, Dobriner and associates,[7] and the principal results are summarized in Table IX. The figures given are in some instances averages of results for 5 – 20 steroids of the structural types indicated; in the region of most of the measurements (5.7 – 6.0 μ; 1750 – 1670 cm.$^{-1}$) the maximum deviation from the mean is about $\pm 0.010\,\mu\,(\pm 3$ cm.$^{-1})$. A low-intensity band near 2.80 μ (3600 cm.$^{-1}$) was observed for all substances having one or more hydroxyl groups (band A, Figure 1). The position of this band is dependent upon hydrogen-bonding effects and varies with the solvent and

---

[6] For the vibration frequencies characteristic of different groups, see Herzberg, "Infrared and Raman Spectra," Van Nostrand, 1945.

[7] R. N. Jones, V. Z. Williams, Whalen and Dobriner, *J. Am. Chem. Soc.*, 70, 2024 (1948); R. N. Jones, Humphries and Dobriner, *ibid.*, in press.

concentration, and the band appears considerably different in determinations made with crystal films. No positional effects have been discerned. Thus present techniques of infrared spectrometry can establish the presence

TABLE IX. Characteristic Absorption Bands
(R. N. Jones and co-workers, average values)

TYPE	GROUP	$\lambda_{max}^{CS_2}$, μ	$\mu_{max}^{CS_2}$, cm.$^{-1}$	COMMENTS
Hydroxyl	OH (at 3, 11, 17, or 20)	2.809	3560	
Isolated ketonic carbonyl	17-Keto	5.737	1743	
	7-Keto	(5.817)	(1719)	
	3-Keto	5.821	1718	
	11-Keto	5.838	1713	
	12-Keto	5.855	1708	
	20-Keto	5.862	1706	
Two isolated ketonic carbonyls	3,17-Diketo	$\begin{cases} 5.731 \\ 5.817 \end{cases}$	$\begin{cases} 1745 \\ 1719 \end{cases}$	No vicinal effects
	3,20-Diketo	$\begin{cases} 5.817 \\ 5.848 \end{cases}$	$\begin{cases} 1719 \\ 1710 \end{cases}$	
	3,11-Diketo	5.841	1712	
	11,20-Diketo	5.838	1713	
Neighboring carbonyls	11,17-Diketo	$\begin{cases} 5.711 \\ 5.838 \end{cases}$	$\begin{cases} 1751 \\ 1713 \end{cases}$	Vicinal effects
	11,12-Diketo	5.794	1726	
Alkyl esters	$\begin{cases} OCOCH_3 \text{ (at 3, 17, or} \\ \quad 20) \\ COOCH_3 \text{ (bile acid)} \end{cases}$	$\begin{cases} 5.751 \\ 8.078 \\ 5.740 \end{cases}$	$\begin{cases} 1739 \\ 1238 \\ 1742 \end{cases}$	
Aryl esters	$OCOC_6H_5$ (at 3)	5.817	1719	
α,β-Unsaturated ketones	Δ^4-3-Keto	$\begin{cases} 5.970 \\ 6.196 \end{cases}$	$\begin{cases} 1675 \\ 1614 \text{ (CHCl}_3) \end{cases}$	
	Δ^{16}-20-Keto	$\begin{cases} 5.999 \\ 6.297 \end{cases}$	$\begin{cases} 1667 \\ 1588 \text{ (CHCl}_3) \end{cases}$	
	$\Delta^{9\,(11)}$-12-Keto	5.945	1682	

or absence of one or more hydroxyl groups but cannot indicate the number and position of such functions.

Monoketones of the steroid series are characterized by a band of high intensity exhibiting a certain degree of positional specificity. 17-Ketosteroids are sharply differentiated from compounds with carbonyl groups at any of five other positions investigated[8] because the band appears at a dis-

[8] Measurements made with crystal films[4] revealed no difference between 3- and 17-ketones.

tinctly shorter wave length (5.737 μ; 1743 cm.$^{-1}$). The difference between a 3-ketosteroid (5.821 μ; 1718 cm.$^{-1}$) and a 20-ketosteroid (5.862 μ; 1706 cm.$^{-1}$) is beyond the limit of experimental error and hence these structures can also be differentiated. However, a carbonyl group at C_{11} cannot be distinguished by present techniques from one at C_3, C_{12}, or C_{20}. A diketone in which the carbonyl groups occupy distant positions in the molecule has the spectral characteristics of both isolated structural units, and there is no interactional or additive effect. Thus the spectrum of a 3,17-diketone has bands (5.73, 5.82 μ; 1740, 1720 cm.$^{-1}$) corresponding to those of 17-ketones (5.74 μ; 1740 cm.$^{-1}$) and of 3-ketones (5.82 μ; 1720 cm.$^{-1}$). Δ^5-Pregnene-3,20-dione similarly gives bands at 5.817 and 5.848 μ (1719 and 1710 cm.$^{-1}$) recognizable as due to the two separate functions; pregnane-3,20-dione also gives two bands. In an 11,17-diketone the functional groups are sufficiently near to one another to permit vibrational interaction, for although one band (5.838 μ; 1713 cm.$^{-1}$) can be identified as that characteristic of the C_{11}-group, the other (5.711 μ; 1751 cm.$^{-1}$) exhibits some displacement attributable to a vicinal effect (C_{17}-ketone: 5.737 μ; 1743 cm.$^{-1}$). A vicinal effect is observed also in the spectrum of an 11,12-diketone, which shows a single band displaced to a wave length shorter than that of the bands characteristic of either isolated ketonic group.

The carbonyl group of both steroid acetates and bile acid esters displays selective absorption in the same region as that of the 17-ketosteroids. The two types can of course be distinguished by saponification experiments, but a differentiation by spectrometry is also possible, at least in the case of the acetates; these show also a strong band at 8.078 μ (1238 cm.$^{-1}$) that is lacking in the spectrum of the 17-ketones. With the acyl derivative of a phenol or enol the absorption band associated with the carbonyl group is displaced to shorter wave lengths:

Estradiol diacetate
$\lambda \, ^{CS_2}_{max} \, 5.659\mu$ (1767 cm.$^{-1}$)

Testosterone enol dipropionate
$\lambda \, ^{CS_2}_{max} \, 5.701\mu$ (1754 cm.$^{-1}$)

Vicinal effects resulting from carbonyl interactions of neighboring acetate and ketonic functions have been noted. Thus the two absorption bands for a 20-keto-21-acetoxy steroid are both displaced to shorter wave lengths than observed when the two functional groups are distant. No vicinal effects are noted with free 20-keto-21-hydroxy compounds, with 11-keto-17-acetoxy derivatives, or with 11,20-diketones.

In the spectra of α,β-unsaturated ketones the band characteristic of the corresponding saturated ketone is shifted to longer wave lengths by amounts varying from 0.04 to 0.09 μ (27 – 43 cm.$^{-1}$) in the three known cases; the three unsaturated ketones are not distinguishable with respect to this band.

$$\begin{array}{cc}
\text{CH}_2\text{OCCH}_3 & \text{CH}_2\text{OH} \\
\text{CO} \quad \text{O} & \text{CO}
\end{array}$$

(Vicinal effect)   (No vicinal effect)

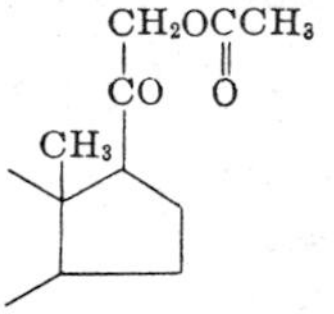

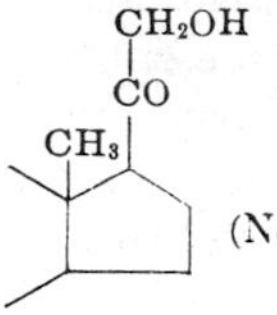

$\lambda \ ^{\text{CS}_2}_{\text{max}}$ 5.642, 5.692μ $\lambda \ ^{\text{CS}_2}_{\text{max}}$ 5.862μ (1706 cm.$^{-1}$)
(1732, 1757 cm.$^{-1}$)

However, Furchgott, Rosenkrantz and Shorr[4] found that at least two of the ketonic types can be differentiated with reference to a second band at about 6.2 μ (1600 cm.$^{-1}$) observable in spectra determined with crystal films. Both carbon bisulfide and carbon tetrachloride absorb strongly in this region, but Blout, Fields and Karplus[9] used chloroform successfully as solvent for exploration of this part of the spectrum. The measurements of Jones and co-workers in chloroform (Table IX) show that the position of this band definitely differentiates between Δ^4-3-ketones and Δ^{16}-20-ketones.

Infrared spectrometry by present techniques cannot be relied upon for the determination of the presence or absence of a double bond in a steroid. With both saturated and unsaturated compounds a strong absorption band appears in the region 3.3 – 3.6 μ (3000 – 2800 cm.$^{-1}$) due to —C—H vibrations of the ring and side chain (band C, Figure 1). In unsaturated compounds in which the double bond carries at least one hydrogen atom a minor shoulder or inflection often appears at the base of this main band at 3.312 μ (3020 cm.$^{-1}$) that is attributable to =C—H vibrations. Sometimes this inflection fails to appear in determinations in solution because the concentration is too low, and positive identification can be made better by the crystal film technique. With a $\Delta^{8(14)}$-steroid (ditertiary double bond) this structural characteristic is missing and the inflection is completely absent.

OPTICAL ACTIVITY

Specific rotations have been determined routinely by most sterol chemists and the constants have proved of great value for purposes of characterization and as criteria of purity. In the past decade optical rotatory data have found significant application in the determination of structure and configuration, and the theoretical interpretation of rotational effects in this

[9] Blout, Fields and Karplus, *J. Am. Chem. Soc.*, **70**, 194 (1948).

series offers intriguing problems for the future. Unfortunately there are many gaps in the existing literature. A report of rotatory power has not always been recognized as an obligatory part of the description of each new compound, derivative, or intermediate encountered; yet the optical data are likely to be of far greater ultimate value than melting points, even though useful applications may not be apparent when the compounds are first prepared.

The existing records also suffer from the shortcoming that the specific rotations recorded were determined in a variety of solvents. Chloroform is a favored solvent for the characterization of sterols and their acyl derivatives and has been advocated as a reference standard (Wallis; Barton). However, chloroform does not have adequate solvent power for many bile acids and for the highly hydroxylated steroids of the adrenal cortex, and in the latter instances the favored solvents are alcohol, acetone, and dioxane. A few direct comparisons[1, 2] indicate that specific rotations (in the range of $-40°$ to $+100°$) in acetone or alcohol are some $8 - 10°$ more positive than the rotations of the same compounds in chloroform; rotations determined in dioxane (peroxide-free!) are $4 - 6°$ more positive than those in chloroform. Since dioxane occupies a median position and has high solvent power for compounds of many types, this would seem to be the preferred solvent for general use. Much of the recorded data, however, refers to chloroform solution; a sparingly soluble substance sometimes can be brought into solution by the addition of ethanol in amount insufficient to significantly affect the rotation. Acyl and ester derivatives often differ considerably in solubility characteristics from the parent compounds, but the use of different solvents for the determination of specific rotations imposes an unnecessary limitation on the usefulness of the data. The comparison of the rotatory powers of a typical steroid alcohol and its acyl derivatives is of particular significance. Acetylation greatly increases the mass of the oxygen function and the dissymmetry at the position concerned, and the dextro- or levorotatory character of the asymmetric center is thereby accentuated and becomes more easily recognizable.

The basis of comparison in the following discussions is the molecular rotation, M_D, defined as follows:

$$M_D = \frac{[\alpha]_D \times \text{Molecular Weight}}{100}$$

The experimental error in the determination of specific rotations is about $1 - 3$ percent, and hence M_D is uncertain to the extent of $5 - 10$ units.

[1] Plattner and Heusser, *Helv. Chim. Acta.*, **27**, 748 (1944).
[2] Barton, *J. Chem. Soc.*, 1116 (1946).

Method of Molecular Rotation Differences. Callow and Young[3] initiated the analysis of optical rotational data by pointing out that all natural sterols having a 5,6-double bond are levorotatory. They also observed that among sterols, bile acids, and members of the androstane series an inversion at C_3 from the β- to the α-configuration usually leads to slightly increased dextrorotation, and that the increase is much greater in nuclear-unsaturated stenols than in stanols. Callow and Young noted further that a 4,5-double bond increases dextrorotation, whereas a 5,6-double bond augments levorotation, regardless of the basic nature of the steroid. The investigation of the effects of structural changes on optical activity was extended by Wallis and co-workers,[4] and then Barton perfected a method for the analysis of molecular rotation differences and applied it with considerable success to the revision of a number of proposed formulas.[5] One method of approach is illustrated by the data in Table X for a group of 3β-hydroxy A/B-trans stanols that differ in the structure and configuration of the side chain. The less common sterols from which these stanols are derived are discussed in Part 3 of this chapter; they carry a methyl or

TABLE X.[a] Molecular Rotation Differences for Stanol Derivatives

STEROL	SIDE CHAIN SUBST.	M_D (CHCl$_3$)				M_D (DERIV.) $-$ M_D (STEROL)		
		Sterol	Acetate	Benzoate	Ketone	ΔAc	ΔBz	ΔKet
Cholestanol........	none	+ 93	+ 60	+ 98	+ 158	− 33	+ 5	+ 65
Ergostanol........	24b—CH$_3$	+ 64	+ 27		+ 140	− 37		+ 76
Campestanol.......	24a—CH$_3$	+ 125	+ 80			− 45		
Stellastanol........	24a—CH$_3$	+ 88	+ 62			− 26		
Stigmastanol.......	24b—C$_2$H$_5$	+ 100	+ 69	+ 104	+ 170	− 31	+ 4	+ 70
Poriferastanol[b].....	24a—C$_2$H$_5$	+ 90	+ 70		+ 171	− 20		+ 81
"γ"-Sitostanol.....	24a—C$_2$H$_5$	+ 83	+ 46		+ 157	− 37		+ 74

[a] Data from Barton, Part I, except as noted.
[b] Data from W. Bergmann and Low, *J. Org. Chem.*, **12,** 67 (1947).

[3] R. K. Callow and F. G. Young, *Proc. Roy. Soc.*, **A157,** 194 (1936).
[4] Bernstein, Kauzmann and Wallis, *J. Org. Chem.*, **6,** 319 (1941); Bernstein, E. J. Wilson, and Wallis, *ibid.*, **7,** 103 (1942).
[5] Barton, "The Application of the Method of Molecular Rotation Differences to Steroids," Part I (Natural Sterols), *J. Chem. Soc.*, 813 (1945); Part II (Unsaturated Sterols), *ibid.*, 512 (1946); Part III (Steroidal Hormones and Bile Acids), *ibid.*, 1116 (1946); Barton and J. D. Cox, Part IV (Optical Anomalies), *ibid.*, 783 (1948); Part V (Unsaturation at the 7,8-Position), *ibid.*, in press; Part VI (Neosterol), *ibid.*, in press; Part VII (Olefinic Unsaturation at the 8,9-Position), *ibid.*, in press; Part VIII (22-Dihydroergosterol D), *ibid.*, in press; Barton and E. Miller, Part IX ("u" Ergostadienol), *ibid.*, in press; Barton and Klyne, Survey of Some Steroid Molecular Rotations, *Chemistry and Industry*, in press.

ethyl group at C_{24} in the two possible orientations, a and b, and stellastanol is probably the C_{20}-epimer of campestanol. These changes in the side chain produce differences in molecular rotation of as much as 61 units, and a compound under study could not be recognized as belonging or not belonging to this group on the basis of the absolute M_D value. However, the difference in M_D between the acetates and the free stanols (Δ^{Ac}) is a fairly constant value (av. -33) regardless of the absolute value of M_D and hence this difference is an identifying characteristic of the series. The increments in M_D attending benzoylation ($\Delta^{Bz} + 4.5$) and conversion to the 3-stanones ($\Delta^{Ket} + 73$) are quite different from Δ^{Ac} and are further constants characteristic of the common ring system and 3β-hydroxyl group. Correspondence with all three Δ values for the more exactly characterized stanols within the limits of error in the determination of $[\alpha]_D$ constitutes sure evidence of homogeneity and of correspondence in type. Certain substances previously regarded as members of the group were recognized by Barton as grossly impure because of the anomalous Δ values. The rare 24a-methyl compounds are very difficult to obtain completely free from the more levorotatory 24b-epimers, and Bergmann and Low[6] employed M_D differences to advantage in estimating the degree of purity of various samples and in establishing configurations. The rotational contribution of the 24b-methyl group can be evaluated reliably by comparison of the M_D values of a series of ergostanol derivatives with those of cholestanol, as shown in Table XI, and the contribution of the 24b-ethyl group is evaluated by comparison of stigmastanol with cholestanol. These three series

TABLE XI. M_D Contributions of 24-Alkyl Groups ($CHCl_3$)

DERIVATIVE	ΔM_D FROM THAT OF CHOLESTANOL ANALOG			
	Ergostanol	Campe-stanol	Stigma-stanol	Porifera-stanol
	24b-CH₃	24a-CH₃	24b-C₂H₅	24a-C₂H₅
Stanol	-29	$+32$	$+7$	-3
Stanyl acetate	-33	$+20$	$+9$	$+10$
Stanyl benzoate			$+6$	
Stanone			$+12$	$+13$
Δ^5-Stenol	-33	$+19$	$+2$	-2
Δ^5-Stenyl acetate	-19	$+25$	$+6$	-5
Δ^5-Stenyl benzoate	-32	$+14$	-9	-19
Δ^5-Stenyl m-Dinitrobenzoate			$+20$	-4
Δ^4-Stenone			-3	-27
Average	-29	$+22$	$+6$	-5

6 W. Bergmann and Low, *J. Org. Chem.*, **12**, 67 (1948).

of compounds have been studied extensively and carefully and the individual Δ values show considerable constancy; the contribution of the 24b-methyl group (–29) is clearly much greater than that of the 24a-ethyl group (+ 6). The Δ values reported for the 24a-methyl group are based upon data for derivatives of campestanol, known from chemical evidence to be the 24a-epimer of ergostanol. The increment expected for a 24a-methyl group, on the basis of the reliable data for the 24b-methyl compounds, is + 29, and the fact that the observed average (+ 22) is in agreement with this expectation within the permissible error establishes the essential purity of the campestanol compounds. The same conclusion applies to porifera-stanol (last column).

The method of molecular rotation differences has been of great value in establishing the structure and homogeneity of unsaturated sterols. One method of analysis employed by Barton consists in calculation of the effect of a double bond in various locations on the M_D increments for the acylation and for the oxidation of the 3β-hydroxyl group. Table XII gives Barton's average values and the maximum deviations observed. It is evi-

TABLE XII.[a]   Effect of Double Bonds on M_D-Values (CHCl$_3$) for Derivatives of 3β-Hydroxy Sterols

COMPOUND	M_D (DERIVATIVE) − M_D (STEROL)		
	Δ^{Ac}	Δ^{Bz}	Δ^{Ket}
Stanol	− 34 ±11(7)	+ 2 ±3(2)	+ 73 ±9(5)
Δ^5-Stenol	− 35 ±16(12)	+ 81 ±16(11)	+ 124(1)[b]
			+ 480 ±39(7)[c]
Δ^7-Stenol	− 15 ±15(2)	+ 20 ±14(2)	(+ 90)
Δ^8-Stenol	− 46.5 ±1(2)	+ 11.5 ±3.5(2)	
$\Delta^{8 (14)}$-Stenol	− 40 ±17(4)	− 42 ±1(3)	+ 75(1)
Δ^{14}-Stenol	− 35 ±6(3)	+ 30 ±21(3)	+ 73(2)
$\Delta^{5,7}$-Stadienol	+ 120 ±43(4)	+ 185 ±15(5)	

   [a] Data from Barton, Part I. The figure following ± indicates the range within which the Δ values fall; the figure in parentheses gives the number of comparisons.
   [b] Δ^5-Cholestenone-3.
   [c] Δ^4-3-Ketones.

dent that the changes in the Δ values associated with the introduction of a double bond at each of the positions listed are sufficiently pronounced to be characteristic of each structural type. A 5,6-double bond is not revealed by the increment for the acetates (Δ^{Ac}) but is characterized by marked shifts in the values for the benzoates, for a 3-ketone, and for the α,β-unsaturated ketones that result on oxidation and bond migration. Δ^7-Stenols have low and nearly identical Δ^{Ac} and Δ^{Bz} values of opposite sign.

Δ^8-Stenols are only slightly different in Δ values from Δ^5-stenols but are easily differentiated by virtue of their resistance to hydrogenation. An 8,14-double bond is characterized particularly by the negative value of Δ^{Bz} and a 14,15-double bond by negative and positive values for Δ^{Ac} and Δ^{Bz}. Barton has employed these relationships in deducing the structures of a number of stenols of the cholesterol and ergosterol series and of some of the rare unsaturated sterols of natural occurrence.

A second method for the analysis of data for unsaturated compounds is calculation of the effect on the molecular rotation of a parent saturated compound produced by introduction of a double bond in various positions. Average values of the rotational contributions of double bonds in nuclear positions of both stanols (5α-series) and bile acids (5β-series), and of side-chain double bonds introduced into stanols, are recorded in Table XIII. Marked differences between the effects in the 5α- and 5β-series are noted in most instances where the double bond is not separated from C_5 by at least three saturated carbon atoms. The optical anomalies observed when an unsaturated group is adjacent to or near an asymmetric center are designated both as "vicinal effects" and as "optical exaltations"; the former term is applied also to anomalies associated with neighboring centers of asymmetry bearing polar substituents. A 2,3-double bond is one carbon atom removed from the centers of asymmetry at C_5 and C_{10}, but the pronounced difference in the effect in the 5α- and 5β-series is evidence of a strong vicinal action. Differences indicative of vicinal action are evident in steroids with double bonds at the 7,8-, 9,11-, and 8,14-positions; in the latter instance the vicinal effect is transmitted through two saturated carbon atoms. The 11,12-double bond is only two carbon atoms removed from C_5 but apparently does not produce vicinal action and is listed in Table XIII with still more remote double bonds with which differences between the 5α- and 5β-series vanish. The data of Table XII also bear evidence of vicinal action of double bonds neighboring position 3; the Δ values for the 3-ketones (Δ^{Ket}) show that the vicinal effect disappears when the double bond is separated from C_3 by at least three carbon atoms. No theoretical interpretations have been advanced for the very large dextrorotatory effect of a 4,5-double bond and the still more pronounced levorotatory contribution of a 5,6-double bond; in each case the asymmetry at C_5 is destroyed and the double bond is in a position favorable for strong exaltation of the rotational contribution of carbon atom 10, and yet the pronounced effects are of opposite sign.

The data of Table XIII show that the $\Delta^{C=C}$ values of Δ^7 and $\Delta^{8(14)}$-stenols differ from those of the corresponding unsaturated compounds of the bile acid series; the increment in M_D for introduction of a Δ^{14}-double bond is the same in the two series. Failure to recognize the fact that correlations

TABLE XIII.[a] Molecular Rotation Contributions of Double Bonds ($CHCl_3$)

DOUBLE BOND	5α-SERIES (A/B-TRANS)	5β-SERIES (A/B-CIS)
2,3	$+ 152$ (1)	$- 41$ (1)
4,5	$+ 159^b$	
5,6	$- 298^b$	
7,8	$- 68 \pm 17(2)$	$+ 119 \pm 12(2)$
8,9	$+ 96 \pm 4(2)$	
8,14	$- 16 \pm 8(4)$	$- 37$
9,11	$+ 109 \pm 17(3)$	$+ 49 \pm 3(4)$
	COMBINED 5α- AND 5β-SERIES	
11,12	$+ 33 \pm 12(5)$	
14,15	$+ 28(2)$	
16,17	$+ 31 \pm 9(6)$	
17,20	$+ 35$ (1)^c	
	5α-SERIES	
22,23	$- 61 \pm 20(5)$	
24,25	$- 4 \pm 9(3)$	
24,28	$- 20(1)$	
2,3; 4,5	$+ 531(1)$	
3,4; 5,6	$- 363(1)$	
4,5; 6,7	$- 75(1)$	
5,6; 7,8	$- 538 \pm 40(5)$	
7,8; 9,11	$+ 27(1)$	
7,8; 14,15	$- 252(1)$	
8,9; 14,15	$- 152 \pm 28(2)$	

[a] Data largely from Barton and Klyne, Part X. The figure following ± indicates the range within which the Δ values fall; the figure in parentheses gives the number of comparisons.

[b] Referred to the 5α-saturated compound.

[c] A C_{21} steroid.

established in the one series may not be applicable in the other has led to errors in interpretation of data.

Barton and Cox (ref. 5, Part IV) have tentatively suggested a correlation between optical rotational anomalies in steroids and the ultraviolet absorption characteristics of the same compounds. Homoannular dienic systems ($\Delta^{2,4}$, $\Delta^{5,7}$) generally produce a very great exaltation of rotation (Table XIII) and give rise to ultraviolet absorption of long wave length (265 – 285 mμ); heteroannular dienes ($\Delta^{3,5}$-, $\Delta^{4,6}$-, $\Delta^{7,9(11)}$-, $\Delta^{7,14}$-, $\Delta^{8,14}$-) usually have less influence on molecular rotation and absorb ultraviolet light of shorter wave length (230–250 mμ).

Individual Rotatory Contributions. Tentative inferences concerning the sign and magnitude of the rotatory contributions of individual centers of asymmetry can be drawn from comparisons of the molecular rotations of compounds that differ in the configuration at a single asymmetric center (Table XIV). The differences between the representative pairs of saturated C_5-epimers 1, 3, and 4 are slight, but the difference for the benzoates (No. 2) is sufficiently pronounced to suggest that carbon atom 5 is weakly levorotatory in the α-orientation. More decisive information is provided by comparison of the pair of unsaturated epimers, No. 5. Unsaturation adjacent to an asymmetric center produces strong exaltational effects, but the influence may extend beyond the sphere of the center or centers in the immediate environment and inferences concerning the effect at a single center do not appear to be very reliable. However, it seems safe to take the direction of the molecular rotation difference between two unsaturated epimers as an index of the sign of rotation at the center of epimerization. Comparison 5 then indicates that $C_5\alpha$ is definitely levorotatory. The rotations of the unsaturated compounds afford no guide to the magnitude of the rotatory contribution, but those of the saturated epimers show that $C_5\alpha$ is weakly levorotatory (average $\Delta^{\beta-\alpha} = +18$; contribution of $C_5\alpha$, $-18/2$, or about -10). A comparison of the acetates (5) with the benzoates (2) shows that exaltation of $C_5\beta +$ (and elsewhere in the molecule) produces a positive shift of 600 units whereas exaltation of $C_5\alpha -$ results in a negative shift of only 50 units. Although the directions of shift here follow the sign of the exalted center, the magnitude of shift is in one case so low as to suggest that in other instances the rule may not be followed.

Comparison of ergosterol with lumisterol (6) shows that the transposition of the angular methyl group from the front (β) to the rear (α) position is attended with a very pronounced positive shift in M_D; therefore $C_{10}\beta$ must be levorotatory. Comparisons can also be made between two other C_{10}-epimers of the ergosterol-irradiation series, but one member of each pair is of the pyrocalciferol type and has the unnatural configuration at both C_9 and C_{10}. Since a double inversion at adjacent centers may evoke strong vicinal effects, such data are considered invalid and will not be employed for analysis of the relationships at C_{10} or at C_9. The unsaturated C_9-epimers isopyrocalciferol and ergosterol (8) differ very markedly in rotation in a direction indicating that $C_9\beta$ is positive and hence that the natural $C_9\alpha$-orientation is negative. Data available for saturated C_{10} (No. 7) and C_9 (No. 9) epimers show merely that the rotatory contribution at each center is very feeble. A slight apparent difference between the free C_{10}-epimers (in the unexpected direction) disappears on acetylation. One of the saturated C_9-epimers (No. 9), perhydroisopyrocalciferol has been prepared only once and the sample exhibited an unsharp melting point ($68 - 80°$)

TABLE XIV.   Differences in Molecular Rotation Due to Epimerization at a Single Center (C*)

NO.	EPIMERS	C*	M_D	$M_D^\beta - M_D^\alpha$
1	Coprostanol Cholestanol	5β 5α	+ 109 Chf + 93 Chf	+ 16
2	Coprostanol benzoate Cholestanol benzoate	5β 5α	+ 152 Chf + 98 Chf	+ 54
3	Lithocholic acid 3α-Hydroxyallocholanic acid	5β 5α	+ 120 Al + 95 Al	+ 25
4	Epicoprostanol Epicholestanol	5β 5α	+ 123 Chf + 109 Chf	+ 14
5	$\Delta^{6,8}$-Coprostadienol-3β acetate Isodehydrocholesterol acetate	5β 5α	+ 751 + 46	+ 705
6	Ergosterol Lumisterol	10β 10α	− 515 Chf + 760 An	− 1275
7	Ergostanol; acetate Lumistanol; acetate	10β 10α	+ 64 Chf; + 27 Chf + 38 Chf; + 22 An	?
8	Isopyrocalciferol Ergosterol	9β 9α	+ 1310 Chf − 515 Chf	+ 1825
9	Perhydroisopyrocalciferol acetate Ergostanol acetate	9β 9α	(− 28 Chf) + 64 Chf	?
10	Estrone 8-Isoestrone	8β 8α	+ 445 Chf + 254 Chf	+ 191
11	Estradiol-17β 8-Isoestradiol-17β	8β 8α	+ 220 Al + 49 Di	+ 171
12	d-Isoequilenin Equilenin	14β 14α	+ 391 Di + 232 Al	+ 159
13	Methyl 3β-acetoxy-14-iso-17-isoetio-allocholanate Methyl 3β - acetoxy -17 - isoetioallo-cholanate	14β 14α	+ 91 Chf − 139 Chf	+ 230
14	Methyl 14-iso-17-isoetioallocholan-ate Methyl 17-isoetioallocholanate	14β 14α	+ 118 Chf − 102 Chf	+ 220

TABLE XIV. *Continued*

NO.	EPIMERS	C*	M_D	$M^\beta_D - M^\alpha_D$
15	Estrone	13β	+ 445 Chf	+ 561
	Lumiestrone	13α	− 116 Di	
16	Androsterone	13β	+ 275 Al	+ 565
	Lumiandrosterone	13α	− 290 Al	
17	Estradiol-17β	13β	+ 220 Al	+ 176
	Lumiestradiol-17β methyl ether	13α	+ 44 Chf	
18	Progesterone	17β	+ 603 Al	+ 603
	17-Isoprogesterone	17α	± 0 Al	
19	Δ^5-Pregnene 3β ol 20 one	17β	+ 89 Al	+ 522
	Δ^5-17-Isopregnene-3β-ol-20-one	17α	− 433 Al	
20	Methyl etioallocholanate	17β	+ 155 Di	+ 281
	Methyl 17-isoetioallocholanate	17α	− 129 Di	

Chf = Chloroform, Al = Alcohol, An = Acetone, Di = Dioxane

after repeated crystallization. In view of the substantial evidence of the sign of rotation, the natural $C_{10}\beta$- and $C_9\alpha$-orientations can be considered to make minor contributions of − 5 units each.

The two comparisons of the effect of epimerization at C_8 (10, 11) seem to provide a reliable index of the direction and magnitude of the rotation at this center because the benzenoid ring is one carbon atom removed from it. Natural $C_8\beta$ is thus a strongly positive rotophore (+ 90 units). In the first (12) of the three pairs of C_{14}-epimers listed the center concerned is adjacent to an aromatic ring and the M_D increment is not so reliable an index as the other two agreeing values (220 − 230) for the difference in M_D between saturated compounds (13, 14); $C_{14}\alpha$ is strongly levorotatory, and the estimated contribution is − 110. Comparison of estrone (15) and androsterone (16) with the lumi-epimers in which the angular methyl group at C_{13} is inverted from the β- to the α-orientation shows $C_{13}\beta$ to be dextrorotatory but does not afford a reliable estimate of the magnitude of the effect because of the probable exaltation by the adjacent carbonyl group at C_{17}. Data are not available for a precise comparison of compounds lacking such disturbing groups, but a comparison of estradiol-17β with the phenolic methyl ether of its epimer (17) seems admissible; the result indicates $C_{13}\beta$ to be strongly positive (175/2, or about + 90 units).

The three representative comparisons of the effect of inversion at C_{17} listed (18 − 20) indicate $C_{17}\beta$ to be positive, but they do not disclose the magnitude of the effect because the keto and carboxylate groups undoubtedly have exalting influences. Thus the molecular rotation of progesterone is 41 percent higher than that of cholestenone (M_D 357 Chf), and the molecular rotation of methyl etioallocholanate (No. 20) is 41 percent higher than that of cholestane (M_D + 91 Chf). Unfortunately, no estimate can be made of the exaltational effects in the 17-iso series, and hence the most that can be said of the rotational contribution of $C_{17}\beta$ is that the effect must be less than observed for the etio esters No. 20 (284/2 = 142 units). Since approximate estimates can be made of the magnitude of the rotations at all other nuclear centers and since the side-chain carbon atom 20, defined as β-oriented in the natural sterols, has only a feeble effect estimated as + 5 units (Chapter V), some idea of the magnitude of the rotational contribution of $C_{17}\beta$ can be made by subtracting the summation of the contributions at all other centers from the molecular rotation of cholestane (M_D + 91 Chf); calculation from the above approximations gives a value of + 35. The estimated effects at the various centers are summarized in the formula for cholestane (I). The signs of rotation seem reasonably secure; the values

Cholestane
M_D + 91 Chf

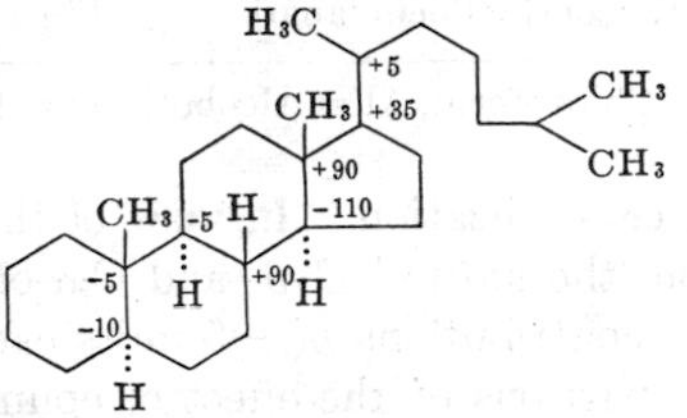

Estimated individual molecular rotation contributions

for the specific M_D contributions are initial approximations that can be revised in the light of more accurate and more extensive data.

According to this analysis, the eight asymmetric carbon atoms of cholestane extending in an unbroken chain from C_5 to C_{20} are oriented in a symmetrical and well neutralized pattern: $---+-+++$. The three most powerful rotophores are of alternate signs and occupy a central portion of the chain. The terminal carbon atoms in the chain of asymmetry are only feebly rotatory. The distribution of dextro- and levorotatory centers resembles those suggested for morphine[7] and for the resin acids (Chapter II). Perhaps the processes of biosynthesis are controlled by a tendency for asymmetric centers to unite in such a manner as to produce a balanced, or neutralized chain.

It is noteworthy that the sterols of the animal organism are weakly rotatory (M_D + 90 to − 150). In spite of the presence of several centers of asymmetry, three of which appear capable of rotational effects in the order

[7] Emde, *Helv. Chim. Acta*, **13**, 1035 (1930).

of ± 100 units, the arrangement is such as to produce almost a complete balance. A hydroxy group at C_3 in either the β- or α-orientation has only a minor influence on the rotation, and the same is true of other common changes in the steroid molecule: inversion at C_5, and change from the sterol to the bile acid side chain. The 5,6-double bond of cholesterol produces a levorotatory shift, but does not lead to pronounced molecular rotation ($M_D - 151$). The steroid hormones secreted in minute amounts in the organism and capable of evoking specific physiological actions are characterized by high dextrorotation, for example: estradiol-17β, $M_D + 220$; estrone, $+ 445$; testosterone, $+ 314$; progesterone, $+ 603$; corticosterone, $+ 734$; Kendall's A, $+ 788$. The high dextrorotation of the hormones in comparison with abundant body steroids and normal products of hormone metabolism suggests the possibility that instances may exist in which optical activity contributes to physiological functioning, possibly by controlling the formation of hormone-enzyme complexes.

Hydroxyl Substitution. The signs of rotation at hydroxylated centers can be deduced from the data of Table XV by the method employed above; the table lists pairs of compounds epimeric at a particular position carrying a hydroxyl group, together with the parent substance or substances having a hydrogen atom at this position (see below for calculation of Δ^{OH} values). Again, comparison of saturated epimers affords a measure of the magnitude of individual rotatory contributions and the data for unsaturated compounds is useful in revealing the sign of rotation. Comparisons 21 and 22 indicate weak contributions at $C_3\beta$-OH of opposite sign, but No. 21 can be taken as the more reliable because the sign of the Δ value agrees with that indicated in comparisons 23 and 24; a 5,6-double bond (No. 23) enhances somewhat the effect of the hydroxyl substituent, and a 4,5-double bond (No. 24) produces a very great exaltation of the effect. The data of examples 32 and 33 illustrate the increased spread in the rotations of epimers resulting from the increase in dissymmetry attending acetylation.

Comparisons 25 and 26 show that $C_3\beta$-OH is less dextrorotatory than $C_3\alpha$-OH in the coprostane series as it is in the cholestane series, and that the magnitude of the effects is about the same; the effects in this instance are slight. The difference between pairs of C_6-OH epimers of the cholestane (29) and coprostane (30) series are large and of opposite sign, probably in consequence of vicinal action of the contiguous centers C_5 and C_6. Therefore the configuration of a member of one series cannot be inferred from a rotational correspondence to a member of the other series unless vicinal effects are known to be inoperative. Plattner and Heusser's[1] deduction of the configurations of the epimeric 7-hydroxycholestanols (31) by optical analogy to 7-epimers of the bile acid series lacked validating evidence on this point, but the configurations are now known from chemical evidence

TABLE XV.   Rotatory Contributions at Hydroxylated Centers

NO.	EPIMERS	PARENT COMPOUND	OH	M_D	$M_D^\beta - M_D^\alpha$
21	Cholestanol Epicholestanol	Cholestane	3β 3α	+ 93 Chf + 109 Chf + 91 Chf	− 16
22	Ergostanol Epiergostanol	Ergostane	3β 3α	+ 64 Chf + 54 Chf + 83 Chf	+ 10
23	Cholesterol Epicholesterol	Δ^5-Cholestene	3β 3α	− 151 Chf − 145 Chf − 207 Chf	− 6
24	Δ^4-Cholestenol Epimer	Δ^4-Cholestene	3β 3α	+ 170 B + 467 B + 248 Chf	− 297
25	Coprostanol Epicoprostanol	Coprostane	3β 3α	+ 109 Chf + 123 Chf + 93 Chf	− 14
26	3β-Hydroxycholanic acid Lithocholic acid	Cholanic acid	3β 3α	+ 98 Al + 120 Al + 102 Al	− 22
27	Cholestane-$3\beta,5\alpha$-diol	Cholestanol	5α	+ 81 Chf + 93 Chf	
28	Tetrahydro-14-anhydroperiplogenin Epimer	3β-Hydroxycholanic acid 3β-Hydroxyallocholanic acid	5β 5α	+ 346 Chf + 90 Chf + 98 Al + 32 Di	+ 256
29	Cholestane-$3\beta,6\beta$-diol Cholestane-$3\beta,6\alpha$-diol	Cholestanol	6β 6α	+ 57 Chf + 154 Chf + 93 Chf	− 97
30	$3\alpha,6\beta$-Dihydroxycholanic acid "α"-Hyodesoxycholic acid	Lithocholic acid	6β 6α	+ 145 Al + 31 Al + 120 Al	+ 114
31	7β-Hydroxycholestanol Epimer	Cholestanol	7β 7α	+ 214 Chf + 33 Chf + 93 Chf	+ 181

TABLE XV. *Continued*

NO.	EPIMERS	PARENT COMPOUND	OH	M_D	$M_D^\beta - M_D^\alpha$
32	7β-Hydroxycholesterol Epimer		7β 7α	+ 29 Chf − 351 Chf	+ 380
33	7β-Hydroxycholesterol diacetate Epimer		7β 7α	+ 252 Chf − 847 Chf	+ 1099
34	Ursodesoxycholic acid Chenodesoxycholic acid	Lithocholic acid	7β 7α	+ 223 Al + 43 Al + 120 Al	+ 180
35	16-Epiestriol Estriol		16β 16α	+ 254 Al + 176 Al	+ 78
36	Estradiol-17β Estradiol-17α	17-Desoxoestrone	17β 17α	+ 220 Al + 147 Di + 228 Al	+ 73
37	Testosterone Epitestosterone		17β 17α	+ 314 Al + 206 Al	+ 108
38	17β-Hydroxy-17-isoprogesterone 17α-Hydroxyprogesterone	17-Isoprogesterone Progesterone	17β 17α	+ 178 Di + 350 Chf 0 Al + 603 Al	− 172
39	12-Epidesoxycholic acid Desoxycholic acid	Lithocholic acid	12β 12α	+ 151 Di + 224 Al + 120 Al	− 73
40	12β-Hydroxycholanic acid Epimer	Cholanic acid	12β 12α	+ 143 An + 164 An + 102 Al	− 21
41	3α,12β-Dihydroxy-Δ⁹⁽¹¹⁾-cholenic acid Epimer		12β 12α	+ 110 + 407 Al	− 297
42	3α,11β-Dihydroxycholanic acid Epimer	Lithocholic acid	11β 11α	+ 206 Al + 86 Al + 120 Al	+ 120
43	Corticosterone acetate 11-Epicorticosterone acetate	Desoxycorticosterone acetate	11β 11α	+ 761 An + 726 An + 648 Di	+ 35

and comparisons 31 and 34 indicate that there is little vicinal action between C_7 and C_5, for 7α- and 7β-hydroxyl groups produce nearly the same effects in both series.

Comparisons 28 (C_5) and 38 (C_{17}) refer to epimeric tertiary alcohols, and here the transposition of the hydroxyl group from one orientation to the other is attended with an inversion of the skeletal structure as well. The parent desoxy compound of each epimer or a close model of a parent compound, is listed. The difference in rotation between the β-OH and α-OH compounds is in each case of the same sign as the difference between the parent β-H and α-H compounds. In example 28 the actual parent substances are known but have not been differentiated; comparison of their optical properties (M_D + 67 and + 21) with those of the cholanic acids taken as desoxy models suggests that the more dextrorotatory isomer has the A/B-cis configuration.

Table XVI lists estimates of the effect on molecular rotation of the substitution of hydroxyl groups in various positions and orientations in saturated compounds of the sterol (A/B-trans) and bile acid (A/B-cis) series.

TABLE XVI. Rotatory Effects of Hydroxyl Groups (ΔM_D)

POSITION	5α-SERIES (A/B-TRANS)		5β-SERIES (A/B-CIS)	
	β-OH	α-OH	β-OH	α-OH
3	+ 2	+ 18	+ 6	+ 24
5		− 26	+ 91	
6	− 36	+ 61	+ 25	− 89
7	+ 121	− 60	+ 103	− 77
17	− 8	− 81		
12			+ 36	+ 83
11			+ 86	− 34

These calculations are limited to the data of Table XV except that those pertaining to position 5 are based upon newly reported data for the 3,5-diols of cholestane and coprostane.[8] Since vicinal action at C_5 does not seem to extend even to C_7, the effects attributed to groups at C_{17}, C_{12}, or C_{11} in one series probably can be assumed to apply equally well in the other.

An oxide bridge between two adjacent centers does not always produce an effect in the direction expected from the effect of hydroxylation at the positions concerned. The expected combined effect of 5β- and 6β-hydroxyl groups, as compared to the effect of 5α,6α-hydroxylation, is + 71 units, and cholesterol β-oxide (M_D + 39 Chf) is distinctly more dextrorotatory than cholesterol α-oxide (M_D − 178 Chf).

[8] Plattner, Heusser and Kulkarni, *Helv. Chim. Acta*, **31**, 1885 (1948).

On the other hand, vicinal effects completely obscure comparison of the epimeric 11,12-oxides. The difference expected between β,β- and α,α-hydroxylation is 73 units; actually methyl $3\alpha,9\alpha,11\alpha,12\alpha$-diepoxycholanate and methyl $3\alpha,9\alpha,11\beta,12\beta$-diepoxycholanate have the same rotation (M_D + 64 Chf). The effect of hydroxyl substitution at C_9 cannot yet be evaluated, but comparison of Δ^{11}-lithocholenic acid (M_D + 162 Al) with its $3\alpha,9\alpha$-epoxide (M_D − 209 Al) shows that the α-oxido linkage extending to C_9 increases the levorotatory contribution at this center.

Rough estimates can be made from the data of Table XVI of the molecular rotations of steroids having nonadjacent hydroxyl groups. Thus for cholic acid (M_D + 151 Al) the value calculated from that of cholanic acid and the separate rotatory effects of the three hydroxyl groups is + 132. Unfortunately, few of the hydrocarbon parents of the steroidal hormones have been characterized (pregnane, M_n + 58 Chf).

Halides. The relationship of a few 3-halides to the corresponding alcohols is shown in Table XVII. Inversion at C_3 from the β- to the α-configuration is attended with a shift of + 16 units with the alcohols and of

TABLE XVII. Molecular Rotations of Alcohols and Halides

C_3	ALCOHOL	M_D	HALIDE	M_D
β	Cholestanol	+ 93	β-Chlorocholestane	+ 110
α	Epicholestanol	+ 109	α-Chlorocholestane	+ 124
β	Cholesterol	− 151	Cholesteryl chloride	− 107
β			Cholesteryl bromide	− 85
β			Cholesteryl iodide	− 59

+ 14 with the chlorides. The saturated chlorides are 15 − 17 units more dextrorotatory than the stanols, and a double bond at C_5 − C_6 augments the difference to + 44 units.

REACTIONS

Cholestanetriols; Oxides. Two of the four possible cholestane-3,5,6-triols that could arise from the hydroxylation of the double bond of cholesterol have been known for many years but their configurations have only recently been elucidated. Hydroxylation with hydrogen peroxide[1] or through the α-oxide[2] gives the isomer commonly known as the trans-triol, whereas oxidation with alkaline permanganate[3] or with osmium tetroxide

[1] Pickard and Yates, *J. Chem. Soc.*, **93**, 1678 (1908).

[2] Westphalen, *Ber.*, **48**, 1064 (1915); Ruzicka and Bosshard, *Helv. Chim. Acta*, **20**, 244 (1937).

[3] Windaus, *Ber.*, **40**, 257 (1907).

gives the cis-triol (Chart 1). In the latter case the preparation through the osmic ester[4] establishes a cis orientation of the hydroxyls introduced. A trans orientation in the isomer was established by the rate of glycol cleavage with lead tetraacetate.[5] Evidence of the orientation at C_5 in the trans-triol was deduced by Ellis and Petrow[6] from the following experiments. Partial hydrolysis of the trans-triol 3,6-diacetate gave the 6-monoacetate, which was oxidized to 3-keto-5-hydroxy-6-acetoxycholestane. This 3-ketone was found to suffer oxidation at $C_2 - C_3$ and bromination at C_2, that is, in the direction characteristic of cholestanone rather than of coprostanone. The ring juncture is therefore trans and the 5-hydroxyl

Chart 1.   CHOLESTANE-3,5,6-TRIOLS

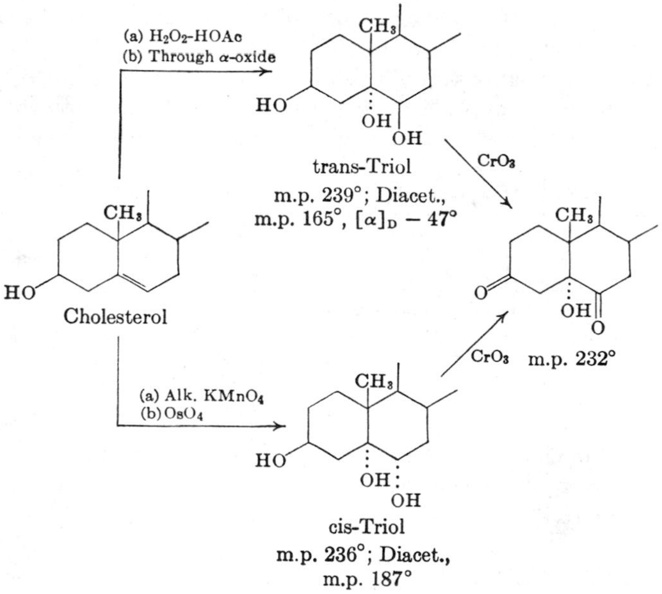

must have the α-orientation; the 6-hydroxyl is trans and therefore β, and the trans-triol is cholestane-3β,5α,6β-triol. Prelog and Tagmann[7] found that, contrary to earlier reports, both the cis and trans triols are converted on oxidation into the same 5-hydroxy-3,6-diketone and therefore correspond in configuration at C_5. The configuration of the cis-triol is there-

4 Ushakov and Lutenberg, *Nature*, **140**, 466 (1937).
5 Criegee, *Ber.*, **65**, 1770 (1932).
6 Ellis and Petrow, *J. Chem. Soc.*, 1078 (1939).
7 Prelog and Tagmann, *Helv. Chim. Acta*, **27**, 1867 (1944).

fore fully established as $3\beta,5\alpha,6\alpha$. These conclusions are confirmed by the relationship of the triols to the two oxides of cholesterol.

The literature prior to 1940 regarding the two 5,6-oxides of cholesterol is confused by the fact that one supposed isomer was not a single individual substance. The other, prepared from cholesterol with perbenzoic acid[2] was known in pure form and fortunately the arbitrary designation α-oxide has turned out to correspond to the actual α-orientation of the oxide ring. The reaction of cholesterol with perbenzoic acid does not proceed entirely in one direction, but the α-oxide predominates and can be purified easily by crystallization. The reaction of cholesteryl acetate with the reagent gives an oxide acetate of sharp melting point,[2] but Hattori[8] concluded on the basis of X-ray and chemical studies that the supposed "β-oxide" is a molecular compound of the true α- and β-forms. Separation into the two pure components has since been achieved by fractional crystallization[9] and by chromatography.[10] A mixture of equal parts of the α- and β-oxide acetates corresponds in melting point and specific rotation to the long-known substance now aptly called[9] the $\alpha\beta$-oxide acetate. A substance prepared from cholesteryl benzoate and monoperphthalic acid[11] is in reality the $\alpha\beta$-oxide benzoate.[9]

The fission reactions of the two oxides are formulated in Chart 2 as conforming to the following rule: the α-oxide ring is cleaved at C_6, the β-oxide ring at C_5; as in the case of other oxides, a Walden inversion occurs at the carbon atom at which a carbon – oxygen bond is ruptured, and again when the oxide ring is reformed. The direction of ring opening is established by the results of fission with hydrogen chloride in chloroform[8, 9] or with pyridine hydrochloride:[11] the α-oxide (II) yields a chlorodiol (I) that forms a monoacetate, which is easily dehydrated to an acetoxychloro-Δ^4-cholestene;[12] the β-oxide (III) yields a chlorodiol (IV) that forms a diacetate. The hydroxyl group generated in the fissions is thus tertiary in I and secondary in IV. Each chlorodiol can be reconverted into the respective oxide by the action of alkali; Hattori[8] separated the two chlorodiols from a mixture and prepared the pure β-oxide for the first time by the ring closure of one of them (IV). The trans-triol is converted by the action of hydrochloric acid into a mixture of the two chlorodiols.[13]

The configurations of the oxides and the steric orientations in the fissions were inferred by Plattner and Lang[14] from the results of hydrogenations.

---

[8] Hattori, *J. Pharm. Soc. Japan*, **60**, 334 (1940) [*C.A.*, **34**, 7294 (1940)].

[9] R. A. Baxter and Spring, *J. Chem. Soc.*, **613** (1943).

[10] Plattner, Petrzilka and Lang, *Helv. Chim. Acta*, **27**, 513 (1944).

[11] P. N. Chakravorty and Levin, *J. Am. Chem. Soc.*, **64**, 2317 (1942).

[12] Spring and Swain, *J. Chem. Soc.*, 1356 (1939).

[13] Windaus and Lüders, *Z. physiol. Chem.*, **117**, 154 (1921).

[14] Plattner and Lang, *Helv. Chim. Acta*, **27**, 1872 (1944).

On hydrogenation of the lower-melting oxide (β) as the 3-acetate the ring opens at C_5 to give a 3,6-diol 3-monoacetate (VII) that was oxidized to a

Chart 2. FISSION REACTIONS OF CHOLESTEROL α- AND β-OXIDES

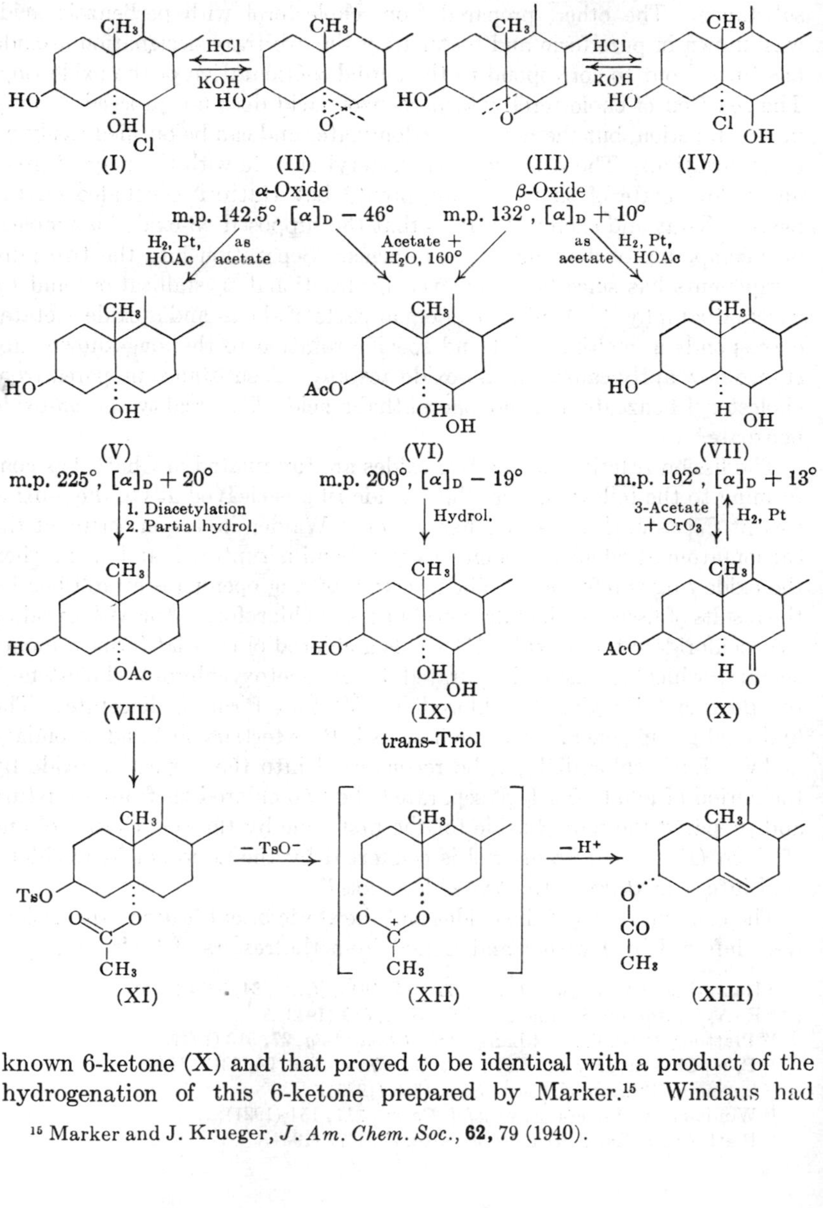

(I) (II) (III) (IV)

α-Oxide β-Oxide
m.p. 142.5°, [α]$_D$ − 46°   m.p. 132°, [α]$_D$ + 10°

H$_2$, Pt, / as   Acetate +   as \ H$_2$, Pt,
HOAc / acetate   H$_2$O, 160°   acetate \ HOAc

(V)   (VI)   (VII)
m.p. 225°, [α]$_D$ + 20°   m.p. 209°, [α]$_D$ − 19°   m.p. 192°, [α]$_D$ + 13°

1. Diacetylation   Hydrol.   3-Acetate ↑ H$_2$, Pt
2. Partial hydrol.   + CrO$_3$ ↓

(VIII)   (IX)   (X)
        trans-Triol

− TsO⁻ →   − H⁺ →

(XI)   (XII)   (XIII)

known 6-ketone (X) and that proved to be identical with a product of the hydrogenation of this 6-ketone prepared by Marker.[15] Windaus had

[15] Marker and J. Krueger, *J. Am. Chem. Soc.*, **62**, 79 (1940).

reduced the ketone with sodium and alcohol and prepared the 6α-epimer of VII.[16] On comparing the rates of hydrolysis of the corresponding diacetates, Plattner and Lang found that the diacetate of the Marker diol VII could be partially hydrolyzed to the 6-monoacetate whereas in the diacetate of the Windaus diol the 3- and 6-acetyl groups were split at the same rate. Stuart models show that a 6β- but not a 6α-hydroxyl is very close to the angular methyl group at C_{10}, and Plattner and Lang therefore concluded that the diacetate showing evidence of hindrance at C_6 has the β-orientation at this position. If the 6-hydroxyl group of the hydrogenation product is β, then the oxide from which it came must have the β-configuration (III). Since the diol VII is obtainable from a ketone (X) known to be of the allo series, the diol must have a configuration at C_5 (α) opposite to that of the oxide, and hence inversion has occurred at the point of fission of the oxide ring.

The higher-melting levorotatory oxide must have the alternate α-configuration. The hydroxyl group formed on hydrogenolysis (V) was shown to be at C_5 by oxidation to a keto alcohol and dehydration to Δ^4 cholestenone-3. This hydroxyl group, although tertiary, is acylable under forcing conditions, from which Plattner and Lang deduced the α-orientation; a 5β-hydroxyl should be strongly hindered by the angular methyl group. The oxide and its product of hydrogenation were thus characterized as 5α-compounds from independent evidence. Further confirmation was seen in the interesting transformation of cholestane-3β,5α-diol 5-acetate (VIII) by treatment with tosyl chloride into epicholesteryl acetate (XIII); the inversion at C_3 is attributed to the transient formation of a 1,3-cis glycol complex (XII).

Application to the process of hydrolysis of the oxides of the rule of fission stated above leads to the prediction that the α- and β-oxides should yield identical products. Plattner and Lang hydrolyzed the pure acetates of the two oxides with water and dioxane at 160° and did indeed obtain an identical product, namely the triol monoacetate VI. This on hydrolysis gives a product identical with cholestane-trans-triol (IX), discussed above. Both sets of evidence indicate the 3β,5α,6β-configuration, and the interpretations thus are mutually strengthened.

The fact that both oxides yield the same triol on hydrolysis has been utilized in an improved process for the preparation of cholesterol α-oxide.[17] The αβ-mixture resulting from the action of perbenzoic acid on cholesteryl acetate is hydrolyzed with dilute sulfuric acid and the resulting 3-acetate of the trans-triol is treated with mesyl chloride to produce the 6-mesyl derivative; this reacts with alkali with closure of the α-oxide ring.

[16] Windaus, *Ber.*, **50**, 133 (1917).
[17] Fürst and Koller, *Helv. Chim. Acta*, **30**, 1454 (1947).

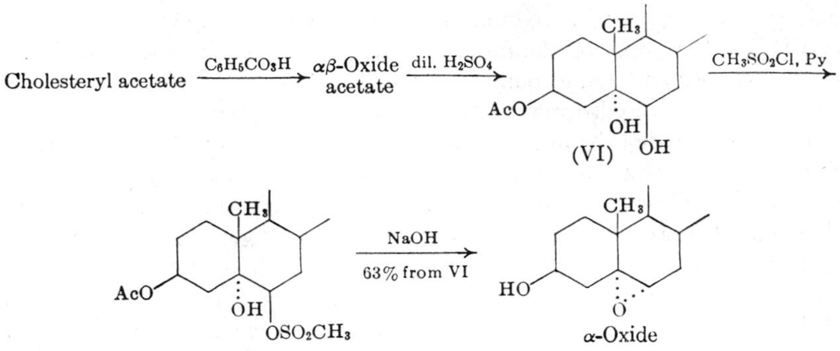

Cholesteryl acetate $\xrightarrow{\text{C}_6\text{H}_5\text{CO}_3\text{H}}$ $\alpha\beta$-Oxide acetate $\xrightarrow{\text{dil. H}_2\text{SO}_4}$ (VI) $\xrightarrow{\text{CH}_3\text{SO}_2\text{Cl, Py}}$

$\xrightarrow[\text{63\% from VI}]{\text{NaOH}}$ α-Oxide

The acetolysis of cholesterol α-oxide acetate[18] follows the course of the other fission reactions, for the product is identical with that obtained by acetylation of the 3-acetate of the trans-triol. The acetolysis of the β-oxide has not been investigated but would be expected to yield the trans-triol triacetate.

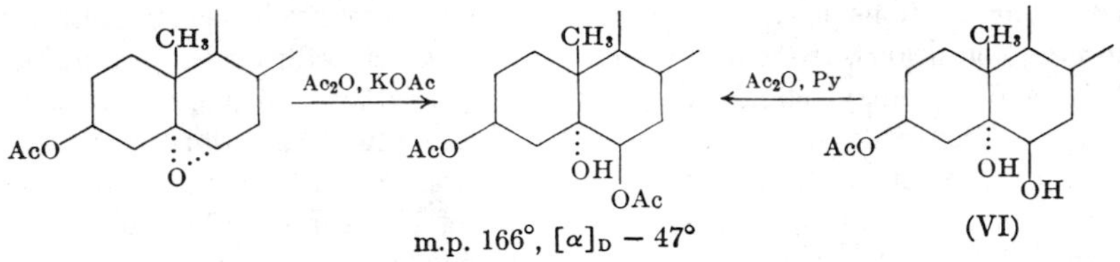

$\xrightarrow{\text{Ac}_2\text{O, KOAc}}$ m.p. 166°, $[\alpha]_D - 47°$ $\xleftarrow{\text{Ac}_2\text{O, Py}}$ (VI)

Ushakov and Madaeva[19] observed no reaction between cholesterol α-oxide and methyllithium or dimethylmagnesium at $80 - 100°$, but found that methylmagnesium iodide reacts slowly in boiling benzene to give a product that forms a monoacetate and a monoketone and that is readily dehydrated. Digitonin precipitates the unsaturated derivative but not the diol. The substance was assumed to be a 6-methyl-3,5-diol, and such a structure would correspond to the opening of the oxide ring in the normal manner (XIVa). The configuration would then be such that the establishment of a 5,6-double bond would require a cis-elimination, and the structure XIVa is therefore unlikely; the Δ^4-structure for the product is less plausible than structure XV because the hydroxyl group at C_3 in the unsaturated derivative is not eliminated on reaction with hot acetic anhydride containing sulfuric acid (unfortunately the optical rotation is not reported). A more likely interpretation is that, under the specific influence of the ionic methylmagnesium iodide, the oxide rearranges to the 6-ketone, which reacts to

[18] Lettré and M. Müller, *Ber.*, **70**, 1947 (1937).
[19] Ushakov and Madaeva, *J. Gen. Chem.* (*U.S.S.R.*), **9**, 436 (1939) [*C. A.*, **33**, 9309 (1939)].

give a diol of the structure XIVb; this formulation accounts adequately for the properties noted and for the dehydration to XV. The nonionic metal alkyls then fail to react with cholesterol oxide because they are incapable of effecting rearrangement.

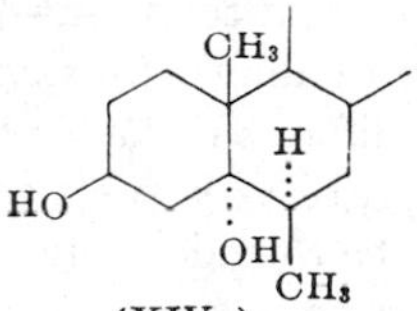

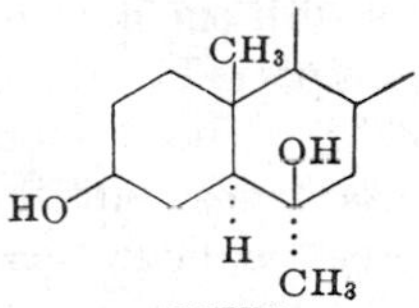

Methylcholestanediol
m.p. 181°

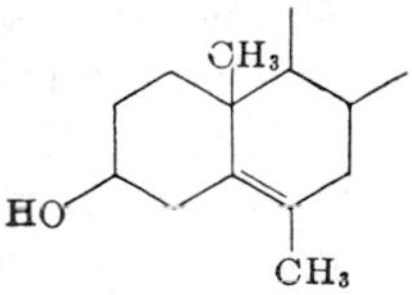

Methylcholesterol
m.p. 135°

Windaus[20] observed that ergosterol on reaction with one equivalent of perbenzoic acid under the usual conditions does not give an oxide but yields the monobenzoate of a 3,5,6-triol. This benzoate has one acylable hydroxyl group and therefore the benzoyl group must be at C_6 and not at C_5.

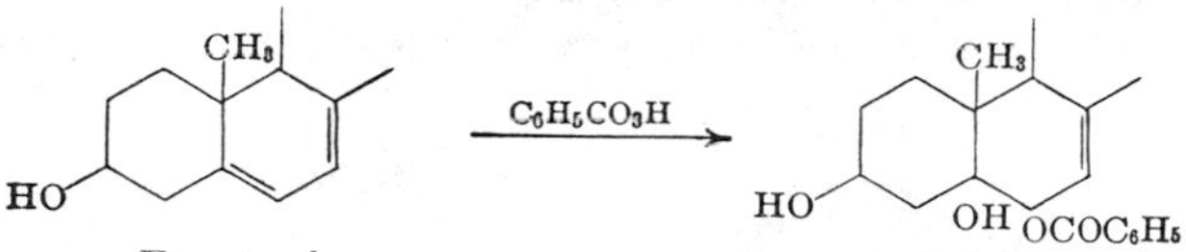

Ergosterol

m.p. 194°, $[\alpha]_D + 49°$

If a 5,6-oxide is formed initially, the oxide linkage extending to C_6 would be under the activating influence of the remaining double bond at $C_7 - C_8$ and probably would be severed whether the configuration were α or β; and hence no inference can be made about the configuration of the product. The reaction is perhaps more plausibly regarded as a direct addition of the reagent as C_6H_5COO—OH. The reaction of isodehydrocholesterol with perbenzoic acid[21] can be interpreted as a similar addition to one of the two

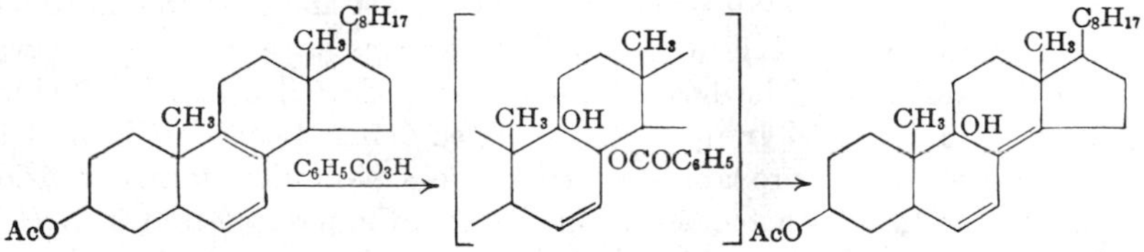

Isodehydrocholesterol
acetate

m.p. 138°, $[\alpha]_D - 18°$
λ_{max}^{ether} 245 mμ

[20] Windaus and Lüttringhaus, *Ann.*, **481**, 119 (1930).
[21] Windaus, Linsert and Eckhardt, *Ann.*, **534**, 22 (1938).

bonds of a conjugated system; here the postulated product of initial addition has a structure favorable for the elimination of benzoic acid and the product isolated is a diene having a tertiary hydroxyl group. The structure was deduced from the absorption spectrum; the substance on dehydration affords a triene (formulated as No. 14, Absorption Spectra).

Stigmasteryl acetate reacts with one mole of perbenzoic acid to give two 5,6-oxides: α-oxide acetate, m.p. 143°, $[\alpha]_D - 37°$ (main product); β-oxide acetate, m.p. 170°, $[\alpha]_D - 32°$.[22] The isomers do not differ as much in rotation as in the cholesterol series, but the original arbitrary prefixes undoubtedly indicate the actual configurations because the α-oxide acetate on hydrogenation yields a diol monoacetate that can be assigned the structure of Δ^{22}-stigmastene-3β,5α-diol 3-acetate on the evidence that the free hydroxyl group is not amenable to acetylation (one hour refluxing with acetic anhydride).

Oxides have been obtained as products of the action of perbenzoic acid on steroids having isolated double bonds at the following positions: 5,6; 7,8; 8,14; 9,11; and 14,15. Another type of reaction was observed by Windaus,[20] who found that a preparation containing Δ^8-cholestenol acetate, XVI, afforded a product having a tertiary hydroxyl group (unacylable) adjacent to the double bond (ready dehydration). Windaus regarded the

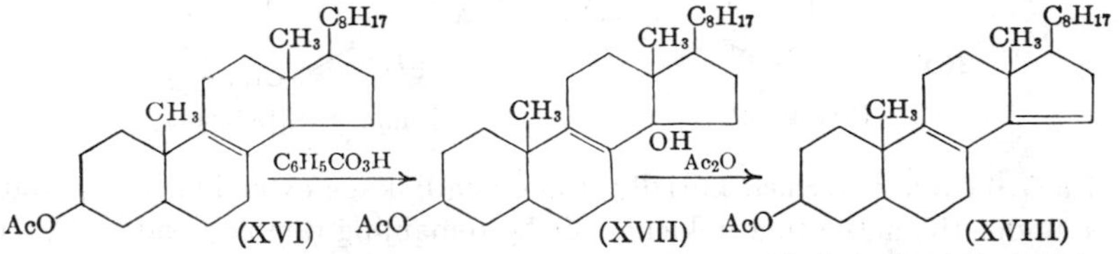

"δ"-Cholestenol acetate (XVI)   (XVII)   Cholestadienol-D acetate (XVIII)

m.p. 99°, λ_{max}^{ether} 245 mμ

reaction as proceeding by addition and elimination and formulated the product of dehydration with acetic anhydride as the $\Delta^{7,9(11)}$-diene (No. 4; Absorption Spectra). A perhaps more likely explanation is that the reaction is a direct allylic hydroxylation to give XVII and that the diene has the $\Delta^{8,14}$-structure (XVIII); the two diene systems have the same absorption characteristics. The heart poison scilliroside (Chapter VII), which contains a 14-hydroxyl group and an isolated double bond that is inert to hydrogenation and is probably located at the 8,9-position, forms an oxide on reaction with perbenzoic acid. In this case the position that in XVI is vulnerable to attack (14) is already oxidized, for the structure is analogous to XVII. Instances cited below (Cholestadienes) in which the action of perbenzoic acid on a monounsaturated compound results in the formation

[22] Fernholz, *Ann.*, **508**, 215 (1934).

of a diene probably proceed by allylic oxidation and dehydration, as in the conversion of XVI through XVII to XVIII.

Oxides are sometimes produced by reagents other than perbenzoic acid. Callow and Rosenheim[23] found that 5-dihydroergosterol (see Stenols) yields the 7,8-oxide (m.p. 111°, $[\alpha]_D - 44°$) on reaction with selenium dioxide at room temperature. Several instances are known of the formation of oxides in chromic acid oxidations (see next section).

The double bond of α,β-unsaturated ketones is not easily hydroxylated by the usual reagents: perbenzoic acid, hydrogen peroxide, or osmium tetroxide; but Butenandt[24] found that a combination of the last two reagents is effective. Thus cholestenone reacts smoothly at 20° with a solution of perhydrol in ether or benzene in the presence of $1/16 - 1/5$ mole of osmium tetroxide to give the diol XIX; Δ^4-cholestene-3,6-dione affords XX in quantitative yield. Δ^1-Cholestenone-3, progesterone, and testosterone can be hydroxylated in the same manner.

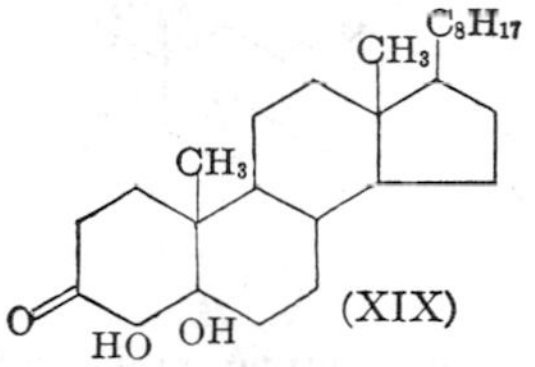

m.p. 208°, $[\alpha]_D + 44°$ m.p. 245°, $[\alpha]_D - 16°$

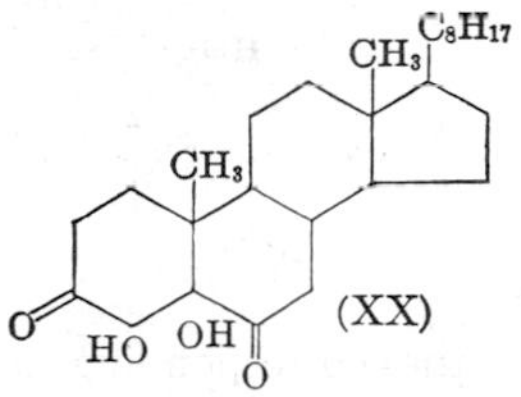

Attack of isolated double bonds by osmium tetroxide is less general than the reaction with perbenzoic acid. Precipitation of the black osmic ester is observed within a few minutes after mixing the reagents when the double bond is located at the 5,6-, 8,9-,[25] 14,15-,[25] or 11,12-position, but the reaction proceeds very slowly or not at all with steroids that have isolated double bonds at 7,8-,[25] 9,11-,[26] or 8,14-positions.[25]

Chromic Acid Oxidation. The chromic acid oxidation of the saturated sterol side chain is discussed in a later section (Androgens); the present section is devoted to a consideration of the oxidation of unsaturated steroids. The examples found in the literature conform to one or the other of two types: either an allylic oxidation at an activated position adjacent to the double bond; or a reaction proceeding through primary attack of the double bond. It seems likely that all reactions of the second type

[23] R. K. Callow and Rosenheim, *J. Chem. Soc.*, 387 (1933); R. K. Callow, *ibid.*, 462 (1936).

[24] Butenandt and Wolz, *Ber.*, **71**, 1483 (1938).

[25] Barton and J. D. Cox, Part VII, *J. Chem. Soc.*, (in press).

[26] Observation of L. H. Sarett.

proceed through the initial formation of an oxide. The formation of oxides in the chromic acid oxidation of simple ethylenes has been established. Thus tetraphenylethylene is oxidized by chromic acid to the oxide, which on more drastic treatment is oxidized to benzophenone.[1] 2,4,4-Trimethylpentene-1 on oxidation with chromic anhydride in acetic anhydride is converted largely into the 1,2-oxide.[2] Reactions to be cited in detail in later sections show that steroids having double bonds at the bridgehead positions $C_8 - C_{14}$ or $C_8 - C_9$ are often oxidized by chromic acid to ketoxides, as in formulations (a) and (b).[3] In example (a) the ketoxide is accom-

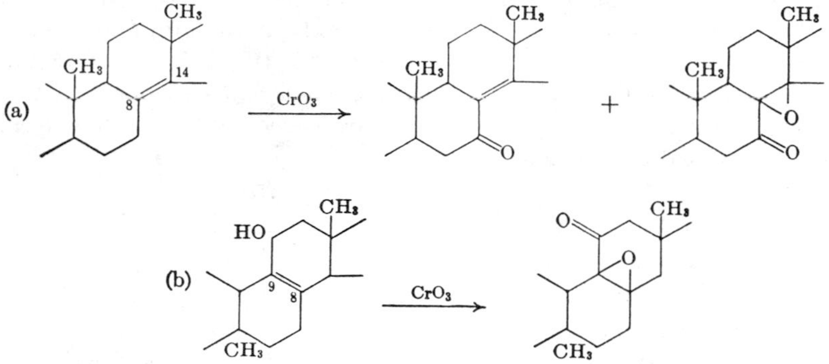

panied by the corresponding α,β-unsaturated ketone and probably is derived from this substance; in example (b) the relationship of the ketoxide to such a precursor is evident. An oxidic linkage extending to a position that carries a hydrogen atom is subject to more ready oxidation by chromic acid. Thus attempts to oxidize cholesterol α-oxide to the 3-keto-5,6-oxide have been unsuccessful;[4, 5] oxidation under very mild conditions afforded only the product of oxide fission as well as of oxidation at C_3: cholestane-3,6-dione-5α-ol. In one rather special case a secondary-tertiary ketoxide

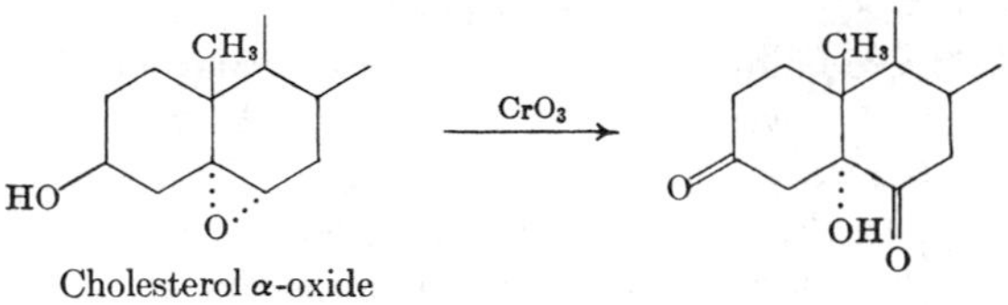

Cholesterol α-oxide

[1] Behr, *Ber.*, **5**, 277 (1872).

[2] Byers and Hickinbottom, *Nature*, **160**, 402 (1947).

[3] Petrow, *J. Chem. Soc.*, 998 (1939); Petrow and Starling, *ibid.*, 60 (1940); Wintersteiner and M. Moore, *J. Am. Chem. Soc.*, **65**, 1513 (1943); Stavely and Bollenback, *ibid.*, **65**, 1285 (1943).

[4] Westphalen, *Ber.*, **48**, 1064 (1915).

[5] Ruzicka and Bosshard, *Helv. Chim. Acta*, **20**, 244 (1937).

has been isolated from a chromic acid oxidation (Petrow and Starling; see Diosterols). The conversion of 5,6-unsaturated steroids into 5,6-oxido derivatives on oxidation with potassium permanganate in acetic acid solution has been established by Ehrenstein and Decker;[6] thus cholesteryl acetate afforded the 5,6-oxide and, probably as a product of further oxidation of the oxide, the 3-acetate of cholestane-3,5-diol-6-one.

Evidence to be cited below (see Stenols, "α"-Spinasterol) indicates that, in contrast with the behavior of compounds with a ditertiary double bond illustrated in formulations (a) and (b), the oxidation of a compound containing the system $R_2C=CHR$ may follow the course (c). Here the initial

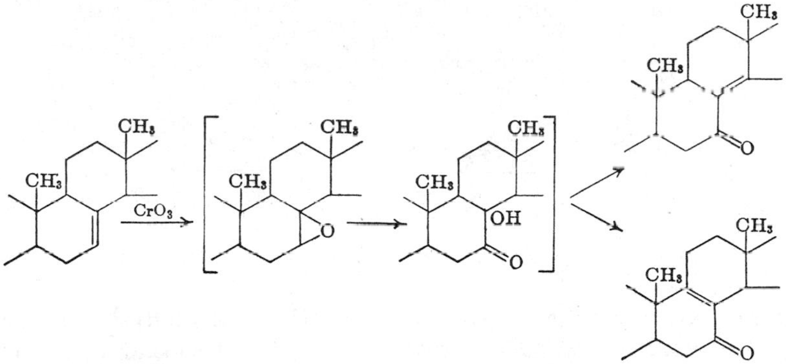

formation of an oxide results in the production of unsaturated ketones (or derived ketoxides) in which the double bond occupies a position different from that in the starting material. This reaction is not the invariable mode of oxidation of compounds of type (c), for some suffer normal allylic oxidation, $R_2C=CHCH_2- \rightarrow R_2C=CHCO-$; but it occurs frequently enough to obscure or invalidate evidence for the location of a double bond based upon the results of chromic acid oxidation. Oxidations of compounds with a ditertiary double bond (a and b) never involve the migration of the double bond from its original position; probably in such a structure allylic oxidation always precedes oxide formation. Thus chromic acid oxidation can be relied upon to furnish valid evidence of the location of a double bond only if this bond has been found to be resistant both to hydrogenation and to isomerization by an active, hydrogen-saturated catalyst (Pt in acetic acid or Pd in an acidic or neutral solution—see Stenols).

The above concept of chromic acid oxidations permits interpretation of certain hitherto unexplained observations. In an investigation of 1896 of

[6] Ehrenstein and Decker, *J. Org. Chem.*, **5**, 544 (1940); Ehrenstein, *ibid.*, **13**, 214 (1948).

the oxidation of free cholesterol with chromic acid in acetic acid solution Mauthner and Suida[7] isolated three products that were later characterized[8-12] as the diketo alcohol III, the unsaturated keto alcohol V, and the unsaturated diketone VI (Chart 3). The products are interrelated by the

Chart 3. OXIDATION OF CHOLESTEROL

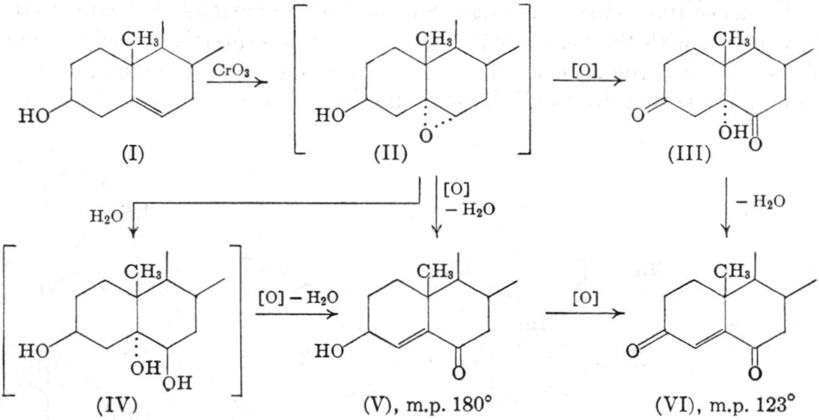

observation that VI can be obtained from III by dehydration and from V by oxidation. Oxidations conducted at steam-bath temperature gave mixtures of V and VI, and at temperatures below 20° III and VI were isolated. Ross[13] reports a yield of VI of 30 percent (crude).

Δ^4-Cholestenone could conceivably be an intermediate to VI, but not to the other two products isolated. A likely interpretation is that the initial product is an oxide or mixture of oxides. It is known that cholestane-3,6-dione-5α-ol (III) is indeed produced by the chromic acid oxidation of preformed cholesterol α-oxide (see above). The unsaturated keto alcohol V may arise by selective oxidation of the oxidic group followed by dehydration, or it may arise through the trans-triol (IV), the product of hydrolysis of both oxides. Evidence is available that this or other 3,5,6-triol intermediate would indeed suffer selective oxidation at the 6- rather than the 3-position. Thus the trans-triol (IV) has been converted by chromic acid

[7] Mauthner and Suida, *Monatsh.*, **17,** 579 (1896).

[8] Windaus, *Ber.*, **39,** 2249 (1906).

[9] Fantl, *Monatsh.*, **47,** 251 (1927).

[10] Windaus, *Ber.*, **40,** 257 (1907).

[11] Pickard and Yates, *J. Chem. Soc.*, **93,** 1678 (1908).

[12] Plattner, Petrzilka and Lang, *Helv. Chim. Acta*, **27,** 513 (1944).

[13] Ross, *J. Chem. Soc.*, 737 (1946).

oxidation under mild conditions into a product identified as cholestane-$3\beta,5\alpha$-diol-6-one;[14] hyodesoxycholic acid $(3\alpha,6\alpha)$ similarly yields a 3-hydroxy-6-ketone, and androstane-$3\beta,5\alpha,6\beta$-triol-17-one yields a 3,5-diol-6-one.[6] The order of reactivity of the hydroxyl groups to chromic acid $(C_6 > C_3)$ thus holds regardless of the configurations at C_3, C_5, and C_6.

Another observation not previously explained is the formation of 5-acetoxy derivatives as by-products in the chromic acid oxidation of cholesteryl acetate[15] and of an analogous bile acid derivative.[16] The oxidation of cholesteryl acetate (VII) has been studied extensively because the 7-keto derivative is an intermediate to 7-dehydrocholesterol. The yield of the

Chart 4. OXIDATION OF CHOLESTERYL ACETATE

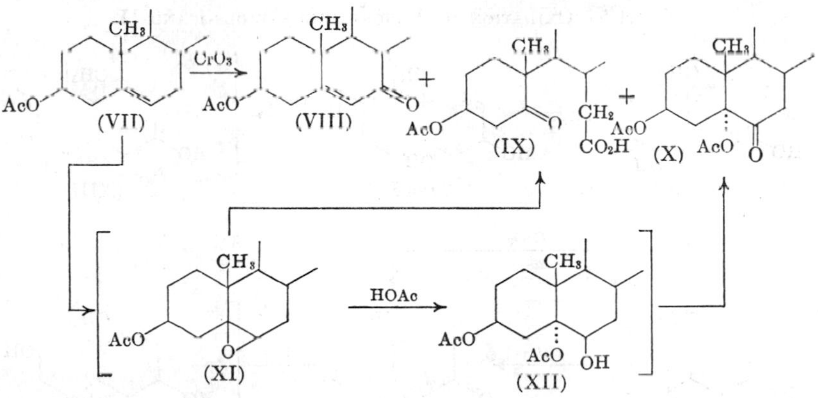

7-ketone is low and the product is accompanied by the keto acid (IX) and by a substance characterized by Schenck as a 3,5-diacetoxy-6-ketone (X) from analytical data and by saponification to the known cholestane-$3\beta,5\alpha$-diol-6-one (oxidation of the trans-triol 3-acetate and hydrolysis). Only one acetyl group was indicated in acetyl determinations conducted in the ordinary way, and more drastic conditions were required for hydrolysis of the tertiary acetoxy group at C_5 (the 5α-hydroxy-3-acetoxy compound, however, can be reacetylated by the action of acetic anhydride catalyzed by potassium bisulfate[14]). The formation of a tertiary acetoxy compound in a reaction conducted in 90 percent acetic acid is difficult to account for except on the assumption that the β-oxide (XI) is formed and suffers acetolysis (XII) in the specific direction established for other fissions (see

[14] Ellis and Petrow, *J. Chem. Soc.*, 1078 (1939).
[15] Fr. Schenck, *Z. physiol. Chem.*, **243**, 119 (1936).
[16] Haslewood, *J. Chem. Soc.*, 224 (1938).

Oxides). This oxide (or the α-isomer) is also a likely precursor of the keto acid IX.

If the foregoing analysis is correct, then the desired allylic substitution leading to VIII competes with an addition reaction leading through the oxide to undesired by-products. More information about the nature of the two reactions might suggest expedients for promoting the one or inhibiting the other.

An initial hydroxylation of a double bond by chromic acid was suggested by Bergmann[17] as a possible explanation of the fact that ergostadienetriol-I (Chart 5) on oxidation gives the same product, $\Delta^{7,22}$-ergostadiene-3,6-dione-5-ol (XV), that is obtained in a normal oxidation from the triol-II. The

Chart 5. OXIDATION OF ERGOSTADIENETRIOLS-I AND II

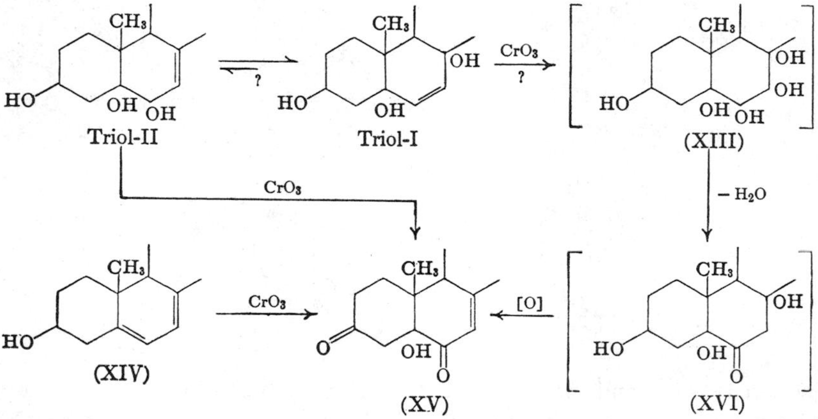

CH₃   HO   OH   OH   Triol-II   ⇌ ?   CH₃   HO   OH   OH   Triol-I   CrO₃ ?   [CH₃   HO   OH   OH   OH   (XIII)]

CrO₃   − H₂O

CH₃   HO   (XIV)   CrO₃ →   CH₃   O   OH   O   (XV)   ← [O]   [CH₃   HO   OH   O   OH   (XVI)]

vic-glycol group produced by hydroxylation to XIII was assumed to undergo dehydration to a 6-keto group in XVI, which could then suffer oxidation and dehydration. This explanation seems unlikely because it calls for a selective elimination of a secondary alcoholic group when two tertiary groups are available. An alternate explanation is that the triol-I or its 3-keto derivative isomerizes in part to a compound of the triol-II type that is removed from the equilibrium by oxidation to XV. Burawoy[18] has reported the direct conversion of ergosterol (XIV) into the unsaturated hydroxydiketone XV by chromic acid oxidation; the reaction probably proceeds through the 5,6-oxide.

Windaus[8] observed the oxidation of $\Delta^{3,5}$-cholestadiene (cholesterylene)

[17] W. Bergmann, F. Hirschmann and Skau, *J. Org. Chem.*, **4**, 29 (1939).
[18] Burawoy, *J. Chem. Soc.*, 409 (1937).

to a product later identified as Δ⁴-cholestene-3,6-dione (Chart 6). The reaction might be interpreted as proceeding by 1,4-hydroxylation to XVIII, but in view of the known reactivity of the 5,6-double bond and the evidence

Chart 6. OXIDATION OF Δ³,⁵-CHOLESTADIENE

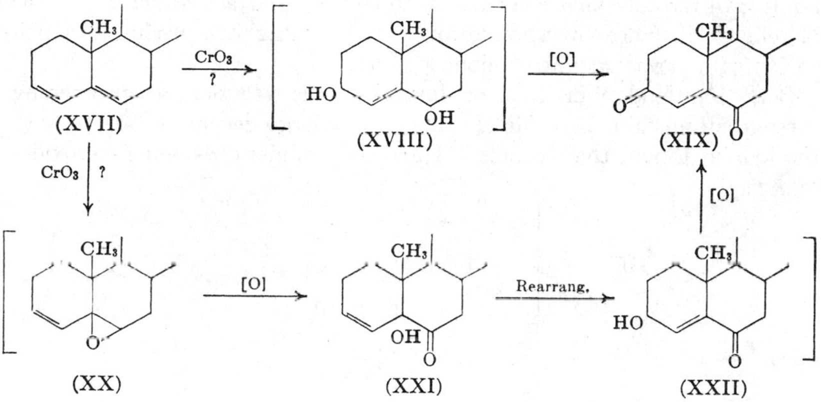

CH₃ (XVII) CrO₃? → [HO— CH₃ OH (XVIII)] [O] → CH₃ O (XIX) O

CrO₃?

[CH₃ O (XX)] [O] → CH₃ OH O (XXI) Rearrang. → [HO CH₃ O (XXII)]

[O]

cited above it seems more likely that the oxidation involves the formation of a 5,6-oxide (XX), oxidation (XXI), allylic rearrangement (XXII), and final oxidation to XIX.

In a discussion of instances of probable bond migration in the course of the chromic acid oxidation of olefinic triterpenoids to α,β-unsaturated ketones, Haworth[19] suggested that the reaction proceeds by hydroxylation of the double bond, dehydration to an allylic alcohol, and oxidation:

—CH=CRCHR— → —CH(OH)CR(OH)CHR— →

—CH(OH)CR=CR— → —COCR=CR—

Barton[20] postulated that the oxidation of Δ⁷-steroids proceeds by this mechanism. The alternate mechanism of oxide formation perhaps offers a more plausible interpretation of this phenomenon (see formulation c, above).

Autoxidation of Cholesterol. Cholesterol in colloidal aqueous solution is very readily attacked by molecular oxygen, even at room temperature.[1] The reaction has been studied in detail by Bergström and Wintersteiner,[2]

[19] R. D. Haworth, *Ann. Repts. Prog. Chem.*, **34**, 327 (1937); see also Noller, *J. Am. Chem. Soc.*, **66**, 1269 (1944).
[20] Barton, *J. Chem. Soc.*, 512 (1946).
[1] Blix and Löwenhielm, *Biochem. J.*, **22**, 1313 (1928).
[2] Bergström and Wintersteiner, *J. Biol. Chem.*, **141**, 597 (1941); **143**, 503 (1942); **145**, 309, 327 (1942).

who prepared the colloid in a phosphate buffer containing sodium stearate as stabilizer. A trace of heavy metal catalyst seems essential. The primary oxidation products were found to be 7-ketocholesterol and 7α- and 7β-hydroxycholesterol; 7-keto-$\Delta^{3,5}$-cholestadiene was isolated but it appears to be a secondary transformation product. The epimeric 7-hydroxycholesterols give the Lifschütz color test with sulfuric and acetic acids like the ill-defined substance "oxycholesterol" that Lifschütz[3] had produced by oxidation with permanganate or dibenzoyl peroxide.

Bergström and Wintersteiner formulate the reaction as proceeding through an unstable peroxide (I) that can undergo decomposition to both the ketone II and the alcohols III and IV (epimeric α- and β-peroxides

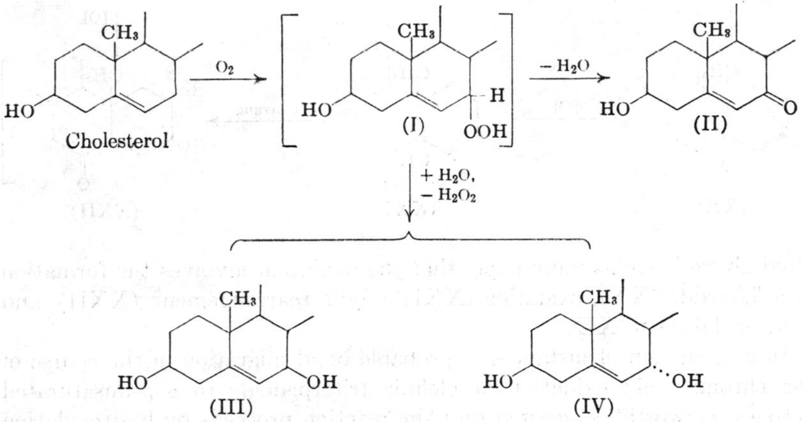

CH₃ ... Cholesterol → O₂ → (I) ... OOH → −H₂O → (II) ... O

+ H₂O, − H₂O₂

(III) ... OH   (IV) ... OH

presumably are formed). The mechanism is consistent with the observation that the cholestenediols are stable under the conditions of the experiment and are not precursors of the ketone. Esterification of the 3-hydroxyl group greatly diminishes the susceptibility to attack by oxygen.

The rapidity of autoxidation of cholesterol in colloidal media casts doubt on the significance of the isolation of 7α- or 7β-hydroxycholesterol from ox[4] and hog[5] liver and from the serum of pregnant mares.[6]

Three crystalline products have been isolated from the digitonin-precipitable fraction of the complex mixture obtained on irradiation of cholesterol with ultraviolet light. One product is an unknown hydroxycholesterol (m.p. 177°; dibenzoate, m.p. 133°); the others probably are 7β-hydroxycholesterol and Δ^4-cholestene-3β, 6β-diol.[7]

[3] Lifschütz, *Z. physiol. Chem.*, **53**, 140 (1907); **117**, 201 (1921).
[4] Haslewood, *Biochem. J.*, **33**, 709 (1939).
[5] MacPhillamy, *J. Am. Chem. Soc.*, **62**, 3518 (1940).
[6] Wintersteiner and Ritzmann, *J. Biol. Chem.*, **136**, 697 (1940).
[7] Windaus, Bursian and Riemann, *Z. physiol. Chem.*, **271**, 177 (1941).

Action of Other Oxidizing Agents. In addition to the oxidations of sterols with chromic acid and oxygen described in the preceding two sections, citations have been made of oxidations with perbenzoic acid, mercuric acetate, permanganate, hydrogen peroxide, osmium tetroxide, and of peroxide formation.

Whereas in the autoxidation reaction cholesterol is attacked at the allylic position 7, the point of attack in the reaction with **selenium dioxide** in acetic acid is at the alternate allylic position 4 to give the unsaturated diol II.[1]

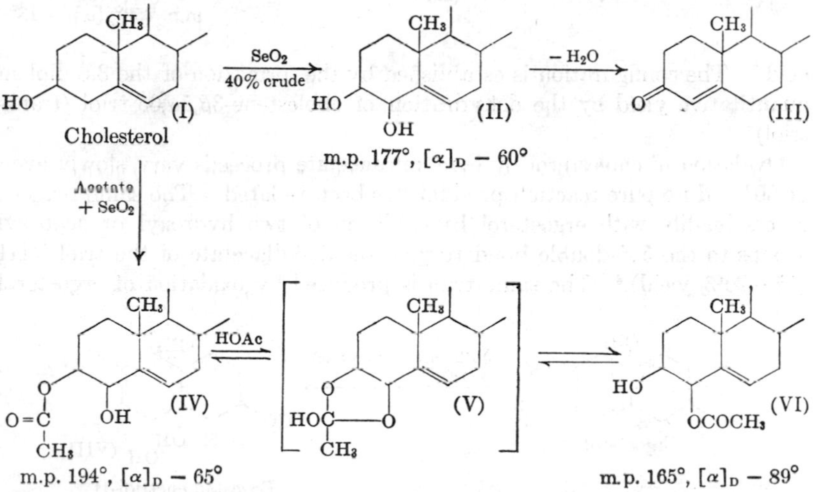

CH₃ ... HO (I) Cholesterol → SeO₂ 40% crude → CH₃ ... HO OH (II) m.p. 177°, [α]D − 60° → − H₂O → CH₃ ... O (III)

Acetate + SeO₂ ↓

CH₃ ... O=C OH (IV) CH₃ m.p. 194°, [α]D − 65° ⇌ HOAc ⇌ [CH₃ ... O HOC—O (V) CH₃] ⇌ CH₃ ... HO OCOCH₃ (VI) m.p. 165°, [α]D − 89°

The 4-hydroxyl group is believed to have the β-configuration because the diol is cleaved by lead tetraacetate at a rate characteristic of cis diols ($k^{20°} = 51$). The diol readily loses water to yield Δ⁴-cholestenone (III), but Rosenheim's suggestion that the diol may be an intermediate in the biological transformation of cholesterol into coprostanol became less attractive with the recognition that autoxidation affords the isomeric 3,7-diol. Selenium dioxide also attacks cholesteryl acetate in the 4-position; at temperatures below 90° the reaction affords the isomeric 3- and 4-monoacetates, IV and VI.[2,3] The second product has been shown to be formed from the first by acyl migration, which probably proceeds through the cyclic acetal V.[3,4]

Oxidation of cholesterol with selenium dioxide in acetic anhydride at 110° or of the acetate in boiling acetic acid yields the diacetate of the 3,6-diol

[1] Rosenheim and Starling, *J. Chem. Soc.*, 377 (1937).
[2] Marker and Rohrmann, *J. Am. Chem. Soc.*, **61**, 3022 (1939).
[3] Petrow, Rosenheim and Starling, *J. Chem. Soc.*, 135 (1943).
[4] Paige, *J. Chem. Soc.*, 437 (1943).

VII (25% yield).[5]   The 3,4-diol II undoubtedly is the intermediate, since it rearranges into the 3,6-diol when heated for five minutes in boiling acetic

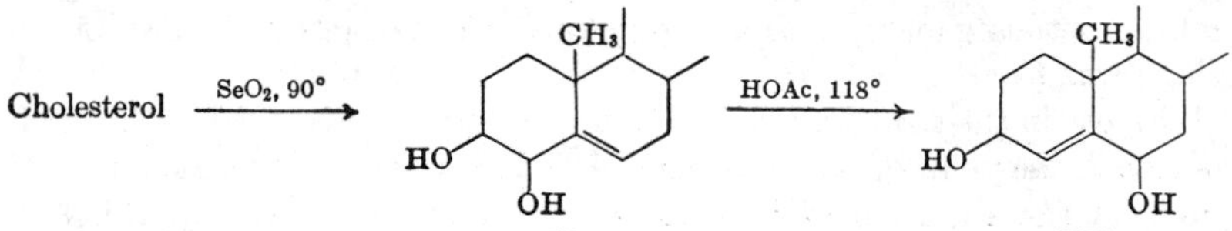

Cholesterol $\xrightarrow{\text{SeO}_2,\ 90°}$

(II)

$\xrightarrow{\text{HOAc, 118°}}$

(VII)
m.p. 258°, $[\alpha]_D$ −13°

acid.[3]   The configuration is established by the formation of the 3,6-diol in quantitative yield by the dehydration of cholestene-3β,5α,6β-triol (trans-triol).

Oxidation of cholesterol by **lead tetraacetate** proceeds very slowly even at 60° and no pure reaction product has been isolated.   The same reagent reacts readily with ergosterol by addition of two hydroxyl or acetoxyl groups to the 5,6-double bond to give the 3,6-diacetate of the triol VIII (15 – 20% yield).[6]   The same triol is produced by oxidation of ergosterol

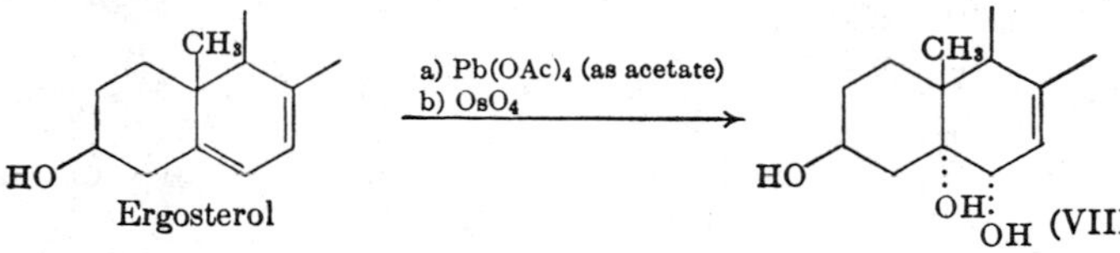

Ergosterol

a) Pb(OAc)₄ (as acetate)
b) OsO₄

$\xrightarrow{\hspace{2cm}}$

(VIII)

Ergostadienetriol-II
m.p. 242°, $[\alpha]_D$ + 29°

with osmium tetroxide[7] (40% yield) or with perbenzoic acid.[8]   The configuration indicated for the triol (3β,5α,6α) is not certain but highly probable, since the product of the reaction of cholesterol with osmium tetroxide (80% yield) is cholestane-3β,5α,6α-triol.[9]

Lead tetraacetate reacts with 7-dehydrocholesterol exactly as it does with ergosterol,[6] and a similar addition to the 5,6-double bond probably occurs in the reaction with vitamin D₂.[6]   The formula IX proposed for the product is based upon the absence of selective absorption indicative of conjugation, hydrogenation to a hexahydrotriol, and oxidation to the $C_{21}H_{34}O$ aldehyde obtained by chromic acid oxidation of vitamin D₂.   Iso-dehydrocholesterol does not possess a double bond at the reactive 5,6-position and the reaction with lead tetraacetate follows a more complex course

⁵ Butenandt and Hausmann, *Ber.*, **70**, 1154 (1937).
⁶ Windaus and Riemann, *Z. physiol. Chem.*, **274**, 206 (1942).
⁷ Criegee, Marchand and Wannowius, *Ann.*, **550**, 114 (1942).
⁸ Windaus and Lüttringhaus, *Ann.*, **481**, 127 (1930).
⁹ Prelog and Tagmann, *Helv. Chim. Acta*, **27**, 1867 (1944).

regarded as proceeding by hydroxylations at positions 6 and 9 and at positions 8 and 9.[10] Oxidation of isodehydrocholesterol with mercuric ace-

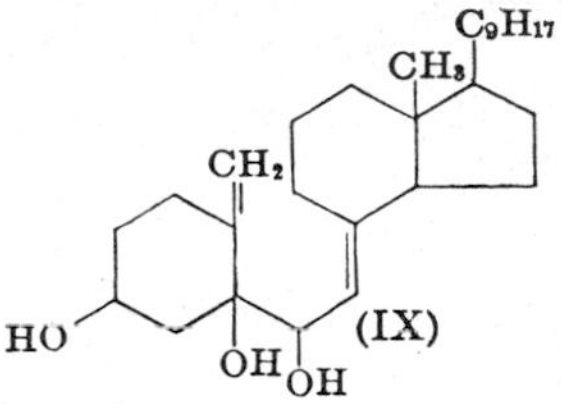

tate[11] gives a mixture of products including a cholestatetraenol (m.p. 115°, $[\alpha]_D$ – 311°, λ_{max}^{ether} 355 mμ, regarded as having the $\Delta^{4,6,8,11}$-system).

The oxidation of cholesterol with alkaline **hypobromite** solution[12] affords an unsaturated substance, the Diels acid, in which ring A has been opened and the double bond is still intact. The ring-carboxyl group is hindered

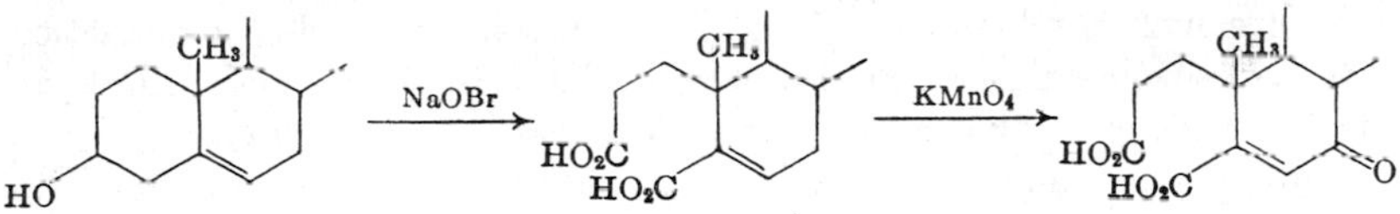

| Cholesterol | Diels acid m.p. 297° | 7-Keto-Diels acid m.p. 217° |

and the acid gives only a mono ester on Fischer esterification. On further oxidation with alkaline permanganate, the substance is converted into 7-keto-Diels acid.[13] The double bond of this keto acid can be reduced by the action of either zinc dust in acetic acid or sodium amalgam to give 7-ketodihydro-Diels acid, m.p. 159°.

Oxidation of Ketones. 3-Ketosteroids of either the normal or allo series are attacked by perbenzoic acid at the 4-position with the production of lactones.[1] The structure of the lactone derived from cholestanone was established by oxidation of the corresponding hydroxy acid methyl ester to a product identical with dihydro-Diels acid. Coprostanone is oxidized to the C_5-epimeric lactone (m.p. 158°, $[\alpha]_D$ + 49°), which is converted by a similar degradation to the same dicarboxylic acid (m.p. 249°) that results from the chromic acid oxidation of coprostanone. Similar lactones have been obtained from methyl 3-keto-12α-acetoxycholanate,[1] methyl 3-keto-Δ^{11}-cholenate,[2] methyl 3-ketocholanate, and etiocholane-17α-ol-3-one.[3] The

[10] Windaus, Riemann, Rüggeberg and Zühlsdorff, *Ann.*, **552,** 142 (1942).
[11] Windaus, Riemann and Zühlsdorff, *Ann.*, **552,** 135 (1942).
[12] Diels and Abderhalden, *Ber.*, **36,** 3177 (1903); **37,** 3092 (1904).
[13] Windaus, *Ber.*, **41,** 614 (1908).
[1] Burckhardt and Reichstein, *Helv. Chim. Acta*, **25,** 1434 (1942).
[2] Burckhardt and Reichstein, *Helv. Chim. Acta*, **25,** 821 (1942).
[3] Ruzicka and co-workers, *Helv. Chim. Acta*, **28,** 618, 1651 (1945).

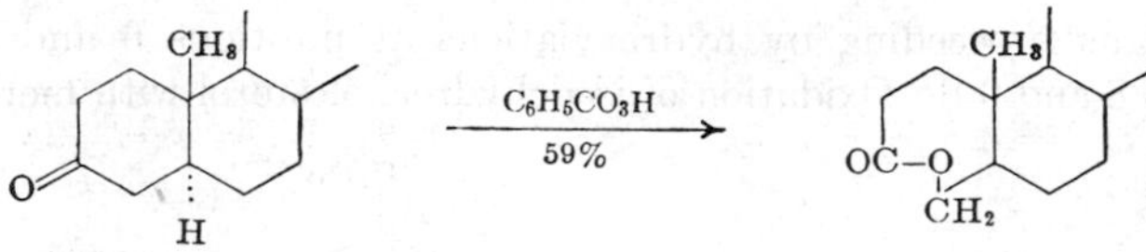

Cholestanone

m.p. 187°, [α]D + 1.2°

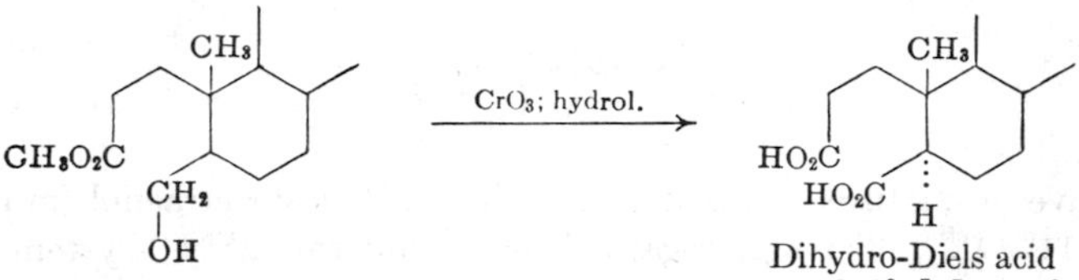

Dihydro-Diels acid
m.p. 249°, [α]D − 9°

oxidation of 17-ketosteroids to lactones has been found to proceed most satisfactorily with the use of peracetic acid in glacial acetic acid in the presence of a little p-toluenesulfonic acid.[4] 7-Ketocholestanol-3β on reaction with perbenzoic acid suffers cleavage at the 7,8-position and affords an ε-lactone; the hydroxy acid reforms the original lactone with ease.[5]

Cholestenone suffers acetoxylation at the 2-position on reaction with **lead tetraacetate.**[6] The structure of the product was established by hydro-

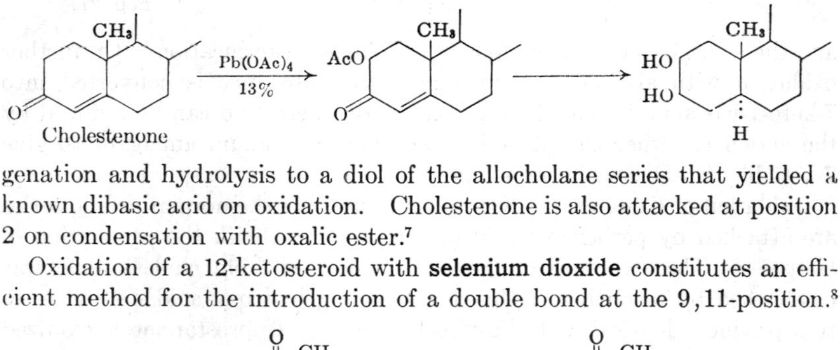

Cholestenone

genation and hydrolysis to a diol of the allocholane series that yielded a known dibasic acid on oxidation.   Cholestenone is also attacked at position 2 on condensation with oxalic ester.[7]

Oxidation of a 12-ketosteroid with **selenium dioxide** constitutes an efficient method for the introduction of a double bond at the 9,11-position.[8]

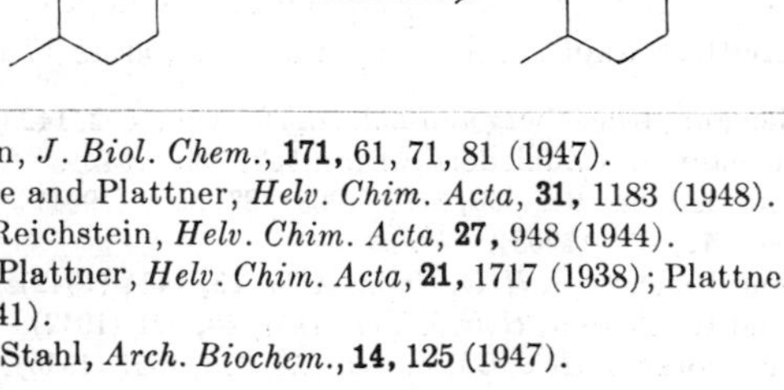

[4] R. P. Jacobsen, J. Biol. Chem., **171**, 61, 71, 81 (1947).

[5] Heusser, Segre and Plattner, Helv. Chim. Acta, **31**, 1183 (1948).

[6] Seebeck and Reichstein, Helv. Chim. Acta, **27**, 948 (1944).

[7] Ruzicka and Plattner, Helv. Chim. Acta, **21**, 1717 (1938); Plattner and Jampolsky, ibid., **24**, 1457 (1941).

[8] Schwenk and Stahl, Arch. Biochem., **14**, 125 (1947).

The oxidation of a 12-ketocholanic acid acetate to the $\Delta^{9(11)}$-12-ketone is an important step in one of the methods for the partial synthesis of cortical hormones (Chapter V).

Δ^4-**Cholestenol** ("**Allocholesterol**"). Δ^4-Cholestenol-3β and its epimer were prepared in a pure form by Schoenheimer and Evans[1] in 1936 by Meerwein-Ponndorf reduction of cholestenone and separation with digitonin. The reduction is effected more efficiently with lithium aluminum hydride, which affords a mixture of about equal parts of the two epimers.[2] The epimers are allylic alcohols like morphine, and they suffer dehydration

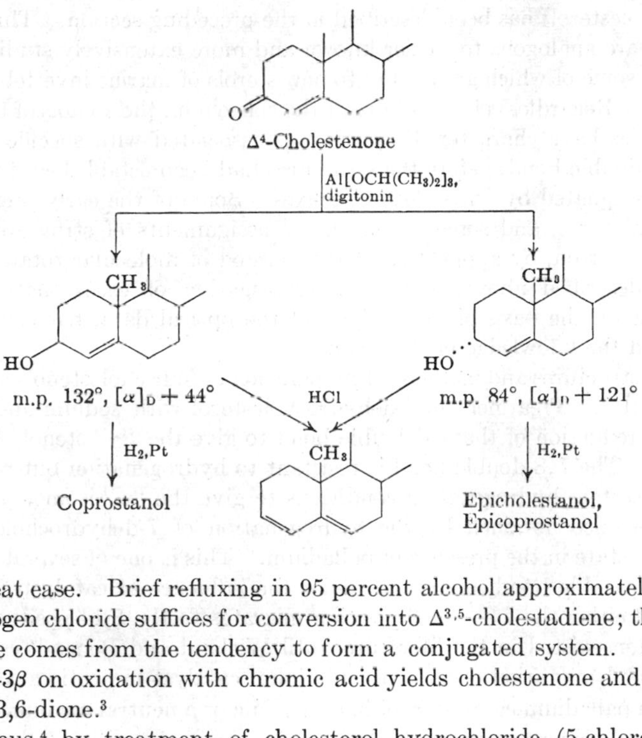

Δ⁴-Cholestenone

Al[OCH(CH₃)₂]₃, digitonin

m.p. 132°, [α]_D + 44°

Coprostanol

HCl

m.p. 84°, [α]_D + 121°

Epicholestanol, Epicoprostanol

with great ease. Brief refluxing in 95 percent alcohol approximately $N/30$ in hydrogen chloride suffices for conversion into $\Delta^{3,5}$-cholestadiene; the driving force comes from the tendency to form a conjugated system. Δ^4-Cholestenol-3β on oxidation with chromic acid yields cholestenone and Δ^4-cholestene-3,6-dione.[3]

Windaus,[4] by treatment of cholesterol hydrochloride (5-chlorocholestanol-3) with potassium acetate, had prepared a substance which he regarded as the Δ^4-isomer of cholesterol and named "allocholesterol"; the substance yielded cholesterol on treatment with mineral acids. Schoen-

[1] E. A. Evans, Jr. and Schoenheimer, *J. Am. Chem. Soc.*, **58**, 182 (1936); Schoenheimer and Evans, *J. Biol. Chem.*, **114**, 567 (1936).

[2] McKennis and Gaffney, *J. Biol. Chem.*, **175**, 217 (1948).

[3] Bonstedt, *Z. physiol. Chem.*, **214**, 173 (1933).

[4] Windaus, *Ann.*, **453**, 101 (1927).

heimer and Evans showed that the material is a mixture of Δ^4-cholestenol with cholesterol and that acid treatment merely dehydrates the first component and liberates cholesterol already present. Although these authors retained the name "allocholesterol" for the pure substance, we prefer in this book to restrict the use of the prefix allo to the definition of a configuration at C_5. Evans and Schoenheimer[5] also showed that another supposed isomer, "β-cholesterol," is in reality a molecular compound containing equal parts of cholestanol and Δ^4-cholestenol-3α.

Stenols. Five cholestenols are known that differ from cholesterol only in the position of the nuclear double bond. One of them, Δ^4-cholestenol (allocholesterol) has been described in the preceding section. Three of the others are analogous to earlier known and more extensively studied ergostenols, some of which are related to new sterols of marine invertebrates and plants. Regardless of the nature of the side chain, the stenols of the different series have characteristic properties associated with specific locations of the double bond; before the structures had been established, the stenols were designated by Greek letter prefixes. Some of the early preparations were mixtures, and some of the initial assignments of structure were in error. Barton, by application of the method of molecular rotation differences described above, and by reinvestigation of cases that appeared dubious on the basis of his analysis of the optical data, has considerably clarified the knowledge of the stenols.

The structures and methods of preparation of four cholestenols are shown in Chart 7. Treatment of 7-dehydrocholesterol with sodium and ethanol effects reduction of the 5,6-double bond to give the "γ"-stenol, Δ^7-cholestenol.[1] The 7,8-double bond is resistant to hydrogenation but rearranges under certain hydrogenating conditions to give the "α"-isomer, $\Delta^{8(14)}$-cholestenol, also obtained by the hydrogenation of 7-dehydrocholesterol in ethyl acetate in the presence of palladium. This is one of several instances of comparable bond migration; under the influence of catalysts, a double bond at either the 7,8- or 8,9-position migrates to the 8,14-position. Some confusion existed in the literature until Wieland and Benend[2] established that bond migration occurs with platinum catalyst in acetic acid solution or with palladium catalyst in either an acidic or a neutral medium, but that no rearrangement occurs with platinum in a neutral medium (ethyl acetate, ether). Stavely and Bollenback[3] observed that bond migration occurs only if the catalyst (Pt or Pd) has been first saturated with hydrogen. Barton[4]

[5] Evans and Schoenheimer, *J. Biol. Chem.*, **115**, 17 (1936).
[1] Fr. Schenck, Buchholz and Wiese, *Ber.*, **69**, 2696 (1936).
[2] Wieland and Benend, *Ann.*, **554**, 1 (1943).
[3] Stavely and Bollenback, *J. Am. Chem. Soc.*, **65**, 1600 (1943).
[4] Barton and J. D. Cox (Part V), *J. Chem. Soc.*, (in press).

has fully confirmed both definitions of the conditions determining whether
or not migration occurs.

Chart 7. CHOLESTENOLS

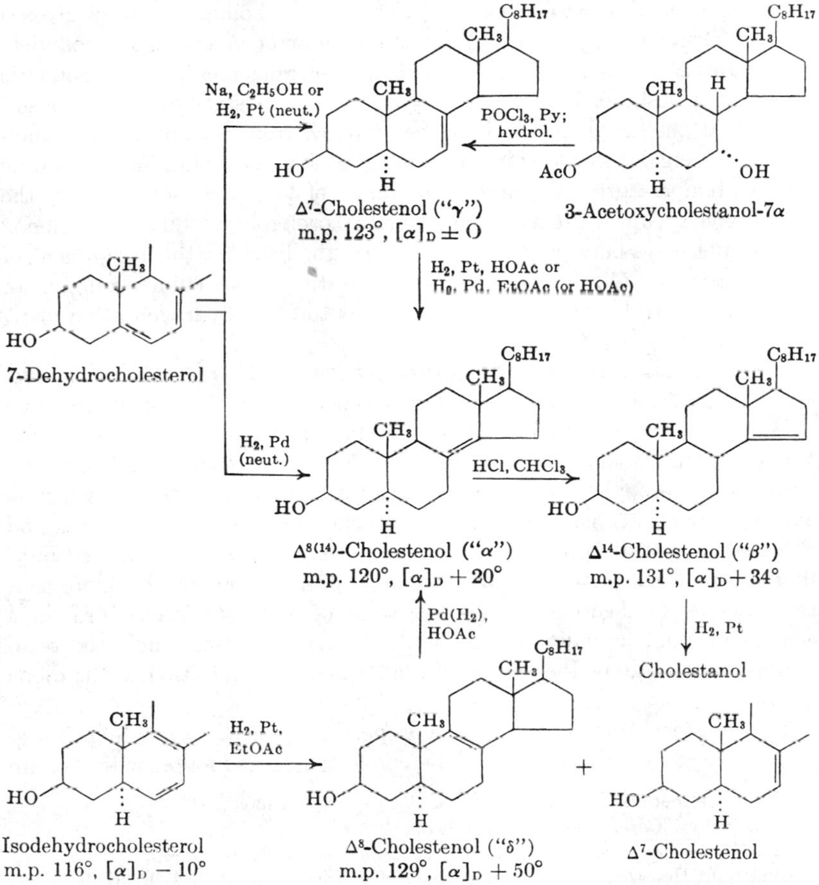

$\Delta^{8(14)}$-Cholestenol ("α") is completely stable to hydrogenation but is
isomerized by dry hydrogen chloride to Δ^{14}-cholestenol ("β"),[1] which is
readily hydrogenated to cholestanol.

Wintersteiner and Moore[5] worked out a method of preparing Δ^7-choles-
tenol (and from it Δ^{14}-cholestenol) more convenient than that through
7-dehydrocholesterol. 7-Ketocholesteryl acetate, available by the chromic

[5] Wintersteiner and M. Moore, *J. Am. Chem. Soc.*, **65**, 1507 (1943).

oxide oxidation of cholesteryl acetate, is hydrogenated in the presence of platinum in a neutral solvent to 7-ketocholestanyl acetate and this is hydrogenated with the same catalyst in acetic acid solution to a mixture of the epimeric 7-hydroxy compounds.[6] Dehydration of 3-acetoxycholestanol-7α by treatment with p-toluenesulfonyl chloride in boiling pyridine gives a mixture of stenol acetates rich in the Δ^7-isomer and convertible in good yield into pure $\Delta^{8(14)}$-cholestenol by catalytic rearrangement. The epimeric 3-acetoxycholestanol-7β resisted dehydration by the same method. Buser[7] found that pure Δ^7-cholestenol can be prepared from 3-acetoxycholestanol-7α by carrying out the dehydration with phosphorus oxychloride in pyridine at room temperature. On similar treatment of 3-acetoxycholestanol-7β the 7-hydroxyl group is replaced by chlorine (probably without inversion).[8] These differences between the epimers form the basis for the assignment of configurations at C_7: the more ready dehydration of one epimer must mean that the hydroxyl group eliminated is trans to the β-hydrogen atom at C_8 and therefore α-oriented.[9]

The only known route to Δ^8-cholestenol ("δ") is by reduction or hydrogenation of isodehydrocholesterol, the $\Delta^{6,8}$-diene available in small amounts as a by-product of the German manufacture of 7-dehydrocholesterol. Windaus, Linsert and Eckhardt[10] reduced isodehydrocholesterol with sodium and isopropyl alcohol, and Wieland and Benend[2] effected selective hydrogenation in a neutral medium not conducive to bond migration and obtained supposedly pure Δ^8-cholestenol. Barton, however, pointed out[11] that the material possessed an anomalous positive acetylation increment and later established[12] that hydrogenation of isodehydrocholesterol in a neutral medium actually affords both Δ^8- and Δ^7-cholestenol; the reaction apparently takes the course of both 1,2- and 1,4-addition to the diene system.

The ergostenols are very similar in properties to the corresponding cholestenols (Chart 8). Ergosterol can be converted by reduction with sodium

[6] Wintersteiner and M. Moore, *J. Am. Chem. Soc.*, **65**, 1503 (1943).

[7] Buser, *Helv. Chim. Acta*, **30**, 1379 (1947).

[8] Fieser, Fieser and R. N. Chakravarti, *J. Am. Chem. Soc.*, (in press).

[9] Plattner, Heusser, Troxler and Segre, *Helv. Chim. Acta*, **31**, 852 (1948), have reported the preparation by pyrolysis of the benzoate or anthraquinone-β-carboxylate of 3-acetoxycholestanol-7α of a substance with properties distinctly different from those of all the known Δ^7-stenols but claimed by these authors to be the first authentic Δ^7-stenol. The evidence of structure is not definitive and Barton (*ibid.*, in press) has pointed out that the M_D differences of the substance and its derivatives are wholly anomalous.

[10] Windaus, Linsert and Eckhardt, *Ann.*, **534**, 22 (1938).

[11] Barton (Part I), *J. Chem. Soc.*, 813 (1945).

[12] Barton and J. D. Cox (Part VII), *J. Chem. Soc.*, (in press).

and alcohol[13,14] or by partial catalytic hydrogenation in a neutral solvent[2,15] into a dihydro derivative that retains the double bond at $C_{22} - C_{23}$ (ozonolysis gives methylisopropylacetaldehyde)[16] and that is now recognized as

Chart 8. ERGOSTENOLS

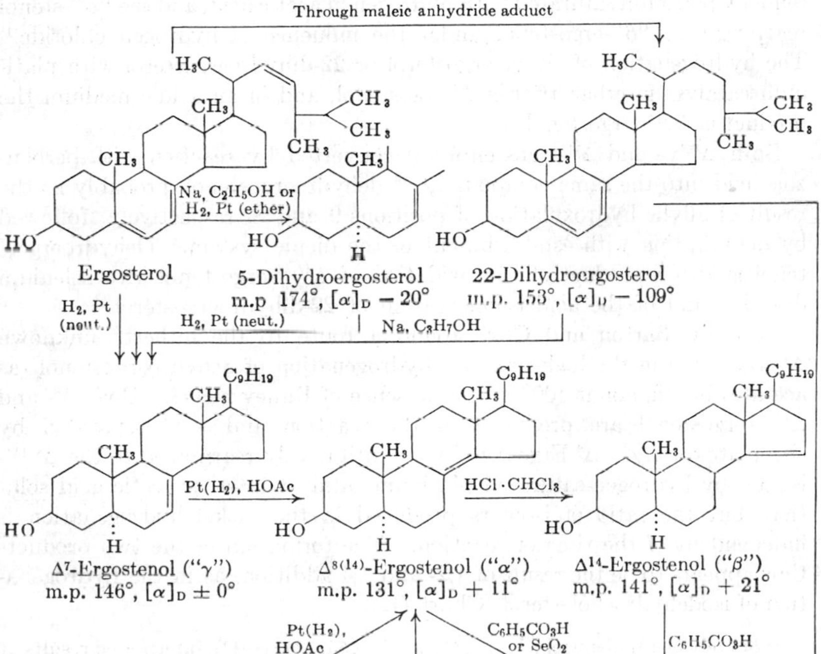

---

[13] Windaus and Brunken, *Ann.*, **460**, 225 (1928); v. Reichel, *Z. physiol. Chem.*, **226**, 146 (1934).
[14] Windaus and Langer, *Ann.*, **508**, 105 (1934).
[15] Heilbron and Sexton, *J. Chem. Soc.*, 921 (1929).
[16] Guiteras, Nakamiya and Inhoffen, *Ann.*, **494**, 116 (1932).

having a nuclear double bond at the "γ"-position $C_7 - C_8$.[17] This 5-di-hydroergosterol is an isomer of the 22-dihydride obtained through the maleic anhydride addition product. On further hydrogenation with platinum in a neutral solvent the double bond in the side chain is saturated and the product is Δ^7-ergostenol.[2] This substance is isomerized to $\Delta^{8(14)}$-ergostenol by platinum saturated with hydrogen in acetic acid, and the "α"-stenol rearranges to "β"-ergostenol under the influence of hydrogen chloride.[18] The hydrogenation of either ergosterol or 22-dihydroergosterol with platinum catalyst in ether affords Δ^7-ergostenol, and in an acidic medium the product is $\Delta^{8(14)}$-ergostenol.

Both $\Delta^{8(14)}$- and Δ^{14}-ergostenol are converted by reaction with perbenzoic acid into the same compound,[19,20] dehydroergostenol, probably as the result of allylic hydroxylation of positions 9 and 8, respectively, followed by dehydration with establishment of the dienic system. Dehydroergostenol is also a product of the oxidation of $\Delta^{8(14)}$-ergostenol with selenium dioxide[21] and of the acid isomerization of 22-dihydroergostérol.[13]

Recently Barton and Cox[12] found a route to the hitherto unknown Δ^8-ergostenol in the high-pressure hydrogenation of dehydroergostenol (as acetate) in ethanol at 100° in the presence of Raney nickel. Both Δ^8- and $\Delta^{8(14)}$-ergostenol are produced in the reaction and were separated by chromatography. Δ^8-Ergostenol is quantitatively rearranged to the $\Delta^{8(14)}$-isomer by hydrogen-saturated platinum catalyst in ether-acetic acid solution, but the ratio of isomers produced in the nickel hydrogenation is independent of the time of reaction. The formation of the two products thus appears to be the result of 1,2- and 1,4-addition, as in the hydrogenation of isodehydrocholesterol (Chart 7).

[17] Stavely and Bollenback, *J. Am. Chem. Soc.*, **65**, 1290 (1943), interpreted results of a study of the oxidation of dihydroergostenyl acetate as indicating the presence of an 8,9-double bond, but they were unaware of the work of Wieland and Benend[2] which proves that the bond is at 7,8. The $\Delta^{7,8}$-structure was confirmed by Barton, *J. Chem. Soc.*, 512 (1946), from M_D data. The formation of the oxidation products on the basis of the $\Delta^{7,8}$-structure can be explained by a mechanism similar to that postulated in Chart 9, below: a labile 7,8-oxidic linkage is first formed and is opened to give an 8-hydroxy-7-ketone that loses water to form the Δ^8-unsaturated 7-ketone isolated. One of the two ketoxides isolated is derived from this ketone, the other probably is the oxide of the $\Delta^{8(14)}$-unsaturated 7-ketone, which could arise from the postulated 8-hydroxy-7-ketone. These structures for the oxidation products all correspond with those deduced by Stavely and Bollenback. The mechanism is essentially that suggested by Barton, who regarded the first step as a hydroxylation.

[18] Reindel, Walter and Rauch, *Ann.*, **452**, 34 (1927); Reindel and Walter, *ibid.*, **460**, 212 (1928); Heilbron and Wilkinson, *J. Chem. Soc.*, 1708 (1932).

[19] Windaus and Lüttringhaus, *Ann.*, **481**, 119 (1930).

[20] Morrison and Simpson, *J. Chem. Soc.*, 1710 (1932).

[21] R. K. Callow, *J. Chem. Soc.*, 462 (1936).

That the double bond of "β"-ergostenol occupies the 14,15-position has been established with certainty.   Ozonolysis[22] of the acetate and pyrolysis of the product gave (after saponification) a keto alcohol[22] $C_{16}H_{26}O_2$ (IV) and

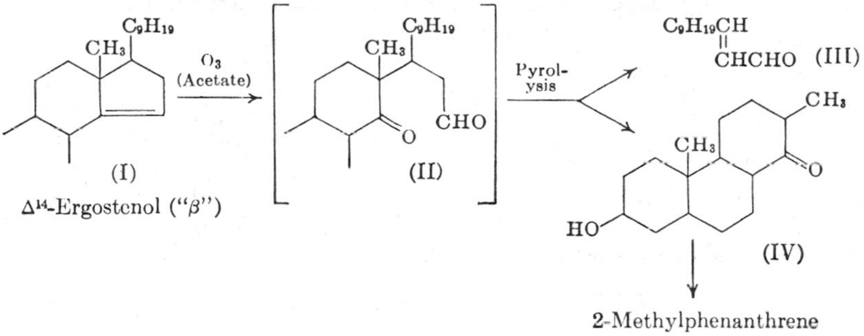

Δ^{14}-Ergostenol ("β")

2-Methylphenanthrene

a C_{12}-aldehyde[23] (probably III).   The keto alcohol was converted by selenium dehydrogenation[23] into a hydrocarbon identified as 2-methylphenanthrene and hence has the structure IV.

The structures of the other ergostenols and of the cholestenols were inferred from the cumulative evidence of the sources, interrelationships, and M_D increments of the isomers in the two series.   The results of oxidation studies have provided confirmatory evidence of the structures of "α"- and "γ"-stenols.   This evidence will not be reviewed in detail, but Chart 9 summarizes the principal products of established structure that have been isolated from oxidations of $\Delta^{8(14)}$-cholestenyl acetate with chromic acid,[24] of $\Delta^{8(14)}$-ergostenyl acetate with chromic acid,[25,26] and of Δ^7-cholestenyl acetate with perbenzoic acid.[5]   The perbenzoic acid oxidation of the Δ^7-isomer VI is anomalous but can be interpreted as proceeding by allylic oxidation (VII), allylic rearrangement (VIII), and oxide formation (IX).   The reaction product IX afforded on further oxidation a ketoxide (XIII) identical with one of the products of the chromic acid oxidation of $\Delta^{8(14)}$-cholestenyl acetate.   The $\Delta^{8(14)}$-stenyl acetates (V) on reaction with chromic acid suffer allylic oxidation to α,β-unsaturated ketones (X) and diketones (XI), and they also afford the isomeric α,β-ketoxides XII and XIII.

Stenols of the $\Delta^{8(14)}$-, Δ^7-, and Δ^8-types give a positive Tortelli-Jaffé color reaction, whereas those of the Δ^{14}-type give no color.   The behavior is consistent with the generalization that the test is distinctive of compounds

[22] Achtermann, Z. physiol. Chem., 225, 141 (1934).

[23] Laucht, Z. physiol. Chem., 237, 236 (1935).

[24] Wintersteiner and M. Moore, J. Am. Chem. Soc., 65, 1513 (1943).

[25] Heilbron, Simpson and Wilkinson, J. Chem. Soc., 1699 (1932).

[26] Stavely and Bollenback, J. Am. Chem. Soc., 65, 1285 (1943).

having a ditertiary double bond ($C_8 - C_9$ and $C_8 - C_{14}$) or a bond capable of migration into such a position ($C_7 - C_8$, $C_9 - C_{11}$).

Chart 9. OXIDATION OF $\Delta^{8(14)}$-AND Δ^7-STENYL ACETATES
(R = C_8H_{17} or C_9H_{19})

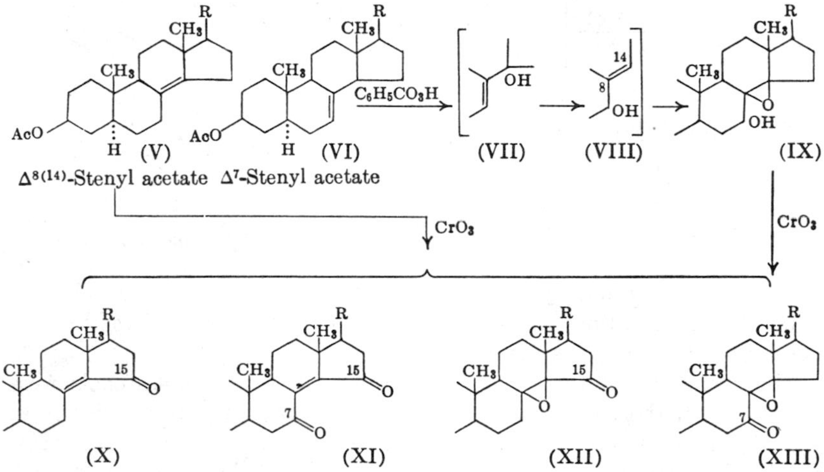

$\Delta^{8(14)}$-Stenyl acetate Δ^7-Stenyl acetate

Cholestenes. Three cholestenes were discovered in the period 1894 – 1909 by Mauthner, who obtained samples of as high purity as any subsequent investigator by the methods illustrated in Chart 10. Δ^2-Cholestene (II) was prepared[1] by the action of quinoline on cholestanyl chloride.   The same hydrocarbon results from the decomposition of epicholestanyl tosylate in boiling methanol;[2] the tosylate of cholestanol is stable under the same conditions.   A convenient preparative method is the decomposition of potassium cholestanyl sulfate in capryl alcohol at 180° in the presence of sodium caproxide[3] (70% yield); the sulfate ester can be prepared in quantitative yield.[4]   Mauthner prepared Δ^5-cholestene (V)[5] by the reduction of cholesteryl chloride (IV) and converted it through the hydrochloride (5-chlorocholestane, VII) into the Δ^4-isomer (VIII).[6]   The structures of the three isomers were established by later evidence. Δ^2-Cholestene on ozonization yields a dibasic acid identified as that derived from cholesterol (III) by conversion into the pyroketone.[2] Δ^5-Cholestene is oxidized by chromic

[1] Mauthner, *Monatsh.*, **30,** 635 (1909).
[2] W. Stoll, *Z. physiol. Chem.*, **246,** 1 (1937).
[3] Sobel and Rosen, *J. Am. Chem. Soc.*, **63,** 3536 (1941).
[4] Sobel and Spoerri, *J. Am. Chem. Soc.*, **63,** 1259 (1941).
[5] Mauthner and Suida, *Monatsh.*, **15,** 85 (1894).
[6] Mauthner, *Monatsh.*, **28,** 1113 (1907).

acid to an unsaturated ketone (VI) that can be transformed into cholestane-
7-one, and hence the double bond has not migrated from the original posi-

Chart 10. Δ^2-, Δ^4-, AND Δ^5-CHOLESTENE

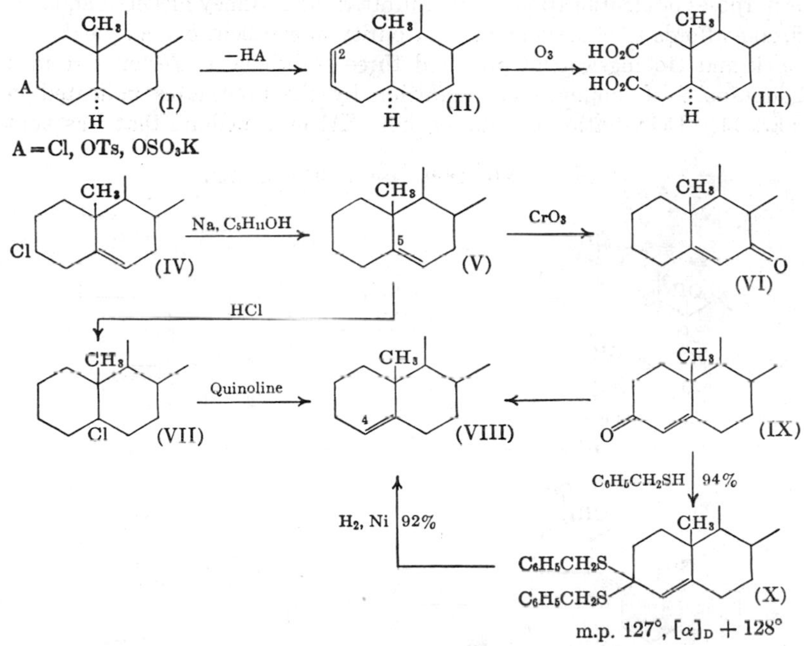

tion.[7] The structure of Δ^4-cholestene is fixed by the formation of an
identical product by Wolff-Kishner reduction of Δ^4-cholestenone (IX);[7]
chromic acid oxidation of the hydrocarbon effects cleavage at the double
bond rather than oxidation at the 3-position.[7]

From the addition of bromine to Δ^5-cholestene, Mauthner[5,8] isolated a
stable form of 5,6-dibromocholestane, m.p. 146°, $[\alpha]_D + 49°$, and a labile
form, m.p. 106°, $[\alpha]_D - 40° \rightarrow + 39°$. The addition product from Δ^4-choles-
tene, 4,5-dibromocholestane,[6] also exhibits mutarotation: m.p. 117°, $[\alpha]_D +
38° \rightarrow + 83°$.

The Wolff-Kishner reduction of cholestenone by the modified procedure
of Huang-Minlon[9] constitutes an improved preparative route to Δ^4-choles-

[7] Lettré, Z. physiol. Chem., **221**, 73 (1933).

[8] Mauthner, Monatsh., **27**, 305 (1906).

[9] Huang-Minlon, J. Am. Chem. Soc., **68**, 2487 (1946); further observations of Dr.
Huang.

tene, and probably a still better method of reduction is that described by
Hauptmann.[10] The condensation of cholestenone with benzyl mercaptan
in the presence of zinc chloride and sodium sulfate affords a dibenzyl mercaptal (X) of such superior crystallizing characteristics that it can be used
for purposes of identification. Desulfuration with Raney nickel in aqueous
dioxane affords Δ^4-cholestene of high purity in excellent overall yield.

Eck and Hollingsworth[11] prepared three additional cholestenes from a
cholestanol-7 of unknown configuration by the procedures indicated in
Chart 11. Dehydration of this alcohol (XI) in a medium that was kept

Chart 11. Δ^7-, $\Delta^{8(14)}$-, AND Δ^{14}-CHOLESTENE

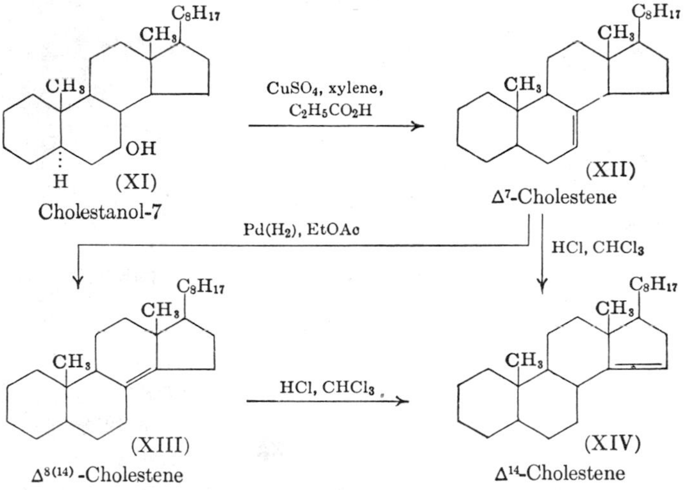

weakly acidic to prevent isomerization gave a cholestene, m.p. 86°, $[\alpha]_D$ +
11°, that afforded one isomer (XIII) under hydrogenating conditions and
another (XIV) on isomerization with mineral acid. The conditions of formation and the relative optical rotations of these substances, in comparison
with corresponding stenols, support the $\Delta^{8(14)}$- and Δ^{14}-formulas assigned
by Eck and Hollingsworth. These authors regarded the initial product of
dehydration as Δ^8-cholestene because chromic oxidation of the hydrocarbon,
followed by reduction of the resulting stenone with sodium and amyl alcohol, and chromic acid oxidation, gave cholestanone-7. Barton,[12] however,
has shown that the increment in molecular rotation for a stenol Δ^8-double
bond is +100, whereas the increment for the substance in question is −48.

[10] Hauptmann, *J. Am. Chem. Soc.*, **69**, 562 (1947).
[11] Eck and Hollingsworth, *J. Am. Chem. Soc.*, **63**, 2986 (1941).
[12] Barton, *J. Chem. Soc.*, 813 (1945); 512 (1946); Part VII, (in press).

The value is closer to that characteristic of Δ^7-stenols (-77), and the formulation of the substance as substantially pure Δ^7-cholestene (XII) is not inconsistent with the chemical evidence, because Δ^7-steroids are now known to afford unsaturated 7-ketosteroids on chromic acid oxidation (see Chromic Acid Oxidation; Stenols).

The physical constants of the six isomers and their behavior on hydrogenation are listed in Table XVIII.

TABLE XVIII.   Cholestenes

Δ	OLD NAME	M.p.	$[\alpha]_D$	HYDROGENATION
2	Neocholestene	68–69°	+ 64°	→ Cholestane
4	Pseudocholestene	78–79°	+ 65°	In ether → coprostane
				In acid soln. → cholestane
5	Cholestene	88 00°	− 56°	→ Cholestane
7		85–86°	+ 11°	Isomerized
8(14)		53–54°	+ 21°	Resistant
14		73 74°	+ 27°	→ Cholestane

Cholestadienes.   In 1896 Mauthner and Suida[1] dehydrated cholesterol by heating it with anhydrous copper sulfate at 200° and obtained a hydrocarbon which they called "cholestcrylene," m.p. 80°, $[\alpha]_D - 104°$. Many subsequent investigators have obtained roughly comparable products of melting point between 75° and 80° and of specific rotations between +1° and $- 116°$ in processes starting with cholesterol or with derived or related substances.[2]   The present evidence indicates that all these preparations are mixtures, but that samples having a levorotation as high as that origi-

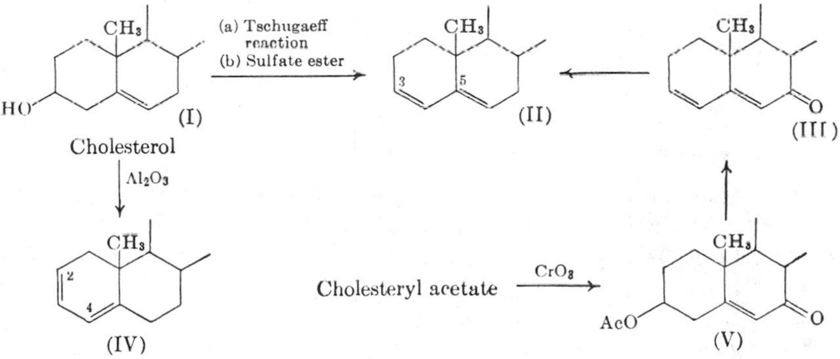

[1] Mauthner and Suida, *Monatsh.*, **17**, 29 (1896).

[2] For reviews, see Stavely and W. Bergmann, ref. 6; Eck and Van Peursem, *Iowa State Coll. J. Sci.*, **13**, 115 (1939); Eck and Hollingsworth, *ibid.*, **13**, 329 (1939); Van Peursem, *ibid.*, **14**, 101 (1939).

nally reported (– 104°) consist very largely of $\Delta^{3,5}$-cholestadiene. In 1939 – 1941 samples of apparently pure $\Delta^{3,5}$-cholestadiene (II) of constant m.p. 80° and $[\alpha]_D$ – 123° were prepared by the following processes, of which the third appears to be the most convenient: (a) pyrolysis of cholesterol methyl xanthogenate,[3] (b) acid dehydration of a mixture of the epimeric Δ^4-cholestenols,[3] and (c) decomposition of potassium cholesteryl sulfate in capryl alcohol containing sodium caproxide.[4,5] Stavely and Bergmann[6] inferred the $\Delta^{3,5}$-structure (of nearly pure hydrocarbon) from the optical and chemical properties (see below) and confirmed it by production of the substance by Wolff-Kishner reduction of $\Delta^{3,5}$-cholestadiene-7-one[1] (III), obtained from cholesteryl acetate through the ketone V. $\Delta^{2,4}$-Cholestadiene (IV) was prepared by Bergmann and co-workers[6,7] by vacuum distillation of cholesterol from freshly activated alumina.

Dimroth and Trautmann[8] prepared 7-dehydrocholestene, or $\Delta^{5,7}$-cholestadiene (XI) from Δ^5-cholestene-7-one (VII), a known[9] product of the oxidation of Δ^5-cholestene.   Reduction with aluminum isopropoxide gave an alcohol,

(VI) →(CrO₃)→ (VII) → (VIII)

Δ^5-Cholestene

Δ^5-Cholestene-7-ol;
benzoate, m.p.
109°, $[\alpha]_D$ + 113.5°

Ac₂O or alc. HCl

Pyrolysis of benzoate

(IX) ← (HCl, CHCl₃) ← (X) ← (Heat) ← (XI)

$\Delta^{3,5}$-Cholestadiene $\Delta^{4,6}$-Cholestadiene   7-Dehydrocholestene

VIII, that afforded the desired hydrocarbon XI on pyrolysis of the benzoate at 125°.   At higher temperatures the $\Delta^{5,7}$-diene was converted into a less dextrorotatory isomer that could be prepared readily in a pure form by the

[3] Eck, Van Peursem and Hollingsworth, *J. Am. Chem. Soc.*, **61**, 171 (1939).
[4] Sobel and Rosen, *J. Am. Chem. Soc.*, **63**, 3536 (1941).
[5] Spring and Swain, *J. Chem. Soc.*, 83 (1941), by a lengthier process obtained material m.p. 80–81°, $[\alpha]_D$ – 129°.
[6] Stavely and W. Bergmann, *J. Org. Chem.*, **1**, 567, 575 (1937).
[7] Skau and W. Bergmann, *J. Org. Chem.*, **3**, 166 (1938).
[8] K. Dimroth and Trautmann, *Ber.*, **69**, 669 (1936).
[9] Windaus, *Ber.*, **53**, 495 (1920).

dehydration of the alcohol VIII with acetic anhydride. Stavely and Bergmann[6] deduced from the properties of this "7-dehydrocholestene isomer" and its relation to other members of the series that it is $\Delta^{4,6}$-cholestadiene, X, and the inference was later verified by Eck and Hollingsworth.[10] Treatment with dry hydrogen chloride[10] in chloroform effects quantitative isomerization to $\Delta^{3,5}$-cholestadiene (IX); therefore the double bonds must be associated with rings A and B. It is interesting that the hydrocarbon can be prepared by dehydration of the alcohol VIII with alcoholic hydrochloric acid[10] and is not isomerized in the polar acidic medium. Oxidation of X with chromic acid and Wolff-Kishner reduction of the resulting cholestenedione gave Δ^5-cholestene, and since the oxidation step is analogous to that of $\Delta^{3,5}$-cholestadiene the observation constitutes evidence of the $\Delta^{4,6}$-structure.

Eck and Hollingsworth[11] reported the preparation of four new cholestadienes starting with the substance described in the preceding section as probably Δ^7-cholestene, and with $\Delta^{8(14)}$-cholestene. Dehydrogenation of Δ^7-cholestene (XII) with mercuric acetate or with bromine gave one isomer

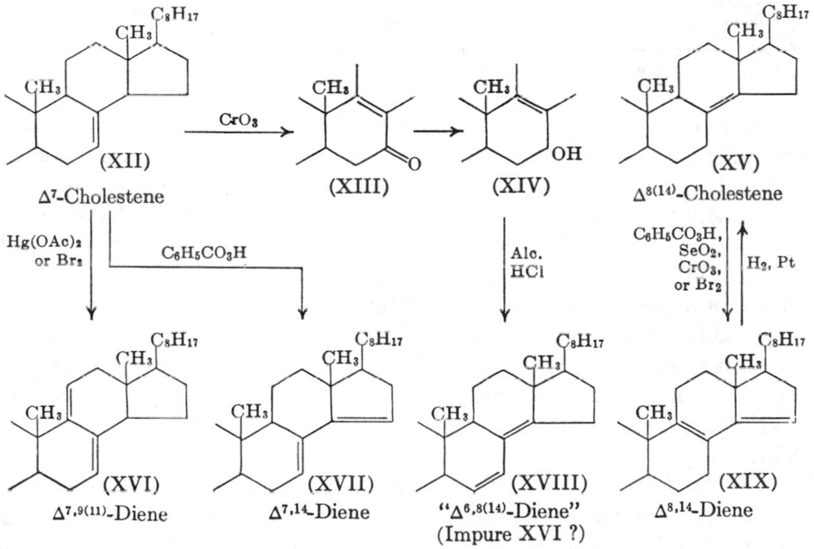

XVI, whereas reaction with perbenzoic acid at 0° gave another, XVII. A third isomer XVIII was obtained from the same starting material through the intermediates XIII and XIV, and a fourth resulted from the oxidation

[10] Eck and Hollingsworth, *J. Am. Chem. Soc.*, **63**, 107 (1941).
[11] Eck and Hollingsworth, *J.Am. Chem. Soc.*, **64**, 140 (1942).

of $\Delta^{8(14)}$-cholestene.   The structures indicated, with the exception of XII, are those suggested by Eck and Hollingsworth.   Formulas XVI, XVII, and XIX are consistent with the preparative reactions (based upon the Δ^7-structure for XII), and the optical rotations (Table XIX) correspond roughly with those of more fully characterized dienic compounds described

TABLE XIX.   Cholestadienes

Δ	M.p.	$[\alpha]_D$	$\lambda_{max}m\mu$	REDN. BY Na, $C_5H_{11}OH$	MALEIC ANHYD. ADDN.	ISOM. BY HCl	CATALYT. HYDROG.
2,4	68.5°	+ 168.5°	275[a]	+	+	+	Coprostane
3,5	79.5–80°	− 123°	234[b]	−	−	−	Cholestane Coprostane
4,6	90–91°	+ 4.3°	238[a]	−	−	+	Cholestane Coprostane
5,7	88–89°	− 127°	273,280[b]				
"6,8(14)"	84–85°	+ 1°	245[c]			−	
7,9(11)	83–84°	+ 32°	243[c]			−	
7,14	82–83°	− 93°	242,250[c]		+		
8,14	83–84°	− 23°	245[c]			−	

[a] Solvent not specified.   [b] In ether.   [c] In alcohol.

in the next section.   The fourth substance was obtained from a cholestenone resulting from chromic acid oxidation of XII and formulated by Eck and Hollingsworth as the Δ^8-ene-7-one XIII (λ_{max} 251 mμ, $[\alpha]_D$ + 3.8°). Such a substance could arise through the 7,8-oxide and the 8-hydroxy-7-ketone derived from it, and the absorption maximum is consistent with formula XIII (calcd., 249 mμ), but Barton[12] has noted that the M_D difference with respect to cholestane is anomalous.   The diene is also anomalous; it is weakly dextrorotatory, whereas the $\Delta^{6,8(14)}$-structure normally produces strong levorotation.   If the unsaturated alcohol has the structure XIV (or contains some of this material), dehydration would be expected to yield XVI rather than XVIII, and hence the product isolated may be impure XVI.

Bergmann[6,13] commented on the contrasting properties of cholestadienes having the conjugated system in one ring (A) and those in which the unsaturated system is distributed between two rings (B).   The former have absorption maxima in the region 260 – 280 mμ, the latter in the range 235 – 250 mμ.   Compounds of the type A are reduced by sodium and amyl alcohol (1,4-addition), add maleic anhydride readily, and are isomerized by heat or by mineral acids in either a polar or nonpolar medium to the

[12] Barton, *J. Chem. Soc.*, 512 (1946).
[13] W. Bergmann and F. Hirschmann, *J. Org. Chem.*, 4, 40 (1939).

more stable isomers of type B.   In the case of the conversion of $\Delta^{2,4}$- to $\Delta^{3,5}$-cholestadiene the change involves a migration of a double bond from the 4,5- to the 5,6-position and the isomerization is characterized by a

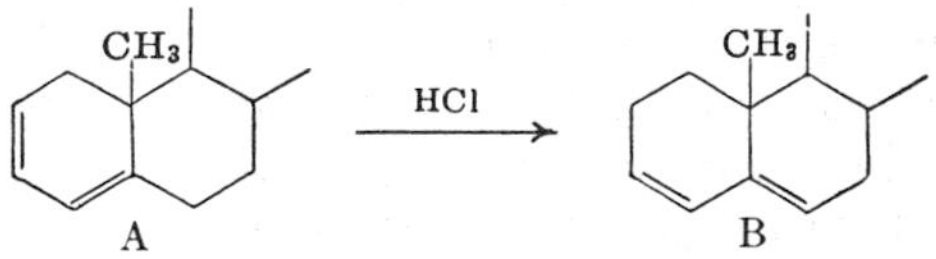

shift from a strong dextro- to a strong levorotation ($\Delta - 291.5°$).   None of the heteroannular dienic hydrocarbons is reduced by sodium and amyl alcohol.   Only one of them reacts with maleic anhydride under nonforcing conditions and this is the $\Delta^{7,14}$-isomer, XVII, in which the double bonds are so arranged that a six-membered ring can form without rearrangement or strain.   One of the hydrocarbons of type B, $\Delta^{4,6}$-cholestadiene, is isomerized by dry hydrogen chloride in chloroform to another hydrocarbon of the same type, but it is stable to alcoholic hydrochloric acid.

Another property characteristic of the homoannular dienic compounds (A) is the ability to add oxygen in the presence of light (artificial) and eosin to form a peroxide comparable to that from ergosterol.   Bergmann and co-workers[7,14] studied the peroxide of $\Delta^{2,4}$-cholestadiene and were able to establish the structure XX through the following observations.   The per-

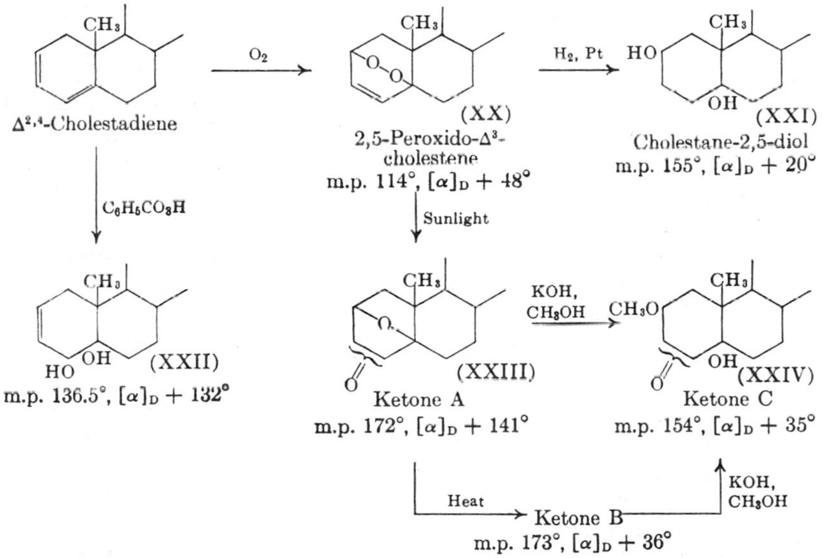

[14] W. Bergmann, F. Hirschmann and Skau, *J. Org. Chem.*, **4**, 29 (1939).

oxide liberates an equivalent amount of iodine from potassium iodide in acetic acid solution. On hydrogenation it yields a diol (XXI) that forms only a monoacetate (therefore one hydroxyl group is tertiary) and that is stable to lead tetraacetate (therefore not a 1,2-diol). These observations rule out the possibility of a 2,3- or 4,5-peroxide structure and show that oxygen has added 1,4 to give a transannular peroxide. On exposure to sunlight the peroxide rearranges to an isomeric ketone, which does not show the presence of a double bond. In analogy to known rearrangements in the terpene series, Bergmann suggested that one oxygen atom leaves the peroxide bridge and adds to the $C_3 - C_4$ double bond to give a transitory oxide that rearranges to a C_3- or a C_4-ketone (XXIII). The ketone (A) rearranges on heat treatment to the isomeric ketone B, and treatment of either A, B, or the peroxide with methanol and potassium hydroxide results in a ketone C of properties suggesting the formulation XXIV. Bergmann and Skau[15] sought to prepare a transannular oxide of the type postulated by the action of perbenzoic acid on $\Delta^{2,4}$-cholestadiene but found that the initial attack is at the 4,5-position to give the unsaturated diol XXII. This formed a monoacetate (one tertiary hydroxyl) and the saturated diol consumed one mole of lead tetraacetate and is therefore cholestane-4,5 diol (m.p. 172°, $[\alpha]_D + 35.5°$).

Isomers of Ergosterol. Studies of the isomerization of ergosterol by various chemical means were undertaken at a time when it seemed possible to produce in this way substances of the type formed in the process of irradiation. This line of investigation lost its original significance with the recognition that irradiation results in the opening of one of the rings, but those isomers that have been adequately characterized constitute an interesting series paralleling in properties corresponding cholestadienes. Additional substances of doubtful homogeneity or unknown structure are omitted from the present discussion.

One way of converting ergosterol into isomeric substances is to proceed through intermediates having two hydrogen atoms more or two hydrogen atoms less than the original sterol. Thus ergosterol-D has been obtained by the oxidation of 5-dihydroergosterol with mercuric acetate,[1,2] perbenzoic acid,[3] or selenium dioxide;[4] it has also been produced by the reduction of dehydroergosterol with sodium ethoxide at 185°.[5] The reduction reaction affords a further indication of the specific reactivity of a 5,6-double bond.

[15] W. Bergmann and Skau, *J. Org. Chem.*, **5**, 439 (1940).
[1] Windaus and Auhagen, *Ann.*, **472**, 185 (1929).
[2] Heilbron, Johnstone and Spring, *J. Chem. Soc.*, 2248 (1929).
[3] Windaus and Lüttringhaus, *Ann.*, **481**, 119 (1930).
[4] R. K. Callow and Rosenheim, *J. Chem. Soc.*, 387 (1933).
[5] Windaus, Dithmar, Murke and Suckfüll, *Ann.*, **488**, 91 (1931).

Ergosterol-D yields ergostanol on hydrogenation but is not reduced by sodium and propyl alcohol and does not add maleic anhydride; the spectrum is also indicative of a conjugated system distributed between two rings.

Chart 12. Isomers of Ergosterol

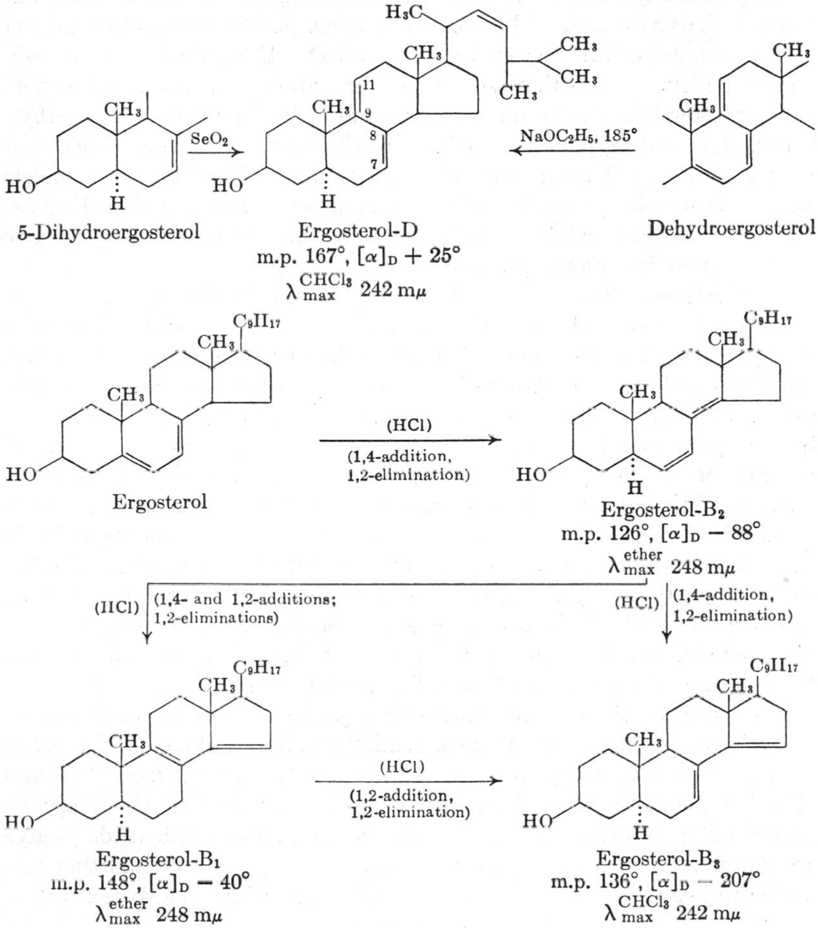
H_3C
CH_3
CH_3
CH_3
CH_3
CH_3
CH_3
CH_3
11
9
8
7
SeO_2
$NaOC_2H_5$, 185°
HO
H
HO
H
5-Dihydroergosterol
Ergosterol-D
m.p. 167°, $[\alpha]_D$ + 25°
$\lambda_{max}^{CHCl_3}$ 242 mμ
Dehydroergosterol
C_9H_{17}
CH_3
CH_3
HO
Ergosterol
(HCl)
(1,4-addition, 1,2-elimination)
C_9H_{17}
CH_3
CH_3
HO
H
Ergosterol-B_2
m.p. 126°, $[\alpha]_D$ − 88°
λ_{max}^{ether} 248 mμ
(HCl) (1,4- and 1,2-additions; 1,2-eliminations)
(HCl) (1,4-addition, 1,2-elimination)
C_9H_{17}
CH_3
CH_3
HO
H
Ergosterol-B_1
m.p. 148°, $[\alpha]_D$ − 40°
λ_{max}^{ether} 248 mμ
(HCl)
(1,2-addition, 1,2-elimination)
C_9H_{17}
CH_3
CH_3
HO
H
Ergosterol-B_3
m.p. 136°, $[\alpha]_D$ − 207°
$\lambda_{max}^{CHCl_3}$ 242 mμ

The presence of a $\Delta^{7,9(11)}$-diene system was inferred by Barton[6] from the optical rotation and the relationship of the isomer to its precursors.

Isomerization of ergosterol (as acetate) with dry hydrogen chloride in

[6] Barton, *J. Chem. Soc.*, 512 (1946); see also W. Bergmann and Klacsmann, *J. Org. Chem.*, **13,** 21 (1948).

chloroform[7] leads to a separable mixture of ergosterols-B_1, B_2, and B_3.[5] Ergosterol-B_3 is also obtained[2,4] from 5-dihydroergosterol by an oxidation reaction that probably involves a migration of the 7,8-double bond. The three isomers are all interconvertible and the rearrangements induced by hydrogen chloride can be formulated as proceeding by the addition-elimination reactions indicated. The isomers have comparable absorption maxima and are similar in this respect to ergosterol-D. Ergosterol-B_3 is the only one of the four isomers that adds maleic anhydride and this isomer differs from ergosterol in absorption spectrum and in its failure to yield methylbenzenetetracarboxylic acid on oxidation with nitric acid (double bonds not both in ring B). The fact that the nuclear double bond of the B_3-maleic anhydride addition product resists hydrogenation in acetic acid in the presence of palladium catalyst[8] indicates that this bond lies between two quaternary carbon atoms (C_8 and C_{14}).

i-Cholesterol. Stoll[1] observed that whereas cholesteryl p-toluenesulfonate is converted by boiling methanol into the normal cholesteryl methyl ether (m.p. 84°, $[\alpha]_D - 46°$), which like cholesterol is levorotatory, the reaction of the ester with methanol in the presence of potassium acetate affords an isomeric, abnormal, dextrorotatory ether (m.p. 79°, $[\alpha]_D + 55°$). Similar pairs of ethers were obtained from other alcohols. Cholesteryl chloride or bromide yields the normal ether when heated with methanol alone at 125°, but gives the abnormal ether in the presence of potassium acetate.[2] Whereas the normal ethers do not react with halogen acids in acetic acid solution at room temperature, the abnormal ethers are converted easily under these conditions into the normal cholesteryl halide (chloride, bromide, or iodide).[3] Ready replacement of the alkoxyl group has been observed also in the reaction of the abnormal ethers with bromine at room temperature;[3] the product is 3,5,6-tribromocholestane.

The abnormal ethers were tentatively regarded as derivatives of epicholesterol[1,3] or Δ^4-epicholestenol[1] until Wallis, Fernholz and Gephart[4] isolated the parent hydroxy compound and showed it to be different from these and all other known isomers of cholesterol. They found that cholesteryl p-toluenesulfonate reacts with potassium acetate in acetic anhydride to give an abnormal, dextrorotatory acetate (m.p. 73°, $[\alpha]_D + 48°$) and that this on hydrolysis yields the new isomer i-cholesterol, which is also dextrorota-

---

[7] Reindel, Walter and Rauch, *Ann.*, **452**, 42 (1927).

[8] Chen, *Ber.*, **70**, 1432 (1937).

[1] W. Stoll, *Z. physiol. Chem.*, **207**, 147 (1932).

[2] Wagner-Jauregg and L. Werner, *Z. physiol. Chem.*, **213**, 119 (1932). These authors state that the abnormal ether rearranges to the normal ether when heated with "one mole HCl" in methanol at 130°, but the experiment is not recorded.

[3] Beynon, Heilbron and Spring, *J. Chem. Soc.*, 907 (1936).

[4] Wallis, Fernholz and Gephart, *J. Am. Chem. Soc.*, **59**, 137 (1937).

tory and is not precipitated by digitonin. Beynon, Heilbron and Spring[5] later reported that i-cholesterol can be prepared in high yield by the hydrolysis of cholesteryl *p*-toluenesulfonate in aqueous acetone in the presence of potassium acetate. i-Cholesteryl acetate does not react with perbenzoic acid or decolorize dilute bromine solution; it shows resistance to hydrogenation under some conditions but in the presence of Adams catalyst in acetic acid it affords cholestanyl acetate in 85 percent yield. It is partially converted into normal cholesteryl acetate when warmed for a few minutes with acetic acid containing a few drops of sulfuric acid. Wallis and co-workers interpreted the reaction of cholesteryl *p*-toluenesulfonate with potassium acetate as a rearrangement reaction of a type common in terpene chemistry and postulated that i-cholesterol contains a bridge bond extending from C_3 to C_5 and a hydroxyl group at C_6 (see formula). Later work

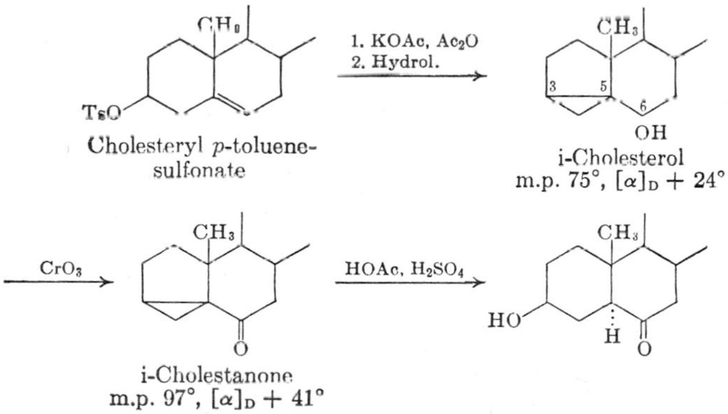

TsO — Cholesteryl *p*-toluene-sulfonate

1. KOAc, Ac₂O
2. Hydrol.

OH
i-Cholesterol
m.p. 75°, [α]D + 24°

CrO₃

i-Cholestanone
m.p. 97°, [α]D + 41°

HOAc, H₂SO₄

confirmed this inference[6] and established that the abnormal ethers of Stoll can be obtained by alkylation of i-cholesterol.[5,6] The position of the hydroxyl group was established by conversion of the corresponding ketone, i-cholestanone,[6,7] into cholestane-6-one[8] by hydrogenation and into cholestane-3β-ol-6-one[9] by hydrolysis. Heilbron, Hodges and Spring[7] found i-cholestanone to be identical with an unidentified product ("heterocholestenone") obtained nearly twenty years earlier by Windaus and Dalmer[10] from intermediates first described by Mauthner and Suida.[11] Cholesteryl

[5] Beynon, Heilbron and Spring, *J. Chem. Soc.*, 1459 (1937).
[6] E. G. Ford and Wallis, *J. Am. Chem. Soc.*, **59**, 1415 (1937); E. G. Ford, P. Chakravorty and Wallis, **60**, 413 (1938); Ladenburg, P. Chakravorty and Wallis, *ibid.*, **61**, 3483 (1939).
[7] Heilbron, Hodges and Spring, *J. Chem. Soc.*, 759 (1938).
[8] Windaus and Dalmer, *Ber.*, **52**, 168 (1919).
[9] Windaus, *Ber.*, **36**, 3754 (1903).
[10] Windaus and Dalmer, *Ber.*, **52**, 162 (1919).
[11] Mauthner and Suida, *Monatsh.*, **15**, 104 (1894).

chloride is nitrated at the 6-position (II), and reduction of the product affords 3-chlorocholestanone-6 (III).[12] The chloroketone is converted into

(I)   (II)   (III)   (IV)

a substance identical with i-cholestanone (IV) on treatment with alcoholic potassium hydroxide[10] or on vacuum sublimation.[13]

One use of the i-cholesterol derivatives is for preparation of cholesteryl halides, noted above; the iodide was prepared for the first time by this method.[3] Higher ethers of cholesterol also can be prepared; for example i-cholesteryl methyl ether reacts with *n*-propanol in the presence of *p*-toluenesulfonic acid to give the normal *n*-propyl ether of cholesterol in 77 percent yield.[14] Cholesteryl *p*-toluenesulfonate reacts with liquid ammonia at 98° to give both i-cholesterylamine and cholesterylamine; the former is the precursor of the latter.[15] i-Cholesterylamine hydrochloride, m.p. 214°, $[\alpha]_D + 20°$, is soluble in ether, whereas cholesterylamine hydrochloride is insoluble.[16] Another use is in affording temporary protection of the 5,6-double bond.[17] Thus stigmasterol yielded an i-methyl ether and when this was hydrogenated in the presence of a weak palladium catalyst the double bond in the side chain was effectively saturated without disturbance of the bridge bond in ring A; treatment of the product with zinc acetate in boiling acetic acid[18] effected rearrangement with the formation of the normal sterol acetate.

3-Halides. Cholesterol is converted by either thionyl chloride or phosphorus pentachloride into a single, sterically pure epimer, cholesteryl chloride, and the reactions of i-cholesteryl methyl ether with hydrogen halides[1] or of cholesteryl methanesulfonate with hydrogen iodide[2] afford 3-halides that all have the same configuration and afford cholesterol (3β) on hydrol-

---

[12] An analogous substitution is the reaction of cholesterol with mercuric acetate, followed by treatment with sodium chloride, to give cholesteryl-6-mercuric chloride; this on iodination affords 6-iodocholesterol; Levin and Spielman, *J. Am. Chem. Soc.*, **62**, 920 (1940).

[13] Windaus and v. Staden, *Ber.*, **54**, 1059 (1921).

[14] McKennis, *J. Am. Chem. Soc.*, **69**, 2565 (1947); **70**, 675 (1948).

[15] Julian, Magnani, E. W. Meyer and Cole, *J. Am. Chem. Soc.*, **70**, 1834 (1948).

[16] Windaus and Adamla, *Ber.*, **44**, 3051 (1911).

[17] Fernholz and Ruigh, *J. Am. Chem. Soc.*, **62**, 3346 (1940).

[18] Beynon, Heilbron and Spring, *J. Chem. Soc.*, 406 (1937).

[1] Beynon, Heilbron and Spring, *J. Chem. Soc.*, 907 (1936).

[2] Helferich and Günther, *Ber.*, **72**, 338 (1939).

Chart 13. REPLACEMENT REACTIONS

Cholesterol (β)

SOCl₂ or PCl₅
(91% yield)
KOAc; hydrol.

Cholesteryl chloride (β)
m.p. 97°, [α]_D − 26°

H₂, Pt

H₂, Pt

Cholestanol (β)
m.p. 142°, [α]_D + 23°

SOCl₂

3β-Chlorocholestane
("α"-Cholestanyl chloride)
m.p. 115°, [α]_D + 27°

PCl₅   KOAc, hydrol.
β/α =88/12

PCl₅   KOAc, hydrol.
α/β =85/15

3α-Chlorocholestane
("β"-Cholestanyl chloride)
m.p. 105°, [α]_D + 30.5°

SOCl₂

Epicholestanol (α)
m.p. 184°, [α]_D + 26°

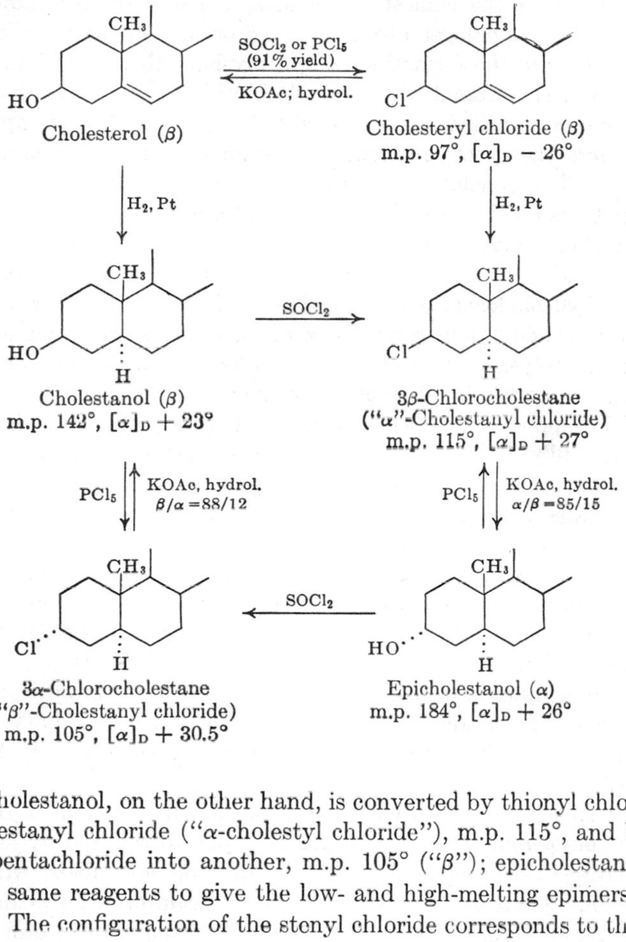

ysis. Cholestanol, on the other hand, is converted by thionyl chloride into one cholestanyl chloride ("α-cholestyl chloride"), m.p. 115°, and by phosphorus pentachloride into another, m.p. 105° ("β"); epicholestanol reacts with the same reagents to give the low- and high-melting epimers, respectively.[3] The configuration of the stenyl chloride corresponds to that of the higher-melting stanyl chloride, into which it is converted on hydrogenation, but the facts cited do not reveal the configurations or indicate which replacement reactions proceed with Walden inversion. Inferences[4] based upon small and irregular differences in the melting points of several pairs of comparable epimers[5] have proved to be erroneous.

[3] Marker, *J. Am. Chem. Soc.*, **57**, 1755 (1935); Marker, Whitmore and O. Kamm, *ibid.*, **57**, 2358 (1935).

[4] Fieser, THIS BOOK, 2nd Ed., pp. 392–393.

[5] Ruzicka, Wirz and J. Meyer, *Helv. Chim. Acta*, **18**, 998 (1935); Barr, Heilbron and Spring, *J. Chem. Soc.*, 737 (1936).

Substantial evidence is now available from two sources. Crowfoot's X-ray analyses[6] of the cholesteryl halides, particularly the iodide, have established that the halogen atom has the β-orientation and hence that no inversions occur in the formation or hydrolysis of the stenyl halides or in the reaction of cholestanol with thionyl chloride to give the chloride m.p. 115°. The same conclusion was arrived at by Shoppee[7] from an application of the modern theory of replacement reactions, particularly as developed by Ingold.[8] The conclusion is based upon a theoretical analysis of the transformations cited above and of the results of a study of the acetolysis of the two cholestanyl chlorides with potassium acetate in *n*-valeric acid at 185° and subsequent saponification. The predominating reaction in each case was dehydrohalogenation to yield Δ^2-cholestene, but the relative proportion of the cholestanols resulting from that portion of the material that underwent acetolysis was nevertheless significant. Both chlorides yielded both epimeric stanols but in markedly unequal and inverse proportions, from which Shoppee concluded that the acetolysis proceeds, as in the case of saturated alkyl halides of less elaborate structure, predominately with inversion. From the observed ratios of epimeric stanols produced (Chart 13) he estimated that bimolecular acetolysis (mechanism S_N2; inversion, no racemization) is accompanied to the extent of some 24 – 30 percent by monomolecular acetolysis (S_N1; chiefly inversion, some racemization). It follows that inversion also occurs in the reactions of the stanols with phosphorus pentachloride but not with thionyl chloride and that the unsaturated compounds undergo replacement reactions without inversion. The relationships are summarized in the chart. The difference in optical rotation of the cholestanyl chlorides is slight but conforms to the rule that substances of the 3α-configuration are somewhat more dextrorotatory than the β-epimers.[9]

The retention of configuration in the replacement reactions of the Δ^5-unsaturated compounds is analogous, for example, to the hydroxylation and methoxylation of α-bromo- and α,β-dibromopropionic acids, which take place without inversion.[8] In these cases cyclic intermediates have been postulated, and it may be that intermediates of the i-cholesterol type are involved in the reactions of the sterols and stenyl chlorides.[10] Since the ethers of i-cholesterol are much more reactive than the normal cholesteryl

[6] Carlisle and Crowfoot, *Proc. Roy. Soc. (London)*, **A184**, 64 (1945); Crowfoot, *Vitamins and Hormones*, **II**, 409 (1944).

[7] Shoppee, *J. Chem. Soc.*, 1138, 1147 (1946).

[8] Cowdrey, Hughes, Ingold, Masterman and Scott, *J. Chem. Soc.*, 1252 (1937); Dostrovsky, Hughes and Ingold, *ibid.*, 188 (1946).

[9] Bernstein, Hicks, D. Clark and Wallis, *J. Org. Chem.*, **11**, 646 (1946).

[10] Dodson and Riegel, *J. Org. Chem.*, **13**, 424 (1948).

ethers, such a mechanism would account for the fact that cholesteryl halides and tosylates undergo acetolysis much more readily than the saturated derivatives. In a kinetic study that confirms and extends the work

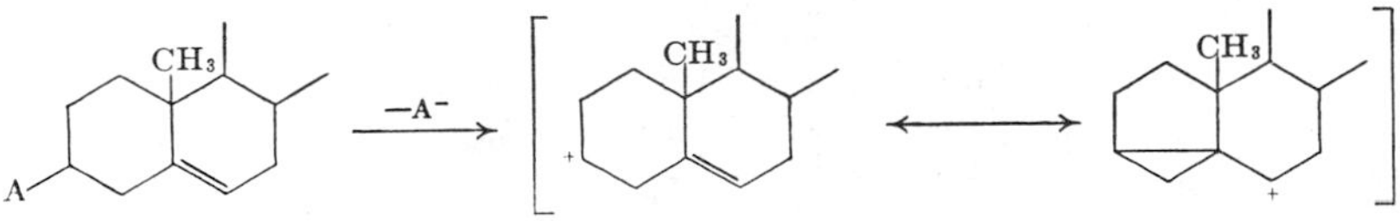

of Shoppee, Winstein[11] observed a difference of 100 in the first order rate constants of the tosylates.

Whereas cholesteryl chloride reacts with acetate or hydroxyl ion without inversion, some inversion occurs when the Grignard derivative of the unsaturated halide is oxygenated. This reaction was employed in the first preparation of epicholesterol (m.p. 141°, $[\alpha]_D - 37.5°$); the substance can be isolated from the mixture by removal of the cholesterol by precipitation with digitonin[12] or by crystallization of the acetates and then the benzoates.[13] Epicholesterol has also been prepared by acetolysis of 7-keto-cholesteryl chloride, which gives a mixture of the two epimeric keto acetates, and Wolff-Kishner reduction.[14] Another method is hydrogenation of Δ^5-cholestenone in the presence of Raney-nickel catalyst and separation of the epimers as above.[15] Epicholesterol is no more sensitive to dehydration by mineral acids than cholesterol. A further method of effecting epimerization at C_3 is through the tosyl ester.[16] Thus the tosylate of 3α-hydroxy-etioallocholanic acid when refluxed with sodium acetate in acetic acid afforded 3β-hydroxyetioallocholanic acid, along with an etioallocholenic acid as a by-product.

Cholesteryl chloride reacts with magnesium in ether only very slowly, even with assistance from added ethylmagnesium bromide,[12,13,17] and the Grignard reagent is invariably accompanied by a product of coupling, 3-cholesteryl-Δ^5-cholestene.[17] The bromide reacts more rapidly but affords the same by-product. Cholesterylmagnesium halides can be carbonated almost quantitatively, but condensations with aldehydes are attended with the formation of large amounts of cholestene.[17]

Substitution Reactions of Ketosteroids. The course of substitution of

[11] Winstein and Rowland Adams, *J. Am. Chem. Soc.*, **70**, 838 (1948).

[12] Marker, Oakwood and Crooks, *J. Am. Chem. Soc.*, **58**, 481 (1936).

[13] Marker, O. Kamm, Oakwood and Laucius, *J. Am. Chem. Soc.*, **58**, 1948 (1936).

[14] Marker, O. Kamm, Fleming, Popkin and Wittle, *J. Am. Chem. Soc.*, **59**, 619 (1937).

[15] Ruzicka and M. W. Goldberg, *Helv. Chim Acta*, **19**, 1407 (1936).

[16] Plattner and Fürst, *Helv. Chim. Acta*, **26**, 2266 (1943).

[17] R. H. Baker and Squire, *J. Am. Chem. Soc.*, **70**, 1487 (1948).

a 3-ketosteroid that has activated α-methylene groups available at both the 2- and 4-positions is determined by the configuration at C_5. 3-Ketones of the normal 5β-series (A/B cis) are substituted at the 4-position; the allo isomers yield C_2-substitution products. Oxidative ring cleavage of the epimeric ketones proceeds in accordance with this general rule.

Bromination is of importance as the first step in the introduction of a double bond; the substitution usually proceeds smoothly, but the dehydro-bromination often gives trouble. Coprostanone and cholestanone are monobrominated exclusively at positions 4 and 2, respectively,[1] and anal-ogous reactions have been observed with 3-keto bile acids.[2] The same rules

Chart 14. BROMINATION OF 3-KETOSTEROIDS

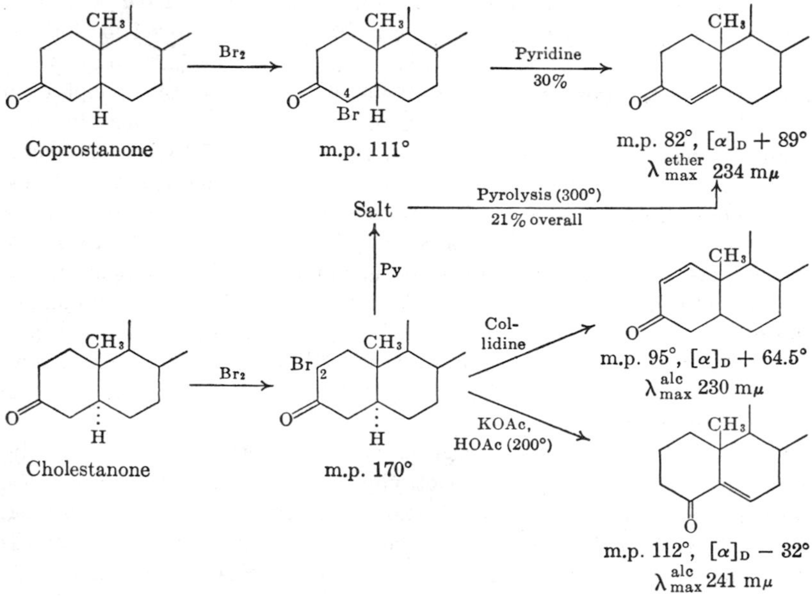

of substitution apply to bromination of 3-ketones with N-bromosuccinimide (which proceeds without formation of hydrogen bromide);[3] cholestenone is brominated by this reagent at position 6.[4] 4-Bromocoprostanone reacts with boiling pyridine to give the normal product of dehydrohalogenation,

[1] Butenandt and Wolff, *Ber.*, **68,** 2091 (1935).

[2] Butenandt and Mamoli, *Ber.*, **68,** 1854 (1935).

[3] Djerassi and Scholz, *Experientia*, **3,** 107 (1947).

[4] Meystre and Wettstein, *Experientia*, **2,** 408 (1946).

Δ^4-cholestenone (Chart 14), but the yield is low and a part of the bromo ketone is converted into a sparingly soluble nitrogen-containing salt,[1] initially assumed to be the pyridinium bromide.[2] Under comparable conditions 2-bromocholestanone reacts with pyridine to give a similar salt in high yield and no dehydrohalogenation occurs.[1] Ruzicka[5] found that the salt can be converted by pyrolysis into an unsaturated ketone but that a rearrangement occurs and the product is Δ^4-cholestenone. The peculiar rearrangement reaction proceeds in only poor yield and is not general (pyrolysis of the salt from 2-bromoallopregnanedione gave Δ^1-allopregnenedione).[6] Butenandt[6] found that normal dehydrohalogenation to Δ^1-cholestenone can be accomplished with the use of collidine (2,4,6-trimethylpyridine), and the reagent has proved useful in other instances.[7] The methyl groups evidently block the formation of salts of the type frequently formed from pyridine. These interfering salts have not been fully characterized, but have been shown to have the composition[8,9] of the sum of the components, in accordance with the assumed formulation (a). Inhoffen and co-workers[9]

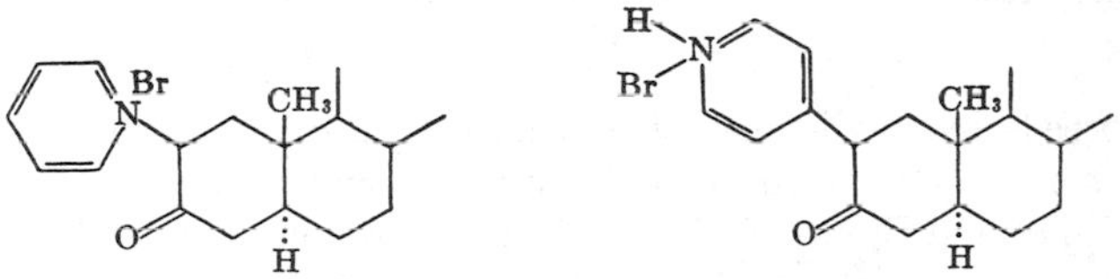

(a)   (b)

observed that 2-bromocholestanone reacted with 2,6-dimethylpyridine to give a comparable salt but reacted with 2,4-dimethylpyridine to give Δ^1-cholestenone as the chief product. From this indication that salt-formation is blocked more effectively by a para-methyl than by an ortho-methyl group, the authors reasoned that the pyridine ring is linked at the para position and that the salt is a pyridinium hydrobromide (b). This point has not been demonstrated, however, and the behavior of 4-bromo-coprostanone cited above shows that pyridine itself can exhibit both reactions established for the dimethyl homologs.

The dehydrohalogenation of 2-bromocholestanone with potassium acetate at 200° leads to the formation of a "hetero-Δ^1-cholestenone"[1] that was eventually identified as Δ^5-cholestenone-4 by the following observations.[10]

[5] Ruzicka, Plattner and Aeschbacher, *Helv. Chim. Acta*, **21**, 866 (1938).
[6] Butenandt, Mamoli, Dannenberg, Masch and Paland, *Ber.*, **72**, 1617 (1939).
[7] The original reaction, however, has been reinvestigated by Jacobsen, *J. Am. Chem. Soc.*, **62**, 1620 (1940), with much less favorable results.
[8] Schwenk and Whitman, *J. Am. Chem. Soc.*, **59**, 949 (1937).
[9] Inhoffen, Zühlsdorff and Huang-Minlon, *Ber.*, **73**, 451 (1940).
[10] Butenandt and Ruhenstroth-Bauer, *Ber.*, **77**, 397 (1944).

Hydrogenation over Raney nickel gives the known cholestanone-4;[11] oxidation with permanganate in boiling acetone gives a diol which contains only one acylable hydroxyl group; the absorption spectrum is that of an α,β-unsaturated ketone in which the double bond is secondary-tertiary and not in the same ring as the carbonyl group (calcd. λ_{max}^{alc} 242 mμ).

Further bromination of 4-bromocoprostanone affords 4,4-dibromocoprostanone.[12,13] The first product of the dibromination of cholestanone or of the bromination of the 2-bromoketone[12] is 2,2-dibromocholestanone,[14] which rearranges readily in the reaction mixture to the 2,4-dibromo ketone.[15,16] The migration of bromine from the 2- to the 4-position prob-

CH$_3$ Br$_2$ O   H

$\xrightarrow{\text{HBr}}$

CH$_3$ Br   O   Br   H

$\xrightarrow[\text{50\%}]{\text{Collidine}}$

CH$_3$ O

2,2-Dibromocholest- anone. m p. 140°

2,4-Dibromocholest- anone. m.p. 194°, $[\alpha]_D$ + 3°

$\Delta^{1,4}$-Cholestadienone-3, m.p.112°, $[\alpha]_D$ + 28° λ_{max}^{ether} 236 mμ

ably proceeds by allylic rearrangement of the enolic form.[16] Hydrogen bromide markedly catalyzes both the initial bromination and the rearrangement. Wilds and Djerassi[17] observed that dibromination of a 3-ketosteroid in ordinary glacial acetic acid gave the 2,4-dibromo compound whereas the 2,2-isomer resulted when the reaction was carried out in acetic acid that has been distilled from potassium permanganate, and Djerassi and Scholz[18] found that the difference is due to inhibition of the rearrangement by a trace of water formed in the treatment with permanganate. Water inhibits both the formation and rearrangement of the 2,2-dibromide; M. Rubin and Hershberg[19] observed that hydrogen peroxide also inhibits rearrangement, even in the presence of hydrogen bromide.

The yield of $\Delta^{1,4}$-cholestadienone-3 by the dehydrohalogenation with pyridine was only 11 percent,[20] whereas substitution of collidine raised the yield to 50 percent.[6] Collidine is generally a better reagent than pyridine but it is far from ideal and the yields are sometimes no better than 10 per-

[11] Windaus, Ber., 53, 488 (1920).
[12] Butenandt, Schramm, Wolff and Kudszus, Ber., 69, 2779 (1936).
[13] Ruzicka, Bosshard, W. Fischer and Wirz, Helv. Chim. Acta, 19, 1147 (1936).
[14] Dorée, J. Chem. Soc., 95, 648 (1909).
[15] Inhoffen, Ber., 70, 1695 (1937).
[16] Inhoffen and Zühlsdorff, Ber., 76, 233 (1943).
[17] Wilds and Djerassi, J. Am. Chem. Soc., 68, 2125 (1946).
[18] Djerassi and Scholz, J. Am. Chem. Soc., 69, 2404 (1947).
[19] Communication from Dr. E. B. Hershberg.
[20] Inhoffen and Huang-Minlon, Ber., 71, 1720 (1938).

cent. Cholestanone has been isolated as one of the products formed from 2-bromocholestanone by the action of collidine[7] and it is the principal product of the action of dimethylaniline on the bromo ketone.[8] Dane[21] introduced an apparently useful method for elimination of hydrogen bromide which consists in the use of silver nitrate in pyridine solution at room temperature; $\Delta^{4,6}$-cholestadienone-3 was prepared by this method. A new method for the dehydrohalogenation of 4-bromo-3-keto steroids of the bile acid series reported by Kendall[22] utilizes 2,4-dinitrophenylhydrazine. The reagent reacts at room temperature to give the dinitrophenylhydrazone of the Δ^4-3-ketosteroid and the derivative is subsequently hydrolyzed with use of pyruvic acid (Chapter V, Chart 27).

Windaus found that the usual rule regarding the direction of substitution holds in general for the reaction of 3-ketosteroids with a mixture of concentrated sulfuric acid and acetic anhydride with the formation of water-soluble sulfonic acid derivatives.[23,24] Cholestanone yields the 2-sulfonic acid deriva-

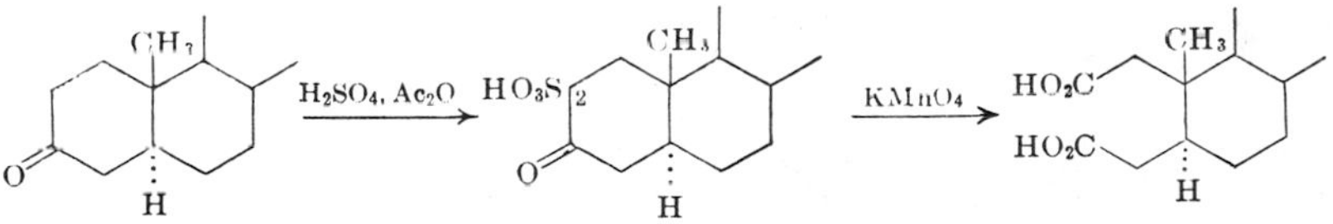

Cholestanone — H_2SO_4, Ac_2O → Cholestanone-2-sulfonic acid — $KMnO_4$ →

tive; the structure was established by oxidation to a known dibasic acid. The product most easily isolated from coprostanone (as the methyl ester) is the 2-sulfonic acid,[23] but the more soluble 4-sulfonic acid[24] is actually the predominating product of the reaction. Cholestenone (I) is converted smoothly into a derivative shown by oxidative degradations to be the 6-sulfonic acid, II.[23] Kuhr[25] postulated that the reaction proceeds through the enol form of cholestenone and found evidence in the smooth conversion of the enol acetate (IV) into the same sulfonic acid. The reactions were conceived as 1,4-additions of sulfuric acid to the enol or enol acetate to give intermediates of the type V. 3-Chloro-$\Delta^{3,5}$-cholestadiene reacts in an analogous manner. The reaction of cholestenone enol acetate with bromine in acetic acid containing potassium acetate to give 6-bromo-Δ^4-cholestenone-3[26] is interpreted most simply as a similar 1,4-addition. Cholestenone-6-sulfonic acid sodium salt has marked power to bring water-

[21] Dane, Wang and Schulte, *Z. physiol. Chem.*, **245**, 80 (1936).
[22] Mattox and Kendall, *J. Am. Chem. Soc.*, **70**, 882 (1948).
[23] Windaus and Kuhr, *Ann.*, **532**, 52 (1937).
[24] Windaus and Mielke, *Ann.*, **536**, 116 (1938).
[25] Kuhr, *Ber.*, **72**, 929 (1939).
[26] Inhoffen, *Ber.*, **69**, 2141 (1936).

insoluble substances into aqueous solution or emulsion (cholesterol, vitamin D, camphor, carcinogenic hydrocarbons). The sulfonate forms salts with

Chart 15.   Δ[4]-CHOLESTENE-3-ONE-6-SULFONIC ACID

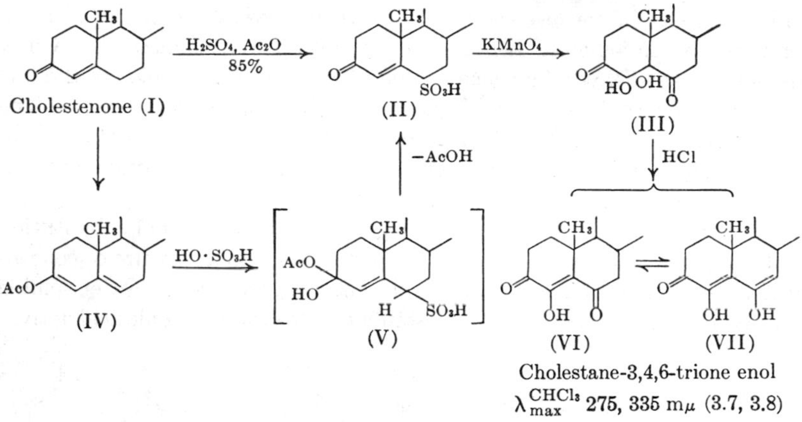

Cholestenone (I)

(II)

(III)

(IV)

(V)

(VI)   (VII)

Cholestane-3,4,6-trione enol

$\lambda_{max}^{CHCl_3}$ 275, 335 mμ (3.7, 3.8)

amino acids that crystallize from absolute alcohol and offers some possibilities as a resolving agent.[27]

The product of dehydration of cholestane-4,5-diol-3,6-dione (III, Chart 15) presents a point of interest. This substance, III, was also obtained by oxidation of Δ[4]-cholestene-3,6-dione with potassium permanganate in acetone solution. Dehydration is effected by boiling alcoholic hydrochloric acid and gives a product formulated by Windaus[23] as the enol VI. This structure accounts for an intense absorption band at 275 mμ (calcd., $\lambda_{max}^{CHCl_3}$, 278 mμ). A second band of still higher extinction coefficient at 335 mμ may possibly be associated with the location of the enolic hydroxyl between the two carbonyl groups, or it may be indicative of an equilibrium mixture containing the dienediolone VII (calcd. $\lambda_{max}^{CHCl_3}$, 332 mμ).

As in other substitutions, cholestanone is oxidized by selenium dioxide in alcohol at the 2-position;[28] coprostanone under the same conditions reacts to only a slight extent. The product of oxidation is not the 2,3-dione (IV, Chart 16) but an equilibrium mixture from which Stiller and Rosenheim isolated two enols of the probable structures III and V. One, enol-A (III), can be isolated through the sparingly soluble potassium salt and is isomerized by hydrochloric acid to enol-B (V). The enols form different monoacetates. Ruzicka[29] has reported the preparation of enol-A (through the

[27] Triem, *Ber.*, **71**, 1522 (1938).

[28] Stiller and Rosenheim, *J. Chem. Soc.*, 353 (1938).

[29] Ruzicka, Plattner and Furrer, *Helv. Chim. Acta*, **27**, 524 (1944).

K-salt) in somewhat better overall yield by the method of Kröhnke: conversion of cholestanone through the 2-bromo derivative to the 2-pyridinium

Chart 16. ENOLIC FORMS OF CHOLESTANE-2, 3-DIONE

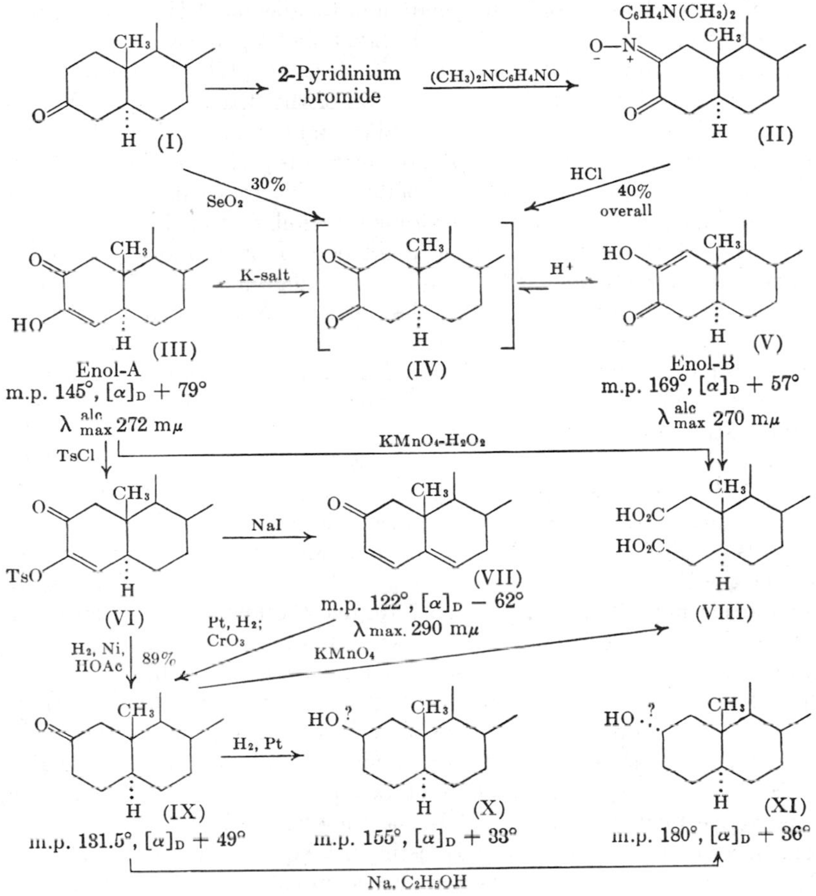

CH₃ (I) H

2-Pyridinium bromide   (CH₃)₂NC₆H₄NO

C₆H₄N(CH₃)₂
O—N⁺ CH₃ (II) H

30% SeO₂

HCl 40% overall

CH₃ (III) H
HO
Enol-A
m.p. 145°, [α]_D + 79°
λ_max^alc 272 mμ

K-salt

CH₃ (IV) H
O
O

H⁺

HO CH₃ (V) H
O
Enol-B
m.p. 169°, [α]_D + 57°
λ_max^alc 270 mμ

TsCl

KMnO₄-H₂O₂

CH₃ (VI) H
TsO
O

NaI

CH₃ (VII) H
O
m.p. 122°, [α]_D − 62°
λ max. 290 mμ

HO₂C CH₃ (VIII) H
HO₂C

H₂, Ni, HOAc 89%

Pt, H₂; CrO₃

KMnO₄

CH₃ (IX) H
O
m.p. 131.5°, [α]_D + 49°

H₂, Pt

HO ? CH₃ (X) H
m.p. 155°, [α]_D + 33°

HO ? CH₃ (XI) H
m.p. 180°, [α]_D + 36°

Na, C₂H₅OH

bromide and condensation of this with *p*-nitrosodimethylaniline to the nitrone II, which on acid hydrolysis yields the dione-enol mixture. Enols A and B both yield the same quinoxaline derivative and on oxidation are converted to a dibasic acid (VIII) identical with that resulting from the oxidation of cholestanone-3.

Ruzicka found that the tosylate (VI) of the lower-melting enol-A on reaction with sodium iodide loses *p*-toluenesulfonic acid with the formation of a conjugated dienone-2 with an absorption maximum close to the calculated value (λ_{max}^{alc} 286 mμ) and therefore formulated as VII. Such a substance could hardly arise from an enol of structure V, but its formation from the tosylate VI can be interpreted as a migration of the double bond from C_3 – C_4 to C_4 – C_5 (equilibrium) and 1,4-elimination. Furthermore, hydrogenation of the tosylate VI, or hydrogenation of the dienone VII and oxidation, yields a cholestanone different from the 3-ketone (m.p. depression) but convertible by oxidation into the same dibasic acid VIII; the substance is therefore cholestanone-2 (IX). Reduction of the 2-keto group by hydrogenation gives one cholestanol-2 (m.p. 155°) and reduction with sodium and alcohol gives the epimer (m.p. 180°); the former is precipitated by digitonin and the latter is not. In melting points, specific rotations, and behavior toward digitonin the epimers are strikingly similar to cholestanol-3β and -3α (with which they give melting point depressions), and on this basis Ruzicka tentatively assigned the β- and α-configurations. The 4-cholestanols[30] do not resemble the 3-cholestanols in physical constants and neither is precipitated with digitonin.

The bromination of 6-ketocholestanyl acetate (I, Chart 17) was investigated by Heilbron[31] in the search for a new route to 7-dehydrocholesterol. Bromination at a low temperature gave a substance identified as the 5-bromo derivative V by dehydrohalogenation and hydrolysis to the allylic alcohol II, which was isomerized by hot alkali to cholestane-3,6-dione, III (migration of the double bond to C_3 – C_4 and ketonization). The 5-bromide was also hydrolyzed to a diol having but one acylable hydroxyl group. Under the influence of hydrogen bromide, the bromine atom of V readily migrates from position 5 to position 7 to give the lower-melting isomer X (bottom). This substance was the type of intermediate sought, but it proved to be very resistant to dehydrohalogenation; the stability indicates that the bromine atom is probably cis to the hydrogen atom at C_8 (not trans as stated by Heilbron) and therefore of β-orientation. Under forcing conditions the substance slowly reacted with silver nitrate and pyridine to give a product of hydrolysis and oxidation that was characterized as a mono-enol (one active hydrogen), XIa or XIb, of cholestane-6,7-dione-3-ol acetate. The absorption spectrum does not distinguish between structures XIa and XIb, for the two unsaturated systems are identical in chromophoric power; the exaltation due to the enolic hydroxyl group in this case amounts to a shift of 31 mμ.

Further bromination of the monobromides afforded two 5,7-dibromo derivatives regarded by Heilbron as differing in the orientation of the

[30] Tschesche and Hagedorn, *Ber.*, **68**, 2251 (1935).
[31] Heilbron, E. R. H. Jones and Spring, *J. Chem. Soc.*, 801 (1937); Heilbron, Jackson, E. R. H. Jones and Spring, *ibid.*, 102 (1938).

Chart 17. BROMINATION OF 6-KETOCHOLESTANYL ACETATE (I)

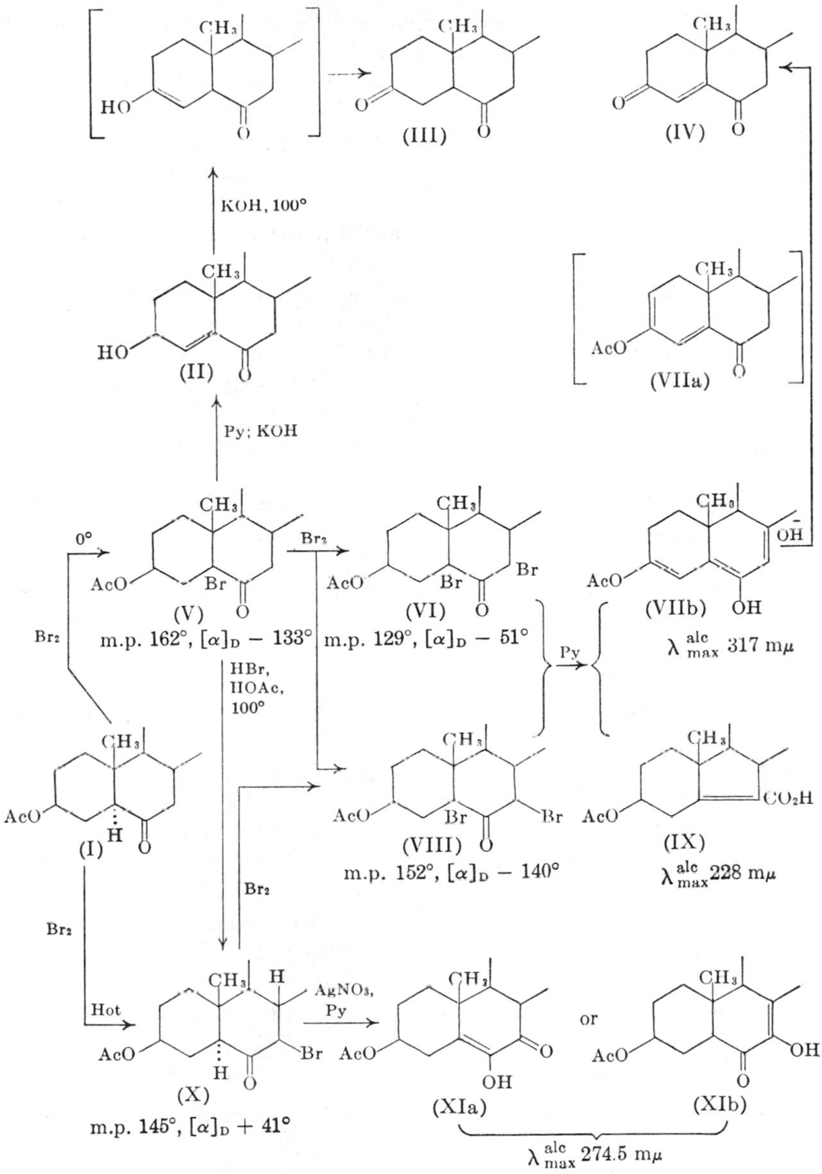

(III)   (IV)

KOH, 100°

(II)

(VIIa)

Py; KOH

0°

AcO   Br   (V)
m.p. 162°, [α]_D − 133°

Br₂

AcO   Br   (VI)
m.p. 129°, [α]_D − 51°

AcO   (VIIb)   OH
λ_{max}^{alc} 317 mμ

Br₂

(I)

HBr,
HOAc,
100°

Br₂

AcO   Br   Br   (VIII)
m.p. 152°, [α]_D − 140°

Py

AcO   CO₂H   (IX)
λ_{max}^{alc} 228 mμ

Br₂

Hot

AcO   Br   (X)
m.p. 145°, [α]_D + 41°

AgNO₃,
Py

AcO   OH   (XIa)

or

AcO   OH   (XIb)

λ_{max}^{alc} 274.5 mμ

bromine atom at position 5.   Both isomers on treatment with boiling pyridine yielded the same two products.   One, m.p. 229°, was formulated as a Δ^4-6-ketone, but Woodward[32] noted that the absorption maximum (228 mμ) is too low for such a structure and proved that the product is indeed the α,β-unsaturated acid IX and is formed as a result of a rearrangement; the absorption maximum is close to that of 3β-hydroxy-$\Delta^{5,16}$-etiocholadienic acid[33]: λ_{max} 230 mμ (log ϵ 4.1).   The predominating product of the reaction was formulated by Heilbron as the dienone VIIa, partly because the substance on hydrolysis yields Δ^4-cholestene-3,6-dione (IV).   It is difficult to see how a double bond can arise at the 2,3-position as pictured, and the absorption maximum of 317 mμ is inconsistent with structure VIIa (calcd. 296 mμ).   The structure of a trienediol acetate, VIIb, is in good accord with the spectrographic evidence ($\Delta^{3,5,7,22}$-ergostatetraene, λ_{max}^{alc} 316 mμ) and accounts for the dehydrohalogenation as follows: formation of a 4,5-double bond; migration of hydrogen from C_3 to produce a $\Delta^{3,5}$-diene-6-ol system; cis elimination of hydrogen bromide at $C_8 - C_7$ promoted by the tendency for extension of the conjugated system.   The formation of IV on hydrolysis may follow the course of ketonization at C_3, migration of the double bonds to positions of conjugation, and further ketonization.   Heilbron considered structures with a Δ^7-double bond to be ruled out by the observation that the compound did not give a positive Tortelli-Jaffé reaction; but it is now recognized that a test conducted on a highly unsaturated substance is significant only if the additive capacity of the substance for bromine is first fully satisfied.

Bromination of 7-ketocholestanyl acetate (XII, Chart 18) proceeds less readily.[34]   The main product, m.p. 175°, is accompanied by an isomer into which it can be converted by the action of hydrogen bromide.   Both bromo compounds on reaction with boiling pyridine (6 – 8 hrs.) yield the same products, XIV and XV, and therefore are epimeric 6-bromo derivatives. The higher-melting isomer reacts more readily and also reacts with silver nitrate in pyridine to give the normal product XIV, whereas the lower-melting isomer in this instance resists normal dehydrohalogenation and is oxidized to the ketol XI.   The orientation of the bromine atom in respect to the C_5-hydrogen atom must therefore be trans in the former isomer (XIII) and cis in the latter (XVI).   Heilbron observed an interesting difference in the low-intensity absorption bands associated with the carbonyl groups of these epimers.   The band at 287 mμ (log ϵ 1.6) of the parent ketone XII is displaced to 313 mμ (log ϵ 2.2) by the 6β-bromine atom of XIII, but is not

[32] Woodward, J. Am. Chem. Soc., **63**, 1123 (1941); Woodward and Clifford, ibid., **63**, 2727 (1941).

[33] Ruzicka, Hardegger and Kauter, Helv. Chim. Acta, **27**, 1164 (1944).

[34] Barr, Heilbron, E. R. H. Jones and Spring, J. Chem. Soc., 334 (1938).

influenced much by the 6α-bromine atom of XVI (λ_{max} 282 mμ, log ε 1.6).

7-Ketocholanic acid (XVII, Chart 18) is also brominated in the 6-position, as shown by transformation of the reaction product (XVIII) into

Chart 18. BROMINATION OF 7-KETOCHOLESTANYL ACETATE (XII) AND 7-KETO-CHOLANIC ACID (XVII)

Thilobilianic acid

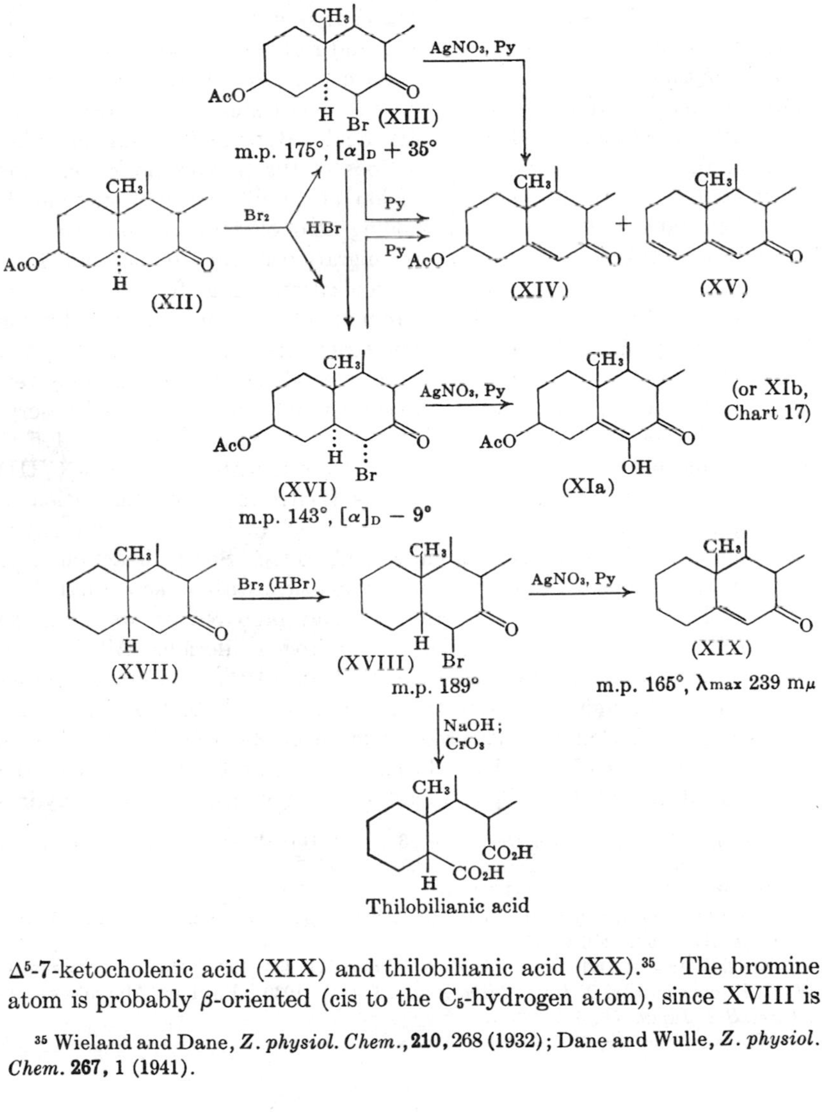

Δ⁵-7-ketocholenic acid (XIX) and thilobilianic acid (XX).[35] The bromine atom is probably β-oriented (cis to the C₅-hydrogen atom), since XVIII is

[35] Wieland and Dane, *Z. physiol. Chem.*, **210**, 268 (1932); Dane and Wulle, *Z. physiol. Chem.* **267**, 1 (1941).

very resistant to dehydrohalogenation (stable in refluxing pyridine solution). Similar bromo derivatives have been obtained from other 7-ketocholanic acids.[36] The bromination of 12-ketosteroids is surveyed in Chapters V and X. **Diosterols.** The name diosterol is applied to two enolic forms of Δ^5-cholestene-3,4-dione, one of which was first encountered by Inhoffen[1] and by Butenandt and Schramm[2] in extensive studies of the bromination of 5,6-dibromocholestanone, the oxidation product of cholesterol dibromide. The first point of attack is at position 4, and Butenandt regarded this as an indication that the dibromoketone has the coprostane configuration (5β-Br). The bromine introduced at C_4 assumes different steric orientations when bromination is conducted in acetic acid (Butenandt) and in ether (Inhoffen). Some of the transformations of the polybromo ketones are illustrated in Chart 19. The conversion of 5,6-dibromocholestanone (I) into cholestane-3,6-dione (II) by boiling alcohol[3] may proceed through the 6-bromo-Δ^4-ketone by hydrolysis, migration of the double bond from the 4,5- to the 5,6-position, and ketonization. The formation of the saturated 3,4-dione II from the tribromoketone III involves a reduction and possibly proceeds through I. The structures III, IV, VII, VIII, and IX assigned to the polybromoketones seem established by the interconversions, and structures VIII and IX are consistent with the observed absorption spectra of the unsaturated ketones. The conversion of 4,4,5,6-tetrabromocholestanone (VII) into 4,6,6-tribromo-Δ^4-cholestenone (VIII) can be accounted for on the hypothesis (Butenandt) of elimination of hydrogen bromide with establishment of a 5,6-double bond and allylic rearrangement of one bromine atom from C_4 to C_6. Several reactions lead to the bromine-free substance V, which is identical with an enol ethyl ether of Δ^4-cholestene-3,6-dione that Windaus[4] had prepared by warming the unsaturated diketone (VI) with alcoholic hydrogen chloride. All the reactions of the various polybromoketones that afford the enol ether V probably proceed through conversion to the key intermediate 4,6-dibromo-Δ^4-cholestenone (IX), and a plausible sequence of steps leading to V is as follows: hydrolysis of the allylic bromine atom at C_6, migration of the double bond from C_4-C_5 to C_5-C_6 (equilibrium), ketonization, loss of hydro-

[36] Hoehn and Linsk, *J. Am. Chem. Soc.*, **67**, 312 (1945); Grand and Reichstein, *Helv. Chim. Acta*. **28**, 344 (1945); Lardon, *ibid.*, **30**, 597 (1947).

[1] Inhoffen, *Ber.*, **69**, 1134, 2141 (1936).

[2] Butenandt and Schramm, *Ber.*, **69**, 2289 (1936); Butenandt, Schramm and Kudszus, *Ann.*, **531**, 176 (1937).

[3] Urushibara and Ando, *Bull. Chem. Soc. Japan*, **11**, 434 (1936); Ruzicka, Bosshard, W. H. Fischer and Wirz, *Helv. Chim. Acta*, **19**, 1147 (1936); Fujii and Matsukawa, *J. Pharm. Soc. Japan*, **56**, 642 (1936).

[4] Windaus, *Ber.*, **39**, 2249 (1906).

Chart 19. BROMINATION OF 5,6-DIBROMOCHOLESTANONE-3

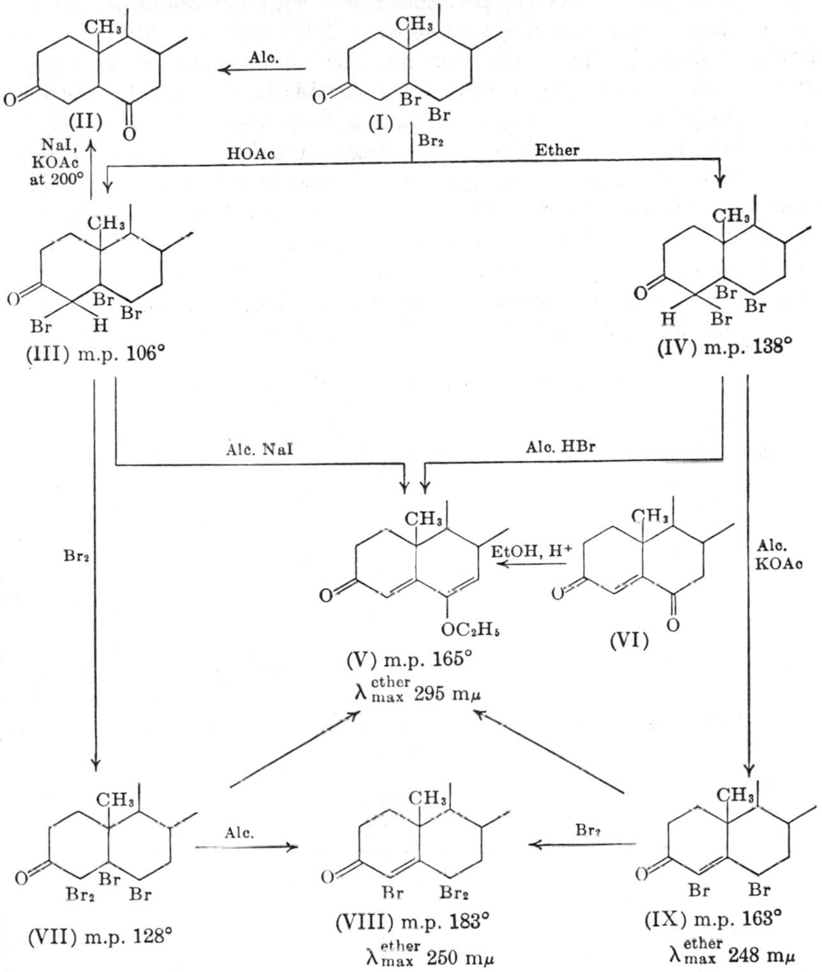

gen bromide to give the known enedione VI, and enol ether formation.
Diosterol-I (m.p. 163°) was prepared by Inhoffen and by Butenandt by

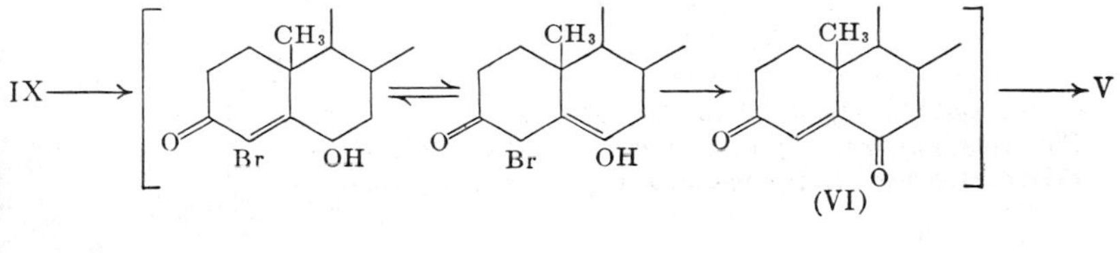

various processes that probably all proceed through 4,6-dibromo-Δ^4-cholestenone (IX, Charts 19, 20); this reacts with potassium acetate in boiling ethanol to give an enol acetate (m.p. 159°) that on acid hydrolysis affords diosterol-I. The substance has the composition of a cholestenedione and has reducing properties comparable to diosphenol. Petrow and Starling[5] later prepared the substance here designated diosterol-II (m.p. 136°, $[\alpha]_D + 31°$), which is isomerized by acids to diosterol-I and which yields the enol acetate that is the precursor of this substance. Inhoffen ascribed to the enol acetate and to diosterol-I the structures (a) and (b), Chart 20; Petrow and Starling concurred in this view and formulated diosterol-II as (c), in accordance with the mode of preparation from X. Dannenberg,[6] however, pointed out that the absorption maximum of the enol acetate, λ_{max} 238 mμ (ether[1]), 245 mμ (alcohol[7]), is much too low for

Chart 20. DIOSTEROLS; ORIGINAL FORMULATION

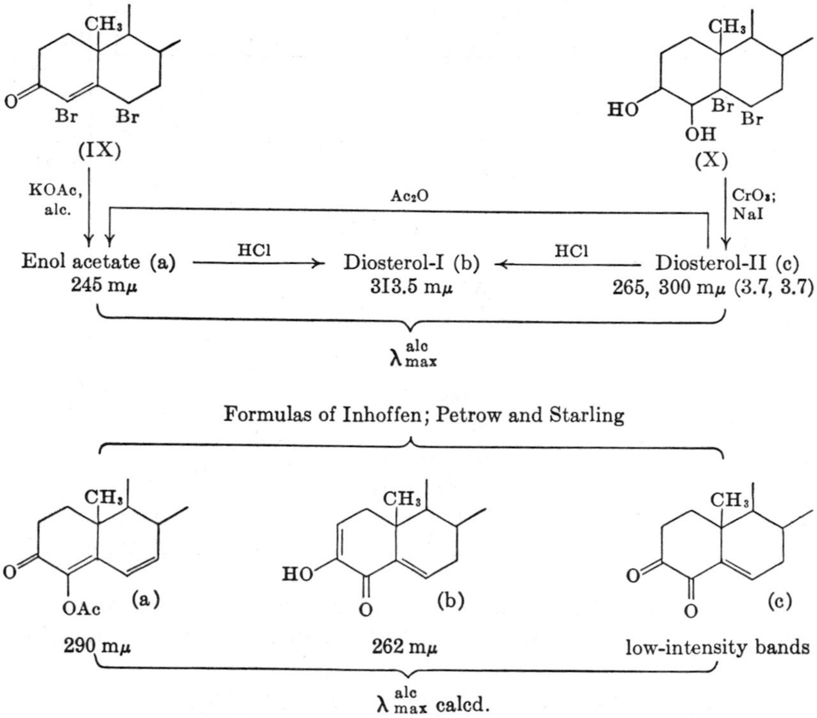

Formulas of Inhoffen; Petrow and Starling

---

[5] Petrow and Starling, *J. Chem. Soc.*, 60 (1940).

[6] Dannenberg, *Abhandl. preuss. Akad. Wiss.*, **21**, 3 (1939).

[7] Fieser, Fieser and Rajagopalan, *J. Org. Chem.* (in press).

the structure (a), as can be seen from comparison with the calculated value given in the Chart. It occurred to us, further, that the maximum reported by Inhoffen for diosterol-I is distinctly too high for the structure (b), and we undertook with Rajagopalan[7] a reinvestigation of the compounds. Determination of the absorption spectrum of diosterol-II, not previously reported, revealed that formula (c) is also in error, for the substance exhibits strong absorption at 265 mμ and 300 mμ and bears no resemblance to known α-diketones, which show two bands of higher wave length and of extinction coefficients in the range log ϵ 1.6–2.0.

The strong band shown by diosterol-I at 313.5 mμ seemed suggestive of the presence of a dienolone or a trienediol system, but either structure would seem inconsistent with Inhoffen's statement that the compound could not be acetylated. Rajagopalan, however, succeeded in preparing a monobenzoate, which is isomeric with the benzoate of diosterol-II, resulting from the action of sodium benzoate in alcohol on 4,6-dibromocholestenone, IX, and which was shown by infrared spectroscopy to contain no further, unacylated hydroxyl group. The infrared spectra showed further that diosterols-I and II both contain a hydroxyl group and an α,β-unsaturated ketonic group. The formulas XI, XIII, and XIV now proposed for diosterol-II, diosterol-I, and the enol acetate (Chart 21), largely on the basis of the spectrographic evidence, afford a rational interpretation of the properties, mode of formation, and reactions of the compounds. The ultraviolet maxima calculated for structures XIII and XIV are in good agreement with the values found.[8] The intense band at 265 mμ found for diosterol-II corresponds to that calculated for structure XI; the equally intense band at 300 mμ most likely is attributable to the presence of the trienediol XII in solution in equilibrium with XI; this may be an intermediate in the acid isomerization of diosterol-II into diosterol-I. The tautomerism is analogous to that suggested in explanation of the double-banded spectrum of cholestane-3,4,6-trione enol (Chart 15).

The production of the enol acetate XIV by the action of potassium acetate on the unsaturated dibromoketone XXI in alcoholic solution must proceed by a special mechanism to account for acetylation under non-acetylating conditions, and the following path is suggested: allylic shift of bromine (XX), replacement of both bromine atoms by acetoxyl groups (XIX), acetyl migration from C_4 to C_3 through the cyclic acetal XVII (for analogy: see page 235), and loss of acetic acid. That diosterol-II on oxidation with hydrogen peroxide yields the Diels acid[2] whereas diosterol-I yields 7-keto-Diels acid[1] is explained by the presence in diosterol-I of a

[8] The calculations are based upon the more powerful of two alternate chromophores present; that in XIV is the Δ^5-4-ketonic system, whereas that in XI is the Δ^2-4-ketonic system carrying the strongly bathochromic enolic hydroxyl group.

double bond extending to position 7; a likely hypothesis is that hydrogen peroxide adds 1,4 to the $\Delta^{4,6}$-diene system to give the intermediate XVI.

Chart 21. DIOSTEROLS; REVISED FORMULATION
(WITH ABSORPTION MAXIMA CALCULATED FOR ALCOHOLIC SOLUTION)

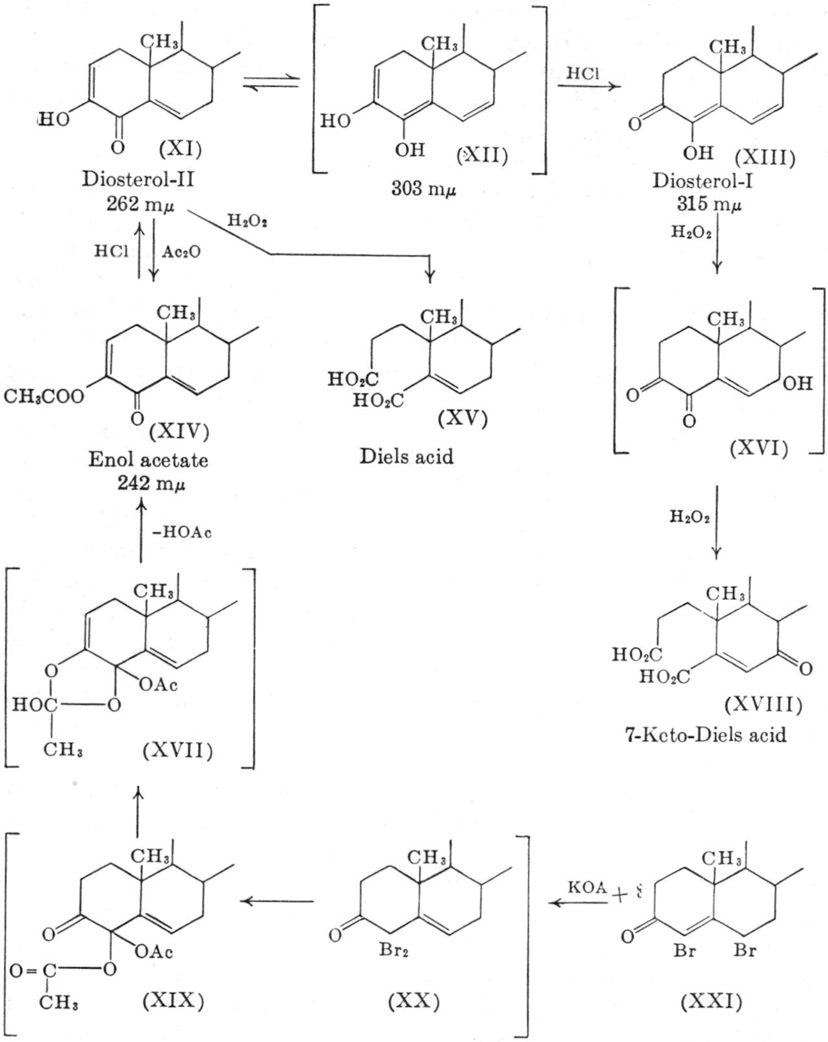

(XI)
Diosterol-II
262 mμ

(XII)
303 mμ

(XIII)
Diosterol-I
315 mμ

(XIV)
Enol acetate
242 mμ

(XV)
Diels acid

(XVI)

(XVIII)
7-Keto-Diels acid

(XVII)

(XIX)

(XX)

(XXI)

Petrow and Starling found a new method of obtaining diosterol-I that consists in controlled chromic acid oxidation of Δ^5-cholestene-3β,4β-diol

3-monoacetate (XXII) to a ketoxide and hydrolysis of this substance. The structure XXIII is now suggested for the ketoxide (orientation of oxide ring

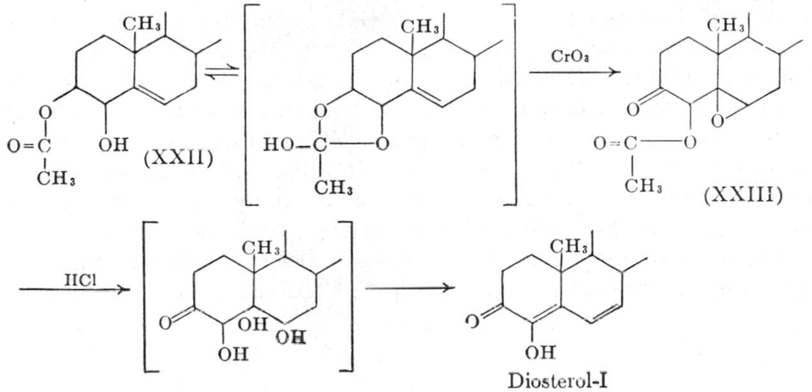

Diosterol-I

arbitrary) and its formation attributed to an initial migration of the acetyl group from the 3- to the 4-position and oxidation; the remaining steps of hydrolysis and dehydration are then understandable.

Westphalen's Diol. In a research reported by Windaus in 1915, Westphalen[1] obtained by the dehydration of trans-cholestane-3,5,6-triol 3,6-diacetate (II) a new diol that may result from a retropinacol rearrangement with displacement of the angular methyl group from C_{10} to C_5. Lettré and Müller[2] suggested that such a rearrangement is involved and the work of Petrow and associates[3, 4] indicated the specific formulation I. The

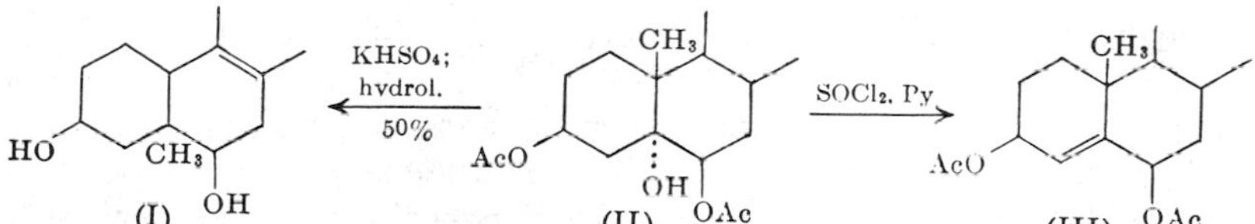

Westphalen's diol
$[\alpha]_D + 119°$; diacetate:
m.p. 128°, $[\alpha]_D$

m.p. 136°, $[\alpha]_D - 13°$

abnormal diol diacetate is produced in improved yield by the use of potassium acid sulfate, and the product is the same whether the solvent is acetic or propionic anhydride,[4] which shows that the acetoxy groups are at

[1] Westphalen, Ber., **48**, 1064 (1915).

[2] Lettré and M. Müller, Ber., **70**, 1947 (1937).

[3] Petrow, Rosenheim and Starling, J. Chem. Soc., 677 (1938).

[4] Petrow, J. Chem. Soc., 998 (1939).

the original positions 3 and 6. The strong dextrorotation was suggestive of an abnormal structure, and dehydration of cholestanetriol diacetate with thionyl chloride and pyridine (Darzen's method[5]) afforded the product of normal dehydration,[3] the diacetate (III) of the known Δ^4-cholestene-3,6-diol. The normal diol on oxidation afforded the known Δ^4-cholestene-3,6-dione, whereas Westphalen's diol yielded an unsaturated diketone (m.p. 106°) that showed no absorption above 230 mμ and in which the double bond is therefore nonconjugated. The dehydrogenation[4] (Se) of the abnormal diol to the second Diels hydrocarbon shows that the original ring system is preserved and that the methyl group occupies an angular position, and the facts cited substantiate the postulated migration to C_5.

The following oxidations of Westphalen's diol or the diacetate provide evidence that the double bond is at C_8–C_9.[4] An oxido derivative, V, gave

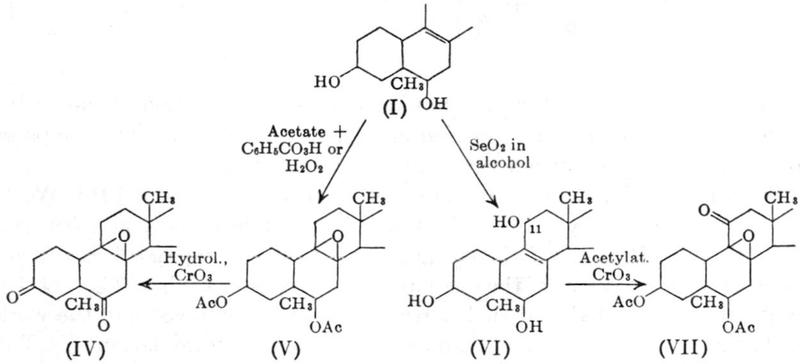

on hydrolysis an oxido-diol that afforded an oxido-diketone (IV) on chromic acid oxidation. The stability of the oxide linkage to oxidation must mean that it extends between two quaternary carbon atoms, since one located at a position such as C_5–C_6 is opened by chromic acid at room temperature (cholesterol α-oxide → cholestane-3,6-dione-5-ol[1]). On reaction with selenium dioxide, Westphalen's diol suffered allylic oxidation to a triol (VI) in which only two of the alcoholic groups could be acetylated (in cold pyridine). The third, inert group, which evidently is the one introduced in the oxidation, also resisted benzoylation and Oppenauer oxidation, but its secondary character was established by oxidation of the diacetate with chromic acid to a ketoxide VII, the carbonyl group of which was inert to carbonyl reagents. The triol did not react with lead tetraacetate, and hence the new hydroxyl group cannot be at position 7, adjacent to a double bond at either C_8–C_9 or C_8–C_{14}; Petrow suggested that the hydroxyl group

[5] Darzens, *Compt. rend.*, **152**, 1601 (1911).

is at C_{11} and the double bond at C_8-C_9. The inert character of the new hydroxyl group may be a further indication of its location at C_{11},[4] in analogy to compounds of the corticosteroid series, but the degree of hindrance in a substance lacking the C_{10}-methyl group can hardly be estimated. The displacement of the methyl group alters some of the properties associated with a normal C_8-C_9 unsaturated steroid. Thus, in contrast with Δ^8-cholestenol, Westphalen's diol (diacetate) is not isomerized (or hydrogenated) by palladium-hydrogen in alcohol-acetic acid and is not isomerized by hydrogen chloride in chloroform.[3]

The products of oxidation of Westphalen's diol with perbenzoic acid (V) and selenium dioxide (VI) are both converted by dehydrating agents into a mixture of two dienediols. The more abundant isomer (m.p. 102°) has an absorption band of high intensity at 244 mμ and reacts with maleic anhydride only at 135°; the other isomer (m.p. 182°) has a band of low intensity at 238 mμ and adds maleic anhydride at 80°. The structures suggested by Petrow are not consistent with the absorption characteristics.

Part 3. Less Common Sterols

All known natural sterols have a methyl group at C_{20}, and in all instances where a correlation has been accomplished the configuration at C_{20} corresponds to that of cholesterol. The pregnanediols and certain steroids of the adrenal cortex have a two-carbon side chain with a secondary alcoholic group at C_{20}, but these two series have not yet been correlated with each other or with cholesterol with respect to the configuration at C_{20} by secure chemical evidence (a tentative correlation of the cortical steroids to cholesterol suggested in Chapter V is based upon a speculative interpretation of optical rotations). Most of the sterols to be discussed in the following sections carry at C_{24} a methyl or ethyl group and a hydrogen atom and thus have a second center of asymmetry in the side chain. Because of the freedom for rotation about single bonds, the atoms and groups at C_{20} and C_{24}, unlike groups in the nucleus, do not have fixed positions in space with respect to the molecule as a whole. However, an asymmetric carbon atom at C_{20} or C_{24} has a fixed rotatory contribution, either dextro or levo, and the two possible configurations relative to the whole molecule can be represented in models and these can be translated into projection formulas according to an arbitrarily defined convention. Such a definition does not have practical significance unless the configurations in the side chain can be related to that at C_{17} by reference to ring compounds in which rotation is restricted and the side chain thereby locked in a fixed geometrical orientation. In the series of cortical steroids the configurations at C_{17} and C_{20} have been related through cyclic osmic esters in which a ring extends between these two positions, and the relative configurations at C_{20} are designated α and β as defined by a convention for projection formulation (Chapter V). It should be possible to relate the configuration at C_{24} in a given series of compounds to that at C_{20} through investigation of derivatives having a bridge between these two positions, and to relate C_{24} to C_{17} through C_{20}, but these problems remain to be solved. For asymmetric centers in the side chain that are at present nonrelated, we propose that the orientations be denoted by the symbols a and b, which are understood to be arbitrary and specific to a given series, and possibly to be reversed in two nonrelated series.

Among the phytosterols, ergosterol and stigmasterol are taken as the typical reference substances because they correspond to cholesterol in the configuration at C_{20} and because they have been shown to correspond to each other in the configuration at C_{24} (see below). The normal or b-configuration at C_{20} is thus defined as that of the three sterols mentioned and is represented by a full-line bond connecting C_{20} and C_{21}; the b-configuration at C_{24} is defined as that of ergosterol and stigmasterol. The epimeric a-

configurations are represented by dotted-line bonds at C_{20}–C_{21} or connecting a methyl or ethyl group to position 24. Since the known instances of side chain isomerism are few, b-configurations are assumed in the formulas unless information is available to the contrary. We regret that this convention is the opposite of that proposed by Bergmann and Low[1] (Greek letters); Dr. Bergmann has graciously agreed to accept the present revision.

A configurational relationship between ergosterol and stigmasterol with respect to position 24 was inferred by Bergmann and Low[1] from the following evidence. Windaus and Resau[2] had isolated as a product of the chromic acid oxidation of cholesteryl acetate a volatile fragment, methyl isohexyl ketone, that retains all the original carbon atoms of the side chain; the yield is markedly increased (to 300 mg. of semicarbazone from 30 g. of cholesteryl acetate) by the addition of potassium persulfate.[3] In similar oxidations of derivatives, ergosterol[4] yielded l-5,6-dimethylheptanone-2 (II, R = CH_3), and β-sitosterol,[3] which has been characterized as 22-dihydrostigmasterol,

[1] W. Bergmann and Low, *J. Org. Chem.*, **12**, 67 (1947).

[2] Windaus and Resau, *Ber.*, **46**, 1246 (1913).

[3] Dirscherl and Nahm, *Ann.*, **555**, 57 (1943).

[4] Guiteras, Nakamiya and Inhoffen, *Ann.*, **494**, 116 (1932).

afforded d-6-methyl-5-ethylheptanone-2 (II, R $=$ C_2H_5). The difference in sign of rotation of the homologous ketones (semicarbazones, M_D -33 and $+4$) does not imply that the two sterols have opposite configurations

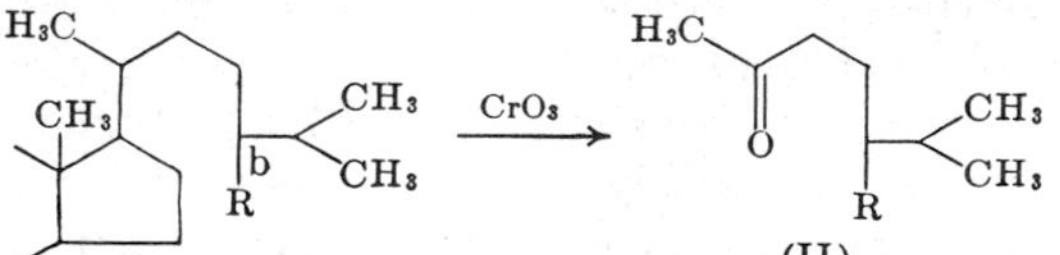

	M_D	
	$R=CH_3$	$R=C_2H_5$
Semicarbazones:		
	-33	$+4$

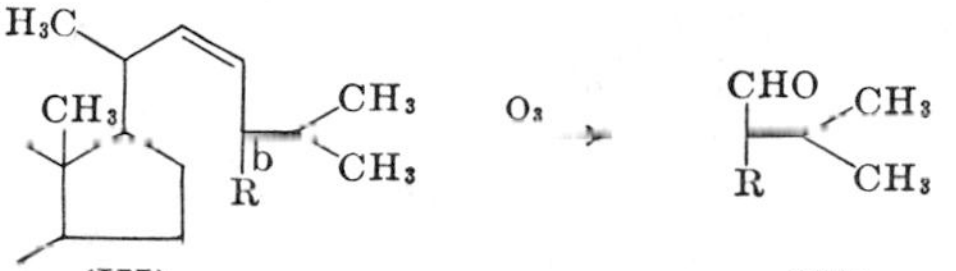

	Semicarbazones:	
	-82	$+16$
Dinitrophenylhydrazones:		
	-106	-9

at C_{24}; Bergmann and Low pointed out that on the contrary the l-dimethyl-heptanone and the d-methylethylheptanone can be expected on the basis of the empirical rule formulated by Marker[5] to have the same configuration. In confirmation of this conclusion they cited the fact that the differences in molecular rotations between the semicarbazones and the 2,4-dinitro-phenylhydrazones of the aldehydes (IV) obtained from ergosterol and from stigmasterol are of the same direction and comparable magnitude. Ergosterol and stigmasterol therefore have the same configuration (b) at C_{24}.

Brassicasterol. This sterol of rapeseed oil (*Brassica rapa*) was isolated by Windaus[6] through the acetate tetrabromide, the analysis of which pointed to the formula $C_{28}H_{46}O$ for the sterol itself. Later analyses of the 3,5-dinitrobenzoate[7] suggested the formula $C_{29}H_{48}O$, but chemical investigations[8] that established the structure showed the original formulation to be

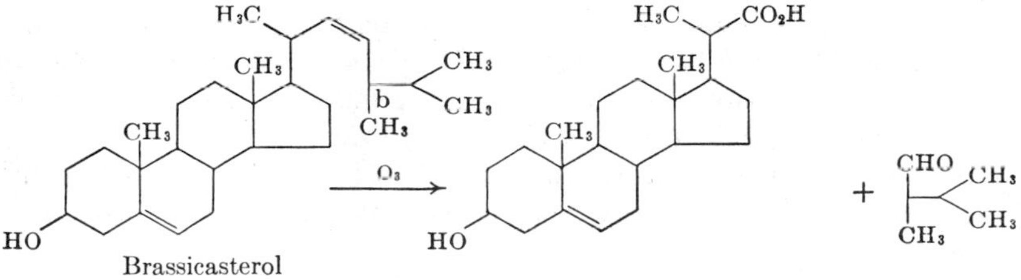

Brassicasterol
m.p. 148°, $[\alpha]_D$ $-64°$

[5] Marker, *J. Am. Chem. Soc.* **58**, 976 (1936).
[6] Windaus and Welsch, *Ber.*, **42**, 612 (1909).
[7] Fernholz and Stavely, *J. Am. Chem. Soc.*, **61**, 142 (1939).
[8] Fernholz and Stavely, *J. Am. Chem. Soc.*, **62**, 428, 1875 (1940).

correct. Ozonization leads to 3β-hydroxybisnorcholenic acid and methylisopropylacetaldehyde, and the fully saturated derivative, brassicastanol, is identical with ergostanol (C_{24}b).

Campesterol has been isolated from rapeseed oil derived from *Brassica campestris*, from soybean oil, and from wheat germ oil.[9] The empirical formula, $C_{28}H_{48}O$, and the result of perbenzoic acid titration both pointed to the presence of one double bond, probably at C_5–C_6, since the $[\alpha]_D$ value is negative and since a dextrorotatory i-methyl ether can be prepared. Chromic acid oxidation of the saturated and acetylated derivative, campes-

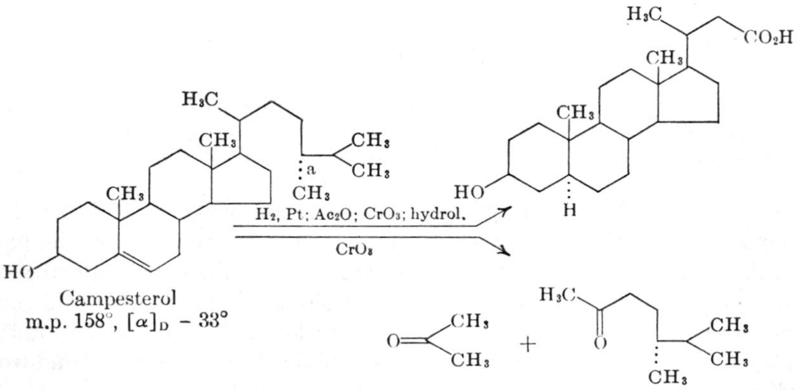

Campesterol
m.p. 158°, $[\alpha]_D$ – 33°

tanyl acetate, leads to 3β-hydroxynorallocholanic acid, which shows that campestanol corresponds to cholestanol and ergostanol in the configurations at all nuclear centers of asymmetry and also at C_{20}. Campestanol (m.p. 147°, $[\alpha]_D$ + 31°), however, is isomeric with ergostanol, and the nature of the isomerism was revealed by chromic acid oxidations that afforded volatile products derived from the side chains. Campesterol (as acetate) yielded acetone (scission at C_{24}–C_{25}) and *d*-5,6-dimethylheptanone-2 (scission at C_{17}),[10] the epimer of the levorotatory ketone isolated as a product of the oxidation of ergostanol.[4] Campesterol therefore has the opposite configuration at C_{24} from ergosterol and is a 24a-sterol. Campesterol is not identical with the 22,23-dihydro derivative of brassicasterol, prepared through a derivative in which the 5,6-position was temporarily blocked;[11] the observation confirms evidence cited above that brassicasterol is a 24b-compound.

Spinasterols. "α"-Spinasterol, isolated from spinach,[1] from senega

[9] Fernholz and MacPhillamy, *J. Am. Chem. Soc.*, **63**, 1155 (1941).

[10] Fernholz and Ruigh, *J. Am. Chem. Soc.*, **63**, 1157 (1941).

[11] Fernholz and Ruigh, *J. Am. Chem. Soc.*, **62**, 3346 (1940).

[1] Hart and Heyl, *J. Biol. Chem.*, **95**, 311 (1932).

root,[2] and from alfalfa,[3, 4] is a doubly unsaturated sterol ($C_{29}H_{48}O$). One double bond was located at C_{22}–C_{23} by isolation of ethylisopropylacetaldehyde as a product of ozonization.[5] The slight negative rotation (– 2.7°) showed that the nuclear double bond is not at C_5–C_6, and a positive Tortelli-Jaffé reaction suggested location at the 7,8-, 8,9-, or 8,14-position. Larsen and Heyl[6] found that hydrogenation with platinum catalyst in acetic acid effected saturation of only the double bond in the side chain but that the resulting stenol could be isomerized with hydrogen chloride to a substance that readily absorbed hydrogen and yielded stigmastanol. Fernholz and Ruigh[5] obtained the same, hydrogenation-resistant dihydride by hydrogenation of "α"-spinasterol with palladium catalyst in ether, and they prepared an identical stigmastenol by similar hydrogenation of 7-dehydrostigmasterol. They shook a solution of "α"-spinasterol with platinum catalyst in the absence of hydrogen (which would attack the side chain) and on finding that the substance was not isomerized concluded that the double bond was already in the inert 8,14-position.

Stavely and Bollenback[7] pointed out that the negative result in the attempted isomerization was inconclusive because of the absence of hydrogen and sought to establish the structure by a study of the action of chromic acid on "α"-spinasterol acetate. They isolated three oxidation products (Chart 1: V, VI, VIII) and two further transformation products (VII, IX) that were all analogous to substances obtained from 5-dihydroergosterol, and since the nuclear double bond of this dihydride was at the time thought to be at the 8,9-position, Stavely and Bollenback concluded that "α"-spinasterol is a $\Delta^{8,22}$-compound. However, the nuclear double bond in the comparison compound is now known from the hydrogenation studies of Wieland and Benend and of Barton to be at the 7,8-position. Barton[8] noted that the optical rotation properties of "α"-spinasterol are indicative of a Δ^7-structure and that the products of oxidation can arise from such a structure. The interpretation suggested in Chart 1 is that the oxidation proceeds through the 7,8-oxide and 7-keto-8-hydroxy derivative.

The inference that "α"-spinasterol has the $\Delta^{7, 22}$-structure I has been verified by two independent researches. The conditions previously em-

[2] Simpson, *J. Chem. Soc.*, 730 (1937).

[3] Dam and co-workers, *Helv. Chim. Acta*, **22**, 313 (1939); Fernholz and M. L. Moore, *J. Am. Chem. Soc.*, **61**, 2467 (1939).

[4] A substance bessisterol ([α] $_D$ – 13.5°) isolated from *Mormordica cochinchinensis* Spreng is believed to be identical with "α"-spinasterol; Kuwada and Yoshiki, *J. Pharm. Soc. Japan*, **57**, 155 (1937); **60**, 232 (1940) [*C. A.*, **31**, 8542 (1937)].

[5] Fernholz and Ruigh, *J. Am. Chem. Soc.*, **62**, 2341 (1940).

[6] Larsen and Heyl, *J. Am. Chem. Soc.*, **56**, 2663 (1934).

[7] Stavely and Bollenback, *J. Am. Chem. Soc.*, **65**, 1600 (1943).

[8] Barton, *J. Chem. Soc.*, 813 (1945).

Chart 1. "α"-Spinasterol

(ALL REACTIONS CONDUCTED WITH ACETATES OR BENZOATES)

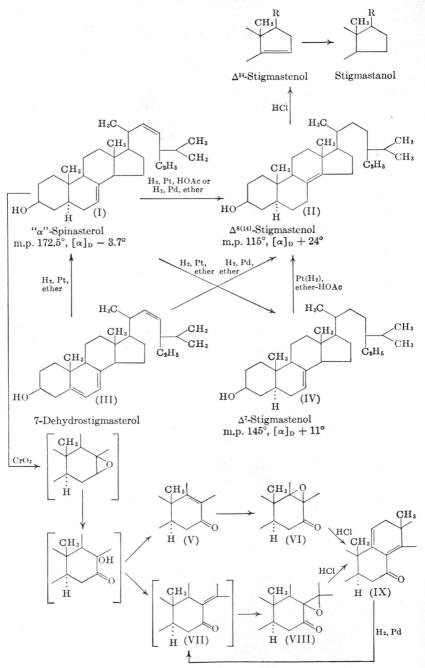

Δ14-Stigmastenol → Stigmastanol

HCl

"α"-Spinasterol
m.p. 172.5°, [α]D − 3.7° (I)

H₂, Pt, HOAc or
H₂, Pd, ether

Δ8(14)-Stigmastenol
m.p. 115°, [α]D + 24° (II)

H₂, Pt,
ether

H₂, Pt,
ether

H₂, Pd,
ether

Pt(H₂),
ether-HOAc

7-Dehydrostigmasterol (III)

Δ7-Stigmastenol
m.p. 145°, [α]D + 11° (IV)

CrO₃

(V)

(VI)

HCl

(IX)

HCl

(VII)

(VIII)

H₂, Pd

ployed for the hydrogenation of "α"-spinasterol (Pt-HOAc or Pd-ether) are conducive to the migration of a Δ^7-stenol to a $\Delta^{8(14)}$-stenol; Barton and Cox[9] found that under nonisomerizing conditions (Pt-ether) the product of hydrogenation is Δ^7-stigmastenol (IV); this can be rearranged by the usual procedure into $\Delta^{8(14)}$-stigmastenol (II). Fieser, Fieser, and R. N. Chakravarti[10] effected the synthetic preparation of "α"-spinasterol by the hydrogenation of 7-dehydrostigmasterol (III) under nonisomerizing conditions. The properties of three other spinasterols of unknown structure are recorded in Table I. All four isomers yield $\Delta^{8(14)}$-stigmastenol on hydrogenation under isomerizing conditions. In consideration of the optical rotation properties, Barton[8] has suggested the possibility that they all belong to the Δ^7-series and differ in the position of the double bond in the side chain.

TABLE I. Spinasterols

TRIVIAL DESIGNATION	STEROLS		ACETATES	
	M.p.	$[\alpha]_D$	M.p.	$[\alpha]_D$
"α"-$(\Delta^{7,22})$	168°	−2.7°	187°	−5°
"β"-a	148–150°	+5.9°	153–155°	+5.1
"γ"-b	159.5–160°	0c	139.5–140°	−14.1°c
"δ"-d	143–144°	+6.2	132–133.5°	+0.8°

a From spinach, Heyl and Larsen, *J. Am. Pharm. Assoc.*, **22**, 510 (1933); from alfalfa seed oil, L. C. King and C. D. Ball, *J. Am. Chem. Soc.*, **64**, 2488 (1942).

b From spinach, Heyl and Larsen, *J. Am. Chem. Soc.*, **56**, 942 (1934).

c $[\alpha]_{546}$ values.

d From alfalfa seed oil, King and Ball.a

Sitosterols. Ordinary preparations of sitosterol (Gr. *sito-*, grain), the most widely distributed of plant sterols, were found by Anderson and co-workers[1] to consist of mixtures of at least three monounsaturated substances, designated "α"-, "β"-, and "γ"-sitosterol, and of a dihydro-"β"-sitosterol. The least soluble component, "γ"- sitosterol, was obtained in a relatively pure condition by crystallization of the acetate dibromide. The "β"-sterol was more difficult to purify and the preparation was undoubtedly contaminated with the "γ"-isomer. "α"-Sitosterol was obtained from the most soluble fraction only as an admittedly crude mixture; purification could not be effected through the dibromide because bromination resulted

9 Barton and J. D. Cox, (Part V), *J. Chem. Soc.* (in press).

10 Fieser, Fieser and Chakravarti, *J. Am. Chem. Soc.* (in press).

1 R. J. Anderson, *J. Am. Chem. Soc.*, **46**, 1450 (1924); Anderson, Nabenhauer and Shriner, *J. Biol. Chem.*, **71**, 389 (1927); Anderson and Shriner, *ibid.*, **71**, 401(1927); *J. Am. Chem. Soc.*, **48**, 2976 (1926); Anderson, Shriner and Burr, *ibid.*, **48**, 2987 (1926); Nabenhauer and Anderson, *ibid.*, **48**, 2972 (1926).

in some substitution (HBr evolved). The characterization of the sitosterols is beset with unusual difficulties of purification and identification. In this series substances known to be different have failed to show melting point depressions on admixture, and hence conclusions regarding identity or nonidentity are necessarily qualified.

"α"-**Sitosterols.** Further processing of the "α"-sterol by fractional crystallization of the *m*-dinitrobenzoates has afforded apparently homogeneous sitosterols designated "α_1"-,[2] "α_2"-,[2] and "α_3"-sitosterol.[2, 3] All three substances are precipitated by digitonin. The "α_1"- and "α_3"-sitosterols are isomers of the formula $C_{29}H_{48}O$; they both contain two nonconjugated double bonds; "α_2"-sitosterol is believed to be a homolog, $C_{30}H_{50}O$. A formulation tentatively suggested for "α_1"-sitosterol[4] has been withdrawn on the basis of optical rotatory data.[5]

"β"-**Sitosterol** is the main sterol of cottonseed oil[6] and of Calycanthus oil;[7] it has been isolated from tall oil,[8] wheat germ oil,[9] and crepe rubber;[10]

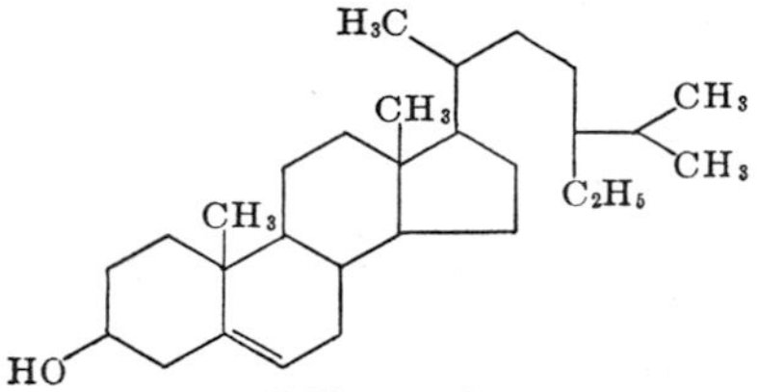

"β"-Sitosterol
m.p. 140°, $[\alpha]_D - 36°$

the substance cinchol, isolated from cinchona bark[11] or wax,[12] is identical with "β"-sitosterol.[13, 14, 15] The same substance appears to be a constituent of the sitosterols of rye germ oil[16] and of corn oil.[9] Preparations from

[2] Wallis and Fernholz, *J. Am. Chem. Soc.*, **58**, 2446 (1936).
[3] Gloyer and Schuette, *J. Am. Chem. Soc.*, **61**, 1901 (1939).
[4] Bernstein and Wallis, *J. Am. Chem. Soc.*, **61**, 2308 (1939).
[5] Bernstein, E. J. Wilson and Wallis, *J. Org. Chem.*, **7**, 103 (1942).
[6] Wallis and P. N. Chakravorty, *J. Org. Chem.*, **2**, 335 (1938).
[7] Cook and Paige, *J. Chem. Soc.*, 336 (1944).
[8] Sandqvist and Bengtsson, *Ber.*, **64**, 2167 (1931).
[9] R. J. Anderson and Shriner, *J. Am. Chem. Soc.*, **48**, 2976 (1926); R. J. Anderson, Shriner and Burr, *ibid.*, **48**, 2987 (1926).
[10] Heilbron, E. R. H. Jones, Roberts and Wilkinson, *J. Chem. Soc.*, 344 (1941).
[11] Liebermann, *Ber.*, **17**, 868 (1884); **18**, 1803 (1885).
[12] O. Hesse, *Ann.*, **228**, 288 (1885).
[13] Dirscherl and Nahm, *Ann.*, **555**, 57 (1943); **558**, 231 (1947).
[14] Windaus and Deppe, *Ber.*, **66**, 1689 (1933).
[15] Dirscherl, *Z. physiol. Chem.*, **257**, 239 (1938).
[16] Gloyer and Schuette, *J. Am. Chem. Soc.*, **61**, 1901 (1939).

the sources indicated are not always homogeneous,[17] and unfortunately the early chemical investigations were carried out with preparations now known to have been contaminated with other sitosterols, but the conclusions are probably valid.

"β"-Sitosterol is a monounsaturated alcohol of the formula $C_{29}H_{50}O$.[8, 18] Comparisons of the dihydride, "β"-sitostanol, and its derivatives indicate its identity with stigmastanol.[19] Furthermore, a substance identical with "β"-sitosterol has been obtained from stigmasterol by selective hydrogenation of the double bond in the side chain (as the acetate in ethyl acetate with palladium catalyst).[20] The oxidation to d-6-methyl-5-ethylheptanone-2 was mentioned above. "β"-Sitosterol has also been degraded to 3β-hydroxynorallocholanic acid[21] and (through the epidihydro acetate) to androsterone.[22] The substance is thus fully characterized as 22-dihydrostigmasterol.

The sitosterols are usually accompanied by a saturated stanol fraction, which consists mainly of dihydro-"β"-sitosterol (stigmastanol).[23]

"γ"-**Sitosterol.** This substance is the principal sterol of soybean oil[1] and is a minor component of the sitosterol mixtures of wheat germ oil[2] and rye germ oil.[3] Although the "γ"-component can be isolated with relative ease, the structure is still in doubt. It is an isomer of "β"-sitosterol (C_{29}-$H_{50}O$); the derivatives in the "γ"-series melt at slightly higher temperatures

"γ"-Sitosterol
m.p. 148°, [α]$_D$ − 43°

Oxidation of
acetate dichloride

Dehydroepiandrosterone

[17] E. R. H. Jones, Wilkinson and Kerlogue, *J. Chem. Soc.*, 391 (1942); Barton and E. R. H. Jones, *ibid.*, 599 (1943). Rhamnol [Windaus and Deppe, *Ber.*, **66**, 1254 (1933)] also is probably identical with "β"-sitosterol; communication from Dr. D. H. R. Barton.

[18] Windaus, v. Werder and Gschaider, *Ber.*, **65**, 1006 (1932).

[19] Bengtsson, *Z. physiol. Chem.*, **237**, 46 (1935); see also Marker and Whittle, *J. Am. Chem. Soc.*, **59**, 2704 (1937).

[20] Bernstein and Wallis, *J. Org. Chem.*, **2**, 341 (1938).

[21] P. N. Chakravorty, *Dissertation*, Göttingen (1935).

[22] Dalmer, v. Werder, v. Honingmann and Heyns, *Ber.*, **68**, 1814 (1935).

[23] R. J. Anderson, Nabenhauer and Shriner, *J. Biol. Chem.*, **71**, 389 (1927); Anderson and Shriner, *ibid.*, **71**, 401 (1927).

[1] Bonstedt, *Z. physiol. Chem.*, **176**, 269 (1928); Bengtsson, *ibid.*, **237**, 46 (1935).

[2] R. J. Anderson, Shriner and Burr, *J. Am. Chem. Soc.*, **48**, 2987 (1926).

[3] Gloyer and Shuette, *J. Am. Chem. Soc.*, **61**, 1901 (1939).

(3–8°) and have specific rotations slightly more negative (2–8°) than the "β"-isomers. Oppenauer[4] degraded "γ"-sitosterol to dehydroepiandrosterone and thereby established that the·nucleus corresponds in structure and configuration to that of "β"-sitosterol. Dirscherl and Nahm[5] oxidized "γ"-sitosteryl acetate with chromic acid and isolated acetone and *l*-6-methyl-5-ethylheptanone-2. The side chain thus corresponds to that of "β"-sitosterol in structure but differs in configuration at C_{24}; whether or not the C_{20}-center has the usual b-configuration has not been established. From an analysis of molecular rotations, Bergmann and Low[6] conclude that "γ"-sitosterol probably is the C_{24}-epimer of "β"-sitosterol but that the samples described contain a more levorotatory component.

Sterols of Algae.[1] The characteristic sterol of *Chlorophyceae* (freshwater green algae) is the common phytosterol (mixture) of higher plants, sitosterol.[2] The typical sterol of the marine brown algae, *Phaeophyceae*, is **fucosterol**, a doubly unsaturated alcohol, $C_{29}H_{48}O$.[3] Both double bonds can be hydrogenated readily with the formation of stigmastanol, and one of

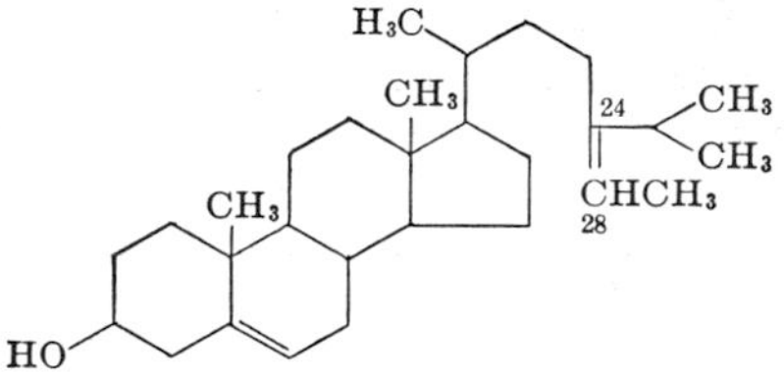

Fucosterol
m.p. 124°, $[\alpha]_D$ − 38°

the double bonds is located at C_5–C_6 by the observation that Oppenauer oxidation gives a substance (fucostadienone, m.p. 94°) showing the spectrum characteristic of an α,β-unsaturated ketone.[4] The second double bond cannot be at C_{22}–C_{23}, for no ethylisopropylacetaldehyde is formed on ozonization;[3] it is not at an inert position associated with C_8 (readily reduced; negative Tortelli-Jaffé test) or conjugated with the double bond at C_5–C_6 (no reaction with maleic anhydride). Heilbron considered the C_{14}–C_{15} position a likely location, but this is inconsistent with the properties of two dihydrides resulting from partial catalytic hydrogenation;[5] one is

[4] Oppenauer, *Nature*, **135**, 1039 (1935).

[5] Dirscherl and Nahm, *Ann.*, **555**, 57 (1943); **558**, 231 (1947).

[6] W. Bergmann and Low, *J. Org. Chem.*, **12**, 67 (1947).

[1] Heilbron, *J. Chem. Soc.*, 79 (1942).

[2] Carter, Heilbron and Lythgoe, *Proc. Roy. Soc. (London)*, **B128**, 82 (1939).

[3] Heilbron, Phipers and Wright, *J. Chem. Soc.*, 1572 (1934).

[4] E. R. H. Jones, Wilkinson and Kerlogue, *J. Chem. Soc.*, 391 (1942).

[5] Coffey, Heilbron, Spring and Wright, *J. Chem. Soc.*, 1205 (1935); Coffey, Heilbron and Spring, *ibid.*, 738 (1936).

identical with 22-dihydrostigmasterol, but the other ("β"-dihydrofucosterol, m.p. 133°, $[\alpha]_D$-30°; acetate, m.p. 122°, $[\alpha]_D$-39°) is not identical with the expected Δ^{14}-stigmastenol. Barton[6] regards the "β"-compound as a mixture. Finally MacPhillamy[7] found positive evidence that the second double bond is at the C_{24}-C_{28} position by the isolation of acetaldehyde in 30 percent yield as a product of the ozonization of fucosterol.

Yeast Sterols. Ergosterol is the principal sterol of yeast but is accompanied by several minor sterols that have been characterized particularly by Wieland and co-workers in investigations of residues from the German industrial production of ergosterol.[1, 2]

Zymosterol ($C_{27}H_{44}O$), the second most abundant sterol of yeast fat, was discovered by Smedley-MacLean;[3] it can be isolated by a process of fractional crystallization, chromatography, and purification through the benzoate,[4] or isolated through the dibromide.[5] Perbenzoic acid titrations established the presence of two double bonds,[6] one of which is susceptible to hydrogenation whereas the other is resistant.[7] The initially formed zymostenol can be isomerized with hydrogen chloride to a stenol that is easily hydrogenated to a saturated alcohol[7] identified[5, 8] as cholestanol. The easily reducible double bond was shown by the isolation of acetone as a product of ozonization to be present in a terminal isopropylidine group.[5, 8] Heath-Brown, Heilbron, and Jones[5] hydrogenated zymosterol in acetic acid-ether and identified the dihydride formed as $\Delta^{8(14)}$-cholestenol; they regarded this as evidence that the nuclear double bond of zymosterol is at the 8,14-position. Wieland, Rath and Benend,[8] however, found that zymosterol can be hydrogenated (Pt) in a neutral medium to a different dihydride that, under hydrogenating conditions in the presence of acetic acid, is isomerized to $\Delta^{8(14)}$-cholestenol. Zymosterol gives a positive Tortelli-Jaffé test, and since the new zymostenol differed from Δ^7- and Δ^8-cholestenol, according to the characterizations of these substances on record at the time, Wieland[8, 9] suggested that the nuclear double bond of zymosterol is at the only other available position, C_9-C_{11}. Later Barton and Cox,[10]

[6] Barton, *J. Chem. Soc.*, 512 (1946).
[7] MacPhillamy, *J. Am. Chem. Soc.*, **64**, 1732 (1942).
[1] Wieland and Asano, *Ann.*, **473**, 300 (1929).
[2] Wieland and Gough, *Ann.*, **482**, 36 (1930).
[3] Smedley-MacLean, *Biochem. J.*, **22**, 22 (1928).
[4] Wieland and Kanaoka, *Ann.*, **530**, 146 (1937).
[5] Heath-Brown, Heilbron and E. R. H. Jones, *J. Chem. Soc.*, 1482 (1940).
[6] Reindel and Weickmann, *Ann.*, **475**, 86 (1929).
[7] Reindel and Weickmann, *Ann.*, **482**, 120 (1930).
[8] Wieland, Rath and Benend, *Ann.*, **548**, 19 (1941).
[9] Wieland and Benend, *Ber.*, **75**, 1708 (1942).
[10] Barton and J. D. Cox, Part VII, *J. Chem. Soc.* (in press.)

as noted above (Stenols), showed that the previously known "Δ^8-choles-tenol" is a mixture from which they isolated pure Δ^8-cholestenol for the first time. This substance proved to be identical with the isomerizable

Chart 2. ZYMOSTEROL

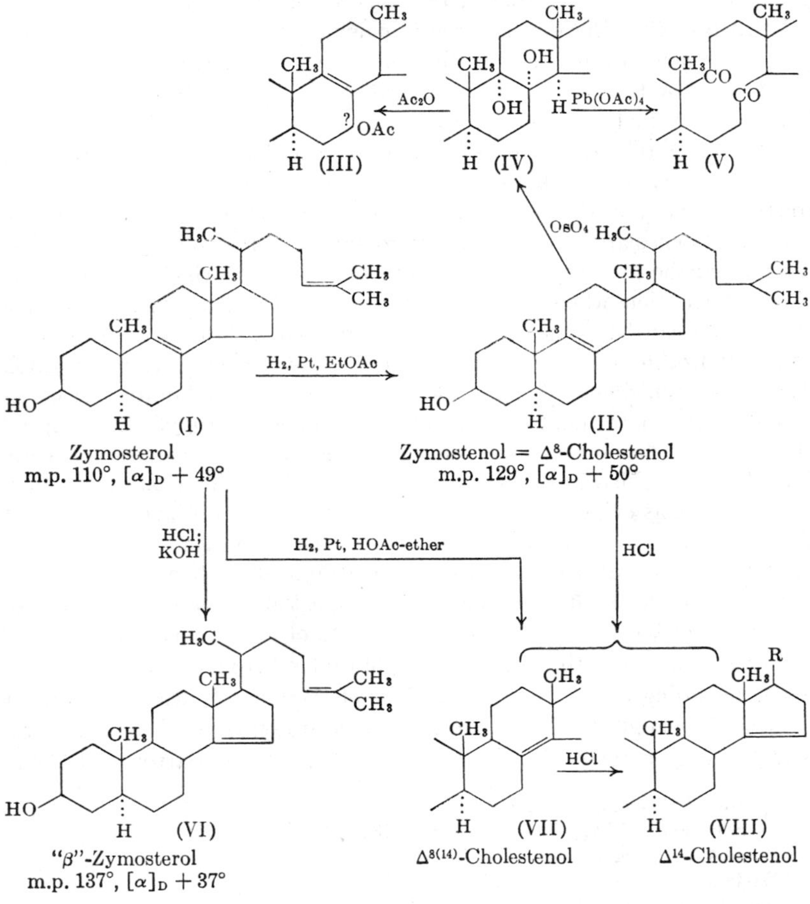

Zymosterol
m.p. 110°, $[\alpha]_D + 49°$

Zymostenol = Δ^8-Cholestenol
m.p. 129°, $[\alpha]_D + 50°$

"β"-Zymosterol
m.p. 137°, $[\alpha]_D + 37°$

$\Delta^{8(14)}$-Cholestenol

Δ^{14}-Cholestenol

zymostenol of Wieland, Rath, and Benend.[8] Zymosterol therefore is $\Delta^{8,24}$-cholestadiene-3β-ol (I, Chart 2). The hydrogenation of the double bond in the side chain without migration of the nuclear double bond (II) and with migration (VII), depending upon whether the medium is neutral or acidic, parallels the behavior of other Δ^8-stenols. In investigating the isomerization of zymostenol (II, as benzoate) to Δ^{14}-cholestenol (VIII) with hydrogen chloride in chloroform, Wieland and Görnhardt[11] observed that when the reaction was conducted for only a brief period $\Delta^{8\,(14)}$-cholestenol (VII) can be isolated along with the end product VIII. Wieland and Benend[9] found that the nuclear double bond of zymosterol itself migrates under the influence of hydrogen chloride in chloroform; in this case a crystalline hydrochloride (benzoate, m.p. 199°, $[\alpha]_D + 28°$) is formed by addition to the 24,25-double bond, but dehydrohalogenation affords an isomeric "β"-sterol (VI) that yields acetone on ozonization and therefore has the original side-chain structure. The original work was confused by the presence of cholesterol in the batch of crude companion sterols used; this arose through inadvertent admixture by the supplying firm of the yeast-sterol residue with a cholesterol-containing mother liquor from another process.[11]

Wieland and Benend[9] state that zymostenol benzoate was hydroxylated with osmium tetroxide to give, after hydrolysis, a cholestanetriol that formed a diacetate in cold pyridine solution and that was cleaved by lead tetraacetate to a substance of the composition of a ketoaldehyde. On the basis of the present evidence, the two hydroxyl groups introduced must be tertiary (IV) and the product of cleavage must be a diketone (V).[10] The statement that the triol forms a diacetate is in error, for the reported theoretical composition required for $C_{31}H_{52}O_5$ is miscalculated. Actually the analysis reported indicates that the substance is the diacetate of a monoanhydro derivative.

Calcd. for $C_{31}H_{50}O_4$: C, 76.50; H, 10.35
Found: C, 76.50; H, 10.55

If one of the tertiary hydroxyl groups is eliminated with a hydrogen atom at either C_7 or C_{11}, the resulting unsaturated alcohol could undergo allylic rearrangement to a substance with an acylable hydroxyl group, for example, III. The attack by osmium tetroxide probably is at the less hindered rear side of the molecule to give the $3\beta,8\alpha,9\alpha$-triol (IV), in which the cis orientation of the 8-hydroxyl group and the 14-hydrogen atom is unfavorable for the establishment of an 8,14-double bond.

Ascosterol and Fecosterol. These minor sterols of yeast[1, 4] (named from *Ascomyces* and from *faex*, yeast) are doubly unsaturated isomers of the formula $C_{28}H_{46}O$.[12] The two sterols give practically identical colors in the Liebermann-Burchard and Tortelli-Jaffé tests, and in the latter test they differ appreciably from zymosterol with respect to speed and tone.[1] Wieland, Rath, and Hesse[12] found that both sterols on hydrogenation in acetic acid solution afford $\Delta^{8\,(14)}$-ergostenol, and that ascosterol is isomerized

[11] Wieland and Görnhardt, *Ann.*, **557**, 248 (1947).
[12] Wieland, Rath and Hesse, *Ann.*, **548**, 34 (1941).

to fecosterol by the action of platinum catalyst in ethyl acetate solution under nitrogen. They also observed that fecosterol on ozonization affords formaldehyde in 30% yield but did not investigate the behavior of ascosterol. Wieland assumed that the conversion of ascosterol into fecosterol involved migration of a double bond from the 9,11- to the 8,14-position, and later commented[13] on one unusual feature of the reaction: isomerization induced by a mild catalyst in a presumably neutral medium. Another anomaly is that the change occurred in the absence of hydrogen (see Stenols). Barton[14] questioned the fact of isomerization but regarded both compounds as $\Delta^{9\,(11)}$-steroids on the basis of evidence from molecular rotations that he has since revised.[15] The two sterols are closely analogous to zymosterol, as is apparent from the differences in M_D for the sterols and their derivatives as compared with the parent stanols and their derivatives (Table II). Comparison of zymosterol with zymostenol shows that a

TABLE II. Effect of Unsaturation on Molecular Rotations $(CHCl_3)$[15]

	ΔM_D		
	Sterol	Acetate	Benzoate
Zymosterol.............................	+104	+86	+107
Zymostenol..............................	+103	+85	+96
Ascosterol..............................	+115	+70	+119
Fecosterol..............................	+103	+61	+99

double bond in the side chain produces very little contribution to the molecular rotation. Since zymosterol is now established to be Δ^8-unsaturated,[15] the two other yeast sterols must have a double bond at the 8,9-position. The fragmentary facts seem to us to suggest that the bond migration reported by Wieland occurs in the side chain, and a possible formulation is suggested in Chart 3. If the migration is not from one nuclear position to another, there is no reason to suppose that the change cannot occur under conditions milder than those required for a nuclear shift. The postulated migration of the extracyclic double bond from C_{23}–C_{24} to C_{24}–C_{28} may be implemented by a steric effect, particularly if in ascosterol the isopropyl group is cis to the large group including the nucleus.

Episterol,[2] from yeast (m.p. 151°, $[\alpha]_D$–5°), is an isomer of fecosterol and like this substance yields $\Delta^{8(14)}$-ergostenol on hydrogenation and formaldehyde on ozonization (45% yield).[12] The substance is not isomerized by platinum catalyst in a nitrogen atmosphere. Before the recognition

[13] Wieland and Benend, *Ann.*, **554**, 1 (1943).
[14] Barton, *J. Chem. Soc.*, 813 (1945); 512 (1946).
[15] Barton and J. D. Cox, Part VII, *J. Chem. Soc.* (in press).

Chart 3. Ascosterol and Fecosterol

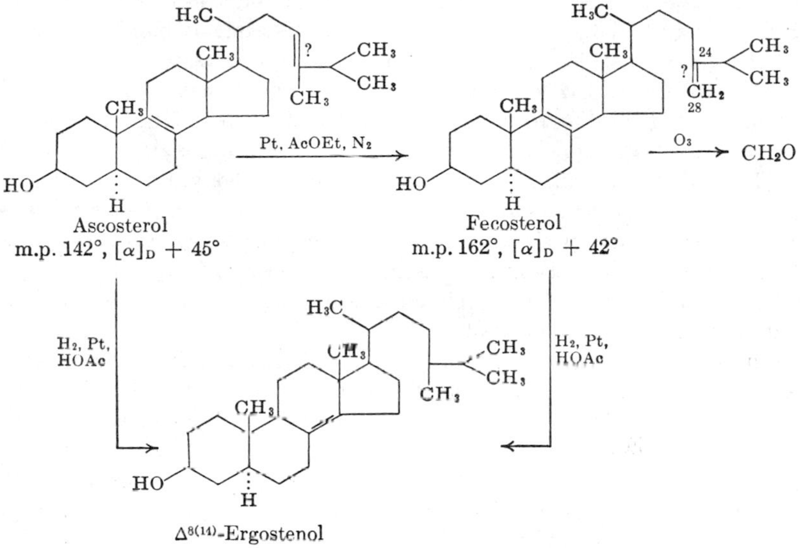

H₃C... CH₃ ? CH₃ CH₃ CH₃ CH₃
HO— H
Ascosterol
m.p. 142°, [α]_D + 45°

Pt, AcOEt, N₂ →

H₃C... CH₃ 24 CH₃ ? CH₂ CH₃ 28 CH₃
HO— H
Fecosterol
m.p. 162°, [α]_D + 42°

O₃ → CH₂O

H₂, Pt, HOAc

H₃C... CH₃ CH₃ CH₃ CH₃ CH₃
HO— H
Δ⁸⁽¹⁴⁾-Ergostenol

H₂, Pt, HOAc

that nuclear bond migrations occur only when the catalyst is saturated with hydrogen, Wicland took the observation to mean that the nuclear double bond is at C₈–C₁₄. Barton,[14] however, has shown by comparison of molecular rotation differences that this bond undoubtedly is at C₇–C₈. The stability of the double bond in the side chain to mild conditions of isomerization suggests a location similar to that in fecosterol.

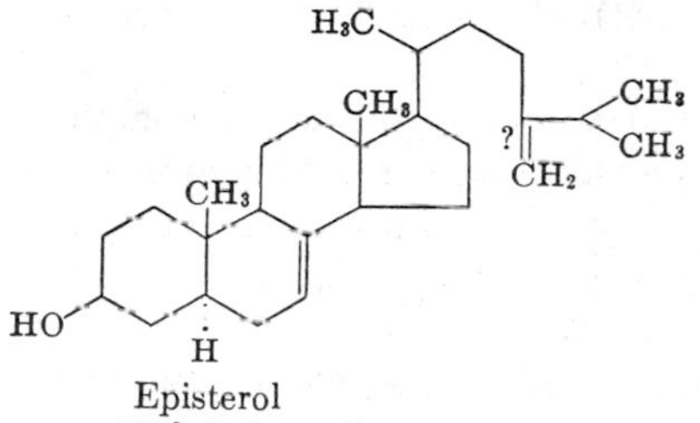

H₃C... CH₃ ? CH₂ CH₃ CH₃ CH₃
HO— H
Episterol
m.p. 151°, [α]_D − 5°

Other Sterols of Yeast. 5-Dihydroergosterol has been isolated as a minor companion of ergosterol.[16,12] Another supposed component "neosterol" has been shown by Barton and Cox[17] to be a mixture of ergosterol

[16] R. K. Callow, *Biochem. J.*, **25**, 87 (1931).
[17] Barton and J. D. Cox, Part VI, *J. Chem. Soc.* (in press).

and 5-dihydroergosterol. Other constituents reported are **anasterol**[2] (m.p. 159°, $[\alpha]_D - 8°$, 2 double bonds); **hyposterol**[12] (m.p. 102°, $[\alpha]_D + 12.5°$, 3 double bonds). A substance **cerevisterol,** isolated in small amounts from yeast[18] (10 g. from 4500 kg. of yeast), has since been isolated from a mushroom (*Amanita phalloides*) and from ergot.[19] Cerevisterol has been assigned the formula $C_{28}H_{46}O_3$[20] and is described as follows: (Bills) m.p. 265°, $[\alpha]_{546}-57°$; (Wieland) m.p. 254°, $[\alpha]_D-79°$. The sterol readily forms a diacetate but does not react with carbonyl reagents or give evidence of the presence of an alkoxyl group. It is resistant to hydrogenation but reacts with perbenzoic acid; the spectrum shows an absorption band of very low intensity at 245 mμ (alcohol). Cerevisterol is not precipitated by digitonin but gives characteristic colors in the Liebermann-Burchard and Rosenheim tests.

Fungisterol (m.p. 149°, $[\alpha]_D - 0.2°$) was discovered by Tanret[21] as a companion of ergosterol in ergot; Tanret's sample, purified by over one hundred crystallizations, was later shown to have still contained a small amount of ergosterol ($[\alpha]_D-22°$; autoxidizable). The pure sterol was characterized by Wieland and Coutelle[19] and shown to be identical with Δ^7-ergostenol; subsequent evidence[13] invalidated the method of separation employed but not the identification.

Phytosterols of Unknown Structure. A crystalline substance that may be a sterol has been isolated from *Euphorbia tirucalli:*[22] $C_{27}H_{42}O$, m.p. 119°, $[\alpha]_D + 57°$; oxime, m.p. 195°. Two sterols have been isolated from alfalfa;[23] one is probably "α"-spinasterol and the other, m.p. 133°, $[\alpha]_D-22.5°$, appears to be an isomer ($C_{29}H_{48}O$). The substance **nycosterol,** m.p. 222°, $[\alpha]_D + 91°$, has been isolated from *Nyctanthes arbortristis.*[24] **Artostenone** ($C_{30}H_{50}O$, m.p. 109°, $[\alpha]_D + 20°$), isolated from *Artocarpus integrifolia,* is believed to be a $\Delta^{9(11)}$-12-ketosteroid with the side chain $C_{11}H_{23}$.[25]

Pseudosterols. The yeast sterols are accompanied by a substance initially regarded as a sterol and called kryptosterol.[26] It is precipitated by digitonin and was originally regarded a C_{27}-compound, but later analyses

[18] Bills and Honeywell, *J. Biol. Chem.,* **80,** 15 (1928).

[19] Wieland and Coutelle, *Ann.,* **548,** 270 (1941).

[20] Honeywell and Bills, *J. Biol. Chem.,* **99,** 71 (1932); **103,** 515 (1933).

[21] Tanret, *Compt. rend.,* **147,** 75 (1908).

[22] Dutta and Karimullah, *J. Sci. Ind. Research (India),* **3,** 212 (1944) [*C. A.,* **39,** 3173 (1945)].

[23] Dam, Geiger, Glavind, P. Karrer, W. Karrer, Rothschild and Salamon, *Helv. Chim. Acta,* **22,** 313 (1939).

[24] Vasistha, *J. Benares Hindu Univ.,* **2,** 343 (1938) [*C. A.,* **33,** 4447 (1939)].

[25] Nath, *Z. physiol. Chem.,* **247,** 9 (1937); **249,** 71, 76, 78 (1937); Nath, Chowdhury and Uddin, *J. Ind. Chem. Soc.,* **23,** 245 (1946).

[26] Wieland and Stanley, *Ann.,* **489,** 31 (1931).

of various derivatives indicate the formula $C_{30}H_{50}O$, which places the substance in the class of the triterpenoids.[27] Kryptosterol on hydrogenation forms only a dihydro derivative, but the presence of a second inert double bond is established by conversion of the dihydride into an oxide; therefore kryptosterol contains four rings. The oxygen is present as a secondary hydroxyl group (oxidation to a ketone). The formation of acetone in good yield on ozonization locates the active double bond in the group $>C=C(CH_3)_2$.[28] The dihydro derivative is rearranged by treatment with hydrochloride to isodihydrocryptosterol, in which the remaining double bond is still not susceptible to hydrogenation.

Tho substances **lanosterol** and **agnosterol** isolated from wool fat[29] were initially regarded as sterols of the formulas $C_{30}H_{50}O$ and $C_{30}H_{48}O$, but the former substance was later found to yield 1,2,8-trimethylphenanthrene on selenium dehydrogenation.[30] Ruzicka and co-workers[31] found that lanosterol is actually a nonseparable mixture of kryptosterol and dihydrokryptosterol.[31]

STEROLS OF MARINE INVERTEBRATES

The highly diverse sterols of marine invertebrates have been investigated extensively by W. Bergmann and others both in the hope of discovering possible starting materials for the preparation of steroid hormones and in order to explore biogenetic relationships to possible dietary precursors.[1,2] The characteristic sterols of vertebrates are C_{27}-compounds (cholesterol and cholestanol), and at the time the researches under discussion were undertaken the known phytosterols had been characterized as C_{28}- or C_{29}-compounds (ergosterol, stigmasterol). The isolation from the oyster and other mollusks of a C_{28}- or C_{29}-alcohol, ostreasterol,[3] suggested the possibility that invertebrates may be dependent upon exogenous plant sterols and incapable of effecting the full synthesis of the sterols that they require. Since 1940, however, it has become evident that phytosynthesis is not limited to the production of C_{28}- and C_{29}-sterols but that the group of phytosterols includes C_{27}-compounds as well (zymosterol). Furthermore,

[27] Wieland, Pasedack and Ballauf, *Ann.*, **529**, 68 (1937).
[28] Wieland and Benend, *Z. physiol. Chem.*, **274**, 215 (1942).
[29] Windaus and Tschesche, *Z. physiol. Chem.*, **190**, 51 (1930).
[30] H. Schulze, *Z. physiol. Chem.*, **238**, 35 (1936).
[31] Ruzicka, Rey and Muhr, *Helv. Chim. Acta*, **27**, 472 (1944); Ruzicka, Denss and Jeger, *ibid.*, **28**, 759 (1945).
[1] W. Bergmann, Schedl and Low, *J. Org. Chem.*, **10**, 580 (1945).
[2] W. Bergmann, McLean and Lester, *J. Org. Chem.*, **8**, 271 (1943).
[3] W. Bergmann, *J. Biol. Chem.*, **104**, 317, 553 (1934).

cholestanol has been isolated from certain sponges[4] and cholesterol from a number of snails.[5, 6, 6a] From these and other facts, Bergmann and Low[7] concluded that the early hypothesis is untenable. Gastropods (snails) have been found to contain cholesterol regardless of their feeding habits; cholesterol is the principal sterol of herbivorous land snails and also of the marine gastropod *Haliotis*, which feeds exclusively on algae. Bergmann and Low point to interesting differences in the sterol content of gastropods and pelecypods (bivalves): the average fat content of the latter (1%) is half that of the former, and the principal sterols are of the C_{28}- to C_{29}-type, rather than cholesterol.

The sterols of bivalves consist of complex and difficultly separable mixtures of homologs and epimers of varying degree of unsaturation, and the isolation of individual components of assured purity is a difficult task. The

TABLE III.   Sterols of Marine Invertebrates

STEROL	FORMULA	DOUBLE BONDS	M.p.	$[\alpha]_D$	OCCURRENCE
Chalinasterol[a]	$C_{28}H_{46}O$	2	144°	−42°	Sponge
Ostreasterol[b]	$C_{28}H_{46}O$	2	143°	−44°	Oyster, clam
Stellasterol[c]	$C_{28}H_{46}O$	2	complete separation		⎫ Starfish
Stellastenol[c]	$C_{28}H_{48}O$	1	not effected		⎭
Neospongosterol[d]	$C_{28}H_{48}O$	1	153°	+10°	Sponge
Poriferasterol[e]	$C_{29}H_{48}O$	2	156°	−49°	Sponge
Clionasterol[f]	$C_{29}H_{50}O$	1	138°	−42°	Sponge

[a] W. Bergmann, Schedl and Low, *J. Org. Chem.*, **10**, 587 (1945).
[b] Ref. 3.
[c] W. Bergmann and Stansbury, *J. Org. Chem.*, **9**, 281 (1944).
[d] Ref. 4.
[e] Valentine and W. Bergmann, *J. Org. Chem.*, **6**, 452 (1941); Lyon and W. Bergmann, *ibid.*, **7**, 428 (1942).
[f] Valentine and W. Bergmann, *J. Org. Chem.*, **6**, 452 (1941); Kind and W. Bergmann, *ibid.*, **7**, 341 (1942); Mazur, *J. Am. Chem. Soc.*, **63**, 883, 2442 (1941).

accompanying table lists those new sterols isolated from marine invertebrates that appear, for the most part, to be homogeneous substances. The discussions below follow the order of listing in Table III.

Chalinasterol, the sterol of the sponges *Chalina arbuscula* Verrill and *Tetilla laminaris* Wilson, has been converted by partial hydrogenation

[4] W. Bergmann, Gould and Low, *J. Org. Chem.*, **10**, 570 (1945).
[5] Tsujimoto and Koyanagi, *J. Soc. Chem. Ind.* (*Japan*) *Suppl.*, **37**, 81B (1934); **37**, 436B (1934); **38**, 118B (1935) [*C. A.*, **29**, 3865 (1935)].
[6] Bock and Wetter, *Z. physiol. Chem.*, **256**, 33 (1938).
[6a] Kind, Slater and Vinci, *J. Org. Chem.*, **13**, 538 (1948).
[7] W. Bergmann and Low, *J. Org. Chem.*, **12**, 67 (1947).

either directly or through the i-methyl ether, into campesterol and thereby identified as the 24a-epimer of brassicasterol.

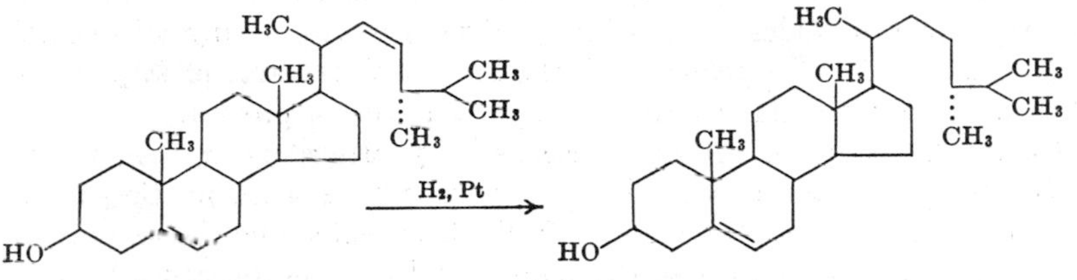

Chalinasterol	Campesterol

Ostreasterol, originally thought to be a C_{29}-compound, is regarded by Bergmann and Low[7] as very probably identical with chalinasterol (C_{28}).

Stellasterol and Stellastenol. The sterol fraction of the starfish *Asterias forbesi* consists of a complex mixture of at least the two components stellasterol and stellastenol, the complete separation of which has not been effected. Some evidence of the structures has been adduced from the characterization of mixtures. All fractions were slightly dextrorotatory, which argues against the presence of a double bond at C_5–C_6, and all showed green colors in the Tortelli-Jaffé test, indicative of a double bond extending to C_8. Stellasterol has a second double bond in the side chain, and ozonization of the mixture gave a substance characterized with probability as *d*-methylisopropylacetaldehyde, which indicates the presence at C_{24} of a methyl group in the a-orientation, the opposite to that of ergosterol. Hydrogenation of the mixture resulted in saturation of the C_{22}–C_{23} double bond of stellasterol and gave a homogeneous product, "α"-stellastenol, having properties characteristic of a $\Delta^{8(14)}$-stenol. "α"-

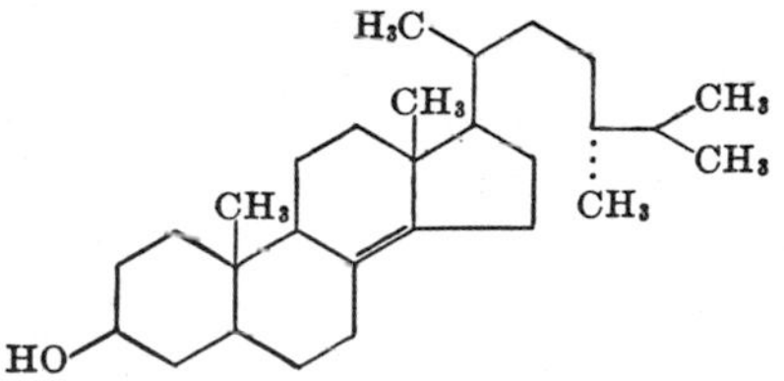

"α"-Stellastenol
m.p. 125°, $[\alpha]_D$ + 19.8°
Stanol: m.p. 143°, $[\alpha]_D$ + 22°

Stellastenol was isomerized with acid to a "β"-isomer that was hydrogenated to stellastanol; this substance and campestanol are both believed to be C_{24a}-methyl stanols, but they are not identical. Barton[8] has observed

[8] Communication from Dr. D. H. R. Barton.

that the optical properties of the mixture ($[\alpha]_D$ + 8°, acetate + 2°, benzoate + 9°; M_D + 32°, + 9°, + 45°) indicate that the doubly unsaturated stellasterol probably has a double bond at the 7,8-position; the positive Δ^{B_2} value (+ 13°) precludes the possibility of the presence of any substantial proportion of $\Delta^{8(14)}$-compounds and the low absolute value of $[\alpha]_D$ shows that no appreciable amount of Δ^8-compounds can be present.

Neospongosterol. A substance isolated by Henze[9] from the sponge *Suberites domuncula* and named spongosterol was isolated by Bergmann from the similar *Suberites compacta* (0.7% dry weight) and shown to be a difficultly separable mixture of cholestanol and the monounsaturated neospongosterol. The substance was fully characterized as the 22-dehydro

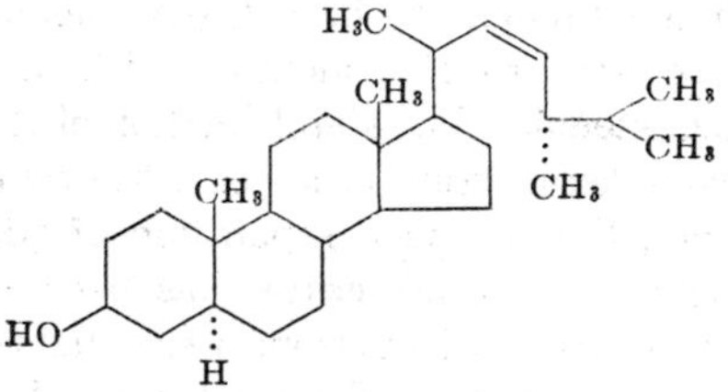

H₃C structure

Neospongosterol

derivative of campestanol by the following evidence: ozonization to 3β-hydroxybisnorallocholanic acid and d-methylisopropylacetaldehyde; hydrogenation to a stanol corresponding in properties to campestanol.

Poriferasterol and Clionasterol. These sterols occur together in certain sponges; on absorption of two moles and of one mole of hydrogen, respectively, they yield the same substance, poriferastanol (m.p. 143°, $[\alpha]_D$ + 25°); this is an isomer of stigmastanol and probably is identical with

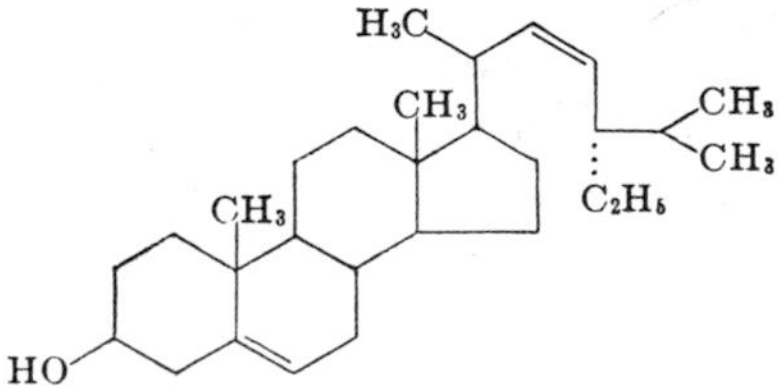

Poriferasterol 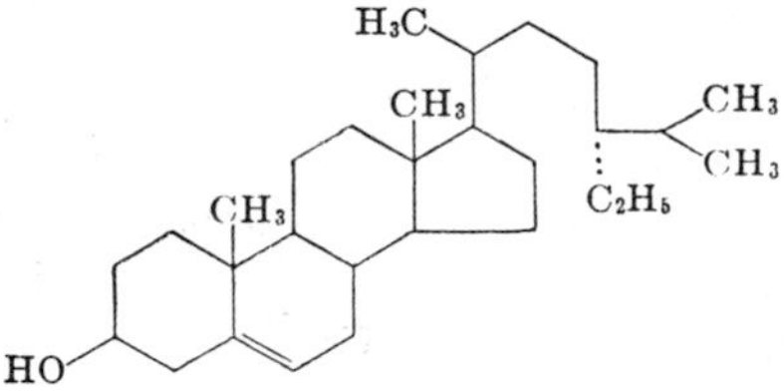   Clionasterol

"γ"-sitostanol. Ozonization of poriferasterol to 3β-hydroxy-Δ⁵-bisnorcholenic acid located the double bonds at C_5–C_6 and C_{22}–C_{23}, and the isolation of d-ethylisopropylacetaldehyde as another product of ozonization established the structure of the terminal part of the side chain and indi-

⁹ Henze, *Z. physiol. Chem.*, **41**, 109 (1904); **55**, 427 (1908).

cated that poriferasterol is the C_{24}-epimer of stigmasterol. This inference has been substantiated by a comparison of the differences in molecular rotations between derivatives of the two stanols and of cholestanol.[7] Poriferasterol has been converted into clionasterol by hydrogenation of the i-methyl ether,[7] and hence clionasterol is 22-dihydroporiferasterol; the relationships between the molecular rotations of derivatives are consistent with the inference that clionasterol is the 24a-epimer of "β"-sitosterol.

Gorgosterol,[2] m.p. 185°, $[\alpha]_D$ − 45°, isolated from the gorgonia *Plexaura flexuosa*, is possibly $C_{30}H_{52}O$ or $C_{31}H_{54}O$; it may be a triterpene alcohol rather than a sterol. **Conchasterol,** isolated from mollusks,[5] is probably identical with ostreasterol and chalinasterol. **Shakosterol,** from the mollusk *Tridacna gigas* ("shako"),[5] may be identical with brassicasterol.[7]

Chapter IV
Sex Hormones

Whereas sterols occur abundantly and have been investigated since the earliest days of chemistry, the sex hormones occur in the organism in extremely small amounts and the isolation of the first known member of the group was accomplished only in 1929. The field, once opened, attracted numerous investigators because of the novelty of the compounds and the prospect of useful applications to medicine. The final solution in 1932 of the problem of the structures of the sterols paved the way both for the elucidation of the structures of the new hormonal substances and for their preparation from available steroids. The highly competitive researches advanced so rapidly that by 1936 sex hormones of three types had been isolated, their structures fully established, and the pure substances made available in quantities adequate for therapeutic use (see chart).

The chemical studies were founded upon the results of extended biological experimentation leading to the recognition that sexual processes of the organism proceed under the influence of specific chemical substances, defined as hormones because they are capable of acting at a site other than that of origin. These substances exert a control over growth processes somewhat broader than is implied by the term sex hormone, but they are usually so designated. There are two types of female sex hormones, exemplified by the estrogens: estradiol, estrone, and estriol; and by progesterone, the sole natural progestational hormone or gestogen. Testosterone, androsterone, and related substances have qualitatively similar male sex hormone activity and are defined as androgens. Estradiol, progesterone, and testosterone appear to be true, primary hormones, whereas the other compounds of related physiological function, as well as a host of inactive companion excretory compounds, are products of metabolic transformation. The primary sex hormones are formed in the testes or ovaries under the stimulation of hormones of another type secreted in the anterior lobe of the pituitary gland: the gonadotropic hormones. The sexogens control the growth and physiological functioning of the reproductive organs and, according to their nature, they promote the development of either male or female secondary sex characteristics. The male hormones control the development of the genital tract and the accessory male organs, and they influence the longevity and mobility of the sperm. The normal growth of secondary marks of the male sex, for example the comb and wattles of the cock, takes place under stimulation by androgens.   In consequence of the greater complexity of the female organism, at least two kinds of hormones

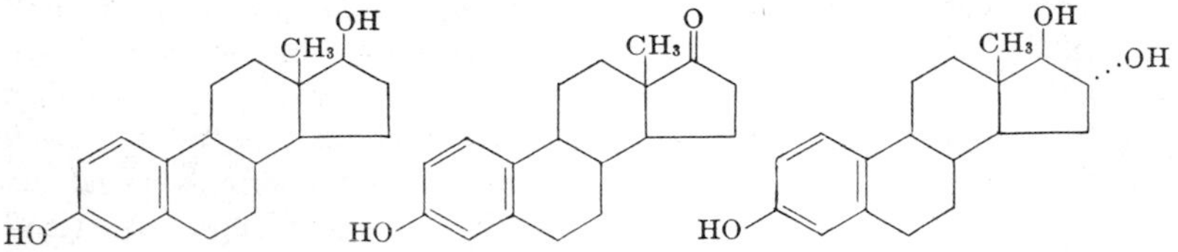

Estradiol   Estrone   Estriol

(Estrogens)

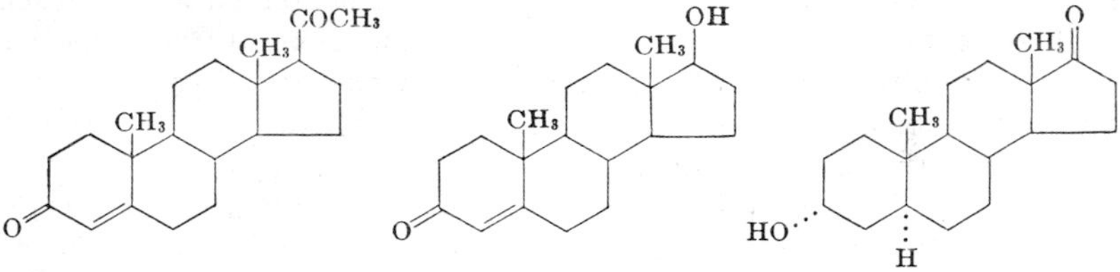

Progesterone   Testosterone   Androsterone
(Gestogen)

(Androgens)

are required to control the various processes in the uterine cycle and in pregnancy.   The estrogen produced in the ovary, probably in the ripening follicles, passes to the uterus and the vagina, and in animals produces the characteristic changes of estrus (sexual heat).   The association with the follicular phase and the easily observable response in test animals occasioned the use of the equivalent terms "follicular hormone" and "estrogen." Progesterone is secreted by the corpus luteum or yellow body of the ovary, an organ formed from the cells lining the follicle after rupture and expulsion of the ovum.   The estrogens act in conjunction with progesterone in control of the uterine cycle.   In humans the cycle consists in the periodic preparation of the uterus for pregnancy in two phases.   The first phase occurs under the hormonal influence of estrogens and consists in growth or proliferation (cell division) of a functional bed or mucosa in the uterus.   In the second, secretory phase, the corpus luteum hormone prepares the bed for the implantation of the fertilized ovum.   In case there is no fertilization leading to pregnancy, the mucosal bed largely degenerates and returns to the unproliferated, or resting, condition.

Gonadotropic Hormones.   However important in the direct regulation of the sex processes, the hormones of the gonads (testes and ovaries) are not in primary control of these processes, for they owe their origin to the stimulating action of hormones secreted by the anterior lobe of the pituitary gland. These hormones pass in the blood stream to the testis or ovary and stimulate the production of either the male or female hormones. That the sexual cycle is under the direct control of the pituitary was first indicated by clinical observations of the connection between certain diseases and dysfunction of the pituitary gland. Confirmation was found in the effects of partial or total removal of the anterior lobe by operation (hypophysectomy). Partial hypophysectomy arrests normal sexual activity; all sexual activity can be inhibited by complete hypophysectomy (Cushing, 1909). With the development of a technique for the study of effects of hypophysectomy in small female animals (Smith, 1927), it was demonstrated that removal of the anterior lobe before puberty leads to continued infantilism, whereas removal at a later period causes cessation of the sex cycle and atrophy of the ovaries. The next advance was the demonstration that implantation of pituitary tissue into hypophysectomized female animals restores the normal cycle with the reappearance of estrus. New follicles are produced and luteinization (corpus luteum formation) occurs. Similar implantation into immature normal females leads to precocious sex maturity (Zondek and Aschheim, 1927; Smith and Engle, 1927). Implantation of the pituitary gland also brings about rejuvenation of reproductive organs in hypophysectomized male animals, but has no effect on castrated animals. This body of evidence clearly establishes the control of the sexual processes by the pituitary.

That this control is purely hormonal in character was established by the production of similar effects with cell-free extracts of the pituitary (Evans, 1928). A physiological method for the determination of the activity is available through observation of changes produced in infant female mammals. A mouse unit is defined as the smallest amount that will bring about follicle-ripening and luteinization in the infant female mouse. Early evidence for the presence of at least two factors (Aschheim and Zondek, 1927) has been generally confirmed and two distinct, highly potent preparations have been obtained.[1] Both are glycoproteins, but show considerable differences in solubility and sensitivity to enzymes. The hormones show differences in their biological activity, but they are not sex-specific, like the hormones produced in the gonads under their stimulation. One stimulates the follicular growth in the ovaries of female animals and the growth of sperm-forming tissues; it is known as thylakentrin or as FSH (follicle-stimulating hormone). This factor has been prepared free from the other known hormones of the anterior pituitary, but the purest preparation now known is not homogeneous. The second factor stimulates the interstitial

---

[1] B. F. Chow, "Purification and Properties of Certain Protein Hormones," *Advances in Protein Chemistry*, I, 153 (1944).

cells of the ovaries with formation of corpora lutea from the follicles; in males, it stimulates the production of the testicular male hormone. It is known as the luteinizing hormone, as metakentrin, as LH, or as ICSH (interstitial cell-stimulating hormone). This factor has been obtained essentially pure from both swine and sheep glands. The metakentrins from these two sources, however, are not identical in their physical properties. In addition the pituitary secretes prolactin, or the lactogenic hormone, which is required for the production of milk in mammals; it also stimulates and maintains the production of progesterone by the corpus luteum.

The physiological relationship between the ovarian hormones and the pituitary hormones is highly complex, for the ovarian hormones can control to some extent the secretory activity of the pituitary.[2] In ovariectomized animals the secretion of the follicle-stimulating hormone is higher than in normal animals; administration of estrogens suppresses secretion of the hormone. Moreover, the secretion of the luteinizing hormone is controlled by progesterone. The delicate balance maintained by the stimulating or inhibiting effects of the various hormones of the ovaries and of the pituitary control the sexual function.

Gonadotropic hormones have been found in sources other than the pituitary gland. Aschheim and Zondek (1927) reported that the urine of pregnant women contains a substance capable of inducing follicle stimulation in the immature female mouse. The biological assay provides a method for the early diagnosis for pregnancy (Aschheim-Zondek reaction), for the hormone is excreted only during this condition (in the first few months). It is also found in all body fluids during this time. The original Aschheim-Zondek test has been largely replaced in this country and in England by a modified test of Friedman (rabbit ovulation). The latter requires a single intravenous injection into a sexually mature rabbit. Highly pure preparations of the hormone, known as chorionic gonadotropin or as PU (pregnancy urine hormone), have been prepared.[3] It is a glycoprotein containing galactose and hexosamine. The factor functions as a luteinizing hormone in primates and in rats; it is probably derived from the placenta.[4]

[2] Fevold, "Gonadotropic Function of the Pituitary Gland," *Chemistry and Physiology of Hormones*, p. 152, Am. Assoc. Advancement Sci. (1944); Laqueur, "Interrelationships between Gonadotrophin and Sex Hormones," *Harvey Lectures*, **41**, 216, (1946); Zondek and Sulman, "Mechanism of Action and Metabolism of Gonadotropic Hormones in the Organism," *Vitamins and Hormones*, III, 297 (1945).

[3] Gurin, "Isolation and Chemistry of Human Chorionic and Pregnant Mare Serum (Equine) Gonadotropins," *Chemistry and Physiology of Hormones*, p. 144, Am. Assoc. Advancement Sci. (1944).

[4] Levin, "Physiology of the Gonadotropic Substances of Blood, Urine, and Non-Hypophyseal Tissues," *Chemistry and Physiology of Hormones*, p. 162, Am. Assoc. Advancement Sci. (1944).

A second gonadotropin occurs in the serum of pregnant mares during a limited period (Cole and Hart, 1930; Zondek, 1930). It is known as mare serum gonadotropin or as PMS. Like the chorionic hormone, it is a glycoprotein; although apparently different in molecular weight, the two hormones are strikingly similar in their chemical properties. Their physiological actions are different. The equine hormone is both follicle-stimulating and luteinizing in immature female rodents; other physiological differences also distinguish the equine factor from the human urine factor. On a weight basis, both hormones are more active than the pituitary hormones.

A third distinct gonadotropin is present in the blood and urine of human castrates and postmenopausal women; it is apparently present in small amounts in the urine of men and women throughout life. It is sometimes referred to as CU (castrate urine hormone). This hormone is apparently primarily a follicle-stimulator.

Biological Investigations of Hormones of the Gonads. The presence of hormones in the testis and ovary and the nature of their specific physiological functions were established by animal experimentation resembling that described above and largely antedating the work on the gonadotropic hormones. With the use of either castrated animals or animals not sufficiently mature to display full sexual activity, various tissues and extracts can be tested for their ability to restore or initiate such activity. Since the removal of both ovaries from a female mammal (double ovariectomy) abolishes the normal cyclic changes, these changes must occur under influence from the ovaries. That the effect is hormonal, that is, due to stimulation by an agent capable of being transported in the body fluid, was established by the observation that the cyclic changes are maintained on autotransplantation of the ovaries to other sites of the body. An advance was made in 1923 by Allen and Doisy,[1] who devised a convenient test for the follicular hormone which depends upon ability to produce the typical estrous reaction when injected into castrated mice or rats. A positive reaction is easily recognized, for the reproductive cycle in the normal animal is characterized by distinct changes in the cell structure of the lining of the vagina. At the height of estrus the lining acquires a unique, cornified character easily distinguished from that typical of the resting period or of the permanent condition of castrated animals. Microscopic examination of vaginal smears gives a reliable indication of the estrous condition of the living animal.

Allen and Doisy prepared alcoholic (cell-free) extracts of ovaries capable of inducing typical estrus in test animals and thereby proved that the active principle is a chemical substance. The activity of a preparation was evalu-

[1] E. Allen and Doisy, *J. Am. Med. Assoc.*, **81**, 819 (1923).

ated in terms of mouse or rat units. A mouse unit of hormone is the quantity that just suffices to produce the estrous response in the castrated animal; in the procedures employed in different laboratories, the mouse unit varies from about 0.04 to 0.1 γ of pure estrone; the international standard of activity has been set as that of 0.1 γ of estrone. The method of bioassay gives reliable and reproducible results and, since the sexual cycle for the mouse is only 4–6 days in duration, the test can be performed rapidly. The ratio of the mouse unit (m.u.) to the rat unit (r.u.) varies with the medium and method of injection but usually is between 1:5 and 1:7.

The Allen-Doisy test was an indispensable guide in the search for a pure estrus-producing hormone. Active material was found in follicular fluid, in mammalian placenta, and in the blood; fairly active extracts of the first two tissues were prepared by several investigators. Organic solvents extract considerable material in addition to the hormone, however, and a separation from the inert material of the tissues proved to be extremely difficult. Little progress in the direction of isolation was made until Aschheim and Zondek[2] in 1927 discovered that estrogenic material is excreted in considerable quantity in the urine of pregnant women. The observation was of enormous value in expediting the chemical investigations, for simple benzene or ether extraction of pregnancy urine affords solutions of hormone of higher biological activity and lower content of interfering contaminants than had been obtained by elaborate purification of tissue extracts. With a convenient source of hormone and a reliable test for physiological activity both available, the chemical work entered a final phase and culminated in 1929 in the isolation in two laboratories of a pure, crystalline hormone. This work will be described below.

Investigations of the male sex hormones[3] date at least to experiments of Berthold in 1849. The castration of a cock leads to the general regression of the characteristic head furnishings of the animal; the comb and wattles soon atrophy and almost completely disappear. Berthold found that transplantation of testis tissue causes the comb of the capon to resume growth. The regeneration of secondary sex characteristics by the implantation or grafting of testicular tissue was demonstrated in later experiments with the same test animal (Pézard, 1911), but the effect was not proved to be of hormonal character until 1927, when McGee,[4] of the Chicago research group of Koch and Moore, prepared a cell-free alcoholic extract of bull testes containing an active principle capable of promoting comb growth in capons. The observation was soon confirmed and extended by others

[2] Aschheim and Zondek, *Klin. Wochschr.*, **6**, 1322 (1927).
[3] See C. R. Moore, "The Biology of Testes" and F. C. Koch, "Biochemistry of Androgens" in E. Allen's *Sex and Internal Secretions*, 2nd Ed. (1939).
[4] McGee, *Dissertation*, Chicago (1927).

(Koch and Moore, Loewe and Voss, Funk and Harrow, Steinach, Dodds, Frattini and Maino), but all initial attempts to isolate an active principle from testes tissue were fruitless. Prompted by the possible analogy to the estrogenic hormone, several workers then investigated normal male urine and found[5] (1928) that androgenic material is indeed excreted in the urine, although in extremely small amounts. The processing of urine, with guidance from bioassays in capons, led to the isolation of androsterone in 1929. Finally, in 1935, testosterone was isolated from testicular extracts.

Chemical studies of the corpus luteum hormone were initiated by the discovery by Corner and Allen in 1929 of a method of bioassay based upon the effect of the active principle on the uterine mucosa of the sexually mature castrated rabbit. The absence of any source of material other than the corpus luteum itself was a great handicap in the investigation, but the isolation of progesterone was achieved in 1934.

ESTROGENIC HORMONES

Isolation of Estrone. The isolation of estrone was accomplished independently in 1929 by Doisy and co-workers[1] at the St. Louis University School of Medicine and by Butenandt[2] at Göttingen. The respective results were announced at Boston in August and at Kiel in October. Early in the following year the Laqueur[3] group at Amsterdam reported the isolation of an apparently identical crystalline substance of high physiological activity. In each case the urine of pregnant women was used as the starting material. When such urine is shaken with ether, butanol, or benzene a considerable portion of the estrogenic material is extracted, for the hormone is readily soluble in all organic solvents and sparingly soluble in water. A better yield is obtained if the urine is submitted to acid hydrolysis before the solvent extraction. Fresh urine is not required, as the hormone does not appear to deteriorate rapidly. In the first step of Doisy's original process[4] the urine was acidified to pH 4, allowed to stand for several days, and extracted with olive oil. The hormone was then extracted with alcohol. Butenandt made use of a technical crude oil supplied by the Schering-Kahlbaum A.-G. This was obtained by the ether extraction of acidified

---

[5] Loewe, H. E. Voss, Lange and Wähner, *Klin. Wochschr.*, **7**, 1376 (1928).

[1] Doisy, Veler and Thayer, *Am. J. Physiol.*, **90**, 329 (1929); *J. Biol. Chem.*, **86**, 499 (1930); **87**, 357 (1930).

[2] Butenandt, *Naturwissenschaften*, **17**, 879 (1929); Butenandt and v. Ziegner, *Z. physiol. Chem.*, **188**, 1 (1930).

[3] Dingemanse, de Jongh, Kober and Laqueur, *Deut. med. Wochschr.*, **56**, 301 (1930).

[4] For later methods see Katzman and Doisy, *Proc. Soc. Exp. Biol. Med.*, **30**, 1196 (1933).

urine, followed by the partial removal of acidic impurities by extraction with very dilute alkali. Bioassays of the dark brown sirup indicated the presence of about 0.3 percent of active material. In the various methods for further purification of these crude extracts, advantage is taken of the stability of the hormone to acids, bases, and heat, and of its weakly acidic (phenolic) character and ketonic properties. After an alkaline hydrolysis of the crude oil, Butenandt[5] distributed the material between 50 percent alcohol and ligroin, when the first solvent retained nearly all the hormone. A further enrichment was attained by extraction of the active principle from the alcoholic phase into benzene. After removal of the solvent the material was subjected to hydrolysis with hot, alcoholic hydrochloric acid and extracted from a solution in ether with 1 N sodium hydroxide. The purified oil on distillation in high vacuum then yielded a crude, yellow crystallizate, and completely pure crystals were obtained on repeated sublimation and crystallization. The hormone was later found to form a very sparingly soluble molecular compound with quinoline, which affords a convenient method of obtaining pure, colorless crystals from the crude distillate.[6] The complex crystallizes almost completely from quinoline and it is decomposed by shaking with ether and dilute acid. Doisy also used the semicarbazone in isolating and purifying the hormone.[7]

Subsequent quantitative studies established that urine must be submitted to rather drastic acid hydrolysis prior to solvent extraction if the maximum yield of estrogenic material is to be obtained;[8, 9] the hormone is present in part in the form of water-soluble, ether-insoluble conjugates. The nature of the conjugation and the determination and isolation of estrone will be discussed further in later sections.

The first sex hormone to be isolated has been known by a number of names: theelin (Doisy), progynon and follicular hormone (Butenandt), oestrin (Marrian), menformon (Laqueur), folliculin (Girard). The name oestrone, proposed by a group of English investigators,[10] was accepted by a League of Nations Conference in London in 1935. This name, or the modernized name estrone employed in the United States, indicates the ketonic nature of the hormone and its most characteristic physiological action, and it is adaptable to a general system of nomenclature (parent hydrocarbon: estrane). The international unit of estrogenic activity,

[5] Butenandt, *Z. physiol. Chem.*, **191**, 127 (1930).

[6] Butenandt and U. Westphal, *Z. physiol. Chem.*, **223**, 147 (1934).

[7] J. M. Curtis, MacCorquodale, Thayer and Doisy, *J. Biol. Chem.*, **107**, 191 (1934).

[8] Borchardt, Dingemanse and Laqueur, *Naturwissenschaften*, **22**, 190 (1934).

[9] S. L. Cohen and Marrian, *Biochem. J.*, **28**, 1603 (1934); **29**, 1577 (1935).

[10] Adam, Danielli, Dodds, King, Marrian, Parkes and Rosenheim, *Nature*, **132**, 205 (1933).

established under the auspices of the Health Organization of the League of Nations,[11] is that of 0.1γ of a standard estrone preparation administered in sesame oil by subcutaneous injection. The oral dose is about forty times the subcutaneous dose.[12]

Girard's Reagent, $[(CH_3)_3{}^+NCH_2CONHNH_2]Cl^-$. Trimethylaminoacetohydrazide hydrochloride (betainehydrazide hydrochloride), described first in a patent,[1] has become recognized as a reagent of general value for the separation of ketonic from nonketonic material.[2] Estrone or comparable ketone can be converted into a water-soluble Girard derivative and subsequently regenerated by hydrolysis. The reagent is easily pre-

17-Ketosteroid   Girard derivative

pared in 83–89 percent yield from ethyl chloroacetate, trimethylamine, and hydrazine hydrate in ethanol;[2, 3] it is hygroscopic and undergoes decomposition in a moist atmosphere. An alternate, less hygroscopic reagent (P) recommended for technical isolations is prepared by substitution of pyridine for the trimethylamine in the usual reagent (T). The condensation is carried out by refluxing a solution of the ketone and Girard reagent in alcohol containing 10 percent of acetic acid for about one-half hour. The solution is then diluted with water and nonketonic material is removed by repeated extraction of the mixture with ether; the aqueous solution of the Girard derivative is clarified, acidified with hydrochloric acid, and warmed briefly to effect hydrolysis. The regenerated ketonic material is then recovered by ether extraction. Estrone can be isolated readily by this process from a dark, oily hormone concentrate from urine.

Reichstein[4] observed that ketones of the cholestanone type react readily with the Girard reagent and give hydrazones that can be hydrolyzed with very dilute mineral acid; those of the cholestenone type also react readily with the reagent but a considerably higher concentration of acid is required for hydrolysis. Mixtures can sometimes be fractionated either by selective partial condensation with the reagent or by hydrolysis at progressive levels of acidity.[4] Aldehydes react readily to form hydrazone derivatives so

[11] *J. Am. Med. Assoc.*, **101**, 377 (1933).
[12] de Jongh, Kober and Laqueur, *Biochem Z.*, **270**, 17 (1934).
[1] Girard and Sandulesco, Brit. Pat. Appl. 6640, March (1934).
[2] Girard and Sandulesco, *Helv. Chim. Acta*, **19**, 1095 (1936).
[3] Girard, *Organic Syntheses*, Coll. Vol. II, 85 (1943).
[4] Reichstein, *Helv. Chim. Acta*, **19**, 1107 (1936).

stable to acid hydrolysis that a sharp separation of ketones from aldehydes can be made; no practicable method has been found for the regeneration of aldehydes. Diaryl ketones react only very slowly with Girard's reagent. The isolation of the pure Girard derivative of a ketone can be accomplished as follows:[5] a suspension of the components in glacial acetic acid is warmed briefly on the steam bath and the solution is then evaporated to dryness under reduced pressure; the residual product is then crystallized, for example from methanol-acetone.

Henbest and Jones[6] have pointed out instances where, in the process of separation of ketonic from nonketonic steroids by reaction with Girard's reagent in methanol or ethanol solutions containing acetic acid, nonketonic allylic alcohols are converted into the corresponding methyl or ethyl ethers.

Anchel and Schoenheimer[7] investigated reagents that convert ketones into alkali-soluble derivatives. Carboxymethoxylamine ($H_2NOCH_2CO_2$-H), easily prepared from the sodium derivative of acetoxime and ethyl chloroacetate,[8] reacts rapidly with a steroid ketone in alcoholic solution and the product can be separated from inert material by extraction from ether with potassium carbonate solution. The oxime acids are stable, solid derivatives; they can be split efficiently by refluxing alcoholic hydrogen chloride. A second reagent, p-carboxyphenylhydrazine (H_2NNHC_6-H_4CO_2H), is of particular value for the separation of saturated and α,β-unsaturated ketones. The hydrazone derivative of cholestanone is easily cleaved by alcoholic formaldehyde solution at the reflux temperature, whereas the derivative of cholestenone is not attacked under these conditions but can be split by the action of pyruvic acid in boiling alcohol. The p-carboxyphenylhydrazones are autoxidizable.

Other Sources of Estrone. The average estrogenic activity of the urine of pregnant women is about 10,000 mouse units per liter, or 1 mg. of hormone calculated as estrone. In 1930 Zondek[1] discovered a better source of hormone in the urine of pregnant mares, the average activity of which is 100,000 m.u. per liter, or ten times that of human urine. Zondek[2] estimated that a single mare during pregnancy excretes about 30 g. of estrogenic material. The hormone is present in mare urine as an ether-insoluble conjugate to an even greater extent than in human urine, and only 10–25 percent of material is directly extractable.[3] Thorough acid hydrolysis is

[5] Wolfe, Hershberg and Fieser, *J. Biol. Chem.*, **136**, 660 (1940).
[6] Henbest and E. R. H. Jones, *Nature*, **158**, 950 (1946).
[7] Anchel and Schoenheimer, *J. Biol. Chem.*, **114**, 539 (1936).
[8] Borek and H. T. Clarke, *J. Am. Chem. Soc.*, **58**, 2020 (1936).
[1] Zondek, *Klin. Wochschr.*, **9**, 2285 (1930).
[2] Zondek, *Naturwissenschaften*, **21**, 33 (1933).
[3] Zondek, *Arkiv Kemi, Mineral. Geol.*, **11B**, No. 24 (1933) [*C. A.*, **28**, 3119 (1934)].

thus required prior to solvent extraction.   Processes suitable for the working of human pregnancy urine require considerable revision for application to mare's urine.[4]   Mare's urine is one of the key sources of estrone for the pharmaceutical industry.

Zondek[5] made the further surprising discovery that, according to bioassays, estrogenic hormone is present in astonishingly large amounts in the genital glands and excretions of certain male mammals.   The richest source found was the testis of the horse.   Stallion urine was also found to be richer in estrus-producing material than the urine of pregnant mares, as shown in the table.   The stallion excretes nearly twice as much estrogen as the pregnant mare and an inordinately greater amount than the nonpregnant woman.   The paradoxical higher excretion of female sex hormone by the male than by the female animal has been found only with equines

Estrogen Content of Urines (Zondek, 1934)

	PER LITER	PER DIEM
	m.u.	*m.u.*
Stallion	170,000	1,700,000
Mare	200	2000
Pregnant mare	100,000	1,000,000
Sexually mature woman	30–200	45–300
Pregnant woman	10,000	15,000

(horse, zebra, ass, kiang).   For the bull, for example, the assays indicated only 330 m.u. of estrogen per liter of urine.   In spite of the high estrogen content indicated by bioassays, stallion urine has not proved to be a practicable source of estrogens.

Pure, crystalline preparations fully identified as estrone have been isolated from the following sources: mare pregnancy urine,[6] stallion urine,[7] human male urine,[8] human placenta,[9] stallion testes,[10] beef adrenal glands,[11] and the bile of pregnant cows.[12]

A surprising discovery is that estrone occurs in the vegetable kingdom.

[4] J. M. Curtis, *J. Biol. Chem.*, **100**, XXXIII (1933); J. M. Curtis, MacCorquodale, Thayer and Doisy, *ibid.*, **107**, 191 (1934); Beall and Marrian, *J. Soc. Chem. Ind.*, **53**, 309T (1934); Beall and Edson, *Biochem. J.*, **30**, 577 (1936).
[5] Zondek, *Arkiv Kemi, Mineral Geol.*, **11B**, No. 24 (1933); *Nature*, **133**, 209, 494 (1934).
[6] Cartland, R. K. Meyer, L. C. Miller and Rutz, *J. Biol. Chem.*, **109**, 213 (1935).
[7] Deulofeu and Farrari, *Z. physiol. Chem.*, **226**, 192 (1934); Häussler, *Helv. Chim. Acta*, **17**, 531 (1934).
[8] Dingemanse, Laqueur and Mühlbock, *Nature*, **141**, 927 (1938).
[9] Westerfeld, MacCorquodale, Thayer and Doisy, *J. Biol. Chem.*, **126**, 195 (1938).
[10] Beall, *Biochem. J.*, **34**, 1293 (1940).
[11] Beall, *Nature*, **144**, 76 (1939).
[12] W. H. Pearlman, Rakoff, Cantarow and Paschkis, *J. Biol. Chem.*, **170**, 173 (1947).

The observation[13] of estrogenic activity in extracts from various flowers, lower animals, and bituminous substances is of little significance in view of the existence of numerous synthetic estrogens (see below), but in two instances the active principle has been identified. Butenandt and Jacobi[14] isolated pure estrone (18 mg.) from a palm kernel extract (50 kg.), and Skarzynski[15] obtained from female willow flowers (65 kg.) a crystallizate of pure estriol (7 mg.). The substances isolated from the plants produced the typical estrous response in castrated animals. Estrogens do not appear to have any influence on plant growth.

Structure of Estrone. Investigations that eventually led to the elucidation of the structure of estrone were carried out simultaneously with the study of an inactive, higher-melting companion substance, pregnanediol, isolated from pregnancy urine in 1929 by Marrian.[1] Butenandt,[2] who had accumulated nearly 2 g. of the same substance from the residues of the extraction of estrone from 1000–2000 liters of urine, established that pregnanediol is a fully saturated disecondary alcohol (oxidation to pregnanedione) of the formula $C_{21}H_{36}O_2$, which therefore must contain four rings, like a sterol or bile acid. The similarity was extended by the further oxidation of pregnanedione to a ketodicarboxylic acid resembling lithobilianic acid to the extent that on pyrolysis it lost carbon dioxide and afforded a pyrodiketone (Chart 1). One of the alcoholic groups therefore is on a six-membered ring; the observation that the ketodicarboxylic acid, like pregnanediol itself, gives a positive iodoform reaction showed that the other hydroxyl group is present in the side chain: —$CH(OH)CH_3$. The suspected relationship was then established by Clemmensen reduction of pregnanedione to a hydrocarbon, pregnane, identical with 17-ethyletiocholane, prepared for comparison from bisnorcholanic acid. Later work established the position and configuration of the nuclear hydroxyl group.

The correlation of pregnanediol with the bile acids revealed nothing about the structure of estrone, for no relationship between the hormone and the inactive companion substance had been established. Analyses of estrone and various derivatives established the formula $C_{18}H_{22}O_2$.[3,4] One oxygen atom was recognized as ketonic by the preparation of an oxime (Butenandt) and the other was characterized as phenolic (Butenandt, Doisy, Marrian).

[13] Aschheim and Hohlweg, *Deut. med. Wochschr.*, **59**, 12 (1933).

[14] Butenandt and H. Jacobi, *Z. physiol. Chem.*, **218**, 104 (1933).

[15] Skarzynski, *Bull. intern. acad. polonaise, Classe sci. math. nat.*, **BII**, 347 (1933) [*C. A.*, **28**, 4755 (1934)].

[1] Marrian, *Biochem. J.*, **23**, 1090 (1929).

[2] Butenandt, *Ber.*, **63**, 659 (1930); **64**, 2529 (1931).

[3] Butenandt, *Z. physiol. Chem.*, **191**, 140 (1930); Butenandt and F. Hildebrandt, *ibid.*, **199**, 243 (1931).

[4] Thayer, Levin and Doisy, *J. Biol. Chem.*, **91**, 791 (1931).

Bernal[5] presented an X-ray analysis that suggested a long molecule with the hydroxyl group at one end and the carbonyl group at the other, but an error in calculation led him to conclude that estrone contains only three

Chart 1. DEGRADATION OF PREGNANEDIOL

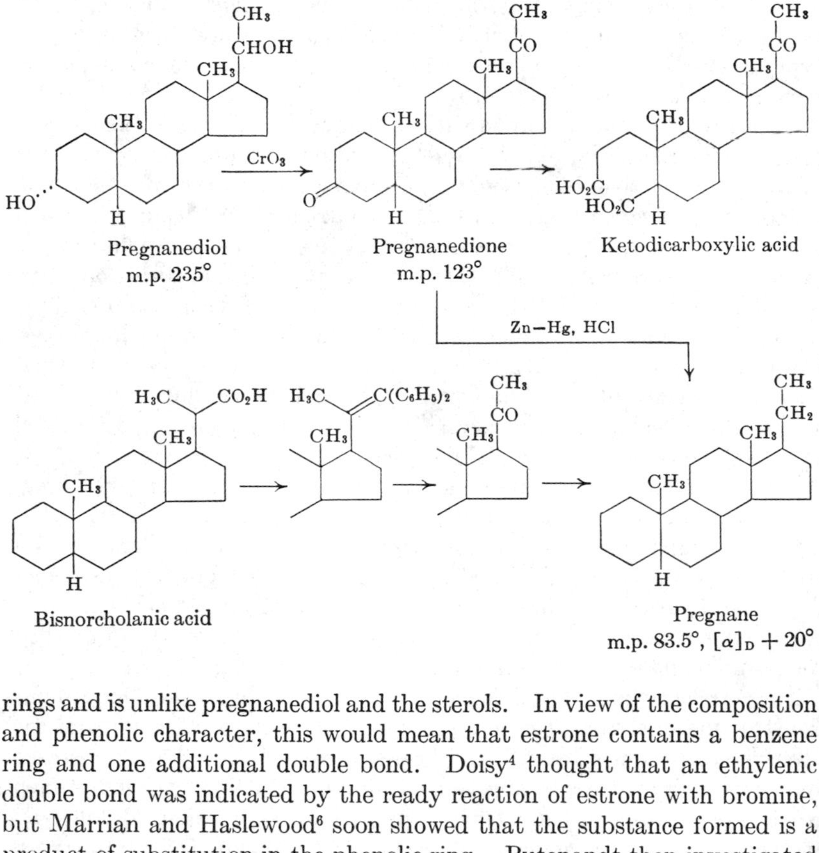

Pregnanediol
m.p. 235°

Pregnanedione
m.p. 123°

Ketodicarboxylic acid

Zn—Hg, HCl

Bisnorcholanic acid

Pregnane
m.p. 83.5°, $[\alpha]_D + 20°$

rings and is unlike pregnanediol and the sterols.   In view of the composition and phenolic character, this would mean that estrone contains a benzene ring and one additional double bond.   Doisy[4] thought that an ethylenic double bond was indicated by the ready reaction of estrone with bromine, but Marrian and Haslewood[6] soon showed that the substance formed is a product of substitution in the phenolic ring.   Butenandt then investigated the degree of unsaturation by a study of the catalytic hydrogenation and molecular refraction of estrone and in 1932 reported results that pointed to the presence of only three double bonds and therefore indicated a four-ring system.[7]   He therefore postulated the structure that is now known to be

[5] Bernal, *Chemistry and Industry*, **51**, 259 (1932).

[6] Marrian and Haslewood, *J. Soc. Chem. Ind.*, **51**, 277T (1932).

[7] Butenandt, *Nature*, **130**, 238 (1932); *Z. angew. Chem.*, **45**, 655 (1932).   For the final results see Butenandt and U. Westphal, *Z. physiol. Chem.*, **223**, 147 (1934).

correct. Essentially the same formulation was suggested independently by Marrian and Haslewood,[6] and it was not long before the deductions were verified.

A route to a successful degradation was opened by independent observations of Marrian and Haslewood[6] and of the Doisy group[8] concerning the action of fused alkali on estriol, which Butenandt had converted by dehydration into estrone. The fusion product (Chart 2) was characterized as a

Chart 2. DEGRADATION OF ESTRIOL

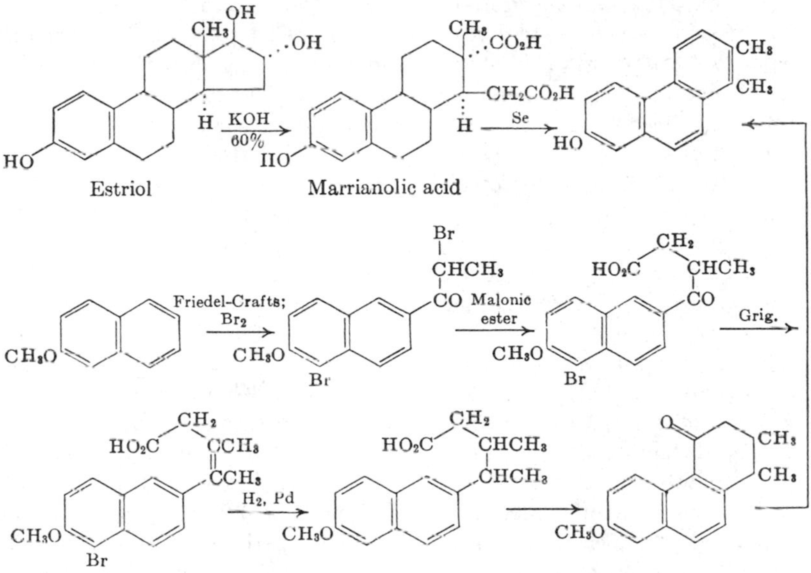

phenoldicarboxylic acid having all the original carbon atoms, and it is now called marrianolic acid. The dibasic acid forms an anhydride and not a ketone when heated with acetic anhydride, which is an indication that the ring opened in the fusion is five-membered. Butenandt[9] then found (1933) that the dibasic acid can be dehydrogenated smoothly to a dimethylphenanthrol that on zinc-dust distillation yielded 1,2-dimethylphenanthrene, prepared for comparison both by synthesis from naphthalene and methylsuccinic anhydride and by dehydrogenation of etiobilianic acid. The original hormone therefore has the phenanthrene skeleton with a five-membered ring joined at least at one of the two positions indicated by the

[8] MacCorquodale, Thayer and Doisy, *J. Biol. Chem.*, **99**, 327 (1933).

[9] Butenandt, Weidlich and H. Thompson, *Ber.*, **66**, 601 (1933).

methyl groups in the degradation product.   That the attachment is probably the same as in the sterols was indicated by the isolation of chrysene
as a minor product of the zinc-dust distillation of estrone,[10] and by the
observation that the cross-sectional area of the hormone molecule found by
unimolecular film measurements (34 ± 2 sq. Å) is close to that calculated
for a structure of the sterol type (33 sq. Å).[11]

The location of the hydroxyl group, and consequently the positions of the
three benzenoid double bonds that confer upon estrone the properties of a
phenol, was established in 1934 by Haworth and by Cook.   Haworth[12]
identified Butenandt's degradation product as 1,2-dimethyl-7-phenanthrol
by the synthesis of the methyl ether shown in Chart 2.   Cook[13] carried the
evidence a step further by the synthesis of another degradation product
containing the five-membered ring (Chart 3).   The synthesis through the
difficultly accessible 5-nitro-2-aminonaphthalene yielded only 0.36 g. of final
product from 900 g. of β-naphthylamine.   2-Methylcyclopentanone was
selected for the Bogert-Cook condensation because the methyl group
hinders spiran formation; the group was eliminated in the final dehydrogenation.   The synthetic 7-methoxy-1,2-cyclopentenophenanthrene was
identical with the product of degradation of estrone methyl ether by elimination of the carbonyl group and dehydrogenation.[14]

As a means of locating the carbonyl group, Cook[15] condensed estrone
methyl ether with methylmagnesium iodide, dehydrated the resulting carbinol, hydrogenated the ethylenic product, and dehydrogenated the saturated compound with selenium.   The methyl group introduced in the
Grignard reaction was expected to appear in a corresponding position in the
final product, but this substance did not prove identical with the 1'-, the
2'-, or the 3'-methyl derivative of 7-methoxy-1,2-cyclopentenophenan-
threne, all of which were synthesized for comparison.   Instead, the compound was found to be identical with synthetic 7-methoxy-3',3'-dimethyl-
1,2-cyclopentenophenanthrene (VI), evidently formed as the result of a
rearrangement in the dehydration of the carbinol IV, with migration of the
angular methyl group from C_{13} to C_{17}.   This interpretation was substantiated by the observation that methyl migration also occurs in the dehydration of the dihydro derivative of estrone methyl ether, VII, for the product
of subsequent dehydrogenation is 7-methoxy-3'-methyl-1,2-cyclopenteno-

[10] Butenandt and H. Thompson, *Ber.*, **67**, 140 (1934).

[11] Danielli, Marrian and Haslewood, *Biochem. J.*, **27**, 311 (1933); Danielli, *J. Am. Chem. Soc.*, **56**, 746 (1934).

[12] R. D. Haworth and Sheldrick, *J. Chem. Soc.*, 864 (1934).

[13] A. Cohen, Cook, Hewett and Girard, *J. Chem. Soc.*, 653 (1934).

[14] Cook and Girard, *Nature*, **133**, 377 (1934).

[15] A. Cohen, Cook and Hewett, *J. Chem. Soc.*, 445 (1935).

Chart 3. Synthesis of Degradation Products

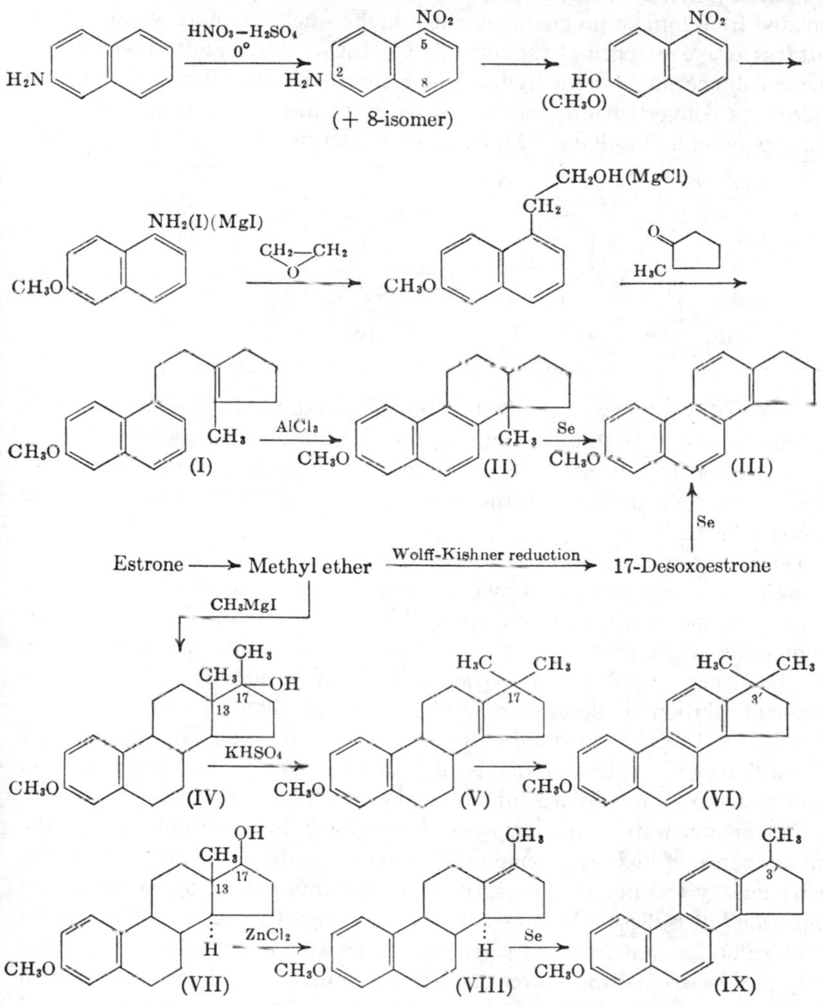

phenanthrene (IX). These transformations provide a rigid proof that the carbonyl group is at C_{17} and the angular methyl group at C_{13} and hence complete the evidence of the structure of estrone. Later observations with synthetic compounds (Bachmann) have shown that the rearrangements occur because the trans ring juncture between rings C and D does not permit a double bond to enter the five-membered ring; the cis arrangement permits dehydration without rearrangement.

Estriol. Shortly after the first isolation of estrone, Marrian[1] in London isolated from human pregnancy urine a higher-melting, more water-soluble but less active estrogen of the formula $C_{18}H_{24}O_3$. Butenandt[2] inferred that the substance might be a hydrate of estrone and established that it can indeed be converted into estrone by vacuum distillation from a mixture with potassium bisulfate. Marrian and Haslewood[3] similarly identified

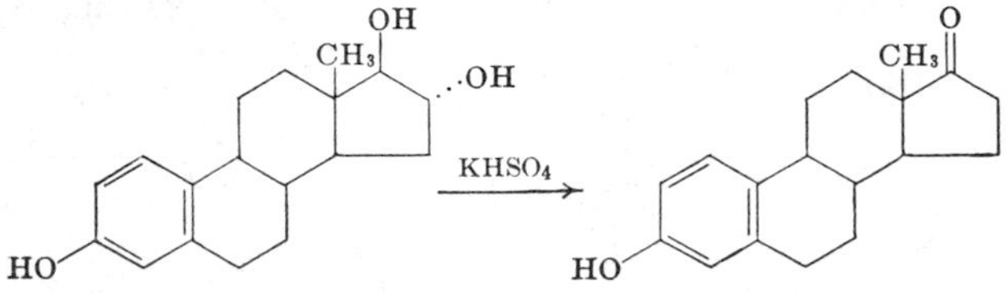

Estriol   Estrone

estrone methyl ether as a product of the dehydration of the ether of estriol. Estriol forms a triacetate and, as noted earlier, the bond linking the hydroxylated carbon atoms can be cleaved by alkali fusion (marrianolic acid). Another product of the cleavage of ring D is described below (doisynolic acid).

Doisy[4] encountered estriol in an active fraction from human pregnancy urine that resisted extraction by ether from a weakly alkaline solution from which estrone was easily extracted. The difference in distribution constants of the two phenols is so great that a nearly quantitative separation can be made:[5] estriol alone is extracted by 0.1 N sodium hydroxide from an ethereal solution of the mixture, and estrone can then be extracted with 1 N alkali. The two substances differ only slightly in acidic strength, and the difference in extractability is probably due to the fact that the triol is considerably more hydrophilic than the hydroxyketone.

The greater water solubility of estriol probably is responsible also for the maintenance of high estrogenic activity on oral administration. Estriol is considerably less potent than estrone when administered by subcutaneous injection but is distinctly more active by the digestive route. Thus estriol is of value for oral therapy, whereas estrone and estradiol are not. The only practicable natural source of estriol is human pregnancy urine, which according to a procedure of Doisy[4] yields about 0.3 mg. of estrone and 1.3

---

[1] Marrian, *Biochem. J.*, **24**, 435, 1021 (1930).

[2] Butenandt, *Z. physiol. Chem.*, **191**, 140 (1930); Butenandt and F. Hildebrandt, *ibid.*, **199**, 243 (1931).

[3] Marrian and Haslewood, *Biochem. J.*, **26**, 25 (1932).

[4] Doisy, Thayer, Levin and J. M. Curtis, *Proc. Soc. Exp. Biol. Med.*, **28**, 88 (1930); Doisy and Thayer, *J. Biol. Chem.*, **91**, 641 (1931); Thayer, Levin and Doisy, *ibid.*, **91**, 655 (1931).

[5] S. L. Cohen and Marrian, *Biochem. J.*, **28**, 1603 (1934)

mg. of estriol per liter; this source is worked commercially for the recovery of both estrogens.

Since estrone can be obtained more abundantly from mare's urine, the requirement for estriol for oral therapy may be met by a process developed independently by Huffman[6] and by Butenandt[7] for the conversion of estrone into estriol.

Chart 4. ESTRIOL FROM ESTRONE

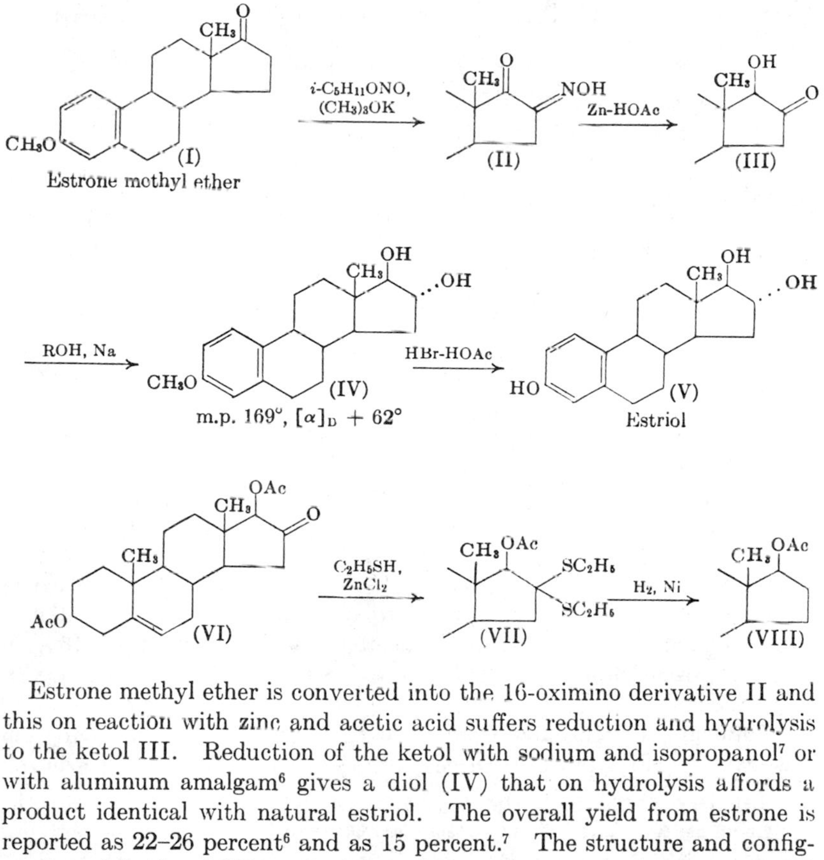

Estrone methyl ether is converted into the 16-oximino derivative II and this on reaction with zinc and acetic acid suffers reduction and hydrolysis to the ketol III. Reduction of the ketol with sodium and isopropanol[7] or with aluminum amalgam[6] gives a diol (IV) that on hydrolysis affords a product identical with natural estriol. The overall yield from estrone is reported as 22–26 percent[6] and as 15 percent.[7] The structure and configuration of the ketol III can be inferred by analogy to the ketol acetate VI prepared in the same way from dehydroepiandrosterone;[6] this ketol yielded

---

[6] Huffman and W. R. Miller, Science, 100, 312 (1944); Huffman, J. Biol. Chem., 169, 167 (1947); Huffman and Lott, J. Am. Chem. Soc., 69, 1835 (1947); Huffman and Lott, J. Biol. Chem., 172, 325 (1948).

[7] Butenandt and Schäffler, Z. Naturforsch., 1, 82 (1946).

a 16-diethylthioacetal (VII), which on hydrogenolysis with Raney nickel catalyst afforded androstenediol diacetate (VIII), a known C_{17} β-hydroxy derivative. Since estriol fails to form an acetonide under forcing conditions,[7] the two alcoholic hydroxyl groups must be in the trans orientation: 16α-OH, 17β-OH. 16-Ketoestrone methyl ether (yellow, m.p. 178°) has been prepared by the oxidation of the ketol III with copper acetate.[8]

Two stereoisomers of estriol are known. 16-Epiestriol (isoestriol-A),[9] obtained by the reduction of the ketol III with hydrogen and platinum catalyst in dilute alkali, must have a C_{17} β-hydroxyl group like estriol; since

Chart 5. EPIMERS OF ESTRIOL

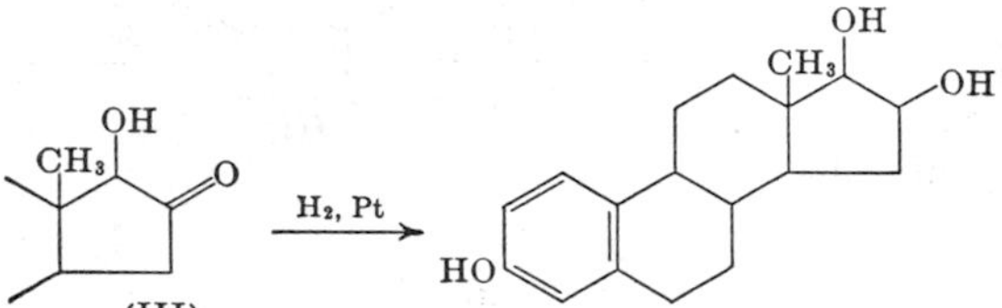

(III)

16-Epiestriol
m.p. 269°, $[\alpha]_D + 88°$

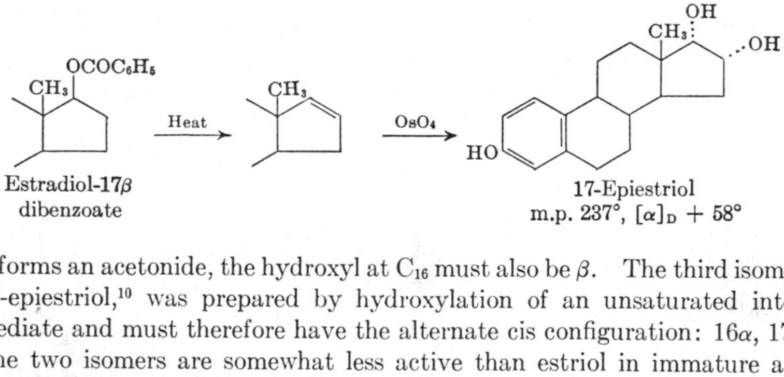

Estradiol-17β
dibenzoate

17-Epiestriol
m.p. 237°, $[\alpha]_D + 58°$

it forms an acetonide, the hydroxyl at C_{16} must also be β. The third isomer, 17-epiestriol,[10] was prepared by hydroxylation of an unsaturated intermediate and must therefore have the alternate cis configuration: 16α, 17α. The two isomers are somewhat less active than estriol in immature and castrated rats.[11]

Equilenin, Equilin, and Isomers of Estrone. In 1932–33 Girard and associates[1] in Paris processed large quantities of mare's pregnancy urine and

[8] Huffman, *J. Biol. Chem.*, **167**, 273 (1947).
[9] Huffman and Darby, *J. Am. Chem. Soc.*, **66**, 150 (1944); Huffman and Lott, *ibid.*, **69**, 1835 (1947).
[10] Prelog, Ruzicka and P. Wieland, *Helv. Chim. Acta*, **28**, 250 (1945).
[11] Huffman and Grollman, *Endrocrinology*, **41**, 12 (1946).
[1] Girard, Sandulesco, Fridenson and Rutgers, *Compt. rend.*, **194**, 909 (1932); Girard, Sandulesco, Fridenson, Guadefroy and Rutgers, *ibid.*, **194**, 1020 (1932); Girard, Sandulesco, Fridenson and Rutgers, *ibid.*, **195**, 981 (1932); Sandulesco, Tchung and Girard, *ibid.*, **196**, 137 (1933); Girard, *Bull. soc. chim. biol.*, **15**, 562 (1933).

isolated the new estrogens equilenin and equilin (the isolation of a third substance, hippulin, has not been confirmed). These substances are now known to be di- and mono-dehydro derivatives of estrone, but they possess much lower estrogenic activity. Equilenin is characterized as a naphthalene derivative by the formation of a picrate, through which it can easily be separated from companion substances. Equilenin can be recognized by

Chart 6. EQUILENIN AND EQUILIN

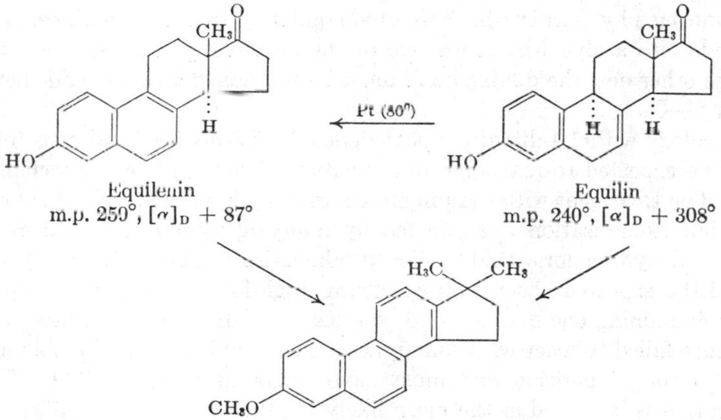

Equilenin
m.p. 259°, [α]ᴅ + 87°

Pt (80°)

Equilin
m.p. 240°, [α]ᴅ + 308°

7-Methoxy-3′,3′-dimethyl-1,2-cyclo-
pentenophenanthrene

a sensitive test based upon conversion into an amorphous red product when heated in air. Girard found that samples of estrone from mare's urine contain traces of equilenin, but no equilenin has been detected in human urine. The substance appears in mare's urine only after about the 175th day of pregnancy and becomes particularly abundant during the last months of burden. Since the quantity of estrone excreted decreases as the quantity of equilenin increases, it appears that, as pregnancy progresses, estrone is partially dehydrogenated in the animal organism to the less active equilenin (and equilin).

In a process analogous to that applied to estrone, both equilenin and equilin have been degraded through the methyl ether 17-methylcarbinol to 7-methoxy-3′,3′-dimethyl-1,2-cyclopentenophenanthrene;[2] the reaction establishes the location of the hydroxyl, methyl, and carbonyl groups. In the case of equilenin this evidence, coupled with that indicating the presence of a naphthalene nucleus (picrate, spectrum), fully establishes the structure.

[2] A. Cohen, Cook and Hewett, J. Chem. Soc., 445 (1935).

Equilin contains a benzenoid ring and a further double bond, and since the absorption maximum is identical with that of estrone (λ_{max}^{alc} 280 mμ, low intensity), this bond is not conjugated with the benzenoid ring.[3] The attempted palladium hydrogenation of equilin to estrone or an isomer has been unsuccessful, because, even in the presence of hydrogen, catalysts exert a dehydrogenating action and the substance is transformed into equilenin.[4] The ready conversion must mean that the nonconjugated double bond is associated with ring B and probably is at C_7-C_8.[3] This location was confirmed by Serini,[5] who converted equilin by treatment with osmium tetroxide into a glycol in which one of the alcoholic groups was acylable and the other not; the double bond must be secondary-tertiary, and therefore at C_7-C_8.

In analogy with 1,4-dihydronaphthalene, the 7,8-double bond of equilin would be expected to rearrange to a position of conjugation. No change resulted on treatment with sodium alkoxides or hydrogen chloride in chloroform, but isomerization was effected by refluxing equilin in a mixture of acetic and hydrochloric acid.[6] The product, isoequilin-A (Chart 7), exhibited the expected absorption spectrum (high-intensity band) of a substance containing one double bond conjugated with a benzene ring. The substance failed to react with osmium tetroxide and hence the double bond is not at the 6,7-position and must have migrated to 8,9 or 9,11. The 8,9-location is indicated as the more likely by the fact that isoequilin-A is dehydrogenated readily by palladium at 80°; the product is not equilenin as in the dehydrogenation of equilin itself, but an epimer, *d*-isoequilenin.[7] This substance is identical with one of the stereoisomers of equilenin produced by total synthesis (Bachmann, see below). *d*-Isoequilenin, rather than equilenin, also has been identified as the product of dehydrogenation of estrone.[8] This could mean either that the two natural estrogens differ in configuration at C_{13} or C_{14} or that inversions occur in the dehydrogenation of estrone and in the formation or dehydrogenation of isoequilin-A. Although a rigid proof is not available, the burden of evidence strongly

[3] Cook and Roe, *Chemistry and Industry*, **54**, 501 (1935).

[4] Dirscherl and Hanusch, *Z. physiol. Chem.*, **233**, 13 (1935); **236**, 131 (1935); Dirscherl, *Z. angew. Chem.*, **48**, 399 (1935).

[5] Serini and Logemann, *Ber.*, **71**, 186 (1938).

[6] H. Hirschmann and Wintersteiner, *J. Biol. Chem.*, **126**, 737 (1938).

[7] Heer and Miescher, *Helv. Chim. Acta*, **31**, 1289 (1948), recently prepared by total synthesis a substance regarded as *dl*-8-dehydroestrone of C/D-cis orientation (m.p. 204°; very slight estrogenic activity; Pd-dehydrogenation of the methyl ether at 110° gave *dl*-14-isoequilenin methyl ether, m.p. 126°). Preliminary characterization suggests that this substance is not, as expected, the racemate of isoequilin-A (highly purified sample; m.p. 235°, $[\alpha]_D$ + 234°, potency 1/100 that of estrone).

[8] Butenandt, Wolff and Karlson, *Ber.*, **74**, 1308 (1941).

indicates that epimerizations at position 14 occur in the dehydrogenation of estrone and in the acid isomerization of equilin to isoequilin-A; the chemistry of the stenols suggests that the acid isomerization may proceed through

Chart 7. CORRELATION OF EQUILIN WITH ESTRONE

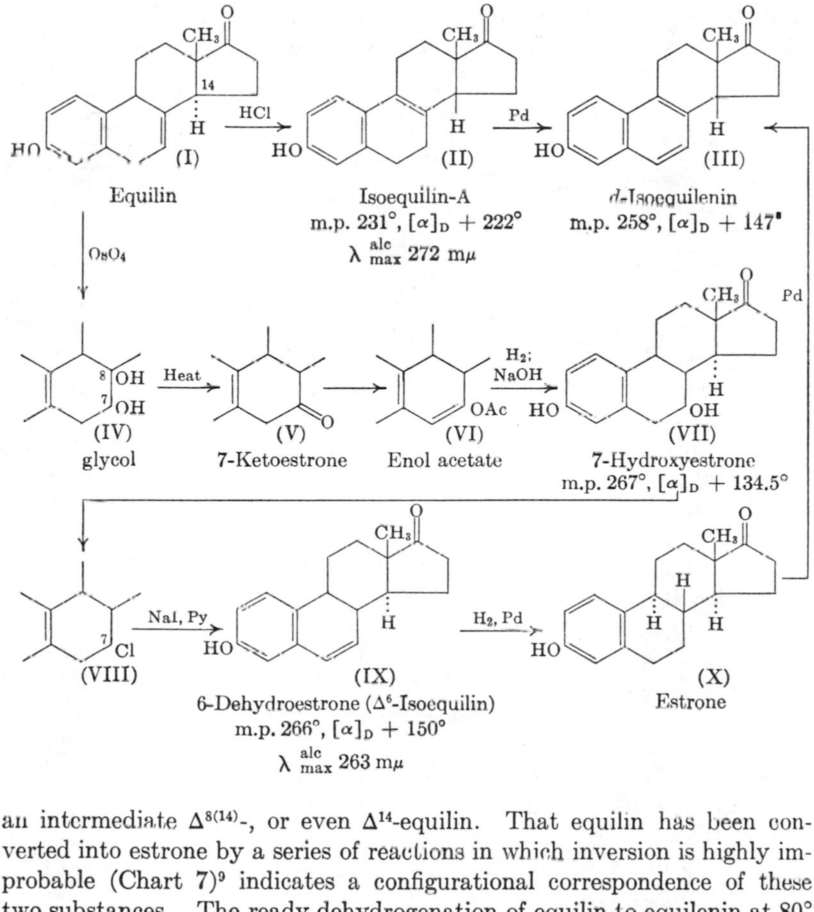

Equilin

Isoequilin-A
m.p. 231°, $[\alpha]_D$ + 222°
λ_{max}^{alc} 272 mμ

d-Isoequilenin
m.p. 258°, $[\alpha]_D$ + 147°

(IV)
glycol

(V)
7-Ketoestrone

(VI)
Enol acetate

(VII)
7-Hydroxyestrone
m.p. 267°, $[\alpha]_D$ + 134.5°

(VIII)

(IX)
6-Dehydroestrone (Δ^6-Isoequilin)
m.p. 266°, $[\alpha]_D$ + 150°
λ_{max}^{alc} 263 mμ

(X)
Estrone

an intermediate $\Delta^{8(14)}$-, or even Δ^{14}-equilin. That equilin has been converted into estrone by a series of reactions in which inversion is highly improbable (Chart 7)[9] indicates a configurational correspondence of these two substances. The ready dehydrogenation of equilin to equilenin at 80° noted above is also much less likely to involve an inversion than the acid isomerization of equilin, and hence, in all probability, estrone and equilenin have the same configurations at C_{13} and C_{14} and the dehydrogenation of estrone is attended with an inversion at C_{14}. Klyne[10] has presented further

[9] W. H. Pearlman and Wintersteiner, J. Biol. Chem., 130, 35 (1939); 132, 605 (1940).
[10] Klyne, Nature, 161, 434 (1948).

evidence from molecular rotation differences confirming the conclusion that estrone and equilenin have the same C/D-trans ring fusion.

Although attempts to saturate the nonconjugated double bond of equilin by palladium hydrogenation have been unsuccessful,[4] the hydrogenation of the double bond subsequent to reduction of the carbonyl group with sodium and alcohol, has been accomplished with the use of Raney nickel.[5] The product is not estradiol but an isomer, regarded as 8-isoestradiol be-

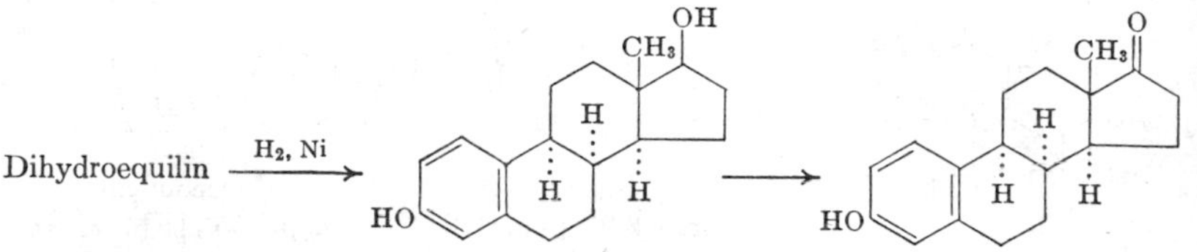

Dihydroequilin $\xrightarrow{H_2, Ni}$

8-Isoestradiol
m.p. 181°, $[\alpha]_D + 18°$

8-Isoestrone
m.p. 247°, $[\alpha]_D + 94°$

cause of the probability that the addition of hydrogen to the 7,8-double bond gives the unnatural configuration at C_8. Oxidation at C_{17} gives 8-isoestrone, which has about one-third the physiological activity of natural estrone (rats).

A further physiologically inactive isomer of estrone, lumiestrone, has been prepared by a process analogous to the isomerization of ergosterol to lumisterol: irradiation of estrone with ultraviolet light of wave length 313 $m\mu$.[8, 11] Absorption of light in this region is probably limited to the carbonyl group, since 17-desoxoestrone is stable to irradiation at the same wave length. Butenandt therefore postulated that the change occurring on irradiation is an epimerization at C_{13} adjacent to the carbonyl group. The dehydrogenation of lumiestrone affords an isomer of equilenin corresponding in all properties to Bachmann's synthetic l-isoequilenin. The substance indeed is the 13α,14α-antipode of d-isoequilenin (III, Chart 7), which was inferred to have the 13β,14β-configuration from independent evidence. The concordance in the conclusions from the two sets of observations greatly strengthens the interpretation as a whole.

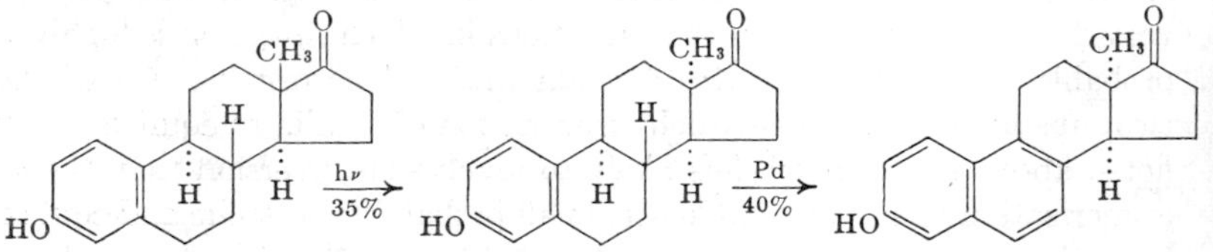

Estrone

Lumiestrone
m.p. 269°, $[\alpha]_D -43°$

l-Isoequilenin
m.p. 258°, $[\alpha]_D -147°$

[11] Butenandt and co-workers, *Ber.*, **75**, 1931 (1942); **77**, 392 (1944).

A structural isomer of estrone isolated from the nonphenolic fraction of equine pregnancy urine has been assigned the structure of $\Delta^{5,7,9}$-estratriene-3-ol-17-one on the following evidence.[12] The substance forms an

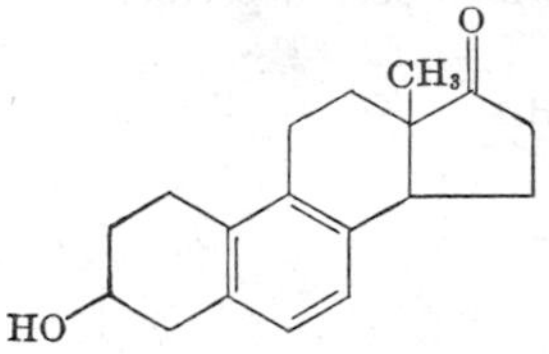

$\Delta^{5,7,9}$-Estratriene-3-ol-17-one
m.p. 139.5°, $[\alpha]_D + 59°$
λ_{max}^{alc} 269.5 mμ (logϵ 2.5)

acetate and an oxime; it take up one mole of hydrogen to yield a diol identical with a product of the reduction of equilenin with sodium and amyl alcohol;[13] the absorption spectrum is similar to that of neoergosterol; the color in the Zimmermann test is indicative of a 17- rather than a 3-keto group. This hydroxyketone probably arises from equilenin by reduction of ring A.

The same structure is claimed for folliculosterone (m.p. 248.5°, $[\alpha]_D +$ 162°, high intensity absorption, $\lambda_{max}^{CHCl_3}$ 280 mμ), a substance obtained by an incompletely described oxidation of neoergosterol.[14] Folliculosterone is said to be as active biologically as estrone. The absorption spectrum is not consistent with the proposed structure.

Estradiol. Of the estrogenic substances isolated from natural sources before 1935, estrone was found to be the most potent in the Allen-Doisy test. Estrone, however, was soon found to be surpassed in activity by products derivable from it by chemical transformation. The most potent and important is a dihydro derivative first prepared by Schwenk and Hildebrandt[1] in a somewhat impure condition due to contamination with a higher-melting C_{17}-epimer of less potency. The lower-melting isomer has been known by the arbitrary designation "α"-estradiol, but is here described as estradiol-17β. Later workers found that estradiol-17β is the exclusive product of hydrogenation in a neutral or alkaline medium[2] or of reduction with sodium and alcohol.[3] The higher-melting estradiol-17α is formed under other conditions, for example on reduction with Raney nickel alloy

---

[12] Heard and M. M. Hoffman, *J. Biol. Chem.*, **135**, 801 (1940); **138**, 651 (1941).

[13] Marker, Rohrmann, Wittle and Tendick, *J. Am. Chem. Soc.*, **60**, 2440 (1938).

[14] Remesow, *Rec. trav. chim.*, **55**, 797 (1936); **56**, 1093 (1937).

[1] Schwenk and F. Hildebrandt, *Naturwissenschaften*, **21**, 177 (1933).

[2] Dirscherl, *Z. physiol. Chem.*, **239**, 53 (1936).

[3] Girard, Sandulesco and Fridenson, *Compt. rend. soc. biol.*, **112**, 964 (1933).

in aqueous potassium hydroxide,[4] but it never constitutes more than 10–20 percent of the reaction mixture. A separation is facilitated by the use of digitonin, for only the 17β-epimer forms a sparingly soluble digitonide (m.p. 265°).[5] A urea complex has also been described for this purpose.[6] Hydro-

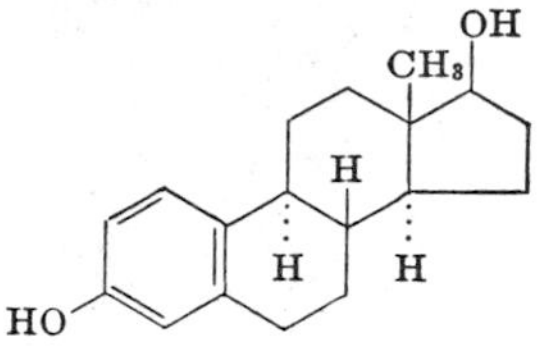

Estradiol-17β
m.p. 178°, $[\alpha]_D$ +81°
λ_{max}^{alc} 280 mμ

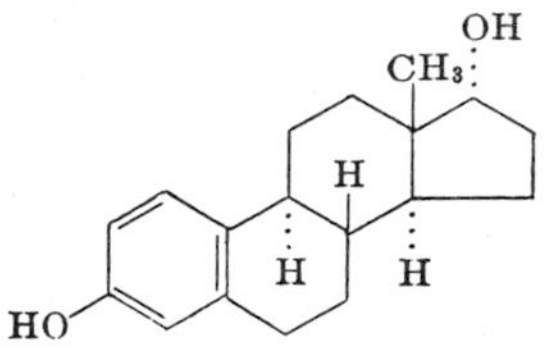

Estradiol-17α
m.p. 223°, $[\alpha]_D$ +54°
λ_{max}^{alc} 280 mμ

genation of estrone in acetic acid solution or in alcohol containing hydrochloric acid leads to attack of the aromatic nucleus, usually even before reduction of the carbonyl group.[2] Estrone is converted into estradiol-17β in the presence of fermenting yeasts.[7]

The highly potent estradiol-17β was introduced as a therapeutic agent in the form of the 3-monobenzoate (Progynon B; rat unit 0.16 γ). Ester derivatives of the estrogens are characterized by a protracted, persistent action. One large dose of an ester has an effect equivalent to several injections of smaller doses of free hormone.

The early realization that estradiol-17β is more active than estrone led workers in the field to suspect that even the most potent of the substances excreted in the urine may not be a primary hormone responsible for normal physiological changes in the body. The investigation of the constituents of ovarian tissue presented many difficulties, but in 1935 Doisy[8] reported the isolation of a crystallizate of high potency identical with estradiol-17β. The substance was best isolated as the sparingly soluble di-α-naphthoate; preparation of the derivative was carried out in pyridine solution and the excess α-naphthoyl chloride was removed by adding excess glycine and subsequently extracting the resulting α-naphthoylglycine from ether with sodium bicarbonate solution. The processing of four tons of sow ovaries afforded about half of a total of 25 mg. of estrogen present, as estimated from bioassays. The structure of the ovarian hormone had been estab-

[4] Whitman, Wintersteiner and Schwenk, *J. Biol. Chem.*, **118**, 789 (1937); Butenandt and Goergens, *Z. physiol. Chem.*, **248**, 129 (1937).

[5] Wintersteiner, *J. Am. Chem. Soc.*, **59**, 765 (1937).

[6] Priewe, U. S. Patent 2,300,134 (1942).

[7] Wettstein, *Helv. Chim. Acta*, **22**, 250 (1939).

[8] MacCorquodale, Thayer and Doisy, *Proc. Soc. Exp. Biol. Med.*, **32**, 1182 (1935); *J. Biol. Chem.*, **115**, 435 (1936).

lished and the substance had been introduced to use in therapy before the isolation had been accomplished.

Estradiol-17β has since been isolated from mare pregnancy urine,[9] from late human pregnancy urine[10] (the amount increases with duration of pregnancy), from human placenta,[11] and from horse testes.[12] The investigation of the last source was prompted by an early observation of Zondek[13] that extracts obtained from horse testes had higher estrogenic activity than extracts from the same weight of mare's ovaries. The actual amounts isolated from 28 kg. of horse testes were 0.21 mg./kg. of estradiol-17β and 0.36 mg./kg. of estrone. Stallion urine is probably the richest known source of estradiol; the estrogen has been isolated as the di-α-naphthoate in an amount equivalent to 5 mg. of free hormone per liter of urine.[14] Estradiol-17α has been isolated from mare pregnancy urine[15] and from the urine of rabbits fed estradiol-17β or estrone.[16]

The results of comparative assays vary somewhat with details of the test methods. In general, estradiol-17β appears to be 8–10 times as active as estrone and about 40 times as potent as estradiol-17α (see Properties).

	NATURAL		17-EPIMER	
	M.p.	$[\alpha]_D$	M.p.	$[\alpha]_D$
Testosterones	154.5°	+109°	221°	+71.5°
Estradiols	178°	+81°	223°	+54°

The evidence for the configurations at C_{17} indicated above is based partly on analogy with testosterone and 17-epitestosterone.[17] With the C_{17}-epimeric estradiols, as with the testosterones, the natural (or more abundant) steroid has the lower melting point, the higher dextrorotatory power, and the higher physiological potency; in both series, moreover, reduction of a C_{17}-keto group affords chiefly the epimer of natural configuration. From this analogy it is safe to infer that natural estradiol has the same configuration at C_{17} as testosterone. An initial deduction regarding the orientation

[9] Wintersteiner, Schwenk and Whitman, *Proc. Soc. Exp. Biol. Med.*, **32**, 1087 (1935).
[10] Huffman, MacCorquodale, Thayer, Doisy, G. Van S. Smith and O. W. Smith, *J. Biol. Chem.*, **134**, 591 (1940).
[11] Huffman, Thayer and Doisy, *J. Biol. Chem.*, **133**, 567 (1940).
[12] Beall, *Biochem. J.*, **34**, 1293 (1940).
[13] Zondek, *Nature*, **133**, 209 (1934).
[14] Levin, *J. Biol. Chem.*, **158**, 725 (1945).
[15] Hirschmann and Wintersteiner, *J. Biol. Chem.*, **122**, 303 (1938).
[16] Fish and Dorfman, *J. Biol. Chem.*, **140**, XL (1941); Heard, Bauld and M. M. Hoffman, *ibid.*, **141**, 709 (1941).
[17] Ruzicka and Kägi, *Helv. Chim. Acta*, **19**, 842 (1936).

of the hydroxyl group of testosterone was made by Ruzicka on the basis
of the observation that esters of testosterone are hydrolyzed somewhat
more readily than corresponding esters of epitestosterone;[18] Ruzicka
assumed that the evidently less hindered 17-hydroxyl group of testosterone
must be trans to the C_{13}-methyl group and therefore in the α-orientation.
This assumption has been invalidated by studies of the relative ease of
hydrolysis of epimeric etiocarboxylic esters of C_{17}-configurations that are
known unambiguously from correlations with sterols. Ruzicka[19] found
that on treatment with 0.1 N potassium hydroxide for one hour under
reflux, 44–48 percent of etioallocholanic acid methyl ester (I) was hydro-

		M.p.	$[\alpha]_D$			M.p.	$[\alpha]_D$
A = H	(I)	140°	+48°	A = H	(Ia)	135°	−41°
A = AcO	(II)	149°	+36°	A = AcO	(IIa)	114°	−37°

lyzed, but only 18 percent of the $C_{17}\alpha$-epimer, 17-isoetioallocholanic acid
methyl ester (Ia), was hydrolyzed. Reichstein[20] observed a comparable relationship between the 17β- and 17α- epimeric 3β-acetoxy esters II and IIa.
In each case the less hindered epimer is that in which the carboxylate group
is cis to the angular methyl at C_{17}. Reichstein observed that according to
molecular models the methylene group at C_{12} should exert hindrance on an
ester group of C_{17} comparable to that of the angular methyl group. On the
basis of this evidence the less hindered, natural testosterone has a 17β-
hydroxyl group, and the estradiol found in the ovaries is estradiol-17β.[21]
The 17-hydroxy compounds then follow the pattern of the 17-esters with
respect to optical rotation but not melting point: the alcohols and esters of
17β-orientation are both more dextrorotatory than the 17α-epimers; the
higher-melting epimers in the two series are the 17α-alcohols and the 17β-
esters.

The conclusion that the 17-hydroxyl group is β-oriented is strengthened
by further analogies cited in Chapter V and is strongly supported by the
following independent evidence. In numerous examples of the reactions
of 17-ketosteroids with Grignard reagents and with potassium acetylide

[18] Ruzicka, Furter and M. W. Goldberg, *Helv. Chim. Acta*, **21**, 498 (1938).
[19] Heusser, Meier and Ruzicka, *Helv. Chim. Acta*, **29**, 1250 (1946).
[20] von Euw and Reichstein, *Helv. Chim. Acta*, **30**, 205 (1947).
[21] M. W. Goldberg, Sicé, Robert and Plattner, *Helv. Chim. Acta*, **30**, 1441 (1947).

that have been studied the reaction proceeds almost exclusively by opening
of the rear member of the double bond and formation of a product with an
α-side chain and a 17β-hydroxyl group. The addition of lithium aluminum
hydride to carbonyl compounds is strictly analogous to that of these
organometallic compounds, and the observation that reduction of estrone
with lithium aluminum hydride affords natural estradiol in excellent yield[22]
is sure evidence of the 17β-configuration of this hormone.

The 17-epimeric alcohols exhibit differences in color tests with mineral
acids.[23] The β-compounds show no color under mild conditions to which
the α-epimers respond. Since the reaction presumably involves dehydration, the less hindered β-compounds apparently undergo dehydration less
readily than the epimers. Unfortunately the digitonin precipitation reaction, which has been of great diagnostic value for C_3-hydroxy compounds,
is of no use in the investigation of C_{17}-hydroxy epimers because the formation of a sparingly soluble digitonide in the case of estradiol-17β is apparently an isolated instance. Neither one of the testosterones nor of the
17-dihydroequilenins forms an insoluble digitonide.

One of the 17-dihydroequilenins[24] (m.p. 217°, $[\alpha]_D$ − 5°, 1/200 as active
as estradiol-17β[25]) was isolated from the urine of pregnant mares. At about
the same time Marker[26] prepared both this substance and its 17-epimer
(m.p. 248°, 1/120 as active as estradiol-17β[25]) by Meerwein-Ponndorf reduction of equilenin. Both epimers are less active than equilenin. The one
isolated from urine is the less active of the two by a slight margin and has
the lower melting point; the α-configuration is suggested by these relationships, but unfortunately the optical rotation of the epimer is not recorded.

Prelog and Führer[27] have reported the isolation from pregnant mare's
urine of 3-desoxyequilenin, m.p. 157°, $[\alpha]_D$ + 117°, rat unit 100–150 γ.
Hydrogenation of the ketone in acetic-hydrochloric acid (Pt) gave 3-desoxy-
hexahydroequilenin, also obtained by the hydrogenation of equilenin.

---

[22] A. C. Ott and M. F. Murray, *Abst. A. C. S. 138th Meeting*, Chicago (1948): The
reduction is conducted in ether solution, and because of the slight solubility of estrone the material is leached from a Soxhlet extractor. The observation has been
confirmed by Dr. E. B. Hershberg, who estimates the percentage of estradiol-17β as
90–95 percent.

[23] Miescher and Kägi, *Chemistry and Industry*, **16**, 276 (1938); *Helv. Chim. Acta*, **22**,
683 (1939); Woker and Antener *ibid.*, **22**, 1309 (1939).

[24] Wintersteiner, Schwenk, H. Hirschmann and Whitman, *J. Am. Chem. Soc.*, **58**,
2652 (1936); H. Hirschmann and Wintersteiner, *J. Biol. Chem.*, **122**, 303 (1938). This
substance is one component of an estrogenic crystallizate (δ-follicular hormone)
isolated by Schwenk and F. Hildebrandt, *Naturwissenschaften*, **20**, 658 (1932).

[25] Selye, *Encyclopedia of Endocrinology* (1943).

[26] Marker and co-workers, *J. Am. Chem. Soc.*, **59**, 768 (1937); **61**, 3314 (1939); Ruzicka and co-workers, *Helv. Chim. Acta*, **21**, 1394 (1938).

[27] Prelog and Führer, *Helv. Chim. Acta*, **28**, 583 (1945).

17α-Ethinylestradiol. Treatment of estrone with potassium acetylide in liquid ammonia leads almost exclusively to one epimeric 17-ethinyl-estradiol.[1] The 17-hydroxyl group has the same β-orientation as that of estradiol-17β and the derivative is as active as the ovarian hormone on subcutaneous injection (rat). It is distinctly more active than the hormone

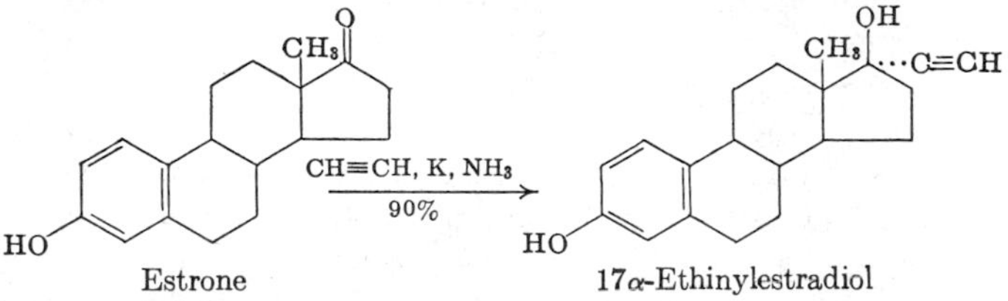

Estrone   17α-Ethinylestradiol

when administered orally to rats, and in humans the substance is also extraordinarily active by mouth.[2] The corresponding ethinyl derivatives prepared from equilenin and equilin also show enhanced estrogenic activity.[1] Reduction of the ethinyl to a vinyl group decreases the activity to about one-half that of the parent ketone.[1]

A great many other derivatives and transformation products of the natural hormones have been prepared and assayed, but no highly potent compound other than 17α-ethinylestradiol has been encountered. Modifications of the molecule other than esterification usually result in marked

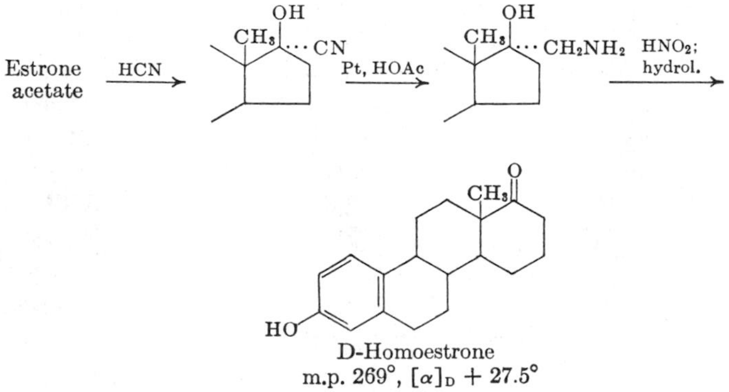

D-Homoestrone
m.p. 269°, [α]ᴅ + 27.5°

loss in activity. D-Homoestrone and D-homoestradiol[3] (m.p. 233°, [α]ᴅ + 88°), for example, are both only about 1/30 as active in rats as estrone.

[1] Inhoffen, Logemann, Hohlweg and Serini, *Ber.*, **71**, 1024 (1938).

[2] W. M. Allen, *J. Am. Med. Assoc.*, **39**, 1 (1942); E. V. Clarke and Selye, *J. Pharmacol.*, **78**, 187 (1943).

[3] M. W. Goldberg and Studer, *Helv. Chim. Acta*, **24**, 478, 295 E (1941).

Properties of the Estrogens; Occurrence as Conjugates. The accompanying table lists the physical properties of five natural hormonal substances and of 17α-ethinylestradiol. The relative physiological potencies are indicated in the last two columns by closely agreeing assay data reported by Inhoffen[1] and by Schwenk.[2]

Properties of Estrogens

COMPOUND	M.p. (corr.)	$[\alpha]_D$	λ^{alc}_{max}	pK_a	SOLUBILITY, mg./ 100 g.			ESTROGENIC ACTIVITY IN RATS, ED_{50} IN γ	
					Water $^{18°}$	Methanol $^{20°}$	Toluene $^{20°}$	Subcut.	Oral
			$m\mu$						
Estradiol-17β	178°	+81°	280			411	4.6	0.1[a], 0.07[b]	50[a]
Estrone	260°	+165°	280	9.36	0.21	63	9.9	0.8[a], 0.7[b]	60[a], 50[b]
Estriol	280°	+61°	280	9.11		202	0.3	10[a]	10[a]
Equilin	240°	+308°	280					1–1.5[a]	40[a]
Equilenin	259°	+87°	280,342					15–20[a]	
17α-Ethinylestradiol	146°	+1°						0.1[a], 0.08[b]	3[a], 7[b], 3[c]

[a] Inhoffen;[1] in aqueous solution.
[b] Schwenk;[2] in oil.
[c] Schwenk;[2] in alcohol.

Bioassays of ether extracts of urines before and after ether extraction established the fact that estrogens are present in part in a free condition and in part as nonextractable conjugates. At least some of the conjugated estrogen of pregnant mare's urine is estrone sulfate.[3] Isolation proved difficult and only a small amount of material was obtained; hence the possible presence of other conjugates is not excluded. Estrone is also present in stallion urine as the sulfate.[4] Estrone sulfate has been prepared by the esterification of estrone with chlorosulfonic acid in pyridine;[5] it is hydrolyzed readily in hot aqueous mineral acid solution and also by the enzyme phenolsulfatase. The sulfate ester is only about one-seventh as active as estrone when given by subcutaneous injection but is about twice as active by mouth.

[1] Inhoffen, Logemann, Hohlweg and Serini, *Ber.*, **71**, 1024 (1938).
[2] Results of assays in the Biological Laboratories of Schering Corporation kindly supplied by Dr. E. Schwenk.
[3] Schachter and Marrian, *J. Biol. Chem.*, **126**, 663 (1938).
[4] H. Jensen, Larivière and Elie, *Rev. can. biol.*, **4**, 535 (1945) [*C. A.*, **40**, 2184 (1946)].
[5] Butenandt and Hofstetter, *Z. physiol. Chem.*, **259**, 222 (1939).

The conjugated form of estriol in human pregnancy urine is a glucuronide ($C_{24}H_{32}O_9$) in which the glucuronic acid is linked through the terminal glycosidic group to the 16- or 17-alcoholic hydroxyl group of estriol.[6] The glucuronide is extracted from a urine concentrate with butanol at pH 3 and then extracted into aqueous alkali as the sodium glucuronidate: $ROC_5H_8O_4COONa$. The presence of a free phenolic group was inferred from an observed shift in absorption maximum from 280 to 295 mμ in the presence of alkali, indicative of salt formation; confirmation was found by methylation and hydrolysis, which afforded estriol 3-methyl ether. The glucuronide is hydrolyzed less readily than the sulfate ester of estrone; this difference accounts for the fact that hydrolysis of equine urine proceeds more readily than that of human urine. Administered by subcutaneous injection, the glucuronide is much less active than estriol; but given orally it is about ten times more effective.[7]

Influence of Estrogens on Carcinogenesis. That female sex hormones may be connected with the initiation of certain forms of malignant growth was suggested by the results of investigations of the incidence of cancer in mice in relationship to estrogenic substances. Notable contributions to the problem were made by Leo Loeb long before the development of the chemistry of the hormones.[1] In breeding experiments (1907–19) Loeb found that different strains of mice can be developed in each of which the incidence of spontaneous mammary cancer is approximately constant, whereas from strain to strain it varies from nearly 0 to almost 100 percent. In some strains practically none of the mice develop tumors; in others nearly all the females are subject to cancer of the breast, the prevalent tumor in this species. Males, even of high cancer rate strains, usually do not develop mammary tumors. The cancer rate remains approximately constant in successive generations, and both the incidence of cancer and the age at which tumors appear are characteristic of each strain.

Loeb found that, with female mice of known high-incidence strains, removal of the ovaries at the age of 3–4 months led to a marked decrease in the incidence of cancer. Castration at a sufficiently early period reduced the cancer rate to zero. Extirpation of the ovaries at later periods was less effective, and when the operation was performed at the age of 8–10 months, the cancer rate was practically the same as that of the noncastrated mice, although tumors appeared at a later age. The results suggested that ovarian hormones, acting in cooperation with hereditary factors, influence

---

[6] S. L. Cohen and Marrian, *Biochem. J.*, **30**, 57 (1936); S. L. Cohen, Marrian and Odell, *ibid.*, **30**, 2250 (1936); Marrian, *ibid.*, **40**, XIX (1946).

[7] Odell, Skill and Marrian, *J. Pharmacol.*, **60**, 420 (1937).

[1] See review by Loeb, "Estrogenic Hormones and Carcinogenesis," *J. Am. Med. Assoc.*, **104**, 1597 (1935).

the transformation of normal tissue of the mammery gland into cancerous tissue.

Loeb then attempted to induce tumor formation by transplanting ovaries of female mice into castrated males of high cancer rate strains, but with negative results. Successful experiments in this direction have been carried out with the use of pure hormone preparations. Lacassagne[2] and others,[3, 4, 5] using pure hormone preparations, have induced mammary tumors in male mice in which they normally would not have appeared. The estrogens are most effective when applied to mice of strains in which the females show a high incidence of spontaneous mammary tumors. Breeding is about as effective as estrogen administration for the induction of mammary tumors in female mice.[3, 6] Large doses of estrogens can inhibit the incidence of mammary tumors.[7]

Marked species specificity has been noted in the effectiveness of estrogens in promoting carcinogenesis. Rats are much more resistant than mice,[8] and monkeys, rabbits, and dogs are apparently entirely resistant.[9]

Estrogens also have been observed to promote induction of uterine tumors and lymphosarcomas in mice.[2] Benign fibroid uterine growths in female guinea pigs and tumorous growths in the prostatic region of castrated male guinea pigs have been induced by continued estrogen administration.[10] A low incidence of lesions of the uterine cervix has been noted in mice after prolonged administration of estrogens;[11] mice ordinarily do not develop spontaneous carcinoma of the cervix. Nonsex tissues also appear to be subject to influence; thus estrogens have been observed to induce leukemia, or lymphoid tumors, in mice.[12]

[2] Lacassagne, *Compt. rend.*, **195**, 630 (1932); Lacassagne and Nyka, *Compt. rend. soc. biol.*, **116**, 844 (1934); Lacassagne, *Am. J. Cancer*, **37**, 414 (1939).

[3] Shimkin and Andervont, *J. Natl. Cancer Inst.*, **2**, 611 (1912).

[4] Cramer, *Am. J. Cancer*, **38**, 463 (1940).

[5] E. Allen, *Endocrinology*, **30**, 942 (1942).

[6] Shimkin, "Hormones and Mammary Tumors in Mice," Publications of Am. Assoc. Advancement Sci. (1945); Gardner, "Studies on Steroid Hormones in Experimental Carcinogenesis," *Recent Progress in Hormone Research*, I, 217 (1947).

[7] Gardner, *Endocrinology*, **28**, 53 (1941).

[8] Eisen, *Cancer Research*, **2**, 632 (1942); W. O. Nelson, *Yale J. Biol. Med.*, **17**, 217 (1944).

[9] Gardner, *Surgery*, **16**, 8 (1944).

[10] Lipschütz and co-workers, *Cancer Research*, **2**, 45, 200, 204 (1942); **4**, 18, 24, 179 (1944); **5**, 515 (1945).

[11] Gardner, *Arch. Path.*, **27**, 138 (1939); E. Allen and Gardner, *Cancer Research*, **1**, 359 (1941).

[12] Lacassagne, *Compt. rend. soc. biol.*, **126**, 193 (1937); Gardner, Kirschbaum and Strong, *Arch. Path.*, **29**, 1 (1940); Gardner, Dougherty and W. L. Williams, *Cancer Research*, **4**, 73 (1944).

Colorimetric Determination.   A number of color reactions have been investigated with the view to the development of rapid and accurate methods for the colorimetric assay of estrogenic hormones.   The total estrogen fraction of an extract from hydrolyzed urine, or from plasma, or other tissue, can be separated from androgens, cholesterol, and other neutral products by extraction of the phenolic material with alkali.   Since the three principal estrogens differ greatly in biological potency but are all phenols of comparable structure, the nature and proportion of the components cannot be inferred from bioassays, from determination of the intensity of the absorption band at 280 mμ characteristic of all three hormones,[1] or by application of color reactions dependent merely upon the common phenolic structure in ring A.   Color reactions still more specific and sensitive than those listed below would be welcomed for application in clinical medicine.

Kober test.[2]   A pink color develops when estradiol, estrone, or estriol is heated with phenolsulfonic acid and sulfuric acid, followed by the addition of water.   The reaction has been applied to the colorimetric determination of hormones in urinary extracts;[3] a simplified procedure has been described,[4] but this is regarded by some as unreliable for use with impure extracts.[5] Factors promoting maximum stabilization and intensification of the color have been reported.[6]   One difficulty is that nonestrogenic substances produce a brown color that interferes in analysis of urinary extracts of low estrogen content; a simple method of correction is based upon the observation that when the solution is heated at 100° for one and one-half hours the pink color due to the estrogens fades completely but the brown color is unaltered.[7]   The color test is more sensitive when guiacolsulfonic acid is used in place of phenolsulfonic acid;[8] in this modification estrone and estradiol are positive whereas estriol is essentially negative.

Diazo coupling test.[9]   Orange or red colors develop on coupling of an estrogen with diazotized p-nitroaniline or sulfanilic acid.

---

[1] Chevallier, Cornil and Verdollin, *Bull. acad. méd.*, **114**, 171 (1935).

[2] Kober, *Biochem. Z.*, **239**, 209 (1931); *Acta Brevia Neerland., Physiol. Pharmacol. Microbiol.*, **5**, 34 (1935); *Biochem. J.*, **32**, 357 (1938).

[3] S. L. Cohen and Marrian, *Biochem. J.*, **28**, 1603 (1934).

[4] Cartland, R. K. Meyer, L. C. Miller and Rutz, *J. Biol. Chem.*, **109**, 213 (1935).

[5] Pincus, Wheeler, G. Young and Zahl, *J. Biol. Chem.*, **116**, 253 (1936).

[6] Venning, Evelyn, Harkness and Browne, *J. Biol. Chem.*, **120**, 225 (1937).

[7] M. F. Stevenson and Marrian, *Biochem. J.*, **41**, 507 (1947).

[8] Szego and Samuels, *Proc. Soc. Exp. Biol. Med.*, **43**, 263 (1940); *J. Biol. Chem.*, **151**, 587 (1943).

[9] Schmulovitz and Wylie, *J. Lab. Clin. Med.*, **21**, 210 (1935).   Modified and improved procedure: Talbot, Wolfe, MacLachlan, Karush and A. M. Butler, *J. Biol. Chem.*, **134**, 319 (1940).

David test.[10] A typical blue color is produced on reaction of estriol with sulfuric acid and arsenic acid. The test is specific to estriol.

Bachman test.[11] In this test, also specific to estriol, a stable violet-pink color is produced on reaction with sodium *p*-toluenesulfonate in phosphoric acid.

Benzoyl chloride test.[5] The extract is evaporated to dryness and the residue treated in chloroform with benzoyl chloride and a solution of zinc chloride in acetic acid. Estrone gives rise to an intense absorption band at 502 mμ; estradiol gives a less intense band of the same wave length; with estriol the test is essentially negative.

Zimmermann test (see Sterols). Since this test is specific for ketones, it can afford the basis for the specific determination of estrone in estrogen mixtures.

Girard test.[12] In this test, also specific to the ketonic estrone, the aqueous solution of the Girard derivative is treated with mercuric and potassium iodide, whereupon a colored complex precipitates. Gravimetric determination can be made of the precipitate.[13]

Fractionation of Urinary Estrogens. Since all three natural estrogens occur in the urine of pregnant and nonpregnant females and probably also in the urine of normal males,[1] the problem of separation and determination of the individual active components has attracted considerable attention. A serious difficulty is encountered at the outset in effecting complete hydrolysis of the ether-insoluble conjugates with minimum destruction of the freed estrogens. Sodium hydroxide (2 N) effects only partial hydrolysis at 120° in 6–8 hours, and under these conditions both estrone and estradiol are partially destroyed.[2] Thus all the various procedures employ acid hydrolysis. In that of Marrian[2] the urine is adjusted to pH 1 and further acidified with 33 cc. of 12 N hydrochloric acid per liter, and then autoclaved at 120° for two hours. In the procedure of Smith and Smith[3] 150 cc. of 12 N hydrochloric acid is added per liter of urine and the mixture is boiled for ten minutes and then cooled rapidly. The addition of powdered zinc during hydrolysis was found to increase the yield of estrogen as determined by bioassay;[4] the effect could be due either to the prevention

[10] David, *Acta Brevia Neerland.*, **4**, 64 (1934).

[11] C. Bachman, *J. Biol. Chem.*, **131**, 463 (1939).

[12] Girard and Sandulesco, *Helv. Chim. Acta*, **19**, 1095 (1936).

[13] Hughes, *J. Biol. Chem.*, **140**, 21 (1941).

[1] Only estrone has been isolated, but the presence of estradiol and estriol is indicated.

[2] S. L. Cohen and Marrian, *Biochem. J.*, **29**, 1577 (1935).

[3] O. W. Smith and G. Van S. Smith, *Am. J. Physiol.*, **112**, 340 (1935); Smith, Smith and Schiller, *Endocrinology*, **25**, 509 (1939).

[4] G. Van S. and O. W. Smith, *Endocrinology*, **28**, 740 (1941).

of air oxidation or to some reduction of the carbonyl group of the estrone present. Koch[5] recommends acidification of urine to pH 1–1.2 with hydrochloric acid followed by boiling for fifteen minutes. In another procedure the urine is acidified to pH 0.4–0.6 and allowed to stand at room temperature for at least four weeks.[6]

In a procedure of fractionation described by Pincus,[7] the urine sample is hydrolyzed according to Smith and Smith except that the boiling time is reduced to seven minutes. The hydrolyzate is extracted with ether and the total estrogen fraction removed by extraction with 2 N sodium hydroxide; the extract is adjusted to pH 2–3 and again the estrogenic material is extracted with ether. The material is transferred to benzene and the solution extracted three times with 0.3 M sodium carbonate to remove the estriol, which is recovered by ether extraction of the acidified aqueous extract. The benzene solution is evaporated and treated with Girard's reagent for the separation of the ketonic estrone from the nonketonic estradiol. The estrogen content of each of the three fractions is then determined by bioassay.

A procedure for chromatographic fractionation is reported by Stimmel.[8] The total estrogen fraction from a 24-hour urine, dissolved in methanol-benzene, is adsorbed on activated alumina and developed with pure benzene. Estrone, estradiol, and estriol are then eluted by 2, 5, and 30 percent methanol-benzene mixtures, respectively. Thus estrone and estradiol are adsorbed much less strongly than estriol and are fairly similar in adsorbability. Stimmel assayed each fraction colorimetrically as follows: estrone by the Zimmermann test, estradiol by the Kober test, and estriol by the Bachman test.

Estradiol from Cholesterol. The investigation of the conversion of steroids into aromatized derivatives was undertaken by Inhoffen in Windaus' laboratory with the original objective of clarifying the aromatization that occurs in the pyrolysis of the so-called ergopinacol, but the elucidation of the structures of the estrogenic hormones introduced the new objective of converting an abundant steroid into a hormone. An initial trial in the cholesterol series led to a disappointing result. Inhoffen and Huang-Minlon[1] sought to aromatize ring A by elimination of methane from $\Delta^{1,4}$-cholestadienone-3 by pyrolysis but found that the methyl group has a strong tendency to migrate to position 1 to give the abnormal product

[5] F. C. Koch, *Ann. Rev. Biochem.*, **9**, 327 (1940).

[6] Edson and Heard, *J. Biol. Chem.*, **130**, 579 (1939).

[7] Pincus, *J. Clin. Endocrinology*, **5**, 291 (1945); see also Friedgood, Garst and Haagen-Smit, *J. Biol. Chem.*, **174**, 523 (1948).

[8] Stimmel, *J. Biol. Chem.*, **153**, 327 (1944); **162**, 99 (1946); **165**, 73 (1946).

[1] Inhoffen and Huang-Minlon, *Naturwissenschaften*, **26**, 756 (1938).

sterophenol.[1,2,3] On treatment with acetic anhydride and a trace of sulfuric acid,[1] the dienone is isomerized to sterophenol in almost quantitative yield.[1,2,4] The reaction is analogous to the isomerization of santonin to desmotroposantonin.[5]

H₃C.

CH₃

CH₃

CH₃

CH₃

O

$\Delta^{1,4}$-Cholestadienone-3

Ac₂O, H₂SO₄
93%

H₃C.

CH₃

CH₃

CH₃

CH₃

HO

Sterophenol
m.p. 140°, [α]_D + 161°

In spite of this adverse result, Inhoffen pursued parallel work in the androstane series and in 1940 announced the preparation of estradiol from cholesterol through a long series of steps culminating in an aromatization in the desired direction but in very low yield.[6] The starting material was derived from androstenediol (I, p. 336), an intermediate in the commercial preparation of testosterone from cholesterol. The conversion of androstenediol into androstanolone (II, as acetate) had been worked out by Butenandt and by Ruzicka: formation of the diacetate or dibenzoate, hydrogenation, partial hydrolysis (at C₃), and oxidation (see Testosterone). In a confirmation of Inhoffen's work, Wilds and Djerassi[7] obtained II (as the hexahydrobenzoate) in yields of 72–75 percent from the 3-acetate-17-benzoate of I. By reactions analogous to those known in the cholestanone series, two double bonds were introduced by bromination and dehydrohalogenation;[8, 9] in the last reaction the desired product VI is formed in satisfactory yield but is accompanied by the isomeric $\Delta^{4,6}$-androstadiene-17β-ol-3-one (V).[9,7]

Inhoffen and Zühlsdorff[6] conducted the final step of aromatization by heating the dienone VI in an evacuated sealed tube at 325° for twelve minutes; the product was purified through the digitonide and identified

[2] Inhoffen and Zühlsdorff, Ber., 74, 604 (1941).

[3] Confirmed by Wilds and Djerassi, J. Am. Chem. Soc., 68, 1712 (1946).

[4] The yield shown in the chart (material of m.p. 144–145°) was obtained by Dr. Huang-Minlon in a reinvestigation at the Harvard Laboratory.

[5] Clemo, R. D. Haworth and Walton, J. Chem. Soc., 1110 (1930); Huang-Minlon, Lo and Chu, J. Am. Chem. Soc., 65, 1780 (1943); 66, 1954 (1944).

[6] Inhoffen, Angew. Chem., 53, 471 (1940); Inhoffen and Zühlsdorff, Ber., 74, 1911 (1941).

[7] Wilds and Djerassi, J. Am. Chem. Soc., 68, 2125 (1946).

[8] Inhoffen, Zühlsdorff and Huang-Minlon, Ber., 73, 451 (1940).

[9] Inhoffen and Zühlsdorff, Ber., 76, 233 (1943).

as estradiol (VII). The yield reported was 5 percent. The product of rearrangement, 1-methylestradiol (VIII) was also isolated.[6,7] Inhoffen[10] has reported yields of 20–60 percent by the use of a high-boiling hydro-

Chart 8. Estradiol from Androstenediol

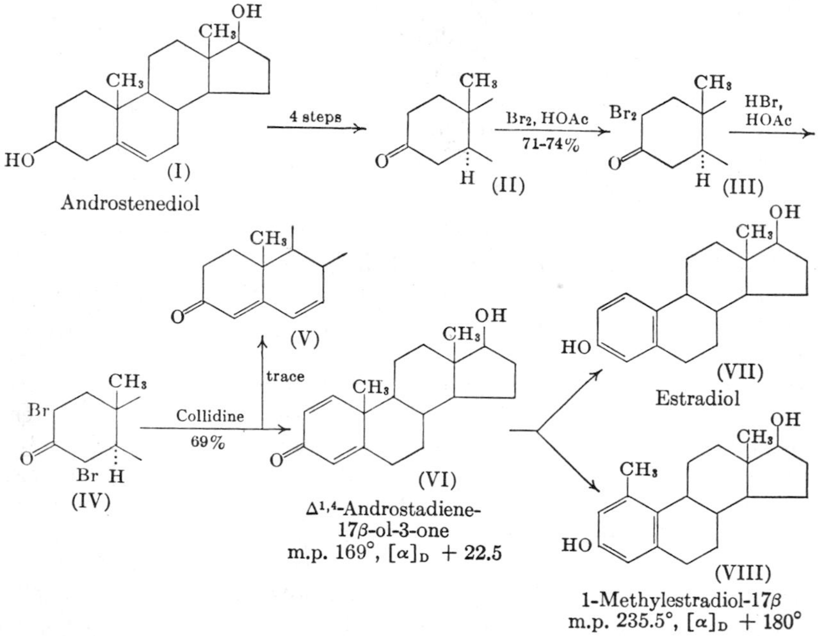

gen-donating solvent such as tetralin.[11] Wilds and Djerassi[7] investigated various conditions and hydrogen donors and their highest yield (in 9,10-dihydrophenanthrene) was 10 percent. The rearrangement product 1-methylestradiol-17β can be prepared in 62 percent yield with the use of acetic anhydride-sulfuric acid; it has no estrogenic activity.

Total Synthesis. The total synthesis of estrone, and hence of the more useful estradiol and estriol, has been the goal of many investigators since the elucidation of the structure of the hormone. The problem is rendered particularly difficult by the fact that estrone is one of sixteen possible stereoisomers. The synthesis of a natural product of such complexity has been a prominent target of synthetic chemistry, particularly

[10] Inhoffen, U. S. Patent 2,361,847 (1944); *Angew. Chem.*, **59**, 207 (1947).

[11] Addinall, Field Information Agency Technical Report No. 996, states that in 1942 Schering A. G. manufactured 29 kg. of estradiol, presumably by the Inhoffen process.

in view of the prospect of useful application to the pharmaceutical industry. Estrone from urine is very costly. Inhoffen's process starting with cholesterol, which is neither cheap nor abundantly available, involves a large number of steps, one of which (removal of the side chain) proceeds in a yield of a few percent at best and another (aromatization) is also limited. Even an elaborate synthesis might well replace present methods of production. Nonsteroid synthetic estrogens find current use in therapy largely because the natural hormones are extremely expensive, but the latter, if available at a more nearly comparable price, might eventually find wider use than the synthetic substitutes.

Equilenin, which contains only two asymmetric carbon atoms and is therefore one of only four stereoisomers, presented the obvious target for initial synthetic attack. The problem was brilliantly solved by the synthesis of equilenin by Bachmann, Cole and Wilds[1] in 1939 by one method and by W. S. Johnson, Petersen and Gutsche[2] in 1945 by another. Equilenin does not possess sufficient estrogenic potency to be of any value in therapy. It is possible that an efficient method can be found for the reduction of the naphthalenoid equilenin to the benzenoid estrone or estradiol, although reduction with sodium and alcohol or by hydrogenation with platinum in the presence of hydrochloric acid results almost exclusively in the reduction of ring A.[3]

The syntheses of Bachmann and of Johnson both employ the same intermediate: 7-methoxy-1-keto-1,2,3,4-tetrahydrophenanthrene. This substance (VIII, Chart 9) was first prepared by Butenandt and Schramm[4] by the process A. The azo dye intermediate Cleve's acid (I) was submitted to alkali fusion and the autoxidizable aminonaphthol isolated as the stable N-monoacetate II. This was transformed into 1-iodo-6-methoxynaphthalene (IV) and, in the original synthesis, the Grignard reagent from IV was condensed with the MgI-salt of succinic acid half-aldehyde to the unsaturated acid VII, which was then hydrogenated to VI prior to ring closure to VIII. Cook and co-workers[5] prepared 1-iodo-6-methoxynaphthalene (IV) by a less practicable preparative route from β-naphthylamine already described (Chart 3), but they introduced the much improved scheme of converting IV into the cylic ketone VIII by way of β-(6-methoxynaphthyl)-

[1] Bachmann, Cole and Wilds, *J. Am. Chem. Soc.*, **61**, 974 (1939); **62**, 824 (1940).

[2] W. S. Johnson, Petersen and Gutsche, *J. Am. Chem. Soc.*, **67**, 2274 (1945); **69**, 2942 (1947).

[3] Ruzicka, P. Müller, Mörgeli, *Helv. Chim. Acta*, **21**, 1394 (1938); compare Windaus and Deppe, *Ber.*, **70**, 76 (1937).

[4] Butenandt and Schramm, *Ber.*, **68**, 2083 (1935).

[5] A. Cohen, Cook, Hewett and Girard, *J. Chem. Soc.*, 653 (1934); A. Cohen, Cook and Hewett, *ibid.*, 445 (1935).

ethanol (V).　The yields shown in the chart are those of the best procedures developed by Butenandt, by Cook, and by Bachmann.

More recently a much simpler synthesis of the unsaturated ketone VIII has been worked out by Stork (Chart 9, B).　Stork[6] first found conditions

Chart 9.　7-METHOXY-1-KETO-1,2,3,4-TETRAHYDROPHENANTHRENE

A. From Cleve's acid

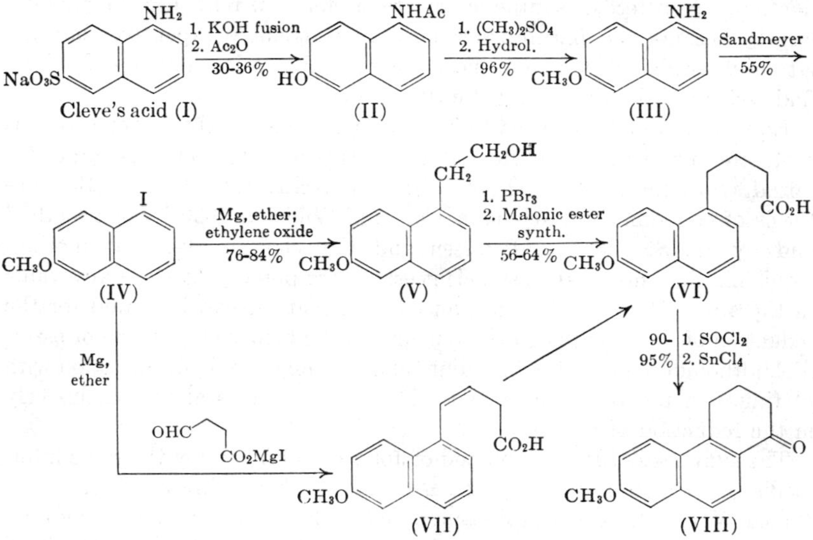

B. From β-naphthol

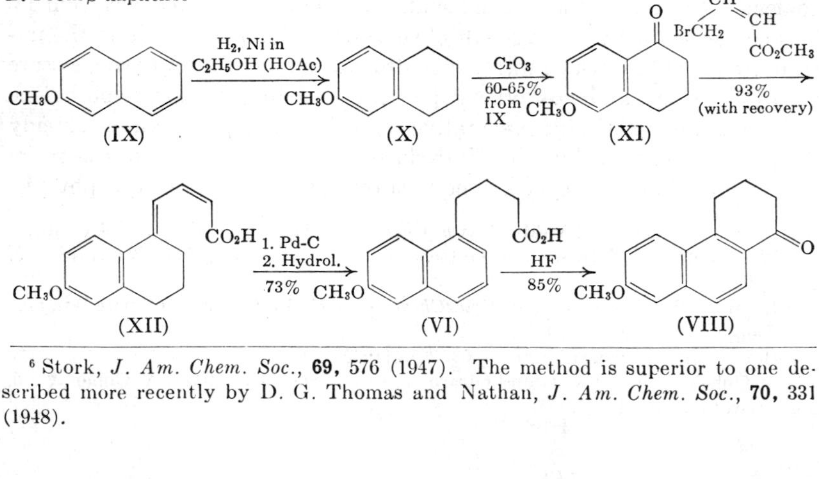

[6] Stork, *J. Am. Chem. Soc.*, **69,** 576 (1947).　The method is superior to one described more recently by D. G. Thomas and Nathan, *J. Am. Chem. Soc.*, **70,** 331 (1948).

under which β-methoxynaphthalene can be hydrogenated almost exclusively in the unsubstituted ring to give a product rich in 6-methoxytetralin (X) and convertible by a known method of oxidation[7] into 6-methoxytetralone-1 (XI). This was then[8] condensed with methyl γ-bromocrotonate in a Reformatsky reaction and the dienic acid XII was isomerized to the

Chart 10. BACHMANN'S TOTAL SYNTHESIS OF EQUILENIN

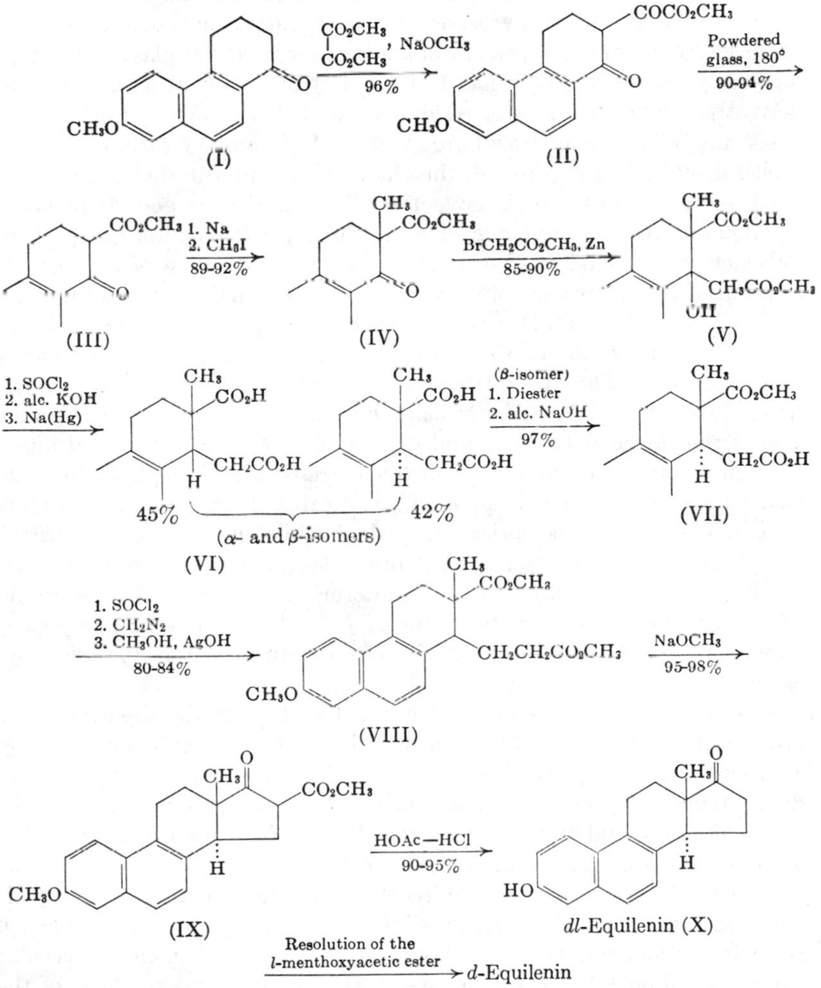

[7] Burnop, Elliott and Linstead, *J. Chem. Soc.*, 727 (1940).
[8] Stork, *J. Am. Chem. Soc.*, **69**, 2936 (1947).

known naphalenoid acid (VI), which was then cyclized. The ketone VIII is thus available in a five-step process in overall yield of 36 percent; process A involves eight steps and the overall yield is 8 percent.

Bachmann's synthesis of equilenin is formulated in Chart 10. 7-Methoxy-1-keto-1,2,3,4-tetrahydrophenanthrene was condensed with dimethyl oxalate in the presence of sodium methoxide under nitrogen to the glyoxalate II. Difficulty was experienced at first in effecting the elimination of carbon monoxide by pyrolysis, but a smooth conversion to III was achieved by the simple expedient of adding powdered soft glass. An angular methyl group was introduced at C_2 (IV) by methylation of the sodio derivative, and an acetic ester residue was added at C_1 (V) by Reformatsky reaction. When the hydroxyl group of the Reformatsky carbinol (V) was replaced by hydrogen (through the chloride, the unsaturated ester, reduction) subsequent hydrolysis gave two dl-acids, (VI, α and β) in about equal amounts. Selective hydrolysis of the unhindered ester group of the β-diester was effected nearly quantitatively by the action of a 1 percent solution of one equivalent of sodium hydroxide in methanol, and the side chain of the half-ester VII was then lengthened by Arndt-Eistert reaction. Dieckmann cyclization of VIII to IX proceeded smoothly in the presence of sodium methoxide in a nitrogen atmosphere; finally, the keto ester IX was refluxed in a mixture of acetic and hydrochloric acids to effect elimination of the carboxylate group and demethylation and so converted into a substance that proved to be dl-equilenin, for resolution through the l-menthoxyacetic ester afforded d-equilenin, identical with the natural substance from mare's urine. The optical antipode, l-equilenin, was isolated through the d-menthoxyacetic ester. The other two stereoisomers of natural equilenin were synthesized from the intermediate α-acid (VI); d-isoequilenin is described above (see Equilenin). l-Equilenin was found to possess only about one-thirteenth the activity of the natural d-form; the other two isomers are even less active.

The Johnson synthesis of equilenin is based upon the discovery of a novel cyclization reaction by which ring D can be formed in a single step. Johnson initially explored the condensation of a β-keto nitrile (a) with diethyl succinate and potassium t-butoxide in the expectation that the nitrile group would not interfere with the Stobbe condensation of the α-methylene group of the ester with the carbonyl group. Instead of the expected half-ester derivative, the reaction afforded the unsaturated cyclic keto ester (f). One of several possible mechanisms discussed by Johnson is an initial addition to the carbonyl group (a → b), an intramolecular Thorpe addition (c), further changes probably analogous to those of the ordinary Stobbe reaction (d, e), and decarboxylation (f).

The manner in which this new reaction was utilized in the synthesis is

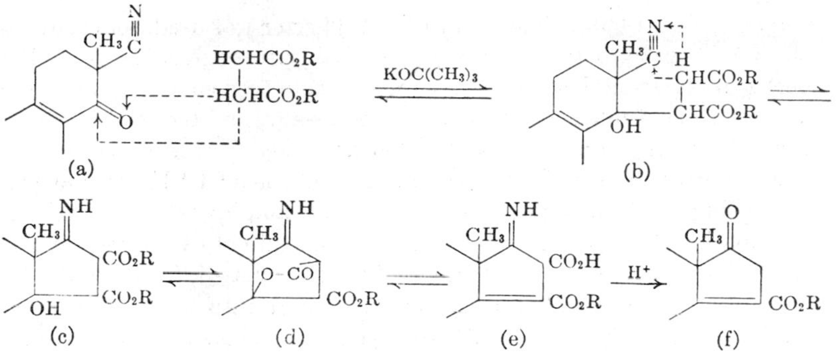

(a)   KOC(CH₃)₃   (b)

(c)   (d)   (e)   (f)

shown in Chart 11. 7-Methoxy-1-keto-1,2,3,4-tetrahydrophenanthrene (I) was condensed with ethyl formate to the formyl derivative II, and this afforded the isoxazole III by brief heating in acetic acid with hydroxylamine

Chart 11. Johnson's Total Synthesis of Equilenin

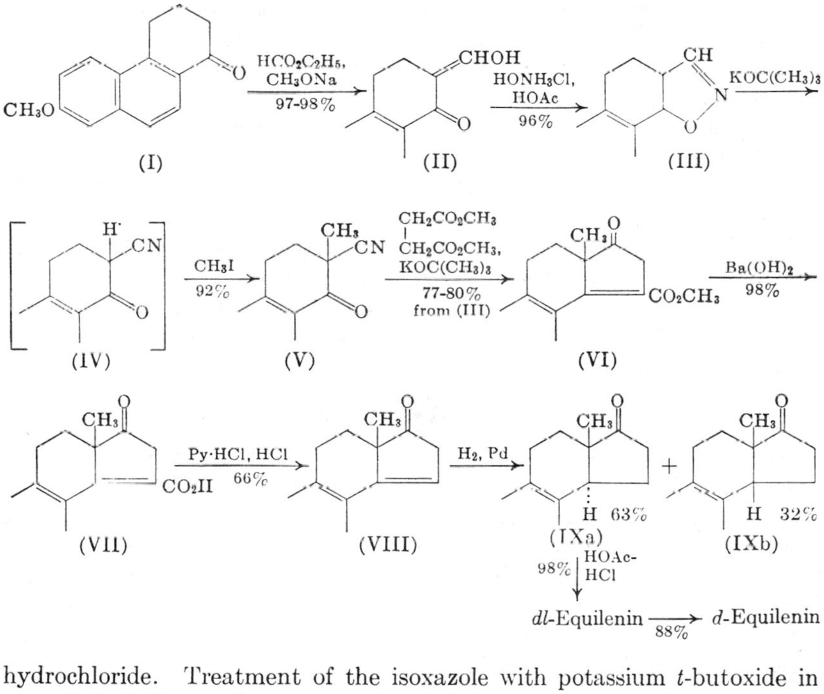

(I)   (II)   (III)

(IV)   (V)   (VI)

(VII)   (VIII)   (IXa)   (IXb)

dl-Equilenin $\xrightarrow{88\%}$ d-Equilenin

hydrochloride. Treatment of the isoxazole with potassium *t*-butoxide in *t*-butyl alcohol gave the potassio derivative of the keto nitrile IV, and this derivative was directly methylated to V. The next step of cyclization by the method discussed above was best carried out with dimethyl succinate and potassium *t*-butoxide; when the diethyl ester was used, some reduction of the carbonyl group of V occurred, probably through a Meerwein-Ponndorf type of reduction by potassium ethoxide formed in a side reaction. The isolation of intermediate V was unnecessary, and the reaction mixture from the methylation was evaporated and used in the next step. The unsaturated keto ester VI was saponified and the acid VII decarboxylated in a boiling mixture of pyridine hydrochloride and hydrochloric acid. Hydrogenation then gave an easily separable mixture of two isomers in which the C/D-trans product IXa fortunately predominated, for it proved to be *dl*-equilenin methyl ether and was converted into *d*-equilenin by the methods of Bachmann. The Δ^{14}-structure was assigned to the unsaturated ketone VIII because it yielded the two racemates on hydrogenation, whereas an isomeric ketone obtained as a product of pyrolytic decarboxylation gave only *dl*-isoequilenin and therefore can be regarded as having the alternate Δ^{15}-structure.

These syntheses by Bachmann, Cole, and Wilds and by Johnson, Petersen, and Gutsche are characterized not only by masterly pilot experimentation but by the development, through careful investigation and repeated trial at each step, of procedures that leave little to be desired with respect to yield. By the shorter synthesis of Johnson, it is possible to prepare 3.3 g. of *dl*-equilenin from 10 g. of starting ketone in seven operations.

An ingenious synthesis devised by Robinson[9] took a steric course the opposite of that desired and afforded *dl*-isoequilenin (Chart 12). In the initial steps (I → III), Robinson employed a known[10] but little used process in which an aryl methyl ketone is condensed with furfural and the furfurylidene derivative (II) is hydrolyzed with a boiling mixture of alcohol and hydrochloric acid. The hydrolytic fission of the furan ring is attended with a process of oxidation-reduction that affords a saturated diketo acid (III) in about 50 percent yield:

$$\text{ArCOCH}{=}\text{CHCOCH}_2\text{CH}_2\text{CHO} \xrightarrow{\text{H}_2\text{O}} \text{ArCOCH}_2\text{CH}_2\text{COCH}_2\text{CH}_2\text{COOH}$$

Smooth cyclization of the diketo acid III to IV was accomplished by the action of 2 percent aqueous potassium hydroxide solution, and the unsaturated acid IV was hydrogenated in the presence of palladinized strontium carbonate and the reduced acid cyclized to V; the yield in the cyclization could not be raised above 25 percent. The diketone V has one carbonyl group (C_4) that is inert to hydrazine derivatives; being adjacent to an aromatic ring, however, this group is reducible to a methylene group by hydrogenation. The reduction product, VI, lacks only the angular

[9] R. Robinson, *J. Chem. Soc.*, 1390 (1938); Koebner and R. Robinson, *ibid.*, 1994 (1938); Birch, Jaeger and R. Robinson, *ibid.*, 582 (1945).

[10] Kehrer and Igler, *Ber.*, **32**, 1176 (1899); Kehrer, *ibid.*, **34**, 1263 (1901).

methyl group of the equilenin structure.   In order to force methylation
to proceed in the position desired, it was necessary to block the more
reactive alternate position adjacent to the carbonyl group.   This was done

Chart 12.   Robinson's Synthesis of *dl*-Isoequilenin

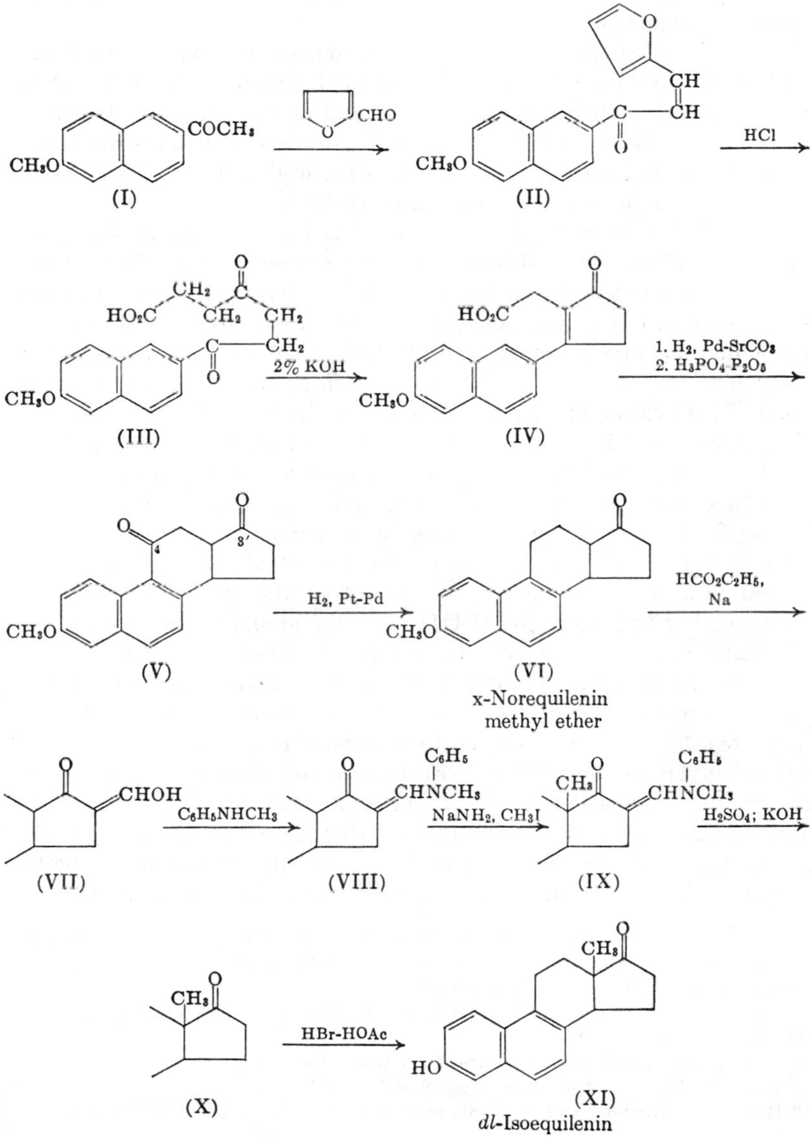

(I)   (II)   (III)   (IV)   (V)   (VI) x-Norequilenin methyl ether   (VII)   (VIII)   (IX)   (X)   (XI) *dl*-Isoequilenin

by formylation (VII) and condensation to the methylanilinomethylene derivative VIII, which could indeed be methylated as desired (IX). The blocking group was removed by treatment with aqueous alcohol-sulfuric acid (cleavage to the formyl derivative) and then with alcoholic potassium hydroxide;[11] demethylation of X afforded a substance identical with Bachmann's *dl*-isoequilenin.

The first synthetic substance fully characterized as having the estrone structure is an isomer of the natural hormone designated estrone-A. Substances synthesized by Dane and Schmitt[12] and by Breitner[13] may be structural isomers. The structure of a substance designated x-norestrone[14] has not been unambiguously proved.[6] A structural isomer of equilenin, 3-hydroxy-16-equilenone, has been synthesized.[15]

The synthesis of estrone-A was accomplished by Bachmann, Kushner, and Stevenson[16] as follows (Chart 13). The condensation product I from β-*m*-methoxyphenylethyl bromide and malonic ester was acylated with the acid chloride of ethyl hydrogen glutarate and the keto ester II cyclized with sulfuric or orthophosphoric acid to III. This triester was converted by saponification, decarboxylation, and esterification into the unsaturated diester IV, which on reaction with sodium methoxide followed by methyl iodide underwent Dieckmann cyclization and methylation in one operation and afforded the unsaturated tricyclic keto ester V. A Reformatsky reaction with zinc and methyl bromoacetate and dehydration of the carbinol with dry hydrogen chloride in benzene gave a doubly unsaturated ester, probably VII, which was crystalline (the first ethylenic bond had been retained as long as possible in order to reduce the number of isomers). The product of hydrogenation (VIII) was a liquid and probably consisted of a mixture of stereoisomers; this was put through the successive procedures of the equilenin synthesis and gave a resinous mixture of stereoisomeric estrones from which a single racemic form, estrone-A, readily crystallized. Estrone-A was found to correspond to estrone in its reactions with carbonyl reagents, in the Kober color test, and in absorption spectrum; the structure was definitely fixed by conversion into 7-methoxy-3′,3′-dimethyl-1,2-cyclopentenophenanthrene. Estrone-A has only about 1/250 the estrogenic activity of the natural hormone and therefore cannot be *dl*-estrone. The oily residual mixture was about 1/50 as active as estrone.

---

[11] The method of removing a benzylidene group devised by W. S. Johnson, *J. Am. Chem. Soc.*, **65**, 1317 (1943), was not applicable in this instance.

[12] Dane and Schmitt, *Ann.*, **537**, 246 (1939).

[13] Breitner, *Med. u. Chem.*, **4**, 317 (1942). See Heer and Miescher, *Helv. Chim. Acta*, **31**, 219 (1948).

[14] R. Robinson and Rydon, *J. Chem. Soc.*, 1394 (1939).

[15] Wilds and Close, *J. Am. Chem. Soc.*, **69**, 3079 (1947).

[16] Bachmann, Kushner and A. C. Stevenson, *J. Am. Chem. Soc.*, **64**, 974 (1942).

CH₂
CH₂ CH₂CO₂R
COCl

CH₃O

CH(CO₂R)₂
CH₂
CH₂

(I)

CH₂
CH₂ CH₂CO₂R
O=C
C(CO₂R)₂
CH₂
CH₃O CH₂

(II)

H₂SO₄

CH₂
CH CH₂CO₂R
(CO₂R)₂
CH₃O

(III)

3 steps

CH₂
CH₂ CH₂CO₂CH₃
CO₂CH₃
CH₃O

(IV)

NaOCH₃,
CH₃I

CH₃
CO₂CH₃
CH₃O

(V)

CH₃
CO₂CH₃
CH₂CO₂CH₃
OH
CH₃O

(VI)

HCl

CH₂
CO₂CH₃
CHCO₂CH₃

(VII)

CH₃
CO₂CH₃
CH₂CO₂CH₃

(VIII)

CH₃
CO₂CH₃
CH₂CO₂H

(IX)

Arndt-
Eistert

CH₃
CO₂CH₃
CH₂CO₂CH₃
CH₂

(X)

CH₃
CO₂CH₃

(XI)

CH₃O

(XII)
Estrone-A
m.p. 214-214.5°

2 steps

CO₂CH₃
CH₃O O

(XIII)

CH₃ CO₂CH₃
O

(XIV)

CH₃ CO₂CH₃
CH₂CO₂CH₃
OH

(XV)

2 steps

CH₃
CO₂CH₃
CH₂CO₂CH₃

(XVI m.p. 96°)
(XVII m.p. 92°)

5 steps

CH₃ O

(XVIII, racemate)

3 steps

CH₃ O

HO

(XIX)
Estrone

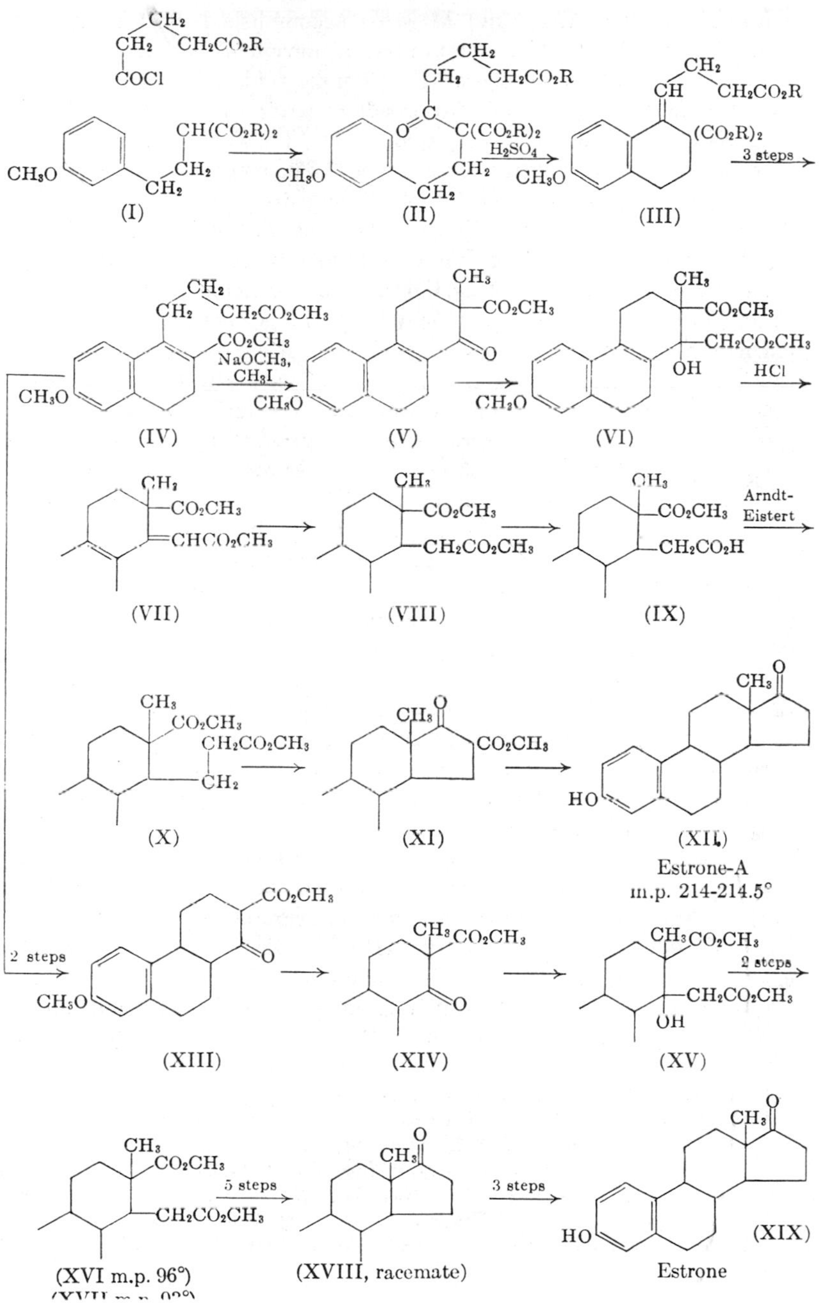

Finally, in 1948, Anner and Miescher accomplished the total synthesis of natural estrone.[17] This outstanding achievement was an outcome of Anner and Miescher's synthesis of doisynolic acids described in the next section (Chart 17). The key intermediate is the saturated tricyclic keto ester XIV (Chart 13), first prepared (as ethyl ester) by Robinson[18] from 1-keto-7-methoxyoctahydrophenanthrene. The methyl ester was prepared by Bachmann as an incidental part of the estrone-A research by hydrogenation of IV, cyclization (XIII), and methylation. The methyl and ethyl esters of XIV had been known only as oils, but Anner and Miescher succeeded in isolating three of the four possible racemates in crystalline form. From the results of the doisynolic acid synthesis, they could infer that a particular one of the racemates (m.p. 135°) must have the proper configuration for the construction of the molecule of natural estrone. This ester was consequently put through a sequence of transformations similar to those employed by Bachmann: Reformatsky reaction (XV), dehydration and hydrogenation to a mixture of two racemates, one of which (XVI) afforded racemic estrone methyl ether (XVIII, m.p. 140°) and racemic estrone (m.p. 250°). Resolution was effected by crystallization of the *l*-menthoxyacetate; the less soluble ester on hydrolysis gave a product identical with natural estrone. The lower-melting ester (XVII) yielded in a similar manner a second estrone racemate, m.p. 127°, differing in the juncture of rings C and D; this proved to be physiologically inactive.

Estrogenolic Acids. In 1932 Marrian and Haslewood[1] isolated from the alkali fusion of estriol a dibasic acid which they correctly formulated as $C_{18}H_{22}O_5$ and which served a useful purpose in degradative studies of the hormone structure. A year later Doisy[2] confirmed the observation and further reported the preparation, by alkali fusion of estrone, of a monobasic acid (m.p. 195°) mistakenly regarded as "$C_{17}H_{22}O_3$." Doisy initially stated that these and related degradation products arising by fission of ring D possess several times the estrogenic potency of pure estrone, but in 1934 the statement was retracted and the degradation products declared to be devoid of significant activity.[3] Hohlweg and Inhoffen[4] of the Schering firm made patent claim to the production of potent estrogenic acids by alkali fusion of estradiol, equilenin, equilin, and dihydroequilenin.

The first systematic investigation of the vague and conflicting claims was

[17] Anner and Miescher, *Experientia*, **4**, 25 (1948).

[18] R. Robinson and J. Walker, *J. Chem. Soc.*, 747 (1936); **183** (1938).

[1] Marrian and Haslewood, *J. Soc. Chem. Ind.*, **51**, 277T (1932).

[2] MacCorquodale, Thayer and Doisy, *J. Biol. Chem.*, **99**, 327 (1933); MacCorquodale, Levin, Thayer and Doisy, *ibid.*, **101**, 753 (1933); U. S. Patent 2,069,096 (1937).

[3] MacCorquodale, Levin and Thayer, *J. Biol. Chem.*, **105**, lv (1934).

[4] Hohlweg and Inhoffen, German patents 705,862 (1941), 719,572 (1942).

reported in 1944 by Miescher of the Swiss firm Ciba.[5] Miescher named the dibasic acid discovered by Marrian marrianolic acid; the monobasic acid, which he showed actually to have the formula $C_{18}H_{24}O_3$, he named doisynolic acid. The structure of marrianolic acid was already known (see Structure of Estrone); that of doisynolic acid (Chart 14) was established by catalytic dehydrogenation to 1-ethyl-2-methyl-7-phenanthrol, which on zinc-dust distillation was converted into 1-ethyl-2-methylphenanthrene.[6]

Chart 14. Estrogenolic Acids from Hormones

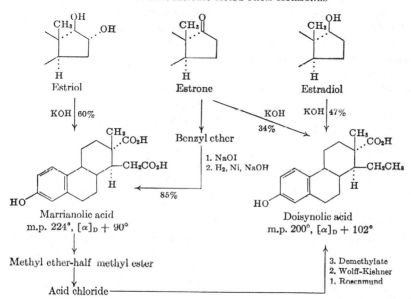

The rupture of ring D of estrone with generation of a carboxyl and an ethyl group is a purely hydrolytic process; the conversions of estriol and estradiol into marrianolic and doisynolic acid, respectively, are oxidative fissions. The best procedure for the preparation of marrianolic acid utilizes the action of hypoiodite on the benzyl ether of estrone, followed by nickel hydrogenation, which removes the benzyl group.[7] Since this low-temperature conversion gives the same, single stereoisomer that is formed in the alkali fusion of estriol and since marrianolic acid has been converted into doisynolic acid by the nondrastic reactions indicated at the bottom of the

[5] Miescher, *Helv. Chim. Acta*, **27**, 1727 (1944).
[6] Heer and Miescher, *Helv. Chim. Acta*, **28**, 156 (1945).
[7] Heer and Miescher, *Helv. Chim. Acta*, **28**, 156 (1945); **29**, 1895 (1946); **30**, 550 (1947). See confirmation by Heer and Miescher, *ibid.*, **31**, 405 (1948),

chart,[7] it is safe to conclude that the two acids are configurationally related to each other and to the three hormones.

Marrianolic acid, as all other dibasic acids like it, is completely inactive. Pure doisynolic acid, however, is about as active as estrone in rats by subcutaneous injection and distinctly more active than estrone when given by mouth.[8] The methyl ether is as active as the free phenol.

This initial finding prompted extensive further studies, which led to the discovery of still more potent members of the series. One is a levorotatory bisdehydrodoisynolic acid (− 116°) produced, along with a nearly inactive dextrorotatory diastereoisomer (+ 33°), by the alkali fusion of equilenin or of dihydroequilenin.[5,9] The two acids, formed in about equal amounts, both yield 1-ethyl-2-methyl-7-phenanthrol on dehydrogenation and hence are of the doisynolic type. Evidently an inversion occurs in the formation of one acid or the other, and fortunately evidence is available to show that the physiologically potent isomer is the one resulting from inversion. The reasoning can be followed with reference to Chart 15, in which the active bisdehydrodoisynolic acid derived from equilenin (I) is represented by formula II and the inactive epimer by IV. The latter inactive acid (IV) was obtained also by the dehydrogenation of doisynolic acid (VII), from estrone. In this case dehydrogenation is known not to be accompanied by inversion, since the same bisdehydrodoisynolic acid (IV) is obtained from equilenin through the bisdehydromarrianolic acid (hypoiodite) and reduction and since the configurational correspondence of estrone and equilenin has been established. The dehydrogenation of estrone to d-14-isoequilenin (as ether X) has been shown to proceed with inversion at C_{14}; hence the conversion of d-14-isoequilenin through the bisdehydromarrianolic acid derivative V to a product identical with the highly active bisdehydrodoisynolic acid II establishes that this substance is formed from equilenin with inversion and is the 1-epimer of IV.

In an independent series, lumiestrone[7] (XI), postulated to be 13-isoestrone, was converted through the marrianolic (VIII) and doisynolic (VI) acids into a bisdehydrodoisynolic acid (III) that proved to be the antipode of the highly active isomer II. That the configuration indicated for III, with the methyl and hydrogen both in the α-orientation, is just that expected from the independent inference regarding the configuration of the antipode II, strengthens both sets of independent inferences. It appears, then, that doisynolic acids can be dehydrogenated without inversion (cases VI and VII) but that in an alkali fusion of a naphthalenoid compound or a dehydrogenation to such a compound inversion may occur at position 14

[8] Tschopp, *Helv. Physiol. Pharmacol. Acta*, **4**, C28, 401 (1946) [*C. A.*, **41**, 1810 (1947)].

[9] Heer, Billeter and Miescher, *Helv. Chim. Acta*, **28**, 991 (1945).

Chart 15. CONFIGURATIONAL RELATIONSHIPS

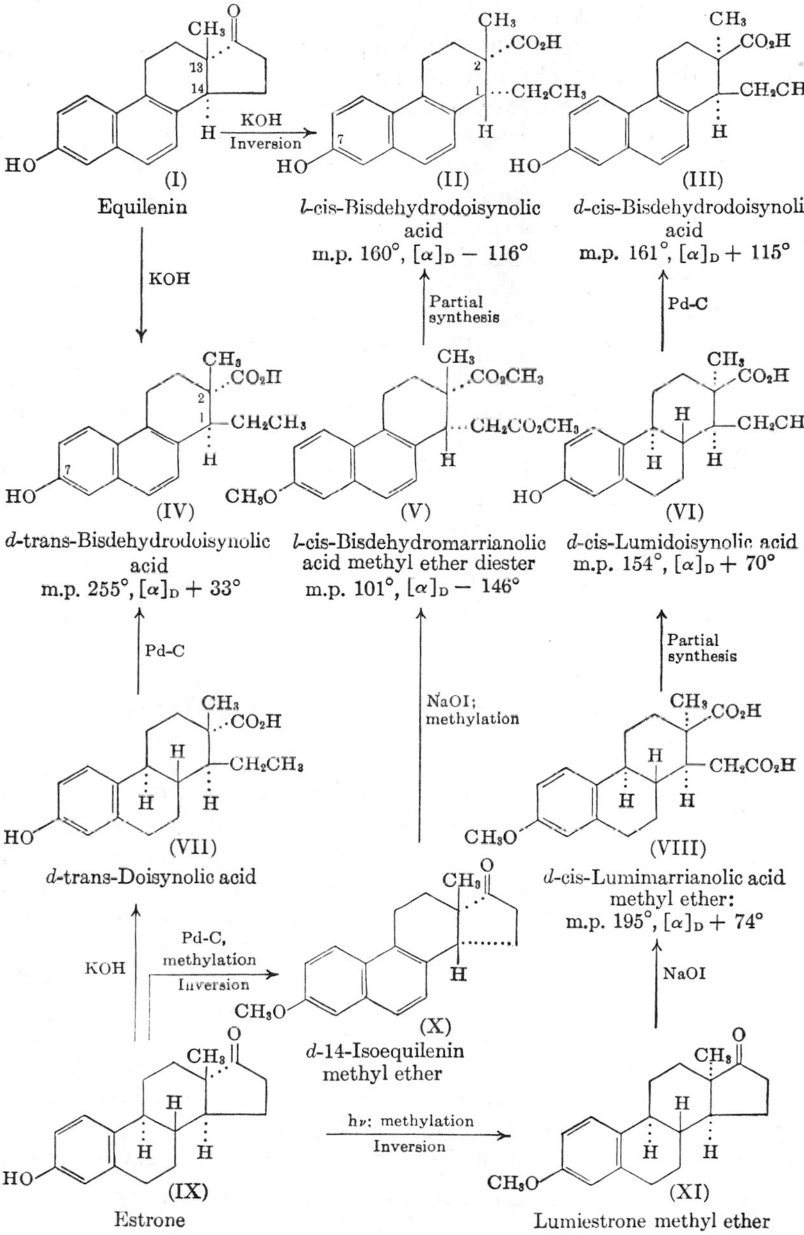

(I)
Equilenin

(II)
l-cis-Bisdehydrodoisynolic acid
m.p. 160°, $[\alpha]_D - 116°$

(III)
d-cis-Bisdehydrodoisynolic acid
m.p. 161°, $[\alpha]_D + 115°$

KOH
Inversion

KOH

Partial synthesis

Pd-C

(IV)
d-trans-Bisdehydrodoisynolic acid
m.p. 255°, $[\alpha]_D + 33°$

(V)
l-cis-Bisdehydromarrianolic acid methyl ether diester
m.p. 101°, $[\alpha]_D - 146°$

(VI)
d-cis-Lumidoisynolic acid
m.p. 154°, $[\alpha]_D + 70°$

Pd-C

NaOI; methylation

Partial synthesis

(VII)
d-trans-Doisynolic acid

(VIII)
d-cis-Lumimarrianolic acid methyl ether:
m.p. 195°, $[\alpha]_D + 74°$

KOH

Pd-C, methylation
Inversion

NaOI

(X)
d-14-Isoequilenin methyl ether

(IX)
Estrone

hν: methylation
Inversion

(XI)
Lumiestrone methyl ether

adjacent to the aromatic system (case I → II, along with the normal product IV; case IX → X).

The system of nomenclature here applied to both physiologically active and inactive estrogenolic acids is based upon the relative orientations of the methyl group and hydrogen atom of the two asymmetric centers; the acid is designated cis if these have either the α,α- or β,β-orientation, and otherwise trans. At a time when the relationships were thought to be the reverse of those now recognized, Miescher employed the designations "iso" (cis) and "normal" (trans); he then changed to the designations "α" (cis) and "β" (trans). We prefer the cis-trans terminology because it obviates any possible confusion with the α-β system for indication of relative configurations in the steroid nucleus.

The marrianolic acids listed in Chart 15, as well as d-trans-bisdehydro-marrianolic acid (from equilenin; m.p. 245°, $[\alpha]_D$ + 102°) and marrianolic acid itself are all devoid of physiological activity. The most potent monobasic acid listed is l-cis-bisdehydrodoisynolic acid (II); this is related in configuration to the inactive d-14-isoequilenin, whereas the inactive d-trans isomer IV has the configuration of the active equilenin. Thus, among the naphthalenoid compounds, the estrogenolic acids of the higher physiological activity are those having the configuration of the less active 17-keto-steroids. The doisynolic acid derived from estrone is active; but the relationship just noted suggests that the C_1-epimer of the cis series might be extremely potent (see below).

For the exploration of additional stereoisomers and related compounds, and with the objective of finding a more practical preparative route to the active bisdehydrodoisynolic acid, Miescher turned to synthesis. Intermediates described by Bachmann afforded a ready approach to the structures desired. The keto ester I (Chart 16), an intermediate in Bachmann's synthesis of equilenin, was employed in one synthesis (A) of the two dl-bisdehydrodoisynolic acids.[10] The reaction with ethylmagnesium bromide gave a mixture of two epimeric carbinols in which the higher-melting IIa predominates. Dehydration of IIa afforded a mixture of cis-trans isomers IIIa and IIIb, but hydrolysis of the mixture with methanolic potassium hydroxide at 200° gave a single unsaturated acid, IV, which on hydrogenation (Rupe nickel) yielded a dl-bisdehydrodoisynolic acid (m.p. 204°) of high activity. When the mixture of unsaturated esters (III) was hydrogenated and then hydrolyzed with pyridine hydrochloride, both the 204° dl-acid and a trace of a second, inactive dl-acid (m.p. 240°) were isolated. A second, simpler synthesis[11] (B) proceeded through the intermediates VI and VII to similar mixtures of carbinols (II) and unsaturated

[10] Heer, Billeter and Miescher, *Helv. Chim. Acta*, **28**, 1342 (1945).
[11] Anner and Miescher, *Helv. Chim. Acta*, **29**, 586 (1946).

Chart 16. SYNTHESIS OF BISDEHYDRODOISYNOLIC ACIDS

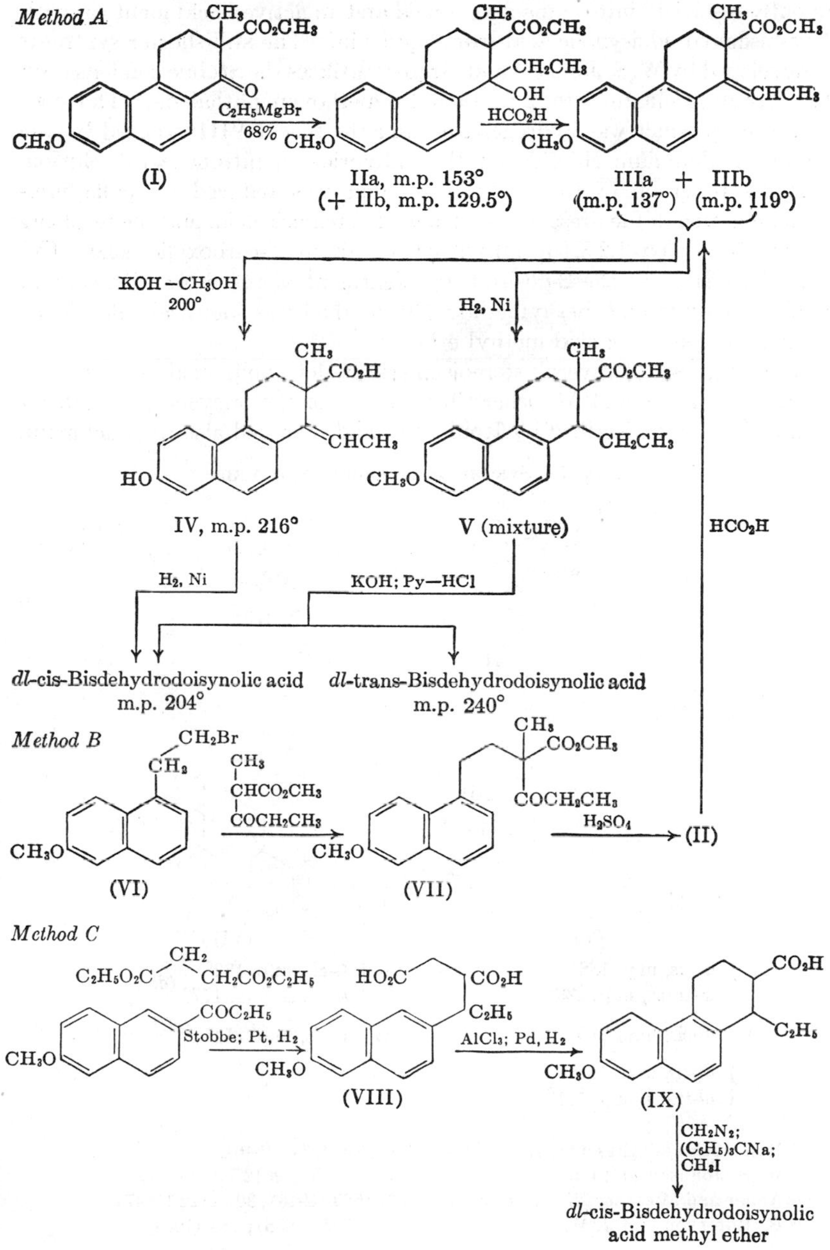

Method A

(I)

C_2H_5MgBr 68%

IIa, m.p. 153°
(+ IIb, m.p. 129.5°)

HCO_2H

IIIa + IIIb
(m.p. 137°) (m.p. 119°)

KOH–CH₃OH
200°

H_2, Ni

IV, m.p. 216°

V (mixture)

HCO_2H

H_2, Ni   KOH; Py—HCl

dl-cis-Bisdehydrodoisynolic acid
m.p. 204°

dl-trans-Bisdehydrodoisynolic acid
m.p. 240°

Method B

(VI)

$\begin{array}{l} CH_2Br \\ CH_3 \\ CHCO_2CH_3 \\ COCH_2CH_3 \end{array}$

(VII)

H_2SO_4

(II)

Method C

$\begin{array}{l} CH_2 \\ C_2H_5O_2C\!\!-\!\!CH_2CO_2C_2H_5 \\ COC_2H_5 \end{array}$
Stobbe; Pt, H_2

(VIII)

$AlCl_3$; Pd, H_2

(IX)

CH_2N_2;
$(C_6H_5)_3CNa$;
CH_3I

dl-cis-Bisdehydrodoisynolic
acid methyl ether

esters (III). The physiologically active *dl*-acid m.p. 204° was subsequently resolved[12] into an inactive *d*-acid and an active *l*-acid identical with *l*-cis-bisdehydrodoisynolic acid from equilenin. The still shorter synthesis C developed by W. S. Johnson and Graber[13] utilizes the Stobbe condensation of diethyl succinate with 2-propionyl-6-methoxynaphthalene. The condensation product was hydrogenated and the diacid VIII cyclized by the action of aluminum chloride on the anhydride in nitrobenzene solution. The 4-keto group of the cyclized product was reduced by palladium-hydrogenation in the presence of a trace of perchloric acid, and the resulting 1-ethyl-7-methoxy-1,2,3,4-tetrahydrophenanthrene-2-carboxylic acid (IX) was methylated at the 2-position by treatment of the ester with sodium triphenylmethyl and methyl iodide; the product was identical with *dl*-cis-bisdehydrodoisynolic acid methyl ether.

The synthesis of several stereoisomeric *dl*-doisynolic acids was accomplished by Anner and Miescher[14] by the use of the tricyclic keto ester I (Chart 17), first described by Robinson[15] and prepared also by Bachmann

Chart 17.   SYNTHESIS OF DOISYNOLIC ACIDS

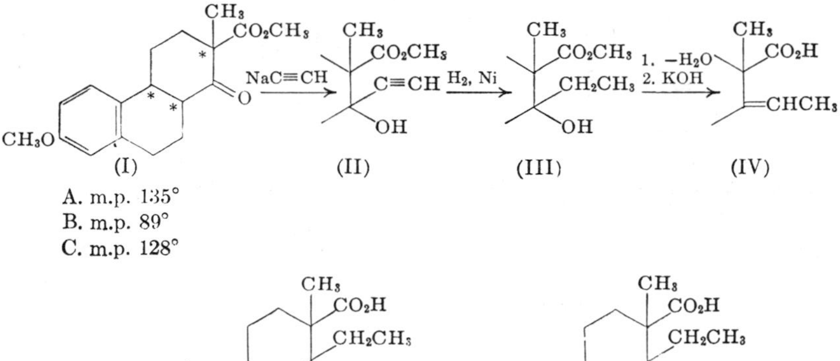

(I)
A. m.p. 135°
B. m.p. 89°
C. m.p. 128°

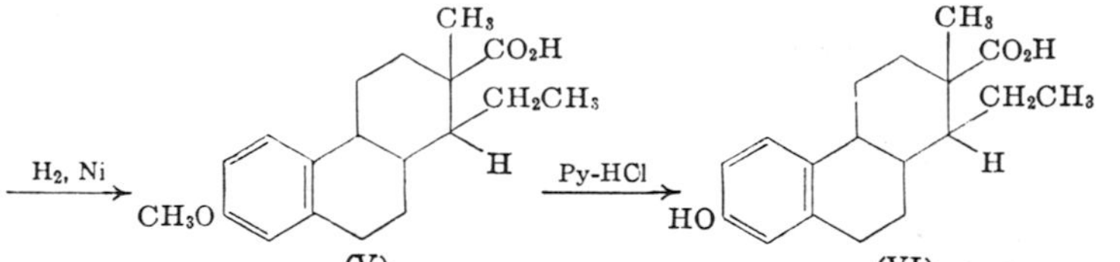

(II)   (III)   (IV)

(V)
A $\begin{cases} dl\text{-cis, m.p. } 188° \\ dl\text{-trans, m.p. } 229° \end{cases}$

B   *dl*-cis, m.p. 215°

C $\begin{cases} dl\text{-cis, m.p. } 181° \\ dl\text{-trans, m.p. } 191° \end{cases}$

(VI)
A $\begin{cases} dl\text{-cis, m.p. } 182° \\ dl\text{-trans, m.p. } 177° \end{cases}$ (*dl*-Doisynolic acid)

B   *dl*-cis, m.p. 214°   (*dl*-Lumidoisynolic acid)

[12] Rometsch and Miescher, *Helv. Chim. Acta*, **29**, 1231 (1946).
[13] W. S. Johnson and Graber, *J. Am. Chem. Soc.*, **70**, 2612 (1948).
[14] Anner and Miescher, *Helv. Chim. Acta*, **29**, 1889 (1946); **30**, 1422 (1947).
[15] R. Robinson and J. Walker, *J. Chem. Soc.*, 747 (1936); 183 (1938).

(Chart 13). The ester I has three centers of asymmetry and can exist in four *dl*-forms; Anner and Miescher isolated from the oily product three crystalline racemates, each of which was used separately for the synthesis of doisynolic acids by the scheme shown in the chart. Five of the eight theoretically possible methyl ethers of formula V were isolated, and three of the ethers were demethylated to crystalline *dl*-doisynolic acids (VI). The configurational relationships indicated for the different isomers were tentatively inferred by Miescher, in part from melting-point comparisons of synthetic *dl*-acids and optically active acids derived from hormones and in part from the results of dehydrogenations to bisdehydrodoisynolic acids.

One of the synthetic doisynolic acids has remarkably high estrogenic potency, namely the *dl*-cis acid of the A-series (m.p. 182°). This racemate is active in rats orally or subcutaneously at a dosage of 0.05 γ and is the most potent estrogen of the series yet described. The assay data in the

Estrogenic Activity[8]

	ACTIVE DOSE (RATS), γ
dl-cis-Doisynolic acid-A	0.05*
l-cis-Bisdehydrodoisynolic acid	0.05–.07*
d-trans-Doisynolic acid	0.7–1.0
Estrone	10–15**
	0.7–1.0***
d-cis-Bisdehydrodoisynolic acid	10*
d-cis-Lumidoisynolic acid	250
d-trans-Bisdehydrodoisynolic acid	200–300

* Single injection of a water solution of the sodium salt.
** Single injection in dilute alcohol.
*** Two injections in oil.

accompanying table show that the synthetic *dl*-acid is slightly more potent than even *l*-cis-bisdehydrodoisynolic acid; since one antipode is probably inactive, or nearly so, the other must possess extraordinarily high potency. According to Miescher's inferences, this epimer must have the opposite configuration at C_1 from that of estrone at C_{14} but must conform to estrone at the other two asymmetric centers; the relationship to the hormone is thus the same as the relationship of the potent *l*-cis-bisdehydrodoisynolic acid to equilenin.

At the outset of his investigations Miescher[5] discussed the possibility that doisynolic acids are involved in the biological functioning of the hormones and that the inactive marrianolic acids are concerned in the process of the excretion of the hormones. The former possibility now seems excluded, for otherwise *d*-14-isoequilenin would be more active than equilenin, whereas it is inactive.

Many compounds structurally related to bisdehydrodoisynolic acid have been prepared.[16]   The 1-methyl derivative is as active as the parent compound, but the 1-ethyl derivative is only one-tenth as active.   All other modifications tried have reduced the estrogenic activity.

Estrolic Acid.   Jacobsen[17] has investigated a series of lactones resulting from the opening of ring D of estrone and other 17-ketosteroids by peroxide oxidation.   The initially formed hydroxy acid from estrone is called estrolic acid and probably results from cleavage of the C_{16}–C_{17} bond.   Related lactones are described as androlactone, bisdehydroestrolactone, testololactone, etc.   Estrolic acid, in aqueous solution, has little estrogenic activity but can inhibit secretion of gonadotropic hormones by the pituitary gland. The most satisfactory method of preparation consists in oxidation of estrone acetate with peracetic acid in glacial acetic acid containing a little p-toluenesulfonic acid.   Jacobsen's estrolactone obtained by saponification of the acetate and relactonization, appears to be related to but different from a lactone obtained by Westerfeld[18] by oxidation of estrone in alkaline solution with hydrogen peroxide, since the latter is about one-fourteenth as active as estrone.

Nonsteroid Synthetic Estrogens.   Even before the evidence for the structure of estrone was complete, Cook and Dodds[1] investigated a number of synthetic compounds bearing some minor structural similarity to the hormone and soon found that estrogenic activity is remarkably unspecific and that the estrous change can be induced by adequate doses of a host of compounds, some of which are wholly unrelated to estrone.   1-Ketotetrahydrophenanthrene, for example, produces the full estrous response including uterine changes in castrated rats at a dosage of 100 mg./rat.   This, to be sure, is a huge amount of chemical (about 400 mg./kg.) and it is doubtful if much significance is to be attached to the estrogenic activity of comparable low order found for such other compounds as neoergosterol, 3,4-benzpyrene, and 5,6-cyclopenteno-1,2-benzanthracene.   The observation

[16] Heer and Miescher, *Helv. Chim. Acta*, **28**, 1506 (1945); Anner and Miescher, *ibid.*, **29**, 586 (1946); Billeter and Miescher, *ibid.*, **29**, 859 (1946); Anner, Heer and Miescher, *ibid.*, **29**, 1071 (1946); Anner and Miescher, *ibid.*, **29**, 1889 (1946); Ehmann and Miescher, *ibid.*, **30**, 413 (1947); Heer and Miescher, *ibid.*, **30**, 777 (1947); **31**, 229 (1948); Billeter and Miescher, *ibid.*, **31**, 1302 (1948). The last paper cited includes an account of the opening of six-membered lactone rings by diazomethane with production of unsaturated esters.

[17] Jacobsen, *J. Biol. Chem.*, **171**, 61 (1947); H. Levy and Jacobsen, *ibid.*, **171**, 71 (1947); Jacobsen, Picha and H. Levy, *ibid.*, **171**, 81 (1947).

[18] Westerfeld, *J. Biol. Chem.*, **143**, 177 (1942).

[1] Cook, Dodds and Hewett, *Nature*, **131**, 56 (1933); Cook and Dodds, *ibid.*, **131**, 205 (1933); Cook, Dodds, Hewett and Lawson, *Proc. Roy. Soc.* (London), **B114**, 272 (1934).

of weak estrogenic activity in some of the carcinogenic hydrocarbons prompted the study of oxygenated derivatives of closer analogy to the natural estrogens, as exemplified by the diols obtained by the action of Grignard reagents on 1,2,5,6-dibenzanthraquinone. The activity rises to

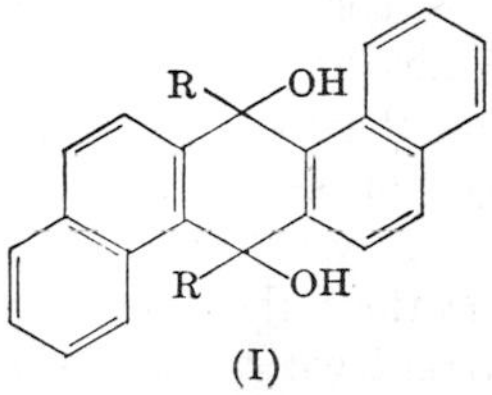

(I)

R	*Rat dose, mg.*
CH_3	Inactive
CH_2CH_3	10
$CH_2CH_2CH_3$	0.025
$CH_2CH_2CH_2CH_3$	1
$CH_2CH_2CH_2CH_2CH_3$	Inactive

a maximum in the di-*n*-propyl diol and then falls off. The most potent member is still only about 1/40 as active as estrone, but the marked improvement over the earlier compounds prompted an investigation of other dihydroxy aromatic compounds that proved fruitful.

Dodds and Lawson[2] found several such compounds to be estrogenic: 4,4'-dihydroxydiphenyl (100 mg. dose; 2,2'-isomer inactive); 4,4'-dihydroxydiphenyl ether (100 mg.); 4,4'-dihydroxydiphenylethane (100 mg.); 4,4'-dihydroxystilbene (10 mg.); 4,4'-dihydroxytolane (10 mg.); stilbene itself is active in 25-mg. doses. A few active compounds were discovered in the series of still simpler hydroxy compounds having only one aromatic ring, and of these *p-n*-propylphenol was the most active. By analogy with stilbene and its *p,p'*-dihydroxy derivative, Dodds and Lawson thought that *p*-propenylphenol, or anol, should be still more active. The subsequent events were briefly as follows.[3] The English workers attempted the demethylation of anethole with potassium hydroxide and alcohol in a sealed

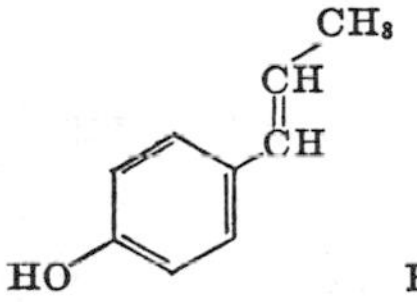

Anol

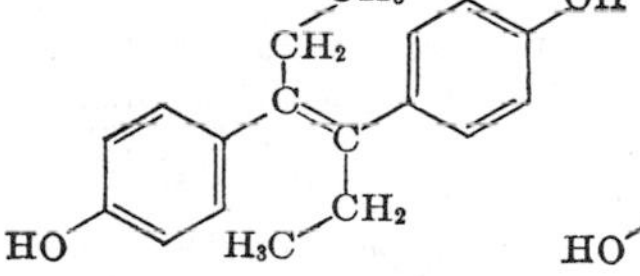

Stilbestrol
(*trans*, m.p. 171°)
Rat dose 0.4γ

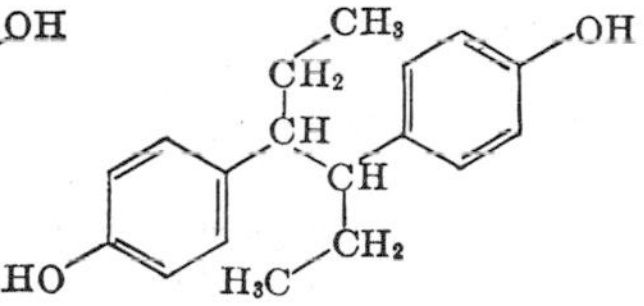

Hexestrol
(*meso* m.p. 186°)
Rat dose 0.2γ

tube, but obtained only a crude, oily preparation of anol, which was submitted as such to assay. On the basis of the results, they reported that anol is as strongly estrogenic as estrone. Attempts to confirm the report

[2] Dodds and Lawson, *Proc. Roy. Soc.* (*London*), **B125**, 222 (1938).

[3] For detailed accounts see Solmssen, *Chem. Revs.*, **37**, 481 (1945); Wessely, *Angew. Chem.*, **53**, 197 (1940); Masson, *Rev. can. biol.*, **3**, 491 (1944).

in several laboratories soon led to the recognition that pure anol itself has very little activity but that the crude product of attempted demethylation contains a highly potent estrogen. That this may be a product of dimerization was suggested by the observation of Serini and Steinruck[4] that anethole is converted by the action of Grignard reagents into products of demethylation, dimerization, and alkylation that possess considerable estrogenic potency (probably alkyl derivatives of p,p'-dihydroxydiphenylethane). Dodds, Golberg, Lawson, and R. Robinson,[5] on the hypothesis that the active by-product might be stilbestrol ("diethylstilbestrol," see formula), synthesized this compound and found it to be highly active. The active estrogen has been assigned the trans configuration; the less active cis isomer (m.p. 151°) can be isomerized by treatment with alcoholic hydrochloric acid.[6] The active contaminant in the crude anol was subsequently isolated[7] and found to be the dihydro derivative hexestrol, which is somewhat more active than stilbestrol. Both substances are more active than estrone and approach estradiol in potency; they have found use in therapy, and much work has been done on the development of practical methods of synthesis. The original synthesis of stilbestrol[5] from anisaldehyde through desoxyanisoin was not very efficient but superior to several subsequent syntheses.[8] Probably the best of the syntheses reported is that of Kharasch[9] (Chart 18.)

The first synthesis[7] of hexestrol started with the reaction of anisaldazine with ethylmagnesium bromide, but the overall yield of the active meso isomer was only 0.7 percent. Hydrogenation of stilbestrol leads to the less active, lower-melting (128°) dl-hexestrol.[5, 10] A synthesis that affords the meso isomer in 7–20 percent yield depends upon the coupling action of sodium or magnesium on anethole hydrobromide, followed by demethylation.[11] The best present synthesis of this estrogen is also due to Kharasch:[12]

[4] Serini and Steinruck, *Naturwissenschaften*, **25**, 682 (1947).

[5] Dodds, Golberg, Lawson and R. Robinson, *Proc. Roy. Soc. (London)*, **B127**, 140 (1939).

[6] Walton and Brownlee, *Nature*, **151**, 305 (1943).

[7] N. R. Campbell, Dodds and Lawson, *Proc. Roy. Soc. (London)*, **B128**, 253 (1940).

[8] Wessely and co-workers, *Naturwissenschaften*, **27**, 131, 567 (1939); *Monatsh.*, **73**, 127 (1940); Kuwada and co-workers, *J. Pharm. Soc. Japan*, **60**, 93, 553 (1940); Peteri, *J. Chem. Soc.*, 833 (1940); Vargha and Kovacs, *Ber.*, **75**, 794 (1942); Rubin, Kozlowski and Salmon, *J. Am. Chem. Soc.*, **67**, 192 (1945); Wilds and Biggerstaff, *ibid*, **67**, 789 (1945).

[9] Kharasch and Kleiman, *J. Am. Chem. Soc.*, **65**, 11 (1943).

[10] Wessely and Welleba, *Ber.*, **74**, 777 (1941); Docken and Spielman, *J. Am. Chem. Soc.*, **62**, 2163 (1940).

[11] Girard and Sandulesco, French patent 855,879; W. F. Short, *Chemistry and Industry*, **18**, 703 (1940); Bernstein and Wallis, *J. Am. Chem. Soc.*, **62**, 2871 (1940).

[12] Kharasch and Kleiman, *J. Am. Chem. Soc.*, **65**, 491 (1943).

the reaction of anethole hydrobromide with phenylmagnesium bromide in the presence of cobaltous chloride.

Chart 18. SYNTHESIS OF STILBESTROL AND HEXESTROL

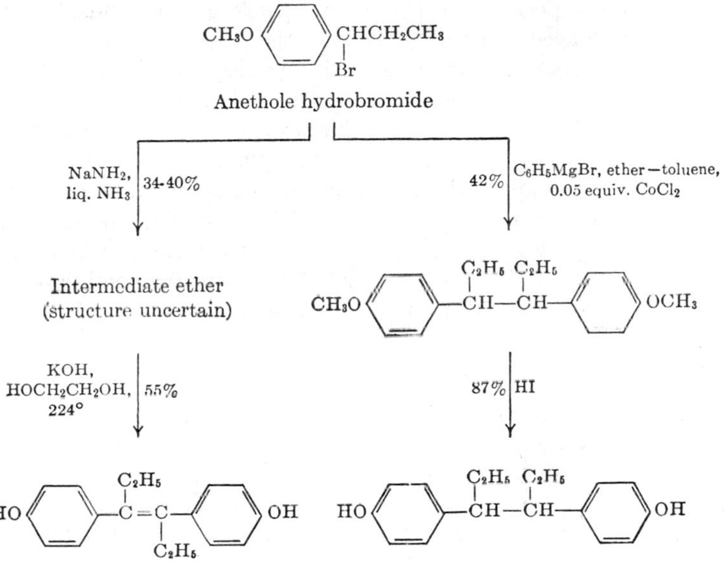

$$CH_3O \langle \rangle CHCH_2CH_3$$
$$\underset{Br}{|}$$

Anethole hydrobromide

| NaNH$_2$, liq. NH$_3$ | 34-40% | | 42% | C$_6$H$_5$MgBr, ether—toluene, 0.05 equiv. CoCl$_2$ |

Intermediate ether (structure uncertain)

$$CH_3O \langle \rangle \overset{C_2H_5}{\underset{|}{C}H} - \overset{C_2H_5}{\underset{|}{C}H} \langle \rangle OCH_3$$

KOH, HOCH$_2$CH$_2$OH, 224° | 55%

87% | HI

$$HO \langle \rangle \overset{C_2H_5}{\underset{\underset{C_2H_5}{|}}{C}} = C \langle \rangle OH$$

Stilbestrol

$$HO \langle \rangle \overset{C_2H_5}{\underset{|}{C}H} - \overset{C_2H_5}{\underset{|}{C}H} \langle \rangle OH$$

Hexestrol

Another member of the same group that shows comparable biological activity is known as dienestrol or hexadiene (3,4-di-*p*-hydroxyphenyl-2,4-hexadiene).[5] Estrogenic activity has also been encountered among trialkyl derivatives of 1,3-di-*p*-hydroxyphenylpropane, the most active of which is known as benzestrol,[13] one of four racemic forms that have been prepared. The formula of benzestrol can be written in such a way that

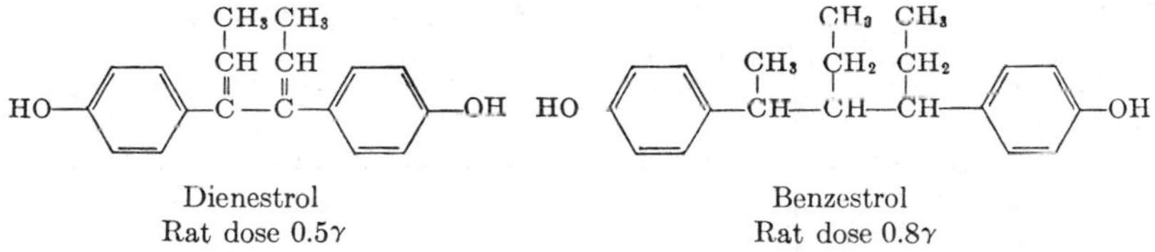

$$HO \langle \rangle \overset{CH_3}{\underset{|}{C}H} \overset{CH_3}{\underset{|}{C}H} \overset{}{\underset{}{C}} - C \langle \rangle OH$$

Dienestrol
Rat dose 0.5γ

$$HO \langle \rangle \overset{CH_3}{\underset{|}{C}H} \overset{CH_2}{\underset{|}{C}H} \overset{CH_2}{\underset{|}{C}H} \langle \rangle OH$$

Benzestrol
Rat dose 0.8γ

the carbon skeleton corresponds to that of the potent carcinogen 9,10-dimethyl-1,2-benzanthracene.[14]

[13] Stuart, Shukis, Tallman, McCann and Treves, *J. Am. Chem. Soc.*, **68,** 729 (1946).
[14] R. H. Martin, *Chemistry and Industry*, **94,** (1944).

Estrogenic activity is also found in triphenylethylene derivatives,[15] for example, triphenylethylene, $(C_6H_5)_2C=CHC_6H_5$, and eht more active triphenylchloroethylene, $(C_6H_5)_2C=CClC_6H_5$. Although direct comparisons with other synthetic estrogens have not been reported, the activity of the triphenylethylenes appears to be of a lower order; the compounds, however, exert a more prolonged action than those of the stilbestrol type.

Stilbestrol exhibits qualitatively all the physiological effects of the true hormones. Toxic effects in experimental animals have been noted but apparently can be prevented by whole liver extracts.[16] In human therapy toxic symptoms (nausea, anorexia, vertigo, skin rash) probably appear only when large doses are used.[17] Stilbestrol, a comparatively inexpensive product, apparently has found a definite place in clinical usage.[18] Like estrone or estradiol, it is said to be of value in treatment of carcinoma of the prostate,[19] but occasionally it seems to aggravate the condition.[20] In experimental animals stilbestrol can act as a carcinogenic agent.[21]

MALE HORMONES

Isolation of Androsterone. The following functions are characteristic of the testicular hormone present in the inner secretions of the testis: control of the development of the male genital organs (seminal vesicles, prostates, Cowper glands, vas deferens, and penis); influence on the secretory activity of the accessory glands and on the character of the sperms; development of secondary sex characteristics. The most satisfactory methods for the detection and quantitative bioassay of the hormone are those depending upon its influence on the development of the seminal vesicles of castrated male rodents (Loewe and Moore test) and upon the ability of the hormone to promote comb growth in capons (coxcomb test of Koch). The second method, which originated with Pézard[1] and which was placed upon a

---

[15] Robson and Schönberg, *Nature*, **140**, 196 (1937); Dodds, Fitzgerald and Lawson, *ibid.*, **140**, 772 (1937); Robson, Schönberg and Fahim, *ibid.*, **142**, 292 (1938).

[16] Chamelin and Funk, *Arch. Biochem.*, **2**, 9 (1943).

[17] Rauscher, *Klin. Wochschr.*, **21**, 855 (1942) [*C. A.*, **38**, 2711 (1944)]; Thiel, *Farm. Peruana*, **1**, 24 (1943) [*C. A.*, **38**, 166 (1944)].

[18] Council on Pharmacy and Chemistry: "Stilbestrol." *J. Am. Med. Assoc.*, **113**, 2312 (1939).

[19] Dean, H. Q. Woodward and Twombly. *Surgery*, **16**, 169 (1944) [*C. A.*, **39**, 4951 (1945)].

[20] Herbst, *J. Am. Med. Assoc.*, **120**, 1116 (1942).

[21] Nelson, *Yale J. Biol. Med.*, **17**, 217 (1944); Šavnik and Premru, *Z. Krebsforsch.*, **51**, 337 (1941); [*Chem. Zentr.*, II, 1157 (1941)]; Swaab, *Nederland. Tijdschr. Geneeskunde*, **85**, 4058 (1941) [*C. A.*, **37**, 3181 (1943)]; Shimkin and Grady, *J. Natl. Cancer Inst.*, **1**, 119 (1940); Lacassagne, *Compt. rend. soc. biol.*, **129**, 641 (1938).

[1] Pézard, *Compt. rend.*, **153**, 1027 (1911).

quantitative basis by Gallagher and Koch[2] was employed by Butenandt and Tscherning[3] in work leading to the first isolation of a male sex hormone. In the technique[4] employed by these investigators, the capon unit (c.u.) is defined as the amount of substance which, when administered to each of three capons on two successive days, produces in the course of the third and fourth day an average increase of 20 percent in the area of the comb. The area is measured on a shadowgraph of the comb by means of a planimeter.

The amount of hormone present in the genital organs is extremely small and early attempts of several investigators to obtain pure material from testis tissue met with failure. Small amounts of a male hormone, however, occur in the blood and in the urine of normal males, and the systematic investigation of the latter source by Butenandt and Tscherning eventually led to success. From a crude extract supplied by the Schering-Kahlbaum Company, these investigators achieved the first isolation of a crystalline hormone in 1931. In the original work some 15,000 liters of urine yielded only 15 mg. of the hormone. Once the method of separation had been perfected, higher yields were obtained. According to bioassay, 1 liter of male urine contains approximately 1 mg. of the hormone (500–600 c.u.).

In the first step of the process[5] the urine was acidified, concentrated, and extracted with chloroform. A large amount of inert material was removed from the chloroform solution by extraction with alkali, and steam distillation of the neutral fraction removed an additional quantity of inactive material. Further enrichments were accomplished by subjecting the residue to alkaline hydrolysis and to hydrolysis with hydrochloric acid. The unhydrolyzed residue containing the hormone was then dissolved in benzene and the solution diluted extensively with petroleum ether and extracted with 60 percent alcohol. A highly active extract was obtained (1 c.u. = 1–1.4 mg.), but it was not improved by the further application of similar methods. In the course of the separations the male hormone had behaved so much like estrone, except for the absence of acidic properties, as to suggest a similarity in structure. The purified oil was thus treated with various reagents for the hydroxyl and for the carbonyl group and any change in physiological activity noted. The active principle was found to be ketonic in character, for with hydroxylamine a crystallizate was obtained which removed nearly all activity from the oil. The purified oxime yielded on hydrolysis a mixture of substances that could be separated

[2] Gallagher and F. C. Koch, *J. Biol. Chem.*, **84,** 495 (1929).

[3] Butenandt, *Z. angew. Chem.*, **44,** 905 (1931).

[4] Butenandt and Tscherning, *Z. physiol. Chem.*, **229,** 167 (1934).

[5] For a detailed account see Butenandt and Tscherning, Ref. 4, also, Tscherning, *Ergeb. Physiol. exp. Pharmakol.*, **35,** 301 (1932).

by fractional sublimation in high vacuum and by crystallization. The principal component was a ketone melting at 178° and containing one capon unit in 150–200 γ (0.15–0.20 mg.) of material. On the basis of further chemical characterization, which indicated that the substance is a sterol-like ketone, Butenandt named the hormone androsterone (Gr. *andro-*, male). Androsterone was found to be completely saturated, and the presence of an alcoholic hydroxyl group was established by the preparation of an acetate. The great difficulty of isolation imposed serious limitations on the work of characterization, and the combustion of the hormone presented a further difficulty. Reliable analyses of the acetate,[6] however, pointed to the formula $C_{19}H_{30}O_2$ or $C_{18}H_{28}O_2$. Either formula would indicate a carbon skeleton containing four reduced rings, and the nature of both oxygen atoms was clear from the character of the derivatives. This information, though meager, was suggestive (and accurate), for it pointed to a structural relationship to the sterols and a still closer relationship to estrone, a C_{18}-hydroxyketone having a four-ring system. On the basis of this analogy, Butenandt suggested what has proved to be the correct formula for androsterone at a time (1932) when no more than 25 mg. of the hormone had been obtained in a pure condition!

Androsterone from Cholesterol. At the time when the problem had reached this highly suggestive but still uncertain state, Ruzicka[1] (1934) undertook an investigation of the question of structure by the preparative route. It seemed possible that androsterone arises in the organism as a degradation product of a reduced sterol or of lithocholic acid, and Ruzicka attempted to produce a ketone of the structure suggested by Butenandt by oxidative degradation of cholestanyl acetate. Windaus had shown that the side chain of the sterols can be degraded to that of the bile acids by chromic acid oxidation, and Ruzicka applied this method to cholestanyl acetate in the hope of isolating a nuclear fragment. Most of the material was acidic, but a small neutral fraction yielded a crystalline semicarbazone and from this a hydroxyketone of the expected composition was obtained. The substance differed in melting point from androsterone, but it showed definite if weak activity in the comb-growth test and therefore seemed likely to be a stereoisomer. Androsterone has seven asymmetric carbon atoms and is therefore one of 128 theoretically possible stereoisomers. However, all natural sterols and bile acids known at the time have the nuclear configuration of either cholestane or coprostane and contain a C_3-hydroxyl group in either the α- or β-orientation. Therefore androsterone most

[6] Butenandt, *Z. angew. Chem.*, **45**, 655 (1932); *Naturwissenschaften*, **21**, 49 (1933).
[1] Ruzicka, M. W. Goldberg and Brüngger, *Helv. Chim. Acta*, **17**, 1389 (1934); Ruzicka, M. W. Goldberg, J. Meyer, Brüngger and Eichenberger, *ibid.*, **17**, 1395 (1934); Ruzicka, Brüngger, Eichenberger and J. Meyer, *ibid.*, **17**, 1407 (1934).

likely is one of three specific stereoisomers of the hydroxyketone from cholesterol. Fortunately, satisfactory methods of preparing epicholestanol and coprostanol had just become available through discoveries of Vavon (1933) and Grasshof (1934); a route to epicoprostanol was developed by Ruzicka.

The chromic acid oxidation of each stanol as acetate proceeded in very low (unspecified) yield but afforded a hydroxyketone. That from epicholestanol proved to be identical with androsterone, and the structure inferred by Butenandt was thereby established. The hormone is now recognized as the 3α-hydroxy-17-ketone of the allo series. The 3-epimer,

Chart 1. ANDROSTERONE AND ISOMERS

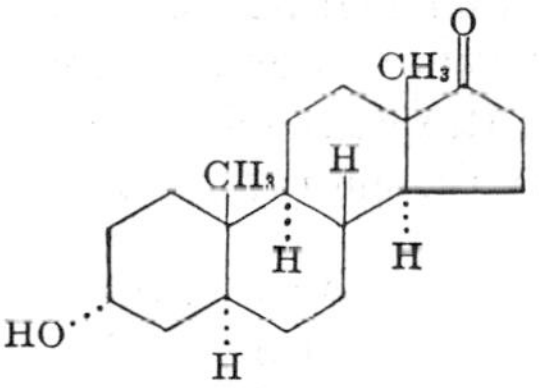

Androsterone
m.p. 183°, [α]$_D$ + 94.5
I. U. 100 γ

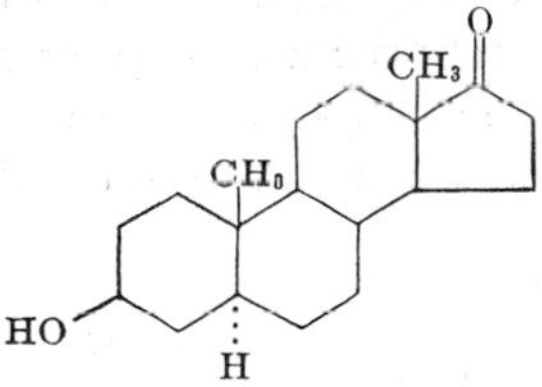

Epiandrosterone
m.p. 174.5°, [α]$_D$ + 88°
I. U. 700 γ

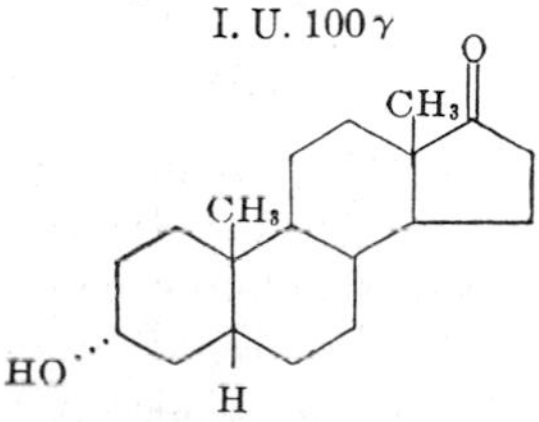

5-Isoandrosterone
m.p. 151°, [α]$_D$ + 105°
Inactive

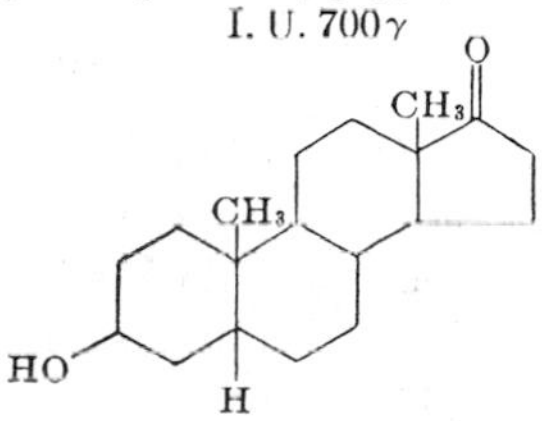

3β-Hydroxyetiocholanone-17
m.p. 152°, [α]$_D$ + 89°
Inactive

prepared from cholestanol, has been known as "isoandrosterone" but is here called epiandrosterone in accordance with a general scheme in which the prefixes epi- and iso- indicate deviations from a natural or typical steroid in configurations at hydroxylated positions and at centers involving the orientation of a carbon–carbon linkage, respectively.[2] The isomer of androsterone that is inverted at C$_5$ has been known as 3α-hydroxyetiocholanone-17 but is here called 5-isoandrosterone. Comparative assays[3]

[2] See Preface.

[3] The observation was confirmed by Butenandt and Cobler, *Z. physiol. Chem.*, **234**, 218 (1935), who prepared epiandrosterone from stigmasterol. See also Wallis and Fernholz, *J. Am. Chem. Soc.*, **57**, 1511 (1935); Dirscherl, *Z. physiol. Chem.*, **235**, 1 (1935).

by Tschopp indicated that epiandrosterone is only one-seventh as active as androsterone and that 5-isoandrosterone, as well as its 3-epimer, is completely inactive.

Ruzicka's complete process[4] for the preparation of androsterone involves the following transformations:

Cholesterol → cholestanol → cholestanone →
epicholestanol → acetate → androsterone acetate
(semicarbazone) → androsterone.

The yield in the oxidation step is extremely low. Callow and Deanesley[5] made various improvements, including separation of androsterone with Girard's reagent, and under the best conditions obtained the hormone in 0.2 percent overall yield from cholesterol. A temperature of 85–90° during the chromic acid oxidation is apparently optimum for androsterone formation; from oxidations at lower temperatures Ruzicka[6] isolated by-products of the side-chain structures I–III. Probably the most satisfactory method

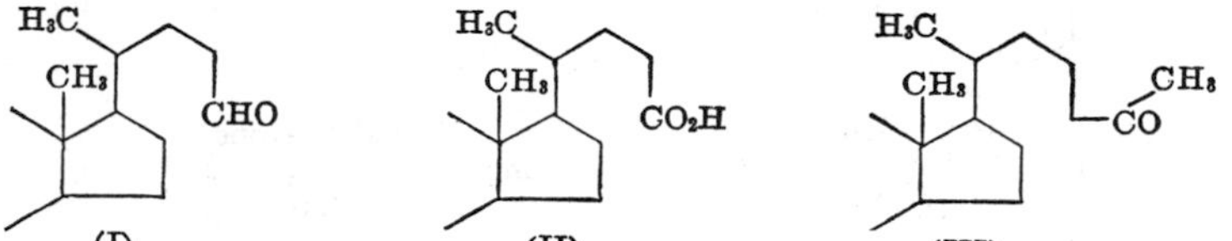

(I)   (II)   (III)

of preparation is from dehydroepiandrosterone (IV), an intermediate in the preparation of testosterone and other hormones from cholesterol. This is converted through the chloride V,[7,8] the saturated chloro compound VI,[9] and the acetate VII (with inversion, as in the sterol series) to androsterone (VIII). In an alternate process described by Marker[10] cholesterol is converted into β-cholestanyl chloride and this is oxidized with chromic acid to the intermediate 3β-chloroandrostanone (VI); again the yield in the oxidation step is low (700 g. of β-cholestanyl chloride → 9.2 g. of VI semicarbazone). Ruzicka[11] carried out the same oxidation of β-cholestanyl chloride, prepared in this instance by the action of phosphorus pentachloride on

[4] Ruzicka and Eichenberger, *Helv. Chim. Acta*, **18**, 430 (1935); French patent 779,132 (1935).

[5] R. K. Callow and Deanesley, *Biochem. J.*, **29**, 1424 (1935).

[6] Ruzicka, Oberlin, Wirz and J. Meyer, *Helv. Chim. Acta*, **20**, 1283 (1937).

[7] Wallis and Fernholz, *J. Am. Chem. Soc.*, **59**, 764 (1937).

[8] Configuration: Shoppee, *J. Chem. Soc.*, 1138 (1946).

[9] Butenandt and Dannenbaum, *Z. physiol. Chem.*, **229**, 192 (1934).

[10] Marker, *J. Am. Chem. Soc.*, **57**, 1755 (1935); Marker, Whitmore and O. Kamm, *ibid.*, **57**, 2358 (1935).

[11] Ruzicka, Wirz and J. Meyer, *Helv. Chim. Acta*, **18**, 998 (1935).

epicholestanol (inversion). The isomeric 3α-chloroandrostanone (m.p. 128°, $[\alpha]_D$ + 94°) is obtained by oxidation of α-cholestanyl chloride.[12]

Chart 2. RELATIONSHIP OF DEHYDROEPIANDROSTERONE TO ANDROSTERONE

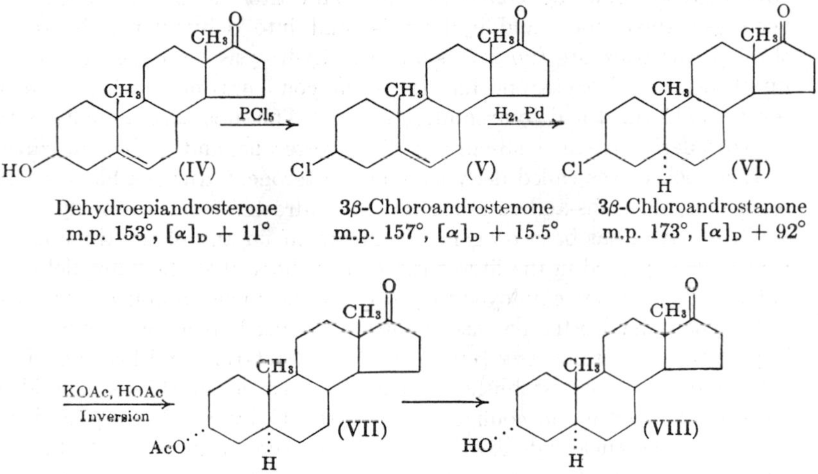

Dehydroepiandrosterone (IV)
m.p. 153°, $[\alpha]_D$ + 11°

$\xrightarrow{PCl_5}$

3β-Chloroandrostenone (V)
m.p. 157°, $[\alpha]_D$ + 15.5°

$\xrightarrow{H_2,\ Pd}$

3β-Chloroandrostanone (VI)
m.p. 173°, $[\alpha]_D$ + 92°

$\xrightarrow[\text{Inversion}]{KOAc,\ HOAc}$

Androsterone acetate (VII)

$\longrightarrow$

Androsterone (VIII)

Other routes to androsterone were actively investigated in the period when this was the only known natural androgen of significant potency, but the substance promptly lost any temporary importance in hormone therapy with the discovery of the more potent testosterone. Application of the Ruzicka procedure of oxidation, however, proved of value in the determination of the orientation of the C_3-hydroxyl group in a number of sterols (stigmasterol,[13] ergosterol,[13] cinchol,[14] sitosterol;[15] all found to be $C_3\beta$) and bile acids (lithocholic acid,[16] $C_3\alpha$). Androsterone has been obtained from 3α-hydroxyallocholanic acid by stepwise Barbier-Wieland degradation to 3α-hydroxyetioallocholanic acid, conversion of this acid into the diphenylethylene, and ozonization.[17]

Dehydroepiandrosterone. This second, weakly androgenic hydroxyketone (IV, Chart 2) was isolated from urine in 1934 by Butenandt along with an inactive unsaturated chloroketone (m.p. 157°) that proved to be

[12] Ruzicka, M. W. Goldberg and Brüngger, *Helv. Chim. Acta*, **17**, 1389 (1934).
[13] Fernholz and P. N. Chakravorty, *Ber.*, **67**, 2021 (1934).
[14] Dirscherl, *Z. physiol. Chem.*, **235**, 1 (1935); **237**, 52, 268 (1935).
[15] Ruzicka and Eichenberger, *Helv. Chim. Acta*, **18**, 430 (1935).
[16] Ruzicka and M. W. Goldberg, *Helv. Chim. Acta*, **18**, 668 (1935).
[17] Dalmer, v. Werder, Honigmann and Heyns, *Ber.*, **68**, 1814 (1935).

merely the chloride of dehydroepiandrosterone formed by the action of hydrochloric acid on this substance in the course of the acid hydrolysis of urine (V, Chart 2).[18] The steric course of the hydrolysis of 3-halosteroids was not known at the time and when Butenandt found that the unsaturated chloroketone could be converted into androsterone by hydrogenation, acetolysis (inversion), and hydrolysis, and into dehydroepiandrosterone through the benzoate (no inversion) and hydrolysis he assumed that the unsaturated hydroxyketone has the same configuration at C_3 as androsterone and named it dehydroandrosterone. The substance actually is the dehydro derivative of the 3-epimer of androsterone, and in the first edition of this book it was called dehydroisoandrosterone. Ruzicka has used the name dehydro-trans-androsterone (OH in androsterone cis to the hydrogen at C_5). There has been no general agreement on any of the three names that have appeared in the literature, and we hope that the name dehydroepiandrosterone here employed may prove to be an acceptable compromise.

Dehydroepiandrosterone was at once recognized as a compound of key importance because of its relationship to androsterone and because of the suspected and soon established correspondence of this 17-ketosteroid to cholesterol in both the configuration of the C_3-hydroxyl group and the location of the nuclear double bond. At the time of its isolation the substance was regarded as a possible natural precursor of both androgens and estrogens.

Chromic Acid Degradation of the Steroid Side Chain. The preparation of dehydroepiandrosterone from cholesterol was reported in 1935 from four laboratories,[1,2,3,4,5] and a preparation from sitosterol was reported from a fifth laboratory.[6] The method consists in the chromic acid oxidation of cholesteryl acetate dibromide at 45–65° over a period of six to eight hours, debromination of the extracted organic material with zinc and acetic acid, separation of an acidic fraction of which 3β-hydroxy-Δ^5-cholenic acid is the chief component, and treatment of the neutral residue with semicarbazide hydrochloride and sodium acetate in ethanol. The semicarbazone acetate of dehydroepiandrosterone is less soluble than the derivatives of other ketones present (see below) and can be easily separated in pure form;

[18] Butenandt and Dannenbaum, *Z. physiol. Chem.*, **229,** 192 (1934); Butenandt and Tscherning, *ibid.*, **229,** 167 (1934); Butenandt, Dannenbaum, Hanisch and Kudszus, *ibid.*, **237,** 57 (1935).

[1] Butenandt, Dannenbaum, Hanisch and Kudszus, *Z. physiol. Chem.*, **237,** 57 (1935).

[2] Ruzicka and Wettstein, *Helv. Chim. Acta,* **18,** 986 (1935).

[3] Wallis and Fernholz, *J. Am. Chem. Soc.,* **57,** 1379, 1504 (1935).

[4] Schoeller, Serini and Gehrke, *Naturwissenschaften,* **23,** 337 (1935).

[5] French patent, 834,941 (1938) [*C. A.,* **33,** 4602 (1939)].

[6] Oppenauer, *Nature,* **135,** 1039 (1935).

hydrolysis to dehydroepiandrosterone is effected by ethanolic sulfuric acid. Wallis and Fernholz[3] report an overall yield of about 1 percent. Butenandt[1] obtained a higher yield (2.8 percent) by addition of sulfuric acid to the oxidation mixture; the acid permits a lower temperature (50°) and a shorter time of reaction (three hours). A Schering patent[5] claims a yield of about 6.5 percent by oxidation essentially by Butenandt's procedure.[7]

Ruzicka[8] isolated two additional ketones from the semicarbazone residue remaining after separation of dehydroepiandrosterone semicarbazone (II and III, Chart 3). The formation of these ketones is favored by a low temperature of oxidation (28–30°). One product, pregnenolone (II), had

Chart 3. Oxidation of Cholesteryl Acetate Dibromide
(AFTER DEBROMINATION AND HYDROLYSIS)

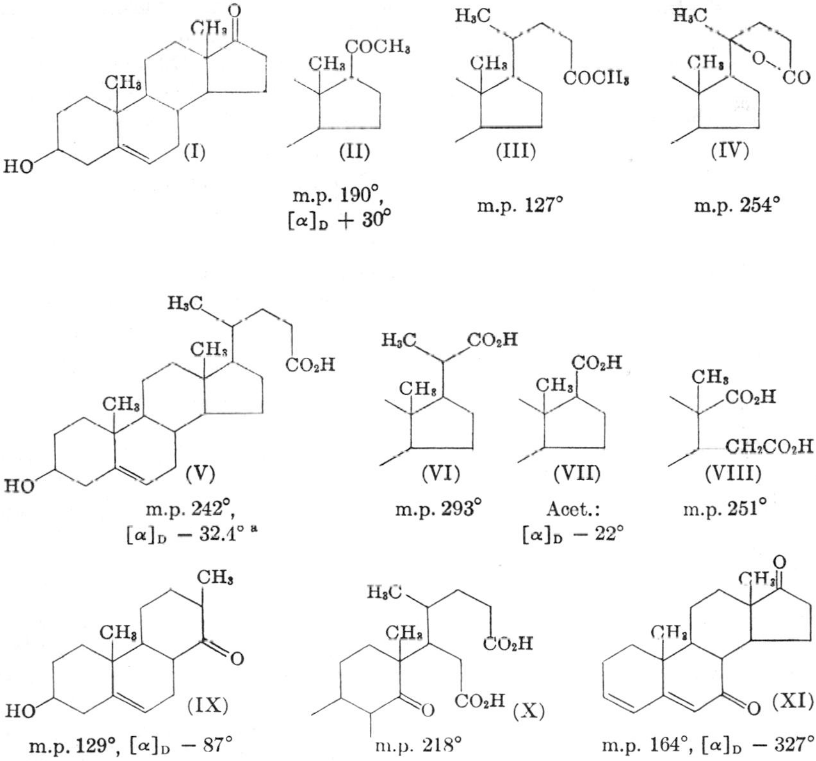

(I)

(II)
m.p. 190°,
$[\alpha]_D + 30°$

(III)
m.p. 127°

(IV)
m.p. 254°

(V)
m.p. 242°,
$[\alpha]_D - 32.4°$ [a]

(VI)
m.p. 293°

(VII)
Acet.:
$[\alpha]_D - 22°$

(VIII)
m.p. 251°

(IX)
m.p. 129°, $[\alpha]_D - 87°$

(X)
m.p. 218°

(XI)
m.p. 164°, $[\alpha]_D - 327°$

[a]Dioxane; communication from Dr. E. Schwenk.

[7] The addition of ammonium nitrate is said to increase the yield slightly: Kiprianov and Frenkel, *J. Gen. Chem.* (*U. S. S. R.*), **9**, 1682 (1939) [*C. A.*, **34**, 3756 (1940)].

[8] Ruzicka and W. H. Fischer, *Helv. Chim. Acta*, **20**, 1291 (1937).

been isolated previously by Japanese investigators.[9] Whitman and
Schwenk[10] describe a procedure for the isolation of this 20-ketone by acetylation of the mixture and selective precipitation of the digitonide of pregnenolone acetate. Ruzicka regards the second ketonic by-product as the
24-ketone (III).

The hydroxylactone IV was isolated from the mother liquors of the
neutral fraction[11] and its structure established[12] by conversion through a
Grignard reaction to the known diphenyldiene:

$$-C(CH_3)=CHCH=C(C_6H_5)_2$$

The chief product isolated from the acid fraction is 3β-hydroxy-Δ^5-cholenic
acid (V),[1,2,3,10,13] a useful intermediate for hormone preparations. Two
products of the further shortening of the side chain have been isolated in
small amounts: 3β-hydroxy-Δ^5-bisnorcholenic acid[14] (VI) and 3β-hydroxy-
Δ^5-etiocholenic acid (VII). The bilianic acid VIII[15] and the ketone IX[16]
result from attack of ring D; the ketone is probably the product of decarboxylation of the β-keto acid. The ketonic dibasic acid X was isolated from
the more soluble sodium salt mixture of the acid fraction.[14] $\Delta^{3,5}$-Andro-
stadiene-7,17-dione[17] (XI) probably is not a primary oxidation product but
arises from a 3β-acetoxy precursor during acid hydrolysis.

Simpler compounds having isoalkyl side chains have been found to be
convertible into tertiary alcohols by oxidation with chromic acid in the
usual way (about 10% water present), or better with chromic anhydride in
anhydrous acetic acid; the tertiary alcohols formed are subject to ready
oxidative fission by the same reagent:[17]

$$-(CH_2)_nCH(CH_3)_2 \rightarrow -(CH_2)_nC(OH)(CH_3)_2 \rightarrow -(CH_2)_{n-1}COOH + O=C(CH_3)_2$$

The isolation from the above oxidation of the hydroxylactone IV is evidence
of the formation of a tertiary alcohol as a phase in the oxidation of the
steroid, and it may be that all the neutral and acidic products shown in

[9] Fujii and Matsukawa, *J. Pharm. Soc. Japan*, **56**, 24, 93 (1936) [*Chem. Zentr.*, II, 1354 (1936)].

[10] Whitman and Schwenk, U. S. patent 2,221,826 (1940) [*C. A.*, **35**, 1412 (1941)].

[11] Miescher and W. H. Fischer, *Helv. Chim. Acta*, **22**, 155 (1939).

[12] Billeter and Miescher, *Helv. Chim. Acta*, **30**, 1409 (1947); see also Veer and Gold-schmidt, *Rec. trav. chim.*, **66**, 75 (1947). We are informed by Dr. K. Miescher that later evidence places the lactone linkage at C_{17} rather than at C_{20}.

[13] Riegel, Vanderpool and Dunker, *J. Am. Chem. Soc.*, **63**, 1630 (1941).

[14] P. Wieland and Miescher, *Helv. Chim. Acta*, **31**, 211 (1948).

[15] Kuwada, *J. Pharm. Soc. Japan*, **56**, 75 (1936); Kuwada and Miyasaka, *ibid.*, **56**, 631 (1936).

[16] Köster and Logemann, *Ber.*, **73**, 298 (1940).

[17] Fieser, *J. Am. Chem. Soc.*, **70**, 3237 (1948).

Chart 3, as well as methyl isohexyl ketone derived from the side chain, arise through initial hydroxylations at the various tertiary positions; direct further oxidation of the alcohols seems more likely than oxidation through anhydro derivatives.[12]

The oxidative removal of the bile acid side chain as a route to hormone intermediates has been investigated with less success.[18] The nature and yields of five products isolated from the large-scale chromic acid oxidation of the methyl ester diacetate of desoxycholic acid are shown in Chart 4.

Chart 4. OXIDATION OF BILE ACID DERIVATIVE

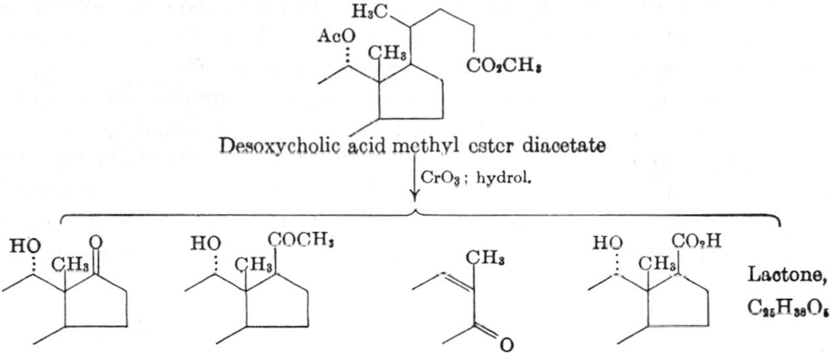

H₃C

AcO
CH₃   CO₂CH₃

Desoxycholic acid methyl ester diacetate

CrO₃; hydrol.

(XII) 0.1%   (XIII) 0.1%   (XIV) 0.2%   (XV) 0.1%   (XVI) 0.1%

Lactone, C₂₅H₃₈O₄

The ketones XII and XIII, the acid XV, and probably the lactone XVI, are analogous to products derived from cholesteryl acetate dibromide, but the yield of the 17-ketone is much lower in this instance. The α,β-unsaturated ketone XIV has an unreactive carbonyl group and was isolated from the nonketonic fraction, but it has typical ultraviolet absorption characteristics; it is analogous to product IX, Chart 3.

Ketonic oxidation products are isolated most satisfactorily through their sparingly soluble semicarbazones. Since the ketones are produced in very low yield and hence at considerable expense, the process of hydrolysis of the semicarbazones has been studied extensively with the view to the elimination of any unnecessary loss. Hydrolysis with sulfuric acid in alcohol[19] or in dioxane[20] with hydrochloric and acetic acids[21] often leads to significant amounts of condensation products or to partial hydrolysis of acetoxy groups.

[18] Reich and Reichstein, *Helv. Chim. Acta*, **26**, 2102 (1943); Reich, *ibid.*, **28**, 863, 892 (1945).

[19] Ruzicka and Wettstein, *Helv. Chim. Acta*, **18**, 986 (1935).

[20] Addinall, FIAT Report No. 996.

[21] Ruzicka, M. W. Goldberg and Brüngger, *Helv. Chim. Acta*, **17**, 1389 (1934).

A process utilizing nitrous acid in acetic acid[22] affords ketones in high yield but sometimes in an impure condition.[23] Hershberg[23] has perfected a superior method of hydrolysis by exchange with pyruvic acid, a carbonyl compound of particularly favorable semicarbazone-hydrolysis constant.[24] The reaction is conducted in the presence of sodium acetate both to avoid deacetylation and to keep the exchange semicarbazone in solution when the mixture is diluted with water. Thus 10 g. of pure dehydroepiandrosterone acetate semicarbazone (m.p. 280°) in 30 cc. of acetic acid was treated at 110° with a solution of 3.2 g. of sodium acetate and 7 g. of 50 percent aqueous pyruvic acid in 20 cc. of acetic acid; after ten minutes, a total of 100 cc. of water was added dropwise under reflux to cause separation of the product in a crystalline condition. The yield of pure dehydroepiandrosterone acetate, m.p. 170.2–170.9°, was 8.28 g. (97%).

Testosterone. By 1935 a number of compounds derived from androsterone and dehydroepiandrosterone had been prepared and assayed for androgenic activity in capons. The α,β-unsaturated Δ^4-androstenedione-3,17, prepared[1,2,3] by the oxidation of dehydroepiandrosterone dibromide and debromination with zinc and acetic acid, attracted attention because of the structural relationship to progesterone, because the compound con-

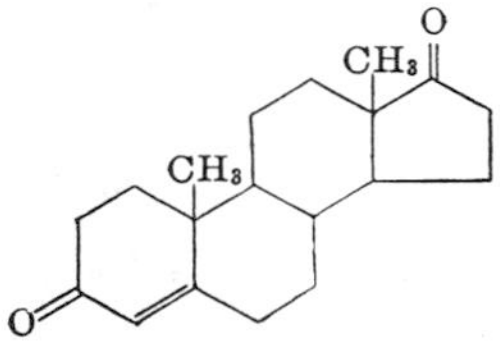

Δ^4-Androstenedione-3, 17
m.p. 174°, $[\alpha]_D + 190°$

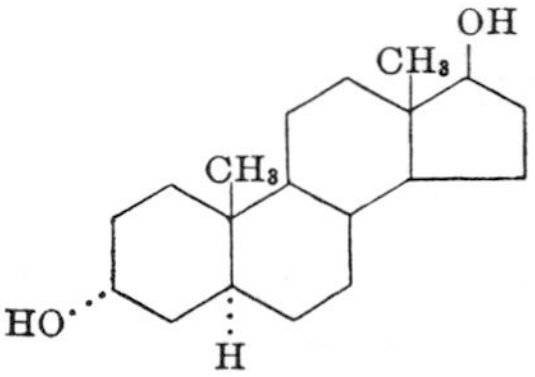

Androstanediol-3α, 17β
m.p. 223°, $[\alpha]_D + 13°$

ceivably could yield androsterone and dehydroepiandrosterone on reduction and estrone by the elimination of methane, and because it was found to be nearly as potent in the capon test as androsterone and also to show estrogenic activity of a low order (in immature rats and mice but not in castrates).[3,4] Also of interest was the dihydro compound resulting from the reduction of the carbonyl group of androsterone with sodium and propyl

[22] Goldschmidt and Veer, *Rec. trav. chim.*, **65**, 796 (1946); **66**, 238 (1947); Wolfrom, *ibid.*, **66**, 238 (1947).

[23] Hershberg, *J. Org. Chem.*, **13**, 542 (1948).

[24] Conant and Bartlett, *J. Am. Chem. Soc.*, **54**, 2881 (1932).

[1] Ruzicka and Wettstein, *Helv. Chim. Acta*, **18**, 986 (1935).

[2] Wallis and Fernholz, *J. Am. Chem. Soc.*, **57**, 1511 (1935).

[3] Butenandt and Kudszus, *Z. physiol. Chem.*, **237**, 75 (1935).

[4] Butenandt and Hanisch, *Ber.*, **68**, 1859 (1935).

alcohol[5] or by hydrogenation in an acidic medium:[6] androstanediol-3α, 17β (configuration later established by correlation with testosterone). As in the case of estrone, the reduction is attended with a marked increase in physiological activity; androstanediol is about three times as potent as androsterone. The observation suggested the possibility that hormones more potent than androsterone might be found.

Still more enlightening were the results of comparisons of the biological actions of androsterone and of testicular extracts. Androsterone was found to produce enlargement of the seminal vesicles, the prostate, and the penis of castrated rats in a manner qualitatively similar to the effects produced by extracts from testes. However, quantitative differential bioassays conducted by Laqueur[7] at Amsterdam (1935) revealed differences. The administration to castrated rats of urinary and testicular extracts of the same capon unitage produced markedly different effects in the rate of growth of the seminal vesicles. In a typical experiment the average weights of the vesicles of the controls, the animals receiving androgen from urine, and those receiving testicular extracts were in the ratios: 1:11:67. The material from testes has about five times the activity per capon unit as androsterone in promoting the growth of the seminal vesicles. Gallagher and Koch[8] then observed highly active testicular extracts to show notable decrease in activity when boiled with alkali; such instability to alkali is not typical of the urinary androgens but is exhibited by the α,β-unsaturated ketone progesterone. The similarly constituted androstenedione shares this property,[1,2] and of all the known compounds assayed, androstenedione had shown particularly high potency in the rat test.[9] At this stage androstenedione appeared to be similar to but not identical with the testicular hormone, because assays of purified concentrates of the latter pointed to higher potency than that of androsterone in both the rat and capon tests.

Then, in June 1935, Laqueur[10] reported the isolation of a testicular hormone, m.p. 154°, to which he gave the name testosterone. About 10 mg. of the pure hormone was isolated from 100 kg. of steer testis tissue.[11] Pure testosterone was found to be about ten times as powerful as androsterone in promoting comb growth; the activity per capon unit in the rat test is about seven times that of androsterone. Testosterone has the absorption spectrum of an α,β-unsaturated ketone and it yields Δ4-androstenedione-3,17

[5] Butenandt and Tscherning, *Z. physiol. Chem.*, **234**, 224 (1935).
[6] Ruzicka, M. W. Goldberg and J. Meyer, *Helv. Chim. Acta*, **18**, 994 (1935).
[7] Dingemanse, Freud and Laqueur, *Nature*, **135**, 184 (1935); David and Freud, *Acta Brevia Neerland.*, **5**, 13 (1935).
[8] Gallagher and F. C. Koch, *Endocrinology*, **18**, 107 (1934).
[9] Tschopp, *Nature*, **136**, 258 (1935).
[10] David, Dingemanse, Freud and Laqueur, *Z. physiol. Chem.*, **233**, 281 (1935).
[11] David, *Acta Brevia Neerland.*, **5**, 85, 108 (1935).

on oxidation. These facts, and the known high potency of androstanediol as compared with that of androsterone, strongly suggested that the hormone is the 17-dihydride of androstenedione. This inference was soon verified by synthetic preparations of an identical product reported by Butenandt[4,12] in September and shortly afterward by Ruzicka.[13,14] In the first method[4,12,13] dehydroepiandrosterone was reduced with sodium and propyl alcohol to androstenediol and this was converted by partial hydrolysis of the diacetate into the 17-monoacetate. An apparent improvement,[14] unfortunately reported without citation of yields, takes advantage of the greater resistance of a benzoate than an acetate group to saponification. Dehydroepiandrosterone acetate (Chart 5) on hydrogenation with a nickel catalyst is selectively reduced at the carbonyl group, and benzoylation of the product gives the 3-acetate-17-benzoate. In the partial saponification of this mixed ester in methanol with one mole of alkali, the alkali functions catalytically to produce methyl acetate by ester interchange and only about 0.1 mole is consumed. The 17-benzoate was initially converted into testosterone benzoate by oxidation of the 5,6-dibromide and debromination with sodium iodide or zinc; Oppenauer[15] later effected oxidation of the 17-acetate with aluminum *t*-butoxide and acetone in benzene.

By far the simplest and most efficient method of preparing testosterone from dehydroepiandrosterone is the microbiological process of Mamoli (Chart 5, B). The steps of oxidation[16] and reduction[17] were first conducted separately, and later combined into one operation[18] as follows. Oxidation to androstenedione is accomplished by shaking a suspension of finely divided dehydroepiandrosterone and oxidizing yeast in a phosphate buffer with oxygen for two days. The solid matter containing the dione is then collected and extracted with alcohol, and the concentrated extract added slowly to an actively fermenting yeast in a sugar medium (yield 81%).

Of the other methods listed (Chart 5, C), the first is not practicable but demonstrates that androstenediol can be oxidized selectively at C_3 by the Oppenauer method.[19] Testosterone is also formed in low yield by the dehydrobromination of androstenediol dibromide.[20] Miescher[21] found that

[12] Butenandt and Hanisch, *Z. physiol. Chem.*, **237**, 89 (1935).

[13] Ruzicka, *J. Am. Chem. Soc.*, **57**, 2011 (1935); Wettstein, *Schweiz. med. Wochschr.*, **65**, 912 (1935); Ruzicka and Wettstein, *Helv. Chim. Acta*, **18**, 1264 (1935).

[14] Ruzicka, Wettstein and Kägi, *ibid.*, **18**, 1478 (1935).

[15] Oppenauer, *Rec. trav. chim.*, **56**, 137 (1937).

[16] Mamoli and Vercellone, *Ber.*, **71**, 1686 (1938).

[17] Mamoli and Vercellone, *Ber.*, **70**, 470 (1937).

[18] Mamoli, *Ber.*, **71**, 2278 (1938).

[19] Kuwada and Joyama, *J. Pharm. Soc. Japan*, **57**, 247, 914 (1937).

[20] Galinovsky, *Ber.*, **74**, 1624 (1941).

[21] Miescher and W. H. Fischer, *Helv. Chim. Acta*, **22**, 158 (1939).

Chart 5. Testosterone from Dehydroepiandrosterone

A. Butenandt-Ruzicka Method

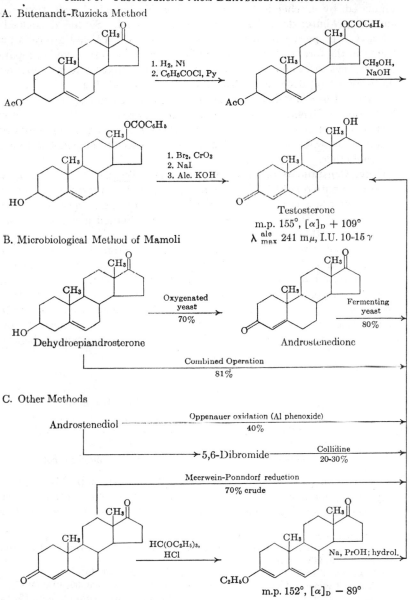

1. H₂, Ni
2. C₆H₅COCl, Py

CH₃OH,
NaOH

1. Br₂, CrO₃
2. NaI
3. Alc. KOH

Testosterone
m.p. 155°, [α]_D + 109°
λ_{max}^{alc} 241 mμ, I.U. 10-15 γ

B. Microbiological Method of Mamoli

Dehydroepiandrosterone

Oxygenated
yeast
70%

Androstenedione

Fermenting
yeast
80%

Combined Operation
81%

C. Other Methods

Androstenediol ———— Oppenauer oxidation (Al phenoxide) ————
40%

➤5,6-Dibromide———— Collidine
20-30%

Meerwein-Ponndorf reduction
70% crude

HC(OC₂H₅)₃,
HCl

Na, PrOH; hydrol.

m.p. 152°, [α]_D − 89°

the selective microbiological reduction of androstenedione at C_{17} can be simulated by a chemical process: Meerwein-Ponndorf reduction with aluminum t-butoxide and secondary butyl alcohol. Serini[22] developed a method of preparing testosterone in which the C_3-carbonyl group is protected in the form of the 3-enol ethyl ether.[23] The derivative is prepared by the reaction of androstenedione with ethyl orthoformate in benzene in the presence of alcoholic hydrogen chloride; the substance is formulated in the chart as a $\Delta^{3,5}$-diene because this structure should be stable to acid. Reduction at C_{17} and hydrolysis afforded testosterone. A saturated ketone such as cholestanone reacts with ethyl orthoformate to give the 3-diethylacetal, which when heated in xylene loses one molecule of alcohol and yields the enol ether.

Other Constituents of Testicular Extracts. Testosterone has been isolated in minute quantities from horse testes,[1] and its presence in fractions from swine testes is indicated by the infrared absorption spectrum.[2] The processing of extracts from other species has afforded a number of substances other than testosterone.

Ogata and Hirano[3] isolated five substances from boar testes. One substance (m.p. 130°) possesses high androgenic activity and has a melting point close to that of androstenedione, but it is not identical with this compound. A second substance named testalolone ($C_{21}H_{32}O_3$, m.p. 264°) forms an insoluble digitonide, a monobenzoate, and a dioxime; it has a saturated ring system and shows reducing properties and has been assigned the provisional formula indicated below (Hirano). Another substance is believed

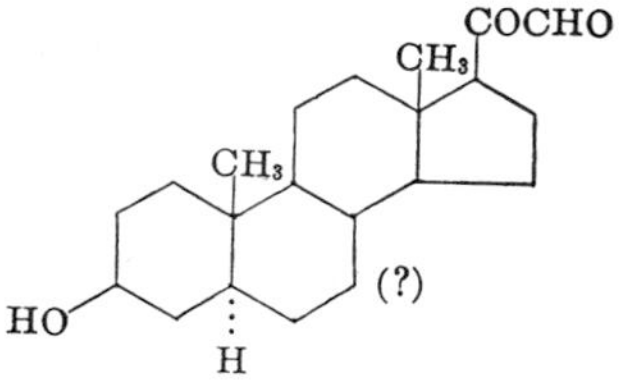

Testalolone

$$CH_2O(CH_2)_{15}CH_3$$
$$|$$
$$CHOH$$
$$|$$
$$CH_2OH$$

Testriol = Chimyl alcohol

to be the monopalmitate of propanediol-1,2; another (m.p. 224°) is probably a C_{23-24} compound containing three atoms of oxygen; another, testriol, was regarded as an open-chain triatomic alcohol but has since been isolated

[22] Serini and Köster, *Ber.*, **71**, 1766 (1938).

[23] A process utilizing the 3-semicarbazone is less satisfactory; Westphal and Hellmann, *Ber.*, **70**, 2136 (1937).

[1] Tagmann, Prelog and Ruzicka, *Helv. Chim. Acta*, **29**, 440 (1946).

[2] Prelog, Tagmann, Lieberman and Ruzicka, *Helv. Chim. Acta*, **30**, 1080 (1947).

[3] Ogata and Hirano, *J. Pharm. Soc. Japan*, **54**, 199 (1934); Hirano, *ibid.*, **56**, 122, 717 (1936).

from swine testes[4] and from swine spleen[5] and identified as chimyl alcohol.[6] Extended examination of the constituents of swine testis tissue by Prelog, Ruzicka, and co-workers[7] has led to the isolation of a number of substances, some of them related to cholesterol, namely:

Δ^4-Cholestenone-3
$\Delta^{4,6}$-Cholestadienone-3
Cholestanetriol-3β,5α,6β
Cholestane-3β-ol-6-one
Δ^4-Cholestenediol-3β,6
7β-Hydroxycholesterol
$\Delta^{3,5}$-Cholestadiene-7-one

Some of these steroids contain oxygen substituents at positions 3 and 6 and may be related to the 3,6-dihydroxycholanic acids of swine bile. The 7-oxygenated compounds may arise by autoxidation of cholesterol, also a constituent of testis tissue. A small amount of friedelin, the triterpene of cork, was isolated. Prelog also isolated the following already known steroids: Δ^5-pregnene-3β-ol-20-one,[8] allopregnane-3β-ol-20-one, and allopregnane-3α-ol-20-one.

One of the nonketonic fractions of the swine testis extract was observed to have a pronounced musklike odor, and chromatographic separation yielded two crystalline monounsaturated alcohols of the formula $C_{19}H_{30}O$. One alcohol forms an insoluble digitonide, the other does not. Both alcohols (but not their dihydro derivatives) give a positive Kägi-Miescher color test characteristic of steroids containing or capable of forming a 16,17-double bond. These observations suggested the formulas shown in Chart 6, which were verified by the synthetic preparation[9] of identical alcohols through Δ^{16}-androstenone-3. These alcohols bear some structural analogy to civetone, a large-ring unsaturated ketone of musk odor which can be similarly formulated. Of the two alcoholic derivatives, the 3α-hydroxy compound has the more intense musk odor. The saturated ketone, androstanone-3, has a penetrating "urine" smell.[10] The two cis-decalin epimers, Δ^{16}-etiocholenol-3α and -3β, are odorless.[11]

[4] Prelog, Ruzicka and Steinmann, *Helv. Chim. Acta*, **27**, 674 (1944).
[5] Prelog and Beyerman, *Helv. Chim. Acta*, **28**, 350 (1945).
[6] Baer and H. O. L. Fischer, *J. Biol. Chem.*, **140**, 397 (1941).
[7] Ruzicka and Prelog, *Helv. Chim. Acta*, **26**, 975 (1943); Prelog, Ruzicka and Stein, *ibid.*, **26**, 2222 (1943); Prelog, Tagmann, Lieberman and Ruzicka, *ibid.*, **30**, 1080 (1947).
[8] Also isolated from the same source by Haines, R. H. Johnson, Goodwin and Kuizenga, *J. Biol. Chem.*, **174**, 925 (1948).
[9] Prelog, Ruzicka and P. Wieland, *Helv. Chim. Acta*, **27**, 66 (1944).
[10] Prelog, Ruzicka, Meister and P. Wieland, *Helv. Chim. Acta*, **28**, 618 (1945).
[11] Derivatives with 3- and 17-alkyl groups are described by Ruzicka, Prelog and Meister, *Helv. Chim. Acta*, **28**, 1651 (1945); Ruzicka, Meister and Prelog, *ibid.*, **30**, 867 (1947).

Chart 6. CONSTITUENTS OF TESTICULAR EXTRACTS

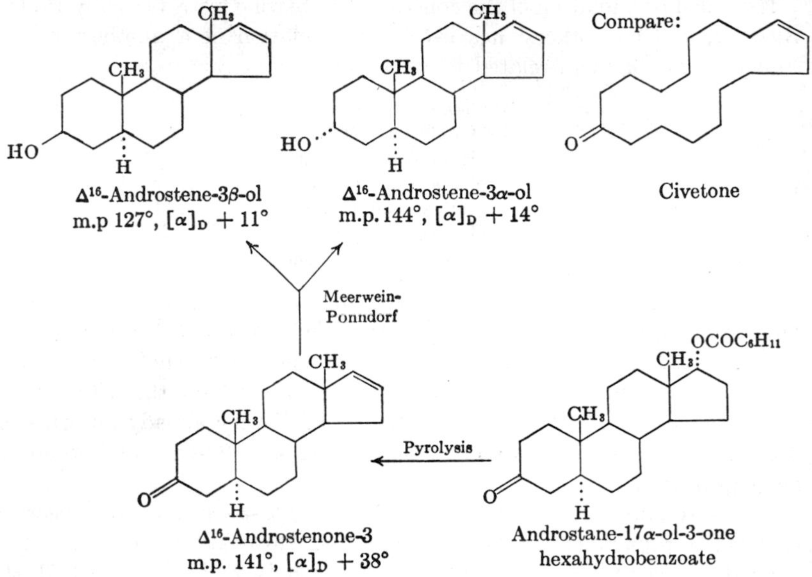

Δ^{16}-Androstene-3β-ol
m.p 127°, $[\alpha]_D$ + 11°

Δ^{16}-Androstene-3α-ol
m.p. 144°, $[\alpha]_D$ + 14°

Compare:

Civetone

Meerwein-
Ponndorf

Pyrolysis

Δ^{16}-Androstenone-3
m.p. 141°, $[\alpha]_D$ + 38°

Androstane-17α-ol-3-one
hexahydrobenzoate

Physiological Activity of Related Substances. A great many compounds related to testosterone or androsterone have been assayed for androgenic activity, for the most part in capons by one of the following two procedures. In the test method of Tschopp[1] the substance is administered subcutaneously in oil for six consecutive days; one capon unit is the minimal daily dose required to produce a 20 percent increase in the area of the comb in a group of at least five leghorn capons. The international unit (I.U.) is the androgenic activity of 0.1 mg. (100 γ) of androsterone. The test employed by Butenandt[2] is described above and differs only in minor details. Several other test procedures have been described; the comb-growth activities summarized in the table are largely those found by the Tschopp test.

None of the related compounds surpass testosterone in comb-growth activity. As in the estradiol series, the hydroxyl group must be in the β-orientation for highest physiological potency. Epitestosterone, which

[1] Tschopp, *Klin. Wochschr.*, **14**, 1064 (1935); Ruzicka, M. W. Goldberg and J. Meyer, *Helv. Chim. Acta*, **18**, 210 (1935).

[2] Butenandt and Tscherning, *Z. physiol. Chem.*, **229**, 185 (1934); Butenandt, Dannenbaum, Hanisch and Kudszus, *ibid.*, **237**, 57 (1936).

Androgenic Activity (Comb-growth Test)

COMPOUND	M.p.	$[\alpha]_D^{alc}$	I.U., γ
Testosterone (17β-ol)	155°	+109°	15
Epitestosterone (17α-ol)	201°	+71.5°	400
17α-Methyltestosterone	164°	+76°	25–30
17α-Ethyltestosterone	143°	+71°	70–100
17α-Methylandrostane-3α,17β-diol	185°		35
17α-Methylandrostane-3-one-17β-ol	193°		15
Androsterone	183°	+94.5°	100
Acetate	165°	+86°	130
Oxime	215°		500
Lumiandrosterone	146°	−100°	Inactive
Epiandrosterone	175°	+88°	700
Androstane-3α,17β-diol	223°	+13°	20–25
Androstane-3α,17α-diol	228°		350
Androstane-3β,17β-diol	164°	+4.2°	500
Androstane-3β,17α-diol	214°		
Androstane-17β-ol-3-one	181°		32°	20
Androstane-17α-ol-3-one	180°		300
Δ^5-Androstene-3α,17β diol	209°	−56°	35
Δ^5-Androstene-3β,17β-diol	184°	−50°	500
Dehydroandrosterone (Δ^5-3α-ol-17-one)	223°	0°	100
Dehydroepiandrosterone (Δ^5-3β-ol-17-one)	153°	+11°	200
Δ^4-Androstene-3β-ol-17-one	130°		150–200
Androstanedione-3,17	133°	+111°	120–130
Δ^4 Androstenedione	174°	+190°	120
$\Delta^{4,6}$-Androstadiene-17β-ol-3-one	211°		200

has a 17α-oriented hydroxyl group, is much less active than testosterone; the same relationship is seen between the C_{17}-epimeric androstane-3α,17-diols[3] and androstane-17-ol-3-ones. Thus androstane-17β-ol-3-one, or

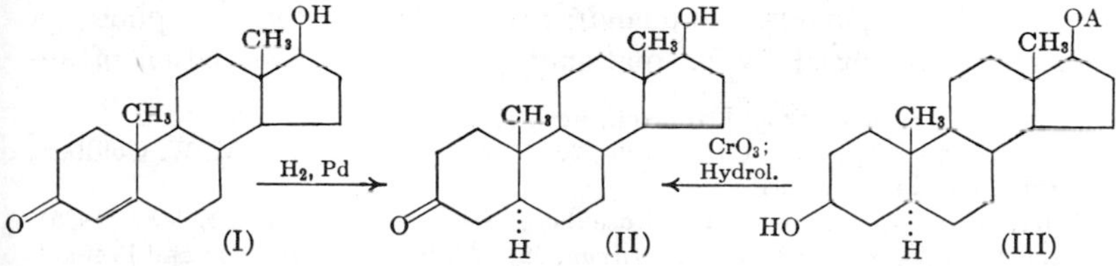

(I)   (II)   (III)

Testosterone   Androstane-17β-ol-3-one

$A \begin{cases} COC_6H_5 \\ COCH_2CH_2CO_2H \end{cases}$

[3] Preparation of the four androstane-3,17-diols: see Testosterone, Refs. 5 and 6; Ruzicka and Kägi, *Helv. Chim. Acta*, **20**, 1557 (1937); Ruzicka, M. W. Goldberg and Rosenberg, *ibid.*, **18**, 1487 (1935); Ruzicka and Rosenberg, *ibid.*, **19**, 357 (1936); Butenandt, Tscherning and Hanisch, *Ber.*, **68**, 2097 (1935); Mamoli and Schramm, *Ber.*, **71**, 2698 (1938).

4-dihydrotestosterone (II), is nearly as active as testosterone whereas the
17α-ol is only weakly active; the substance (II) has been prepared by the
hydrogenation of testosterone[4] and from dehydroepiandrosterone through
the intermediate esters III.[5]

17α-Methyltestosterone (VI), readily prepared by the action of a tenfold
excess of methyl Grignard reagent on dehydroepiandrosterone and oxidation of the dibromide[6] or by the Oppenauer method (40% yield),[7] is slightly

(IV)   (V)   (VI)
                    17α-Methyltestosterone

less active than testosterone in the capon test but may be somewhat more
active in the rat test.   That the Grignard addition results almost exclusively in the β-hydroxy-α-methyl orientation at C_{17} can be inferred from
analogy to a number of additions of established orientation observed in the
cortical hormone series.   The high potency of 17α-methyltestosterone is
not shared by carbinols with larger alkyl or aralkyl groups.   Difficulties
were encountered in the preparation of 17α-ethyltestosterone because the
17-carbonyl group is to some extent reduced (in the usual steric sense) by
the action of ethyl Grignard reagent.[8]   The compound is more readily
prepared by hydrogenation of 17α-ethinylandrostene-3β,17β-diol and
Oppenauer oxidation.[9]   17α-Ethinyltestosterone is almost inactive in the
capon test but has progestational activity.

Comparison of 3-epimers of the androsterone, androstanediol, and androstenediol series shows that the 3α-compounds are invariably more active
than the 3β-compounds.   Lumiandrosterone (VII), the C_{13}-epimer of
androsterone produced by irradiation,[10] is inactive.   Acetylation of an-

[4] Butenandt, Tscherning and Hanisch, *Ber.*, **68**, 2097 (1935).

[5] Ruzicka and Kägi, *Helv. Chim. Acta*, **20**, 1557 (1937); Ruzicka, M. W. Goldberg
and Grob, *ibid.*, **24**, 1151 (1941).

[6] Ruzicka, M. W. Goldberg and Rosenberg, *Helv. Chim. Acta*, **18**, 1487 (1935);
Fujii and Matsukawa, *J. Pharm. Soc. Japan*, **55**, 1333 (1935); Kiprianov and Frenkel,
J. Gen. Chem. (U. S. S. R.), **9**, 1682 (1939) [*C. A.*, **34**, 3756 (1940)].

[7] Chinaeva, Ushakov and Marchevskiĭ, *J. Gen. Chem. (U. S. S. R.)*, **9**, 1865 (1939)
[*C. A.*, **34**, 4073 (1940)].

[8] Butenandt, Cobler and Josef Schmidt, *Ber.*, **69**, 448 (1936); Butenandt and
Schmidt-Thomé, *ibid.*, **69**, 882 (1936); Butenandt, Schmidt-Thomé and Paul, *ibid.*,
71, 1313 (1938); Ruzicka and Rosenberg, *Helv. Chim. Acta*, **19**, 357 (1936).

[9] Ruzicka, K. Hofmann and Meldahl, *Helv. Chim. Acta*, **21**, 597 (1938).

[10] Butenandt and Poschmann, *Ber.*, **77**, 394 (1944).

drosterone alters the effective dose only slightly, but the acetate exhibits a markedly protracted action. In the series of higher esters the activity in the comb-growth test falls off with increasing molecular weight but the activity in the rat test increases.[11] Initial attempts to prepare the Δ^1-isomer of testosterone (VIII) by the action of potassium acetate on

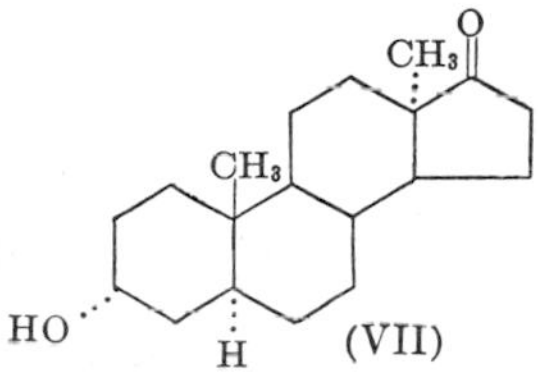

(VII)	(VIII)	(IX)
Lumiandrosterone	Δ^1-Androstene-17β-ol-3-one	Δ^5-Androstene-
	m.p. 150°, $[\alpha]_D$ + 53.5°	17β-ol-4-one
	λ_{max}^{alc} 230 mμ	m.p. 159°, $[\alpha]_D$ − 42°
		$\lambda_{max}^{CHCl_3}$ 240 mμ

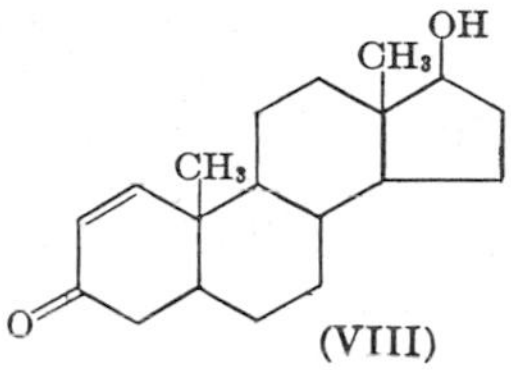

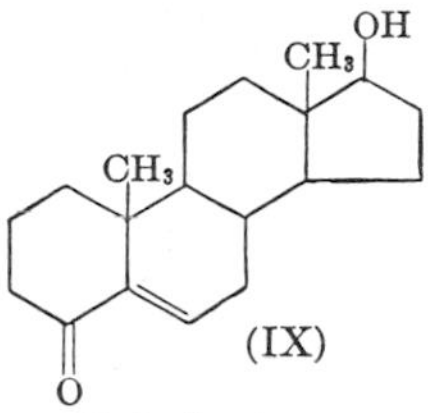

2-bromoandrostane-17β-ol-3-one gave a substance identified as the Δ^5-unsaturated 4-ketone IX.[12] The true Δ^1-isomer VIII was obtained by dehydrohalogenation with collidine; it has about half the androgenic activity of androsterone.[13] The isomeric 4-ketone IX has no androgenic activity but is a weakly active estrogen (200 γ).

Certain steroids that are not androgens exhibit male hormone activity of a special type described by Selye.[14] Pregnenolone (Δ^5-3β-ol-20-one) has no ordinary androgenic activity, but it prevents testicular atrophy that normally follows estradiol treatment or hypophysectomy.[15] Δ^5-Androstene-3β,17β-diol exhibits this spermatogenic action in higher order than other substances assayed (rat dose, 0.5 mg.); the 17α-methyl derivative of the diol is half as active and the 17β-methyl epimer is one-quarter as active. Testosterone, 17α-methyltestosterone, pregnenolone, and progesterone are effective at a dosage of 10 mg.

D-Homosteroids. An interesting type of compound in which ring D is enlarged by one carbon atom was encountered in attempts to employ two different synthetic methods for the introduction of the two-carbon side chain of progesterone or of the cortical hormones. The Darzens condensation of dehydroepiandrosterone acetate with ethyl α,α-dichloropropionate, followed by alkali treatment and decarboxylation, gave both the

[11] Ruzicka and Wettstein, *Helv. Chim. Acta*, **19**, 1141 (1936).

[12] Butenandt and Dannenberg, *Ber.*, **71**, 1681 (1938); Butenandt and Ruhenstroth-Bauer, *ibid.*, **77**, 397 (1944).

[13] Butenandt and Dannenberg, *Ber.*, **73**, 206 (1940).

[14] Selye, *Endocrinology*, **30**, 437 (1942).

[15] Masson, *Am. J. Med. Sci.*, **209**, 324 (1945); **212**, 1 (1946).

expected Δ^5-pregnenolone (IV, Chart 7) and an isomeric substance[1,2] named neopregnenolone (Miescher), now known to have the structure V. The ratio of the isomers varies with the conditions of decarboxylation. A product related to the anomalous isomer was encountered in the attempt to hydrate the 17-ethinylcarbinol VI to the 17-acetocarbinol VIII;[3] at the

Chart 7. ENLARGEMENT OF RING D

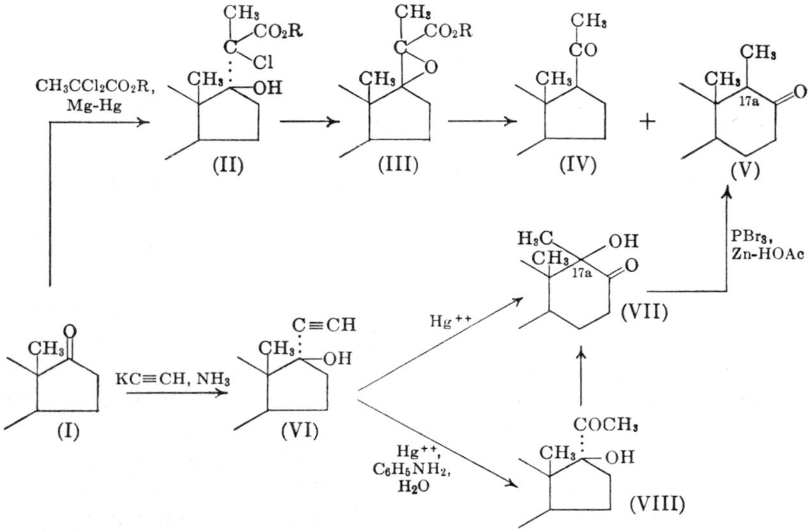

time it was not known that orientation of the ethinyl and hydroxyl groups in VI are the opposite of the orientations in the natural C_{21}-steroids. Direct hydration in the presence of mercuric salts, or addition of acetic acid to the triple bond and hydrolysis, gave a D-homo hydroxyketone (VII) convertible into Miescher's neopregnenolone (V).[4,5] The presence of a 6-membered D-ring was established by selenium dehydrogenation of the saturated diol corresponding to VII to a product identified as 1-methylchrysene.[6]

Stavely[5] later effected the hydration of the ethinylcarbinol to the normal product VIII (Δ^5-pregnene-3β,17β-diol-20-one); Shoppee and Prins[7] found

[1] Yarnall and Wallis, *J. Am. Chem. Soc.*, **59**, 951 (1937).

[2] Miescher and Kägi, *Chemistry and Industry*, **16**, 276 (1938); *Helv. Chim. Acta*, **22**, 184 (1939).

[3] Ruzicka and K. Hofmann, *Helv. Chim. Acta*, **20**, 1280 (1937).

[4] Ruzicka and Meldahl, *Helv. Chim. Acta*, **22**, 421 (1939).

[5] Stavely, *J. Am. Chem. Soc.*, **61**, 79 (1939); **62**, 489 (1940); **63**, 3127 (1941).

[6] Ruzicka and Meldahl, *Helv. Chim. Acta*, **23**, 364 (1940).

[7] Shoppee and Prins, *Helv. Chim. Acta*, **26**, 185, 201, 1004 (1943).

that the diacetate of VI can be converted into the diacetate of VIII in 78 percent yield by Stavely's method. The structure of VIII was established by degradation to dehydroepiandrosterone.[5] The normal product VIII readily rearranges to the D-homo derivative under the influence of base or acetic anhydride and boron fluoride; Shoppee and Prins[7] interpret the reaction as a pinacolic rearrangement. Either of the two C_{17a}-epimers can be obtained in quantitative yield; one (m.p. 277°, $[\alpha]_D$ – 110°) with potassium hydroxide in methanol, the other (m.p. 178°, $[\alpha]_D$ – 62°) by treatment with alumina. The tertiary alcoholic group of the higher-melting and more levorotatory epimer shows evidence of greater hindrance (BF_3-catalyzed acetylation; initial rate of hydrolysis) than that of the isomer presumably because of proximity to the C_{12}-methylene group, and therefore probably has the α-orientation.[7] The rearrangement resulting in ring enlargement is not dependent upon the steric orientation at C_{17}, since 17α-hydroxyprogesterone yields epimeric D-homo derivatives on treatment with methanolic potassium hydroxide.[8]

A route to D-homosteroids that are more closely analogous to sex hormones is application of the Tiffaneau ring-enlargement reaction.[9] Thus D-homoandrosterone (XI) was prepared from androsterone cyanohydrin (IX) by reduction of the cyano group and treatment of the amine X with

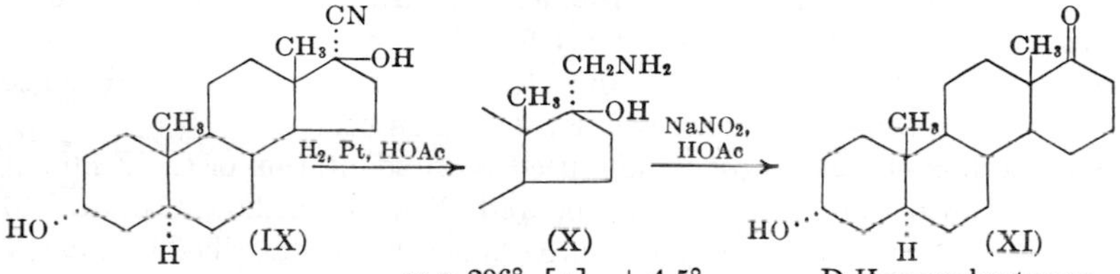

(IX)

(X)
m.p. 206°, $[\alpha]_D$ + 4.5°

(XI)
D-Homoandrosterone
m.p. 205,° $[\alpha]_D$ – 35.5°

nitrous acid.[10] D-Homoepiandrosterone (m.p. 195°, $[\alpha]_D$ – 66.5°) was prepared similarly from dehydroepiandrosterone and the structure established by degradation to 1-methylchrysene.[7] Both epimers possess androgenic activity but, in contrast to the relationship between the weakly active epiandrosterone and the potent androsterone, the 3β-hydroxy compound D-homoepiandrosterone is the more active and is about as potent as androsterone. D-Homoepiandrosterone, a 3-ol-17a-one, was converted through the 3-acetate-17a-benzoate to the 3-one-17a-ol isomer D-homodihydrotestosterone, which was found to have physiological activity

[8] von Euw and Reichstein, *Helv. Chim. Acta*, **24**, 879 (1941).
[9] Tiffeneau, Weill and Tchoubar, *Compt. rend.*, **205**, 54 (1937).
[10] M. W. Goldberg and Monnier, *Helv. Chim. Acta*, **23**, 376, 840 (1940).

comparable to dihydrotestosterone (androstane-3-one-17β-ol). D-Homotestosterone and D-homoandrostene-3,17-dione have also been prepared.[11]

A-Homodihydrotestosterone, m.p. 199°, $[\alpha]_D$ + 108.5°, has been prepared by the same method from the cyanohydrin of 17β-acetoxydihydrotestosterone.[12] The structure is uncertain with respect to the position of the carbonyl group in the enlarged ring A. In contrast with D-homodihydrotestosterone, the A-homo compound is practically inactive (I.U. 500 γ).

17-Ketosteroids of Urine. Androsterone, dehydroepiandrosterone, and 5-isoandrosterone are the principal constituents of the neutral ketonic fraction derived from normal male and female urines, but they are accompanied by a host of other excretory products of hormone metabolism. A systematic investigation of the ketosteroids of normal and pathological urines conducted at Memorial Hospital has led to the isolation of forty-two crystalline products, eleven of which had been isolated previously.[1] The nature of these substances and the significance of the findings are discussed below (Steroid Metabolism); the present section is limited to a brief survey of chemical and physical methods of determination of value in clinical studies of the association of hormone production to health and disease. The steroids excreted in the urine are all products of metabolic transformations of true glandular hormones and provide only an indirect index of specific glandular productivity. It is probably fortuitous that some possess androgenic activity of varying degree and that others are inactive, and hence bioassays of the 17-ketosteroid fraction lack significance.

The method of assay most widely used is an adaptation of the Zimmermann color reaction (m-dinitrobenzene and alkali) by Callow, Callow, and Emmens.[2] Other modified procedures have been described.[3] Pincus[4] has reported an alternate colorimetric method based upon the formation of colored complexes of 17-ketosteroids with antimony trichloride in acetic acid-acetic anhydride; a disadvantage of the test is that dehydroepiandrosterone gives only a weak color. A preliminary report[5] indicates that improvements can be effected by the use of modified reagents, for example: $SbCl_3$-nitrobenzene(or phenol)-acetyl chloride-acetic anhydride; $BiCl_3$-acetyl chloride; $SbCl_3$-benzoyl chloride-nitrobenzene.

[11] M. W. Goldberg, Sicé, Robert and Plattner, *Helv. Chim. Acta*, **30**, 1441 (1947).

[12] M. W. Goldberg and Kirchensteiner, *Helv. Chim. Acta*, **26**, 288 (1943).

[1] Dobriner, Lieberman and Rhoads, *J. Biol. Chem.*, **172**, 241 (1948); Lieberman, Dobriner, Hill, Fieser and Rhoads, *ibid.*, **172**, 263 (1948).

[2] N. H. Callow, R. K. Callow and Emmens, *Biochem. J.*, **32**, 1312 (1938).

[3] Friedgood and Whidden, *Endocrinology*, **25**, 919 (1939); **28**, 237 (1941); Cahen and Salter, *J. Biol. Chem.*, **152**, 489 (1944).

[4] Pincus, *Endocrinology*, **32**, 176 (1943).

[5] L. C. Clark, Jr. and H. Thompson, *Science*, **107**, 429 (1948).

A new approach to the problem was suggested by Wolfe, Hershberg, and Fieser,[6] who showed that the 17-ketosteroids present in neutral urinary extracts can be determined with accuracy in amounts in the order of 10 γ by condensation with Girard's reagent and polarographic analysis of a buffered aqueous solution of the reaction mixture. Unlike cyclopentanone Girard derivatives, the cyclohexanone derivatives are not reducible at the dropping mercury electrode, and hence saturated 3-ketosteroids do not interfere with the determination of 17-ketosteroids. The latter are characterized by a half-wave potential at about − 1.4 v.; α,β-unsaturated ketosteroids show a wave at a lower potential of − 1.1 v. and are determinable simultaneously in the same specimen. Estrone is also determinable by the same method. Dehydroepiandrosterone (and cholesterol) can be determined by microanalytical Oppenauer oxidation to the α,β-unsaturated ketosteroids and polarography of the Girard derivatives.[7] The polarographic method of estimating urinary 17-ketosteroids has been confirmed and extended by others. Werthessen and Baker[8] introduced a technique for spreading the polarographic wave; Barnett, Henly and Morris[9] developed a further improvement consisting in permanganate oxidation of the urinary extract to destroy interfering material and their modified procedure appears satisfactory for routine assays.

A standardized procedure for the separation and fractionation of the 17-ketosteroids of urine is described by Dobriner, Lieberman, et al.[1] Urine is hydrolyzed by short refluxing with sulfuric acid, extracted with ether, and the acidic and phenolic constituents removed by extraction with bicarbonate and then sodium hydroxide. The ketonic material is then separated by treatment with Girard's reagent T,[10] usually repeated on both ketonic and nonketonic fractions to achieve more complete separation. The ketonic fraction is then separated with digitonin into a 3α- and 3β-hydroxyketone fraction, and each of these is submitted to chromatography (alumina and magnesium sulfate). The material is adsorbed on the column from a 2−5 percent solution in ligroin-benzene or benzene and eluted with solvent mixtures of increasing polarity in five fractions. Each fraction is processed with Girard's reagent again, recovered, and chromatographed once more.

[6] Wolfe, Hershberg and Fieser, *J. Biol. Chem.*, **136**, 653 (1940).
[7] Hershberg, Wolfe and Fieser, *J. Biol. Chem.*, **140**, 215 (1941).
[8] Werthessen and C. F. Baker, *Endocrinology*, **36**, 351 (1945).
[9] J. Barnett, Henly and C. J. O. R. Morris, *Biochem. J.*, **40**, 445 (1946); Butt, Henly and C. J. O. R. Morris, *ibid.*, **42**, 447 (1948).
[10] Pincus and Pearlman, *Endocrinology*, **29**, 413 (1941); Talbot, A. M. Butler and MacLachlan, *J. Biol. Chem.*, **132**, 595 (1940); Talbot, Berman and MacLachlan, *ibid.*, **143**, 211 (1942).

PROGESTERONE

In the human ovary, following the ripening and rupture of the follicle, there is formed a tissue which, on account of the abundance of yellow carotene present, is called the corpus luteum or yellow body. The main functions[1] of the corpus luteum are connected with the preparation for and maintenance of pregnancy. The uterine mucosa, which grows to a certain stage under the influence of estradiol, proliferates further under the stimulation of secretions from the corpus luteum and so is prepared for the reception of the fertilized ovum. If no fertilization occurs, the corpus luteum degenerates after about two weeks and the excess mucosa is carried away in the menstrual flow. A new one ordinarily appears in the course of the next menstrual cycle. In the event of fertilization, the corpus luteum undergoes no regression but performs the following functions: it (1) suppresses ovulation, (2) maintains a condition in the uterus essential to the development of the embryo, (3) inhibits uterine motility, and (4) in conjunction with estradiol induces mammary gland development.

That the corpus luteum is a gland with inner secretions, was suggested by the work of Fraenkel (1903),[2] who showed that with rabbits the removal of the corpora lutea shortly after ovulation terminates pregnancy, or prevents the attachment of the ovum to the uterus. In 1928 the American investigators G. W. Corner and W. M. Allen[3] made the important observation that, after the progestational changes have been prevented by the extirpation of the early corpus luteum, activity can be restored by the use of extracts of corpora lutea. Rabbits castrated shortly after mating and then given subcutaneous injections of such extracts develop within a few days a progestational condition similar to that during early pregnancy. Implantation of the fertilized egg occurs and pregnancy can be maintained to the point of normal birth. These experiments proved that the internal secretions of the corpus luteum contain a hormone that controls pregnancy. The work of Corner and Allen provided a convenient test method. Adult female rabbits are castrated at the proper stage of follicle ripening, as determined by mating. The administration of a hormone extract produces after the fifth day a progestational proliferation of the mucosa easily recognized by histological examination. Clauberg[4] developed a modified

---

[1] See W. M. Allen, "Biochemistry of the Corpus Luteum Hormone, Progesterone," pp. 901–930, in *Sex and Internal Secretions*, 2nd ed. (1939).

[2] Fraenkel, *Arch. Gynaekol.*, **68,** 438 (1903).

[3] Corner and W. M. Allen, *Am. J. Physiol.*, **86,** 74 (1928); **88,** 326 (1929); W. M. Allen and Corner, *ibid.*, **88,** 340 (1929).

[4] C. Clauberg, *Die weiblichen Sexualhormone*, Berlin (1933).

test[5] which dispenses with castration and with histological control. In place of the estrous type of uterine mucosa of the adult animal, a similar endometrium is produced artificially in the infantile rabbit by the administration of follicular hormone for six to eight days. This serves as an indicator of the progestational activity of a preparation and the characteristic changes can be observed after the substance has been injected over a period of five days.

Isolation and Properties. After the investigations of Corner and Allen the younger of these workers, W. M. Allen, developed methods for the extraction and concentration of hormone preparations.[6] By 1932 physiologically active, if very crude, crystallizates had been secured from the corpus luteum by Allen[7] at Rochester, and by the research groups of F. L. Hisaw[8] at Wisconsin and of H. K. Slotta[9] at Breslau. The preparations were active in doses of as little as 3 mg., but the degree of purity was not sufficient to permit a chemical characterization.

The isolation of the pure hormone was beset with difficulties. The starting material was expensive and contained only traces of the active principle. The hormone, particularly in an impure condition, was found to be very sensitive to alkalis and to oxidizing agents, and it is accompanied by chemically similar substances. It was not long, however, before the isolation was accomplished. In 1934 the independent preparation of the pure corpus luteum hormone was announced from no less than four laboratories. In April, Butenandt[10,5] reported the isolation of two physiologically active diketones, m.p. 128.5° and 120°, together with an inactive hydroxyketone, m.p. 194°. In July, Slotta, Ruschig, and Fels[11] described the preparation from corpus luteum extract of closely corresponding substances, m.p. 128°, 119°, and 186°. In August, Allen and Wintersteiner[12] announced the isolation,[13] in the laboratories of the Universities of Rochester and Columbia, of preparations melting at 128°, 121°, and 190°. Hartmann

[5] Butenandt, U. Westphal and Hohlweg, *Z. physiol. Chem.*, **227**, 84 (1934).

[6] W. M. Allen, *Am. J. Physiol.*, **92**, 174, 612 (1930); **100**, 650 (1932); W. M. Allen and R. K. Meyer, *ibid.*, **106**, 55 (1933).

[7] W. M. Allen, *J. Biol. Chem.*, **98**, 591 (1932).

[8] Fevold, Hisaw and Leonard, *J. Am. Chem. Soc.*, **54**, 254 (1932); Fevold and Hisaw, *Proc. Soc. Exp. Biol. Med.*, **29**, 620 (1932).

[9] Fels and Slotta, *Proc. II Internat. Congr. for Sex Research*, p. 361, London (1930); *Zentr. Gynaekol.*, **55**, 2765 (1931).

[10] Butenandt, *Verhandl. deutsch. Ges. innere Med.*, Wiesbaden, April 11; *Wien Klin. Wochschr.*, **30**, 934 (1934).

[11] Slotta, Ruschig and Fels, *Ber.*, **67**, 1270 (1934). See also Slotta and Ruschig, *Z. physiol. Chem.*, **228**, 207 (1934).

[12] W. M. Allen and Wintersteiner, *Science*, **80**, 190 (1934).

[13] Wintersteiner and W. M. Allen, *J. Biol. Chem.*, **107**, 321 (1934); see also W. M. Allen and Goetsch, *J. Biol. Chem.*, **116**, 653 (1936).

and Wettstein,[14] of the Gesellschaft für Chemische Industrie, Basel, published in July an account of the isolation of a crystallizate, m.p. 175–177°, which was taken to be an individual hormone; but they later (October) recognized that this was an error and succeeded in obtaining pure compounds melting at 129°, 120°, and 197°. Contrary to early views of Slotta, the two active diketones are polymorphic forms of a single substance. The prism form, m.p. 128°, separates on slow crystallization from aqueous alcohol; the needle form, m.p. 121°, can be obtained by crystallization from petroleum ether. The two forms have the same physiological activity, they yield identical derivatives, and they are interconvertible.[13,15]

Although progesterone has been detected in the placenta[16] and in pregnancy urine,[17] these sources do not appear at all practicable and all the above investigators used corpus luteum tissue from sow ovaries. The ovary of the sow contains several corpora lutea, whereas ovaries of other available animals, like human ovaries, contain but one corpus luteum. The ovaries from a single sow weigh about 12 g. and yield about 3 g. of yellow-body tissue and 0.08 mg. of crude hormone. In the preparation at the Schering-Kahlbaum laboratory of a purified hormone extract for Butenandt's work, about 625 kg. of ovaries from 50,000 sows yielded 12.5 g. of an extract active in doses of 3.5 – 5.5 mg.; this afforded 20 mg. of pure progesterone (prism form). On the basis of the activity of the purified extract, 10 – 15 sows are required to produce enough hormone to cause the characteristic physiological changes in the uterus of a single rabbit!

All the investigators employed Allen's procedures[6] (1930) of solvent extraction and distribution for the preparation of purified extracts. On distribution between petroleum ether and 33 percent alcohol, the corpus luteum hormone is found in the former layer and estrogens concentrate in the latter. At a stage where a concentration of one rabbit unit (rb.u.) per 4 – 5 mg. is reached, practically all the active material can be precipitated as the sparingly soluble semicarbazone. After hydrolysis, further purification can be accomplished by sublimation in high vacuum, selective adsorption, and crystallization. The inactive hydroxyketone (allopregnanol-3β-one-20) accompanies the hormone through all these processes and can be separated as the acetate, which is distinctly less soluble in alcohol than progesterone. A quantitative separation can be made by treatment of the mixture with chlorosulfonic acid in pyridine and then with soda; the

[14] M. Hartmann and Wettstein, *Helv. Chim. Acta*, **17**, 878, 1365 (1934).

[15] Butenandt and Josef Schmidt, *Ber.*, **67**, 1901, 2088 (1934); Fernholz, *ibid.*, **67**, 2027 (1934); Hohlweg and Josef Schmidt, *Klin. Wochschr.*, **15**, 265 (1936).

[16] Adler, de Fremery and Tausk, *Nature*, **133**, 293 (1934).

[17] de Fremery, Luchs and Tausk, *Arch. ges. Physiol.*, **231**, 341 (1931); Loewe and H. E. Voss, *Schweiz. med. Wochschr.*, **64**, 1049 (1934).

hydroxyketone affords an ether-insoluble sulfate ester, and progesterone is not affected.[18]

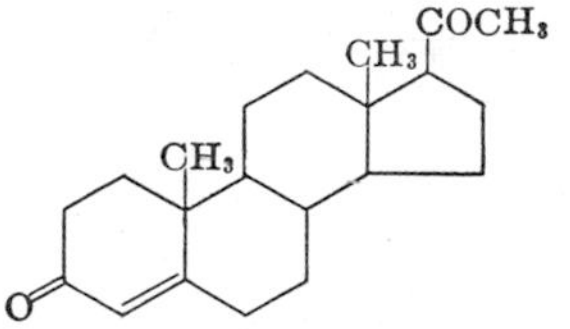

Progesterone
m.p. 121°, 128°; [α]$_D$ + 192°
λ $_{max}^{alc}$ 240 mμ
rb.u. 1.0 mg.

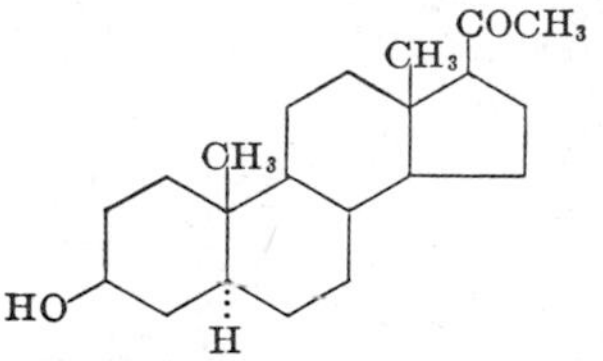

Allopregnanol-3β-one-20
m.p. 194°, [α]$_D$ + 91°
Inactive

A biogenetic and hence a structural relationship between progesterone ($C_{21}H_{30}O_2$) and the inactive hydroxyketone ($C_{21}H_{34}O_2$) seemed indicated by the empirical formulas of the substances and by their occurrence together. A relationship of the companion substance to pregnandiol from pregnancy urine was suspected, and the fact that the hydroxyketone and the diol yield different diketones on oxidation (allopregnanedione-3,20, m.p. 200°, [α]$_D$ + 127°; and pregnanedione-3,20, m.p. 123°) was correctly attributed to a difference in configuration at C_5. The absorption spectrum of progesterone indicated the presence of an α,β-unsaturated keto grouping,[19] and X-ray studies pointed to a sterol-like molecule.[20] On the basis of these limited observations, Slotta[19] proposed a formula which very shortly was proved to be correct by partial synthesis.

Progesterone from Other Steroids. The first synthetic preparation of a substance identical with natural progesterone proceeded from the starting material 3β-hydroxy-Δ⁵-bisnorcholenic acid (II, Chart 1), which Fernholz[1] had just prepared from stigmasterol by ozonization of the acetate dibromide, debromination, and hydrolysis. Butenandt[2] and Fernholz[3] independently converted the acid II through the ester and the diphenylethylene III to pregnenolone (IV). In the original work pregnenolone was converted by oxidation of the 5,6-dibromide and debromination into a substance identical with progesterone. The structure of the companion hydroxyketone was established by the preparation of the substance from hydroxybisnorcholenic

[18] Butenandt and U. Westphal, *Ber.*, **69**, 443 (1936).
[19] Slotta, Ruschig and Fels, *Ber.*, **67**, 1624 (1934); Wintersteiner and W. M. Allen, *J. Biol. Chem.*, **107**, 321 (1934).
[20] Neuhaus, *Ber.*, **67**, 1627 (1934).
[1] Fernholz, *Ann.*, **507**, 128 (1933).
[2] Butenandt, U. Westphal and Cobler, *Ber.*, **67**, 1611 (1934); Butenandt and U. Westphal, *ibid.*, **67**, 2085 (1934).
[3] Fernholz, *Ber.*, **67**, 1855, 2027 (1934).

acid (II) by hydrogenation to 3β-hydroxybisnorallocholanic acid and degradation of the side chain through the diphenylethylene.[4] A further

Chart 1. PROGESTERONE FROM STIGMASTEROL AND FROM PREGNANEDIOL

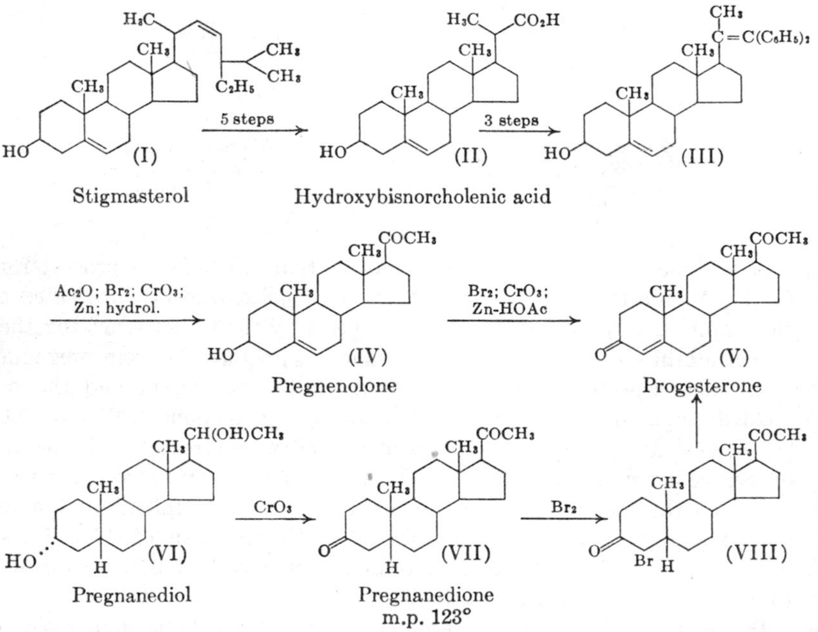

5 steps

(I)
Stigmasterol

3 steps

(II)
Hydroxybisnorcholenic acid

(III)

Ac₂O; Br₂; CrO₃;
Zn; hydrol.

(IV)
Pregnenolone

Br₂; CrO₃;
Zn-HOAc

(V)
Progesterone

(VI)
Pregnanediol

CrO₃

(VII)
Pregnanedione
m.p. 123°

Br₂

(VIII)

synthetic preparation of progesterone described by Butenandt[5] (Chart 1) utilized pregnanediol from pregnancy urine; the diketone VII obtained by oxidation was selectively brominated at the 4-position and the product dehydrobrominated.

One of several commercial processes operated in Germany for the production of progesterone[6] utilized the Butenandt-Fernholz procedure as applied to the phytosterol mixture from soybean oil, which consists mainly of "γ"-sitosterol (saturated side chain) but contains 12 – 16 percent of stigmasterol. The intermediate pregnenolone was converted directly into progesterone by Oppenauer oxidation (76% yield from 2.5 kg. of pregnenolone). Myles[7] has described a process for the preparation of

[4] Butenandt and Mamoli, *Ber.*, **67**, 1897 (1934); Fernholz, *Z. physiol. Chem.*, **230**, 185 (1934).

[5] Butenandt and Josef Schmidt, *Ber.*, **67**, 1901 (1934).

[6] C. R. Addinall, Field Information Agency Technical Report No. 996.

[7] J. R. Myles, U. S. patent 2,205,045.

hydroxybisnorcholenic acid consisting in partial bromination of the total soyasterol acetates and ozonization of the mixture. Riegel[8] found that the double bond and hydroxyl group of stigmasterol can be protected during ozonization by conversion into the i-sterol methyl ether; hydroxybisnorcholenic acid methyl ether ester was obtained in this way from the total soyasterols in 4 percent overall yield.[9] A certain amount of progesterone is also produced from the pregnenolone isolated as a by-product in the preparation of dehydroepiandrosterone from cholesterol. An alternate method for the conversion of hydroxybisnorcholenic acid into pregnenolone, and hence into progesterone, was developed by Ruschig[6] of the I. G. Farbenindustrie and is based upon a modified Curtius degradation (Chart 2).

Chart 2. CURTIUS DEGRADATION OF HYDROXYBISNORCHOLENIC ACID (II)

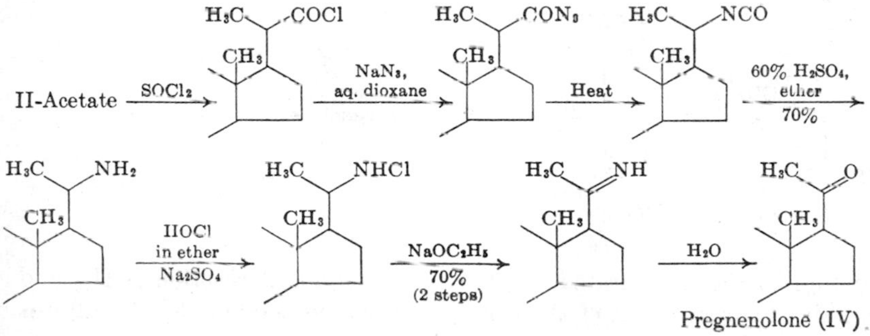

II-Acetate $\xrightarrow{SOCl_2}$ [H₃C–COCl, CH₃] $\xrightarrow[\text{aq. dioxane}]{NaN_3,}$ [H₃C–CON₃, CH₃] $\xrightarrow{Heat}$ [H₃C–NCO, CH₃] $\xrightarrow[\text{ether}]{\underset{70\%}{60\% \ H_2SO_4,}}$

[H₃C–NH₂, CH₃] $\xrightarrow[\substack{\text{in ether} \\ Na_2SO_4}]{HOCl}$ [H₃C–NHCl, CH₃] $\xrightarrow[\substack{70\% \\ (2 \text{ steps})}]{NaOC_2H_5}$ [H₃C–NH, CH₃] $\xrightarrow{H_2O}$ [H₃C–O, CH₃]

Pregnenolone (IV)

The reaction of the acid chloride with sodium azide proceeded smoothly in aqueous dioxane or acetone. The hydrolysis of the isocyanate was accomplished by stirring an ethereal solution of the substance with 60 percent sulfuric acid, and conversion of the amine into the unstable chloroamine was accomplished as follows. The hypochlorous acid generated by passing chlorine into sodium bicarbonate solution was extracted with ether and the solution dried quickly at a low temperature and the titer determined. An ethereal solution of one equivalent of the amine was added at 0° in the presence of sodium sulfate to retain the water formed. The chloroamine was thus obtained as a crystalline solid and on reaction with sodium ethoxide it afforded a solid ketimine that was easily hydrolyzed to pregnenolone. The overall yield of pregnenolone from hydroxybisnorcholenic acid is stated to be about 45 percent.

Another commercial process is based upon a synthetic procedure of

[8] Riegel, E. W. Meyer and Beiswanger, *J. Am. Chem. Soc.*, **65,** 325 (1943).
[9] Riegel, Gouley and Beiswanger, *J. Am. Chem. Soc.* (in press).

Butenandt[10] starting with dehydroepiandrosterone (IX, Chart 3). One carbon atom of the side chain is introduced by way of the cyanohydrin (X), obtained as a mixture of the two C_{17}-epimers. Dehydration of the

Chart 3. PROGESTERONE FROM DEHYDROEPIANDROSTERONE

Dehydroepiandrosterone   Epimers,
acetate   m.p. 195°, 206°

m.p. 216°, λ_{max}^{ether} 237 mμ

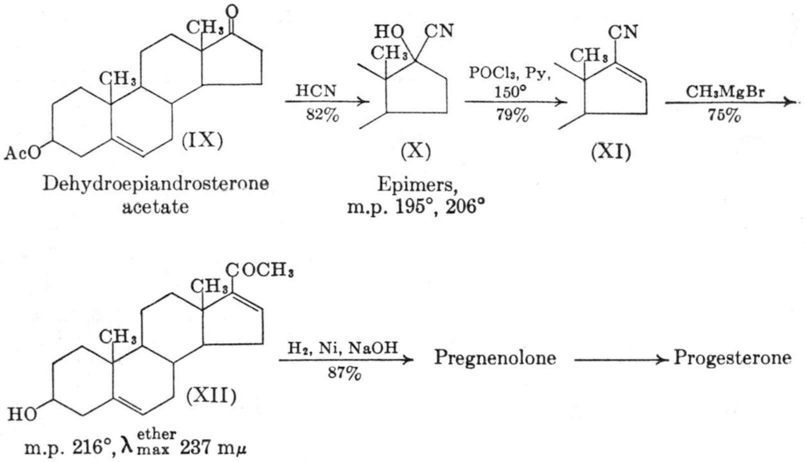

mixture to the unsaturated nitrile (XI), a Grignard reaction (XII), and selective hydrogenation of the conjugated double bond at $C_{16} - C_{17}$ affords pregnenolone.

In 1944 Meystre and Miescher[11] described a highly efficient new method for degrading the bile acid side chain, and in 1946 they reported the partial synthesis of progesterone[12] from 3β-hydroxy-Δ^5-cholenic acid, a by-product in the production of dehydroepiandrosterone from cholesterol for which no previous use had been found. The reactions shown in Chart 4 include various alternate routes to progesterone, depending upon the order in which the different operations are conducted. The most satisfactory was through I, II, III, IV, V, VIII, IX to XII. Thus the methyl ester (I) of the unsaturated acid was converted into the diphenylethylene III, the more reactive nuclear double bond was protected by the addition of hydrogen chloride (IV), and bromine was introduced adjacent to the double bond of the side chain (V) by bromination with N-bromosuccinimide according to

[10] Butenandt and Schmidt-Thomé, Ber., 71, 1487 (1938); 72, 182 (1939).

[11] Meystre, Frey, Wettstein and Miescher, Helv. Chim. Acta, 27, 1815 (1944); Meystre, Ehmann, Neher and Miescher, ibid., 28, 1252 (1945). See also Ettlinger and Fieser, J. Biol. Chem., 164, 451 (1946).

[12] Meystre, Frey, Neher, Wettstein and Miescher, Helv. Chim. Acta, 29, 627 (1946); Meystre, Wettstein and Miescher, ibid., 30, 1022 (1947).

Ziegler; this reaction is usually catalyzed by either light[11] or a peroxide.[13] The action of dimethylaniline on V resulted in the splitting of both hydrogen bromide and hydrogen chloride to give VIII, which was converted by

Chart 4. PROGESTERONE FROM 3β-HYDROXY-Δ⁵-CHOLENIC ACID

Chart 4. Progesterone from 3β-Hydroxy-Δ⁵-cholenic Acid

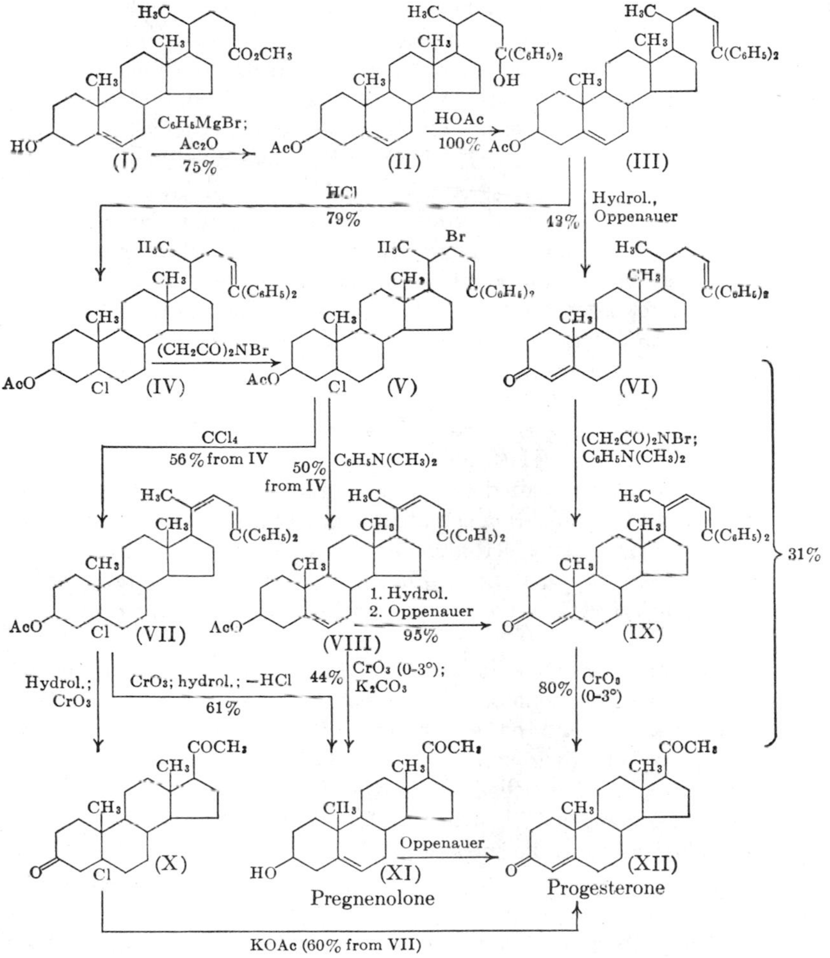

hydrolysis and Oppenauer oxidation into a substance (IX) having the desired structure in ring A and a dienic side chain. By controlled chromic acid oxidation the dienic system was eliminated with the formation of

[13] H. Schmidt and Karrer, *Helv. Chim. Acta*, **29**, 573 (1946).

progesterone (XII); the predominant by-product, identified as β,β-diphenylacrolein, $(C_6H_5)_2C{=}CHCHO$,[14] can be separated easily as the bisulfite addition product.[15] The dehydrohalogenation of the 5-chloro derivative V leads predominately to the formation of the Δ^5-derivative, but probably the Δ^4-isomer is present as well in the initial mixtures; 5-chlorocholestane gives chiefly Δ^4-cholestene, and cholesterol hydrochloride gives a mixture of cholesterol and Δ^4-cholestenol. Thus an overall yield of 23 percent based upon isolated products was raised to 33 percent by conducting the successive operations without isolation of intermediates.

A shorter synthesis that does not involve protection of the nuclear double bond is by the sequence: I, II, III, VI, IX, XII. The overall yield is only about 10 percent, but the process demonstrates that allylic bromination in the side chain of VI proceeds more readily than bromination adjacent to the α,β-unsaturated ketonic group of the nucleus. Other variations are possible starting with the selective elimination of the reactive bromine atom of V with retention of the C_5-chlorine atom. The resulting VII can be converted into progesterone through either the chloroketone X (20% yield overall) or pregnenolone (XI); pregnenolone is also available through the other route (VIII).

The preparation of progesterone from various sapogenins by Marker[16] is described in Chapter VIII (Chart 4).

Progesterone has been isolated as a product of the oxidation of cholesterol dibromide with potassium permanganate in a two-phase acidic medium and debromination;[17] the yield as determined by bioassays is 0.2 percent. Dirscherl has reported the isolation of progesterone and Δ^4-androstenedione-3,17 in unspecified yield from the chromic acid oxidation of Δ^4-cholestenone-3.[18]

Isoprogesterones. Butenandt observed that allopregnanolone[1] from pregnancy urine and pregnenolone[2] (I) can both be isomerized in part at the asymmetric center adjacent to the carbonyl group by the action of 5 percent methanolic potassium hydroxide. The reactions are reversible, and in each case equilibrium is reached at a ratio of about 70 parts of normal ketone (I) to 30 parts of 17-isoketone (II). Attempts to isomerize progesterone at first met with no success, partly because the 17-iso derivative

[14] Miescher and Schmidlin, *Helv. Chim. Acta*, **30**, 1405 (1947).

[15] Kohler and Larsen, *J. Am. Chem. Soc.*, **57**, 1451 (1935).

[16] Marker, R. B. Wagner, Ulshafer, Wittbecker, Goldsmith and Ruof, *J. Am. Chem. Soc.*, **69**, 2173 (1947); Marker, *ibid.*, **69**, 2395 (1947).

[17] Spielman and R. K. Meyer, *J. Am. Chem. Soc.*, **61**, 893 (1939).

[18] Dirscherl and Hanusch, *Z. physiol. Chem.*, **252**, 49 (1938). See also German patent 712,591 (1941) [*C. A.*, **37**, 4534 (1943)].

[1] Butenandt and Mamoli, *Ber.*, **68**, 1847 (1935).

[2] Butenandt and Fleischer, *Ber.*, **70**, 96 (1937).

is in this case more labile. Thus the oxidation of 17-isopregnenolone (II) through the dibromide was attended with reversion to the more stable orientation at C_{17} and the product was progesterone.[3] Oppenauer oxidation however afforded 17-isoprogesterone (III).[3] The substance proved to be

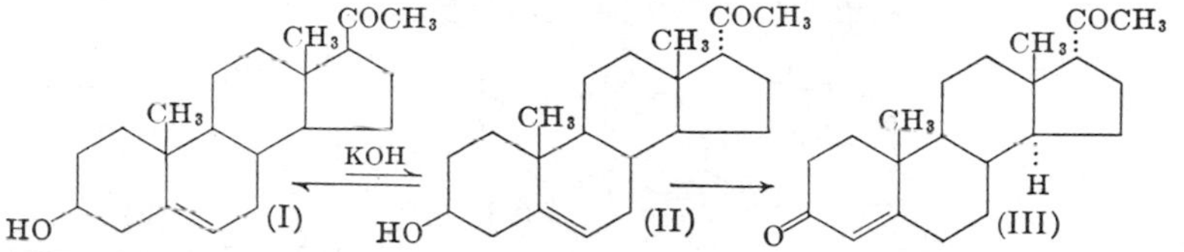

17-Isoprogesterone

inactive; it is easily isomerized to progesterone by the action of alcoholic hydrochloric acid. The accompanying table lists the properties of the different members of the normal (17β) and iso (17α) series. There is no

	NORMAL COMPOUND		17-ISO COMPOUND		17-ISO-14-ISO COMPOUND	
	M.p.	$[\alpha]_D$	M.p.	$[\alpha]_D$	M.p.	$[\alpha]_D$
Progesterone	128°	+192°	145°	0°	107°	+139°
Δ^5-Pregnenol-3β-one-20	190°	+28°	173°	−140°	205°	−14°
Acetate	147°	+20°	171°	−126°	159°	−18°
Allopregnanol-3β-one-20	194°	+91°	148°	+6°		
Acetate	144°		101°			
Allopregnanedione-3,20	200°	+127°	135°	−15°		

general trend in the melting points, but the 17-iso compounds are invariably more levorotatory and less stable than the normal compounds. The stability relationship is further evidence that a C_{17}-group in the α-orientation is more strongly hindered then a 17β-group. In both this series of isomeric 17-aceto compounds and that of the etio acids, the more stable, less hindered 17β-epimers are more dextrorotatory than the 17α-epimers.

Butenandt found that 17-isopregnanol-3β-one-20, like the normal compound, is precipitated by digitonin; Δ^5-isopregnenol-3β-one-20, on the other hand, is not precipitated. A further anomaly is that both allopregnanol-3β-one-20 acetate and allopregnanedione-3,20 (but not the iso compounds) form sparingly soluble digitonides; a difference from the usual behavior is that the complexes separate very slowly (2–4 hours). Usually neither acetyl nor ketonic derivatives form digitonides.

The third isomer of progesterone listed in the table differs from the hormone in the configuration at both C_{14} and C_{17}. It was prepared by

[3] Butenandt, Schmidt-Thomé and Paul, *Ber.*, **72**, 1112 (1939).

Plattner[4] through an intermediate (IV) obtained by methods developed for the synthesis of substances related to the cardiac aglycones (Chapter VII). The two double bonds in ring D are particularly reactive and can be

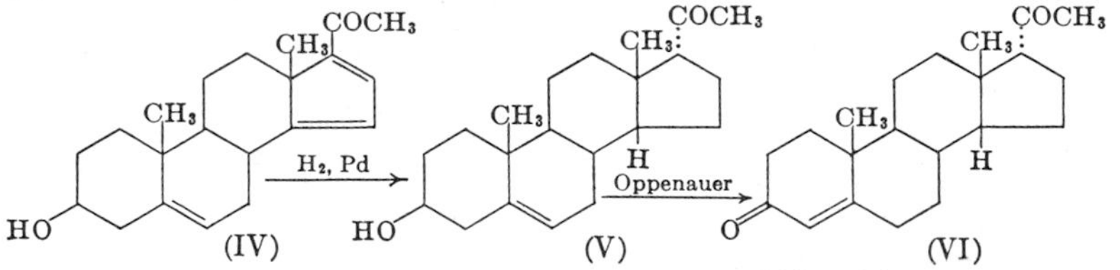

14-Iso-17-isoprogesterone
λ max 242 mμ (4.2), 305 mμ (2.0)

saturated without disturbance of the 5,6-double bond. The addition of hydrogen to this system gives the abnormal configuration at both C_{17} and C_{14}. The result is in accord with other observations[5] showing that hydrogenation of the 14,15-double bond leads to the normal sterol configuration (14α) if the substituent at C_{17} has the normal (β) orientation and to the 14-iso configuration (β) if the substance belongs to the 17-iso series (α). Oppenauer oxidation of V gave 14-iso-17-isoprogesterone (VI); this substance has no progestational activity.

Progestational Activity and Structure. Progesterone exerts a specific physiological action only at a dosage level vastly higher than that at which the other sex hormones are effective. The international unit of progestational activity is that produced by 1 mg. of progesterone in rabbits. The pregnancy hormone also differs from the other hormones of the gonads in possessing higher structural specificity. Very few of the many substances of related structure that have been examined display significant progestational (luteoid) activity.

One of the most interesting of the related compounds is the 17α-ethinyl derivative of testosterone (III, Chart 5); the name 17-isopregneninolone is sometimes used for this substance in order to emphasize the fact that it possesses significant luteoid, but not testoid, activity. It is prepared by the addition of acetylene to dehydroepiandrosterone[1] and Oppenauer oxidation of the predominating product II.[2] Reichstein[3] isolated the epimeric addi-

[4] Plattner, Heusser and Segre, *Helv. Chim. Acta*, **31**, 249 (1948).

[5] Plattner, Ruzicka and co-workers, *Helv. Chim. Acta*, **29**, 942 (1946); **30**, 385, 1342 (1947); Kuno Meyer, *ibid.*, **29**, 719 (1946).

[1] Ruzicka and K. Hofmann, *Helv. Chim. Acta*, **20**, 1280 (1937); Kathol, Logemann and Serini, *Naturwissenschaften*, **25**, 682 (1937).

[2] Inhoffen, Logemann, Hohlweg and Serini, *Ber.*, **71**, 1024 (1938).

[3] Reichstein and Meystre, *Helv. Chim. Acta*, **22**, 728 (1939); Reichstein and Gätzi, *ibid.*, **21**, 1185 (1938).

tion product I by careful chromatographic fractionation and effected degradations of the two products to the hydroxyetiocholanic acids and thereby
established the configurations at C_{17}. The addition of acetylene to 17-

Chart 5. RELATED COMPOUNDS

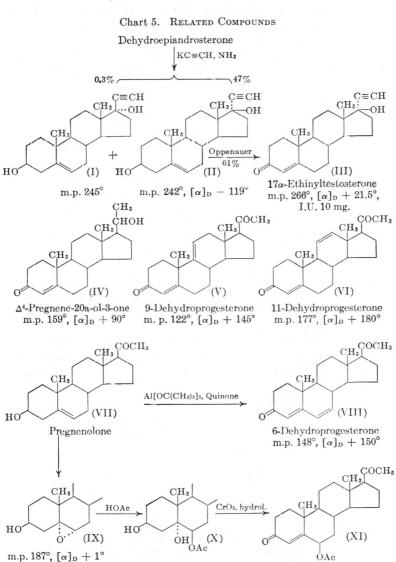

Dehydroepiandrosterone

KC≡CH, NH₃

0.3% ⌐———————————⌐ 47%

(I)
m.p. 245°

(II)
m.p. 242°, [α]D − 119°

(III)
17α-Ethinyltestosterone
m.p. 266°, [α]D + 21.5°,
I.U. 10 mg.

Oppenauer
61%

(IV)
Δ⁴-Pregnene-20a-ol-3-one
m.p. 159°, [α]D + 90°

(V)
9-Dehydroprogesterone
m. p. 122°, [α]D + 145°

(VI)
11-Dehydroprogesterone
m.p. 177°, [α]D + 180°

(VII)
Pregnenolone

Al[OC(CH₃)₃]₃, Quinone

(VIII)
6-Dehydroprogesterone
m.p. 148°, [α]D + 150°

(IX)
m.p. 187°, [α]D + 1°

HOAc

(X)

CrO₃, hydrol.

(XI)
6β-Acetoxyprogesterone
m.p. 146°, [α]D + 90°

ketones was initially carried out with potassium acetylide in liquid ammonia, but Stavely[4] introduced a more convenient procedure consisting in the use of potassium t-butylate at room temperature (yields $80-85\%$). The ethinyl group in the chief product of addition (II) has the α-orientation, which is opposite to that of the two-carbon side chain of the cortical hormones. Although 17α-ethinyltestosterone (III) has only about one-third the activity of progesterone by subcutaneous injection, it is much more active than progesterone on oral administration (4 mg. active; progesterone inactive at 60 mg.). The substance was introduced into clinical medicine in 1941 under the name Proluton C. Reduction of the ethinyl group to vinyl decreases the activity somewhat (I.U. 20 mg.; 15 mg. active by mouth).

The Δ^4-3-keto grouping in ring A seems to be an essential feature of structure, for related saturated diketones and 3-hydroxy derivatives are inactive. Reduction of the 20-keto group might be expected to enhance the physiological activity, as in the case of estrone, androsterone, and androstenedione, but the dihydro derivative IV is inactive at doses of 1 mg.; IV has been prepared from pregnane-20a-ol-3-one through the 4-bromo derivative[5] and from Δ^5-pregnene-3β,20a-diol.[6] Neither Δ^1-allopregnenedione-3,20[7] nor Δ^5-pregnenedione-3,20[8] is active.

9-Dehydroprogesterone (V),[9] from corticosterone, is active at a dosage of 8 mg. 11-Dehydroprogesterone (VI)[10] is no less than three times as potent as progesterone in the Clauberg test (I.U. 0.2 mg.; progesterone, 0.6 mg.).[10a] 6-Dehydroprogesterone (VIII) was first prepared[11] in low yield by a process involving the dehydrohalogenation of a 5,6-dibromo-3-ketone (silver nitrate and pyridine in the last step); a novel new method[11] consists in the Oppenauer oxidation of pregnenolone in the presence of aluminum t-butoxide with use of quinone as the hydrogen acceptor; the normal dehydrogenation of the alcoholic group is accompanied by further dehydrogenation to produce VIII in one step. The reaction does not proceed through the Δ^4-3-ketone, since this is not attacked under the same conditions, but the Δ^5-3-ketone can be oxidized to VIII by the modified Oppenauer procedure

[4] Stavely, *J. Am. Chem. Soc.*, **61**, 79 (1939).

[5] Butenandt and Josef Schmidt, *Ber.*, **67**, 2092 (1934).

[6] Marker, Crooks and Wittbecker, *J. Am. Chem. Soc.* **63**, 777 (1941).

[7] Butenandt and Mamoli, *Ber.*, **68**, 1850 (1935).

[8] U. Westphal and Schmidt-Thomé, *Ber.*, **69**, 889 (1936).

[9] Shoppee and Reichstein, *Helv. Chim. Acta*, **24**, 351 (1941).

[10] Hegner and Reichstein, *Helv. Chim. Acta*, **26**, 715 (1943).

[10a] Communication from Dr. A. Wettstein regarding comparative assays with a newly prepared specimen; Meystre, Tschopp and Wettstein, *Helv. Chin. Acta*, **31**, 1463 (1948).

[11] Wettstein, *Helv. Chim. Acta*, **23**, 388 (1940).

and therefore is a likely intermediate. 6-Dehydroprogesterone has about one-third the activity of progesterone. 16-Dehydroprogesterone[12] is only about one one-hundredth as active as the hormone.

Desoxycorticosterone, which is the 21-hydroxy derivative of progesterone, has marked activity (I.U. 10 mg.). 6β-Acetoxyprogesterone[13] (XI) has about the same activity; the substance was prepared from the main product of the action of perbenzoic acid on pregnenolone, probably the α-oxide X. 17-Hydroxyprogesterone, a constituent of the adrenal cortex (Chapter 5) and also available by partial syntheses, has no progestational activity at a dosage of 5 mg.; it shows some androgenic activity in castrated rats and increases comb growth when applied directly.[14]

20-Norprogesterone (XIV) has been prepared[15] through the inter-mediates XII and XIII. The substance is midway between testosterone

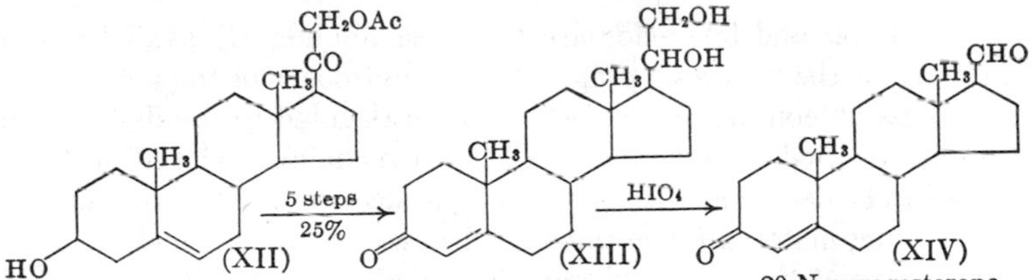

CH₂OAc / CH₃ / CO / CH₃ / HO / (XII) — 5 steps 25% → CH₂OH / CHOH / CH₃ / CH₃ / (XIII) — HIO₄ → CH₃ / CHO / CH₃ / (XIV) 20-Norprogesterone m.p. 153°, [α]$_D$ + 159°

and progesterone in structure and it exhibits the physiological activity of both hormones to a mild degree; it possesses slight testoid activity and shows gestational activity at a dosage of 10 – 20 mg. Several of the androgens elicit typical progestational proliferation of the endometrium; 17α-methyltestosterone is the most active (30 mg. dose).[16] The next higher homolog of progesterone, 21-methylprogesterone,[17] is about one-tenth as active as the hormone; 21-ethylprogesterone[16] has no significant activity. These substances were prepared by the malonic ester synthesis from 3β-hydroxy-Δ^5-etiocholenic acid. Δ^4-Norcholene-3,22-dione[18] (XV), another homolog, is likewise inactive. Both epimers are known; the preparation

[12] Butenandt and Schmidt-Thomé, Ber., 72, 182 (1939); Marker, Tsukamoto and D. L. Turner, J. Am. Chem. Soc., 62, 2525 (1940).

[13] Ehrenstein and T. O. Stevens, J. Org. Chem., 6, 908 (1941).

[14] Butenandt, Naturwissenschaften, 30, 4 (1942).

[15] Steiger and Reichstein, Helv. Chim. Acta, 21, 171 (1938); Miescher, Hunziker and Wettstein, ibid., 23, 400, 1367 (1940).

[16] Ruzicka and Rosenberg, Helv. Chim. Acta, 19, 357 (1936).

[17] Wettstein, Helv. Chim. Acta, 23, 1371 (1940).

[18] Wettstein, Helv. Chim. Acta, 24, 311 (1941); Cole and Julian, J. Am. Chem. Soc., 67, 1369 (1945).

involves the reaction of dimethylcadmium with the acid chloride of 3β-hydroxy-Δ⁵-bisnorcholenic acid followed by Oppenauer oxidation.

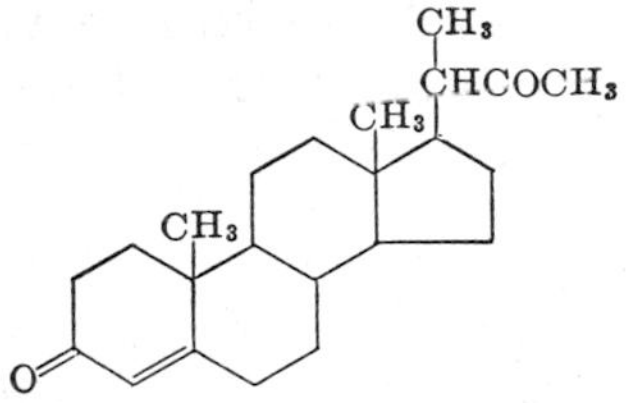

Δ⁴-Norcholene-3,22-dione
XVa m.p. 208°, [α]ᴅ + 54°
XVb m.p. 191°, [α]ᴅ + 67°

DEGRADATION OF BILE ACIDS TO C_{19}–C_{21} STEROIDS

Since sterols and bile acids are the most abundantly available starting materials for the synthetic preparation of hormones of the gonads and the adrenal gland, considerable effort has been devoted to the development of improved methods of degradation of the side chains. The Δ^{22}-unsaturated sterols can be degraded with ease, and the soyasterol mixture is one important starting material for hormone syntheses. The only method available for the removal of a saturated sterol side chain is the nonspecific and highly wasteful process of chromic acid oxidation (see Androsterone, Dehydroepiandrosterone); the yields of useful products from cholesterol are very low, but nevertheless the process is operated commercially.

The carboxyl group of a bile acid offers opportunity for a variety of methods of attack. The classical degradation of Barbier-Wieland has been applied in several instances already discussed and improved in several details. Mason and Hoehn[1] studied the various steps in the degradation of desoxycholic acid (Chart 6) to the 20-methyl ketone (VII) and etiodesoxycholic acid (X) and improved the yields in the oxidations of the diphenylethylenes (IV, VI) by conducting the reactions at 15°. The overall yield of the 20-methyl ketone VII was 8 percent. The classical method of oxidation of the ternordiphenylethylene VI to etiodesoxycholic acid (X) proceeded in only 15 percent yield, and the longer route through the ketone VII, the benzal derivative VIII, and the glyoxal IX proved preferable. The overall yield of etiodesoxycholic acid was 3.1 percent. Kendall and co-workers[2] applied the same degradation to the bromo-oxido ester derivative XI of 11-ketocholanic acid and by introduction of various improvements in the experimental procedures (large excess of Grignard

---

[1] Mason and Hoehn, *J. Am. Chem. Soc.*, **60**, 1493, 2824 (1938).
[2] Communication from Dr. E. C. Kendall.

Chart 6. Barbier-Wieland Degradation

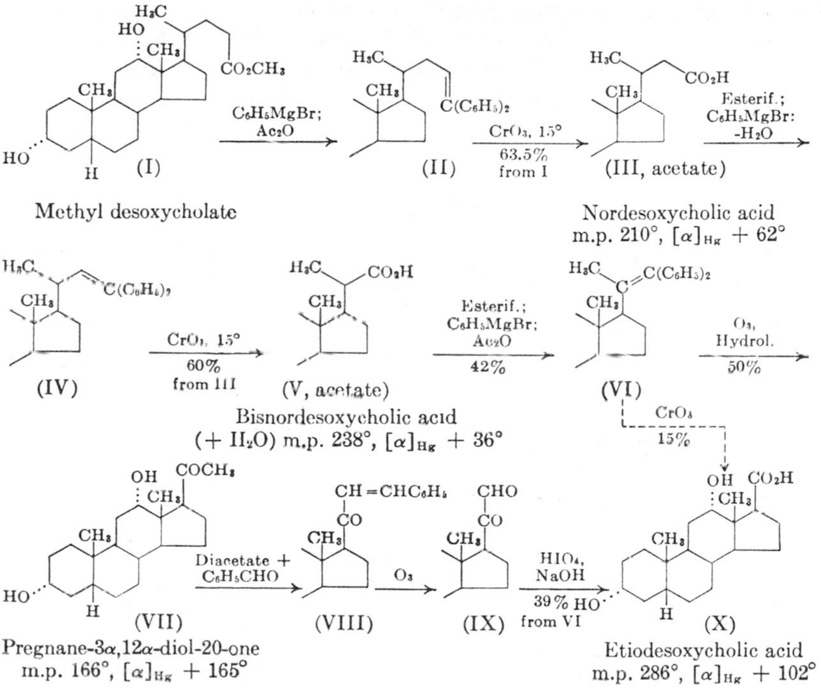
C6H5MgBr; Ac2O
CrO3, 15°
63.5% from I
Esterif.; C6H5MgBr: -H2O
(I)
(II)
(III, acetate)
Methyl desoxycholate
Nordesoxycholic acid m.p. 210°, [α]Hg + 62°
CrO3, 15°
60% from III
Esterif.; C6H5MgBr; Ac2O
42%
O3, Hydrol.
50%
(IV)
(V, acetate)
(VI)
Bisnordesoxycholic acid (+ H2O) m.p. 238°, [α]Hg + 36°
CrO3
15%
Diacetate + C6H5CHO
O3
HIO4, NaOH
39% from VI
(VII)
(VIII)
(IX)
(X)
Pregnane-3α,12α-diol-20-one m.p. 166°, [α]Hg + 165°
Etiodesoxycholic acid m.p. 286°, [α]Hg + 102°

reagent; Grignard reaction in benzene or benzene-ethylmorpholine at a low temperature) succeeded in degrading the side chain to a carboxyl group in about 10 percent overall yield.

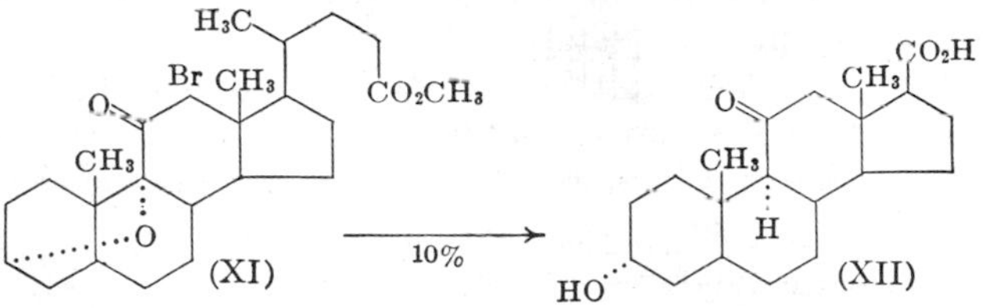
(XI)
10%
(XII)

For the degradation of the bile acid side chain to the stage of a 20-methyl ketone, the classical method is now superseded by the much shorter and more efficient process of Meystre and Miescher already described (Progesterone Synthesis, Chart 4), in which the initial diphenylethylene is converted by Ziegler bromination and dehydrohalogenation into a diphenyl-

diene that on oxidation affords the 20-methyl ketone. This degradation
has been applied to desoxycholic acid (overall yield 36%);[3] to cholic acid;[4]
to cholanic acid;[4] to 3β-hydroxyallocholanic acid;[5] and to lithocholic
acid.[5] The product of the last degradation is pregnane-3α-ol-20-one (XIV),
isolated from the pregnancy urine of man[6] and of sow.[7] The degradation

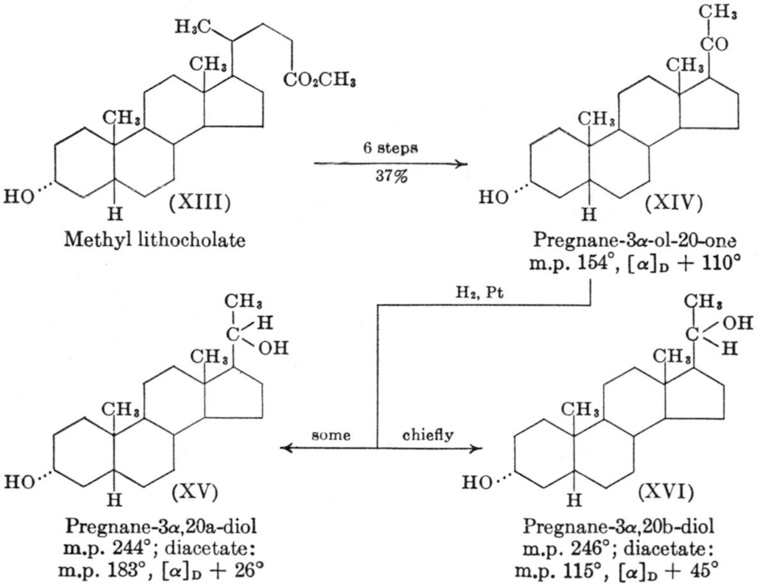

Methyl lithocholate (XIII)

6 steps
37%

Pregnane-3α-ol-20-one (XIV)
m.p. 154°, [α]$_D$ + 110°

H$_2$, Pt

Pregnane-3α,20a-diol (XV)
m.p. 244°; diacetate:
m.p. 183°, [α]$_D$ + 26°

some   chiefly

Pregnane-3α,20b-diol (XVI)
m.p. 246°; diacetate:
m.p. 115°, [α]$_D$ + 45°

also furnishes a route through this ketone to the pregnanediol XV isolated
from urine by Marrian; this epimer has been assigned the arbitrary designation of a 20a-alcohol.[8] Both epimers are formed in reductions with sodium
and alcohol or with nickel and hydrogen;[9] XVI is the chief product of
hydrogenation with platinum catalyst.[8,5]

Miescher[9] has described a further degradation, as applied to 3β-hydroxy-
allocholanic acid, that involves oxidation of the allylic bromo derivative
(XVII) of the diphenylethylene. The desired bromo acid XVIII was

[3] Meystre, Frey, Wettstein and Miescher, Helv. Chim. Acta, 27, 1815 (1944); Meystre, Ehmann, Neher and Miescher, ibid., 28, 1252 (1945).

[4] Meystre and Miescher, Helv. Chim. Acta, 28, 1497 (1945).

[5] Meystre and Miescher, Helv. Chim. Acta, 29, 33 (1946).

[6] Marker and O. Kamm, J. Am. Chem. Soc., 59, 1373 (1937); W. H. Pearlman and
Pincus, Fed. Proc., 1, 66 (1942).

[7] Marker and Rohrmann, J. Am. Chem. Soc., 61, 3476 (1939); see note, p. 506.

[8] Marker and co-workers, J. Am. Chem. Soc., 59, 2291 (1937).

[9] P. Wieland and Miescher, Helv. Chim. Acta, 30, 1876 (1947).

invariably accompanied by 3β-hydroxybisnorallocholanic acid, XX. Dehydrohalogenation of the bromo acid afforded 3β-acetoxy-$\Delta^{20(22)}$-norallocholenic acid methyl ester (XIX). No yields are reported.

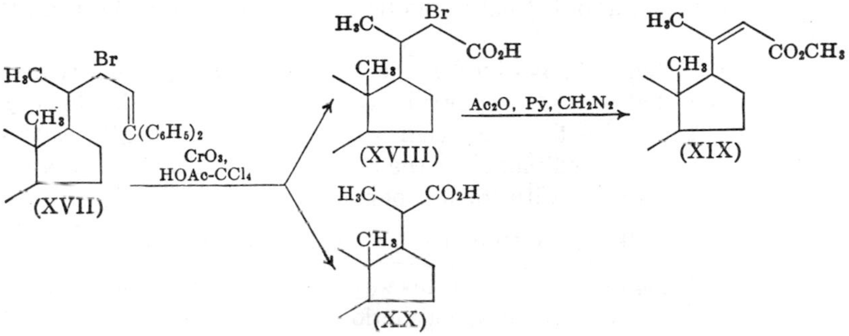

Another method of degradation, reported by Jacobsen[10] in a preliminary note, proceeds from the acid chloride (I) through the phenyl ketone (II) and its α-bromo- and α-acetoxy derivatives (III, IV) to the α-diketone V; the enol acetate VI can be oxidized to the bisnor acid VII. Hoehn and

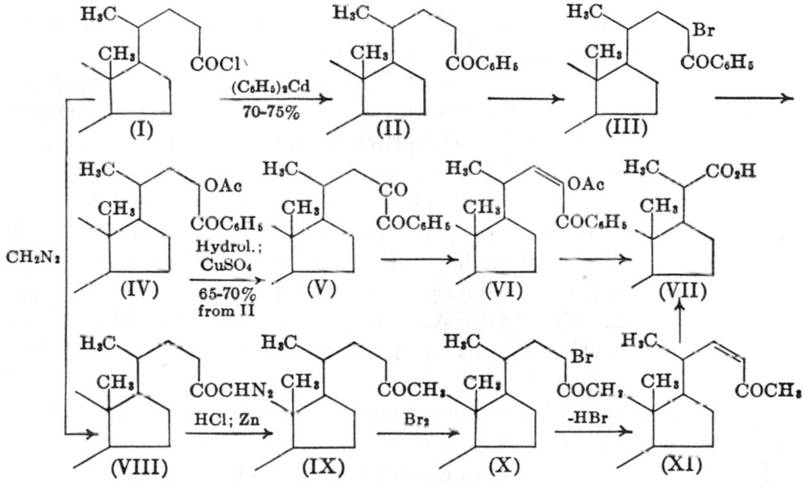

Moffett[11] investigated the direct oxidation of phenyl ketones of the type II (as acetates) but found that the nor acids are produced in only very small yield. A scheme of degradation[12] similar to that of Jacobsen but actually

[10] Jacobsen, *J. Am. Chem. Soc.*, **66**, 662 (1944).
[11] Hoehn and Moffett, *J. Am. Chem. Soc.*, **67**, 740 (1945).
[12] Hollander and Gallagher, *J. Biol. Chem.*, **162**, 549 (1946).

found to be less promising is illustrated by the partial formulas I → VIII → XI → VII. The yields in the steps leading to the α-bromomethyl ketone X were satisfactory, but dehydrohalogenation gave an oily product (XI) that on oxidation afforded only minute amounts of isomeric bisnor acids (VII).

The use of i-ether derivatives in the Barbier-Wieland degradation has been explored but is unsatisfactory because dehydration of the diphenylcarbinol is attended with rearrangement to the normal ether.[13] Another degradation investigated[14] involves the reaction of the silver salt of a cholanic acid with bromine with the loss of one carbon atom:

$$-CH(CH_3)CH_2CH_2CO_2Ag \rightarrow -CH(CH_3)CH_2CH_2Br$$

23-Bromocholane was obtained in this way from cholanic acid in 25 percent yield, but attempted dehydrohalogenation of this compound and of 22-bromonorcholane with collidine, piperidine, silver nitrate, or sodium ethoxide was unsuccessful.

Some of the methods explored for the degradation of 20-methyl ketones to 17-ketones are summarized in Chart 7. According to Reichstein's evaluation, the first three processes are unsatisfactory.[15] Methods proceeding through the etio acid (II) are handicapped at the start because the best of the two degradations of I to II shown in Chart 6 proceeds in only 39 percent yield. The degradation of the acid through the diphenylcarbinol and diphenylethylene (IV) was successful in one case[16] and completely unsuccessful in another.[17,15] Dimethylcarbinols (III, R = CH₃) are obtainable in good yield by the action of methylmagnesium iodide on the 20-methyl ketone (I), and instances are reported of their degradation through the 17-ethylenes (IV) to the 17-ketones X in yield of about 10 percent.[18] A reinvestigation[15] of one of these examples showed that under most conditions the chief product of dehydration is the 20-pregnene VII (90% yield with $POCl_3$-pyridine); under some conditions (P_2O_5-benzene) dehydration affords an abnormal product probably resulting from a rearrangement.

The degradation of 20-ketopregnane derivatives with persulfuric acid (Caro's reagent) gives a mixture of the two products V and VI, the first of which results from the elimination of the two-carbon side chain.[19] Accord-

---

[13] Riegel and E. W. Meyer, *J. Am. Chem. Soc.*, **68,** 1097 (1946).

[14] Brink, M. Clark and Wallis, *J. Biol. Chem.*, **162,** 695 (1946).

[15] Koechlin and Reichstein, *Helv. Chim. Acta*, **27,** 549 (1944).

[16] Dalmer, v. Werder, Honigmann and Heyns, *Ber.*, **68,** 1814 (1935).

[17] Reichstein and v. Arx, *Helv. Chim. Acta*, **23,** 747 (1940).

[18] Butenandt and Cobler, *Z. physiol. Chem.*, **234,** 218 (1935); Butenandt and G. Müller, *Ber.*, **71,** 191 (1938).

[19] Marker and co-workers, *J. Am. Chem. Soc.*, **62,** 525, 650, 2543, 2621, 3003 (1940).

ing to Reichstein[15] the yield is very low and the process is less promising than another process due to Marker[20] starting with the bromination of the ketone I to a mixture of the 17,21-dibromide (VIII) and the 17-monobro-

Chart 7. DEGRADATION OF 20-METHYL KETONES TO 17-KETONES

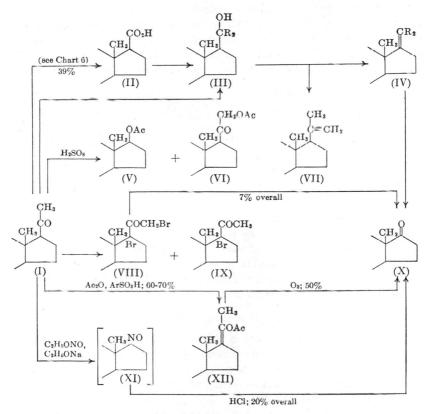

mide (IX). Treatment of the crude mixture with potassium hydroxide converts IX into two hindered esters, whereas VIII yields an unsaturated acid, $>C=CHCOOH$, that on ozonization affords the 17-ketone X in low yield.[15]

The best of the degradations shown are the two illustrated at the bottom of Chart 7. In one[21] the 20-methyl ketone is submitted to nitrite cleavage

[20] Marker and co-workers, *J. Am. Chem. Soc.*, **64**, 210. 213, 817 (1942), Plattner, Heusser and Boyce, *Helv. Chim Acta*, **31**, 603 (1948).
[21] Ettlinger and Fieser, *J. Biol. Chem.*, **164**, 451 (1946).

and the resulting nitroso-oxime derivative hydrolyzed without being isolated. The other[22] consists in the ozonization of the enol acetate (XII), prepared by treatment of the 20-ketosteroid with acetic anhydride and *p*-toluenesulfonic acid. In one instance both the cis and trans forms of the enol acetate were isolated.

A degradative reaction similar to oxidation with Caro's acid was investigated by Sarett,[23] who studied the oxidation of 20-ketopregnanes with perbenzoic acid. The results varied greatly with the nature of the compound oxidized. The substance XIII, which has an inert C_{11}-carbonyl group (3-ketosteroids are converted into lactones), was oxidized very

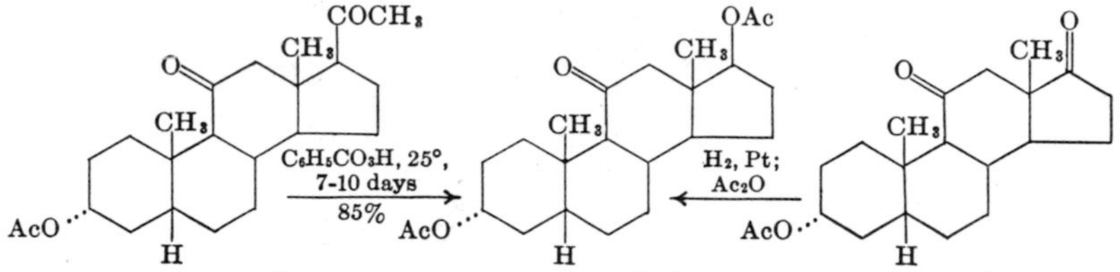

smoothly to the 17-acetoxy derivative XIV; the acetoxyl group probably has the β-orientation because the product is identical with that resulting from the hydrogenation of the 17-ketone XV and acetylation. When the 3-benzoate corresponding to XIII was oxidized in the same way the yield was only 19 percent. Oxidation of pregnane-3α,12α-diol-20-one diacetate by the same method proceeded in 61 percent yield.

Sex Hormone Therapy[1]

Intelligent use of sex hormones in therapy requires an understanding of the various interrelationships of endocrine glands. Various abnormalities of sex characteristics may be due to pituitary or to adrenal dysfunction and obviously cannot be corrected by estrogenic or androgenic therapy. The literature contains many conflicting claims, probably owing to faulty diagnosis of the condition treated. A definitive evaluation of medical applications of the hormones cannot yet be made; the substances have become available only recently, and the high cost of the preparations has limited widespread trial. The following survey is not intended to be complete, but merely presents a few of the more firmly established uses.

[22] C. W. Marshall, Kritchevsky, Lieberman and Gallagher, *J. Am. Chem. Soc.*, **70**, 1837 (1948).

[23] Sarett, *J. Am. Chem. Soc.*, **69**, 2899 (1947).

[1] Grollman, *Essentials of Endocrinology*, Lippincott (1947); Hamblen, *Endocrinology of Women*, Thomas (1945).

The female sex hormones[2] can often improve cases of ovarian inadequacy not due to pituitary failure. Thus a cyclic estrone-progesterone program sometimes initiates or restores normal ovarian function in young women with an ovulatory failure (absence of ovulation and corpus luteum formation). When such treatment is unsuccessful, additional therapy with gonadotropins is occasionally effective. At the present time only the gonadotropins from human pregnancy urine and placenta and from the serum of pregnant mares are available commercially.

Various types of hypoestrogenism are known; if ovarian failure alone is the cause, estrogen therapy is justified even though it must be continued indefinitely. In certain pituitary diseases (acromegaly, pituitary basophilism) estrogens are used to depress pituitary activity. Inhibition of the pituitary lactogenic hormone provides the basis for use of estrogens to suppress lactation. Testosterone is more effective in this respect. Other clinical uses of estrogens depend upon their ability to stimulate growth of epithelial tissues; they are used in senile vaginitis, in bacterial infection of the vaginal mucosa of children (sulfa medication probably more effective), in atrophic rhinitis, and in hypomastia. The rather widespread use of estrogens for treatment of climacteric symptoms probably is not always justified. Estrogens should not be used indefinitely for this purpose, for they merely postpone a natural process.

Progesterone may have some value in prevention of abortion. Some endocrinologists favor its use in pregnancies induced by hormone therapy and in those with a previous record of abortion. Many instances have been reported, however, in which progesterone failed to prevent abortion preceded by low pregnanediol values. Another use is based upon the ability of progesterone to inhibit uterine motility (treatment of afterpains).

Testosterone[3] has definite value in maintenance of normal male characteristics in eunuchs and castrates. It has no permanent effect, and treatment must be continued indefinitely if results are to be maintained. Its use in normal men is contraindicated, because it depresses spermatogenic activity by inhibition of the pituitary. The androgens exert various effects on the female organism, such as inhibition of lactation and suppression of menstruation; they are used clinically to some extent.[4]

Testosterone has recently been shown to have another interesting physio-

---

[2] Fluhmann, "Ovarian Dysfunctions and Their Treatment," *Glandular Physiology and Therapy* (1942).

[3] Hamilton, "Therapeutics of Testicular Dysfunction," *Glandular Physiology and Therapy* (1942); Heller and Maddock, "Clinical Uses of Testosterone in the Male," *Vitamins and Hormones*, V, 393 (1947).

[4] A. C. Carter, E. J. Cohen and Shorr, "The Use of Androgens in Women," *Vitamins and Hormones*, V, 317 (1947).

logical action: it promotes protein repletion and hence improves debilitation that accompanies certain diseases associated with dysfunction of the endocrine glands: Addison's disease, Cushing's syndrome, Simmonds' disease, and progeria.[5] Testosterone is the most active protein anabolic steroid known, but urinary extracts have been prepared that are more effective.

[5] Kochakian, "The Protein Anabolic Effects of Steroid Hormones," *Vitamins and Hormones*, IV, 255 (1946); Albright, *Harvey Lectures*, **38**, 123 (1942–43); Kochakian, "The Role of Hydrolytic Enzymes in Some of the Metabolic Activities of Steroid Hormones," *Recent Progress in Hormone Research*, I, 177 (1947).

Chapter V

Adrenal Cortical Hormones

Chemical investigations of the constituents of the adrenal cortex were initiated by the discovery that extracts of this organ are capable of extending the life span of adrenalectomized dogs, which otherwise would survive only a few days.[1] The adrenal cortical principle, cortin, actually contains a number of active and inactive substances and the former exert, to varying degrees, not only life-maintenance activity, but several other partly interrelated physiological actions (see later section). Thus assays for various forms of cortin activity have been employed in the processing of glandular extracts; in general the assays are less convenient and the results less exact than the assays for sex hormones. However, chemical studies initiated in 1935 by Kendall, by Wintersteiner and Pfiffner, and by Reichstein led within three years to the isolation of twenty-one crystalline substances, six of which are able to maintain life in adrenalectomized animals; since then seven more substances have been isolated.[2] The residual amorphous fractions still possess physiological activity but the nature of the active components is unknown.

Crude concentrates are prepared from whole beef glands, even though the active principles are present only in the cortex. First extraction is made with acetone or alcohol, which precipitate protein constituents. Advantage is taken of the relatively high water-solubility of the hormones, and various processes of partition yield an aqueous concentrate free from fats.[3] Weak acid or alkali can be used to remove basic or acidic contaminants. Reichstein introduced the use of Girard's reagent for the separation of reactive ketones from nonketonic or inert ketonic material; since the ketones show varying degrees of reactivity, fractionation can be accom-

[1] Rogoff and G. N. Stewart, *J. Am. Med. Assoc.*, **92**, 1569 (1929); Swingle and Pfiffner, *Science*, **71**, 321 (1930).

[2] For review articles see *Ann. Rpts.*, **33**, 395 (1936); **35**, 281 (1938); **37**, 332 (1940); **40**, 147 (1943); **48**, 200 (1946); Pfiffner, *Advances in Enzymology*, **2**, 325 (1942); Reichstein and Shoppee, *Vitamins and Hormones*, **1**, 346 (1943).

[3] The various procedures for the preparation of concentrates are described in the following papers: Reichstein, *Ergebnisse der Vitamin- und Hormonforschung*, **1**, 334 (1938); Kendall, *Cold Spring Harbor Symposia Quant. Biol.*, **5**, 299 (1937); Grollman, *ibid.*, **5**, 313 (1937); Pfiffner and Vars, *J. Biol. Chem.*, **106**, 645 (1934).

plished in either the formation or hydrolysis of the Girard derivatives.[4] The most efficient method for separation of individual components is chromatographic fractionation of the more stable acetates.[5] Ordinary methods of hydrolysis cause decomposition of the sensitive hormones, but hydrolysis of the acetates can be accomplished satisfactorily with aqueous methanol containing potassium carbonate or bicarbonate at 20°.[6]

Each of the three groups initially engaged in the work of isolation designated their pure products by a series of letters; the letter designations for the active compounds later gave way to names. Thus Substance H (Reichstein) is identical with Compound B (Kendall) and is now called corticosterone. Unless otherwise indicated, the letter designations employed here are those of Reichstein. The six compounds that are active in prolonging the life of adrenalectomized animals are shown in Chart 1. They all have the α,β-unsaturated ketonic grouping in ring A characteristic of testosterone and progesterone and they all possess a ketol side chain; the ketol grouping is highly sensitive to both acids and alkalies. The three compounds in the upper line in Chart 1 differ only with respect to the degree of oxygenation at C_{11}. The already pronounced dextrorotation of the 11-desoxy Compound Q is progressively increased by the introduction of an 11β-hydroxyl group (H) and an 11-keto group (Kendall's Compound A). The compounds in the lower line all have a 17α-hydroxyl substituent and they show the same progressive shift to higher dextrorotation with the introduction of 11β-hydroxyl and 11-keto substituents; the 17α-hydroxyl group decreases dextrorotation.

The approximate amounts of the active materials isolated from 1000 pounds of beef glands are: corticosterone, 333 mg.,[7] 340 mg.;[8] dehydrocorticosterone, 333 mg.,[7] 6 mg.;[8] 17-hydroxycorticosterone, 34 mg.,[9] 37 mg.;[10] 17-hydroxydehydrocorticosterone, 85 mg.,[9] 200 mg.,[8] 500 mg.;[7] desoxycorticosterone, 12.5 mg.;[8] 17-hydroxydesoxycorticosterone, 6 mg.[8] Recently hog adrenals have been found to be a much richer source of at least one of the hormones, 17-hydroxycorticosterone; the amount isolated corresponds to 600 mg. per 1000 lbs. of glands.[11] 17-Hydroxydehydrocorticosterone was isolated from the same source (340 mg. per 1000 lbs.).

[4] Reichstein, *Helv. Chim. Acta*, **19**, 29, 1107 (1936).

[5] Steiger and Reichstein, *Helv. Chim. Acta*, **21**, 546 (1938); Reichstein and von Euw, *ibid.*, **21**, 1197 (1938); **24**, 247E (1941).

[6] Reichstein and von Euw, *Helv. Chim. Acta*, **21**, 1181 (1938); von Euw and Reichstein, *ibid.*, **25**, 988 (1942).

[7] Kendall, *Cold Spring Harbor Symposia Quant. Biol.*, **5**, 299 (1937).

[8] Reichstein and von Euw, *Helv. Chim. Acta*, **21**, 1197 (1938).

[9] Kuizenga and Cartland, *Endocrinology*, **24**, 526 (1939).

[10] Reichstein, *Helv. Chim. Acta*, **20**, 953 (1937).

[11] Kuizenga, J. W. Nelson, Lyster and Ingle, *J. Biol. Chem.*, **160**, 15 (1945).

Chart 1. ADRENAL CORTICAL HORMONES

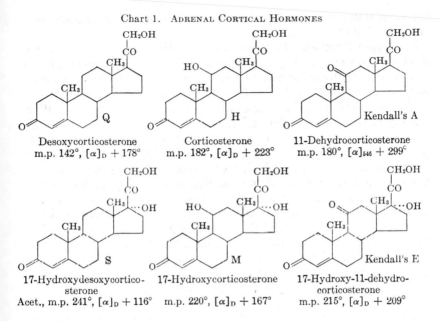

Desoxycorticosterone
m.p. 142°, $[\alpha]_D$ + 178°

Corticosterone
m.p. 182°, $[\alpha]_D$ + 223°

11-Dehydrocorticosterone
m.p. 180°, $[\alpha]_{546}$ + 299°

17-Hydroxydesoxycortico-
sterone
Acet., m.p. 241°, $[\alpha]_D$ + 116°

17-Hydroxycorticosterone
m.p. 220°, $[\alpha]_D$ + 167°

17-Hydroxy-11-dehydro-
corticosterone
m.p. 215°, $[\alpha]_D$ + 209°

A number of companion cortical steroids have been isolated; these all are reduction products lacking either the unsaturated grouping in ring A or the ketol group and they are all inactive. Comparisons of the six active hormones indicate that oxygen functions at C_{11} and C_{17} are not essential to life-maintenance activity but contribute importantly to physiological actions of still greater significance. Desoxycorticosterone is readily available by partial syntheses from sterols and bile acids and indeed was so prepared prior to its isolation, but it falls far short of glandular extracts in meeting some of the requirements of cortical hormone therapy. Since total glandular extracts cannot provide the variety of specific actions afforded by the individual C_{11}- and C_{17}-oxygenated hormones and since the supply of glands in any case is inadequate, synthetic methods have been investigated far beyond the requirements of structure elucidation and in particular with the objective of accomplishing the difficult and important feat of introduction of oxygen functions of proper steric orientation at C_{11} and C_{17}. Since all the synthetic developments have much in common, those that form an essential part of the evidence of structure will be described for the most part in a general section on synthesis.

SPECIFIC STRUCTURAL AND STERIC CHARACTERISTICS

The following paragraphs are devoted to a discussion of certain special structural features of cortical steroids that introduce complications not encountered in other series.

C₁₁-Oxygen Function. In those natural cortical steroids that possess an 11-hydroxyl group, this group has been shown by unequivocal evidence to be β-oriented[1] (for evidence see Chapter X). It is of general significance that the inference of the 11β-configuration independently deducible from hindrance effects, from the course of dehydrations, and from the relative stability of C_{11}-epimers is thus established as correct. The 11β-hydroxyl group resists acetylation by all methods tried, whereas an 11α-hydroxyl group, for example, that in 3α,11α-dihydroxycholanic acid,[2] is easily acetylated; inspection of models shows that the β-oriented group is subject to very pronounced steric hindrance but that an 11α-group is not hindered. On the other hand, the 11β-hydroxysteroids are readily dehydrated and are sensitive even to dilute mineral acids,[3] whereas the 11α-epimers are dehydrated only under forcing conditions normal for secondary alcohols. The double bond resulting from the dehydration of the 11β-hydroxy compounds was at first thought to be at C_{11}–C_{12} rather than at C_9–C_{11} because, unlike the secondary-tertiary 7,8-double bond, it is subject to hydrogenation. This assumption was recognized as false when 11β-hydroxyprogesterone and 12α-hydroxyprogesterone were found to yield different anhydroprogesterones on dehydration; since the latter compound can only yield the

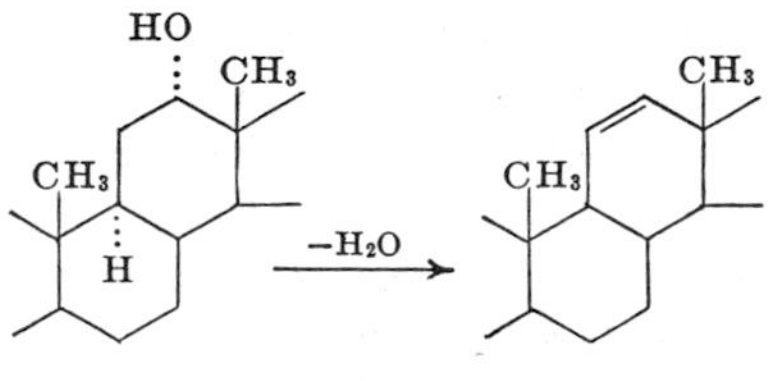

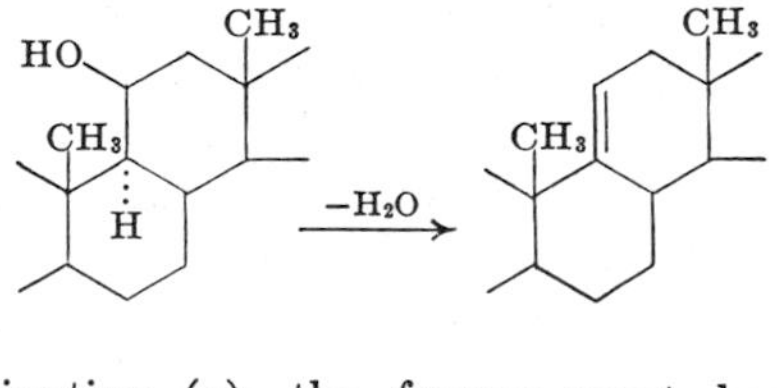

11,12-unsaturated derivative (a), the former must have afforded the $\Delta^{9(11)}$-isomer (b).[4] Therefore the 11β-hydroxyl group is eliminated with

---

[1] von Euw and Reichstein, *Helv. Chim. Acta.*, **30**, 205 (1947).

[2] W. P. Long and Gallagher, *J. Biol. Chem.*, **162**, 511 (1946); Gallagher and W. P. Long, *ibid.*, **162**, 521 (1946).

[3] Shoppee, *Helv. Chim. Acta*, **23**, 740 (1940); Shoppee and Reichstein, *ibid.*, **24**, 351 (1941).

[4] Hegner and Reichstein, *Helv. Chim. Acta*, **26**, 715 (1943).

the 9α-hydrogen atom and the dehydration follows the normal course of trans elimination. The dehydration of corticosterone acetate[5] is interesting. When the substance is heated for one-half hour in hydrochloric-acetic acid (1:9) it is converted partly into the 9-anhydro derivative; an alcoholic substance recovered from the mixture was originally regarded as 11-epicorticosterone acetate but is more likely impure starting material.[6] When

Chart 2. ANHYDROCORTICOSTERONES

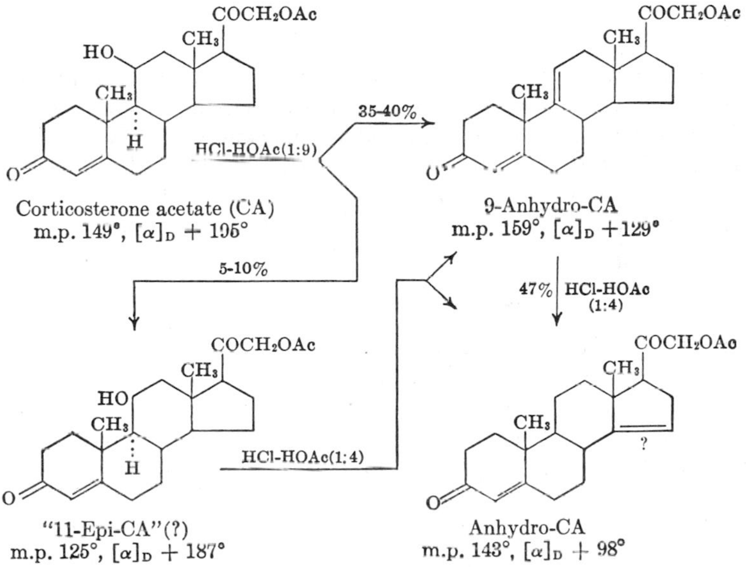

Corticosterone acetate (CA)
m.p. 149°, [α]$_D$ + 195°

9-Anhydro-CA
m.p. 159°, [α]$_D$ +129°

"11-Epi-CA" (?)
m.p. 125°, [α]$_D$ + 187°

Anhydro-CA
m.p. 143°, [α]$_D$ + 98°

the dehydration was carried out with a stronger mineral acid mixture 9-anhydrocorticosterone acetate was the chief product isolated (26% yield) but was accompanied by a substance (m.p. 143°) originally regarded as the Δ^{11}-isomer (17% yield). However 11-anhydrocorticosterone acetate (m.p. 181°, [α]$_D$ + 173°) has since been prepared by unambiguous methods and found to be different from the 143° product.[7] The latter substance, which can be produced by the acid-isomerization of 9-anhydrocorticosterone acetate, is probably the Δ^{14}-isomer.

The carbonyl group at C$_{11}$ is inert to hydroxylamine and to phenylhydrazine, and does not react with hydrazine under conditions of the Wolff-

[5] Shoppee and Reichstein, *Helv. Chim. Acta*, **26**, 1316 (1943).

[6] Observation of Dr. T. F. Gallagher based upon the fact that the supposed epimerization is not attended with as marked a decrease in dextrorotation as would be expected from the relationship between known 11-epimers.

[7] Communication from Dr. A. Wettstein.

Kishner reduction. It is also resistant to catalytic hydrogenation in a neutral medium, but hydrogenation can be accomplished in acetic acid solution. The reaction affords exclusively the hindered 11β-hydroxy de-

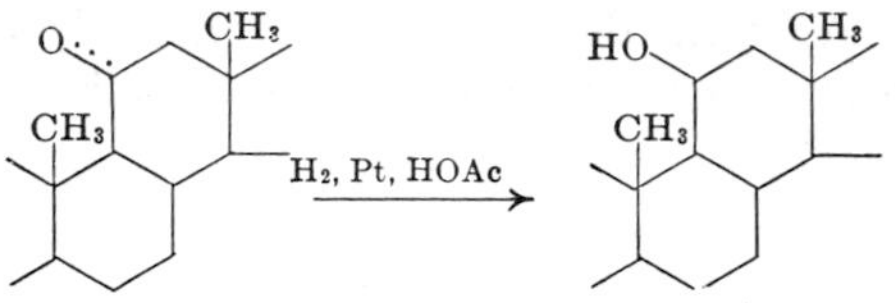

rivative, and hence hydrogen attacks the molecule at the unhindered back side and opens the rear bond of the carbonyl group. Reduction to 11β-hydroxy compounds can be effected particularly smoothly with lithium aluminum hydride.[8] C_{11}-Ketones often can be reduced by the Clemmensen method under vigorous conditions.

Steric Hindrance at C_{17}. Two types of steric hindrance effects associated with position 17 can be defined. One influences the direction of the opening of a double bond extending from position 17; this linkage is conveniently represented by one full line and one dotted line, to indicate that the bonds lie in a plane perpendicular to the plane of ring D. A reaction used extensively in the synthesis of cortical steroids is the hydroxylation of the 17,20-double bond with osmium tetroxide (a); this proceeds by cis addition, and hydrolysis of the cyclic osmic ester affords chiefly products with a β-side chain and a 17α-hydroxyl group. The hydroxylation involves

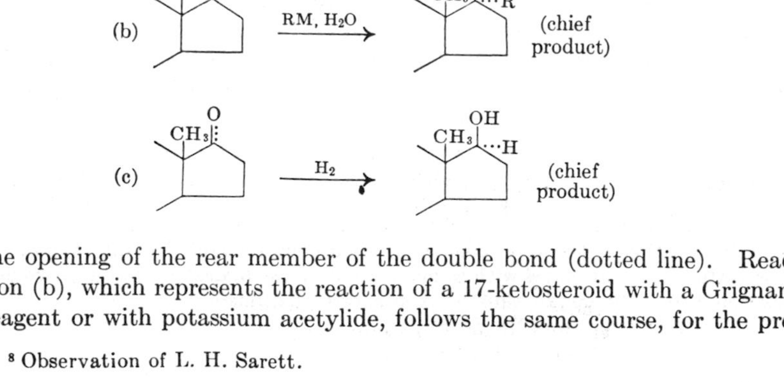

the opening of the rear member of the double bond (dotted line). Reaction (b), which represents the reaction of a 17-ketosteroid with a Grignard reagent or with potassium acetylide, follows the same course, for the pre-

[8] Observation of L. H. Sarett.

dominating product invariably is that resulting from the opening of the rear bond. The reduction or hydrogenation of a 17-ketosteroid (c) proceeds similarly by rear-bond attack and gives chiefly the 17β-alcohol. The course of these reactions would seem to indicate that more space is available for attack by reagents at the back side of the molecule than at the front side.

A second set of facts appears to be at variance with the first: β-oriented etio esters (d) and 17β-acetoxy compounds (e) are more easily hydrolyzed than the 17α-epimers (see Estradiol); a 17β-aceto compound (f) such as

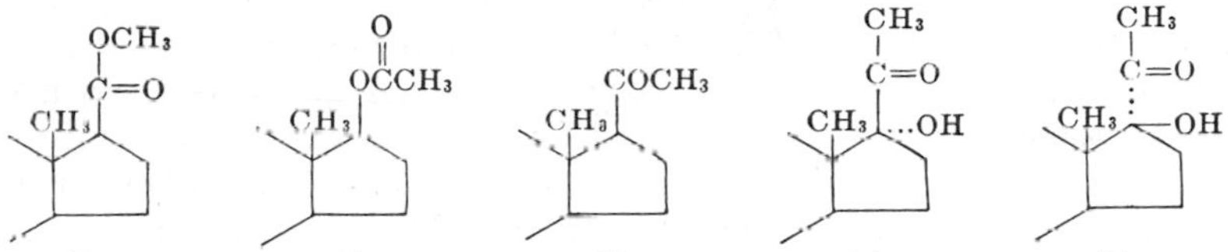

(d)   (e)   (f)   (g)   (h)

progesterone is thermodynamically more stable than the 17α-epimer and predominates in the equilibrium mixture (see 17-Isoprogesterone); in a (natural) 17α-hydroxy-20-ketone (g) the hydroxyl group is not acylable but the carbonyl group possesses normal reactivity, whereas in a (synthetic) 17β-hydroxy-20-ketone (h) the hydroxyl group is acylable and the carbonyl in the rear position is scarcely available for reaction.[1] These observations all point to greater hindrance at the back side of the molecule than at the front.

The two sets of observations refer to phenomena of two distinct types. The opening of a 17-double bond involves an attack at carbon atom 17, and inspection of Stuart models affords some rationalization of the observed preference for attack from the rear. The front side of C_{17} is the same distance from the angular methyl carbon as the rear side is from carbon atom 12, but the vibrating methyl group can dominate more space than the restricted 12-methylene group and so exert a short-range or bond-hindrance effect. The phenomena of the second type are concerned with groups or functional parts of groups occupying space remote from the immediate environment of C_{17}. The hydrolysis of the esters (d) and (e) proceeds through initial attack of the carbonyl groups, and the acetylation of (h) by severance of the oxygen-hydrogen bond; the isomerization of 17-isoprogesterone to progesterone (f) doubtless involves enolization, but the position of equilibrium must be concerned with the space available for the whole acetyl group in the alternate α- and β-orientations. Thus it seems to be an empirical fact that whereas the back side of the molecule offers better opportunity for attack at the 17-carbon atom, the front side

[1] von Euw and Reichstein, *Helv. Chim. Acta*, **30**, 205 (1947).

has more space available for the accommodation of a substituent group. We see no explanation of the group-hindrance effect but present the two sets of correlations in evidence of the regularity of the operation of specific hindrance factors; incidentally the correlations strengthen the case for the 17β-orientation of estradiol and testosterone (see Estradiol).

Configuration at C$_{20}$. Some of the inactive compounds isolated from adrenal cortical extracts contain centers of asymmetry at both the 17- and 20-positions, and Reichstein and associates have established their structures by methods of degradation and synthesis and have shown that the side chain is in all instances β-oriented. Heretofore no absolute correlation of the configurations at C$_{17}$ and C$_{20}$ has been suggested, and Reichstein has employed arbitrary designations (α and β) that have the same status as those (a and b) here adopted for the indication of nonrelative configurations at C$_{20}$ and C$_{24}$ in other steroids. However, we believe that from the accumulation of evidence it is now possible to assign with reasonable assurance absolute configurations (α and β) at C$_{20}$ relative to the whole molecule to most members of both the natural and synthetic series.

The configuration at C$_{20}$ relative to that at C$_{17}$ and the whole ring system is designated α or β according to the convention for projection formulation shown in the chart. The projection is best derived from an actual model;

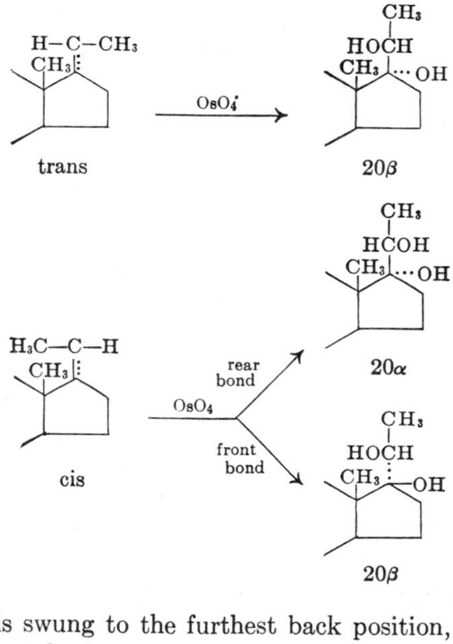

carbon atom 21 is swung to the furthest back position, whether the side chain is attached to the front or back of the model, and therefore appears in the projection in the top position. A given side chain of α- or β-orientation should make the same contribution to the rotatory power of the molecule as a whole whether attached to the front or back side of C_{17}.

Most of the syntheses of 20-hydroxy compounds proceed by osmium tetroxide hydroxylation of a 17-ethylene obtained either by a dehydration reaction or by allylic rearrangement of a 17-vinylcarbinol. The hydroxylation proceeds by cis addition, and the experimentally determined orientation of the side chain shows whether the front or the rear bond has opened. Hence the configuration at C_{20} relative to C_{17} would follow from a knowledge of the configuration of the 17-ethylene. Although direct evidence is not available, reasonable inferences can be made. Inspection of models shows that there is an enormous difference in the spatial characteristics of cis and trans 17-pregnenes; the trans structure presents no unusual features, but the cis structure is very strongly hindered, for the methyl group facing the ring system is closely crowded by both the angular methyl group and the 12-methylene group. Evidence is at hand to show that a substance of so hindered a character is not easily formed. Observations concerning the dehydration of the dimethylcarbinol I were mentioned earlier. Butenandt[1] dehydrated I (20-methylallopregnane-3β,20-diol) with acetic acid and acetic anhydride and isolated the 17-ethylene II in about 10 percent yield

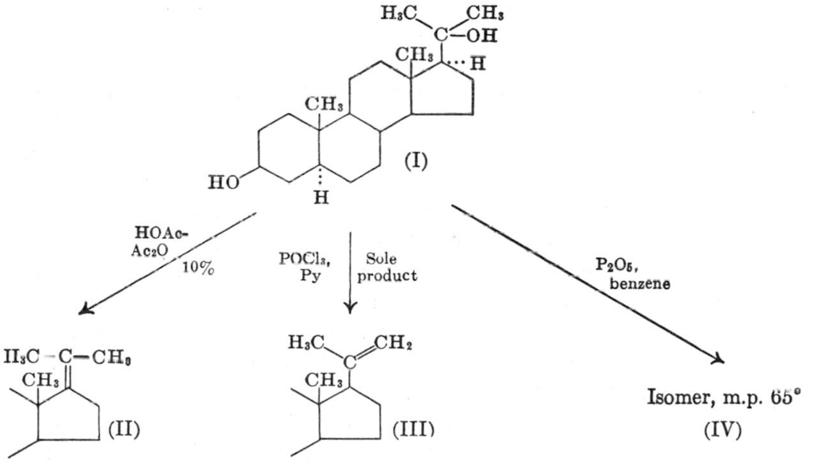

along with traces of two isomers, and he has reported similar results in other dehydrations by the same method or by high-vacuum sublimation.[2] Reichstein reinvestigated the dehydration of I under various conditions and

[1] Butenandt and Cobler, *Z. physiol. Chem.*, **234**, 218 (1935).
[2] Butenandt and G. Müller, *Ber.*, **71**, 191 (1938).

in no case obtained more than a trace of the 17-ethylene.[3]   Refluxing with acetic acid gave chiefly (85%) the 20-ethylene III, and III was the sole product of dehydration with phosphorus oxychloride in pyridine and the only substance isolated on high-vacuum sublimation.   Dehydration with phosphorus pentoxide in benzene gave chiefly a third, unidentified isomer, IV.   Since the structure of the carbinol I permits trans elimination of the hydroxyl group with the tertiary hydrogen atom at C_{17}, the preponderance of other reactions is a clear demonstration of the resistance to the formation of a 17-ethylene with a methyl group cis to the ring system.   Reichstein[3] has reported an instance of the dehydration of a diphenylcarbinol corresponding to I where no material convertible by ozonization to a 17-ketone was produced.   If the 17-ethylene II is formed with difficulty, the same must be true of a cis 17-pregnene.   It seems safe to assume that dehydration reactions that can proceed by normal trans elimination to give either a cis or a trans 17-pregnene yield a preponderant amount of the trans isomer.

The second type of 17-ethylene used for the partial synthesis of cortical steroids is obtained by allylic rearrangement of a vinylcarbinol prepared by the addition of acetylene to a 17-ketone and partial hydrogenation.

Dimroth[4] introduced the useful procedure of effecting the rearrangement with trichloroacetic acid in acetic anhydride and applied it to the carbinols from cyclohexanone and α- and β-trans-decalone.   The yields were excellent and the crystalline acetates from the decalones seemed to be fully homogeneous.   The ready acetylation of the primary alcohol formed by rearrangement, as compared with the starting tertiary alcohol, may contribute to the smoothness of the reaction.   The reaction also proceeds well as applied to the vinylcarbinols from 17-ketosteroids, and although two steric paths are open all rearrangements on record seem to have afforded a single, sterically pure 17-ethylene.   Since the ionic resonance hybrid should be free to give rise to the more stable of the two possible final products, it is probable that these invariable are trans 17-ethylenes.

Serini[5] effected the partial synthesis of Substance K by the allylic rearrangement of V (Chart 3) and hydroxylation.   If the ethylene has the trans structure VI, then K has the 20β-configuration shown.   Substance K,

[3] Koechlin and Reichstein, *Helv. Chim. Acta*, **27**, 549 (1944).

[4] K. Dimroth, *Ber.*, **71**, 1333 (1938).

[5] Serini, Logemann and W. Hildebrand, *Ber.*, **72**, 391 (1939).

as the triacetate, is distinctly more dextrorotatory than the 20α-epimer
prepared, with K, by the hydrogenation of Substance P (as triacetate).[6]

Chart 3. SYNTHESIS OF SUBSTANCE K

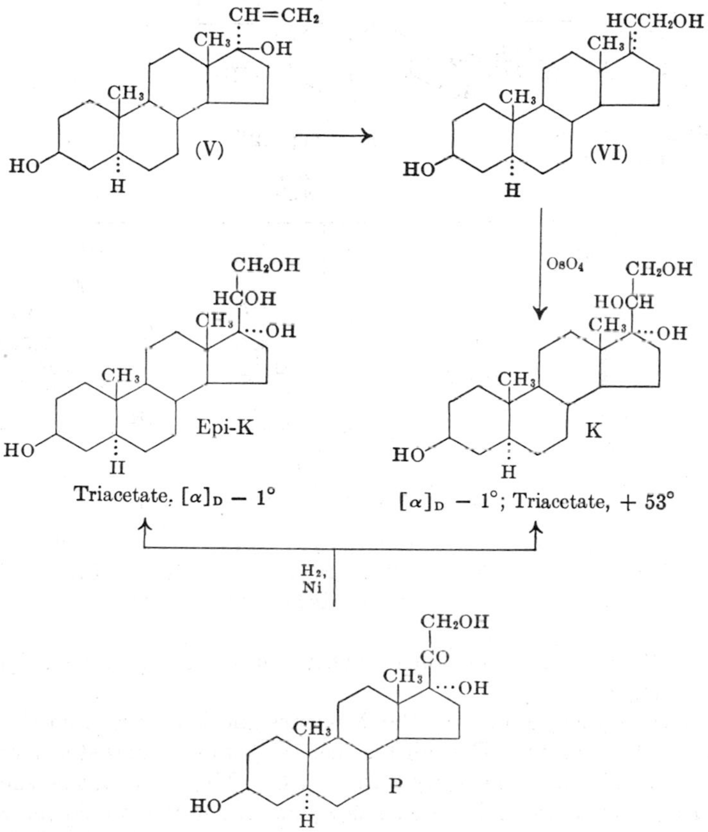

Epi-K

Triacetate. $[\alpha]_D - 1°$

$[\alpha]_D - 1°$; Triacetate, $+ 53°$

Substances J and O, along with a third isomer of the unnatural series,
were synthesized by Reichstein[7] by hydroxylation of the ethylene VIII
resulting from dehydration of VII (Chart 4). This ethylene when fully
purified melted at 120–121.5°, but the preparation hydroxylated melted
over the range 114–117° and evidently contained both geometrical isomers.
Now J and O are known to be C_{20}-epimers with the 17-hydroxyl group in the
α-orientation, and therefore they arise by rear-bond opening of the two
ethylenes. Since J is formed in ten times as high yield as O, it must have

[6] Reichstein and Gätzi, *Helv. Chim. Acta,* **21,** 1185 (1938).
[7] Reich, Sutter and Reichstein, *Helv. Chim. Acta,* **23,** 170 (1940).

Chart 4. Synthesis of J and O

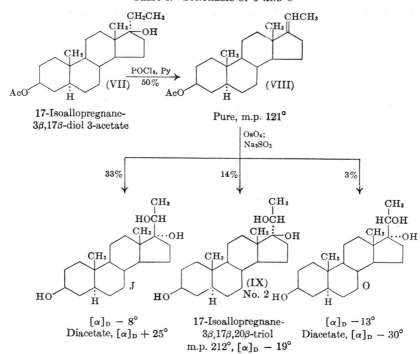

17-Isoallopregnane-
3β,17β-diol 3-acetate

(VII) POCl₃, Py 50% → (VIII)

Pure, m.p. 121°

OsO₄;
Na₂SO₃

33%   14%   3%

J
[α]_D − 8°
Diacetate, [α]_D + 25°

(IX)
No. 2
17-Isoallopregnane-
3β,17β,20β-triol
m.p. 212°, [α]_D − 19°

O
[α]_D −13°
Diacetate, [α]_D − 30°

come from the predominating trans ethylene and therefore can be assigned the 20β-configuration.

Substance O, then, belongs to the 20α-series and is formed from the cis ethylene in the mixture. The third isomer (IX) was recognized as having an α-side chain by its nonidentity with J or O. The configuration shown is based upon evidence to be cited below; the orientation would indicate that the substance arises by front-bond hydroxylation of the cis ethylene.

J-Diacetate and O-diacetate differ in specific rotation by 55°; the difference is of the same magnitude and in the same direction as that between K-triacetate and epi-K-triacetate (54°). Thus reasoning based upon two independent syntheses employing different types of reactions both lead to the conclusion that a 20β-hydroxysteroid in an acetylated condition is significantly more dextrorotatory than the 20α-epimer.

Sarett, in the course of a synthesis of 11-dehydrocorticosterone described below (Chart 24), separated and characterized two C₂₀-epimers of the formula X; these were derived from a mixture evidently containing the cis and trans 17-ethylenes. Each epimer, XA and XB, was converted through the 4-bromo diacetate into the unsaturated derivatives XIA and XIB. The two pairs of diols have nearly the same specific rotation, but both diacetates of the B-series are significantly more dextrorotatory than

Chart 5. Synthesis of T

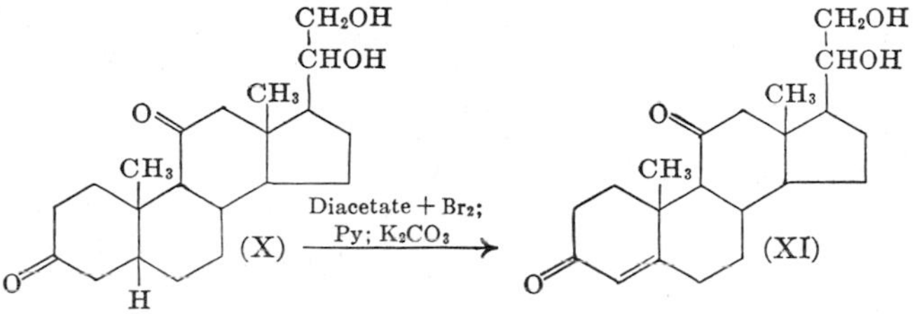

	M.p.	$[\alpha]_D$
Diols	{ A 183°	+ 68.5°
	{ B 168°	+ 61.5°
Diacetates	{ A 181°	+ 45°
	{ B 175°	+ 74°

	M.p.	$[\alpha]_D$
Diols	{ A 195°	+ 176.5°
	{ B 224.5°	+ 176°
Diacetates	{ A 154.5°	+ 133°
	{ B 208°	+ 170°

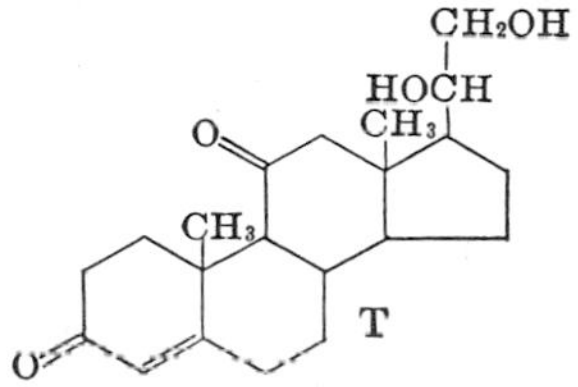

Diol; m.p. 210° (crude)
Diacetate, m.p. 213°

their epimers and hence must belong to the 20β-series. Reichstein's Substance T is known from the course of its oxidation[8] to have the structure XI, and it corresponds in melting point and in that of the diacetate reasonably well with XIB and not at all with XIA. Therefore, Substance T can be assigned the 20β-configuration.

In the first of two syntheses of 17α-hydroxy-11-dehydrocorticosterone by Sarett (Chart 26 below), an intermediate 17,20,21-triol proved to be identical with Substance U. Since the synthesis proceeded through the allylic rearrangement of a 17α-vinyl-17-hydroxy compound similar to V above, followed by osmium tetroxide hydroxylation, U like K must belong to the 20β-series. Two other cortical steroids have been correlated with U by Reichtstein,[9] who oxidized E-diacetate to a substance identical with

---

[8] Reichstein and von Euw, *Helv. Chim. Acta*, **22**, 1222 (1939).
[9] Reichstein and von Euw, *Helv. Chim. Acta*, **24**, 247E (1941).

U-diacetate and hydrogenated E to a substance identical with A; E and A, therefore, also are 20β-compounds.

Chart 6. CORRELATION OF E WITH U AND A

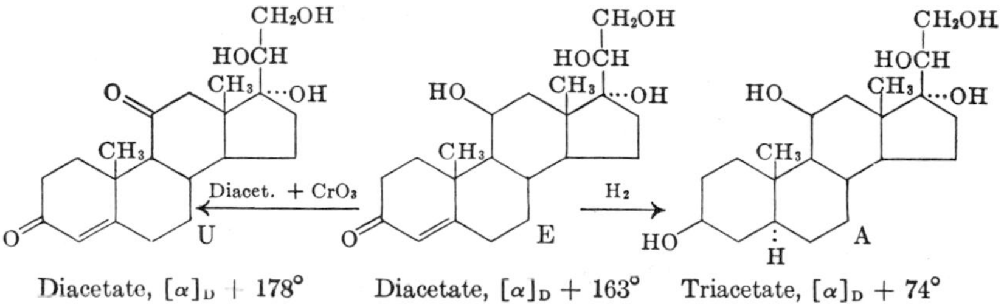

Diacetate, $[\alpha]_D + 178°$ Diacetate, $[\alpha]_D + 163°$ Triacetate, $[\alpha]_D + 74°$

Configurations can thus be assigned to all seven of the known cortical steroids that are asymmetric at C_{20}.   Evidence derived from sources that in some instances are completely independent of each other indicates that six of the substances isolated from the adrenal cortex belong to the same stereochemical series (20β); the seventh, Substance O, is the epimer of J.

Several pairs of 20-epimeric nor and bisnor bile acid derivatives of the normal and 20-iso series have been characterized with respect to optical rotation.   If an acid or ester of either series is compared with a 20-hydroxy-pregnane in terms of Marker's[10] empirical rule for the prediction of configurational relationships on the assumption that the ring system attached to C_{20} has an ordinal number approximately the same as that of an isopropyl group, it is found that substitution of any of these acid or ester groups for the hydroxyl group is not attended with change in configurational series. Each of four known derivatives of 3β-hydroxynorcholanic acid is slightly more dextrorotatory than the corresponding 20-iso compound[11] (average increment in $M_D + 14°$).[12]   Three of four of the 3,12-dihydroxybisnor-cholanic acid derivatives are more dextrorotatory than the 20-epimers[13] (see table); the one instance of reversal is of minor order.   The comparisons

TABLE I.   3,12-Dihydroxybisnorcholanic Acids

HYDROXYL GROUPS	DERIVATIVE	NORMAL SERIES $[\alpha]_D$	20-ISO SERIES $[\alpha]_D$
$3\alpha,12\beta$	Methyl ester	$+38°$	$+10°$
$3\alpha,12\beta$	Methyl ester diacetate	$+59°$	$+20°$
$3\alpha,12\alpha$	Methyl ester	$+40°$	$+21°$
$3\alpha,12\alpha$	Methyl ester diacetate	$+88°$	$+101°$

[10] Marker, *J. Am. Chem. Aoc.*, **58**, 976 (1936).
[11] Plattner and Pataki, *Helv. Chim. Acta*, **26**, 1241 (1943).
[12] W. Bergmann and Low, *J. Org. Chem.*, **12**, 67 (1947).
[13] Sorkin and Reichstein, *Helv. Chim. Acta*, **27**, 1631 (1944); **28**, 875 (1945).

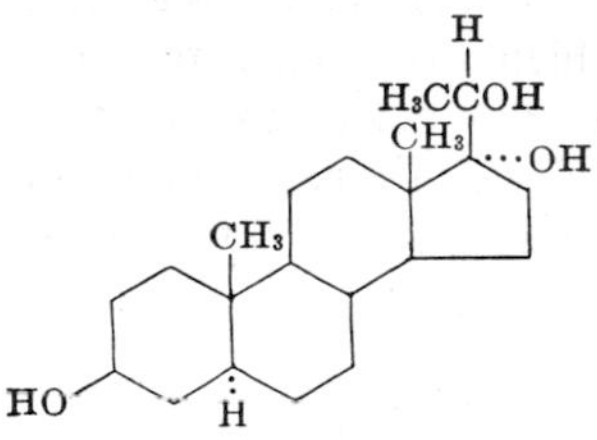

H
H₃CCOH
CH₃
····OH

CH₃

HO
H

Substance J

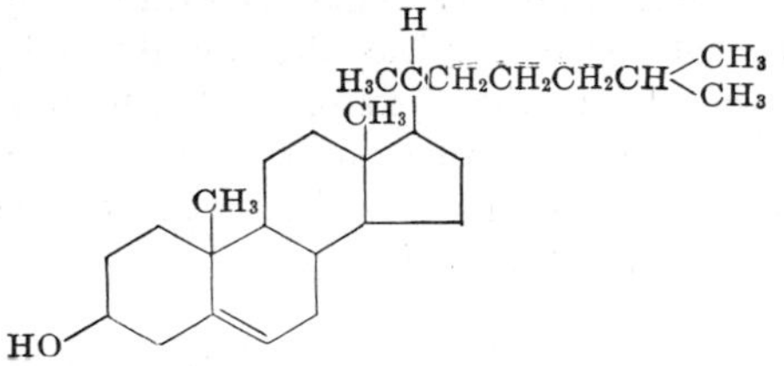

H
H₃CCCH₂CH₂CH₂CH⟨CH₃/CH₃
CH₃

CH₃

HO

Cholesterol

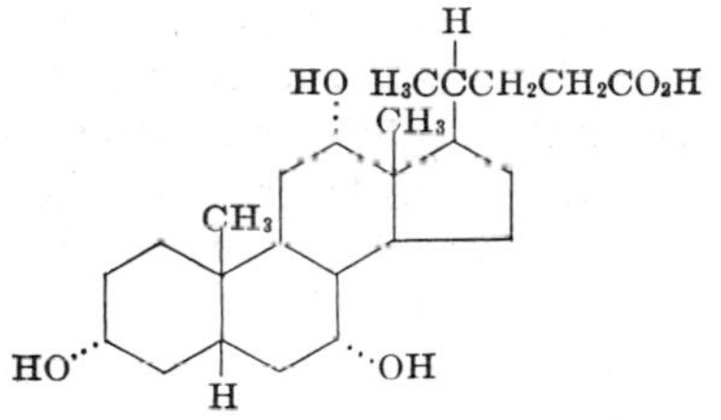

H
HO H₃CCCH₂CH₂CO₂H
CH₃

CH₃

HO····   ····OH
H

Cholic Acid

as a whole thus indicate that these acidic groupings, and hence the terminal parts of the sterol and bile acid chains, probably are in the β-orientation.

Periodic Acid Oxidation. Periodic acid has proved to be a very useful reagent for the characterization of the cortical steroid side chain and for

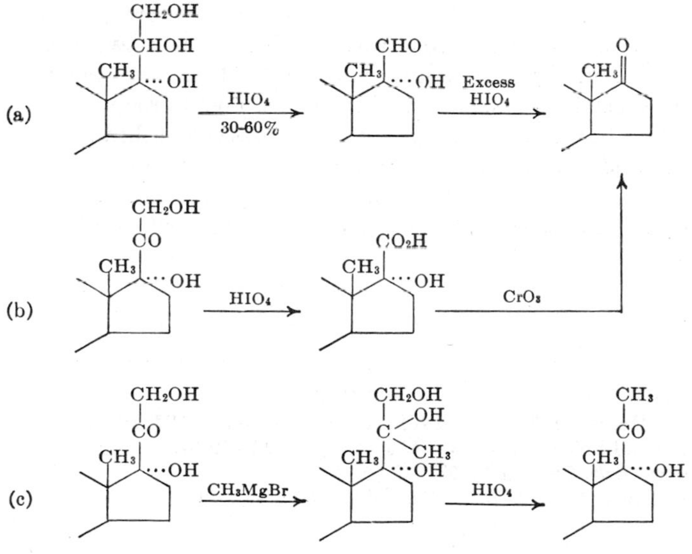

(a)

CH₂OH
CHOH
CH₃····OH
$\xrightarrow[30\text{-}60\%]{\text{HIO}_4}$
CHO
CH₃····OH
$\xrightarrow[\text{HIO}_4]{\text{Excess}}$
O
CH₃

(b)

CH₂OH
CO
CH₃····OH
$\xrightarrow{\text{HIO}_4}$
CO₂H
CH₃····OH
$\xrightarrow{\text{CrO}_3}$

(c)

CH₂OH
CO
CH₃····OH
$\xrightarrow{\text{CH}_3\text{MgBr}}$
CH₂OH
C⟨OH/CH₃
CH₃····OH
$\xrightarrow{\text{HIO}_4}$
CH₃
CO
CH₃····OH

the correlation of compounds that differ only in the side chain. A glycerol-type substance (a) yields first an aldehyde, which with excess reagent is converted into the 17-ketone. A dihydroxyacetone derivative (b) yields an α-hydroxy acid that can be oxidized to the 17-ketone with chromic acid. Periodic acid oxidation is also used in the ingenious process (c) for elimination of a 21-hydroxyl group.

STRUCTURE OF THE ACTIVE COMPOUNDS

Corticosterone. This was the first active principle to be isolated from glandular extracts. It was described by Reichstein[1] and shortly after by Kendall,[2] and the correct empirical formula was deduced in both laboratories. The absorption spectrum (λ_{max}^{alc} 240 mμ) was found to be that characteristic of an α,β-unsaturated ketone, and strong reducing properties indicated the presence of an aldehyde or α-ketol grouping. The ketol structure (I, Chart 7) was established[2] by the observation that oxidation with periodic acid gives one mole of formaldehyde and a carboxylic acid, II, which on oxidation with chromic acid yields a further acid (III) containing, according to Zerewitinoff determination, two carbonyl groups. This transformation gave the first indication of the presence of a secondary alcoholic group in the hormone, for the substance (I) yields only a monoacetate. The C_{11}-carbonyl group in acid III is inert to catalytic hydrogenation in a neutral medium, for under these conditions III can be converted into products of reduction of one or both centers of unsaturation in ring A (V and VI); these products belong to the allo series, since reduction of the 3-keto group leads to the β-configuration (precipitable with digitonin). Clemmensen reduction of V did not afford a crystalline product. The carbon skeleton of corticosterone was established[3] by conversion to allo-pregnane (IX) through the intermediates IV–VIII; the last step involved a successful Clemmensen reduction of the C_{11}-carbonyl group.

A proof of the presence of oxygen at C_3 was first established in an inactive cortical steroid that had been correlated with corticosterone by oxidation to the diketo acid III.[4] A direct proof was achieved in a transformation involving in the first step the replacement of the C_{21}-hydroxyl by hydrogen as follows:[5]

$$-COCH_2OH \xrightarrow{TsCl, Py} \left\{ \begin{matrix} -COCH_2OTs \\ -COCH_2Cl \end{matrix} \right\} \xrightarrow{NaI} -COCH_2I \xrightarrow{Zn} -COCH_3$$

[1] Reichstein, *Helv. Chim. Acta*, **20**, 953 (1937).
[2] Mason, Hoehn, McKenzie and Kendall, *J. Biol. Chem.*, **120**, 719 (1937).
[3] Steiger and Reichstein, *Helv. Chim. Acta*, **21**, 161 (1938).
[4] Shoppee, *Helv. Chim. Acta*, **23**, 740 (1940).
[5] Reichstein and Fuchs, *Helv. Chim. Acta*, **23**, 684 (1940).

The reaction of the ketol with p-toluenesulfonyl chloride (TsCl) yields a mixture of the ester and the chloro ketone, but both components react with sodium iodide to give the iodo ketone, which on reduction with zinc yields the methyl ketone.[6] The product derived from corticosterone is 11-hydroxyprogesterone (X, inactive); this loses water very easily to give

Chart 7. DEGRADATION OF CORTICOSTERONE

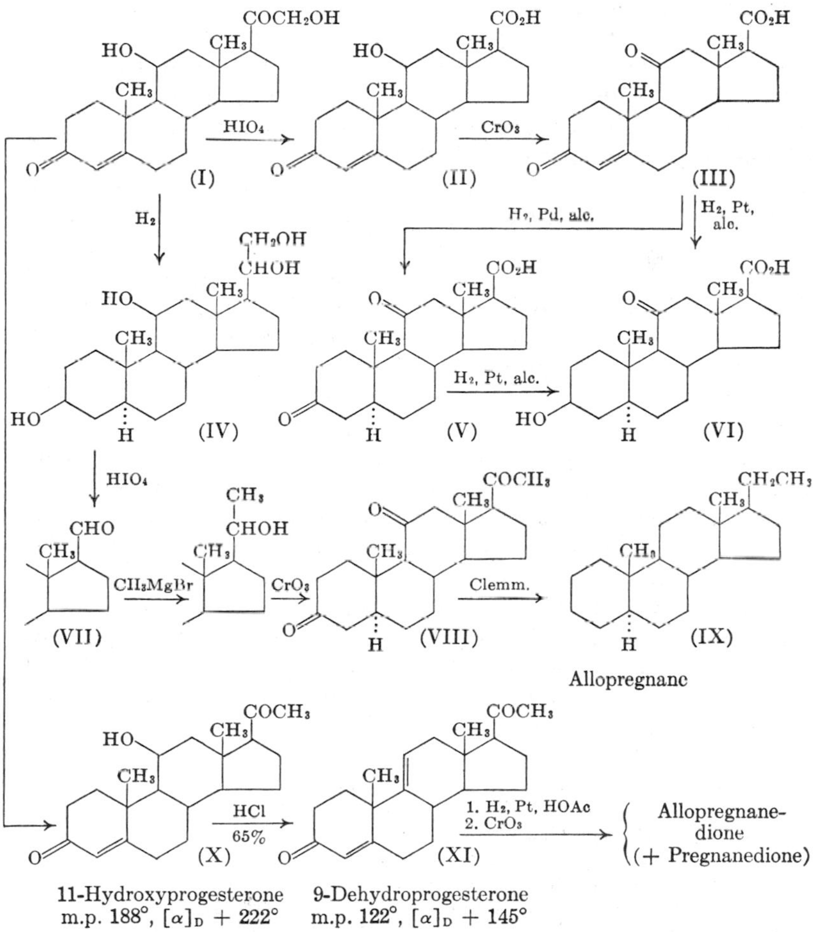

Allopregnane

11-Hydroxyprogesterone   9-Dehydroprogesterone
m.p. 188°, [α]$_D$ + 222°   m.p. 122°, [α]$_D$ + 145°

[6] The reduction of a 17,21-diol-20-one or a 17,20,21-triol by this method is not successful and apparently leads to D-homo compounds; Prins and Reichstein, *Helv. Chim. Acta*, **23,** 1490 (1940).

9-dehydroprogesterone (XI, one-third as active as progesterone).[7] The diunsaturated diketone was hydrogenated in an acidic medium to effect saturation of the 9,11-double bond and the product oxidized to regenerate the two carbonyl groups; the main end product was allopregnanedione, and a trace of pregnanedione was isolated. The degradation proves the presence in corticosterone of oxygen functions at C_3 and C_{20}; it also indicates the presence of a 4,5-double bond, for this structure explains the formation of C_5-epimeric end products. It should be noted that the reduction of a Δ^4-3-ketone does not always yield C_5-epimers. Cholestenone yields coprostanone (H_2, Pd, ether);[8] testosterone and androstenedione yield androstane derivatives (allo series);[9] progesterone gives a mixture of pregnane and allopregnane derivatives in which the latter predominates slightly.[10]

The unreactive hydroxyl group of the hormone was first inferred to be at C_{11} by the process of elimination of other possible positions. The diketone V does not behave like an α- or β-diketone or keto acid, and hence positions 1, 2, 4, and 16 were excluded. Positions 6 and 7 seemed unlikely because known steroids so substituted do not have the special character noted. Position 12 was eliminated by the fact that the degradation product X is an isomer of 12-hydroxyprogesterone and that the acid III differs from 3,12-diketo-Δ^4-etiocholenic acid,[11] prepared for comparison from desoxycholic acid. Final proof that the hydroxyl group is at C_{11} was obtained by partial synthesis (see below).

11-Dehydrocorticosterone was isolated first by Kendall[1] ,and later by Reichstein[2] and by Kuizenga and Cartland.[3] Kendall found that this hormone is converted by chromic acid oxidation into a diketoetiocholenic acid identical with that obtained from corticosterone (III, Chart 7). The direct conversion of corticosterone into 11-dehydrocorticosterone was accomplished by Reichstein[4] by mild oxidation of the 21-acetate.

Desoxycorticosterone had been prepared[5] in 1937 by partial synthesis from 3-acetoxy-Δ^5-etiocholenic acid and found to possess physiological activity, but was only isolated[2] from the adrenals in 1938. The hormone and its acetate were soon introduced to clinical use.

[7] Shoppee and Reichstein, Helv. Chim. Acta, 24, 351 (1941).
[8] Grasshof, Z. physiol. Chem., 223, 249; 225, 197 (1934).
[9] Butenandt, Tscherning and Hanisch, Ber., 65, 2097 (1935).
[10] Butenandt and Fleischer, Ber., 68, 2094 (1935).
[11] Mason and Hoehn, J. Am. Chem. Soc., 60, 2566 (1938).
[1] Mason, Hoehn, McKenzie and Kendall, J. Biol. Chem., 120, 719 (1937).
[2] Reichstein and von Euw, Helv. Chim. Acta, 21, 1197 (1938).
[3] Kuizenga and Cartland, Endocrinology, 24, 526 (1939).
[4] Reichstein, Helv. Chim. Acta, 20, 953 (1937).
[5] Steiger and Reichstein, Helv. Chim. Acta, 20, 1164 (1937). Improved procedure: Reichstein and von Euw, ibid., 23, 136 (1940).

17-Hydroxycorticosterone. This hormone (I, Chart 8) was isolated by Reichstein,[4] by Kendall,[6] and by Kuizenga and Cartland.[3] Reichstein[7] found that on chromic acid oxidation the substance is converted into an

Chart 8. DEGRADATION OF 17-HYDROXYCORTICOSTERONE

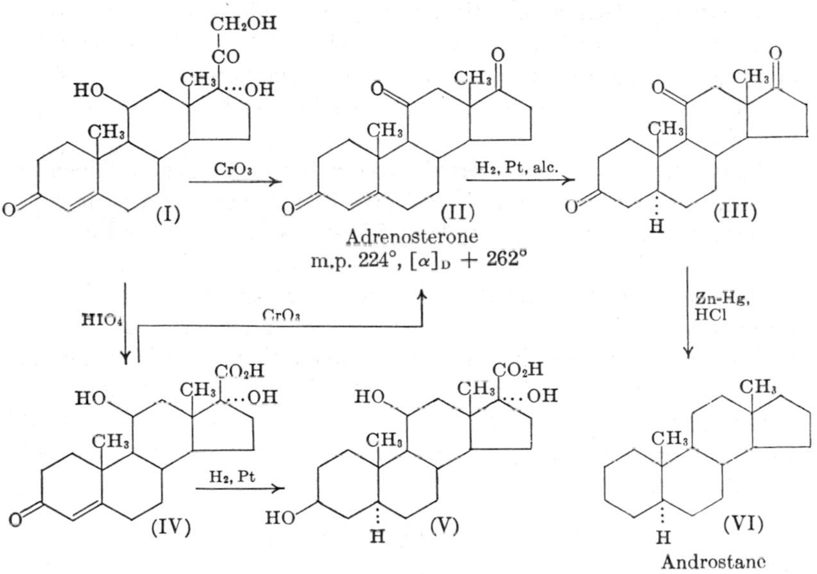

unsaturated triketone identical with a steroid previously isolated[8] from glandular extracts and named adrenosterone (II); it is possible that adrenosterone does not occur in the adrenals but is formed by oxidation during processing. Adrenosterone was characterized by reduction to a hydrocarbon identical with androstane. 17-Hydroxycorticosterone on periodic acid oxidation affords an acid (IV) with one less carbon atom,[6, 9] and this is oxidized by chromic acid to adrenosterone. The elimination of the carboxyl and hydroxyl groups in this oxidation characterizes the substance as an α-hydroxy acid and therefore establishes the presence in the original hormone of a hydroxyl group at C_{17}. Evidence for the α-orientation was furnished by partial synthesis.

The 17α-hydroxyl group present in certain of the cortical hormones is not acylable and it is more sensitive to the action of dehydrating agents

[6] Mason, Hoehn and Kendall, *J. Biol. Chem.*, **124**, 459 (1938).

[7] Steiger and Reichstein, *Helv. Chim. Acta*, **20**, 817 (1937).

[8] Reichstein, *Helv. Chim. Acta*, **19**, 29 (1936).

[9] von Euw and Reichstein, *Helv. Chim. Acta*, **25**, 988 (1942).

than the 11β-hydroxyl group. Substances are available by partial synthesis in which the side chain or carboxyl group is α-oriented, and the 17β-hydroxyl group in these compounds is acylable. Thus $3\beta,17\beta$-dihydroxy-17-isoetioallocholanic acid yields a diacetate,[10] whereas the epimeric $3\beta,17\alpha$-dihydroxyetioallocholanic acid yields only a monoacetate.[11]

17-Hydroxy-11-dehydrocorticosterone, commonly called Kendall's Compound E, was isolated in four laboratories.[12, 13, 14, 3] It differs from 17-hydroxycorticosterone only in that the oxygen function at C_{11} is a carbonyl group, and it has been prepared from this substance by chromic acid oxidation of the acetate.[15]

17-Hydroxydesoxycorticosterone was isolated by Reichstein;[16] identification was for a time uncertain because the hormone and its acetate melt at the same temperatures as 17-hydroxydehydrocorticosterone and its acetate and show no depressions on admixture. A difference in elementary composition was detected, and the substances were found to differ in a color reaction with sulfuric acid first described by Wintersteiner and Pfiffner;[13] the dehydro compound gives an orange color with a green fluorescence and the desoxy compound gives a pure red color. The constitution of the desoxy compound was suggested by the isolation of Δ^4-androstene-3,17-dione as a product of chromic acid oxidation and was later established by partial synthesis.

Inactive Companion Substances.

Estrone,[1] progesterone,[2] and 17-hydroxyprogesterone[3, 4] have been isolated from adrenal cortical extracts. Three derivatives of androsterone also have been isolated: adrenosterone,[5] Δ^4-androstene-3,17-dione,[4] and androstane-$3\beta,11\beta$-diol-17-one.[6, 4] Reichstein has suggested that these substances arise as products of the oxidation of C_{21}-constituents. Fourteen other companion steroids that are evidently reduction products of the active

[10] Miescher and Wettstein, *Helv. Chim. Acta*, **22**, 112 (1939).

[11] Reichstein and Meystre, *Helv. Chim. Acta*, **22**, 728 (1939).

[12] Mason, Myers and Kendall, *J. Biol. Chem.*, **114**, 613 (1936); **116**, 267 (1936).

[13] Wintersteiner and Pfiffner, *J. Biol. Chem.*, **116**, 291 (1936).

[14] Reichstein, *Helv. Chim. Acta*, **19**, 1107 (1936).

[15] Reichstein, *Helv. Chim. Acta*, **20**, 978 (1937).

[16] Reichstein and von Euw, *Helv. Chim. Acta*, **21**, 1197 (1938); Reichstein and Gätzi, *ibid.*, **21**, 1190 (1938).

[1] Beall, *Nature*, **144**, 76 (1939); *J. Endocrinology*, **2**, 81 (1940).

[2] Beall and Reichstein, *Nature*, **142**, 489 (1938); Beall, *Biochem. J.*, **32**, 1957 (1938).

[3] Pfiffner and North, *J. Biol. Chem.*, **132**, 459 (1940); **139**, 855 (1941).

[4] von Euw and Reichstein, *Helv. Chim. Acta*, **24**, 879 (1941).

[5] Reichstein, *Helv. Chim. Acta*, **19**, 29, 223 (1936).

[6] Reichstein and von Euw, *Helv. Chim. Acta*, **21**, 1197 (1938).

hormones are listed in Chart 9; the identifying letter designations are those of Reichstein. These high-melting, and for the most part dextrorotatory, substances have not all been assayed, but those tested have been found

Chart 9. INACTIVE COMPANION CORTICAL STEROIDS

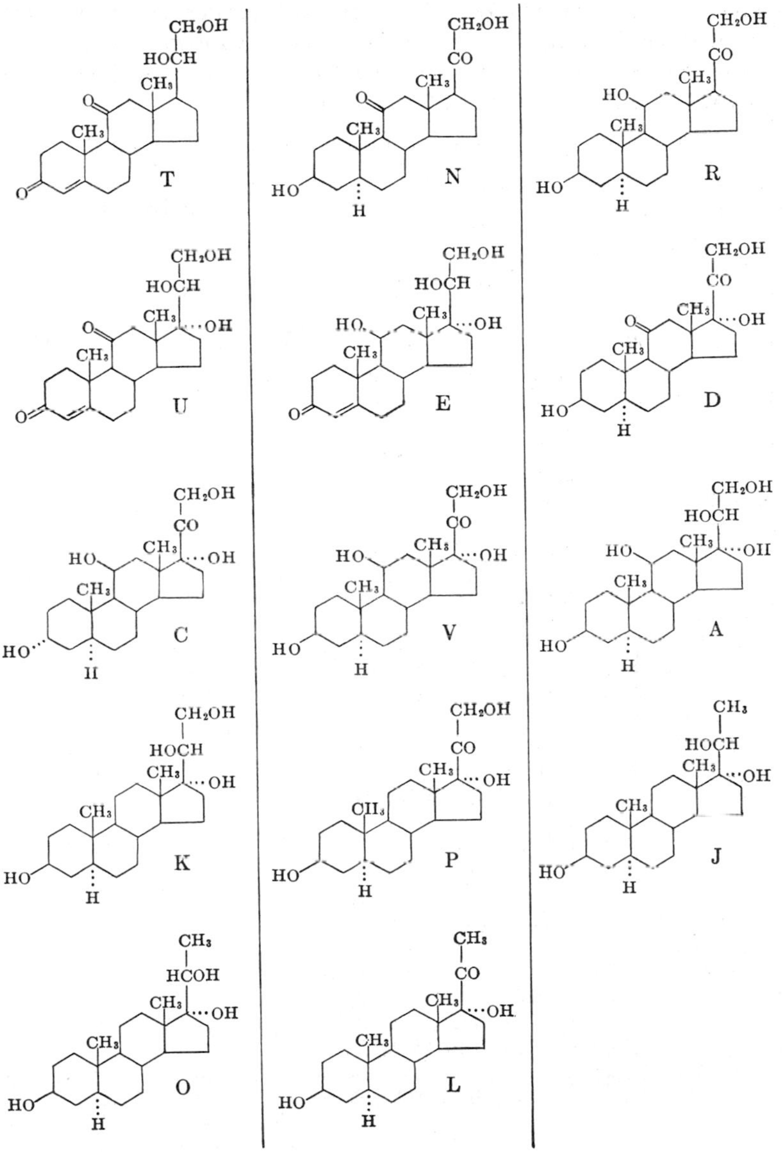

inactive. Seven of the substances are asymmetric at C_{20}, and the absolute configurations at this center relative to C_{17} deduced above are indicated in the formulations; in all but one instance (Substance O), carbon atom 20 has the β-orientation. All the compounds have β-oriented side chains, like all other known natural steroids, and a 17-hydroxyl group if present therefore has the α-orientation. The nuclear-saturated compounds are all allopregnane derivatives. The configuration at C_3 corresponds to that of cholesterol (β) in all but one instance (Substance C); the 3β-hydroxy compounds are all precipitable with digitonin.

TABLE II. Inactive Companion Cortical Steroids (See Chart 9)

REICH-STEIN'S SUBSTANCE	OTHER DESIGNATIONS	ALCOHOL		DI- OR TRIACET.		REFERENCES TO ISOLATION*
		m.p.	$[\alpha]_D$	m.p.	$[\alpha]_D$	
T		210°		213°		(1)
N	H	191°	+94°	145°	+77°	(2),(3),(16)
R		204°		174°	+84°	(4),(5)
U		208°		253°	+178°	(6)
E		125°	+87°	230°	+163°	(7),(8),(9)
D	G, B	242°	+62°	224°	+72°	(7),(10),(11),(12),(13)
C	D, C	276°	+73°	205°	+74°	(12),(7),(11),(13),(14)
V		225°	+51°	227°	+63°	(15)
A	A, D	222°	+16°	220°	+74°	(12),(7),(14)
K		200°	−1°	179°	+53°	(3)
P		239°	+48°	209°	+38°	(16)
J		217°	−8°	160°	+25°	(17)
O		223°	−13°	250°	−30°	(3)
L	G	264°	+38°			(18)

*$H. = Helv. Chim. Acta; J.B.C. = J. Biol. Chem.$

(1) Reichstein and von Euw, *H.*, **22**, 1222 (1939).
(2) Mason, Hoehn, McKenzie and Kendall, *J.B.C.*, **120**, 719 (1937).
(3) Steiger and Reichstein, *H.*, **21**, 546 (1938).
(4) Reichstein and von Euw, *H.*, **21**, 1197 (1938).
(5) Reichstein, *H.*, **21**, 1490 (1938).
(6) Reichstein and von Euw, *H.*, **24**, 247E (1941).
(7) Reichstein, *H.*, **19**, 29 (1936).
(8) Reichstein, *H.*, **20**, 953 (1937).
(9) See ref. 6.
(10) von Euw and Reichstein, *H.*, **25**, 988 (1942).
(11) Mason, Hoehn and Kendall, *J.B.C.*, **124**, 459 (1938).
(12) Wintersteiner and Pfiffner, *J.B.C.*, **111**, 599 (1935).
(13) Kuizenga and Cartland, *Endocrinology*, **24**, 526 (1939).
(14) Mason, Myers and Kendall, *J.B.C.*, **114**, 613 (1936).
(15) von Euw and Reichstein, *H.*, **25**, 988 (1942).
(16) Reichstein and Gätzi, *H.*, **21**, 1185 (1938).
(17) Reichstein, *H.*, **19**, 1107 (1936).
(18) Wintersteiner and Pfiffner, *J.B.C.*, **116**, 291 (1936).

Compounds with Oxygen at C_{11}. Substance **T** (not assayed) has an absorption spectrum similar to that of corticosterone and on chromic acid oxidation yields the same etio acid as is obtained from the hormone. It does not reduce ammoniacal silver hydroxide and it forms a diacetate that is stable to chromic acid oxidation. The properties of synthetic T and its epimer are given in Chart 5. **Substance N** has reducing properties characteristic of an α-ketol and on oxidation with periodic acid yields a 3-hydroxy-11-ketoetio acid identical with that resulting from degradation of corticosterone. **Substance R** has been converted into N by chromic acid oxidation of the diacetate.

The next six steroids listed in Chart 9 are reduced derivatives of 17-hydroxycorticosterone or the 11-dehydro compound. Those with a dihydroxyacetone side chain are distinguished from those of the glycerol type by their ability to reduce alkaline silver solution at room temperature and also by the behavior on periodic acid oxidation. On chromic acid oxidation **U** and **E** yield adrenosterone, and **D, C, V,** and **A** yield the reduction product, androstane-3,11,17-trione. The degradation of **Substance A** (Chart 10) to androstane-3β,17β-diol[1] furnished the first evidence, other than

Chart 10. DEGRADATION OF SUBSTANCE A

Androstane-3β,17β-diol diacetate

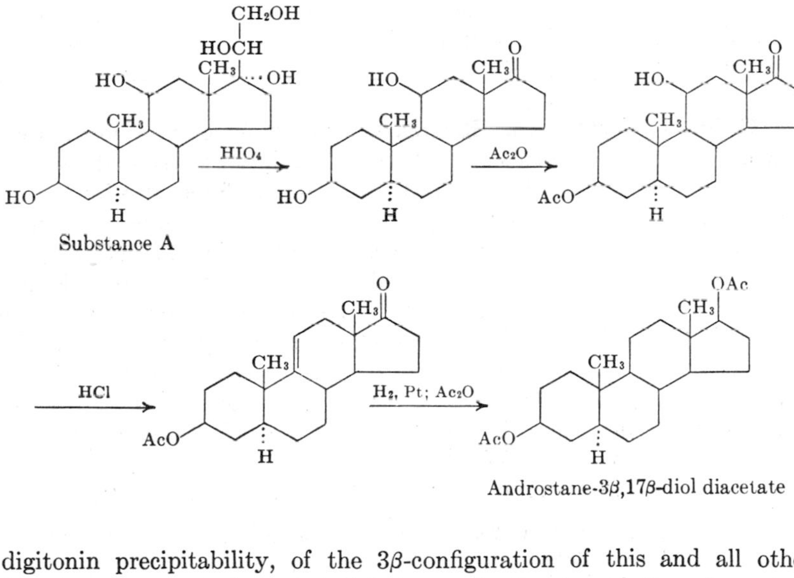

digitonin precipitability, of the 3β-configuration of this and all other 3-hydroxy compounds except **Substance C;** the degradation also estab-

[1] Shoppee, *Helv. Chim. Acta,* **23,** 740 (1940).

lished the A/B-trans ring juncture of the saturated steroids. The ·11-hydroxy compounds **E** and **V** were correlated with the 11-keto compounds **U** and **D** by conversion into these substances by oxidation of the di-acetates.[2] **Substances A, V,** and **C** (the C_3-epimer of **V**) were correlated by conversion into the same 17α-hydroxyetio acid, as shown in Chart ·11.

Chart 11.   CORRELATIONS

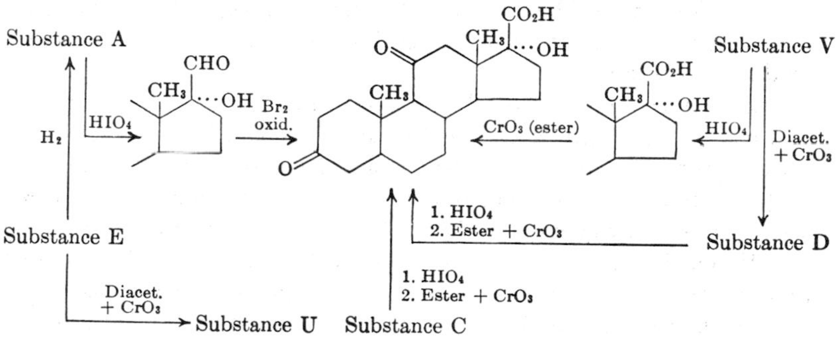

Substance A on partial oxidation with periodic acid yielded an α-hydroxy-aldehyde (positive silver test) that on bromine oxidation afforded an α-hydroxy acid. The oxidation of intermediate compounds with 3- or 11-hydroxyl groups to ketones was accomplished by the action of chromic acid on the methyl esters.

11-Desoxy Compounds.   Reference has been made above to the hydrogenation of P to K and epi-K (Chart 3) and to partial syntheses of K (Chart 3) and of the epimers J and O (Chart 4). **Substance L** was shown to be the 20-ketone corresponding to the last two substances by its conversion by hydrogenation (Raney nickel) to a mixture of J and O in which J predominated.[3] Reichstein succeeded in correlating compounds of the dihydroxyacetone series such as P with those of the 17-hydroxyprogesterone type (L) by periodic acid oxidation of the 20-methylcarbinol from P-diacetate; the yield of L was low (18%), for a considerable amount of the 17-hydroxyetio acid (34%) was formed. Reduction of the 21-hydroxyl group by the procedure through the tosylate and iodide is not applicable to compounds having a 17-hydroxyl group.[4]

17-Hydroxyprogesterone was isolated by Pfiffner and North[5] and later

[2] Reichstein and von Euw, *Helv. Chim. Acta,* **24E,** 247 (1941); von Euw and Reichstein, *ibid.,* **25,** 988 (1942).

[3] Reichstein and Gätzi, *Helv. Chim. Acta,* **21,** 1497 (1938).

[4] von Euw and Reichstein, *Helv. Chim. Acta,* **24,** 418 (1941).

[5] Pfiffner and North, *J. Biol. Chem.,* **132,** 459 (1940); **139,** 855 (1941).

by von Euw and Reichstein.[6] The substance is inactive in the survival test and has no progestational activity, but it is rather strongly androgenic in castrated rats. It has been prepared by partial synthesis.

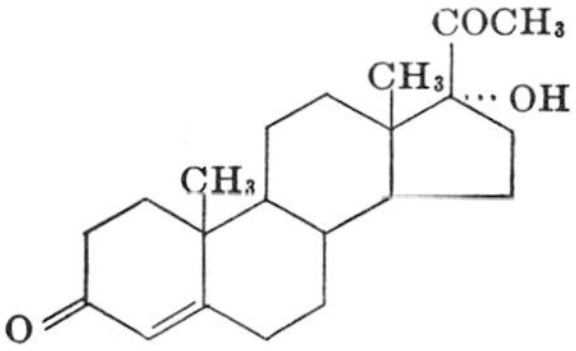

17-Hydroxyprogesterone
m.p. 223°, $[\alpha]_D + 106°$

Synthetic Elaboration of the Side Chain

Some of the methods for the construction of the three types of side chains found in cortical steroids starting with a 17-ketone or an etio acid were developed before the side chain of the natural steroids was known to be β-oriented and before additions to the 17-carbonyl group were known to give predominately products with a 17α-side chain. A synthesis involving such an addition thus yields chiefly an unwanted product of the unnatural series, for example a 17-isoallopregnane rather than an allopregnane. Reichstein, however, was sometimes able by chromatography to isolate the minor reaction products in amounts that sufficed for completion of a partial synthesis. Furthermore, certain of the 17-isoallopregnanes and 17-iso-Δ^5-pregnenes are convertible through the 17-ethylenes into useful products of the natural series. For these reasons substances of both series will be considered in the following discussion.

Alcoholic β-Side Chains. Methods developed for the partial synthesis of cortical steroids having three types of saturated β-oriented side chains are summarized in Chart 12. Substance T and its epimer were intermediates in one of Sarett's syntheses of Kendall's Compound F (see below); the process involved hydroxylation of a 20,21-double bond (a). Syntheses of K, J, and O by hydroxylation of 17-ethylenes, (b) and (c), are given in Charts 3 and 4. Another synthesis of J and O involved hydrogenation of a 20-ketone (d).[1] The intermediate 17-ene-21-ols of synthesis (b) were first prepared (Dimroth, Serini; Chart 3) by allylic rearrangement of the 17-vinylcarbinol with trichloroacetic acid in acetic anhydride. A generally superior modification[2] involves treatment of the tertiary alcohol with phos-

---

[6] von Euw and Reichstein, *Helv. Chim. Acta,* **24,** 879 (1941).
[1] Hegner and Reichstein, *Helv. Chim. Acta,* **24,** 828 (1941).
[2] Ruzicka and P. Müller, *Helv. Chim. Acta,* **22,** 416 (1939).

phorus tribromide. The product is the Δ^{17}-21-bromo derivative, and the halogen atom is readily replaced by acetoxyl on reaction with potassium acetate.

Chart 12. ALCOHOLIC β-ORIENTED SIDE CHAINS

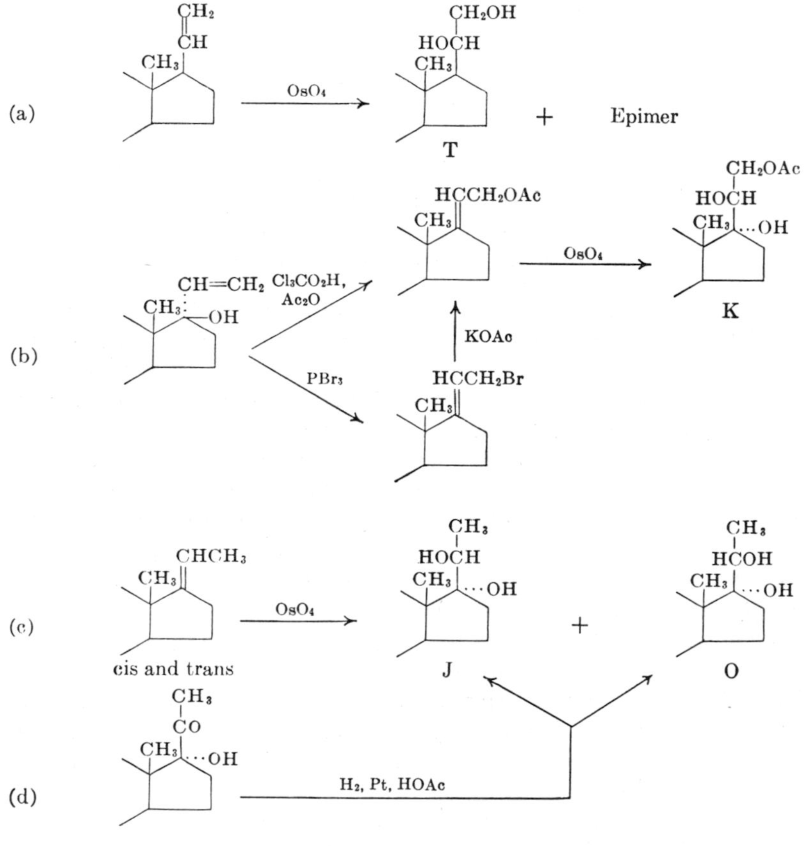

(a)

(b)

(c)

(d)

Alcoholic α-Side Chains. 17-Isoallopregnane-3β,17β,20β-triol (No. ·2) is formed in small amounts in the synthesis of J and O by the scheme (c) above (Chart 4). The 20α-epimer (III) has been prepared from the 17-vinyl derivative I through the aldehyde (II), obtained by ozonization. The configuration indicated is based upon considerations to be presented shortly (see Table III for references).

Three pairs of C_{20}-epimeric 17,20,21-triol derivatives of the structures VII, VIII, and IX (Chart 13) have been prepared by the hydroxylations indicated, each of which affords both possible products. When a double

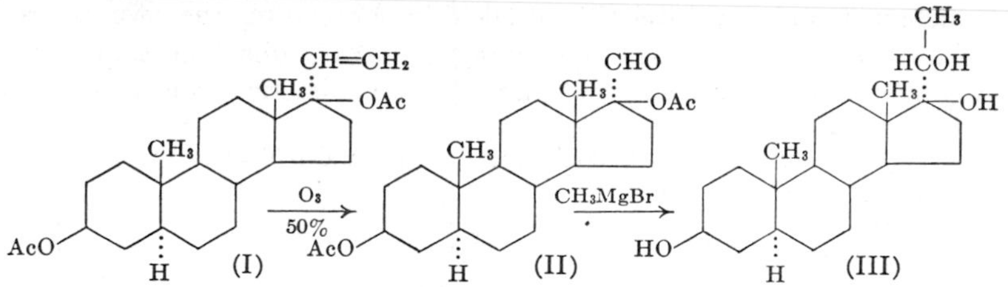

Δ^{20}-17-Isopregnene-3β,17β-
diol diacetate

17α-Formylandros-
tane-3β,17β-diol
diacetate

No. 1

bond is present in the nucleus (V), this is protected with bromine while the
other is hydroxylated (Serini). The double bond of α,β-unsaturated
ketones (VI) is so inert to osmium tetroxide that no protection was required

Chart 13. PREPARATION OF 20-EPIMERIC 17,20,21-TRIOLS

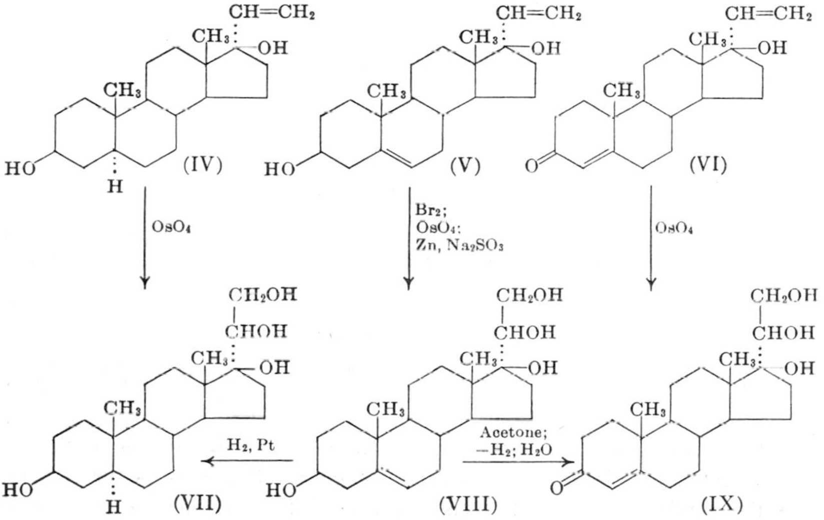

Nos. 3, 4

Nos. 5, 6

Nos. 7, 8

in the reaction of vinyltestosterone (VI) with one mole of reagent (Serini).
The Δ^5-unsaturated epimers (VIII) were related to the saturated compounds (VII) by hydrogenation and to the α,β-unsaturated ketones (IX)
by conversion into the 20,21-acetonide and Oppenauer oxidation (Reichstein). The six interrelated compounds with the 17,20,21-triol grouping
are listed in Table III as No. 3 – No. 8. The pair of epimers with the
17,20-diol grouping are listed as No. 1 and No. 2.

Salamon and Reichstein[1] succeeded in correlating the two series as follows (Chart 14). Δ^{20}-17-Isoallopregnene-3β,17β-diol 3-acetate (XI) on treatment with perbenzoic acid afforded two epimeric oxides (XIII, XV),

Chart 14. CORRELATION OF TRIOLS AND TETROLS

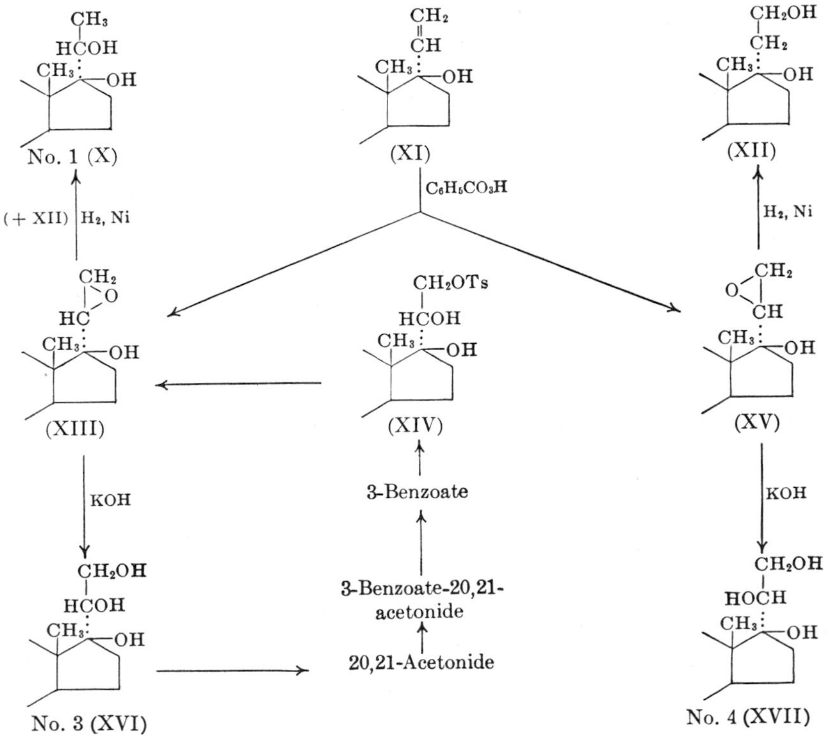

CH₃
HCOH
CH₃ —OH
No. 1 (X)

(+ XII) | H₂, Ni

CH₂
CH‖ (CH)
CH₃ —OH
(XI)

C₆H₅CO₃H

CH₂OH
CH₂
CH₃ —OH
(XII)

| H₂, Ni

CH₂
HC >O
CH₃ —OH
(XIII)

CH₂OTs
HCOH
CH₃ —OH
(XIV)

CH₂
O< CH
CH₃ —OH
(XV)

| KOH

3-Benzoate

| KOH

CH₂OH
HCOH
CH₃ —OH
No. 3 (XVI)

3-Benzoate-20,21-acetonide

20,21-Acetonide

CH₂OH
HOCH
CH₃ —OH
No. 4 (XVII)

each of which could be hydrolyzed with potassium hydroxide in aqueous dioxane to a tetrol, identical with the isomers No. 3 and No. 4, respectively, of Table III. Such a hydrolysis could involve rearrangements and inversions, but one tetrol (XVI) was shown to have the same configuration as the oxide from which it was derived by reconversion through the 3-benzoate-21-tosylate in the manner indicated. Although in the sugar series oxides on hydrogenation open exclusively in such a direction that the oxygen is retained by the carbon poorer in hydrogen atoms, both oxides in this instance gave some of the abnormal product XII. However, the oxide XIII also yielded some of the normal reduction product X, identical with isomer

[1] Salamon and Reichstein, *Helv. Chim. Acta,* **30,** 1929 (1947).

TABLE III. C_{20}-Epimers of the 17-Isopregnane Series

NO.	COMPOUND	FREE		DI- OR TRIACET.	
		M.p.	$[\alpha]_D$	M.p.	$[\alpha]_D$
1[a]	17-Isoallopregnane-3β,17β,20α-triol	235°	−9 Al	203°	−11 Chf
2[b]	20β-Epimer	212°	−17 Al	135°	−11 An
3[c,d,e]	17-Isoallopregnane-3β,17β,20α,21-tetrol	246°	0 Al	126°	−32 An
4[c,d]	20β-Epimer	210°	0 Al	148°	0 An
5[d,f]	17-Iso-Δ⁵-pregnene-3β,17β,20α,21-tetrol	240°	−73 Di	166°	−88.5 Di
6[d]	20β-Epimer	223°		123°	−44 An
7[d]	17-Iso-Δ⁴-pregnene-17β,20α,21-triol-3-one	233°		165°	+22 An
8[c,d]	20β-Epimer	233°	+66 Di	180°	+44 Di

Al = Alcohol, Chf = Chloroform, An = Acetone, Di = Dioxane

[a] Prins and Reichstein, *Helv. Chim. Acta*, **23**, 1490 (1940).
[b] Reich, Sutter and Reichstein, *Helv. Chim. Acta*, **23**, 170 (1940).
[c] Serini, Logemann and Hildebrand, *Ber.*, **72**, 391 (1939).
[d] Prins and Reichstein, *Helv. Chim. Acta*, **25**, 300 (1942).
[e] Ruzicka and K. Hofmann, *Helv. Chim. Acta*, **22**, 150 (1939).
[f] Serini and Logemann, *Ber.*, **71**, 1362 (1938).

No. 1.   No. 1, therefore, has the same configuration at C_{20} as Nos. 3, 5, and 7.

It is now appropriate to consider the evidence for the configurations at C_{20}.   The most reliable basis for comparison of the optical properties of 20-epimers in the synthetic (17-iso) and natural series (17-normal) is by reference to the increments in molecular rotation of the free hydroxy compounds and their typical acetyl derivatives.   In the last column of Table IV M_D increments are listed for a number of natural compounds and other 17-normal derivatives that have been correlated with them.   The eight synthetic compounds described in this section are listed, together with one additional related compound.   Figures representing comparisons in different solvents are enclosed in brackets; for acetone, alcohol, and dioxane the uncertainty due to solvent effect is estimated to be about ±40 units in M_D.   In the natural series the effect of acetylation of the 17α,20β,21-triols K, A, E, and U is in the range of M_D +240 to +410.   The acetylation increments for the 20β,21-diols T and XB and for the 17α,20β-diol J are in the range +110 to +130, and in each instance the increment for the 20α-epimer is of opposite sign and is 140 to 220 units more negative.   In the 17-isoallopregnane series the acetylation increments for two 17β,20β,21-triols are 0 and −40 and those for two 17β,20α,21-triols are −153 and

−166. The magnitude of the difference and the close correspondence to that found in the natural series fully substantiates the configurations assigned. Compounds 1 and 2 differ so little in rotation that comparisons

TABLE IV. Molecular Rotations of 20-Epimers

TYPE	COMPOUND	M_D^a Alcohol	M_D^a Acetate	Δ^{Ac}
	20β-Allopregnane Series			
$17\alpha,20\beta,21$-(OH)$_3$	Substance K	−4 Al	+258 An	(+262)
	Substance A	+87[b] An	+326 An	+239
	Substance E	+317 Al	+730 An	(+413)
	Substance U	+508[c] An	+800 An	+293
	Compound III, Chart 15	+220 Di	+541 Di	+321
$20\beta,21$-(OH)$_2$	Substance T	+610[c] An	+732[c] An	+122
	Compound XB, Chart 5	+214[c] An	+320[c] An	+106
$17\alpha,20\beta$-(OH)$_2$	Substance J	−27 Al	+103 An	(+130)
	5-Dehydro-J, Chart 21	−251[c] Al	−140[c] Al	+111
	20α-Allopregnane Series			
$17\alpha,20\alpha,21$-(OH)$_2$	Epi-K		−5 An	
$20\alpha,21$-(OH)$_2$	Epi-T	+612 An	+594 An	−18
	Compound XA, Chart 5	+239 An	+195 An	−44
$17\alpha,20\alpha$-(OH)$_2$	Substance O	−43 Al	−132 An	(−89)
	20β-17-Isoallopregnane Series			
$17\beta,20\beta,21$-(OH)$_3$	No. 4 (3-ol)	0 Al	0 An	(±0)
	No. 6 (Δ^5-3-ol)		−210 An	
	No. 8 (Δ^4-3-one)	+229 Di	+189 Di	−40
$17\beta,20\beta$-(OH)$_2$	No. 2 (3-ol)	−57 Al	−76 An	(−19)
	5-Dehydro-No. 2, Chart 21	−341 Al	−310 Al	+31
	20α-17-Isoallopregnane Series			
$17\beta,20\alpha,21$-(OH)$_3$	No. 3 (3-ol)	0 Al	−153 An	(−153)
	No. 5 (Δ^5-3-ol)	−256 Di	−422 Di	−166
	No. 7 (Δ^4-3-one)		+96 An	
$17\beta,20\alpha$-(OH)$_2$	No. 1 (3-ol)	−30 Al	−46 Chf	(−16)

[a] Al = Alcohol, An = Acetone, Di = Dioxane, Chf = Chloroform.

[b] Calculated from $[\alpha]_{546}$; nineteen comparisons in this series indicate that $[\alpha]_D$ is 19% (av.) lower than $[\alpha]_{546}$.

[c] Synthetic.

of constants determined in different solvents are not significant; No. 2 appears to be slightly more, rather than less levorotatory, as expected for a 20β-epimer.

Ketol Side Chain: C(OH)COCH₃-β. One route to ketols of this type is through steroids with a glycerol side chain (Chart 15). 17-Hydroxy-

Chart 15. 17-HYDROXYPROGESTERONE; SYNTHESIS A

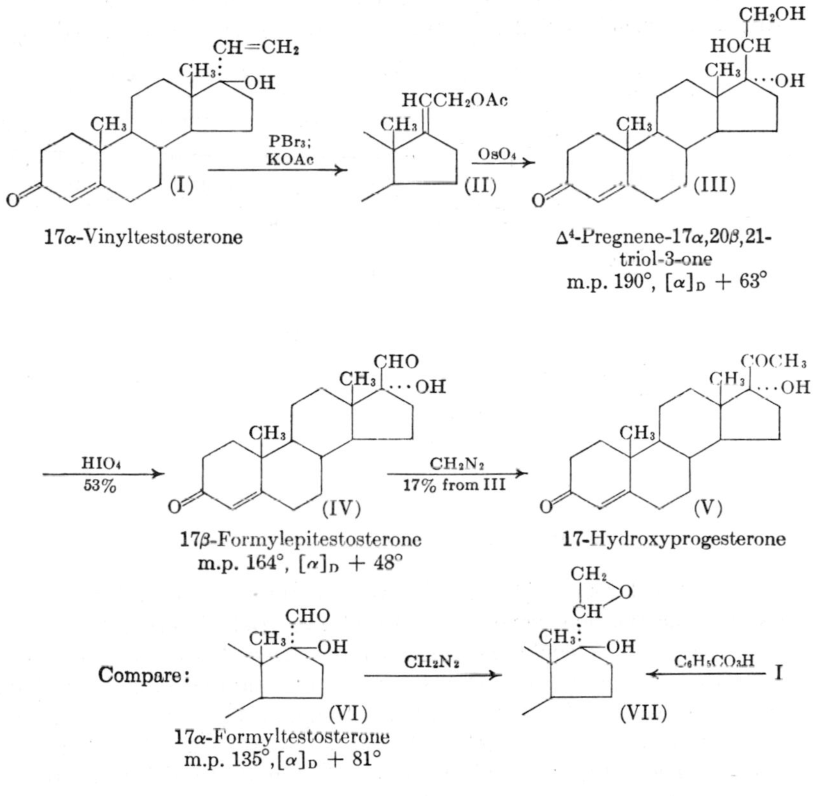

CH=CH₂
CH₃
OH
CH₃
O
(I)
17α-Vinyltestosterone

$\xrightarrow{\text{PBr}_3;\ \text{KOAc}}$

HCCH₂OAc
CH₃
(II)

$\xrightarrow{\text{OsO}_4}$

CH₂OH
HOCH
CH₃
OH
CH₃
O
(III)

Δ⁴-Pregnene-17α,20β,21-triol-3-one
m.p. 190°, [α]ᴅ + 63°

$\xrightarrow[53\%]{\text{HIO}_4}$

CHO
CH₃
OH
CH₃
O
(IV)
17β-Formylepitestosterone
m.p. 164°, [α]ᴅ + 48°

$\xrightarrow[\text{17\% from III}]{\text{CH}_2\text{N}_2}$

COCH₃
CH₃
OH
CH₃
O
(V)
17-Hydroxyprogesterone

Compare:

CHO
CH₃
OH
(VI)
17α-Formyltestosterone
m.p. 135°, [α]ᴅ + 81°

$\xrightarrow{\text{CH}_2\text{N}_2}$

CH₂
O
CH
CH₃
OH
(VII)

$\xleftarrow{\text{C}_6\text{H}_5\text{CO}_3\text{H}}$ I

progesterone (V) has been prepared[1] from the triol III,[2] obtained from 17-ethinyltestosterone by hydrogenation to the vinyl compound I with palladium in pyridine (90% yield), allylic rearrangement, and hydroxylation. Cautious oxidation with periodic acid gave an aldehyde (IV) that reacted with diazomethane with the formation of 17-hydroxyprogesterone. Sub-

[1] Prins and Reichstein, *Helv. Chim. Acta*, **24**, 945 (1941).

[2] Ruzicka and P. Müller, *Helv. Chim. Acta*, **22**, 755 (1939); Logemann, *Naturwissenschaften*, **27**, 196 (1939).

stance K has been converted into L by the same method.[1] The epimeric aldehyde VI with an α-side chain, prepared from the 17β,20α,21-triol described in the preceding section, reacts differently with diazomethane and yields an oxide (VII) identical with one obtained by the action of perbenzoic acid on 17-vinyltestosterone. The relationship between the optical rotations of the epimeric formyl derivatives is the reverse of that shown by the epimeric 17-hydroxyprogesterones.

A less convenient synthesis of 17-hydroxyprogesterone[3] (Chart 16) starts with Δ^5-pregnene-3β,21-diol-20-one diacetate (VIII), an intermediate to

Chart 16.   17-HYDROXYPROGESTERONE; SYNTHESIS B

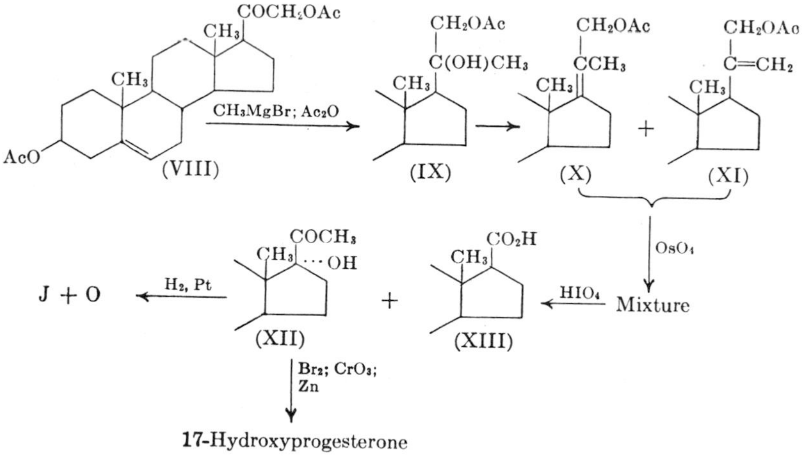

17-Hydroxyprogesterone

desoxycorticosterone. The reaction with methylmagnesium bromide, followed by acetylation, gave a mixture of two triol diacetates ($[\alpha]_D$ −47° and −58°), which could be separated by chromatography. Both gave mixtures of dehydration products, and an unseparated mixture probably containing X and XI was hydroxylated to a mixture that on periodic acid oxidation afforded the ketol XII and 3β-hydroxy-Δ^5-etiocholanic acid (XIII). The ketol was oxidized as the dibromide to 17-hydroxyprogesterone; on hydrogenation it afforded substances J and O.

Sarett[4] developed an efficient method (Chart 17) in which a 20-keto-pregnane (XIV) is converted into the cyanohydrin (XV); this is dehydrated and the product (XVI) treated with osmium tetroxide, when the immediate product of hydroxylation loses hydrogen cyanide with formation of the 17-hydroxy-20-ketone (XVII). 20-Cyanohydrins are rather un-

[3] Hegner and Reichstein, *Helv. Chim. Acta*, **24**, 828 (1941).
[4] Sarett, *J. Am. Chem. Soc.*, **70**, 1454 (1948).

stable, and traces of alkali or pyridine cause regeneration of the 20-ketone, but the stability varies with the nature of the group at C_3. The cyanohydrin (XV) of the 3-acetate is more stable than that of the free hydroxy

Chart 17. CYANOHYDRIN SYNTHESIS

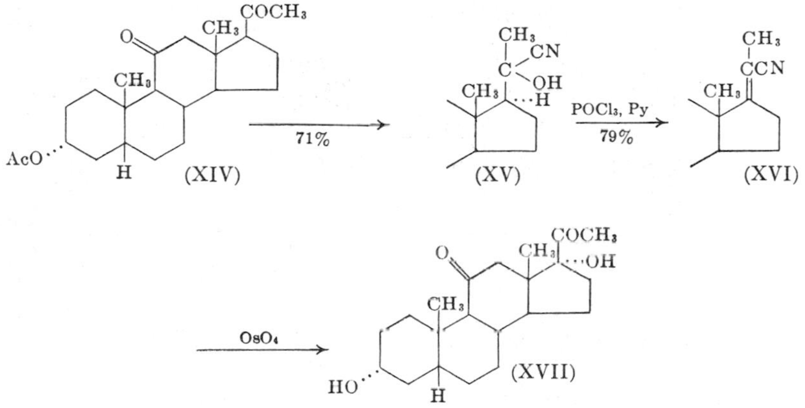

m.p. 208°, $[\alpha]_D$ + 68.5°

compound; the 3-keto-20-cyanohydrin is particularly sensitive to loss of hydrogen cyanide and the yield in the dehydration step in this instance drops to 20 percent. The reaction with osmium tetroxide proceeds extremely slowly under ordinary conditions but is catalyzed by a trace of pyridine.

Ketol Side Chain: C(OH)COCH₃-α. Epimeric 17-hydroxy-20-ketones with the unnatural, α-oriented side chain are obtainable from the carbinols resulting from the addition of acetylene to 17-ketosteroids (Chart 18). The addition reaction was initially conducted by the use of potassium acetylide in liquid ammonia, but a superior method that affords the Δ⁵-diol related to I in 80−85 percent yield consists in the use of potassium t-amylate at room temperature.[1] The diol corresponding to I reacts with acetic anhydride in pyridine at room temperature to give the 3-monoacetate but affords the diacetate I on prolonged refluxing of the solution.[2] Reichstein[3] found that the ethinyl derivative I reacts smoothly in t-butyl alcohol with a solution of hypobromous acid prepared by adding N-bromoacetamide to a sodium acetate buffer. The product is a dibromo ketone (II) and can be reduced in good yield to the known[4] ketone (III). The same ketone

[1] Stavely, *J. Am. Chem. Soc.*, **61**, 79 (1939).
[2] Ruzicka and K. Hofmann, *Helv. Chim. Acta*, **20**, 1280 (1937).
[3] Salamon and Reichstein, *Helv. Chim. Acta*, **30**, 1616 (1947).
[4] Ruzicka and co-workers, *Helv. Chim. Acta*, **21**, 1760 (1938); **22**, 626, 707 (1939); Shoppee and Prins, *ibid.*, **26**, 185 (1943).

can be obtained from the vinylcarbinol IV through the bromohydrin V, which is convertible into the 17-isoallopregnanetri- and tetrols Nos. 1 and 3 (see Table III, above).

Chart 18. KETOLS WITH α-ORIENTED SIDE CHAINS

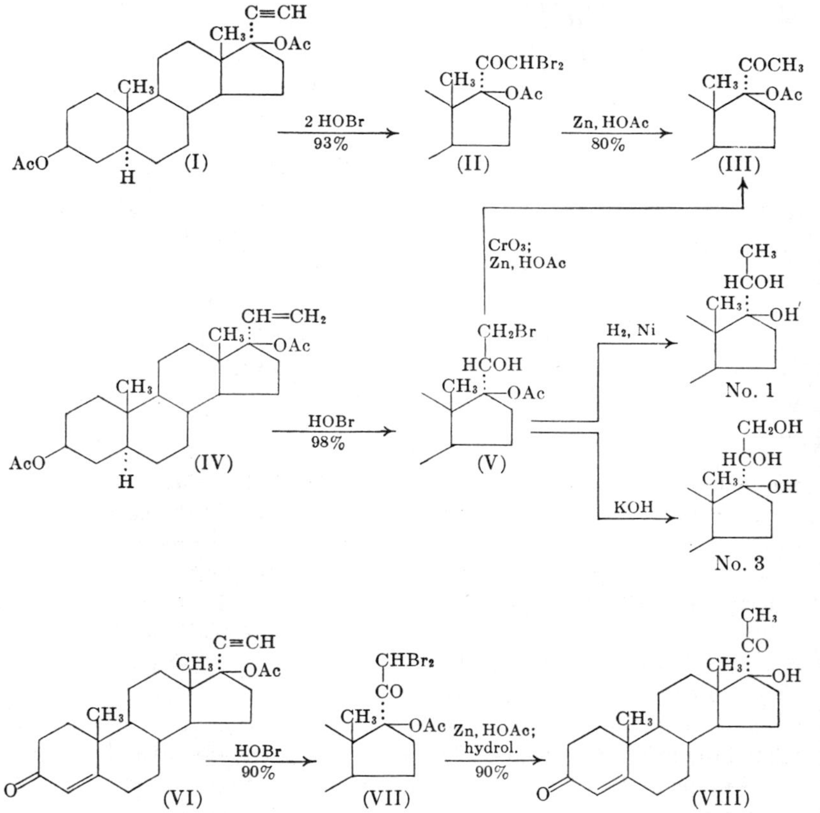

17β-Hydroxy-17-isoprogesterone (VIII) has been prepared[3] by analogous reactions from both 17α-ethinyltestosterone (VI) and 17α-vinyltestosterone; in the latter case the bromohydrin was also converted by hydrolysis into a known triol.   17β-Acetoxy-17-isoprogesterone had been obtained by Ruzicka (1938)[4] by the reaction of 17α-ethinyltestosterone with mercuric sulfate and boron fluoride etherate in acetic acid-anhydride.   Stavely[1] has described a procedure for the transformation of 17α-ethinyl-Δ⁵-androstene-3β,17β-diol into 17-iso-Δ⁵-pregnene-3β,17β-diol-20-one in one step by reaction with aqueous mercuric sulfate at 120°. Whereas progesterone and other 17β-aceto compounds with hydrogen at C_{17} are more dextrorotatory than the 17-iso compounds by nearly 200° in specific rotation, the natural 17-hydroxyprogesterone is only 58° more dextrorotatory than the 17-iso compound.

Ketol Side Chain: CHCOCH₂OH-β; 11-Desoxy Series. Reichstein prepared desoxycorticosterone by synthesis from 3β-acetoxy-Δ⁵-etiocholenic acid (I, Chart 19) in 1937,[1] and has since described several variations of the process. The acid is converted by reaction of the acid chloride with diazo-

Chart 19. Desoxycorticosterone Acetate

CO₂H → COCHN₂ → COCH₂OAc (top row: I, II, III)

SOCl₂; CH₂N₂; KOH, 47%; HOAc, 66%

73% Oppenauer; 20% from I; Br₂; CrO₃; Zn

COCH₂A → COCHN₂ → COCH₂OAc (bottom row: IV, V, VI)

HOAc

A = Cl, OH, OTs, OPO(OH)ONa

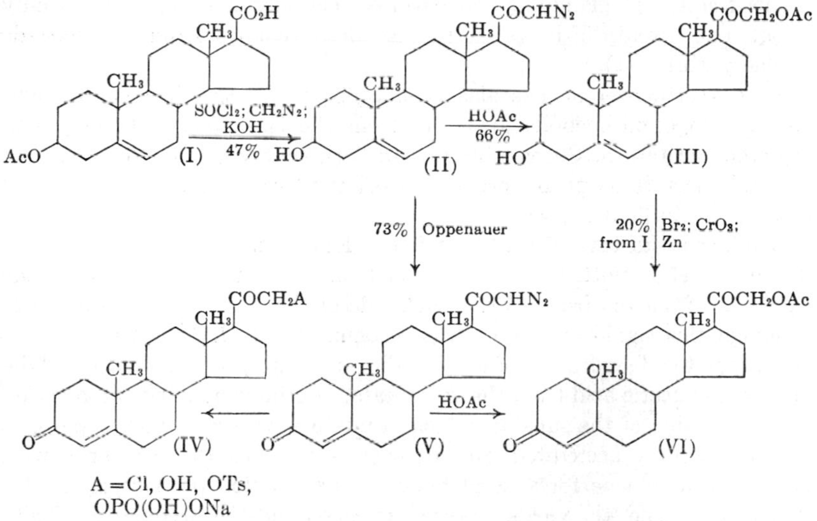

methane into a diazoketone acetate that can be hydrolyzed to the free diazoketone II. This reacts with acetic acid to give the ketol acetate III, which was converted into desoxycorticosterone acetate (VI) through the dibromide. Reichstein later found[2] that the diazoketone is surprisingly stable and can be submitted to Oppenauer oxidation (20°, 2–3 weeks). The oxidation product, diazoprogesterone (V), yields desoxycorticosterone acetate on reaction with acetic acid.[2] By reaction with hydrogen chloride or p-toluenesulfonic acid, the diazoketone V can be converted into 21-chloroprogesterone or into the tosylate of desoxycorticosterone;[3] it can be

[1] Steiger and Reichstein, *Helv. Chim. Acta,* **20,** 1164 (1937).
[2] Reichstein and von Euw, *Helv. Chim. Acta,* **23,** 136 (1940).
[3] Reichstein and Schindler, *Helv. Chim. Acta,* **23,** 669 (1940).

hydrolyzed directly to the ketol with dilute sulfuric acid (unspecified yield). The tosylate cannot be prepared from the ketol with tosyl chloride in pyridine because the ester reacts with pyridine to form a pyridinium salt. The tosylate can be converted into the 21-bromo, chloro, or hydroxy compound by interaction with sodium bromide, tetramethylammonium chloride, or potassium carbonate. The synthesis of the phosphoric ester of desoxycorticosterone was achieved by treatment of the diazoketone with phosphoric acid; the ester has about the same activity as the free ketol or the acetate. The pyridinium salt of the ketol has been converted by the Kröhnke reaction into the ketal derivative,[4] 21-dehydrodesoxycorticosterone (m.p. 106°), which seemed of interest as a possible constituent of the amorphous fraction of glandular concentrates; actually the substance is only about one twenty-fifth as active as desoxycorticosterone (Everse-de Fremery work test).

Desoxycorticosterone has also been prepared by the diazoketone synthesis from etiolithocholic acid and from the 3β-epimer.[5] Desoxycorticosterone acetate has been obtained in 3 percent yield by the action of lead tetraacetate on progesterone; the reaction is of more use in the C_{11}-O series and will be discussed below.

Synthesis with Inversion at C_{17}: Serini Reaction. Serini[1] in 1939 introduced a useful synthetic reaction which involves a transposition of the side chain from the front to the back side of the molecule or the reverse, although this significant point was recognized only later. The reaction consists in the dehydration of a 17,20-diol or, better, the elimination of the elements of acetic acid from the 20-acetate. Serini conducted the reaction by sublimation of the substance from a mixture with zinc dust; a perhaps better procedure accredited[2] to Miescher is to reflux the substance with zinc dust in toluene for several hours. The reaction product is the 17-desoxy-20-ketone; the yields reported are good and the products sterically homogeneous, and the added feature is the fact of inversion. The first example of the reaction illustrated in Chart 20, the synthetic preparation[1] of desoxycorticosterone from a triol obtained from 17α-ethinyltestosterone by reduction to the vinylcarbinol and osmium tetroxide hydroxylation, proceeds with inversion at C_{17} from the α- to the β-configuration. In the second reaction, conducted by Shoppee and Reichstein,[2] the triacetate of Substance A was converted into a 20-ketone identified as the 17-isomer of Substance R diacetate by nonidentity with R diacetate and by oxidation

[4] Reich and Reichstein, *Helv. Chim. Acta,* **22,** 1124 (1939).
[5] Reichstein and Fuchs, *Helv. Chim. Acta,* **23,** 658 (1940).
[1] Serini, Logemann and W. Hildebrand, *Ber.,* **72,** 391 (1939).
[2] Shoppee and Reichstein, *Helv. Chim. Acta,* **23,** 729 (1940).

Chart 20. SERINI REACTION

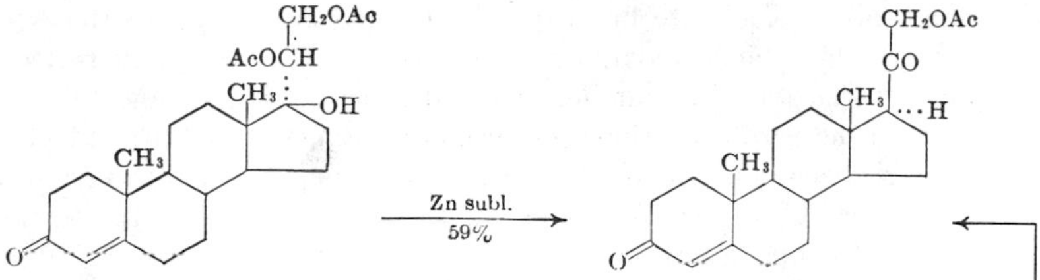

17-Iso-Δ⁴-pregnene-
17β,20β,21-triol-3-one
diacetate
m.p. 180°, [α]D + 47°

Desoxycorticosterone
acetate
[α]D + 169.5°

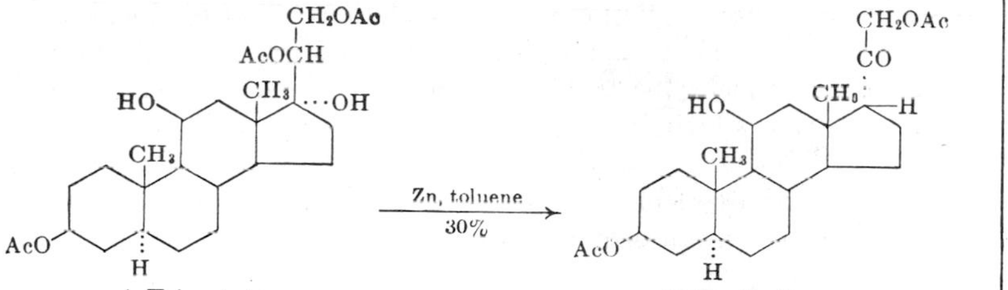

A Triacetate

17-Iso-R diacetate

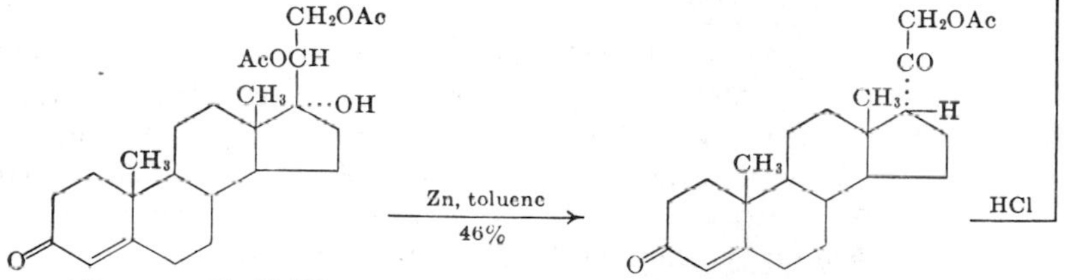

Δ⁴-Pregnene-17α,20β,21-
triol-3-one diacetate
Triol: m.p. 190°, [α]D + 63°

17-Isodesoxycortico-
sterone acetate
m.p. 137°, 174°; [α]D − 26°

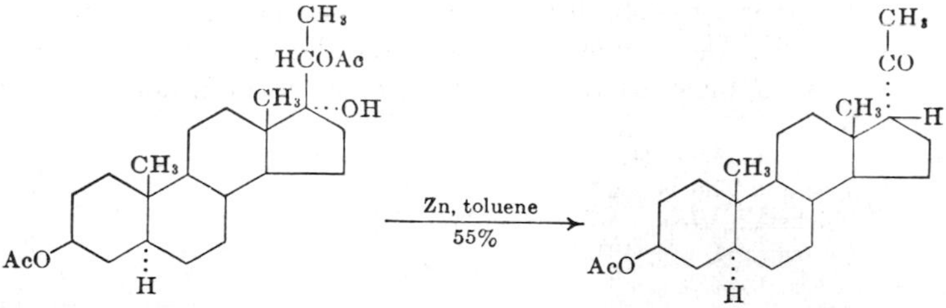

O Diacetate

3β-Acetoxy-17-isoallo-
pregnane-20-one
m.p. 118°, [α]D − 53°

to an 11-keto derivative (the 11-hydroxy group is sensitive to acids) isomeric with Substance N diacetate but capable of being isomerized to this substance by mineral acid (compare 17-isoprogesterone → progesterone). Substance A triacetate was further oxidized to the 11-ketone and this was submitted to the Serini reaction; the product obtained in 60 percent yield was 17-iso-N diacetate.[2] These two reactions thus proceed with inversion at C_{17} from β to α, or just the reverse of the first example. The starting material for the third example of the reaction[3] shown in the chart was the diacetate of a triol prepared as shown in Chart 15 by hydroxylation of an allylic rearrangement product; the substance is thus regarded as a 20β-compound of the 17-normal series. When refluxed with alcoholic hydrochloric acid, 17-isodesoxycorticosterone is largely isomerized (and hydrolyzed) to desoxycorticosterone. Periodic acid oxidation of 17-isodesoxycorticosterone gives 3-keto-17-iso-Δ^4-etiocholenic acid; as expected on theoretical grounds,[4] this acid lacks the lability of the 17-iso aceto compound; it is not affected by acids or bases and the ester is easily hydrolyzed without isomerization. Reichstein[5] has shown that in the bisnorcholanic acid series the free acids are stable to alkali but that the esters, being relatively resistant to hydrolysis, can be partially isomerized with alkali to the 20-iso compounds.

The four examples of the Serini reaction that have been cited all proceed with inversion at C_{17}. The examples include members of both the 17-normal and 17-iso series, but they all have the 20β-configuration. Shoppee[6] has investigated the interesting case of a substance of 20α-orientation, Substance O diacetate (Chart 20), and found that inversion occurs in this case as well and hence that the steric course of the reaction is not dependent upon the configuration at C_{20}. Fieser and Fieser[7] had suggested the possibility of such dependency on the strength of a statement by Butenandt[8] concerning two triols obtained as shown in Chart 21 from dehydroepiandrosterone by reactions analogous to those (Chart 5) leading to Substance J and its 17-isomer, No. 2. Prins and Reichstein[9] later converted the triols by hydrogenation into Substance J and compound No. 2, respectively, and thereby established the configurations. Butenandt recorded the details of the conversion of one triol diacetate by the Serini reaction into 17-iso-Δ^5-pregnene-3β-ol-20-one acetate, but did not indicate

[3] Shoppee, *Helv. Chim. Acta*, **23**, 925 (1940).
[4] Ingold, Shoppee and Thorpe, *J. Chem. Soc.*, 1482 (1926).
[5] Sorkin and Reichstein, *Helv. Chim. Acta*, **28**, 875 (1945).
[6] Shoppee, *Experientia*, **4**, 285 (1948).
[7] Fieser and Fieser, *Experientia* **4**, 285 (1948).
[8] Butenandt, Schmidt-Thomé and Paul, *Ber.*, **72**, 1112 (1939).
[9] Prins and Reichstein, *Helv. Chim. Acta*, **23**, 1490 (1940).

which triol diacetate had been used.   The paper includes the statement, unsupported by experimental details, that the isomeric triol diacetate also yields 17-isopregnenolone.   According   to   the   configurations   now   es-

Chart 21.   OTHER EXAMPLES OF THE SERINI REACTION

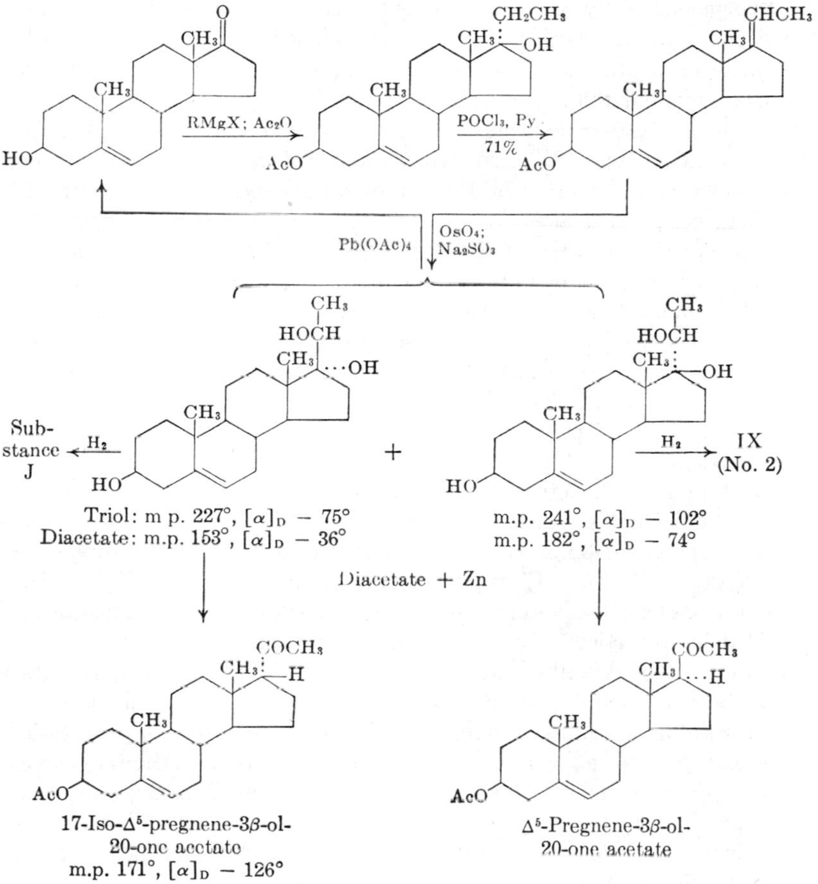

Triol: m p. 227°, [α]_D − 75°
Diacetate: m.p. 153°, [α]_D − 36°

m.p. 241°, [α]_D − 102°
m.p. 182°, [α]_D − 74°

Diacetate + Zn

17-Iso-Δ⁵-pregnene-3β-ol-
20-one acetate
m.p. 171°, [α]_D − 126°

Δ⁵-Pregnene-3β-ol-
20-one acetate

tablished, the formation of the 17-isoketone from the triol diacetate m.p. 182° would mean reaction with retention of configuration.   Fieser and Huang-Minlon[10] repeated the work and found that the more abundant triol diacetate m.p. 153° does indeed react with inversion to give 17-iso-pregnenolone but that the isomer m.p. 182° yields pregnenolone and

[10] Fieser and Huang-Minlon, *J. Am. Chem. Soc.* (in press).

therefore also reacts with inversion, as in all other known examples of the Serini reaction.

The Serini reaction could conceivably proceed through an intermediate Δ^{17}-enol-20-acetate, the double bond of which could open in such a direction as to produce inversion. However, Fieser and Huang-Minlon[10] prepared the two geometrically isomeric Δ^{17}-enol-20-acetates from pregnenolone and found that they are both very easily hydrolyzed (cold aqueous-alcoholic sodium bicarbonate) and that they yield the same product, pregnenolone. Shoppee regarded the Serini transformation as a pinacolic change of an intermediate 17,20-oxide, which suffers inversion on fission of the C_{20}-oxygen bond, and correctly predicted the course of the reaction of Substance O diacetate and the error in Butenandt's work before the experiments cited had been undertaken.[11]

Ketol Side Chain: CHCOCH$_2$OH-β; C$_{11}$-O Series. One synthetic reaction applicable to compounds oxygenated at C_{11} was first reported in an I. G. Farbenindustrie patent for the preparation of desoxycorticosterone and later described by Ehrhart, Ruschig, and Aumüller.[1] The reaction involves the lead tetraacetate oxidation of a 20-ketopregnane to the 21-acetoxy derivative. Thus progesterone affords desoxycorticosterone acetate, but only in 3 percent yield.[2] This poor result is probably attributable to oxidative attack in ring A, for cholestenone on oxidation with lead tetraacetate gives 2-acetoxycholestenone in moderate yield.[3] The oxidation proceeds fairly satisfactorily in the case of fully saturated compounds such as allopregnane-3β-ol-20-one acetate (I, Chart 22) or even Δ^5-pregnene-3β-ol-20-one.[2] Position 17 is attacked to a minor extent (III). This procedure has been used as one step in the partial synthesis[4] of corticosterone and 11-dehydrocorticosterone (IX) from the intermediate ketones IV and VII, prepared as described later (Chart 30). The diazoketone synthesis cannot be employed for the synthesis of corticosterone because the 11β-hydroxyl group is eliminated under the conditions required for preparation of the acid chloride and cannot be acylated for protection. After acetoxylation at C_{21} the alcoholic group at C_3 is oxidized by the Oppenauer reaction, which proceeds rather poorly, probably because of oxidative attack elsewhere in the molecule. The final step of dehydrohalogenation unfortunately usually proceeds in particularly poor yield.

In the earlier syntheses of compounds with the cortical steroid type of

[11] Letter from Dr. C. W. Shoppee of April 16, 1948.

[1] Ehrhart, Ruschig and Aumüller, *Z. angew. Chem.*, **52**, 363 (1939); *Ber.*, **72**, 2035 (1939).

[2] Reichstein and Montigel, *Helv. Chim. Acta*, **22**, 1212 (1939).

[3] Seebeck and Reichstein, *Helv. Chim. Acta*, **27**, 948 (1944).

[4] von Euw, Lardon and Reichstein, *Helv. Chim. Acta*, **27**, 1287 (1944).

Chart 22. ACETOXYLATION AT C_{21}

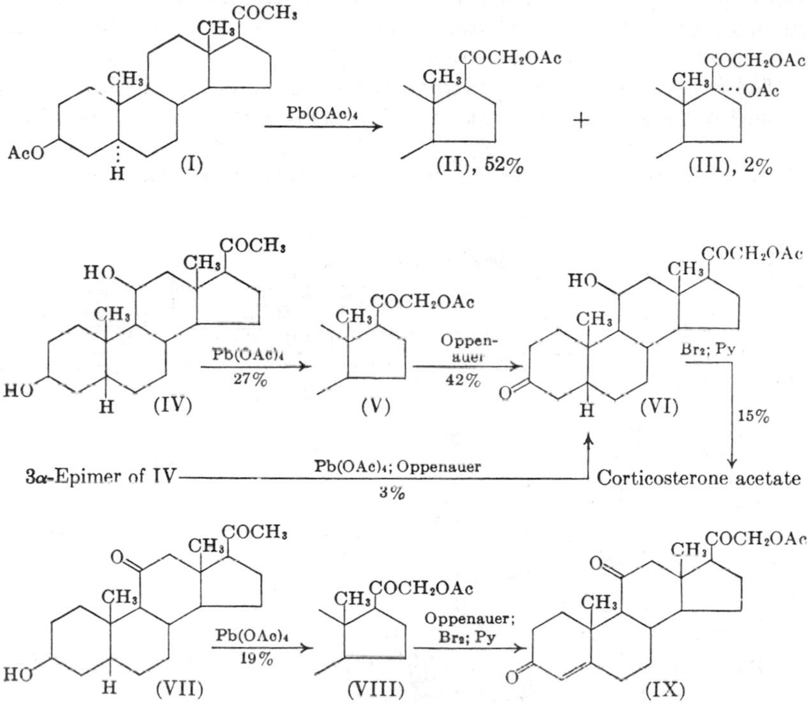

side chain, a suitable cholanic acid was degraded to the etio acid, the 20-ketone, or the 17-ketone. Meystre and Wettstein[5] later found that by a slight modification of the Meystre-Miescher procedure of degradation the ketol side chain can be constructed directly. As demonstrated first in model experiments with desoxycholic acid, the intermediate diene can be brominated at C_{21} by the action of N-bromosuccinimide (under illumination):

$$\underset{\displaystyle -\overset{|}{C}=CHCH=C(C_6H_5)_2}{CH_3} \xrightarrow[69\%]{(CH_2CO)_2NBr} \underset{\displaystyle -\overset{|}{C}=CHCH=C(C_6H_5)_2}{CH_2Br} \xrightarrow{79\%}$$

$$\underset{\displaystyle -\overset{|}{C}=CHCH=C(C_6H_5)_2}{CH_2OAc} \xrightarrow[67\%]{CrO_3} -COCH_2OAc$$

The monounsaturated diphenylethylenes derived from the bisnor acids cannot be brominated in this way. The bromine atom in the product from

[5] Meystre and Wettstein, *Helv. Chim. Acta*, **30**, 1037 (1947).

the diene is very reactive and by the use of an appropriate reagent can be replaced by hydroxyl (CaCO$_3$, H$_2$O), acetoxyl (KOAc), or alkoxyl (ROH) groups. Careful low-temperature oxidation of the 21-acetoxy compound with chromic acid gives the ketol acetate.

The application of the method to the synthesis of 11-dehydrocorticosterone[6] is summarized in Chart 23. The yields in the chromic acid oxida-

Chart 23. 11-DEHYDROCORTICOSTERONE (WETTSTEIN AND MEYSTRE)

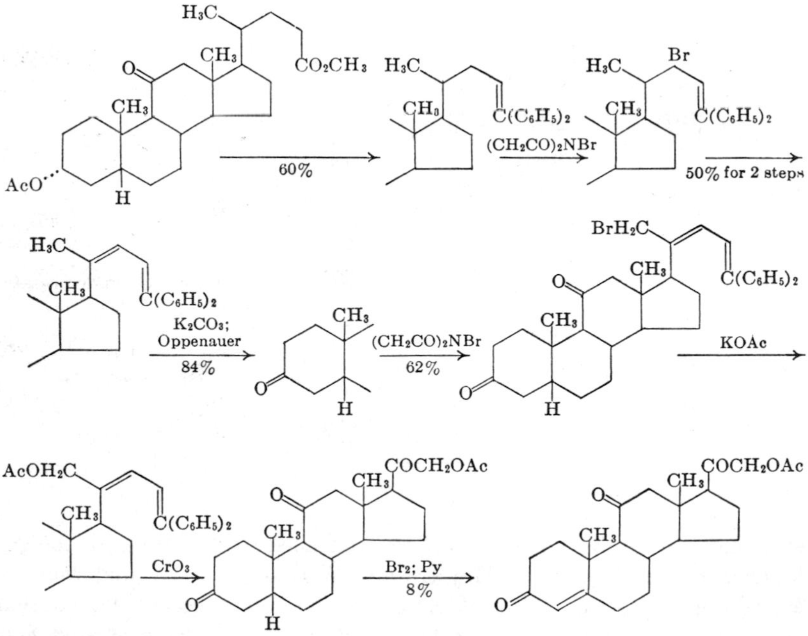

tion and in the preceeding step are not given; that cited for the terminal step is reported by Reichstein.[7] Desoxycorticosterone has been synthesized in the same way;[8] the diene was obtained in about 40 percent overall yield from 3β-hydroxy-Δ^5-cholenic acid and afforded desoxycorticosterone acetate in about 15 percent overall yield (without isolation of intermediates).

Sarett[9] devised another synthesis of 11-dehydrocorticosterone starting with 3α-acetoxy-11-ketobisnorcholanic acid (Chart 24). The acid was

[6] Wettstein and Meystre, *Helv. Chim. Acta*, **30**, 1262 (1947).

[7] Lardon and Reichstein, *Helv. Chim. Acta*, **26**, 747 (1943).

[8] Meystre and Wettstein, *Helv. Chim. Acta*, **30**, 1256 (1947).

[9] Sarett, *J. Biol. Chem.*, **162**, 601 (1946); *J. Am. Chem. Soc.*, **68**, 2478 (1946).

converted by Curtius rearrangement of the azide into the 20-aminopreg-
nane II, which with nitrous acid in pyridine gave a mixture of the epimeric
20-hydroxypregnanes (III, 20%) and the 17- and 20-pregnenes (IV and V,

Chart 24. 11-DEHYDROCORTICOSTERONE (SARETT)

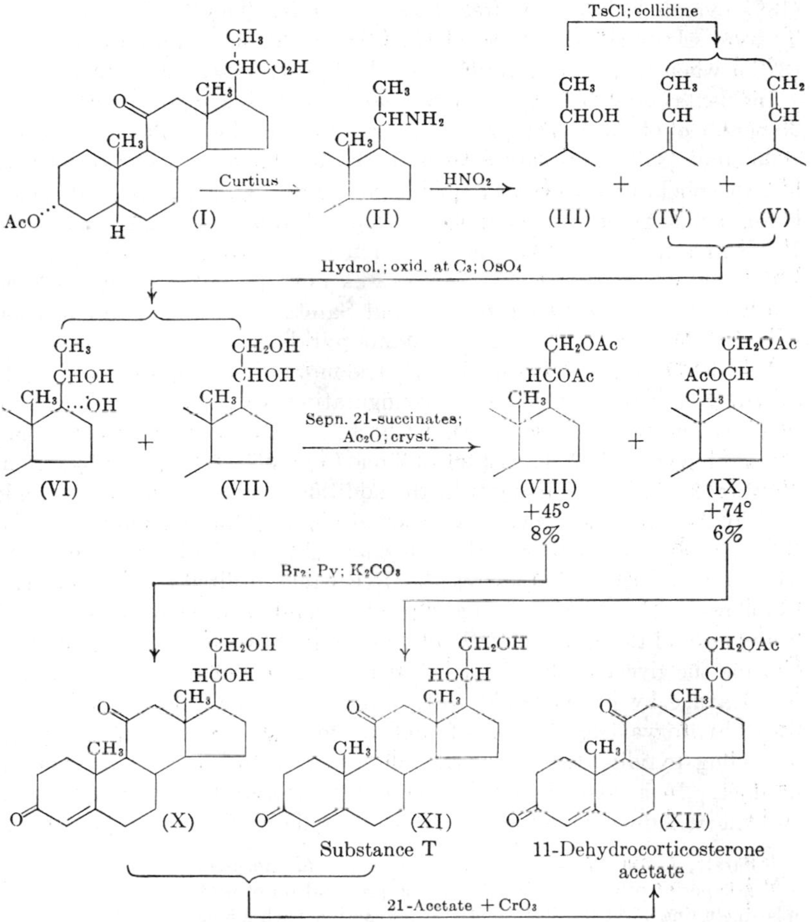

TsCl; collidine

CH_3
$CHCO_2H$
CH_3

CH_3
$CHNH_2$
CH_3

CH_3
$CHOH$

CH_3
CH

CH_2
CH

AcO''   H   (I)   —Curtius→   (II)   —HNO$_2$→   (III)   +   (IV)   +   (V)

Hydrol.; oxid. at C$_3$; OsO$_4$

CH_3
$CHOH$
CH_3...OH
(VI)

CH_2OH
$CHOH$
CH_3
(VII)

Sepn. 21-succinates;
Ac$_2$O; cryst. →

CH_2OAc
$HCOAc$
CH_3
(VIII)
+45°
8%

CH_2OAc
$AcOCH$
CH_3
(IX)
+74°
6%

Br$_2$; Pv; K$_2$CO$_3$

CH_2OH
$HCOH$
CH_3
O   CH$_3$ O   (X)

CH_2OH
$HOCH$
CH_3
O   CH$_3$ O   (XI)
Substance T

CH_2OAc
CO
CH_3
O   CH$_3$ O   (XII)
11-Dehydrocorticosterone
acetate

21-Acetate + CrO$_3$

70%). The mixture was not separated but was treated with tosyl chloride
and then collidine in order to transform the 20-alcohols into the ethylenes.
The mixture of ethylenes thus obtained in 88 percent yield was hydrolyzed
at C$_3$ and oxidized to a mixture of 3-ketones, and this was hydroxylated.
The desired diols (VII) arising from the 20-ethylene (V) reacted selectively
with succinic anhydride in pyridine to give the 21-succinates, which could

be extracted from an unchanged neutral fraction containing VI. The acidic fraction w.is hydrolyzed and acetylated, and crystallization of the mixture afforded the two pure epimers VIII and IX; the assignment of the configurations has been discussed above (Chart 5). Each epimer was brominated at C_4 and a double bond introduced by dehydrohalogenation (13% overall yield). The free diols X and XI (identified as Substance T) were selectively acetylated at C_{21} (21% yield) and cautiously oxidized (82%) when they both afforded 11-dehydrocorticosterone acetate (XII).

Incidental observations by Sarett have shown that hydrogenation of a 20-one-21-ol of the 11-ketopregnane series affords chiefly the 20β-hydroxy compound (85%) and only a trace of the 20α-epimer.[10] The correlation of a 3-alcohol with a 3-ketone required oxidation at C_3 of a compound having a 20,21-diol group protected by acetonide formation.[11] The method of Reich and Reichstein[12] for the oxidation of secondary alcohols with N-bromoacetamide in aqueous acetone was not applicable because of the sensitivity of the acetonide to acid, but Sarett effected smooth oxidation with N-bromoacetamide in dry *t*-butanol-pyridine.

Dihydroxyacetone Side Chain (β). The more difficult synthesis of 17,21-dihyroxy-20-ketones of the proper configuration at C_{17} was first achieved by von Euw and Reichstein as shown in Chart 25. The key intermediate, ω-homo-Δ^4-pregnene-17α,20β,21,22-tetrol-3-one (V) had been prepared by Butenandt[1] by a synthesis starting with the addition of allylmagnesium bromide to dehydroepiandrosterone. Oxidation at C_3, dehydration, and hydroxylation of both double bonds of the side chain gave a mixture of tetrols from which one was isolated in low yield. Reichstein[2] utilized this intermediate as follows. The two hydroxyl groups at the end of the chain were blocked in the form of the acetonide (VI) in order to permit selective acetylation at C_{20}, and the glycol group released on removal of acetone was then available for cleavage by periodic acid with formation of the aldehyde IX. The free dihydroxyaldehyde X was found[3] to undergo Fischer rearrangement[4] in boiling pyridine to give a substance (XI) identical with the natural product. In a later simplified procedure[5] the tetrol V is oxidized with periodic acid directly to the dihydroxyaldehyde X; the overall yield of XI

[10] Sarett, *J. Am. Chem. Soc.*, **70**, 1690 (1948); *ibid.* (in press).

[11] A superior procedure (Sarett) for the preparation of acetonides of steroid glycols, including 17,20,21-triols, consists in reaction with a 5 percent solution of zinc chloride in acetone at room temperature.

[12] Reich and Reichstein, *Helv. Chim. Acta*, **26**, 562 (1943).

[1] Butenandt and D. Peters, *Ber.*, **71**, 2688 (1938).

[2] von Euw and Reichstein, *Helv. Chim. Acta*, **23**, 1258 (1940).

[3] Reichstein and von Euw, *Helv. Chim. Acta*, **23**, 1114 (1940).

[4] H. O. L. Fischer, Taube and Baer, *Ber.*, **60**, 479 (1927).

[5] von Euw and Reichstein, *Helv. Chim. Acta*, **24**, 1140 (1941).

Chart 25. 17-Hydroxydesoxycorticosterone (von Euw and Reichstein)

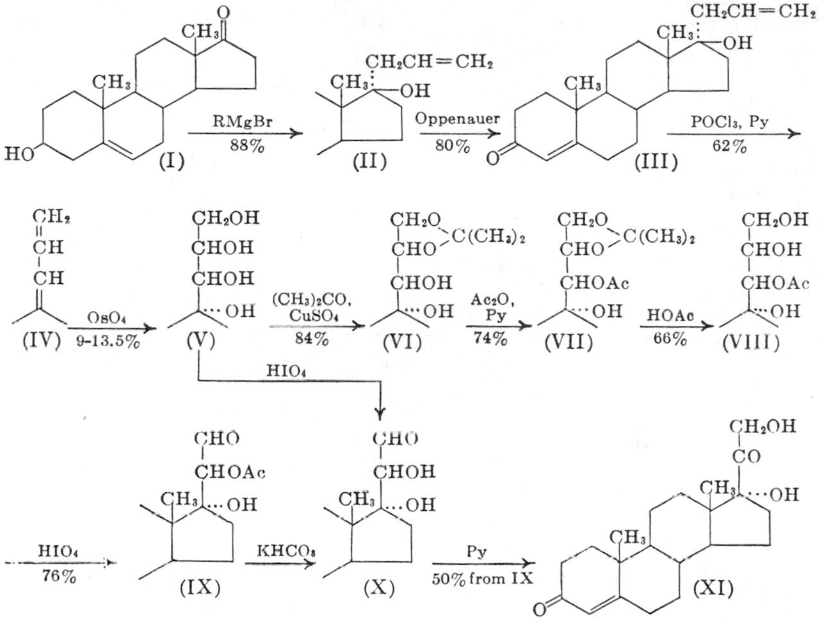

from V by this route is 30 percent. Substance P[6] and Δ^5-pregnene-3β, 17α,21-triol-20-one[7] were synthesized by the earlier procedure.

Sarett achieved the synthesis of Kendall's Compound E by two methods. The first[8] (Chart 26) utilized the mixture of 17- and 20-ethylenes prepared as shown in Chart 24. This was ozonized and the 17-ketone I separated from the etio acid and aldehyde and put through the standard condensation with acetylene, partial hydrogenation, and allylic rearrangement to IV. The activated 21-hydroxyl group was then protected by selective succinoylation to permit oxidation at C$_3$. Hydroxylation then gave a saturated diketone (VII) into which a double bond was introduced by the usual method. The diacetate VIII was hydrolyzed and the diol converted into the 21-monoacetate by partial acetylation, and the synthesis was completed by cautious oxidation at C$_{20}$.

Sarett's second synthesis[9] (Chart 27) utilized the procedure described earlier (Chart 17) for the conversion of an unsaturated nitrile into a ketol

[6] von Euw and Reichstein, *Helv. Chim. Acta*, **24**, 401 (1941).

[7] Fuchs and Reichstein, *Helv. Chim. Acta*, **24**, 804 (1941).

[8] Sarett, *J. Biol. Chem.*, **162**, 601 (1946).

[9] Sarett, *J. Am. Chem. Soc.*, **70**, 1454 (1948).

Chart 26. Kendall's E (Sarett's First Synthesis)

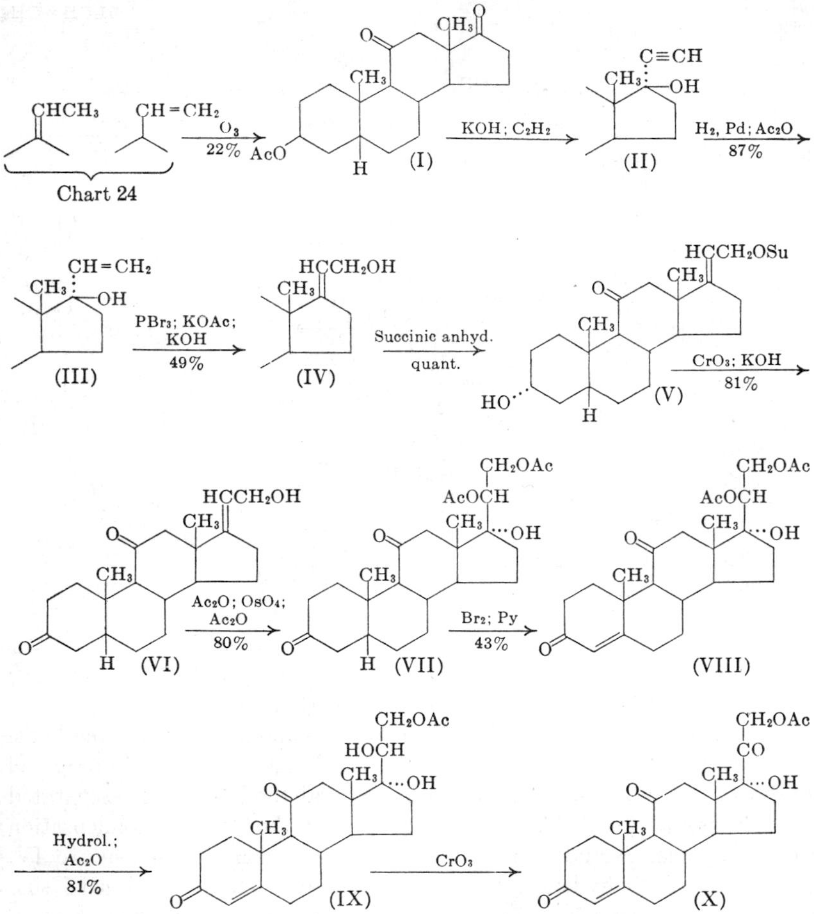

U Acetate

(18%, + 28% adrenosterone)

by hydroxylation. The starting material is pregnane-3α,21-diol-11,20-dione diacetate (I). Sarett originally added hydrogen cyanide to the 21-monoacetate and then oxidized the cyanohydrin at C_3, but the 3-keto group had an adverse effect and the yield in the dehydration to the unsaturated nitrile was only 20 percent. In subsequent work he found[10] that the synthesis is greatly improved by starting with the 3,21-diacetate I. Both the hydrogen cyanide addition (II) and the dehydration reaction (III)

[10] Communication from Dr. L. H. Sarett.

Chart 27. KENDALL'S E (SARETT'S CYANOHYDRIN SYNTHESIS)

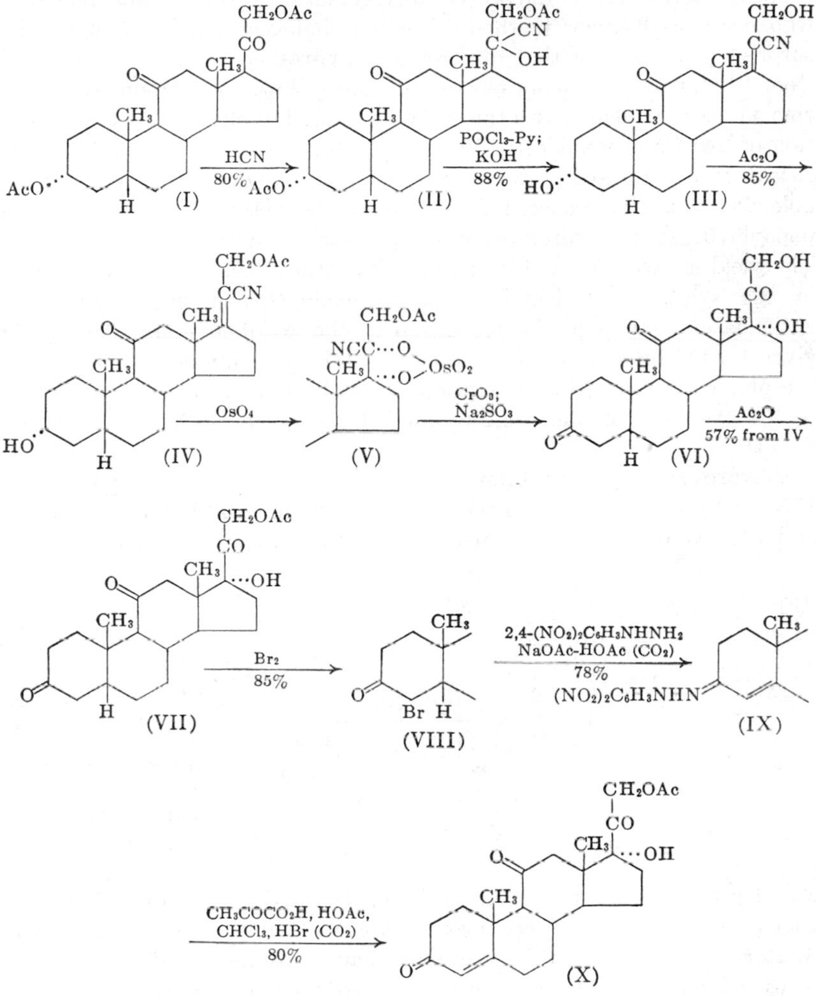

then proceeded in high yield. The 21-acetate (IV) of the unsaturated nitrile was not satisfactory for oxidation, but Sarett found that the osmic ester V is a suitable derivative for efficient oxidation at C_3. Hydrolysis, cleavage of the osmic ester grouping, and acetylation gave VII, which was converted through the 4-bromo derivative (VIII) into Kendall's E. Dehydrohalogenation of VIII with boiling pyridine proceeded so poorly that the introduction of the double bond—the last step in a very long process—

was accomplished only with excessive loss (VII → X, 25% yield). However this shortcoming of the process was remedied by Mattox and Kendall,[11] who introduced a new method of dehydrohalogenation based upon the surprising observation that dinitrophenylhydrazone derivatives prepared from 4-bromo-3-ketones are red rather than yellow. Dinitrophenylhydrazine not only condenses with the carbonyl group but effects smooth elimination of hydrogen bromide (in the presence or absence of sodium acetate) to give an unsaturated phenylhydrazone (IX); this derivative is autoxidizable and must be prepared and used in the absence of oxygen. The phenylhydrazone is hydrolyzed in the presence of pyruvic acid as acceptor. The yield is excellent in this instance and also in the corresponding step in the synthesis of dehydrocorticosterone.[11, 12] The side reaction of autoxidation results in the formation of the $\Delta^{4,6}$-dien-3-one. The yield given for the bromination step (VII → VIII) was obtained by reworking the material recovered after separation of the pure 4-bromo ketone, $[\alpha]_D$ + 102° An; this contains the 2-bromo ketone, which can be debrominated to VII.

Dihydroxyacetone Side Chain (a). Prins and Reichstein[13] synthesized 17-iso-P by hydroxylation of 17-iso-Δ^{20}-allopregnene-3β,17β-diol 3-acetate and selective oxidation of the resulting mixture of epimers. The free triol

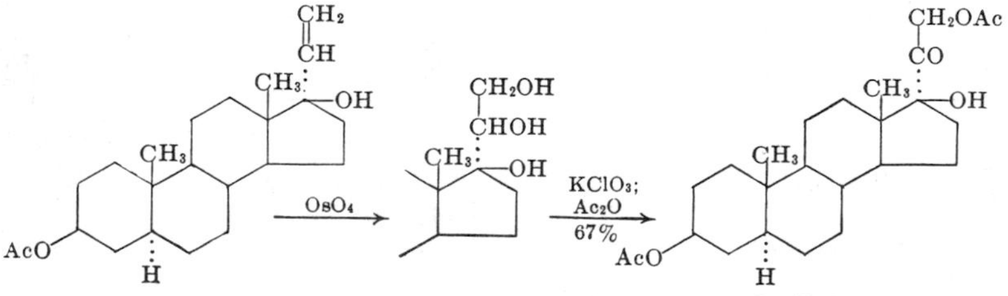

17-Iso-P diacetate
m.p. 163°, $[\alpha]_D$ − 56°

was degraded by periodic acid oxidation to 3β,17β-dihydroxy-17-isoetio-allocholanic acid. 17-Iso-P diacetate is considerably more strongly levorotatory (84°, compared in acetone) than Substance P diacetate; the relationship is similar to that between 17-hydroxyprogesterone and the 17-epimer.

INTRODUCTION OF OXYGEN AT C_{11}

Through Δ^{11}-Derivatives. Early attempts to prepare 11-oxygenated

[11] Mattox and Kendall, *J. Am. Chem. Soc.*, **70**, 882 (1948).
[12] Communication from Dr. E. C. Kendall.
[13] Prins and Reichstein, *Helv. Chim. Acta*, **25**, 300 (1942).

steroids from substances described as 11-hydroxy-12-ketocholanic acid and 11,12-diketocholanic acid, available by bromination of 12-ketocholanic acid,[1] were unsuccessful, for the oxygen at C_{12} could not be eliminated[2] (see, however, Chart 32). Swiss and American workers then investigated the approach through Δ^{11}-unsaturated bile acids available by pyrolysis of 12-hydroxy compounds,[3] or better of the 12-benzoxy derivatives.[4] Chart 28 summarizes methods developed by Reichstein (A) and by Kendall (B) for the production of 3-keto- and 3α-hydroxy-Δ^{11}-bile acid derivatives. 3-Keto-Δ^{11}-cholenic acid methyl ester (V) was obtained by pyrolysis of 3-keto-12α-hydroxycholanic acid,[5] or preferably of the 12-benzoate.[4] 3-Keto-Δ^{11}-etiocholenic acid was prepared in the same way from desoxy-etiocholic acid (27% yield).[6] Reduction of V by the Meerwein-Ponndorf method, by sodium amalgam, or by Raney nickel hydrogenation gave mixtures of 3α- and 3β-hydroxycholenic acids separable with digitonin.[7] Reichstein also investigated the pyrolysis of 3α-acetoxy-12α-benzoxycholanic acid methyl ester, but the yield of the corresponding Δ^{11}-ester was only about 25 percent; the 3-acetoxy group is in part eliminated with the formation of a mixture of choladienic esters.[4] Kendall[8] later reported the preparation of 3α-hydroxy-Δ^{11}-cholenic acid methyl ester (IX) by pyrolysis of methyl 12-benzoxydesoxycholanate (VIII), obtained in the efficient process B. The structure of the unsaturated ester was established by hydrogenation to lithocholic acid and by ozone oxidation[9] to desoxybilianic acid.

The above examples show that pyrolytic formation of Δ^{11}-compounds proceeds better with 12-benzoates than with 12-acetates. In some instances the 12-esters of anthraquinone-β-carboxylic acid have been used to advantage.[10] The thermal dehydration proceeds better when the original

---

[1] Wieland and Posternak, *Z. physiol. Chem.*, **197**, 20 (1931); Wieland and Dane, *ibid.*, **216**, 99 (1933).

[2] Barnett and Reichstein, *Helv. Chim. Acta*, **21**, 926 (1938); **22**, 75 (1939).

[3] Example: 12α-hydroxycholanic acid → Δ^{11}-cholenic acid (m.p. 135°, 40% yield); hydroxylation of the ester with OsO_4 and CrO_3 oxidation gives isothilobilianic acid; Alther and Reichstein, *Helv. Chim. Acta*, **25**, 805 (1942). Hydrogenation of the methyl ester gives methyl cholanate; Barnett and Reichstein, *Helv. Chim. Acta*, **21**, 926 (1938).

[4] Example: 12α-benzoxycholanic acid → Δ^{11}-cholenic acid (50% yield); Lardon, Grandjean, Press, Reich and Reichstein, *Helv. Chim. Acta*, **25**, 1444 (1942).

[5] Burckhardt and Reichstein, *Helv. Chim. Acta*, **25**, 821 (1942).

[6] Lardon and Reichstein, *Helv. Chim. Acta*, **26**, 607 (1943).

[7] Press and Reichstein, *Helv. Chim. Acta*, **25**, 878 (1942).

[8] McKenzie, McGuckin and Kendall, *J. Biol. Chem.*, **162**, 555 (1946).

[9] Gallagher, *J. Biol. Chem.*, **162**, 491 (1946).

[10] von Euw, Lardon and Reichstein, *Helv. Chim. Acta*, **27**, 821 (1944); Lardon and Reichstein, *ibid.*, **28**, 1420 (1945).

Chart 28. Δ^{11}-CHOLENIC ACIDS

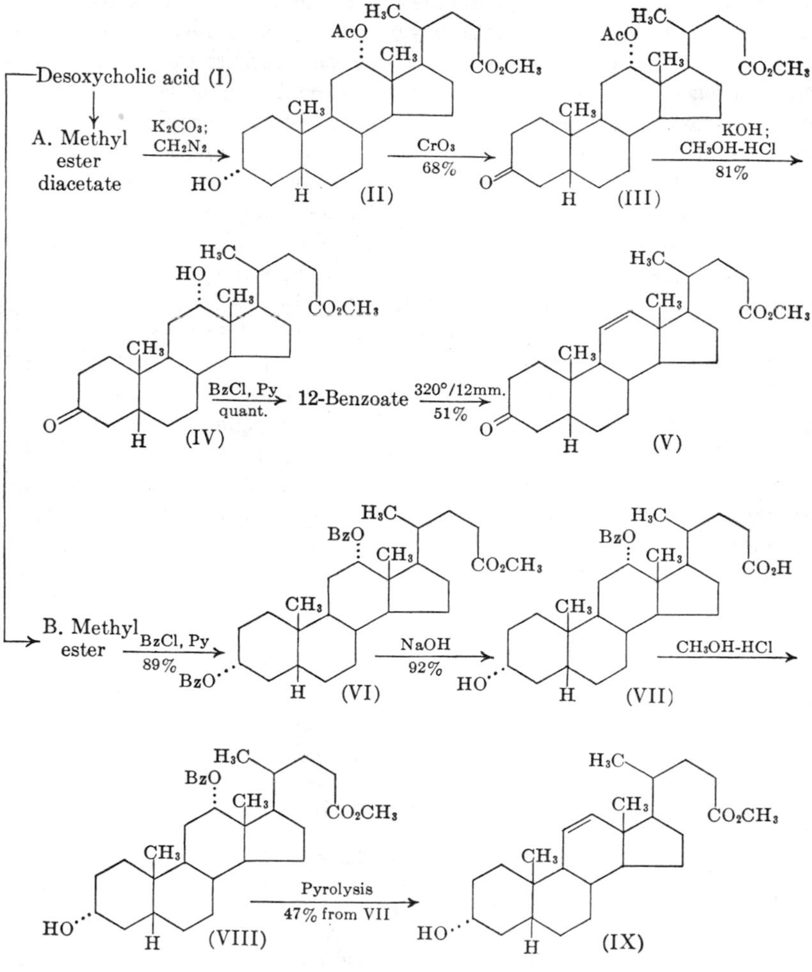

bile acid side chain is intact than when it has been degraded.   In the pyrolysis of 12-acyloxyetiocholanic acids the desired unsaturated acid is always
accompanied by starting material.   An improved procedure for the
preparation of Δ^{11}-etiocholenic acids consists in treatment of the 12-tosylates
with collidine or pyridine under pressure;[11] 3-keto-Δ^{11}-etiocholenic acid has
been obtained by this method in 40 percent yield.

[11] von Euw and Reichstein, *Helv. Chim. Acta*, **29**, 654 (1946).

A general process for the conversion of an 11-ethylene into an 11-ketone is illustrated by Reichstein's synthesis of 11-dehydrocorticosterone.[12] (Chart 29). The addition of hypobromous acid, generated from N-bromo-acetamide in aqueous acetone, gives the desired bromohydrin III, the 11,12-dibromide IV, and the 9-bromo-Δ^{11}-acid V.[13] Only one of the four possible stereoisomeric bromohydrins is produced. Sarett[14] introduced two improvements in the process: the formation of the bromohydrin is markedly catalyzed by a small amount of sulfuric acid; gentle treatment of the reaction mixture with zinc dust in acetic acid reduces the 11,12-dibromide

Chart 29. 11-Dehydrocorticosterone (Reichstein)

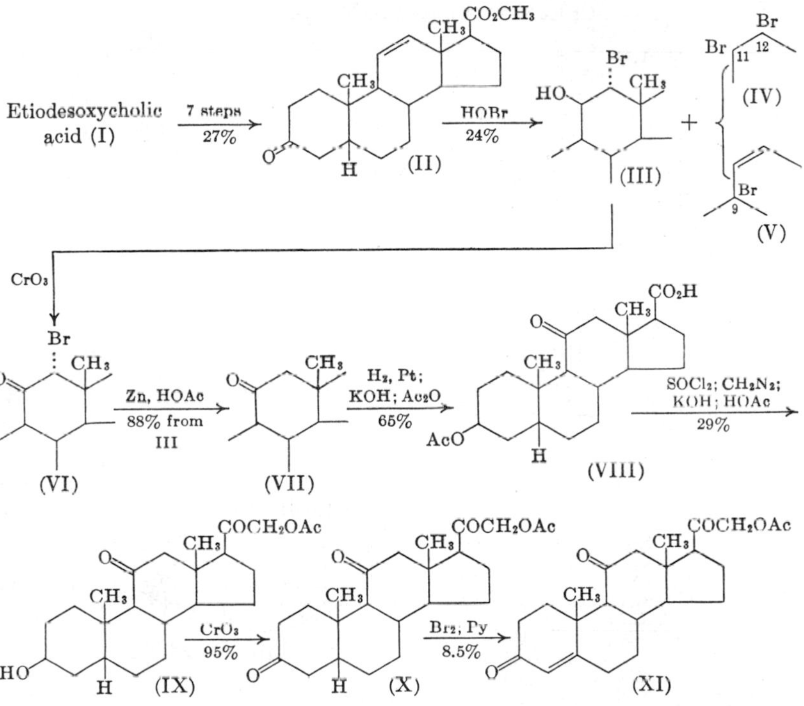

to the starting material, which can be recovered by fractional crystallization. Oxidation of the bromohydrin III gives a ketone (VI) with a labile bromine atom that is easily eliminated by reduction with zinc and acetic acid. The

[12] Lardon and Reichstein, *Helv. Chim. Acta*, **26**, 747 (1943).
[13] Reich and Reichstein, *Helv. Chim. Acta*, **26**, 562 (1943); Lardon and Reichstein, *ibid.*, **26**, 586, 705 (1943).
[14] Sarett, *J. Biol. Chem.*, **162**, 601 (1946).

3-keto group of VII was reduced without attack of the relatively inert 11-keto group, and the acid VIII was then put through the diazoketone synthesis and converted through the 4-bromo-3-ketone into a substance identical with the natural hormone (XI).

The partial syntheses of corticosterone and 11-dehydrocorticosterone by the lead tetraacetate reaction (Chart 22, above) require a pregnanone-20 with oxygen substituents at 3 and 11. Such substances are available from pregnane-3α,12α-diol-20-one (Chart 30A) and from bisnordesoxycholic acid (Chart 30B); both intermediates are degradation products of desoxycholic acid. In Process A[15] the 3,12-diacetate I was partially

Chart 30A. PREGNANE-3β,11β-DIOL-20-ONE

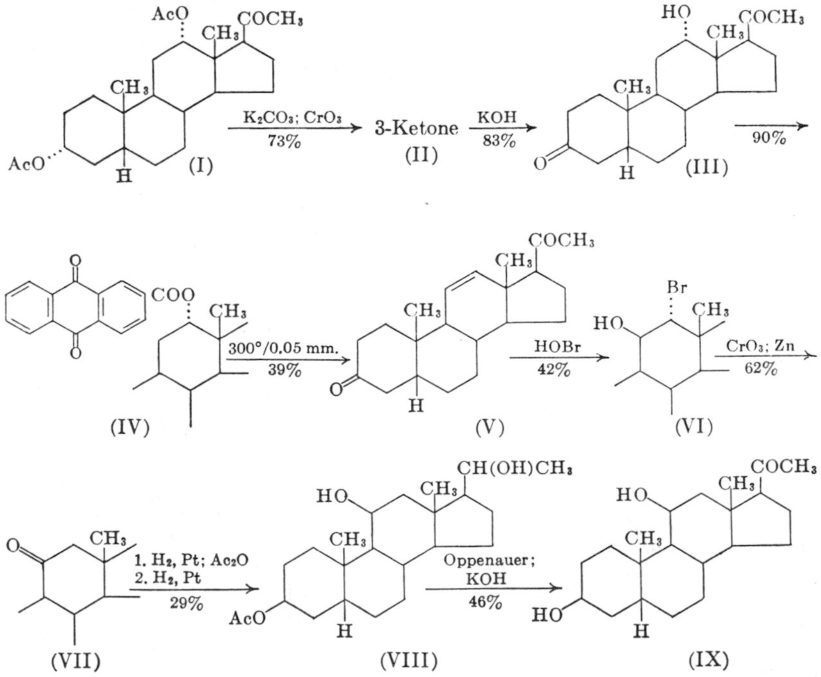

saponified[16] and the product oxidized at C_3 (II).[17]   The 9,11-double bond was introduced by pyrolysis of the anthraquinone-β-carboxylic ester (IV), which proceeded in nearly 40 percent yield; pyrolysis of the benzoate[18]

[15] von Euw, Lardon and Reichstein, *Helv. Chim. Acta*, **27**, 821 (1944).
[16] Reichstein and v. Arx, *Helv. Chim. Acta*, **23**, 747 (1940).
[17] Shoppee and Reichstein, *Helv. Chim. Acta*, **24**, 351 (1941).
[18] Hegner and Reichstein, *Helv. Chim. Acta*, **26**, 721 (1943).

proceeded in only 19 percent yield. Conversion into the 11-keto compound VII was effected through the bromohydrin, and VII was then selectively hydrogenated at C_3, converted to the 3-acetate, and this was hydrogenated more vigorously to reduce the 11- and 20-keto groups (VIII). Oppenauer oxidation with aluminum phenolate and acetone affected only position 20 and afforded, after hydrolysis, the desired pregnane-3β,11β-diol-20-one (IX).

Process B[19] starts with bisnordesoxycholic acid (X), which was converted through the 11-ethylene (XII) and the bromohydrin into the 3,11-diketone

Chart 30B. PREGNANE-3β(AND α),11β-DIOL-20-ONE

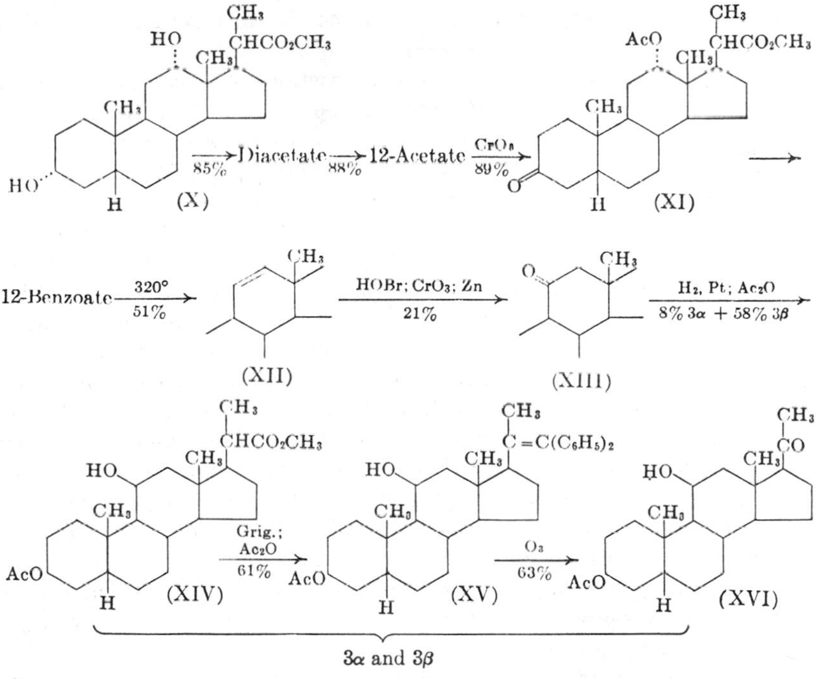

$$\xrightarrow[85\%]{} \text{Diacetate} \xrightarrow[88\%]{} \text{12-Acetate} \xrightarrow[89\%]{CrO_3} \longrightarrow$$

(X)   (XI)

$$\text{12-Benzoate} \xrightarrow[51\%]{320°} \quad \xrightarrow[21\%]{HOBr;\ CrO_3;\ Zn} \quad \xrightarrow[8\%\ 3\alpha\ +\ 58\%\ 3\beta]{H_2,\ Pt;\ Ac_2O}$$

(XII)   (XIII)

$$\text{(XIV)} \xrightarrow[61\%]{\text{Grig.;}\ Ac_2O} \text{(XV)} \xrightarrow[63\%]{O_3} \text{(XVI)}$$

3α and 3β

XIII, which on hydrogenation afforded both 3-epimeric dihydroxyetiocholanic esters XIV. Each was degraded by ozonization of the diphenylethylenes to the pregnanediolone acetates XVI, both of which were converted into corticosterone. The 3-acetates can be oxidized to the 11-ketones, employed for the synthesis of 11-dehydrocorticosterone.

Variation in the Sequence of Reactions. A disadvantageous feature of the syntheses summarized in Charts 26, 27, and 29 is that the α,β-un-

[19] Lardon and Reichstein, *Helv. Chim. Acta*, **27**, 713 (1944).

saturated ketonic grouping in Ring A is introduced at the end of a long series of reactions by a process that proceeded poorly by the procedures available prior to the work of Mattox and Kendall in 1948[1] (Chart 27). Reich and Lardon[2] developed an alternate scheme of synthesis in which the wasteful steps of bromination and dehydrobromination are conducted at an early rather than a late stage of the process.   The Δ^4-3-ketonic grouping as such is incompatible with subsequent operations that have to be performed, but a method was found for conversion into the cholesterol type of structure, from which the Δ^4-3-ketonic system could later be regenerated by Oppenauer oxidation.   This modification was utilized by von Euw and Reichstein[3] in the synthesis of 11-dehydrocorticosterone illustrated in Chart 31.   Etiodesoxycholic acid (I) was converted through the 11-ethylene and the bromohydrin to the unsaturated 3,11-diketone II, and this was transformed into the enol acetate III by reaction with acetyl chloride and acetic anhydride at $90-95°$ according to a procedure of Westphal.[4]   Like comparable enol acetates,[5] III reacts with bromine, or better with N-bromoacetamide and sodium acetate, to give the 6-bromo-Δ^4-3-ketone IV.   Treatment with methanolic hydrochloric acid establishes the 3,6-diketonic grouping (V), probably by hydrolysis of the bromine substituent, migration of the double bond from the 4,5- to the 5,6-position, and ketonization. Hydrogenation of V resulted in reduction of all three carbonyl groups, but the carbonyl at C_{11} was regenerated by partial acetylation at C_3 and C_6 and oxidation.   Several processes are available for the conversion of a 3,6-diol into a compound of the cholesterol type;[2] one efficient method is through the dimesylate, which on reaction with silver acetate yields the 3-acetoxy-Δ^5-unsaturated derivative.   In the synthesis under discussion the substance VII was converted to the 3-succinate dimethyl ester (VIII) and this was dehydrated with phosphorus oxychloride in pyridine (IX). The acid X was then transformed through the diazoketone to the ketol acetate XI, which on Oppenauer oxidation gave 11-dehydrocorticosterone acetate (XII).   Although the yields reported for some of the many steps are low, the overall yield of XII from II without isolation of intermediates is stated to be 8 percent.

It is possible that the process could be greatly simplified by use of a successful procedure described by Wilds and Shunk[6] for the conversion of

[1] Mattox and Kendall, *J. Am. Chem. Soc.*, **70**, 882 (1948).

[2] Reich and Lardon, *Helv. Chim. Acta*, **29**, 671 (1946).

[3] von Euw and Reichstein, *Helv. Chim. Acta*, **29**, 1913 (1946).

[4] U. Westphal, *Ber.*, **70**, 2128 (1937).

[5] Ruzicka and co-workers, *Helv. chim. Acta*, **19**, 1147 (1936); Dane. Wang and Schulte, *Z. physiol. Chem.*, **245**, 80 (1936).

[6] Wilds and Shunk, *J. Am. Chem. Soc.*, **70**, 2427 (1948).

Chart 31. 11-Dehydrocorticosterone; Modified Synthesis

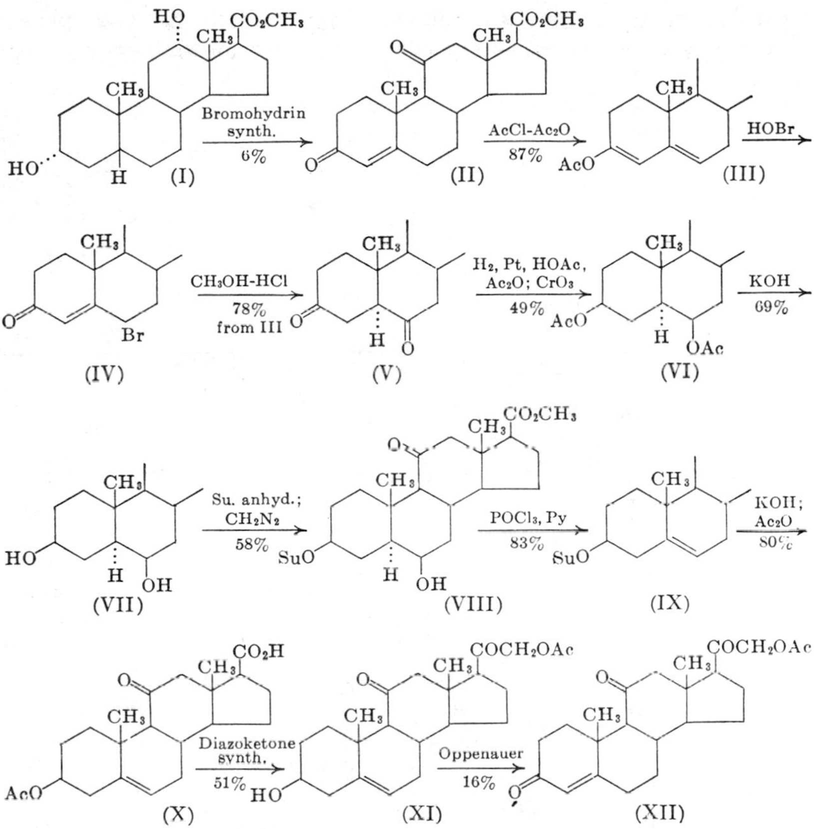

3-keto-Δ^4-etiocholenic acid through the acid chloride and the diazoketone to desoxycorticosterone acetate (overall yield, 59%). The acid chloride is prepared by the reaction of the sodium salt of the unsaturated keto acid with oxalyl chloride in benzene (trace of pyridine) at ice-bath temperature; in the last step the diazoketone is added to boiling acetic acid. If the process is applicable to 11-ketosteroids, the acid corresponding to II would yield XII directly.

Through 11-Bromo-12-ketones. In a second method for the introduction of oxygen at C_{11} worked out by Gallagher, the first step involves bromination of 3α-acetoxy-12-ketocholanic acid methyl ester (I, Chart 32), a reaction first described by Marker and Lawson[1] and later improved by

[1] Marker and E. J. Lawson, *J. Am. Chem. Soc.*, **60**, 1334 (1938).

Longwell and Wintersteiner.[2]   The bromo derivative was obtained in good yield but in an amorphous condition.   More recently the two epimers V and VII were isolated as crystalline esters by chromatography;[3] the

Chart 32.   METHOD OF GALLAGHER

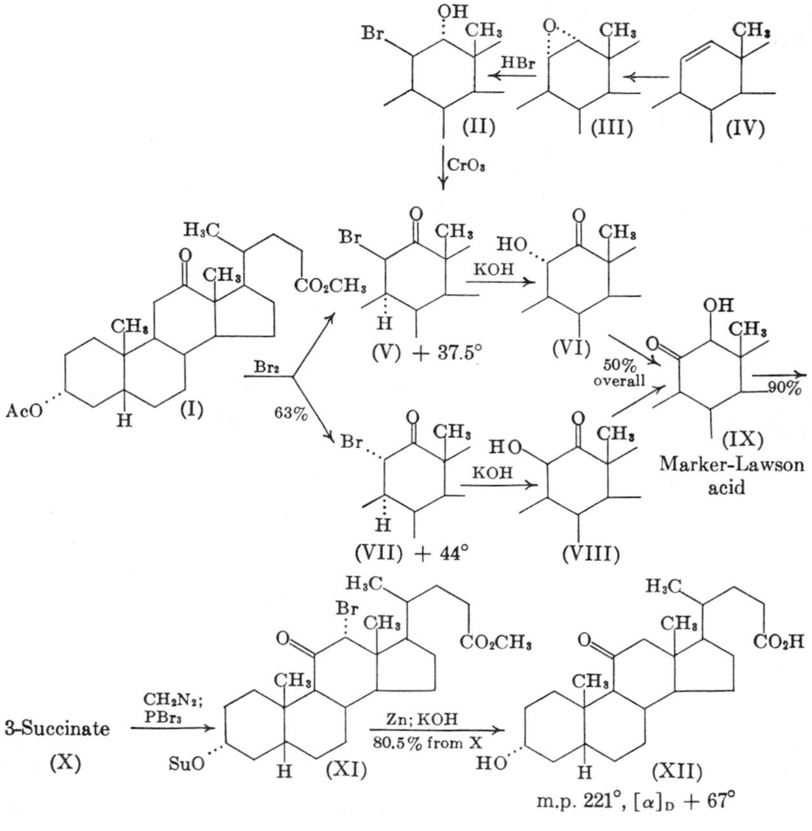

α-bromo epimer predominates.   Gallagher and Long[4] effected the chromatographic separation of the methyl ester acetates.   On dehydrohalogenation (sodium acetate[2] or collidine[3]), both epimers yield the same product, 3α-acetoxy-12-keto-$\Delta^{9(11)}$-cholenic acid methyl ester (m.p. 147°, [α]$_D$ + 111°, λ_{max}^{alc} 241 mμ); the reaction proceeds more readily in the case of the β-bromo compound where the elimination is trans.   The β-bromo ester V

[2] Longwell and Wintersteiner, *J. Am. Chem. Soc.*, **62**, 200 (1940).

[3] Seebeck and Reichstein, *Helv. Chim. Acta*, **26**, 536 (1943).

[4] Gallagher and W. P. Long, *J. Biol. Chem.*, **162**, 521 (1946).

is also available[5] from Δ^{11}-lithocholenic acid methyl ester acetate (IV) through the oxide (III). The oxides obtained by the action of perbenzoic acid on Δ^{11}-lithocholenic acid derivatives[6] and on related Δ^{11}-acids[7] are known to have the α-configuration because on hydrogenation they yield 12α-hydroxy compounds.[8] When the oxide ring is opened with hydrogen bromide (or with acetic acid) inversion occurs at the carbon atom at which the bond to oxygen is severed and the 11β-bromo-12α-hydroxy compound II is formed.[5] Chromic acid oxidation yields the β-bromo-12-ketone V.

The vigorous hydrolysis of either of the bromo ketones or of the amorphous mixture yields a hydroxyketone that Marker and Lawson assumed to be 3,11-dihydroxy-12-keto acid (Marker-Lawson acid, IX, m.p. 202°, $[\alpha]_D$ + 66°). Some doubt was cast on this formulation by the observation that a purified preparation formed no ketonic derivatives.[2] Gallagher later effected hydrolysis with alcoholic potassium hydroxide at room temperature and isolated $3\alpha,11\beta$- (VIII)[9] and $3\alpha,11\alpha$-dihydroxy-12-ketocholanic acid (VI)[10] from the bromo ketones VII and V, respectively, and found them to differ from the Marker-Lawson acid and to form ketonic derivatives. Under the drastic conditions used for the production of the Marker-Lawson acid the ketols VI and VIII undergo rearrangement to the 11-keto-12-ol structure IX.[11, 12] The 12β-orientation of IX is assigned[11] because chromic acid oxidation of $3\alpha,12\beta$-diacetoxy-11β-hydroxycholanic acid methyl ester yields the diacetate methyl ester of IX. Gallagher[13] has shown that the isomerization is reversible but that the equilibria favors the formation of IX. When a highly purified sample of IX was refluxed for two hours in 5 percent aqueous sodium hydroxide, the resulting mixture was found to contain 63 percent of IX, 30 percent of VI, a trace of VIII, and 1 percent of $3\alpha,12\alpha$-dihydroxy-11-ketocholanic acid.

The remaining steps[13] in Gallagher's process for the preparation of 3α-hydroxy-11-ketocholanic acid (XII) from the Marker-Lawson acid consist in succinoylation at C_3, replacement of the 12-hydroxyl group by bromine,

[5] Gallagher and W. P. Long, J. Biol. Chem., **162**, 495 (1946).
[6] Press and Reichstein, Helv. Chim. Acta, **25**, 878 (1942); McKenzie, McGuckin and Kendall, J. Biol. Chem., **162**, 555 (1946).
[7] Burckhardt and Reichstein, Helv. Chim. Acta, **25**, 821 (1942); Reich and Reichstein, ibid., **26**, 562 (1943).
[8] Ott and Reichstein, Helv. Chim. Acta, **26**, 1799 (1943); Berner and Reichstein, ibid., **29**, 1374 (1946).
[9] W. P. Long and Gallagher, J. Biol. Chem., **162**, 511 (1946).
[10] Gallagher and Hollander, J. Biol. Chem., **162**, 533 (1946).
[11] Gallagher, J. Biol. Chem., **162**, 539 (1946).
[12] Wintersteiner, M. Moore and Reinhardt, J. Biol. Chem., **162**, 707 (1946).
[13] Borgstrom and Gallagher, J. Biol. Chem., **164**, 791 (1946); communication from Dr. Gallagher.

and reduction of the bromoketone XI with zinc dust and acetic acid or with chromous chloride in acetone (unsatisfactory unless pure bromoketone is used).

Wolff-Kishner reduction of either the 11α- or the 11β-hydroxy keto acid (VI or VIII) gives 3α,11α-dihydroxycholanic acid (20 – 30%), together with 3α-hydroxy-Δ¹¹-cholenic acid, lithocholic acid, and a 3α,11,12-trihydroxy-cholanic acid.[10, 14] The reduction of VIII involves transposition of the 11-hydroxyl group from the hindered (β) to the unhindered (α) location.

A method for the transformation of the Marker-Lawson acid IX (as ester) into 3α,11β-hydroxycholanic acid is described by Wintersteiner and Moore:[15] the 3-succinate is oxidized with chromic acid to the 11,12-diketone (15% from IX) and this is reduced by the Wolff-Kishner procedure (1.5% yield overall).

Through 3,9-Oxides. A further method for the introduction of an 11-oxygen function was discovered by Kendall and co-workers. 11,12-Oxides of α-orientation are cleaved by acids to 12- and not 11-hydroxy compounds (Chart 32). In the attempt to prepare an oxide of the opposite configuration, which might open in the desired direction, Kendall[1 – 3] investigated the action of dilute alkali on the dibromide of Δ¹¹-lithocholenic acid methyl ester (II, Chart 33). The product, however, was not the oxide but 3α,12-dihydroxy-Δ⁹⁽¹¹⁾-cholenic acid (III), the structure of which was established by Sarett.[4] The 12-hydroxyl group, activated by the 9,11-double bond, is labile and readily replaced by acetoxyl and methoxyl groups and by halogen.[3] The 12-bromo derivative IV is very sensitive to water; when a chloroform solution was washed with water and then evaporated in vacuum, a halogen-free monounsaturated substance was obtained in excellent yield. The substance was found to contain one oxygen function but no acylable hydroxyl group, whereas a free hydroxyl group in the starting material is essential for the reaction. These and other observations indicated that the substance is the 3,9-oxide V, formed by allylic rearrangement and ring closure. Molecular models show that the orientation at the back side of positions 3 and 9 is indeed favorable for the formation of an oxide bridge. The oxide bridge can be opened by hydrogenation in acetic acid (VI); hydrolysis or acetolysis to VII represents the reversal

[14] Gallagher and W. P. Long, *J. Biol. Chem.*, **162**, 521 (1946).

[15] Wintersteiner and M. Moore, *J. Biol. Chem.*, **162**, 725 (1946).

[1] Engel, Mattox, McKenzie, McGuckin and Kendall, *J. Biol. Chem.*, **162**, 565 (1946).

[2] R. B. Turner, Mattox, Engel, McKenzie and Kendall, *J. Biol. Chem.*, **162**, 571 (1946).

[3] Mattox, R. B. Turner, Engel, McKenzie, McGuckin and Kendall, *J. Biol. Chem.*, **164**, 569 (1946).

[4] Sarett, *J. Biol. Chem.*, **162**, 591 (1946).

Chart 33. FORMATION AND REACTIONS OF 3,9-OXIDES

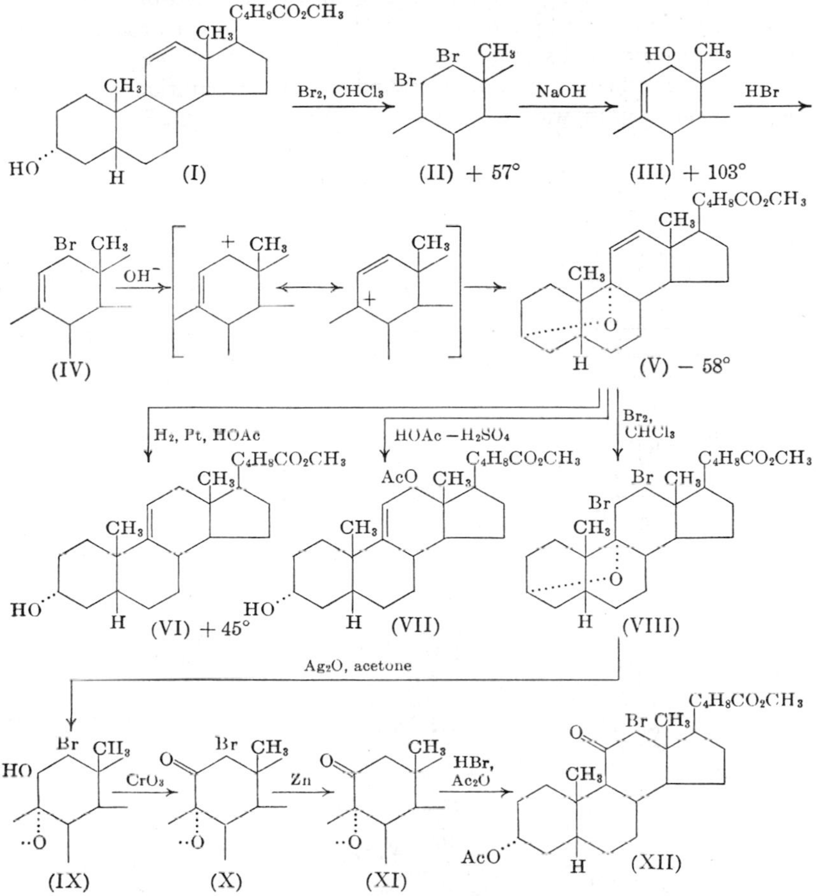

of the reactions by which the substance is formed. The oxide dibromide VIII was investigated[5] particularly, since, unlike II, it cannot lose hydrogen bromide to form a 9,11-double bond. Bromination of V yields two isomeric dibromides, both of which are reconvertible to V on treatment with zinc in acetic acid. In one isomer one of the bromine atoms, fortunately that in the 11-position, is labile and readily replaced by a hydroxyl group. The bromohydrin IX is readily convertible through the bromoketone X to the 11-keto derivative XI. The oxide ring in this substance is not affected

[5] R. B. Turner, Mattox, Engel, McKenzie and Kendall, *J. Biol. Chem.*, **166**, 345 (1946).

by Grignard reagents or by Raney nickel hydrogenation but can be cleaved by hydrogen bromide in chloroform-acetic anhydride at a low temperature with the formation of a bromoketone (XII) that is easily debrominated by reduction with zinc and acetic acid.

The most satisfactory procedure[6] found for the preparation of 11-keto-etiolithocholic acid by way of a 3,9-oxide is shown in Chart 34. The new

Chart 34. 11-KETOETIOLITHOCHOLIC ACID

H_3C
HO
CH_3
CO_2CH_3
CH_3
HO'' H (I)

$\xrightarrow{\text{BzCl, Py}}$ 3-Benzoate (II)

H_3C
O CH_3
CO_2CH_3
CH_3
BzO'' H (III)

$\xrightarrow[\text{90-95\% from I}]{\text{CrO}_3}$

$\xrightarrow[\text{80-85\%}]{\text{SeO}_2; \text{KOH}}$

O CH_3
CO_2H
CH_3
HO'' H (IV) $CH_3OH, H^+; H_2, Pt$

H_3C
HO CH_3
CO_2CH_3
CH_3
HO'' H (V) $\xrightarrow[\text{85\% from IV}]{\text{CH}_3\text{OH, H}^+}$

OCH_3
CH_3
(VI) HCl, CHCl$_3$

Cl CH_3
(VII) $\xrightarrow[\substack{91\% \text{ from VI} \\ 60\% \text{ from I}}]{\text{NaHCO}_3}$

CH_3
CO_2CH_3
O
H (VIII) $\xrightarrow[\text{60\% from VI}]{\text{Br}_2, -78°}$

H_3C
Br CH_3
CO_2CH_3
Br
CH_3
O
H (IX) $\xrightarrow[\text{97\%}]{\text{Ag}_2\text{CrO}_4; \text{CrO}_3}$
m.p. 143°
(+ 20% isomer m.p. 123°)

H_3C
Br CH_3
CO_2CH_3
O
CH_3
O
H (X) $\xrightarrow[\text{84\%}]{\text{ArMgBr;} \\ -\text{H}_2\text{O; CrO}_3}$

H_3C
CH_3
CO_2H
O
CH_3
O
H (XI) $\xrightarrow[\text{84\%}]{\text{Ester,;} \\ \text{HBr; ester.}}$

H_3C
Br CH_3
CO_2CH_3
O
CH_3
HO'' H (XII) $\xrightarrow[\text{80\%}]{\text{Degrad.}}$

CH_3
$CHCO_2CH_3$
(XIII) $\xrightarrow{76\%}$

CH_3
$C=C(C_6H_5)_2$
$\xrightarrow[\text{82\%}]{\text{O}_3}$

CH_3
CO
$\xrightarrow{93\%}$

$CH=CHC_6H_5$
CO
$\xrightarrow[\text{AcO}]{\text{Ac}_2\text{O; O}_3; \\ \text{HIO}_4 \\ 83\%}$

CO_2H
O CH_3
CH_3
AcO'' H (XIV)

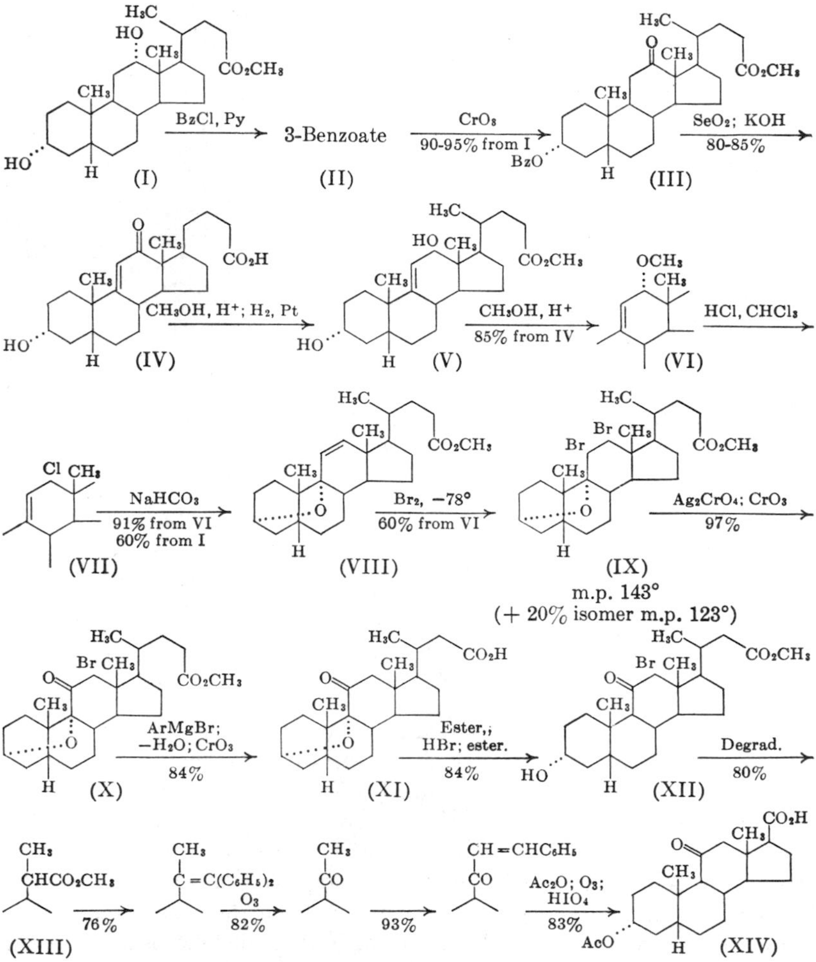

[6] McKenzie, Mattox, Engel, and Kendall, *J. Biol. Chem.*, **173**, 271 (1948).

process does not involve Δ^{11}-lithocholenic acid, available only through a wasteful pyrolytic step. Instead the required $3\alpha,12$-dihydroxy$\Delta^{9(11)}$-cholenic acid (V) is prepared from the corresponding 12-ketone (IV), available by a convenient process described by Schwenk[7] that consists in the selenium dioxide oxidation of 3α-acetoxy-12-ketocholanic acid methyl ester (III). Hydrogenation of the unsaturated keto acid IV (as ester) proceeds rapidly in ethanol-acetic acid and affords a mixture of the epimeric allylic alcohols of the structure V in the ratio $4\beta : 1\alpha$; if the mixture is hydrogenated further in acetic acid solution both epimers suffer hydrogenolysis to the 12-desoxy compound, and the 9,11-double bond of this substance is then slowly saturated.[8] The formation of the 3,9-oxide bridge (VIII) and the reactions through the dibromide to the 12-bromo-11-ketone X proceed as already described. At this point the side chain is conveniently degraded while the oxidic bridge is still intact. The Grignard reaction of the ester X (ether-benzene, 0°) proceeds with reductive elimination of the bromine atom; dehydration of the carbinol in boiling acetic acid is followed by oxidation with chromic acid in an acetic acid—aqueous sulfuric acid—chloroform mixture, which gives the nor acid XI in excellent yield. The acid is esterified (CH₃OH-HCl, 95% yield), and at this stage the oxide bridge is opened (HBr, Ac₂O, CHCl₃, 88% yield) to give, after re-esterification, the 12-bromo-11-keto ester XII. This on Grignard degradation and esterification yields the bisnor ester XIII, which is converted in turn through the diphenylethylene, the 20-methyl ketone, and the benzal derivative to the etio acid XIV.

Physiological Actions[1]

Removal of the adrenal gland from a rat, dog, cat, or rabbit leads to death within a short time. Administration of cortical extract or of an active crystalline steroid isolated from the cortex maintains some of the normal functions in an adrenalectomized animal. In the dog test of Pfiffner, Swingle and Vars,[2] a dog unit is defined as the minimum daily dose of hormone (per kg. body weight) necessary for maintenance of body weight

[7] Schwenk and Stahl, *Arch. Biochem.*, **14**, 125 (1947).

[8] McKenzie, Mattox and Kendall, *J. Biol. Chem.*, **175**, 249 (1948).

[1] General reviews: Swingle and Remington, "The Role of the Adrenal Cortex in Physiological Processes," *Physiol. Rev.*, **24**, 89 (1944); F. G. Young, "Biochemistry of the Adrenal Cortex," *Ann. Repts.*, **42**, 214 (1945); Kendall, "Hormones of the Adrenal Cortex," *Endocrinology*, **30**, 853 (1942); Kendall, "The Adrenal Cortex," *Arch. Path.*, **32**, 474 (1941); Ingle, "Problems Relating to the Adrenal Cortex," *Endocrinology*, **31**, 419 (1942); Pincus, "Studies of the Role of the Adrenal Cortex in the Stress of Human Subjects," *Recent Progress in Hormone Research*, I, 123 (1946).

[2] Pfiffner, Swingle, and Vars, *J. Biol. Chem.*, **104**, 701 (1934).

and normal renal function (urea clearance). One early sign of adrenal insufficiency is a rise of blood urea. The values obtained by this method of bioassay are listed in the first column in Table V; they are in general those summarized by Selye.[3] Desoxycorticosterone is the most active of the hormones in this test; the acetate is about twice as active as the free compound.[4] Corticosterone and its 11-dehydro derivative have about the same activity. Introduction of a 17-hydroxyl group is decidedly unfavorable to this type of activity. Kendall's amorphous fraction is more active than any of the crystalline hormones.[5] Kendall[6] estimates that 90 percent of the renal-function activity of the cortex is present in the amorphous fraction.

In another rather similar method of assay the criterion of activity is maintenance of normal growth in immature adrenalectomized rats.[7] Desoxycorticosterone is again the most active of the hormones. The amorphous concentrate of Kuizenga and Cartland,[8] not necessarily similar to that of Kendall, is slightly less active than desoxycorticosterone.

Only two substances other than the six active cortical steroids are known at the present time that can maintain adrenalectomized animals. One is progesterone, which lacks only the 21-hydroxyl group of desoxycorticosterone. Progesterone protects young rats at rather high dosage levels (1–2 mg. per day protects 50 percent of the test animals).[9] Much more active is 21-acetoxypregnenolone (Δ^5-pregnene-3β,21-diol-20-one 21-acetate), which shows some activity in rats at a dose of 0.25 mg. per day and is fully protective at 0.5 mg. daily dosage.[10] Selye[11] rates this substance as only slightly less active than desoxycorticosterone acetate. Since Δ^5-pregnene-3β-ol-20-one is inactive (at 2 mg. per day),[10] the α-ketol side chain is an important feature of structure. The activity of 21-acetoxypregnenolone and of progesterone is conceivably due to conversion into desoxycorticosterone in the body. The cortical activity of the progestational hormone probably accounts for the fact that pregnant and pseudopregnant animals survive adrenalectomy.

[3] Selye, *Encyclopedia of Endocrinology*, Franks Publishing Co., Montreal (1943).

[4] Kendall, *J. Biol. Chem.*, **128**, li (1939).

[5] Kendall, *J. Am. Med. Assoc.*, **116**, 2394 (1941); Kendall, *Glandular Physiology and Therapy*, p. 273, Am. Med. Assoc., Chicago (1942).

[6] Wells and Kendall, *Proc. Staff Meetings Mayo Clinic*, **15**, 133 (1940).

[7] Hartman and Thorn, *Proc. Soc. Exp. Biol. Med.*, **28**, 94 (1930); Cartland and Kuizenga, *Am. J. Physiol.*, **117**, 678 (1936); Grollman, *Endocrinology*, **29**, 855 (1941).

[8] Kuizenga and Cartland, *Endocrinology*, **24**, 526 (1939).

[9] Gaunt, W. O. Nelson and Loomis, *Proc. Soc. Exp. Biol. Med.*, **39**, 319 (1938); Emery and Greco, *Endocrinology*, **27**, 473 (1940).

[10] Segaloff and W. O. Nelson, *Endocrinology*, **31**, 592 (1942).

[11] Selye, *Science*, **94**, 94 (1941).

TABLE V. Comparative Physiological Activity

SUBSTANCE	LIFE MAINTENANCE (DOG)	EVERSE-DE FREMERY WORK TEST	CARBOHYDRATE METAB.		RETENTION OF Na⁺ (NORMAL DOG)
			Deposition liver glycogen	Ingle test	
	Unit, γ	Unit, mg.	Units/mg.	Units/mg.	Rel. activity
Corticosterone..........	60	0.9	1000	2.3	+
17-Hydroxycorticosterone (M)...........	1000	1.7	1490	6.3	excretion
11-Dehydrocorticosterone..............	60	?	1140	1.6	+
17-Hydroxy-11-dehydrocorticosterone (Kendall's E)..............	500	2	1335	5.0	excretion
Desoxycorticosterone....	15–20	0.07	inactive	inactive	+++
17-Hydroxydesoxycorticosterone (S).....	?	1	inactive	inactive	?
Amorphous fraction.....	9ᵃ 2ᵇ	0.3ᶜ	sl. act.ᵃ	sl. act.ᵃ	++ᵃ

ᵃ Beef adrenals, Kendall; ᵇ Hog adrenals, Kuizenga, J. W. Nelson, Lyster and Ingle, *J. Biol. Chem.*, **160**, 15 (1945); ᶜ Beef adrenals, Reichstein.

The Everse-de Fremery work test[12] (column 2, Table V) has been frequently used for assay, particularly by the Swiss group. It is based on the fact that adrenalectomized animals and Addisonian patients (adrenal insufficiency) show profound muscular weakness. A compound is said to be active if it improves the contractile response of the gastrocnemius muscle of an adrenalectomized rat to short electric stimulation. A unit is the daily effective dose of a given substance. The results obtained by this test are fairly similar to those obtained by the dog test; the discrepancy in the activity of the amorphous fractions may be the result of differences in the preparations. 21-Acetoxypregnenolone is inactive in the work test at a dosage level fifty times that at which desoxycorticosterone is active.[13] Reichstein and Shoppee estimate that one Everse-de Fremery unit is equal to 50–100 dog units.

Assay methods of another type are based on the intimate connection of the cortex with carbohydrate metabolism.[14] Thus the liver glycogen is depleted after adrenalectomy.[15] Long and his associates[16] noted that

[12] Everse and de Fremery, *Acta Brevia Neerland., Physiol. Pharmacol. Microbiol.*, **2**, 152 (1932).

[13] Reichstein and Shoppee, *Vitamins and Hormones*, I, 345 (1943).

[14] C. N. H. Long, "A Discussion of the Mechanism of Action of Adrenal Cortical Hormones on Carbohydrate and Protein Metabolism," *Endocrinology*, **30**, 870 (1942).

[15] Britton and Silvette, *Cold Spring Harbor Symposia Quant. Biol.*, **5**, 357 (1937).

[16] C. N. H. Long, Katzin and E. G. Fry, *Endocrinology*, **26**, 309 (1940).

administration of active cortex principles causes an elevation of carbohydrate in the blood and liver and at the same time increases the excretion of nonprotein nitrogen in the urine, that is, increases the breakdown of protein with consequent liberation of urea and other products of protein metabolism. Quantitative measurements indicated that all the carbohydrate synthesized was derived from protein. Although the main direct effect of the corticoids is apparently on protein metabolism, there is some evidence that the cortical principles promote conversion of glucose into glycogen in the liver[17] and can inhibit oxidation of glucose.[18] The ability of a hormone to promote deposition of glycogen in the liver of fasted, adrenalectomized rats has been developed as an assay method by Reinecke and Kendall[19] and extended by Oslen and co-workers.[20] The activity is expressed in terms of the glycogenic units contained in one mg. of substance; a glycogenic unit is arbitrarily defined as the activity of 1 γ of corticosterone administered to a fasted adrenalectomized rat in four divided doses at two-hour intervals. In the test the two 11,17-oxygenated compounds are the most active; corticosterone and its 11-dehydro derivative are slightly less active. Since desoxycorticosterone and its 17-hydroxy derivative are inactive at rather high dosages (1.2 mg.), an 11-oxygen seems to be essential for glycogenic activity and a 17-hydroxyl group enhances activity but is not sufficient in itself. Kendall's amorphous fraction is practically inactive.

A test developed by Ingle[21] rates the corticoids in very much the same order as the glycogenic test, and hence is also a measure of the same type of physiological activity. The Ingle test is concerned with the ability of a given substance to sustain the muscular responsiveness of the adrenalectomized-nephrectomized rat to repeated faradic stimulation. The gastrocnemius muscle is the test material. An Ingle work unit is defined as the work equivalent of 0.2 mg. of Compound E administered twice during the test. By definition then 1 mg. of E contains five units. There is no evidence that the cortical steroids can improve the working capacity of normal muscles.

Estrone and stilbestrol have some slight activity in the carbohydrate metabolism tests. Long[14] has found that estrone and the synthetic sub-

[17] Britton and Corey, *Am. J. Physiol.*, **131**, 790 (1941).

[18] Thorn, Koepf, Lewis and Olsen, *J. Clin. Invest.*, **19**, 813 (1940); Ingle, *Endocrinology*, **29**, 649 (1941).

[19] Reinecke and Kendall, *Endocrinology*, **31**, 573 (1942).

[20] Olsen, F. H. Jacobs, Richert, Thayer, Kopp and Wade, *Endocrinology*, **35**, 430, 464 (1944); see also Thayer, "Bioassay of Animal Hormones," *Vitamins and Hormones*, IV, 311 (1946).

[21] Ingle, *Am. J. Physiol.*, **116**, 622 (1936); *Endocrinology*, **26**, 472 (1940); *ibid.*, **34**, 191 (1944); Ingle and Kuizenga, *ibid.*, **36**, 218 (1945).

stitute can increase the liver glycogen of fasted adrenalectomized rats but not of hypophysectomized animals. He postulates that the activity of the two estrogens is due primarily to stimulation of the anterior pituitary, which in turn stimulates the adrenal gland.

A bioassay method evidently related to the liver glycogen test and to Ingle's test is based upon the ability of certain corticoids to counteract hypoglycemia provided by insulin. The substances that are active in anti-insulin activity are also those that promote deposition of liver glycogen: Compound E, Substance M, and corticosterone. Desoxycorticosterone and progesterone are practically inactive.[22]

The complicated interrelationship of the various endocrine glands that control carbohydrate metabolism awaits clarification. Thus secretions of the thyroid (thyroxin), pancreas (insulin), and adrenal cortex are known to be required for the delicate normal balance of breakdown and synthesis. Recently Cori and Cori[23] have shown that adrenal cortex extracts and also pituitary fractions can inhibit the activity of hexokinase, an enzyme present in muscle that controls the reversible phosphorylation of glucose, an essential step in the utilization of glucose in the animal organism. This inhibition is counteracted by insulin, although insulin itself has no effect on the hexokinase reaction in the absence of pituitary or cortical inhibition. The pituitary effect is not due to the adrenocorticotropic hormone, which is inactive. The glycogenic 11-oxygen cortical hormones have no inhibitory effect; the amorphous fraction is active. The effect of the cortex extract is not a simple one, however; it is manifested in muscle extracts of diabetic animals but not of normal animals unless the active pituitary fraction is also present.

Another important function of the adrenal cortex is control of electrolyte balance.[24] Thus patients with Addison's disease have a high potassium but a low sodium serum content.[25, 26] In patients suffering from Cushing's syndrome (usually associated with a tumor of the anterior pituitary with consequent cortical hyperactivity) the reverse relationship, low serum potassium and high serum sodium, is usually found.[27] Adrenalectomized

[22] Jensen and Grattan, *Am. J. Physiol.*, **128**, 270 (1940); Grattan and Jensen, *J. Biol. Chem.*, **135**, 511 (1940); Hartman, Brownell, Walther, and Edelmann, *Endocrinology*, **27**, 642 (1940).

[23] C. F. Cori, *Harvey Lectures*, **41**, 253 (1945–46); Colowick, G. T. Cori, and Slein, *J. Biol. Chem.*, **168**, 583 (1947).

[24] Reviews: R. F. Loeb, "The Adrenal Cortex and Electrolyte Behavior," *Harvey Lectures*, **37**, 100 (1942); "Adrenal Cortex Insufficiency," *Glandular Physiology and Therapy*, p. 287, Am. Med. Assoc., Chicago (1942).

[25] Loeb, *Science*, **76**, 420 (1932).

[26] Harrop and co-workers, *J. Am. Med. Assoc.*, **100**, 1850 (1933); **101**, 388 (1933); *J. Exptl. Med.*, **65**, 757 (1937).

[27] E. M. Anderson, Haymaker, and Joseph, *Endocrinology*, **23**, 398 (1938).

cats have been known for some time to show an abnormal serum electrolyte behavior.[28] A diet high in sodium but restricted in potassium has been found to have markedly beneficial effects for patients with Addison's disease, and in many cases is sufficient treatment. Occasionally desoxycorticosterone is also required for complete alleviation, but is not prescribed routinely since it is known to produce atrophy of the adrenal and of the thymus in animals. Desoxycorticosterone happened to be the first cortical hormone available for clinical use, and it has since been found to be by far the most active compound in influence on sodium and chloride retention in normal as well as adrenalectomized animals. The sodium retention activity runs more or less parallel to the life-maintenance (dog) test. Kendall's amorphous fraction, however, is more active in renal function than in sodium retention. As in the dog test, corticosterone and 11-dehydrocorticosterone are definitely less active than desoxycorticosterone. Kendall's E and Substance M actually promote, rather than restrain, excretion of sodium.[29]

Another method of bioassay of cortical activity is based upon the fact that adrenalectomized animals are very susceptible to water. Thus a dose of 150 cc. of water per kg. body weight is fatal to the adrenalectomized dog. Compound E is at least three times as active as desoxycorticosterone in providing protection against water intoxication; the amorphous fraction (Kendall) is definitely less potent than desoxycorticosterone.[30]

Another measure of activity is obtained by determination of the ability to maintain adrenalectomized animals at a low temperature.[31] Kendall's Compound E is the most active in the cold test; 11-dehydrocorticosterone is about one-third as active as Compound E; corticosterone is one-twelfth as active and desoxycorticosterone is one-thirteenth as active as Compound E.[32] According to Kendall[33] the amorphous fraction is only slightly less active than Compound E. The errors are estimated to be in the order of 25–100 percent.

Similarly the cortical hormones are able to protect adrenalectomized animals against shock induced by drugs (morphine and histamine have been used particularly) and by various toxins.[34]

[28] E. J. Baumann and Kurland, *J. Biol. Chem.*, **71**, 281 (1927).

[29] Thorn, Engel and R. A. Lewis, *Science*, **94**, 348 (1941).

[30] Swingle, Remington, Hays and Collings, *Endocrinology*, **28**, 531 (1941); Eversole, Gaunt and Kendall, *Am. J. Physiol.*, **135**, 378 (1942).

[31] Selye and Schenker, *Proc. Soc. Exp. Biol. Med.*, **39**, 518 (1938); Roos, *Endocrinology*, **33**, 276 (1943).

[32] Dorfman, Shipley, Ross, Schiller and Horwitt, *Endocrinology*, **38**, 189 (1946).

[33] Kendall, *Arch. Path.*, **32**, 474 (1941).

[34] Selye, Dosne, Bassett, Whittaker, *Can. Med. Assoc. J.*, **43**, 1 (1940); Parkins, Swingle, Taylor and Hays, *Proc. Soc. Exp. Biol. Med.*, **37**, 675 (1938).

Since adrenalectomy abolishes lactation in experimental animals, the ability of a cortical hormone to maintain lactation in adrenalectomized rats furnishes a method of assay. Desoxycorticosterone is weakly effective in rats, but apparently inhibitory in the guinea pig.[35]

Two colorimetric methods of assay have been described:[36, 37] both are based on the reducing power of the α-ketol side chain present in all the active cortical hormones. Both are modifications of the Folin-Wu method for determination of blood glucose. In one method[37] the reducing action of the steroid on phosphomolybdic acid leads to molybdenum blue, with an absorption maximum at 650–660 mμ. The test is not specific for the cortical steroids, for it is positive for α,β-unsaturated 3-ketosteroids, α,β-diketones, and cyclic α-ketols such as $3\alpha,11\alpha$- or β-dihydroxy-12-ketocholanic acid.

From the above discussion it is evident that the adrenal cortex is concerned with several physiological functions. The two main functions are regulation of the electrolyte balance and of carbohydrate and protein metabolism in the liver and in muscles. Of the isolated hormones desoxycorticosterone is most potent in the first type of activity and the two 17-hydroxy-11-ketosteroids are the most potent in the second type. The renal activity in many respects seems to run parallel with ability to cause retention of sodium; however, one important difference is that Kendall's amorphous fraction is more active than desoxycorticosterone in renal activity. The solubility and analytical composition point to a more highly oxygenated compound than desoxycorticosterone; yet the O_5-compounds that have been isolated do not possess the type of activity shown by the amorphous fraction. Perhaps the fraction contains a hormone of a different structural type or it may contain an activator, as in the case of testicular extracts. The other types of physiological action exerted by the cortical hormones, such as resistance to stress and maintenance of normal growth, may be merely additional manifestations of the more specific functions.

The observation that Compound E causes atrophy of the lymph nodes of adult rats prompted Heilman and Kendall[38] to investigate the effect of this hormone on malignant lymphosarcoma (mice). Prompt regression of the tumors was obtained, but the cures were only temporary; after recurrence the tumors were completely refractory. Inhibitory effects[39] of cortical

[35] Gaunt, Eversole and Kendall, *Endocrinology,* **31,** 84 (1942); W. O. Nelson, Gaunt and Schweizer, *ibid.,* **33,** 325 (1943).
[36] Talbot and co-workers, *J. Biol. Chem.,* **160,** 535 (1945).
[37] Heard and Sobel, *J. Biol. Chem.,* **165,** 687 (1946).
[38] Heilman and Kendall, *Endocrinology,* **34,** 416 (1944).
[39] Murphy and Sturm, *Science,* **98,** 568 (1943); **99,** 303 (1944).

extracts and of desoxycorticosterone on lymphatic leukemia have also been observed in mice.

Urinary Corticoids. Early reports[1] that a benzene extract of human urine prolongs the life of adrenalectomized rats have been fully substantiated in several laboratories. The urinary corticoids, obtained by extraction, preferably with ethylene dichloride, have been shown to protect the adrenalectomized rat against the lethal effects of exposure to low temperatures,[2, 3] to increase deposition of liver glycogen,[4, 5] to affect muscular performance favorably,[6] and to affect electrolyte balance in the same way as adrenal cortical extract.[7] Active extracts were originally prepared by extraction of native urine. The activity can be approximately doubled if the urine is first adjusted to pH 1 and allowed to stand for twenty-four hours at room temperature.[5] Presumably the active constituents are excreted as readily hydrolyzable conjugates. Various partitions and purification processes concentrate the activity,[3] but no pure substance has been isolated. On the basis of bioassay (cold test) the most active extract contains the equivalent of about one mg. of corticosterone. Evidence that the material arises from the adrenal cortex is deduced from the fact that cortinlike activity is seldom detected in the urine of patients with Addison's disease (adrenal insufficiency) but is present in the urine of such patients after treatment with cortical extract (but not after treatment with desoxycorticosterone).[8] Moreover no activity can be detected in the urine of adrenalectomized monkeys, but is found in that of normal or of gonadectomized animals.[9]

The average daily excretion of normal women is equivalent in glycogenic activity to 25–65 γ of 17-hydroxy-11-dehydrocorticosterone; that of normal men is slightly higher: 40–85 γ. No activity is detected in the urine of infants in the first four days of life; thereafter the urinary corticoids increase gradually until at the age of 5–7 the daily excretion is about that of an adult.[10] Greatly increased amounts of active material[11] are obtained from

[1] Perla and Marmorston-Gottesman, *Proc. Soc. Exp. Biol. Med.*, **28**, 1024 (1931); Grollman and Firor, *ibid.*, **30**, 669 (1932–1933).

[2] Dorfman, Horwitt and Fish, *Science*, **96**, 496 (1942).

[3] Venning, M. M. Hofman, and Browne, *Endocrinology*, **35**, 49 (1944).

[4] Horwitt and Dorfman, *Science*, **97**, 337 (1943).

[5] Venning, Kazmin and Bell, *Endocrinology*, **38**, 79 (1946).

[6] Shipley, Dorfman, and Horwitt, *Am. J. Physiol.*, **139**, 742 (1943).

[7] Feil and Dorfman, *Endocrinology*, **37**, 437 (1945).

[8] Dorfman, Horwitt and Shipley, *Endocrinology*, **35**, 121 (1944).

[9] Dorfman, Horwitt, Shipley and Abbott, *Endocrinology*, **35**, 15 (1944).

[10] Venning and Kazmin, *Endocrinology*, **39**, 131 (1946).

[11] Venning and Browne, *10th Conf. on Metabolic Aspects of Convalescence*, Josiah Macy Jr. Foundation, June (1945).

urine of post-operative patients or from urine of patients with Cushing's syndrome. Pregnancy also increases the excretion of corticoids (daily excretion equivalent to 200 – 300 γ of 17-hydroxy-11-dehydrocorticosterone).[12]

Adrenocorticotropic Hormone. Just as the production of the steroid sex hormones of the gonads is controlled by protein hormones of the anterior hypohysis, the formation and release of steroidal hormones of the adrenal cortex is controlled by a hormone of the anterior hypohysis, the adrenocorticotropic hormone (ACTH) or corticotrophin.[1] A relation between the adrenal cortex and anterior pituitary was suggested by early observations that hypophysectomy causes atrophy of the cortex and that crude extracts of the anterior pituitary exert effects somewhat similar to those of the adrenal cortex and can maintain or repair the cortex after hypophysectomy. Preparation of the pure hormone has now been achieved by salt fractionation[2] and by isoelectric precipitation.[3] The hormone is a protein, with an isoelectric point between 4.6 – 4.8 and a molecular weight of approximately 20,000. Administration of the hormone to normal rats affects carbohydrate metabolism in the same way that administration of 17-hydroxycorticosterone does.[4] It is not yet clear whether the protein hormone also affects the mineral metabolism. Increased excretion of urinary steroids has been noted after administration to a normal woman.[5]

[12] Venning, *Endocrinology*, **39**, 203 (1946).

[1] Li and H. M. Evans, "The Properties of the Growth and Adrenocorticotropic Hormones," *Vitamins and Hormones*, V, 197 (1947).

[2] Li, H. M. Evans, and M. E. Simpson, *J. Biol. Chem.*, **149**, 413 (1943).

[3] G. Sayers, A. White and C. N. H. Long, *J. Biol. Chem.*, **149**, 425 (1943).

[4] Ingle and co-workers, *Endocrinology*, **37**, 341 (1945); **39**, 32 (1946).

[5] Mason, Power, Rynearson, Ciaramelli, Li and H. M. Evans, *J. Biol. Chem.*, **169**, 223 (1947).

Chapter VI
Steroid Metabolism

Cholesterol. Even the lower plants (yeast, fungi) can synthesize sterols, and for some time plants alone were believed capable of the synthesis of sterols. Since cholesterol does not occur in plants, the abundant supplies present in animals were thought to arise largely through transformation of phytosterols derived from the diet. Balance studies showed, however, that the amount of cholesterol excreted can exceed the amount consumed, and hence that the sterol apparently can be synthesized in the animal organism. In experiments with the rabbit, whose major sterol is cholesterol, Schoenheimer[1] established that this animal is incapable of converting phytosterols into cholesterol. The rabbit normally consumes only vegetables, and if cholesterol is added to the diet it appears in various organs in morphologically visible deposits and produces a condition resembling human atherosclerosis. The condition is never observed in the absence of added cholesterol, even though the amount of plant sterols in the ordinary diet is ten times the amount of cholesterol required to produce atherosclerosis. Moreover, phytosterols apparently are not even absorbed in the animal organism but are eliminated, chiefly in the feces. A particularly crucial test was possible with ergosterol, which can be detected in minute amounts by spectroscopy and by bioassay of antirachitic activity developed on irradiation. The amount of ergosterol in the animal body cannot be increased by additional dietary sources, though irradiated ergosterol is absorbed readily. The great selectivity of the animal organism is demonstrated by the nonabsorption by the rabbit of cholestanol and of coprostanol, in contrast to cholesterol.

The mode of synthesis presented a more difficult problem. For some time fatty acids were regarded as the probable precursors, since a high fat diet was reported by several investigators[2] to lead to an increase in body cholesterol. Schoenheimer,[3] however, was not able to detect any significant effect of exogenous fat. The discovery of the stable isotope of hydrogen furnished a new tool for the study of intermediary metabolism.

[1] Schoenheimer, *Science*, **74**, 579 (1931).
[2] Eckstein and Treadwell, *J. Biol. Chem.*, **112**, 373 (1936); Minovici, *Bull. soc. chim. biol.*, **17**, 369 (1935); see also Bills, *Physiol. Rev.*, **15**, 1 (1935).
[3] Schoenheimer and Breusch, *J. Biol. Chem.*, **103**, 439 (1933).

One approach is to feed a suspected precursor labeled with deuterium in positions where the isotope is not readily exchangeable (as by enolization) and then to isolate the sterol and determine the deuterium content. A positive result is proof of conversion only if the deuterium content is higher than that of the body fluids. In a second approach to the problem of biosynthesis the uptake of deuterium into cholesterol is determined in animals whose body fluids are enriched with deuterium oxide. The method is valid because the hydrogen atoms of cholesterol, once formed, are not readily exchangeable *in vitro* with deuterium. In such an experiment Rittenberg and Schoenheimer[4] found a high concentration of deuterium in the cholesterol isolated from mice whose drinking water had been enriched for two months with deuterium oxide. They concluded that about half of the hydrogen atoms of cholesterol are derived from water and that the synthesis must consequently involve condensation of a large number of small molecules. The synthesis and degradation of cholesterol is relatively slow. The half-life of cholesterol is 15–25 days (mouse); that of fatty acids, 5–9 days.

At about the same time Sonderhoff and Thomas[5] reported that the sterols synthesized by yeast grown on a medium containing sodium deuterioacetate as the only carbon source contain large amounts of deuterium. They felt that their results justified the conclusion that acetate is utilized directly for synthesis of sterols, since the deuterium content of the fats and carbohydrates was appreciably lower. Some years later Bloch and Rittenberg[6] demonstrated that acetic acid is a precursor of cholesterol in animals. They fed sodium deuterioacetate (containing 9.9 atom percent deuterium) to adult mice and rats and to growing rats for eight days. In all cases the fecal sterols and the body cholesterol of the sacrificed animals contained more than three times as much deuterium as the body fluids. Furthermore, examination of the two fractions of Mauthner pyrolytic degradation showed the deuterium to be distributed between the nucleus and the side chain. Strictly speaking, these experiments only demonstrate that the methyl group, which is labeled, is utilized. In later experiments[7] with isotopic sodium deuterioacetate, $CD_3C^{13}OONa$, cholesterol was isolated that contained both isotopic carbon and deuterium and in such amounts that it can be concluded that acetic acid is a major source of the carbon atoms of cholesterol. The liver has been identified as the site of synthesis.[8] One other C_2-compound, ethyl alcohol, can also serve as a

[4] Rittenberg and Schoenheimer, *J. Biol. Chem.*, **121**, 235 (1937).
[5] Sonderhoff and H. Thomas, *Ann.*, **530**, 195 (1937).
[6] K. Bloch and Rittenberg, *J. Biol. Chem.*, **143**, 297 (1942); *ibid.*, **145**, 625 (1942).
[7] K. Bloch and Rittenberg, *J. Biol. Chem.*, **159**, 45 (1945); *ibid.*, **160**, 417 (1945).
[8] K. Bloch, Borek and Rittenberg, *J. Biol. Chem.*, **162**, 441 (1946).

building unit. This fact has been demonstrated by incubation of rat liver slices with CH_3CD_2OH and isolation of deuteriocholesterol.[9]

Reichstein[10] pointed out that the skeleton of the C_{21}-hormones, C_{24}-bile acids, and C_{27}-sterols is theoretically divisible into C_3- or C_3- and C_6-units; he suggested that the synthesis involves a C_3-intermediate of carbohydrate metabolism, such as glyceraldehyde or dihydroxyacetone. However, various labeled C_3- and C_4-substances, known to be formed in animals or microorganisms from acetic acid, were excluded as possible intermediates.[7] These include propionic acid, butyric acid, and succinic acid. Pyruvic acid, the common C_3-building unit, is also excluded, since it can undoubtedly be formed from alanine in the organism. Only one C_3-compound has been demonstrated to be capable of functioning as a cholesterol precursor; this is acetone.[9] However the possibility that acetone is first oxidized to acetic acid, although unlikely, has not been rigidly excluded. An attractive hypothesis is that the synthesis involves condensation of acetone with acetaldehyde (from ethyl alcohol).

Acetic acid is now known to be a building unit of fatty acids;[11,12] moreover fatty acids are convertible into acetic acid *in vivo*.[13] The latter fact probably accounts for the cholesterol syntheses noted in the early balance feeding experiments.

The body eliminates little cholesterol as such. Undoubtedly some is completely consumed within the organism, for it has been demonstrated[14] that mice can destroy several times the normal body content of cholesterol. A small part is transformed by hydrogenation in the tissues to cholestanol, which is excreted in small amounts in the feces.[15] This reduction product cannot be resorbed from the intestine.[16] Coprostanol and epicoprostanol[17] have not been isolated from tissues but occur in the feces in much larger amounts than cholestanol occurs. Since administered cholesterol causes an increase in coprostanol excretion,[18] coprostanol must be formed from cholesterol. For a time reducing bacteria in the intestines were believed capable of the direct transformation of cholesterol into coprostanol, but

[9] Communication from Dr. D. Rittenberg.

[10] Reichstein, *Helv. Chim. Acta*, **20**, 978 (1937).

[11] Rittenberg and K. Bloch, *J. Biol. Chem.*, **154**, 311 (1944); *ibid.*, **160**, 417 (1945).

[12] H. A. Barker *et al.*, *Proc. Nat. Acad. Science*, **31**, 355, 373 (1945).

[13] K. Bloch and Rittenberg, *J. Biol. Chem.*, **155**, 243 (1944).

[14] Schoenheimer and Breusch, *J. Biol. Chem.*, **103**, 439 (1933).

[15] Windaus and Uibrig, *Ber.*, **48**, 857 (1915).

[16] Schoenheimer and v. Behring, *Z. physiol. Chem.*, **192**, 102 (1930); Schoenheimer and Hrdina, *ibid.*, **212**, 161 (1932).

[17] Marker, Wittbecker, R. B. Wagner and D. L. Turner, *J. Am. Chem. Soc.*, **64**, 818 (1942).

[18] Schoenheimer, Rittenberg and Graff, *J. Biol. Chem.*, **111**, 183 (1935).

Rosenheim[19] and Schoenheimer[18] both questioned this assumption, since in the laboratory hydrogenation of cholesterol under all known conditions results in cholestanol, and they both postulated cholestenone as an intermediate. The more recent observation that both epicoprostanol and coprostanol occur in feces lends support to a 3-ketone intermediate. Cholestenone administered to a dog on a basic meat diet is excreted as coprostanol; when added to a diet of dog biscuits, it is excreted as cholesterol.[19] Labeled coprostanone (4,5-dideuteriocoprostanone) is excreted as deuteriocoprostanol.[19] More precise information was then obtained by feeding experiments with labeled cholestenone, prepared by the rearrangement of Δ^5-cholestenone in an alkaline medium containing deuterium oxide;[20] the product contains four deuterium atoms, all of which are labile. When this was fed the coprostanol isolated from the feces contained deuterium in stable positions. The cholesterol isolated from the body did not contain deuterium. This negative finding may mean that the transformation of cholesterol into cholestenone is not reversible, or merely that the labile deuterium is lost during the reverse transformation. Marker[17] considered the conversion of a Δ^4-3-ketone into a Δ^5-3-hydroxysteroid to be a normal biological process on the basis of the results of feeding experiments with Δ^4-dehydrotigogenone, a steroid sapogenin with the nuclear structure of cholestenone and differing only in the side chain. Sterols corresponding to cholesterol, coprostanol, and epicoprostanol were isolated from the feces. Rosenheim and Webster[21] report that β-sitosterol is converted into 24-ethylcoprostanol;[22] the reduction is entirely analogous to that of cholesterol. Ergosterol and stigmasterol are excreted unchanged. Turfitt[23] found a species of soil bacteria, *Proactinomyces* Spp., that oxidizes cholesterol to cholestenone and then to Δ^4-3-ketoetioallocholanic acid (removal of side chain) and to the ketocarboxylic acid resulting from cleavage of ring A between C_3 and C_4 (also obtained by chemical oxidation of cholestenone).[24] Similar transformations of 3β-hydroxy-Δ^5-cholenic acid, dehydroepiandrosterone, and Δ^5-androstenediol are observed. In the latter case the product is mainly testosterone (42%) with some Δ^4-androstene-3,17-dione (6%). Coprostanol is oxidized to cholestenone. This is the first instance of microbiological oxidation of steroids with the long side chain.

The recent proof that cholesterol is synthesized by the condensation of many small molecules would seem to render unlikely the hypothesis that

[19] Rosenheim and T. A. Webster, *Nature*, **136**, 474 (1935).
[20] Anchel and Schoenheimer, *J. Biol. Chem.*, **125**, 23 (1938).
[21] Rosenheim and T. A. Webster, *Biochem. J.*, **35**, 928 (1941).
[22] Synthesis: Marker and Wittle, *J. Am. Chem. Soc.*, **59**, 2704 (1937).
[23] Turfitt, *Biochem. J.*, **38**, 492 (1944); *ibid.*, **40**, 79 (1946).
[24] Turfitt, *Biochem. J.*, **42**, 376 (1948).

cholesterol is a precursor of the bile acids and sex hormones. It would even seem reasonable that the simpler steroids should be intermediates in the biosynthesis of cholesterol. However Bloch, Berg, and Rittenberg[25] have been able to establish the transformation of cholesterol into cholic acid. They administered deuteriocholesterol[26] to a dog in which a connection between the gallbladder and the kidney had been established by surgery (cholecystonephrostomy) and isolated isotopic cholic acid from the urine. The content of deuterium indicated that if the circulating cholesterol is the immediate precursor, at least two-thirds of the excreted cholic acid arises from cholesterol. The distribution of labeled cholesterol in the various tissues was also determined. The highest amounts were found in the lung and in the liver. No labeled cholesterol was found in the central nervous system (brain and spinal cord), an indication that cholesterol in this site is very inert. The content of the other organs was the same as that of the blood.

Some of the neutral steroids isolated from bile, such as scymnol and pentahydroxybufostane, may represent intermediates in the biological conversion of sterols into bile acids.[27] Pearlman[28] recently investigated the neutral fraction of ox bile, from which five substances were isolated. One was identified as allopregnanediol-3β,20b;[29] the structure of the other compounds is not known. One constituent of the ketonic fraction has the probable formula $C_{27}H_{40}O_3$ and forms a monoacetate and monobenzoate. A nonketonic, digitonin-precipitable component apparently contains 25 or 26 carbon atoms ($C_{25-26}H_{40-42}O_4$). The two other compounds have the probable formulas $C_{24}H_{40}O_3$ and $C_{24}H_{42}O_4$.

The conversion of cholesterol into a C_{21}-steroid of the sex hormone group has also been demonstrated·by Bloch.[30] The hormones themselves are isolated in too small amounts to be detectable by the tracer technique possible with the stable isotope of hydrogen. However pregnanediol, a metabolic product of progesterone (see below), is excreted in relatively large amounts in the later stages of human pregnancy and is readily isolable as the glucuronide. Bloch found that the pregnanediol excreted after ingestion of deuteriocholesterol contained about 60 percent of the amount of deuterium theoretically possible if it had been formed exclusively from cholesterol. Less direct confirmation of the utilization of cholesterol for progesterone synthesis is based on the fact that deposition of cholesterol

[25] K. Bloch, Berg and Rittenberg, *J. Biol. Chem.*, **149**, 511 (1943).

[26] Preparation: K. Bloch and Rittenberg, *J. Biol. Chem.*, **149**, 505 (1943).

[27] Kurauti and Kazuno, *Z. physiol. Chem.*, **262**, 53 (1939).

[28] W. H. Pearlman, *J. Am. Chem. Soc.*, **66**, 806 (1944).

[29] W. H. Pearlman, *J. Biol. Chem.*, **166**, 473 (1946).

[30] K. Bloch, *J. Biol. Chem.*, **157**, 661 (1945).

in the corpus luteum is increased by estrogen administration. The effect is indirect, since it is due to stimulation of gonadotropic hormones (probably ICSH). Cholesterol disappears after administration of lactogen, another pituitary hormone that controls pregnancy.[31] There is some evidence that cholesterol may be a precursor of the adrenal cortical hormones. Thus animals in which shock has been induced by hemorrhage show an increase in the urinary corticoids and a marked depletion of cholesterol in the adrenal gland. Furthermore, administration of the adrenotropic hormone to rats and to guinea pigs increases the production of the 11-oxygenated cortical hormones; at the same time the adrenal cholesterol level falls below normal.[32] Preliminary experiments suggest that ICS hormone (luteinizing hormone) effects androgen synthesis in the testes at their expense of cholesterol.[33]

Further progress in the investigation of metabolism can be expected from the use of radioactive isotopes. The preparation of radioactive cholestenone[34] and of radioactive testosterone[35] has been accomplished by Turner by an interesting reaction in which C^{14} is incorporated into position 3. A Δ^4-3-ketone (I) is ozonized and the resulting keto acid (II) is lactonized. Ester condensation with radioactive phenyl acetate occurs

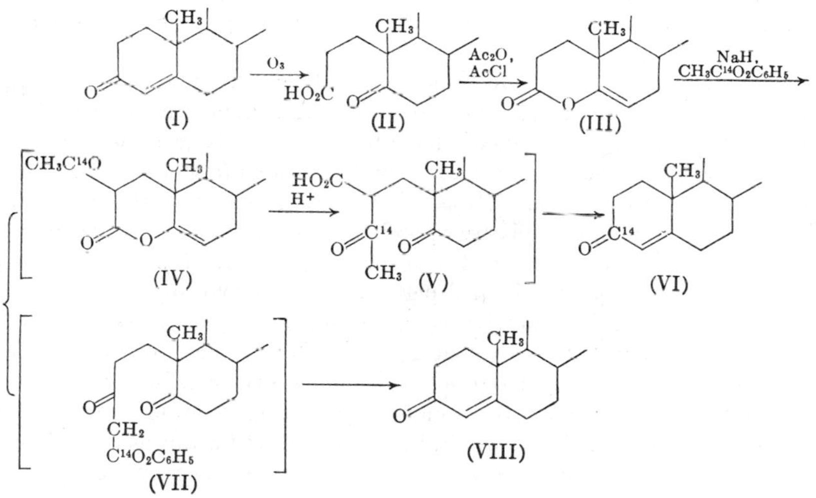

---

[31] Everett, *Endocrinology*, **41**, 364 (1947).

[32] G. Sayers, M. A. Sayers, Liang and C. N. H. Long, *Endocrinology*, **37**, 96 (1945); *ibid.*, **38**, 1 (1946); C. N. H. Long, "Relation of Cholesterol and Ascorbic Acid to the Secretion of the Adrenal Cortex," *Recent Progress in Hormone Research*, I, 99 (1947).

[33] J. Tepperman and H. M. Tepperman, *Endocrinology*, **41**, 187 (1947).

[34] R. B. Turner, *J. Am. Chem. Soc.*, **69**, 726 (1947).

[35] R. B. Turner, *Science*, **106**, 248 (1947).

predominately at position 2 (IV); decarboxylation and cyclization then leads to a radioactive Δ^4-3-ketone. Condensation to give the intermediate VII occurs to a slight extent, for the final product contains only about 90 percent of the radioactivity of the phenyl acetate. Use of methyl-labeled phenyl acetate gives a product labeled at position 4. Reformatsky condensation of radioactive bromoacetic ester, $BrCH_2C^{14}OOCH_3$, with the methyl ester of II was also used for the preparation of 3-radioactive-cholestenone, but the yields were not satisfactory.

Estrogens. The ovaries are not the only site of estrogen synthesis. Estrone, estradiol, and estriol have been isolated from human placenta; furthermore the increase of urinary estrogens during pregnancy and prompt decrease immediately after pregnancy give evidence that this organ can synthesize estrogens. Estrone has been isolated from the adrenal, and the occurrence of estradiol and estriol is indicated. This gland is presumably the source of estrogens encountered in almost normal amounts in ovariectomized women.[1,2] Estrogens are secreted by normal males,[1] and estrone has been isolated from this source (6 mg. from 17,000 l.).[2] Since estrogens are also excreted by eunuchs, the adrenal gland is the presumable site of synthesis in men. However the high estrogen content of the urine of stallions, coupled with the absence in urine of geldings, points to testicular origin in this species.

Estrone and estradiol have been isolated from several species (human, horse, sow), but estriol has been isolated only from human urine and placenta. Equilin and equilenin have been found only in urine of mares.

Most of the estrogen in plasma is bound to protein (β-globulin) in a form that readily dissociates on dialysis. The estrogen in the most active fraction isolated from human plasma is probably mainly estriol. The complex may function as the means of transport.[3] At neutral pH estradiol is twenty-two times as soluble in 3 percent albumin solution as in isotonic saline; γ-globulin is less effective as a dispersing agent.[3a] Testosterone and progesterone also show somewhat greater solubility in protein solution, but the effect is not so pronounced as in the case of estradiol.

The fate of estrogens in the animal organism has been investigated by administration of the hormones in large amount and assay of the urinary estrogens. Unfortunately only about 10 percent of the hormones can be

---

[1] R. T. Frank, *Proc. Soc. Exp. Biol. Med.*, **31**, 1204 (1934); R. T. Frank, Goldberger and Salmon, *ibid.*, **33**, 615 (1936); Dingemanse, Borchardt and Laqueur, *Biochem. J.*, **31**, 500 (1937); N. H. Callow, R. K. Callow, Emmens and Stroud, *J. Endocrinology*, **1**, 76 (1939).

[2] Dingemanse, Laqueur and Mühlbock, *Nature*, **141**, 927 (1938).

[3] Szego and Roberts, *Proc. Soc. Exp. Biol. Med.*, **61**, 161 (1946); Roberts and Szego, *Endocrinology*, **39**, 183 (1946).

[3a] Bischoff and Pilhorn, *J. Biol. Chem.*, **174**, 663 (1948).

accounted for in the urine; maximum excretion of active material occurs within the first twenty hours and practically ceases after ninety hours. Some material is also excreted in the bile; recoveries ranging from 1 to 26 percent have been reported in bile-fistula dogs.[4] Since estradiol is the most potent estrogen and also the principle hormone of follicular fluid, estrone and estriol were assumed to be metabolic transformation products. The conversion of estradiol into estrone has since been demonstrated in the guinea pig,[5] rabbit,[6,7] rhesus monkey,[8] and man.[9,10] Estrone has been isolated in two cases;[5,9] in the other instances, estrone was identified by biological and colorimetric assay of suitable urine fractions. The transformation occurs in the four species in the absence of both the ovaries and the uterus, and in males as well as females. The principal urinary estrogen in rabbits after estradiol administration is not estrone, however, but estradiol-17α.[5,11,12] Thus after administration of 300 mg. of estradiol-17β to normal or to hysterectomized-ovariectomized rabbits 2.6 percent was recovered in the urine as estrone and 12.1 percent as estradiol-17α.[11] According to an indirect method for differential analysis of the epimeric estradiols (based on change in biological activity of the diol fraction after Oppenauer oxidation) little or no estradiol-17α is present in human urine after administration of estrone.[12,13] Inversion of configuration at C_{17} in the rabbit presumably occurs through intermediate formation of estrone. Stroud[14] has obtained a compound which is probably estradiol-17α after administration of estrone to rabbits. It is not certain whether estriol is excreted by rabbits after administration of estradiol. Pincus[6] has presented evidence (based on David color test of a suitable fraction) for such a reaction in female rabbits (functional uterus), but other investigators[11] have not been able to confirm this result.

Estrone administered to men and nonpregnant women is excreted to a

[4] W. H. Pearlman and co-workers, *Endocrinology*, **36**, 284 (1945); *J. Biol. Chem.*, **173**, 175 (1948); Longwell and McKee, *ibid.*, **142**, 757 (1942). Cantarow and co-workers [*Endocrinology*, **31**, 515 (1942)] have reported an almost quantitative recovery of hormone activity in the bile after estrone or estradiol administration. Estrone has been isolated from the bile of pregnant cows [Pearlman and co-workers, *J. Biol. Chem.*, **170**, 173 (1947)].
[5] Fish and Dorfman, *Science*, **91**, 388 (1940); *J. Biol. Chem.*, **140**, 83 (1941).
[6] Pincus and Zahl, *J. Gen. Physiol.* **20**, 879 (1937).
[7] Fish and Dorfman, *J. Biol. Chem.*, **143**, 15 (1942).
[8] Dorfman, Wise and Van Wagenen, *Endocrinology*, **36**, 347 (1945).
[9] Heard and M. M. Hoffman, *J. Biol. Chem.*, **141**, 329 (1941).
[10] Schiller and Pincus, *Arch. Biochem.*, **2**, 317 (1943).
[11] Heard, Bauld and M. M. Hoffman, *J. Biol. Chem.*, **141**, 709 (1941).
[12] W. H. Pearlman and M. R. J. Pearlman, *Arch. Biochem.*, **4**, 97 (1944).
[13] W. H. Pearlman and Pincus, *J. Biol. Chem.*, **147**, 379 (1943).
[14] Stroud, *J. Endocrinology*, **1**, 201 (1939).

limited extent as estradiol and as estriol.[15]   Thus after ingestion of 1.05 g. of estrone (normal men), the estriol fraction contains according to bioassay 28.5 mg. of estriol.   Actually only 0.6 mg. of pure estriol was isolated.[16] In contrast with estrone and estradiol, estriol is not metabolized to so great an extent, for about 50 percent can be recovered (according to bioassay) from the urine after administration to man; increased excretion of estradiol or of estrone is not observed.[17]   Exogenous estradiol is excreted (man) as estradiol (1%), estrone (2.7%), and estriol (5.4%), according to bioassay of the three fractions.

Pincus[6,18] interprets these experimental results on the basis of the following metabolic reactions:

$$\text{Estradiol-17}\beta \rightleftharpoons \text{Estrone} \longrightarrow \text{Estriol}$$
$$\updownarrow$$
$$\text{Estradiol-17}\alpha$$

The interconversions of the diols and of estrone are well established and involve only simple reduction or dehydrogenation.   The formation of estriol is more complex.   Marrian[19] proposed that estriol arises by hydration of the enolic form of estrone.   Another hypothesis[20] is that estrone is converted first into 16-ketoestrone, which on reduction yields 16-keto-estradiol-17β and finally estriol.

The obvious difficulties in the investigation of metabolism by the study of the fate of exogenous estrogens lends importance to the continued search for possible metabolites in urine.   Marker[21] isolated two isomeric diols, $C_{18}H_{30}O_2$, from the nonphenolic carbinol fraction of human nonpregnancy urine.   One is identical with one of the octahydro derivatives of estrone (m.p. 211°, $[\alpha]_D + 7.8°$) obtainable by catalytic hydrogenation of estrone (acetic acid)[22] or of estradiol (ethanol, trace hydrochloric acid).[23]   Both of the diols, estranediol A (m.p. 242°) and estranediol B (m.p. 204°), are dehydrogenated by palladium to equilenin.   They yield different diketones on oxidation, and hence must differ in at least one nuclear center of asymmetry.   The substances are present in traces, 2.95 mg. of A and 43 mg.

[15] Pincus and W. H. Pearlman, *Cancer Research*, **1**, 970 (1941); Pincus and W. H. Pearlman, *Endocrinology*, **31**, 507 (1942).

[16] W. H. Pearlman and Pincus, *J. Biol. Chem.*, **144**, 569 (1942); *ibid.*, **147**, 379 (1943).

[17] Schiller and Pincus, *Arch. Biochem.*, **2**, 317 (1943).

[18] Pincus and W. H. Pearlman, "Intermediate Metabolism of Sex Hormones," *Vitamins and Hormones*, I, 293 (1943).

[19] Marrian, *Harvey Lectures*, **34**, 37 (1938–39).

[20] Huffman and Grollman, *Endocrinology*, **41**, 12 (1947).

[21] Marker, Rohrmann, E. J. Lawson and Wittle, *J. Am. Chem. Soc.*, **60**, 1901 (1938).

[22] Dirscherl, *Z. physiol. Chem.*, **239**, 53 (1936).

[23] Marker and Rohrmann, *J. Am. Chem. Soc.*, **60**, 2927 (1938).

of B from 752 l. urine. These substances arise by reduction of the phenolic ring; a similar reaction accounts for the presence of $\Delta^{5,7,9}$-estratriene-3-ol-17-one in mare's pregnancy urine, which presumably arises by reduction of equilenin in Ring A. The more general reaction in mares, however, is dehydrogenation: estrone → equilin → equilenin.

The marked destruction of estrone and of estradiol in the animal organism can be duplicated by incubation with liver slices *in vitro*,[24] by perfusion through liver,[25] and to a lesser extent by perfusion through kidney.[26] Inactivation by liver is complete within a few hours, but the nature of the final inactive products is entirely obscure. Conjugation is ruled out, for hydrolysis does not restore any activity to the incubated material. Possible metabolic reactions have been discussed by Heard.[9] Cyanide and carbon monoxide inhibit deactivation. There is evidence that the participating enzymes are cytochrome oxidase-cyctochrome c and an unknown dehydrogenase. Atmospheric oxygen is involved.[27]

Biskind and Biskind[28] have observed that female rats maintained on a vitamin B-deficient diet are unable to inactivate estrone (implanted as pellets in the spleen). Drill and Pfeiffer[29] believe that the effect is due to inanition accompanying B-deficiency; their control animals, receiving the same amount of food but also receiving B complex, also did not inactivate estrone. Thiamine, riboflavin, and the amino acid methionine are the essential dietary factors.[30] The implication of estrogens as causative agents in cancer, particularly of the breast and uterus, has prompted an interesting line of research. In a study of twenty cases of human uterine cancer, thiamine deficiency and a high estrogen level were found in 90 percent of the patients.[31] Regression of mammary carcinomas in animals has followed administration of yeast,[32] but use of dietary factors would seem to have more promise as preventative agents than as curative agents.

One possible mode of inactivation is oxidation of the phenolic ring, similar to the oxidation of tyrosine and other monohydric phenols by the enzyme

[24] Zondek, *Skand. Arch. Physiol.*, **70**, 133 (1934); Zondek and Sklow, *Proc. Soc. Exp. Biol. Med.*, **46**, 276 (1941); Heller, *Endocrinology*, **26**, 619 (1940).
[25] Israel, Meranze and Johnston, *Am. J. Med. Science*, **194**, 835 (1937); Schiller and Pincus, *Science*, **98**, 410 (1945).
[26] Schiller, *Endocrinology*, **36**, 7 (1945).
[27] Levy, *Arch. Biochem.*, **14**, 325 (1947).
[28] M. S. Biskind and G. R. Biskind, *Science*, **94**, 462 (1941); *Endocrinology*, **31**, 109 (1942).
[29] Drill and Pfeiffer, *Endocrinology*, **38**, 300 (1946).
[30] Singher and co-workers, *J. Biol. Chem.*, **154**, 79 (1944); *Proc. Soc. Exp. Biol. Med.*, **55**, 254 (1944); Albert Segaloff and Ann Segaloff, *Endocrinology*, **34**, 346 (1944); György and Goldblatt, *Fed. Proc.*, **4**, 154 (1945).
[31] Ayre and Bauld, *Science*, **103**, 441 (1946).
[32] Lewisohn and co-workers, *Cancer Research*, **1**, 799 (1941).

tyrosinase.[33] The reaction in these cases involves introduction of a second hydroxyl group ortho to the first, oxidation to an ortho quinone, and then further destruction of the quinone in an unknown manner. Tyrosinase has been found to inactivate estrone and estradiol.[34] The effect of other known oxidases for phenols has been investigated.[35] Mushroom tyrosinase has no effect, whereas potato tyrosinase and mushroom laccase are very active. In the reaction with the former enzyme three or four atoms of oxygen are consumed; in the latter reaction only one atom of oxygen is taken up. Stilbestrol is similarly inactivated by phenolases.

Testosterone. Two of the principal C_{17}-ketosteroids of normal urine, androsterone and 5-isoandrosterone, are known to be metabolic reduction products of testosterone. Thus they have been isolated in increased amounts after administration of testosterone to hypogonadal men,[1,2] to women,[3] and to chimpanzees;[4] the amounts isolated corresponded to 10 percent, 26 percent, and 18 percent, respectively, of the testosterone administered. In addition some of the testosterone is converted into epi-androsterone,[5] a minor urinary constituent. This substance may not be formed directly from testosterone, since androsterone is converted to a slight extent (8%) into epiandrosterone (in the guinea pig).[6] The reverse reaction, conversion of epiandrosterone into androsterone, has been observed (hypogonadal man).[7] Androsterone is much more resistant than testosterone to metabolic attack, since 24 percent was recovered in the urine after administration to a eunuchoid.[8] Of the four possible isomers that might be expected to arise by saturation of the double bond and reduction of the 3-carbonyl group, one (3β-OH, 5β-H) has never been encountered in urine; the same is true of the corresponding pregnane derivative. If the inactive steroids of the cortex are metabolism products of the hormones, then there is a marked preference in this case for one of the four configurations (3β-OH, 5α-H). No increase in excretion of dehydroepiandrosterone is observed after administration of testosterone, and hence this C_{19}-steroid is probably derived not from the gonads but from the adrenal cortex.

[33] Raper, *Physiol. Rev.*, **8**, 245 (1928).

[34] Westerfeld, *Biochem. J.*, **34**, 51 (1940).

[35] Graubard and Pincus, *Endocrinology*, **30**, 265 (1942).

[1] N. H. Callow, *Biochem. J.*, **33**, 559 (1939).

[2] Dorfman, J. W. Cook and Hamilton, *J. Biol. Chem.*, **130**, 285 (1939).

[3] Schiller, Dorfman and M. Miller, *Endocrinology*, **36**, 355 (1945).

[4] Fish and Dorfman, *Endocrinology*, **35**, 22 (1944).

[5] Dorfman and Fish, *J. Biol. Chem.*, **135**, 349 (1940); Dorfman, *Proc. Soc. Exp. Biol. Med.*, **46**, 351 (1941).

[6] Dorfman, Schiller and Fish, *Endocrinology*, **36**, 349 (1945).

[7] Dorfman, Wise and Shipley, *Endocrinology*, **42**, 81 (1948).

[8] Dorfman and Hamilton, *J. Biol. Chem.*, **133**, 753 (1940).

The intermediates in the metabolism of testosterone are not known. Possibilities are Δ^4-androstenedione, androstanedione, and androstanediol-$3\alpha,17\beta$, since they all give rise to increased androsterone excretion.[8] The action of liver slices on testosterone has been investigated. Under conditions which lead to complete inactivation (absence of band at 238 mμ), androsterone cannot be identified as a product (negative Zimmermann test). The destruction is inhibited by cyanide, iodoacetate, and fluoride, typical inhibitors of enzymes controlling oxidation-reduction processes, and is accelerated by diphosphopyridine nucleotide (DPN) and by citrate.[9,10] Under less drastic conditions, testosterone (51% recovery), 17-epitestosterone (1.2%) and Δ^4-androstenedione (8.5%) can be isolated from the ketonic fraction, together with a trace of an unknown substance, $C_{19}H_{28-30}O_3$, m.p. 201–203°.[11] Δ^4 Androstenedione on incubation under the same conditions gives rise to testosterone and to a lesser amount of 17-epitestosterone; but these two products account for only 20 percent of the material.[12]

Extracts of gonadal tissues were originally believed[13] to effect transformation of testosterone, but the results were later traced to a bacterial contaminate,[14] *Bacillus putrificus* (Bienstock).[15] This organism effects reduction of the nuclear double bond to give the 5β-configuration. In a medium

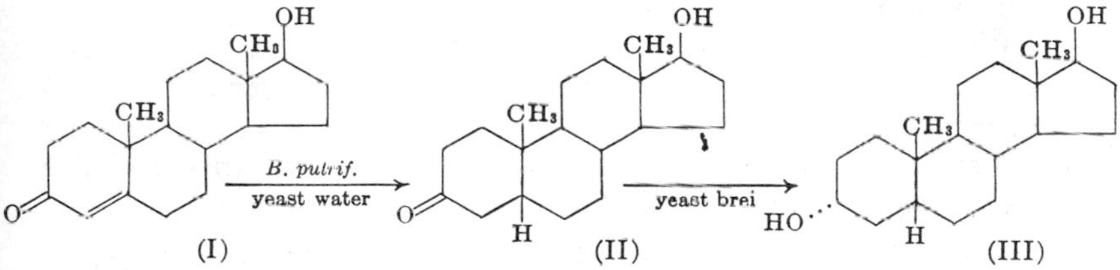

of yeast water, reduction stops at II; in a medium of yeast brei, a mixture of II and of III results. The microorganism effects a corresponding reduction of androstenedione.

The microbiological dehydrogenation of Δ^5-androstenediol-$3\beta,17\beta$ to testosterone has been observed with *Micrococcus dehydrogenans* (from yeast)[16] and with pseudodiphtheria.[17]

[9] Samuels, McCaulay and Sellers, *J. Biol. Chem.*, **168,** 477 (1947).
[10] Sweat and Samuels, *J. Biol. Chem.*, **173,** 433 (1948); **175,** 1 (1948).
[11] L. C. Clark and Kochakian, *J. Biol. Chem.*, **170,** 23 (1947).
[12] L. C. Clark, Kochakian and Lobotsky, *J. Biol. Chem.*, **171,** 493 (1947).
[13] Ercoli, *Ber.*, **71,** 650 (1938).
[14] Mamoli and Schramm, *Ber.*, **71,** 2083 (1938).
[15] Mamoli, R. Koch and Teschen, *Z. physiol. Chem.*, **261,** 287 (1939).
[16] Ercoli, *Z. physiol. Chem.*, **270,** 266 (1941).
[17] Zimmermann and May, *C. A.*, **40,** 4765 (1946).

Progesterone. Progesterone has been isolated from the corpus luteum and from the adrenal gland; progestational activity has been demonstrated in extracts of the placenta,[1] but the hormone has not been isolated from this source. It is accompanied, both in the corpus luteum and in the adrenal gland, by the closely related hydroxyketone allopregnanol-3β-one-20, which was recognized at an early date as a probable metabolite of the hormone. It also seemed reasonable that the three principal alcoholic C_{21}-steroids of urine, pregnanediol, allopregnanediol-3α,20a, and allopregnanediol-3β,20a arise by metabolic reduction of a Δ^4-3-ketone, and more specifically of progesterone, since the diols are excreted in higher quantity during pregnancy than during nonpregnancy. However only pregnanediol has been isolated in increased amount after administration of progesterone,[2] and only in an amount that accounts for 5–20 percent of the hormone. Administered pregnanediol is recovered in the urine only to the extent of 50 percent.

The standard primate laboratory test animal, the rhesus monkey, does not metabolize progesterone in the same way. Neither pregnanediol nor the allopregnanediols have been isolated from urine of this species, and they do not appear as excretory products after administration of progesterone.[3] However both rabbits[4] and dogs[5] have been shown to be capable of reducing progesterone to pregnanediol. Pregnanediol has been found in the pregnancy urine of chimpanzees,[6] mares,[7] and cows,[8] and in the urine of bulls.[8] The steer excretes no detectable quantity.[9] Man and dog excrete pregnanediol as the glucuronide. Although the conjugate can be isolated relatively easily, no trace of it has been found in the urine of bulls,[10] rabbits,[2c,11] cats,[11] and guinea pigs.[6] Venning's method of isolation takes

[1] G. v. S. Smith and Kennard, *Proc. Soc. Exp. Biol. Med.*, **36**, 508 (1937); Pincus and Werthessen, *Am. J. Physiol.*, **124**, 484 (1938); Fish, Dorfman and W. C. Young, *J. Biol. Chem.*, **143**, 715 (1942). Blood plasma of the ovulating hen shows a positive progesterone reaction [Fraps, C. W. Hooker and Forbes, *Science*, **108**, 86 (1948)].

[2] a) Venning, *J. Biol. Chem.*, **119**, 473 (1937); Venning and J. S. L. Browne, *Endocrinology*, **21**, 711 (1937); **27**, 707 (1940); b) Buxton and U. Westphal, *Proc. Soc. Exp. Biol. Med.*, **41**, 284 (1939); c) Heard, Bauld and M. M. Hoffman, *J. Biol. Chem.*, **141**, 709 (1941); d) Hoffman, *Can. Med. Assoc. J.*, **47**, 424 (1942); e) Hamblen, Cuyler and Hirst, *Endocrinology*, **27**, 169, 172 (1940); f) Huber, *Biochem. J.*, **41**, 609 (1947).

[3] Marker and C. G. Hartman, *J. Biol. Chem.*, **133**, 529 (1940).

[4] Heard, Bauld and M. M. Hoffman, *J. Biol. Chem.*, **141**, 709 (1941).

[5] U. Westphal, *Z. physiol. Chem.*, **273**, 1 (1942).

[6] Fish, Dorfman and Young, *J. Biol. Chem.*, **143**, 715 (1942).

[7] Marker and co-workers, *J. Am. Chem. Soc.*, **59**, 2297 (1937); **60**, 1565 (1938); **61**, 2537 (1939).

[8] Marker and co-workers, *J. Am. Chem. Soc.*, **60**, 2442, 2931 (1938).

[9] Marker, *J. Am. Chem. Soc.*, **61**, 1287 (1939).

[10] Strickler, Walton and D. A. Wilson, *Proc. Soc. Exp. Biol. Med.*, **48**, 37 (1941).

[11] U. Westphal and Buxton, *Proc. Soc. Exp. Biol. Med.*, **42**, 749 (1939).

advantage of the extreme solubility in butyl alcohol, by which the glucuronide can be completely extracted from an aqueous solution (preferably neutral). After removal of the organic solvent under reduced pressure, crystallization is induced by a water-acetone mixture. The complex can then be determined gravimetrically, but the total weight should be at least 4–5 mg.[12] In another method the conjugate is hydrolyzed and the glucuronic acid determined by means of its reducing properties.[13] Some laboratories prefer gravimetric assay of pregnanediol itself rather than of the glucuronide in order to eliminate possible errors in the hydrolysis. The conjugate can be hydrolyzed by dilute hydrochloric acid and the free diol purified by crystallization[14] or by chromatography.[2f] A glucuronidase isolated from rat liver effects hydrolysis with less damage than mineral acid.[15] In another procedure the glucuronidate is entrained on barium phosphate and then determined by use of a colorimetric method of assay, the reaction with naphthoresorcinol.[15a]

The pregnanediol glucuronide isolated by Venning's procedure is not entirely homogeneous. Treatment with Girard's reagent T effects separation into a nonketonic fraction (77%), which is pure pregnanediol glucuronide, and a ketonic fraction (23%) consisting of pregnane-3α-ol-20-one glucuronide.[16] The keto alcohol is thus also a metabolite of progesterone.

The complete structure of pregnanediol glucuronide is now established. (I., p. 488). The site of conjugation is at the 3-position of the steroid nucleus, as shown by transformation into the triacetate lactone (II) and hydrolysis to the 20-monoacetate of pregnanediol.[17] The synthesis has been achieved.[18]

The excretion of pregnanediol glucuronide gives an index of the functional activity of the corpus luteum. This body forms within the follicle after ovulation, approximately in the middle of the intermenstrual periods in primates. Thus pregnanediol is not excreted in the follicular phase of the human menstrual cycle, but only in the luteal phase. In this phase it is secreted continuously for a period varying from three to twelve days; peak excretion occurs near the beginning of the secretory phase. The total amount excreted in one menstrual cycle varies from 3–54 mg.[19] The

[12] Venning, *J. Biol. Chem.*, **119**, 473 (1937); *ibid.*, **126**, 595 (1938).

[13] W. M. Allen and Viergiver, *J. Biol. Chem.*, **141**, 837 (1941).

[14] Astwood and G. E. S. Jones, *J. Biol. Chem.*, **137**, 397 (1941); another method for determination of the free diol is described by Rabinovitch, *Nature*, **161**, 605 (1948).

[15] Talbot, Ryan and J. K. Wolfe, *J. Biol. Chem.*, **151**, 607 (1943).

[15a] Bisset, Brooksbank and Haslewood, *Biochem. J.*, **42**, 366 (1948).

[16] Sutherland and Marrian, *Biochem. J.*, **40**, LXI (1946); Dorfman, Ross and Shipley, *Endocrinology*, **42**, 77 (1948).

[17] Heard, M. M. Hoffman, and Mack, *J. Biol. Chem.*, **155**, 607 (1944).

[18] Huebner, Overman and Link, *J. Biol. Chem.*, **155**, 615 (1944).

[19] Venning and J. S. L. Browne, *Endocrinology*, **21**, 711 (1937).

amount of pregnanediol excreted and the duration of excretion are increased by administration of the ICSH.[20]   Administration of estradiol decreases the output[21] in line with the observation that the onset of menstruation can be delayed or even inhibited by injections of estrogens.[22]   If pregnancy follows the luteal phase, excretion of pregnanediol continues; in the first two months about 10 mg. is excreted daily; thereafter excretion rises to a maximum (60–100 mg./24 hrs.) at parturition, after which it drops pre-

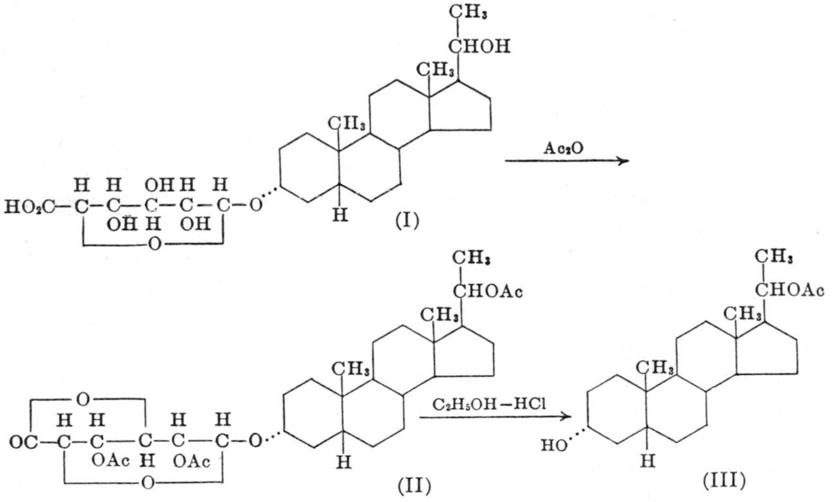

cipitously.[23]   Since in humans the corpus luteum only persists a few months after implantation of the fertilized ovum, the pregnanediol of later pregnancy urine is considered to be derived from the placenta.[24]   Pregnanediol excretion drops to a low level before miscarriage; thus routine assay of pregnancy urine is important clinically.[25]

Pregnenolone is also converted into pregnanediol (man and rabbit); thus after oral administration of 1.08 g. of pregnenolone to men, pregnanediol was isolated from the urine (0.7 mg.) and bile.[26]

Cortical Hormones.   The first studies of the metabolism of desoxycorticosterone revealed extensive reduction to pregnanediol.   In two cases

[20] J. S. L. Browne and Venning, *Am. J. Physiol.*, **123**, 26 (1938).

[21] Pattee, Venning and J. S. L. Browne, *Endocrinology*, **27**, 721 (1940).

[22] Zondek, *Wien. klin. Wschr.*, **49**, 455 (1936).

[23] J. S. L. Browne, Henry and Venning, *J. Clin. Invest.*, **16**, 678 (1937); Venning, *J. Biol. Chem.*, **126**, 595 (1938).

[24] H. W. Jones and Veil, *J. Am. Med. Assoc.*, **111**, 519 (1938).

[25] Gutterman, *J. Am. Med. Assoc.*, **131**, 378 (1946).

[26] W. H. Pearlman and Pincus, *Fed. Proc.*, **5**, 79 (1946).

81 percent and 22 percent of the hormone could be recovered as the diol glucuronidate after administration to healthy men.[1] A similar reaction in women could not be demonstrated.[2] More recently reduction of desoxycorticosterone to the diol has been demonstrated in male and female Addisonians and in a hypogonadal male, but the reduction apparently occurs only to limited extent (1–3%) in such patients.[3] Desoxycorticosterone is also converted into the diol by rabbits,[4] dogs (excreted as glucuronidate),[5] and chimpanzees.[3] The amounts account for 5–20 percent of the hormone. The pregnanediol excreted in small amounts (0.1 mg./l.) by ovariectomized women presumably arises from desoxycorticosterone.[6] In cases of adrenal hyperactivity excretion of pregnanediol is abnormally high (see below). An analogous reduction of dehydrocorticosterone to pregnane-3α,20a-diol-11-one has been demonstrated in a male and in a female Addisonian.[7] The metabolite occurs in normal urine. Dorfman[3] has suggested a mechanism for the biological reduction of the ketol side chain involving reduction at C_{20}, dehydration to the 20-methyl ketone, and further reduction at C_{20}.

It is an attractive hypothesis that C_{21}-cortical hormones are the precursors of some of the C_{19}-steroids found in urine; the hormones that bear a hydroxyl group at position 17 are easily converted by chemical oxidation into 17-ketosteroids. The metabolic degradation of 20-ketones of the progesterone type with elimination of the side chain is also conceivable, but no decisive evidence is available to show that either of these processes actually occurs. Excretion of 17-ketosteroids is not increased during pregnancy.[8] Adrenalectomy leads to reduced output of 17-ketosteroids, but the adrenals are known to synthesize C_{19}-steroids (Δ^4-androstenedione, adrenosterone, and androstane-3β,11β-diol-17-one have been isolated from the gland). In one laboratory[9] an increase in the urinary 17-ketosteroids was observed after administration of desoxycorticosterone (3–14% conversion), but in another[7] no demonstrable difference was detected after administration of dehydrocorticosterone. It should be pointed out that after removal of both the gonads and the adrenals, animals (male and female) continue to excrete 17-ketosteroids at about one-third the preoperative level. Apparently

[1] Cuyler, Ashley and Hamblen, *Endocrinology*, **27**, 177 (1940).

[2] Hamblen, Cuyler, Pattee and Axelson, *Endocrinology*, **28**, 306 (1941).

[3] Horwitt, Dorfman, Shipley and Fish, *J. Biol. Chem.*, **155**, 213 (1944).

[4] U. Westphal, *Z. physiol. Chem.*, **273**, 13 (1942); M. M. Hoffman, Kazmin and J. S. L. Browne, *J. Biol. Chem.*, **147**, 259 (1943).

[5] U. Westphal, *Z. physiol. Chem.*, **273**, 13 (1942).

[6] H. Hirschmann, *J. Biol. Chem.*, **136**, 483 (1940).

[7] Mason, *J. Biol. Chem.*, **172**, 782 (1948).

[8] W. H. Pearlman and Pincus, *Vitamins and Hormones*, I, 294 (1943); Venning, *Endocrinology*, **39**, 203 (1946).

[9] Dorfman, Horwitt, Shipley, Fish and Abbott, *Endocrinology*, **41**, 470 (1947).

some gland other than the gonads and adrenals can function as a source of 17-ketosteroids.

Some of the urinary 17-ketosteroids contain the typical 11-oxygen of the cortical hormones (see next section); they may not be metabolites of the hormones, but merely C_{19}-steroids synthesized by the gland and also bearing the 11-oxygen.

Urinary C_{19}-Steroids.* Table I records approximate data concerning the excretion of the principal 17-ketosteroids: androsterone, 5-isoandrosterone, and dehydroepiandrosterone. These substances occur in about the same amounts in the urines of normal men and women. A female

TABLE I.   Excretion of 17-Ketosteroids

URINE	MILLIGRAMS PER LITER		
	Androsterone	5-Isoandrosterone	Dehydroepiandrosterone
Man (av.)[a]	1.6	1.4	0.2
Woman (av.)[b]	1.3	1.3	.2
Eunuch[c]	0.5	0.9	2.0
Female castrate[d]	1.1	1.2	0.1
Woman, adrenal tumor[e]	0.3	13	88

[a] N. H. Callow, *Biochem. J.*, **33**, 559 (1939).
[b] N. H. Callow and R. K. Callow, *ibid.*, **33**, 931 (1939).
[c] N. H. Callow and R. K. Callow, *ibid.*, **34**, 276 (1940).
[d] H. Hirschmann, *J. Biol. Chem.*, **136**, 483 (1940).
[e] J. K. Wolfe, Fieser and Friedgood, *J. Am. Chem. Soc.*, **63**, 582 (1941).

castrate exhibited about the same excretion pattern as normal women and a eunuch excreted about the same amount of total 17-ketosteroids as normal men, but with a marked increase in the proportion of dehydroepiandrosterone at the expense of the companion substances. Male castrates have been observed in other instances to excrete about normal total amounts of 17-ketosteroids.[1,2] The observations show that the urinary androgens do not arise exclusively from the gonads. One other source undoubtedly is the adrenal gland. In instances of adrenal hyperactivity, for example from malignant proliferation (Table I), the excretion of dehydroepiandrosterone increases enormously. Hyperactivity of the testes results in increased excretion of 17-ketosteroids. In the case of a man with an interstitial tumor of the testes, colorimetric assay indicated an output of 1015 mg. of 17-ketosteroids per 24 hours, and sodium androsterone sulfate (53

* Dorfman, "The Metabolism of Androgens," *Recent Progress in Hormone Research*, II, 179 (1948).

[1] N. H. Callow, R. K. Callow, Emmens and Stroud, *J. Endocrinology*, **1**, 76 (1939).
[2] F. C. Koch, *Biol. Symposia*, **9**, 41 (1942).

mg./l.) was isolated from the butanol extract of the unhydrolyzed urine.[3] In this instance the excretion of androsterone is very much elevated. Androsterone and dehydroepiandrosterone occur in only small amounts (0.01 mg./l.) in the urine of bulls and of pregnant cows, and bioassays indicate that species other than man excrete no more than traces of androgens.

C_{19}-Steroids isolated from urine whose structures are completely or nearly completely established are listed in Table II and formulated in the

TABLE II. Urinary C_{19}-Steroids

NO.	NAME	REFS.*	M.p.	$[\alpha]_D$
1	Androsterone	(1)	183°	+94.5°
2	5-Isoandrosterone	(2)	151°	+105°
3	Dehydroepiandrosterone	(1)	153°	+11°
4	$\Delta^{2(or\ 3)}$-Androstenone-17	(1c), (3), (4)	111°	+148°
5	$\Delta^{3,5}$-Androstadienone-17	(4), (5), (6)	88.5°	−31°
6	3β-Chloro-Δ^5-androstenone-17	(4), (6), (7), (8)	157°	+15.5°
7	Epiandrosterone	(3a), (4), (9)	175°	+88°
8	Androstanedione-3,17	(4)	133°	+111°
9	5-Isoandrostanedione-3,17	(4)	131°	+112°
10	Δ^4-Androstenedione-3,17	(4)	174°	+190°
11	Androstane-3α,11β-diol-17-one	(4), (9), (10)	200°	+98°
12	5-Isoandrostane-3α-ol-11,17-dione	(4), (11)	189°	+96°
13	$\Delta^{9(11)}$-Androstene-3α-ol-17-one	(4), (10b)	187.5°	+136°
14	$\Delta^{9(11)}$-5-Isoandrostene-3α-ol-17-one	(4), (12)	170°	+151°
15	$\Delta^{11?}$-Androstene-3α-ol-17-one	(4), (6)	182°	+122°
16	5-Isoandrostane-3α,17β-diol	(13)	232°	+26°
17	Δ^5-Androstene-3β,17β-diol	(14)	178°	−55.5°
18	Δ^5-Androstene-3β,16α,17β-triol	(8), (15)	260.5°	Acet.−102°
19	Androstane-3β-ol-16(?)-one	(16)	187°	−160°

* See page 492

chart. Additional substances of unknown structure are listed in Table III, below. Some of the substances are transformation products. Thus the unsaturated substances Nos. 4 and 5 undoubtedly are dehydration products formed during acid hydrolysis; the precursors are androsterone sulfate and dehydroepiandrosterone sulfate,[4] the conjugated excretory forms of Nos. 1 and 3. The free hydroxyketones are stable under the hydrolytic conditions employed; but both cleavage of the ester linkage and elimination of sulfuric acid have been shown to occur during acid hydrolysis of androsterone sul-

[3] Venning, M. M. Hoffman and J. S. L. Browne, *J. Biol. Chem.*, **146**, 369 (1942).
[4] Munson, Gallagher and F. C. Koch, *J. Biol. Chem.*, **152**, 67 (1944).

REFRENCES TO TABLE II (p. 491)

(1) Human male: a) Butenandt, Z. angew. Chem., 44, 905 (1931); b) N. H. Callow and R. K. Callow, Biochem. J., 34, 276 (1940); c) Engel, Thorn and Lewis, J. Biol. Chem., 137, 205 (1941).
Human female: d) N. H. Callow and R. K. Callow, Biochem. J., 33, 931 (1939).
Bull and cow (pregnancy): e) Marker, J. Am. Chem. Soc., 61, 944 (1939).

(2) Human: (1b), (1c), (1d).

(3) W. H. Pearlman, Endocrinology, 30, 270 (1942); b) H. Hirschmann, J. Biol. Chem., 136, 483 (1940); c) Venning, M. M. Hoffman and J. S. L. Browne, J. Biol. Chem., 146, 369 (1942).

(4) Lieberman, Dobriner, B. R. Hill, Fieser, and Rhoads, J. Biol. Chem., 172, 263 (1948).

(5) Burrows, J. W. Cook, Roe and Warren, Biochem. J., 31, 950 (1937).

(6) J. K. Wolfe, Fieser and Friedgood, J. Am. Chem. Soc., 63, 582 (1941).

(7) Butenandt and Grosse, Ber., 69, 2776 (1936).

(8) Mason and Kepler, J. Biol. Chem., 161, 235 (1945).

(9) Butler and Marrian, J. Biol. Chem., 119, 565 (1937); 124, 237 (1938); W. H. Pearlman, J. Biol. Chem., 136, 807 (1940); H. Hirschmann, Proc. Soc. Exp. Biol. Med., 46, 51 (1941).

(10) a) Mason, J. Biol. Chem., 162, 745 (1946); b) A. M. Miller, Dorfman and Sevringhaus, Endocrinology, 38, 19 (1946). See also Shoppee, J. Chem. Soc., 1134 (1946).

(11) Lieberman and Dobriner, J. Biol. Chem., 166, 773 (1946).

(12) Dobriner and co-workers, J. Biol. Chem., 169, 221 (1947); Sarett, ibid., 173, 185 (1948).

(13) Butenandt, Z. angew. Chem., 45, 655 (1932); Butenandt, Tscherning and Dannenberg, Z. physiol. Chem., 248, 205 (1937); A. M. Miller and Dorfman, Endocrinology, 42, 174 (1948).

(14) H. Hirschmann and F. B. Hirschmann, J. Biol. Chem., 157, 601 (1945); Schiller, A. M. Miller, Dorfman, Sevringhaus and McCullagh, Endocrinology, 37, 322 (1945).

(15) Marrian, Nature, 154, 19 (1944); Marrian and Butler, Biochem. J., 38, 322 (1944); H. Hirschmann, J. Biol. Chem., 150, 363 (1943).

(16) Mare: Heard and McKay, J. Biol. Chem., 131, 371 (1939); Oppenauer, Z. physiol. Chem., 270, 97 (1941).

fate.[3]   The structure of the diene, No. 5, is certain, since the absorption spectrum corresponds to that of a heteroannular diene (λ_{max} 235 mμ). The same diene can be obtained by treatment of dehydroepiandrosterone with copper sulfate at 200°.   The position of the double bond in No. 4, however, is not settled; it could be at the 2,3- or the 3,4-positions.   In fact the material isolated from the urine or prepared by dehydrohalogenation of 3β-chloroandrosterone[5] is probably a mixture of both isomers, for samples melting at temperatures ranging from 109° to 119° and showing

[5] Butenandt and Dannenbaum, Z. physiol. Chem., 229, 192 (1934); Marker and co-workers, J. Am. Chem. Soc. 59, 1363 (1937); H. Hirschmann, J. Biol. Chem., 136, 483 (1940).

Urinary C_{19}-Steroids

(see Table II)

1.

2.

3.

4.

5.

6.

7.

8.

9.

10.

11.

12.

13.

14.

15.

16.

17.

18.

19.

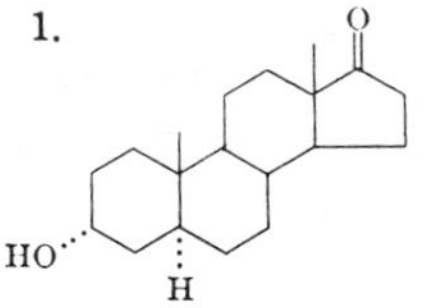

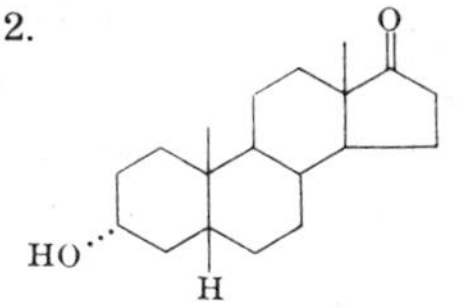

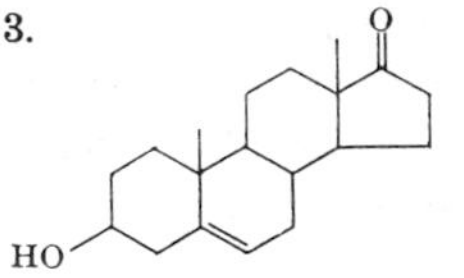

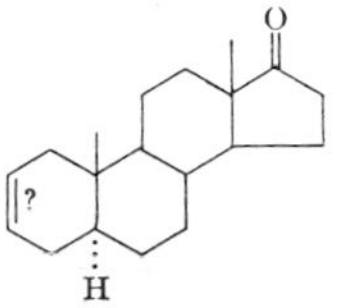

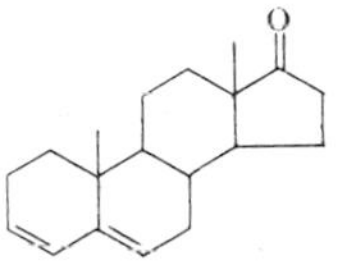

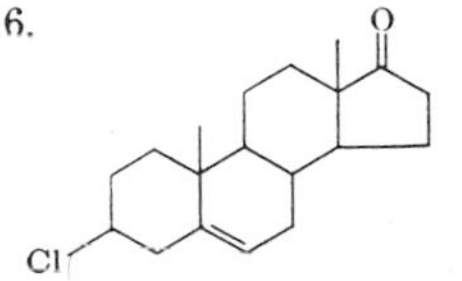

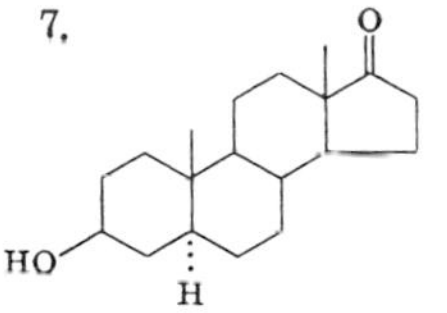

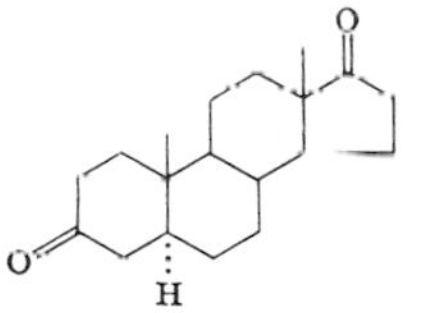

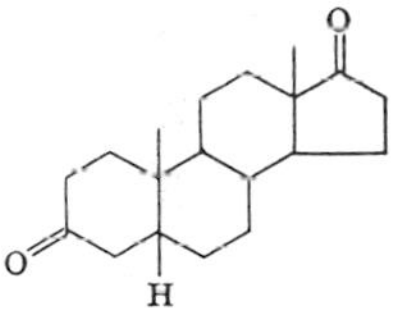

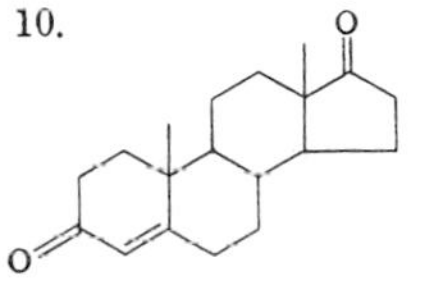

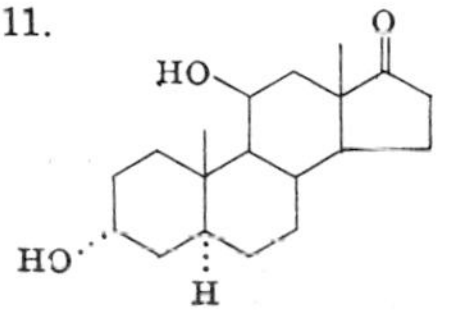

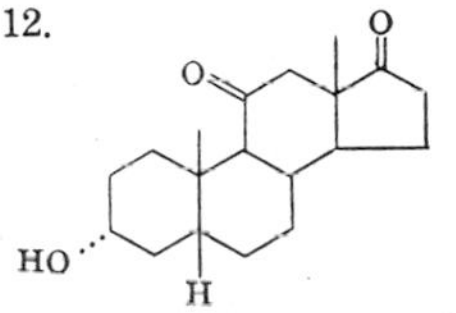

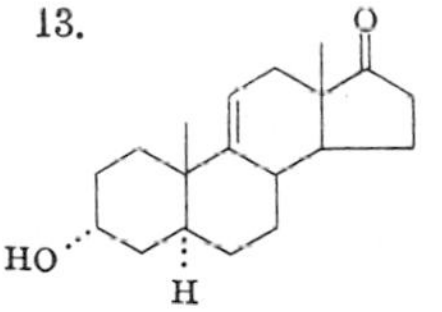

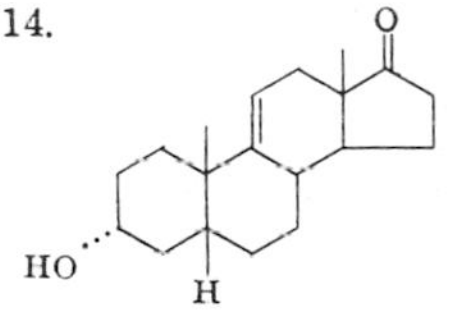

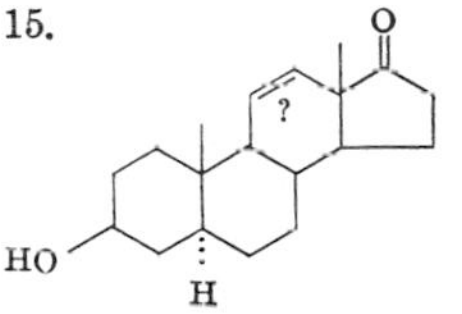

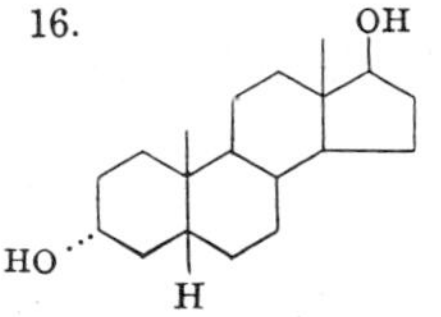

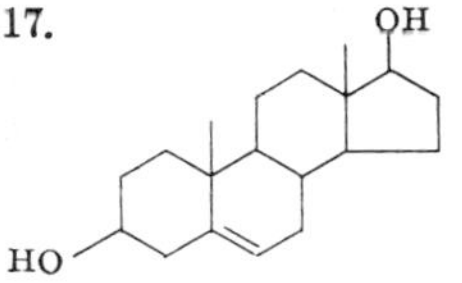

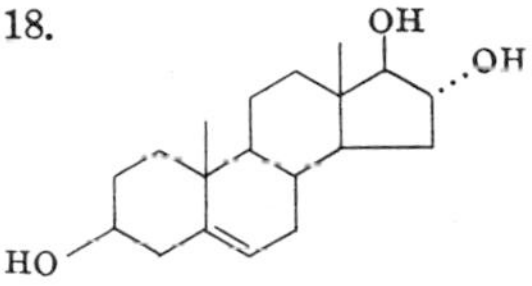

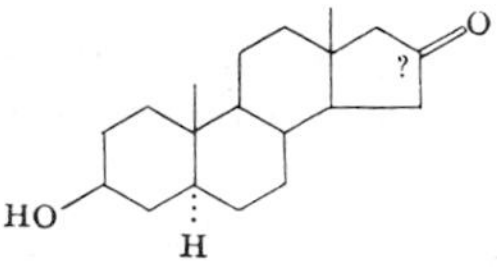

melting point depressions on admixture have been reported. Thus the values reported in Table I for the excretion of androsterone and dehydroepiandrosterone are not entirely accurate, for in some of the cases the dehydration products were also isolated. The urine of the woman with an adrenal tumor contained 25 mg./l. of the diene No. 5 and consequently the

TABLE III. Urinary C_{19} Steroids of Unknown Structure

NO.	FORMULA	DERIVATIVE	M.p.	$[\alpha]_D$	URINE
20	$C_{19}H_{30}O_2$	Acetate	118°	+108°	Man[a]
21	$C_{19}H_{32}O_2$		205°	−26°	Adrenal hyperplasia[b]
22	$C_{19}H_{32}O_2$		209°	+28°	Adrenal tumor[b]
23	$C_{19}H_{28}O_2$	(Oxime)	141°	+121°	Adrenal tumor[c]
24	$C_{19}H_{30}O_2$		191.5°	−171°	Mare, pregnancy[d]
25	$C_{18}H_{24}O_2(?)$	Acetate	169°	+40°	Mare, pregnancy[d]
26	$C_{19}H_{26}O_3$		252°	+94.5°	Mare, pregnancy[e]

[a] Lieberman et al., J. Biol. Chem., **172**, 263 (1948).

[b] Mason and Kepler, ibid., **161**, 235 (1945).

[c] Dingemanse, Huis in't Veld and Hartogh-Katz, Nature, **161**, 848 (1948). The substance has recently been identified as the i-steroid isomer of dehydroepiandrosterone, i-androstane-6-ol-17-one, Dingemanse, Huis in't Veld and Hartogh-Katz, ibid., **162**, 492 (1948), Barton and Klyne, ibid., **162**, 493 (1948).

[d] Oppenauer, Z. physiol. Chem., **270**, 97 (1941).

[e] J. D. Jacobs and Laqueur, Rec. trav. chim., **58**, 77 (1939); Heard, J. Am. Chem. Soc., **60**, 493 (1938); Heard and M. M. Hoffman, J. Biol. Chem., **141**, 329 (1941).

excretion of dehydroepiandrosterone was actually higher than the figure (88 mg./l.) reported. A second transformation product isolated from urine in small amounts is 3β-chloro-Δ⁵-androstenone-17,[6] which can be produced by the action of hydrochloric acid[7] on dehydroepiandrosterone. A further urinary product recently identified (No. 23, Table III above) is the i-steroid isomer of dehydroepiandrosterone, i-androstane-6-ol-17-one. The i-steroid reacts with hydrochloric acid under very mild conditions to give 3β-chloro-Δ⁵-androstenone-17 (4 parts) and dehydroepiandrosterone (1 part); it probably is the immediate precursor of the chloroketone and of at least some of the dehydroepiandrosterone, but the i-steroid itself may be an artifact derived from a conjugate of dehydroepiandrosterone. In addition, acetylation and etherification have been found to accompany hydrolysis of the Girard derivations. Thus a few of the substances listed in Table II were also isolated as the corresponding acetates.

[6] Butenandt and Dannenbaum, Z. physiol. Chem., **229**, 192 (1934); J. K. Wolfe, Fieser and Friedgood, J. Am. Chem. Soc., **63**, 582 (1941); Lieberman and co-workers, J. Biol. Chem., **172**, 263 (1948).

[7] Butenandt and Grosse, Ber., **69**, 2776 (1936).

A long-range program of research on steroid excretion in health and in disease was initiated in 1940 at Memorial Hospital and transferred in 1948 to the Sloan-Kettering Institute for Cancer Research. In this work systematic examination is made of individual urines in amounts adequate for extensive fractionation and chemical characterization (2- to 6-month collections). The techniques of hydrolysis, extraction, and colorimetric determination employed have been described in Chapter IV. The neutral material is processed with Girard's reagent and the ketonic and nonketonic fractions are further separated with digitonin into precipitable (3β) and nonprecipitable (3α) fractions. For the separation of alcohols from nonalcohols, a nonketonic fraction is refluxed with phthalic anhydride in pyridine solution and the resulting phthalic half esters extracted with alkali and saponified by refluxing with sodium methoxide in benzene solution, when sodium methyl phthalate soon precipitates. The neutral fraction thus obtained consists of nonketonic alcohols.

Various constituents of the 3α- and β-hydroxy ketosteroid fractions were isolated by fractional chromatographic separation, preferably with magnesium silicate since alumina is known to cause rearrangements.[8,9] Elution with certain quantities of various solvents (benzene, ether-benzene in varying ratios, ether, finally methyl alcohol) in fixed order yields many fractions, which are rechromatographed. In this manner a nearly quantitative separation of the individual steroids can be achieved. The sequence of elution is always the same, even though the elution of any one compound is influenced by the accompanying impurities; that is, androsterone is always eluted before 5-isoandrosterone. In general the A/B-trans (allo) compounds are eluted before the corresponding A/B-cis (normal) isomers. By this procedure fifteen C_{19}-ketosteroids (No. 1–15, Table II) and nine C_{21}-ketosteroids (next section) were isolated from the ketonic fraction. Most of the substances had been isolated previously. The three diketones, No. 8–10, had not been reported previously. No. 10 is the first instance of the isolation of a Δ^4-3-ketone. These substances are not water-soluble; the known modes of conjugation, by esterification of a hydroxyl group with sulfuric acid or with glucuronic acid, are obviously not possible for these diketones. Lieberman[10] has observed that 3-ketosteroids react with cysteine to form soda-soluble spirothiazolidines; ketones conceivably can be excreted in the form of these derivatives (p. 496). A condensation with sulfhydryl groups of proteins would provide a means of transportation of steroids in the blood. The reaction does not occur with Δ^4-3-ketones, with 6-ketones, or with 20-ketones.

[8] Dobriner, Lieberman and Rhoads, *J. Biol. Chem.*, **172**, 241 (1948).
[9] H. Hirschmann and F. B. Hirschmann, *J. Biol. Chem.*, **167**, 7 (1947).
[10] Lieberman, Brazeau and Hariton, *J. Am. Chem. Soc.*, **70**, 3094 (1948).

Two of the ketones (Nos. 11 and 12) bear an oxygen atom at C_{11}, as the cortical hormones do; and two others (Nos. 13 and 14) obviously are derived from such C_{11}-oxygenated steroids by loss of water, probably during

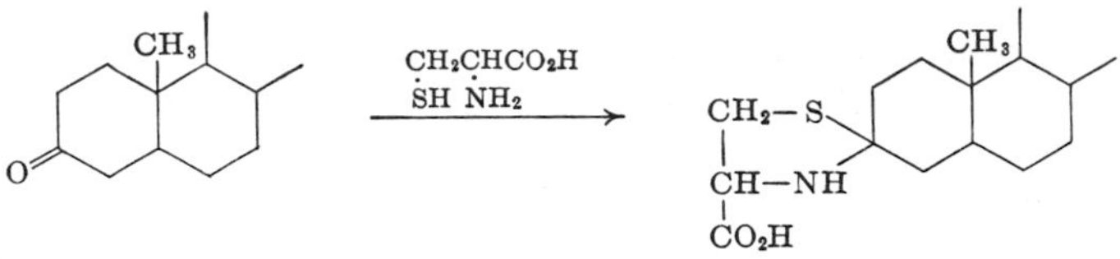

the hydrolytic step. Nos. 11–13 are found in both normal and pathological urine (particularly in case of adrenal dysfunction); No. 14 has been isolated so far only from urine of persons with disease (cancer of the prostate, lymphatic leukemia, essential hypertension, and Cushing's syndrome). The substances mentioned are surely associated with adrenal function; but it cannot be said that they represent with certainty metabolic degradation products of the C_{21}-cortical hormones. No. 15 has been obtained from the urine of several normal persons but is more characteristic of adrenal hyperplasia or adrenal carcinoma. The structure of this substance is uncertain with respect to the position of the double bond; on the basis of the present chemical evidence, the positions possible are 6,7, 7,8, and 11,12.

Isolation of the diol No. 16 has been reported only once from normal urine (175 mg. from 48,500 l. human male urine). It has been isolated recently in small amounts from the urine of a male Addisonian and from the urine of a young woman with virilism. Δ^5-Androstenediol-3β,17β (No. 17) has been found only in two patients with adrenal dysfunction (48 mg./l. and 7.7 mg./l.). It probably is a metabolic reduction product of dehydroepiandrosterone, a predominate urinary steroid in cases of adrenal hyperactivity. Such a conversion has been demonstrated in liver tissue[11] and in Addisonians.[12] No. 18 is also characteristic of adrenal hyperactivity, but is present in urine of normal men and nonpregnant women to a slight extent (0.1 mg./l.). In one case of adrenal carcinoma an occurrence of 7 mg./l. is reported. The structure was established by oxidation of the dihydro derivative to 3-ketoetioallobilianic acid and by partial synthesis from dehydroepiandrosterone.[13] The synthesis is the same as that used in the conversion of estrone into estriol; hence it is reasonable to assume that the 16- and 17-hydroxyl groups have the same configuration as they do in estriol. The structural similarity between the triol and dehydroepiandrosterone suggests that the latter compound is the precursor of the former;

[11] Schneider and Mason, J. Biol. Chem., 172, 771 (1948).
[12] Mason and Kepler, J. Biol. Chem., 167, 73 (1947).
[13] Huffman and Lott, J. Biol. Chem., 164, 785 (1946).

and indeed such a transformation has been demonstrated *in vitro* with liver slices.[11] A further instance of metabolic hydroxylation at C_{16} is encountered in the C_{21}-steroids (see below).

The last substance in Table II, No. 19, was obtained from equine pregnancy urine; it is a hydroxyketone (benzoate, oxime) precipitable with digitonin, and it gives a positive response in the Zimmermann test. It is oxidized to a diketone, which on Clemmensen reduction yields androstane. The carbonyl group is tentatively placed at either C_6, C_{15}, or C_{16}.[14]

Urinary C_{21}-Steroids. The marked increase in excretion of steroid alcohols in human pregnancy is illustrated by the data in Table IV[1] for the three diols mainly responsible for the increase. These diols are also found in

TABLE IV. Excretion of Diols

URINE	MILLIGRAMS PER LITER		
	PREGNANE-DIOL-3α, 20a	ALLOPREGNANE-DIOL-3α, 20a	ALLOPREGNANE-DIOL-3β, 20a
Nonpregnant women	2.1	1.1	0
Ovariectomized woman	0.1	0	0
Pregnant women	13.2	6.6	1.6
Pregnant mares	13.2	6.6	1.6
Pregnant cows	6.6	4.5	0.8
Bulls	26.4	13.2	3.2
Steers (castrated)	0	0	0

about the same high amounts in the pregnancy urine of mares and cows. Whereas normal men excrete only a trace of one of the isomers (pregnanediol), in the bovine species male animals excrete even higher amounts of these three substances than pregnant females. Since the urine of bovine male castrates (steers) contains no detectable quantities of pregnanediol or of the two allopregnanediols, the testes would seem responsible for the production of these substances, at least in this species.

Nineteen C_{21}-steroids of established structure have been isolated from urines (exception: No. 30); these are listed in Table V and formulated in the chart. Pregnanediol (No. 27) and the two allopregnanediols of common occurrence (Nos. 28, 29) all have the same configuration at C_{20}, arbitrarily designated 20a. The only diol of 20b configuration isolated from a natural source is No. 30, which was found in ox bile. Only three of the four possible compounds isomeric at C_3 and C_5 have been encountered.

[14] Heard and McKay, *J. Biol. Chem.*, **140**, lvi (1941); **165**, 677 (1946).

[1] Data chiefly from Marker and co-workers, *J. Am. Chem. Soc.*, **60**, 2931 (1938); result for ovariectomized women from H. Hirschmann, *J. Biol. Chem.*, **136**, 483 (1940).

TABLE V. Urinary C_{21}-Steroids

NO.	NAME	REFS.	M.p.	$[\alpha]_D$
27	Pregnanediol-3α,20a	(1)	242°	+27°
28	Allopregnanediol-3α,20a	(1b), (1c), (1e); (2)	248°	+17°
29	Allopregnanediol-3β,20a	(1b), (3)	216°	
30	Allopregnanediol-3β,20b	(4)	196°	
31	Pregnane-3α-ol-20-one	(5), (6), (7)	149.5°	+106°
32	Allopregnane-3β-ol-20-one	(6), (7), (8), (9)	194°	+91°
33	Allopregnane-3α-ol-20-one	(6), (10)	175°	+96°
34	$\Delta^{2\ (or\ 3)}$-Allopregnenone-20	(6)	129°	+133°
35	Pregnanedione-3,20	(6), (9a)	123°	
36	Allopregnanedione-3,20	(6), (9a)	199°	+127°
37	Pregnanol-3α	(5a)	148°	
38	Allopregnane-3α,6α-diol-20-one	(6)	196°	+105°
39	Δ^5-Pregnenediol-3β,20a	(11)	185°	
40	Pregnane-3α,17α-diol-20-one	(6), (12)	219.5°	+64.5°
41	Pregnanetriol-3α,17α,20a	(12a), (12c)	252°	−4°
42	Δ^5-Pregnene-3β,17α-diol-20-one	(13)	273°	−37°
43	Pregnane-3α,20a-diol-11-one	(14)	219°	+59°
44	Allopregnanetriol-3α,16,20a	(15)	304°	−41°
45	Δ^{16}-Allopregnene-3β-ol-20-one	(16)	207°	

(1) a) Man: Marrian, *Biochem J.*, **23**, 1090 (1929); Butenandt, *Ber.*, **63**, 659 (1930); Engel, Thorn and Lewis, *J. Biol. Chem.*, **137**, 205 (1941); H. Hirschmann, *ibid.*, **136**, 483 (1940); b) Cow: Marker, *J. Am. Chem. Soc.*, **60**, 2442 (1938); c) Mare: Marker and co-workers, *ibid.*, **59**, 2297 (1937); d) Chimpanzee: Fish, Dorfman and W. C. Young, *J. Biol. Chem.*, **143**, 715 (1942); e) Bull: Marker and co-workers, *J. Am. Chem. Soc.*, **60**, 2931 (1938).
(2) M. Hartmann and Locher, *Helv. Chim. Acta*, **18**, 160 (1935).
(3) Marker and Rohrmann, *J. Am. Chem. Soc.*, **61**, 2537 (1939).
(4) Ox bile: W. H. Pearlman, *J. Biol. Chem.*, **166**, 473 (1946).
(5) a) Marker and Lawson, *J. Am. Chem. Soc.*, **60**, 2928 (1938); b) W. H. Pearlman and Pincus, *Fed. Proc.*, **1**, 66 (1942); c) Sutherland and Marrian, *Biochem. J.*, **40**, 1xi (1946); d) Lieberman and Dobriner, *J. Biol. Chem.*, **161**, 269 (1945).
(6) Lieberman, Dobriner, B. R. Hill, Fieser and Rhoads, *J. Biol. Chem.*, **172**, 263 (1948).
(7) Sow: Marker and Rohrmann, *J. Am. Chem. Soc.*, **61**, 3476 (1939).
(8) W. H. Pearlman, Pincus and Werthessen, *J. Biol. Chem.*, **142**, 649 (1942).
(9) Mares: a) Marker and co-workers, *J. Am. Chem. Soc.*, **60**, 1559 (1938); b) Heard and McKay, *J. Biol. Chem.*, **131**, 371 (1939), c) Paterson and Klyne, *Biochem. J.*, **42**, ii (1948).
(10) Marker and Kamm, *J. Am. Chem. Soc.*, **59**, 1373 (1937).
(11) H. Hirschmann and F. B. Hirschmann, *J. Biol. Chem.*, **157**, 601 (1945); Schiller, A. M. Miller, Dorfman, Sevringhaus, and McCullagh, *Endocrinology*, **37**, 322 (1945).
(12) a) G. C. Butler and Marrian, *J. Biol. Chem.*, **119**, 565 (1937); b) Marrian and G. C. Butler, *Nature*, **142**, 400 (1938); c) Mason and Kepler, *J. Biol. Chem.*, **161**, 235 (1945); d) Mason and Strickler, *ibid.*, **171**, 543 (1947).
(13) H. Hirschmann and F. B. Hirschmann, *J. Biol. Chem.*, **167**, 7 (1947).

(SEE TABLE V)

27.	28.	29, 30.
31.	32.	33.
34.	35.	36.
37.	38.	39.
40.	41.	42.
43.	44.	45.

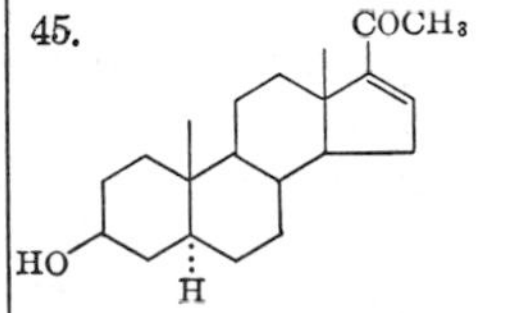

(14) Lieberman, Laurentian Hormone Conference (1947), cited by Mason, *J. Biol. Chem.*, **172**, 783 (1948).

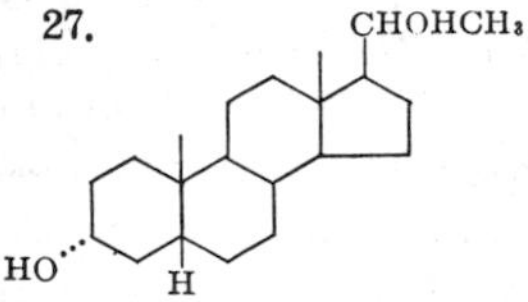

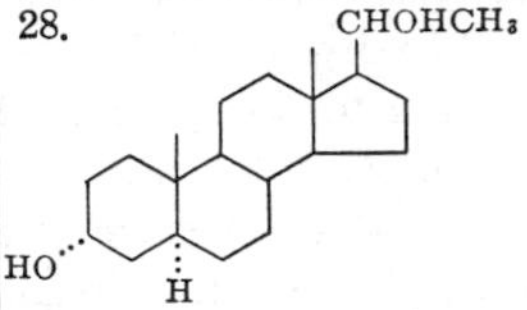

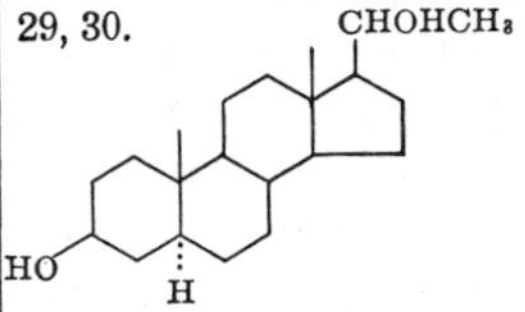

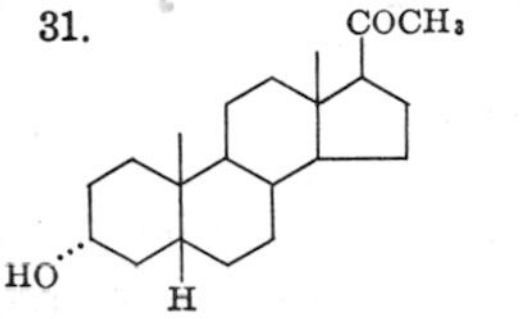

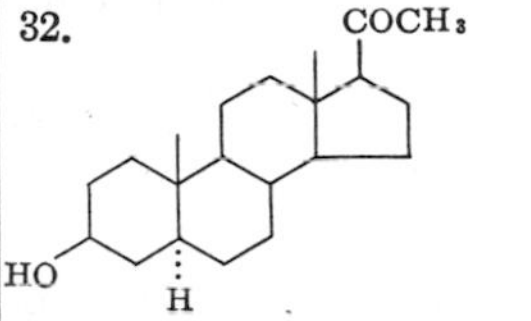

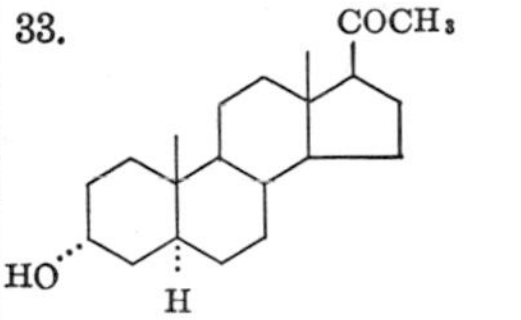

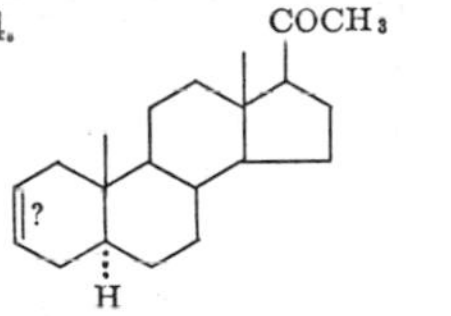

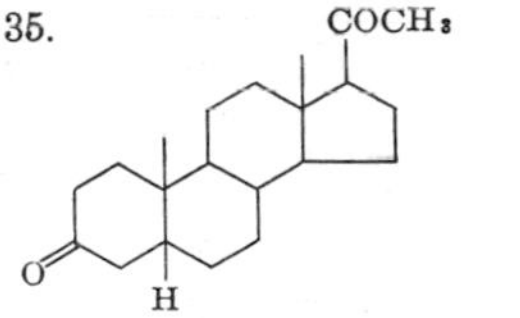

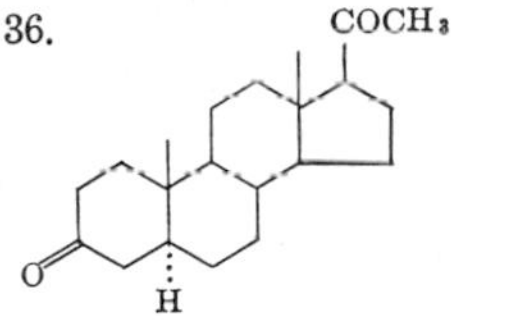

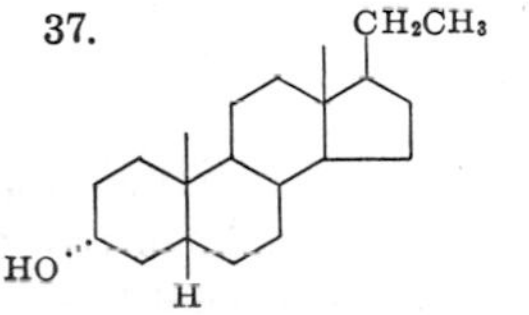

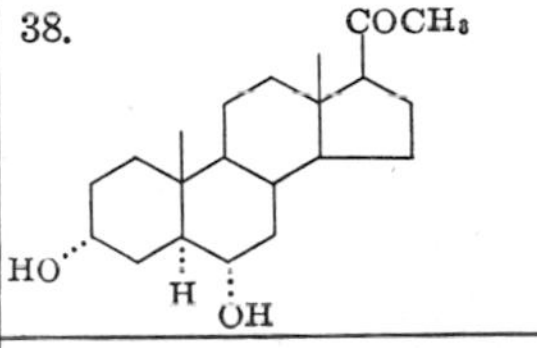

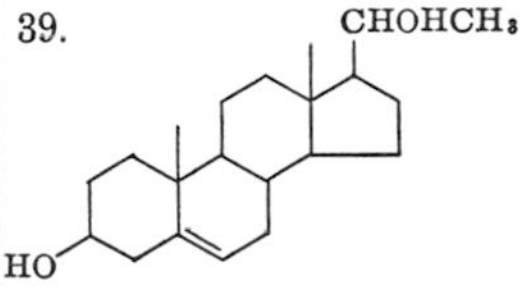

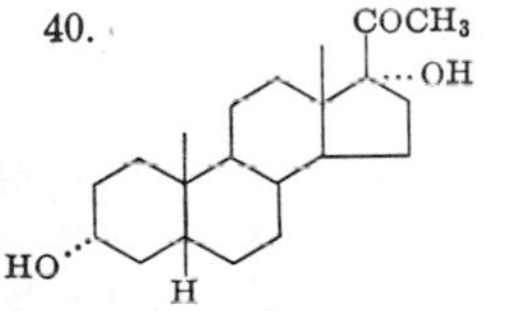

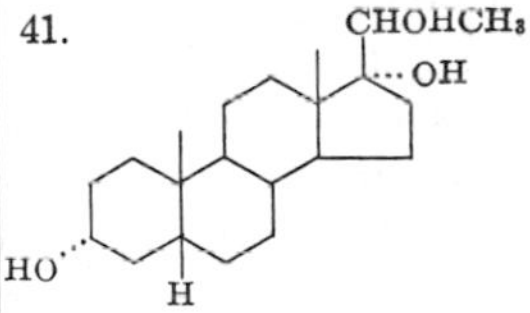

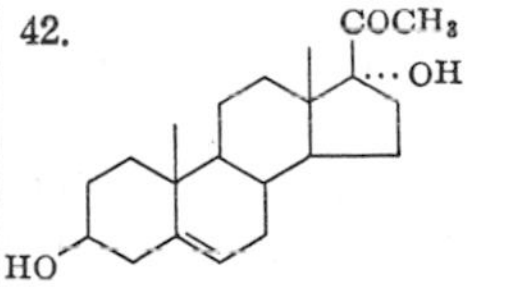

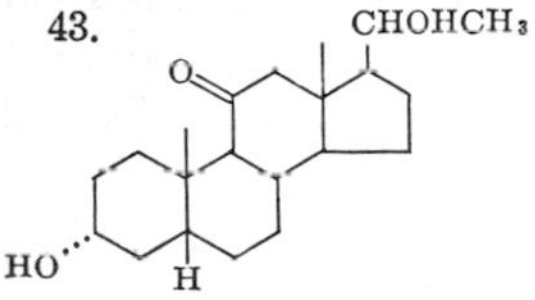

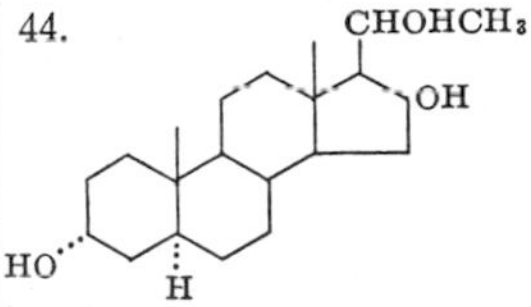

(15) Mare: Haslewood, Marrian and E. R. Smith, *Biochem. J.*, **28**, 1316 (1934); Marker and co-workers, *J. Am. Chem. Soc.*, **60**, 210 (1938).

(16) Klyne and Marrian, *Biochem. J.*, **39**, xlv (1945); Klyne and Paterson, *ibid.*, **42**, i (1948).

The C$_{21}$-diols are evidently reduction products of progesterone or of cortical hormones. The 3-hydroxy-20-ketones Nos. 31–33 are probable intermediates in the reduction to the pregnanediols (No. 34 undoubted'y is an artifact arising from No. 32 or 33 during hydrolysis). The diketones Nos. 35 and 36 are in a lower stage of reduction and are still closer to the hormones. Pregnanol-3α (No. 37) can be regarded as a product of more extensive biological reduction; it occurs in human pregnancy urine in traces (0.65 γ/l).

The 3,6-diol-20-one No. 38 was isolated from human pregnancy urine (0.79 mg./l.) in the detailed investigations of urinary ketosteroids at Memorial Hospital. It is the first instance of a 6-hydroxysteroid in the human species. The molecular rotation indicates that the 6-hydroxyl group has the α-orientation (communication from Dr. D. H. R. Barton): increment for 6-OH = +42. Odell and Marrian[2] have suggested that such a compound could arise by the hydroxylation of a 5,6-double bond, but the addition would have to follow a course the opposite to that of a usual chemical addition. A possible precursor according to this hypothesis is the Δ⁵-unsaturated No. 39, isolated from mare's pregnancy urine and from the urine of a boy with adrenocortical carcinoma. The structure was established by oxidation to progesterone and by reduction (H$_2$, Pd, ethanol) to allopregnanediol-3β,20a.

The next three substances (Nos. 40–42) are interesting because they contain the 17α-hydroxyl group characteristic of some of the cortical hormones. They have been isolated only from urines of patients with adrenal hyperplasia or carcinoma. If C$_{21}$-steroids bearing a 17-hydroxyl group are degraded in the organism to 17-ketones, No. 42 may be a precursor of dehydroepiandrosterone, known to be excreted in abnormal amounts in instances of adrenocortical tumors. In the particular case investigated, the urine contained 11.7 mg./l. of No. 42 and 321 mg./l. of dehydroepiandrosterone. Compound No. 43, with an 11-keto group, bears an obvious relation to the cortical hormones. It has been isolated from the urine of normal individuals, and the inference that it is derived from dehydrocorticosterone is supported by the demonstration of conversion of this hormone to No. 43 in Addisonians (see above).

The saturated triol No. 44 has been isolated only from mare pregnancy urine (1.6 mg./l.). The hydroxyl groups were at first thought to be located at positions 3, 4, and 20,[3] but the substance is completely stable to lead tetracetate and therefore cannot contain a vic-glycol grouping. Odell and Marrian[2] suggested the 3,6,20-arrangement because a derived diketone monoacetate reacted with hydrazine to form a "pyridazone" derivative.

[2] Odell and Marrian, *J. Biol. Chem.*, **125**, 333 (1938).
[3] Marker and co-workers, *J. Am. Chem. Soc.*, **60**, 1067 (1938).

The hydrazine reaction, however, is no longer accepted as evidence of a 1,4-diketonic structure, since polymeric products of the same composition as a true pyridazone can result from substances such as allopregnanedione-3,20.[4] The 3,16,20-formulation is based upon chromic acid oxidation of the triol to 3-ketoetioallobilianic acid and Oppenauer oxidation to Δ^{16}-allopregnene-3,20-dione,[5] available by synthesis.[6] In the latter reaction the 3- and 20-hydroxyl groups are evidently more susceptible to attack than the 16-hydroxyl group, which subsequently is eliminated with the activated 17-hydrogen atom.

A few additional C_{21}-steroids from urine that have not yet been identified are listed in Table VI. Compounds 51 and 52 were both isolated from the

TABLE VI.   Urinary C_{21}-Steroids of Unknown Structure

NO.	FORMULA	DERIVATIVE	M.p.	$[\alpha]_D$	URINE
46	$C_{21}H_{34}O_2$	Acetate	144°	+91.5°	Mare pregnancy[a]
47	$C_{21}H_{34}O_2$		197°	+93°	Mare pregnancy[a]
48	$C_{21}H_{34}O_3$		194°	+66°	Human pregnancy[b]
49	$C_{21}H_{36}O_2$		182°		Man[c]
50	$C_{21}H_{34}O_3$	Triacetate	179.5°		Man[d]
51	$C_{21}H_{36}O_2$		213°	+2°	Mare pregnancy[e]
		Diacetate	160.5°	−32°	
52	$C_{21}H_{36}O_2$		210°		Mare pregnancy[f]
53	$C_{21}H_{36}O_3$		300°		Mare pregnancy[g]

[a] Oppenauer, *Z. physiol. Chem.*, **270**, 97 (1941).

[b] Lieberman, Dobriner, B. R. Hill, Fieser and Rhoads, *J. Biol. Chem.*, **172**, 263 (1948).

[c] Mason and Kepler, *J. Biol. Chem.*, **161**, 235 (1945). The physical constants are close to those of pregnane-3β,20a-diol, Marker and co-workers, *J. Am. Chem. Soc.*, **59**, 2291 (1937).

[d] H. Hirschmann and F. B. Hirschmann, *J. Biol. Chem.*, **157**, 601 (1945); isolated from boy with adrenal cortical tumor.

[e] Klyne, *Biochem. J.*, **40**, lv (1946); isolated as sulfate ester: Klyne and Paterson, *ibid.*, **42**, i (1948).

[f] Marker and co-workers, *J. Am. Chem. Soc.*, **60**, 1561 (1938).

[g] Marker and co-workers, *ibid.*, **60**, 210 (1938).

same source and may be identical (diacetate of No. 52, m.p. 160°).   Marker[7] named compounds 52 and 53 uranediol and uranetriol, respectively, because on oxidation they gave di- and triketones that on Clemmensen reduction afforded the same hydrocarbon, which proved to be an isomer of pregnane

[4] Marker and Wittle, *J. Am. Chem. Soc.*, **61**, 855 (1939).

[5] Marker and D. L. Turner, *J. Am. Chem. Soc.*, **62**, 2540 (1940).

[6] Butenandt, Mamoli and Heusner, *Ber.*, **72**, 1614 (1939).

[7] Marker and co-workers, *J. Am. Chem. Soc.*, **60**, 1061, 1567 (1938).

and allopregnane and was called urane. One carbonyl group of both uranedione and uranetrione was found to be relatively inert, but the diol and triol readily form di- and triacetates, respectively. Marker suggested that one oxygen function is at C_{11} and that urane has the nontypical β-configuration at C_9.

Abnormal Steroid Metabolism. Studies of steroid excretion under various pathological conditions, particularly those associated with dysfunction of the gonads and of the adrenals, have been pursued with a view to diagnosis and improved medical treatment. Results obtained at Memorial Hospital for the excretion of 3α- and 3β-hydroxyketones and of nonketonic alcohols and summarized in Table VII[1,2] demonstrate marked deviations from normalcy in instances of malignancy and hyperplasia. During preg-

TABLE VII. Neutral Steroids from Normal and Pathological Urines

DIAGNOSIS	MILLIGRAM EQUIVALENTS OF ANDROSTERONE PER 24 HRS.		
	Ketonic fraction		Nonketonic alcohols
	3α-Hydroxy	3β-Hydroxy	
Normal males (2)	18.5	1.7	16.0
Normal females (2)	11.9	0.5	7.6
Pregnancy (1)	4.2	.1	15.6
Adrenal hyperplasia (2 females)	53	3.5	40.1
Adrenal tumor (2 females)	80.4	45.8	55.8
Cancer of breast (2)	5.9	0.3	5.4
Cancer of prostate (2)	3.1	.1	5.4

nancy the excretion of 17-ketosteroids decreases, whereas the output of 20-ketosteroids and of nonketonic alcohols (pregnanediol, etc.) increases. In cases of adrenal hyperactivity (hyperplasia and tumor) the excretion of all three categories is greatly increased; but hyperplasia and carcinoma can be differentiated by the excessive excretion of 3β-hydroxyketones in cases of cancer. Cancer of the breast and cancer of the prostate are characterized less sharply by diminished excretion of both ketonic and alcoholic steroids.

Virilism in women can accompany Cushing's syndrome, arrhenoblastoma (due to a type of ovarian tumor), or the adrenogenital syndrome; and a differentiation is often difficult. In this instance assay of the urinary steroids is a distinct aid in diagnosis.[3] In cases of virilism caused by over-

[1] Dobriner, E. Gordon, Rhoads, Lieberman and Fieser, *Science*, **95**, 534 (1942); Dobriner, Rhoads, Lieberman, B. R. Hill and Fieser, *ibid.*, **99**, 494 (1944).

[2] Dobriner, Lieberman and Rhoads, *J. Biol. Chem.*, **172**, 241 (1948).

[3] Dorfman, H. M. Wilson, and J. P. Peters, *Endocrinology*, **27**, 1 (1940).

activity of the cortex (adrenal virilism), an increased excretion of dehydro-epiandrosterone, but not of androsterone, is very general.[4] The situation may be reversed in children; in two instances androsterone, but no dehydro-epiandrosterone, has been shown to be excreted in excessive amounts.[5] This may be a reflection of the different clinical pattern of the adrenogenital syndrome in adults and in children. The disorder is more frequent in children and is manifested in both sexes by enhanced masculinity (androsterone is a much more potent androgen than dehydroepiandrosterone). The syndrome in adult women is accompanied by virilism. Adult men are seldom afflicted; when they are, the disease is manifested by feminism rather than by hypermasculinity as in children. In feminism the estrogen output, as measured by bioassay, is about twenty times that of normal male urine.[6] Adrenal tumors in women are only occasionally accompanied by increased estrogen excretion.[7]

The adrenogenital syndrome[8] is usually associated with adrenal hyper-

TABLE VIII.   Urinary Steroids from Women with Adrenal Tumors and Adrenal Hyperplasia

	CASE NUMBER						
	1a	2	3	4	5b	6	7
	Tumor, mg./l.				Hyperplasia, mg./l.		
C19-Steroids							
Androsterone	1.1	—	6	3.7	3	2	2
Dehydroepiandrosterone	51	69	14	—	1.8	—	0.1
5-Isoandrosterone	4.5	2.3	2.5	—	—	1	—
Δ5-Androstene-3β,17β-diol	1.3	—	0.2	—	—	—	—
Δ5-Androstene-3β,16α,17β-triol	0.2	—	—	—	—	—	—
Androstane-3α,11β-diol-17-one	0.2	—	1.5	—	3.5	2	1.5
C21-Steroids							
Pregnanediol-3α,20a	2.5	2.3	1.8	8.5	0.1	6.4	4
Pregnanediol-3β,20a	—	—	—	—	.7	—	0.1
Pregnanetriol-3α,17α,20a	—	—	—	—	2	—	1.4

ᵃ This case also excreted abnormal amounts of estrogen (2.4 mg. estrone equivalents per 24 hrs.).

ᵇ Male pseudohermaphrodite.

[4] R. K. Callow, *J. Soc. Chem. Ind.*, **55**, 1030 (1936); Crooke and R. K. Callow, *Quart. J. Med.*, **8**, 233 (1939).

[5] Richardson and Doll, *Brit. Med. J.*, **1**, 501 (1939); F. L. Warren, *Cancer Research*, **5**, 49 (1945).

[6] H. Burrows, J. W. Cook, Roe and F. L. Warren, *Biochem. J.*, **31**, 950 (1937).

[7] R. T. Frank, *Proc. Soc. Exp. Biol. and Med.*, **31**, 1204 (1934); S. L. Simpson and Joll, *Endocrinology*, **22**, 595 (1938).

[8] Parkes, "The Adrenal-Gonad Relationship," *Physiol. Rev.*, **25**, 203 (1945); Wintersteiner, "Adrenogenital Syndrome," in *Glandular Physiology and Therapy* (1942).

plasia or adrenal carcinoma and evidently with enhanced production of estrogenic or androgenic factors. Differences in the steroid excretion associated with the two types of lesions are seen in the data of Table VIII, which records an investigation of the urinary steroids of seven patients with adrenal cortical dysfunction, four with tumors and three with hyperplasia (the latter three were pseudohermaphrodites).[9] As in the parallel studies above, excessive amounts of dehydroepiandrosterone are associated with tumors and not with hyperplasia. In addition, the related androstenediol and androstenetriol are found in case of tumor but not of hyperplasia. The inference that these two substances arise from dehydroepiandrosterone is substantiated by an investigation of the metabolism of this and related substances by rabbit liver slices.[10] The main metabolite is the diol and the reduction is reversible, since the diol can give rise to urinary dehydroepiandrosterone (guinea pig).[11] When dehydroepiandrosterone is administered to Addisonians (who normally excrete little or no 17-

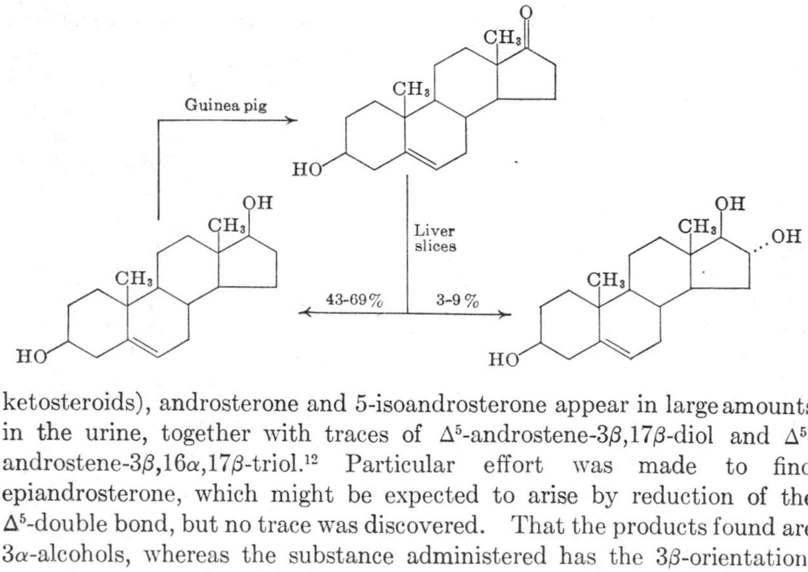

ketosteroids), androsterone and 5-isoandrosterone appear in large amounts in the urine, together with traces of Δ^5-androstene-3β,17β-diol and Δ^5-androstene-3β,16α,17β-triol.[12] Particular effort was made to find epiandrosterone, which might be expected to arise by reduction of the Δ^5-double bond, but no trace was discovered. That the products found are 3α-alcohols, whereas the substance administered has the 3β-orientation, strongly suggests that dehydroepiandrosterone is initially metabolized to a 3-ketone, possibly testosterone,[13] which suffers reduction at C_3 in only one direction. Since the 3α-hydroxy-17-ketosteroid fraction is usually higher

[9] Mason and Kepler, J. Biol. Chem., **161**, 235 (1945).
[10] Schneider and Mason, J. Biol. Chem., **172**, 771 (1948); **175**, 231 (1948).
[11] A. M. Miller and Dorfman, Endocrinology, **37**, 217 (1945).
[12] Mason and Kepler, J. Biol. Chem., **160**, 255 (1945); **167**, 73 (1947).
[13] Pincus, Currents in Biochemical Research, p. 305, Interscience (1946).

than normal in hyperplasia, Mason and Kepler suggest that this fraction arises by metabolism of dehydroepiandrosterone.

Increased amounts of pregnanediol are associated with both types of lesions.[14] In the cases of Table VIII it is unlikely that pregnanediol is derived from progesterone, since ovarian function apparently was completely suppressed. Pregnane-3α,17α,20a-triol seems to be characteristic of hyperplasia and not of tumor. In cases of adrenal carcinoma in a woman[15] and in a young boy,[16] Δ5-pregnene-3β,20a-diol has been isolated in large amounts. The amount excreted by the boy corresponded to 35 mg./l.; that excreted by the woman increased as the disease progressed: 0.33 mg./l. twenty weeks before death, and 24.5 mg./l. two weeks before death. In both cases the urine also contained Δ5-androstenediol (48 mg./l.[15] and 7.7 mg./l.[16]). The urine of the boy also contained Δ5-pregnene-3β,17α-diol-20-one (53 mg./l.). Thus it is evident that carcinoma of the cortex is characterized by increased excretion of 3β-hydroxy-Δ5-steroids, the origin of which is still obscure.

The urinary 17-ketosteroids furnish a partial differentiation between virilism caused by an adrenal tumor and virilism caused by adenoma of the basophil cells of the anterior pituitary (Cushing's syndrome). In the former disease the excretion is about five times the normal amount, in the latter it usually is only slightly above normal.[17] Excretion of estrogens by women with Cushing's syndrome is strikingly decreased.[18]

In a case of Cushing's syndrome associated with severe diabetes mellitus, the urine afforded large amounts of 17-hydroxycorticosterone (191 mg. per 25-day collection).[19] The observation affords evidence that Cushing's syndrome results from an oversupply of carbohydrate-active adrenal cortical hormone.

Addison's disease in women is accompanied by a marked decrease in excretion of urinary androgens (bioassay) but not of estrogens. The urinary levels of androgens in males however is sometimes normal.[20] The

[14] See also G. C. Butler and Marrian, *J. Biol. Chem.*, **119,** 565 (1937); **124,** 237 (1938); Venning, Weil and J. S. L. Browne, *ibid.*, **128,** cvii (1939); U. J. Salmon, Geist and A. A. Salmon, *Proc. Soc. Exp. Biol. Med.*, **47,** 279 (1941).

[15] Schiller, A. M. Miller, Dorfman, Sevringhaus and McCullagh, *Endocrinology,* **37,** 322 (1945).

[16] H. Hirschmann and F. B. Hirschmann, *J. Biol. Chem.*, **157,** 601 (1945); **167,** 7 (1947).

[17] Crooke and R. K. Callow, *Quart. J. Med.*, **8,** 233 (1939); Fraser, Forbes, Albright, Sulkowitch and Reifenstein, *J. Clin. Endocrinology*, **1,** 234 (1941); Talbot, A. M. Butler and Berman, *J. Clin. Invest.*, **21,** 559 (1942); F. L. Warren, *Cancer Research*, **5,** 49 (1945).

[18] Luft, *Acta Med. Scand. Suppl.*, **149,** 119 (1944) [*C. A.,* **39,** 2552 (1945)].

[19] Mason and Sprague, *J. Biol. Chem.*, **175,** 451 (1948).

[20] F. C. Koch, *Biol. Symposia,* **9,** 41 (1942).

effect is explainable on the assumption that the androgens of women are derived from the adrenal cortex. No definite increase in androgen excretion is noted after therapy with desoxycorticosterone or with methyltestosterone.

NOTE

The pregnanediols and allopregnanediols listed in Tables IV and V with the arbitrary designation 20a recently have been correlated through molecular rotation differences with the 20α-series as defined in Chapter V.[21] The constants reported are as follows:

	$[\alpha]_D$	
Pregnane-3α,20α-diol	+27°	Al
Diacetate	+41°	An
Pregnane-3α,20β-diol	+25°	Al
Diacetate	+68°	An
Allopregnane-3β,20α-diol	+23°	Chf
Diacetate	− 0.3°	Chf
Allopregnane-3β,20β-diol		
3-Acetate	− 6°	Chf
Diacetate	+22°	Chf

[21] Sarett. *J. Am. Chem. Soc.* (in press); Klyne and Barton, *ibid.* (in press).

Chapter VII
Cardiac-Active Principles

Two groups of naturally occurring steroids are characterized by their ability to exert a specific and powerful action on the cardiac muscle of man and of animals. The members of one group are products of plant synthesis found in seeds and bark; those of the second group are elaborated in the organism of the toad and are found in skin secretions of the animal. The plant heart poisons are glycosides and on hydrolysis yield sugar-free substances described as cardiac aglycones or genins; for example, digitoxin is hydrolyzed to digitoxigenin and three molecules of the rare sugar digitoxose. The cardiac-stimulating, or cardiotonic, quality of the poisonous principle is associated with the special structure of the aglycone part of the molecule, but the sugar residue contributes fundamentally important distribution characteristics. The toad poisons are composed of structurally related genins conjugated with suberylarginine.

CARDIAC GLYCOSIDES

A very small amount of a cardiac principle can exert a beneficial action on the diseased heart; an excessive dose causes death. The active principles occur in various plants having a wide geographical distribution, particularly those of the order *Apocynaceae.* Others have been found in the *Scrophulariaceae, Liliaceae,* and *Ranunculaceae.* Many species grow in tropical regions and have been used as arrow poisons. Digitalis plants, such as the foxglove, were used in the preparation of poisons for the medieval ordeals, and drugs made from the dried leaves of the plants have long been used as remedies. Digitalis was first employed for the treatment of dropsy and it later met with spectacular success in heart therapy. In the words of Cushny,[1] "digitalis has long been the sheet-anchor in treatment of diseases of the heart." The pharmaceutical preparations of digitalis come from the seeds and leaves of *Digitalis purpurea* (purple foxglove). The sea onion or squill (*Scilla maritima*), a bulbous herb of southern Europe and northern Africa, was used as a medicine by the ancient Egyptians and Romans. It has been employed as an expectorant, a cardiac stimulant, and a diuretic.

---

[1] A. R. Cushny, *Pharmacology and Therapeutics*, 11th Ed., revised by C. W. Edmunds and J. A. Gunn (1937). See also Cushny, *Digitalis and its Allies*, Longmans, Green and Co., London (1925).

Seeds and bark of *Strophanthus* species, such as *Strophanthus kombé*, *S. hispidus*, and *S. gratus*, have been used in tropical Africa as arrow poisons. Certain African tribes employed the root of the uzara as a drug (uzaron). The great potency is illustrated by the fact that 0.07 mg. of strophanthin is sufficient to cause the heart of a 20 g. mouse to stop beating within a few minutes after injection.

The chemical investigations of the active principles of the digitalis plants date from the early part of the nineteenth century (Destouches, 1808; Homolle and Quevenne, 1842). In 1869 Nativelle for the first time isolated a crystalline glycoside (digitalin) in a fairly pure condition. In the following years the chief contributions to the problem of isolation were made by German chemists, particularly by Schmiedeberg, Cloetta, Kiliani, and Krafft. The work of Windaus, undertaken in 1915, furnished the first insight into the structural character of the physiologically active substances, and the extensive investigations (1922–34) of W. A. Jacobs of the Rockefeller Institute, New York, provided a sound foundation for the eventual solution of the major problems of structure.[2]

The chemistry of the cardiac glycosides presents points of unusual complication, and materials suitable for investigation are not easily obtained. The drugs are rare and expensive, they often are of variable character, and the poisonous principles are present in very small quantities. Several physiologically active and closely related substances often occur together in the same plant, and the inactive saponins, digitonin and gitonin, are frequently present and are extracted along with the cardiotonic substances. Usually purification beyond the stage of an amorphous mixture of related compounds, or of mixed crystals, is difficult. The plant heart poisons are all glycosides, and some of them are extremely sensitive to the hydrolytic action of acids, bases, or enzymes. The "melting points" are really points of decomposition and they are only roughly characteristic and afford no sure indication of identity or purity.

The methods of extraction and purification vary with the source and special properties of the individual compounds. The glycosides are all soluble in water and alcohol and sparingly soluble in nonhydroxylic solvents. The dried and powdered seeds, leaves, or roots often are first extracted with ether or ligroin in order to remove fats and resins. By exhaustive extraction with methanol or with 70 percent ethanol the glycosides are brought into solution, leaving a residue consisting largely of cellulose. The alcoholic solution is evaporated in vacuum to a thick syrup and this is taken up in warm water. A crude glycoside mixture often separates at

---

[2] For a survey of the early work, see W. A. Jacobs, "The Chemistry of the Cardiac Glucosides," *Physiol. Rev.*, **13**, 222 (1933).

this point if the solution is allowed to stand for several days, but it usually is advisable to introduce other purification steps. Saponins can be precipitated by the addition of basic lead acetate, and the excess reagent is then eliminated from the filtrate by the addition of either sulfuric acid or sodium phosphate. Extraction of the aqueous solution with ether or chloroform removes tars without the loss of physiologically active material from the water layer. After clarification by these methods, the glycosides can be caused to separate by saturating the water solution with solid ammonium sulfate. The crude glycoside mixture often can be separated effectively by chromatography of the acetates; the free glycosides are recovered by mild hydrolysis with potassium bicarbonate in aqueous methanol.[3]

Acid hydrolysis of a glycoside gives an aglycone, or a secondary product of dehydration, and one or more molecules of a sugar or sugars. Two or more different glycosides may yield the same genin. Thus three glycosides isolated from *Strophanthus kombé* seeds contain strophanthidin as the genin and differ in the nature of the sugar residue:

$$
\left.\begin{array}{l}
\text{k-Strophanthoside} \\
\text{k-Strophanthin-}\beta \\
\text{Cymarin}
\end{array}\right\} \xrightarrow{\ \text{HCl}\ } \text{Strophanthidin} + \left\{\begin{array}{l}
\text{Strophanthotriose} \\
\text{Strophanthobiose} \\
\text{Cymarose } (C_7H_{14}O_4)
\end{array}\right.
$$

By selective enzymatic hydrolysis, A. Stoll[4] was able to relate the three glycosides to one another. Thus the α-glucosidase of yeast, which hydrolyzes only α-glucosidic linkages, cleaves k-strophanthoside into k-strophanthin-β and one molecule of glucose. Strophanthobiase, obtained from the seeds of *S. courmonti*,[5] effects cleavage of two glycosidic linkages and the products are cymarin and glucose. The same enzyme converts k-strophanthin-β into cymarin and glucose. These facts are summarized as follows:

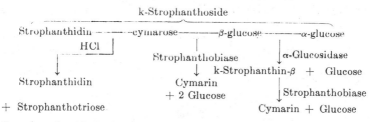

k-Strophanthoside is the main glycoside of *S. kombé* seeds, but the high sugar content makes isolation difficult. Isolation is simplified by acetylation of the crude mixture, for the heptaacetate is less soluble in alcohol than

[3] Rosenmund and Reichstein, *Pharm. Acta Helv.*, **17**, 176 (1942).
[4] Stoll, Renz and Kreis, *Helv. Chim. Acta*, **20**, 1484 (1937).
[5] Jacobs and A. Hoffmann, *J. Biol. Chem.*, **69**, 153 (1926).

the acetates of the other glycosides present. Cleavage of the heptaacetate to the free trioside was accomplished by the action of a trace of barium hydroxide in anhydrous methanol (method of Zemplén); subsequent neutralization with sulfuric acid and filtration gives a solution free of inorganic material. Cymarin is isolated by virtue of·its solubility in chloroform; this solvent extracts cymarin from a water solution of the three glycosides.

Hydrolytic enzymes frequently occur in the plant along with the glycosides, and only by taking special measures to inactivate the enzyme is it possible to isolate the genuine heart poison in unaltered form. This has been demonstrated particularly in the elaborate investigations of A. Stoll[6] and his collaborators at the Swiss firm of Sandoz. Previous investigators had isolated from *Digitalis purpurea* and *Digitalis lanata* the closely related glycosides digitoxin, gitoxin, and digoxin, and these were generally regarded as the original glycosides of the plants. Using a special enzyme-hindering process of extraction which prevents secondary changes, Stoll was able to isolate natural precursors of each of these substances, namely the three digilanides (A, B, and C). These substances occur together in the leaves of *D. lanata*, they decompose at exactly the same temperature (245–248°), they form mixed crystals, and a separation was achieved only by an elaborate process of partition between various solvents. Each of the genuine glycosides can be converted into a known genin and the other hydrolysis products indicated in Table I, and partial hydrolysis by means of enzymes gives the previously known digitoxin, gitoxin, and digoxin by loss of one molecule each of glucose and acetic acid. The older glycosides were thus recognized as progenins, rather than natural glycosides. The two-step hydrolysis to a progenin, acetic acid, and glucose can be accomplished in either of two ways by the careful use of dilute alkali and of the enzyme digilanidase extracted from digitalis leaves, as shown in the formulation. A similar partial enzymatic hydrolysis of a bioside was

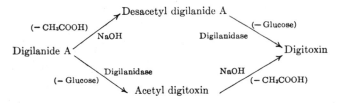

accomplished in the case of scillaren A from squills; the glucose unit was the first eliminated.[7]

    [6] Stoll and Kreis, *Helv. Chim. Acta*, **16**, 1049, 1390 (1933); **17**, 595 (1934); **18**, 120 (1935); Stoll, Kreis and A. Hofmann, *Z. physiol. Chem.*, **222**, 24 (1933); Stoll, A. Hofmann and Kreis, *ibid.*, **235**, 249 (1935).

    [7] Stoll. Suter, Kreis, Bussemaker and A. Hofmann, *Helv. Chim. Acta*, **16**, 703 (1933).

With the exception of glucose and rhamnose, the sugars resulting from the hydrolysis of the plant poisons have not been found elsewhere. Digitoxose was recognized by Kiliani (1922) as a 2,6-desoxyhexose and the configuration was established by Micheel.[8] Digitalose is the 3-methyl ether of a methylpentose.[9] Cymarose was regarded by Windaus and Hermanns[10] as a monomethyl ether of digitoxose. Elderfield [11] established

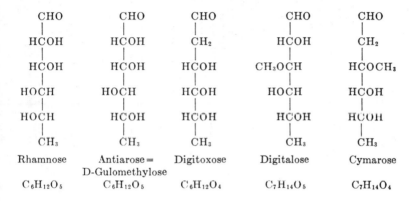

CHO	CHO	CHO	CHO	CHO
HCOH	HCOH	CH$_2$	HCOH	CH$_2$
HCOH	HCOH	HCOH	CH$_3$OCH	HCOCH$_3$
HOCH	HOCH	HCOH	HOCH	HCOH
HOCH	HCOH	HCOH	HCOH	HCOH
CH$_3$	CH$_3$	CH$_3$	CH$_3$	CH$_3$
Rhamnose	Antiarose = D-Gulomethylose	Digitoxose	Digitalose	Cymarose
C$_6$H$_{12}$O$_5$	C$_6$H$_{12}$O$_5$	C$_6$H$_{12}$O$_4$	C$_7$H$_{14}$O$_5$	C$_7$H$_{14}$O$_4$

this relationship and located the ether group at C$_3$. Jacobs and Bigelow[12] consider sarmentose (C$_7$H$_{14}$O$_4$) to be the methyl ether of a 2-desoxy sugar. Antiarose is the 5-epimer of L-rhamnose (p. 547); diginose is 2-desoxy-D-fucose 3-methyl ether;[13] thevetose, identical with cerberose, is L-glucomethylose 3-methyl ether;[14] the sugar of sarmentoside A is L(−)-talomethylose.[15] Digitoxose, cymarose, diginose, and sarmentose are 2-desoxy sugars and possess the high reactivity characteristic of the type. Thus glycosides in which a 2-desoxy sugar is linked to the genin undergo acid hydrolysis with great readiness under mild conditions, and the type can be recognized by the Kiliani test:[16] blue ring at the interface of a solution in acetic acid underlayered with sulfuric acid in the presence of a ferrous salt. 2-Hydroxy sugars can be detached from the genin nucleus only under conditions of hydrolysis so drastic as to promote secondary changes, which usually consist in the elimina-

[8] Micheel, *Ber.*, **63**, 347 (1930). Synthesis: Gut and Prins, *Helv. Chim. Acta*, **30**, 1223 (1947).

[9] O. Th. Schmidt, W. Mayer and Distelmaier, *Ann.*, **555**, 26 (1943). Synthesis: O. Th. Schmidt and Wernicke, *Ann.*, **558**, 70 (1947).

[10] Windaus and Hermanns, *Ber.*, **48**, 979 (1915).

[11] Elderfield, *J. Biol. Chem.*, **111**, 527 (1935).

[12] Jacobs and Bigelow, *ibid.*, **96**, 355 (1932).

[13] Tamm and Reichstein, *Helv. Chim. Acta*, **31**, 1630 (1948).

[14] Blindenbacker and Reichstein, *Helv. Chim. Acta*, **31**, 1669 (1948).

[15] Schmutz, *Helv. Chim. Acta*, **31**, 1719 (1948).

[16] Kiliani, *Arch. Pharm.*, **234**, 273 (1896); **251**, 567 (1913).

TABLE I. Cardiac Glycosides and Aglycones

GLYCOSIDE[a]	FORMULA	[a]D	M.p.	AGLYCONE	M.p.	[a]D	SUGAR
Convallatoxin	$C_{29}H_{42}O_{10}$	±0°	247°	Strophanthidin $C_{23}H_{32}O_6$	235°	+41°	Rhamnose
Cymarin[b]	$C_{30}H_{44}O_9$	+35°	139°				Cymarose
Convalloside[c]	$C_{35}H_{52}O_{18}$	−10°	204°				Rhamnose + Glucose
Cheirotoxin[d]	$C_{35}H_{52}O_{16}$	−17°	211°				Glucose + Methylpentose (or Pentose?)
k-Strophanthin-β	$C_{36}H_{54}O_{14}$	+32°	195°				Cymarose + Glucose
k-Strophanthoside	$C_{42}H_{64}O_{19}$	+14°	200°				Cymarose + 2 Glucose
Cymarol[e]	$C_{29}H_{44}O_9$	+22°	240°	Strophanthidol, $C_{23}H_{34}O_6$	142°	+37°	Cymarose
Periplocymarin[b]	$C_{30}H_{46}O_8$	+29°	212°	Periplogenin $C_{23}H_{34}O_5$	185°	+31.5°	Cymarose
Emicymarin[b]	$C_{30}H_{46}O_9$	+13°	159°				Digitalose
Periplocin	$C_{36}H_{58}O_{13}$	+23°	209°				Cymarose + glucose
Digoxin	$C_{41}H_{64}O_{14}$	+10.5°	265°	Digoxigenin $C_{23}H_{34}O_5$	222°	+18°	3 Digitoxose
α-Acetyldigoxin	$C_{43}H_{66}O_{15}$	+18°	230°				3 Digitoxose + CH₃CO₂H
β-Acetyldigoxin	$C_{43}H_{66}O_{15}$	+30°	258°				3 Digitoxose + CH₃CO₂H
Digilanide C	$C_{49}H_{76}O_{20}$	+33.5°	248°				3 Digitoxose + Glucose + CH₃CO₂H
Somalin[f]	$C_{29}H_{46}O_7$	+9.5°	197°	Digitoxigenin $C_{23}H_{34}O_4$	250°	+18°	Cymarose
Digitoxin	$C_{41}H_{64}O_{13}$	+5°	263°				3 Digitoxose
Desacetyldigilanide A	$C_{47}H_{74}O_{18}$	+12°	268°				3 Digitoxose + Glucose
Digilanide A	$C_{49}H_{76}O_{19}$	+31°	248°				3 Digitoxose + Glucose + CH₃CO₂H
Gitoxin	$C_{41}H_{64}O_{14}$	+3.5°	285°	Gitoxigenin $C_{23}H_{34}O_5$	235°	+34°	3 Digitoxose
Desacetyldigilanide B	$C_{47}H_{74}O_{19}$	+20°	240°				3 Digitoxose + Glucose
Digilanide B	$C_{49}H_{76}O_{20}$	+37°	248°				3 Digitoxose + Glucose + CH₃CO₂H
Oleandrin	$C_{32}H_{48}O_9$	−52°	250°	Gitoxigenin 16-acetate	223°	−8.5°	Oleandrose
Origidin[h]	$C_{23}H_{34}O_{13}$	+12.5°	255°	Dianhydrogitoxigenin	211°	+573°	Glucose + 2,6-Desoxyhexose
Adynerin[*i]	$C_{30}H_{44}O_7$	+7.5°	234°	Adynerigenin, $C_{23}H_{32}O_4$	242°	+18°	Oleandrose

Glycoside	Formula	M.p.	[α]	Genin M.p.	Genin [α]	Genin	Sugar
eriantin*·j	$C_{29}H_{42}O_9$	208°	±0	259°		Neriantogenin, $C_{23}H_{34}O_4$	Glucose
iginin*·k	$C_{23}H_{40}O_7$		−176°	115°	−226°	Diginigenin, $C_{24}H_{26}O_4$	Diginose ($C_7H_{14}O_4$)
zarin	$C_{36}H_{54}O_{14}$	270°	−27°	239° 265°	+5° −29.5°	"α"-Anhydrouzarigenin, $C_{23}H_{34}O_3$ "β"-Anhydrouzarigenin, "	2 Glucose
eriifolin[1,s]	$C_{30}H_{46}O_8$	225°	−50°	220°	+40°	Digitoxigenin	Thevetose ($C_7H_{14}O_5$)
cetylneriifolin[1,s]	$C_{32}H_{48}O_9$	240°	−72.5°				Thevetose + CH_3CO_2H
nevetin[1,s]	$C_{42}H_{66}O_{18}$	193°	−62°				Thevetose + 2 Glucose
t''-Antiarin	$C_{29}H_{42}O_{11}$	240°	−4°	205°	−160°	Dianhydroantiarigenin $C_{23}H_{30}O_5$	Antiarose
''-Antiarin	$C_{29}H_{42}O_{11}$	225°	±0				Rhamnose
abain	$C_{29}H_{44}O_{12}$	200°	−34°	255°	+11°	Ouabagenin, $C_{23}H_{34}O_8$	Rhamnose.
rmentooymarin	$C_{29}H_{46}O_8$	130°	−12.5°	270°	+21.5°	Sarmentogenin, $C_{23}H_{34}O_5$	Sarmentose
lotropin	$C_{29}H_{40}O_9$	221°	+56°	240°	+42°	Anhydrocalotropagenin, $C_{23}H_{32}O_5$	Methylreductinic acid
charidin	$C_{29}H_{40}O_9$	290°		251°		Isoanhydrocalotropagenin	$C_6H_8O_3$ (?)
lotoxin	$C_{29}H_{40}O_{10}$	244°	+74°	242°		Pseudoanhydrocalotropagenin	Hydroxymethylreductinic acid
lonitoxin[m]	$C_{29}H_{44}O_{10}$	263°	−27°	178°		Adonitoxigenin, $C_{23}H_{32}O_5$	Rhamnose
illaren A	$C_{36}H_{56}O_{11}$	270°	−74°	253°	−63°	Scillaridin A, $C_{24}H_{30}O_3$	Rhamnose + Glucose
illaren F	$C_{30}H_{47-48}O_{16}$	165°	+106°			Unknown	Glucose
illiroside[n]	$C_{32}H_{46}O_{12}$	170°	−59°			Unknown	Glucose
ellebrin	$C_{24}H_{52}O_{15}$	273°	−23°			Two isomers: $C_{24}H_{-34}O_6$	Glucose + Rhamnose
rmentoside A°	$C_{35}H_{4c}O_{10}$	280°	−40.5°	262°	−16°	Sarmentosigenin A, $C_{23}H_{34}O_6$	L(−)-Talomethylose
rmentoside B°	$C_{36}H_{56}O_{15}$	269°	−4.5°	133°	+9°	SarmentosigeninB, $C_{23}H_{34}O_6$	Digitalose + Glucose
nghinin[p]	$C_{32}H_{46}O_{10}$	130°	−79°	Amorph.		Tanghinigenin $C_{23}H_{32}O_5$	Thevetose + CH_3CO_2H
ssacetyltanghinin°	$C_{30}H_{44}O_9$	195°	−55°				Thevetose ($C_7H_{14}O_5$)

TABLE I.—Continued

GLYCOSIDE	FORMULA	M.p.	[α]D	AGLYCONE	M.p.	[α]D	SUGAR
eneniferin[a]	$C_{32}H_{48}O_9$	214°	-84°	Veneniferigenin, $C_{23}H_{34}O_4$	Amorph.		Thevetose + CH_3CO_2H
anghiferin[a]	$C_{32}H_{46}O_9$	245°	-64°	Tanghiferigenin, $C_{23}H_{32}O_4$	288°		Thevetose + CH_3CO_2H
onvallamarin[*]	$C_{44}H_{70}O_{19}$	193°	-66.5°	Convallamaretin, $C_{26}H_{40}O_6$	250°	-86°	2 Rhamnose + Glucose
erberin[r,t]	$C_{32}H_{48}O_9$	193°	-78°	Anhydrocerberigenin, $C_{23}H_{32}O_3$	222°	+47°	Cerberose ($C_7H_{14}O_5$)

* Physiologically inactive.
a Early references not given in the footnotes can be found in Elsevier's *Encyclopedia*, Vol. 14 (1940).
b From *Strophanthus Nicholsonii Holm*, von Euw and Reichstein, *Helv. Chim. Acta*, **31**, 883 (1948).
c Schmutz and Reichstein, *Pharm. Acta Helv.*, **22**, 359 (1947).
d Schwarz, Katz and Reichstein, *Pharm. Acta Helv.*, **21**, 250 (1946).
e Blome, Katz and Reichstein, *ibid.*, **21**, 325 (1946).
f Hartmann and Schlittler, *Helv. Chim. Acta*, **23**, 548 (1940).
g [α]₅₄₆
h Mannich and Schneider, *Arch. Pharm.*, **279**, 223 (1941) [*Chem. Zentr.*, I, 1380 (1942)].
i W. Neumann, *Ber.*, **70**, 1547 (1937).
j Schmiedeberg, *Ber.*, **16**, 253 (1883).
k W. Karrer, *Festschr. für E.C. Barell*, p. 238, Basel (1936) [*Chem. Zentr.*, II, 2727 (1936)]; Shoppee and Reichstein, *Helv. Chim. Acta*, **23**, 975 (1940); Press and Reichstein, *ibid.*, 2127 (1947).
l Frèrejacque, *Compt. rend.*, **221**, 645 (1945); **225**, 695 (1947).
m Rosenmund and Reichstein, *Pharm. Acta Helv.*, **17**, 176 (1942); Katz and Reichstein, *ibid.*, **22**, 437 (1947).
n Stoll and Renz, *Helv. Chim. Acta*, **25**, 43, 377 (1942).
o Schmutz and Reichstein, *Pharm. Acta Helv.*, **22**, 167 (1947).
q Frèrejacque and Hasenfratz, *Compt. rend.*, **222**, 149 (1946).
p Frèrejacque and Hasenfratz, *ibid.*, **223**, 642 (1946).
r Matsubara, *Bull. Chem. Soc. Japan*, **12**, 436 (1937) [*Chem. Zentr.*, I, 2887 (1938)]; *J. Chem. Soc. Japan*, **60**, 1195, 1201, 1230, 1237 (1939) [*C. A.*, **36**, 6503 (1942)].
s Helfenberger and Reichstein, *Helv. Chim. Acta*, **31**, 1470 (1948).
t Cerberin was recently shown by Frèrejacque, *Compt. rend.*, **226**, 835 (1948), to be identical with acetylneriifolin. Cerberose is thus identical with thevetose; that the sugar is indeed L-glucomethylose 3-methyl ether, as inferred by Frèrejacque and Hasenfratz, *Compt. rend.*, **222**, 815 (1946), was established by Blindenbacher and Reichstein, *Helv. Chim. Acta*, **31**, 1669 (1948), by synthesis.

tion of water with the formation of a mono-, di-, or trianhydro genin. For example, the intact aglycone of uzarin, a glucoside, has not yet been obtained and only anhydrouzarigenin has been isolated as a hydrolysis product. Voss[17] found that with model glycosides alcoholysis sometimes proceeds as much as one hundred times as fast as hydrolysis and introduced this as a procedure for effecting cleavage under less destructive conditions.[18] Thus, convallamarin, a glucoside-dirhamnoside, was successfully cleaved to convallamaretin without introduction of any new double bonds by allowing the glycoside to stand for several days at 35° in 2 percent methanolic hydrogen chloride; the sugar was split quantitatively as methylglucoside.

Another method of effecting cleavage under sparing conditions was employed by Mannich[19] in the first successful preparation of the true genin from ouabain, a rhamnoside that had afforded only resins or extensive degradation products in all previous attempts to effect hydrolysis. The glycoside is only sparingly soluble in acetone, but when a suspension in acetone containing hydrogen chloride is shaken in the cold the solid soon dissolves in the form of a monoacetonide in which the group introduced is in the sugar residue. On standing for one or two weeks the solution deposits crystals of a monoacetonide of ouabagenin (80% yield), apparently because the genin contains a 1,3-glycol grouping; this feature is by no means essential to the success of the method. The acetonide is hydrolyzed with 0.6 percent sulfuric acid (80–90% yield) or by the action of refluxing dilute alcohol (quantitative yield). The sugar is probably split as the chloro derivative. The method is successful in some other cases but unfortunately not in all, particularly with polyglycosides that are very sparingly soluble in acetone.

Although scillaridin A is a C_{24}-compound, the more typical aglycones of the strophanthus-digitalis group are related C_{23}-compounds, mainly of the formula $C_{23}H_{34}O_{4-8}$. The structures and configurations of several members of the latter group are now known in all detail (for evidence of the stereo-

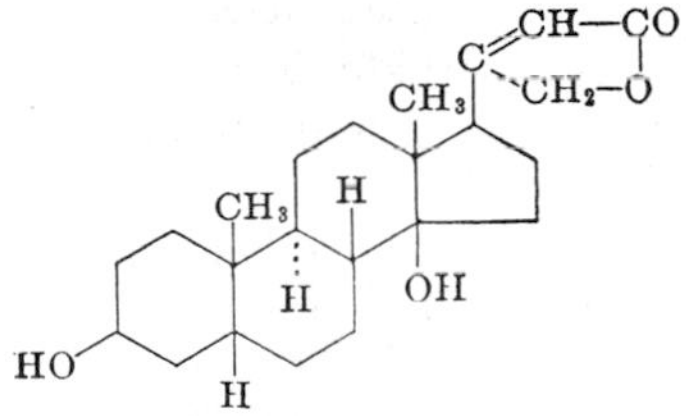

Digitoxigenin

[17] W. Voss and Wachs, *Ann.*, **522**, 240 (1936).

[18] W. Voss and Vogt, *Ber.*, **69**, 2333 (1936).

[19] Mannich and Siewert, *Ber.*, **75**, 737 (1942).

chemical relationships, see Chapter X). The simplest substance is digitoxi-genin. The carbon skeleton corresponds to that of a bile acid except that there is one less carbon atom in the side chain. A secondary alcoholic group at C_3, the angular methyl groups, and the side chain are all β-oriented, as they are in the sterols, and the ring-junctures A/B and B/C are cis and trans, respectively, as in coprostanol. Unlike the orientation in the sterols, the C/D-ring juncture is cis, and a characteristic 14-hydroxyl group thus has the β-orientation. The α,β-unsaturated lactone ring and the 14β-hydroxyl group are the most distinctive features of structure. Stro-phanthidin (next section) differs from digitoxigenin in having an additional, β-oriented hydroxyl group at C_5 and an aldehydic group at C_{10}, instead of the usual methyl group. Because of the presence of this extra functional group, strophanthidin undergoes a greater variety of transformations than the related aglycones and the chemistry is more complicated. The pioneer-ing researches of Jacobs that were directed, by fortuitous circumstance, particularly to the study of strophanthidin led to an array of transformation products that presented a most perplexing problem of interpretation but that ultimately enriched the knowledge of the stereochemical relationships.

STRUCTURE OF STROPHANTHIDIN

Functional Groups. Strophanthidin contains a carbonyl group recogniz-able by absorption at 303 mμ (log ϵ 1.8). That the aglycone forms an oxime but does not reduce Fehling's solution[1] seemed indicative of a ketonic group, but the aldehydic nature of the group was shown by its conversion to carboxyl on oxidation of the aglycone with permanganate in acetone solution to strophanthidinic acid[2] (Chart 1); somewhat higher yields can be obtained by oxidation of strophanthidin 3-acetate with chromic acid.[3] Although the secondary hydroxyl group at C_3 and the double bond in the lactone ring are vulnerable points of attack, only the aldehydic group is attacked by neutral permanganate. Chromic acid oxidation of the methyl ester affords the 3-ketone, strophanthidonic acid methyl ester.[4] This ester is not acylable, whereas strophanthidin forms a monoacetate and a mono-benzoate, and hence the acylable hydroxyl group in the genin is secondary.

Of the two unsaturated centers in strophanthidin, the first to be attacked on catalytic hydrogenation is the double bond in the lactone ring.[5] The product, dihydrostrophanthidin, still bears the intact aldehydic group,

[1] Jacobs and Collins, *J. Biol. Chem.*, **65**, 491 (1925).
[2] Jacobs, *J. Biol. Chem.*, **57**, 553 (1923); Jacobs and Gustus, *ibid.*, **74**, 795 (1927).
[3] Koechlin and Reichstein, *Helv. Chim. Acta*, **30**, 1673 (1947).
[4] Jacobs and Gustus, *J. Biol. Chem.*, **74**, 795 (1927).
[5] Jacobs and Heidelberger, *J. Biol. Chem.*, **54**, 253 (1922).

since it can be oxidized to the corresponding acid. Reduction of the carbonyl group is effected either by aluminum amalgam or by the Meerwein-Ponndorf method;[6] the product, strophanthidol, forms a diacetate and a

Chart 1.* STROPHANTHIDIN; THE ALDEHYDIC FUNCTION

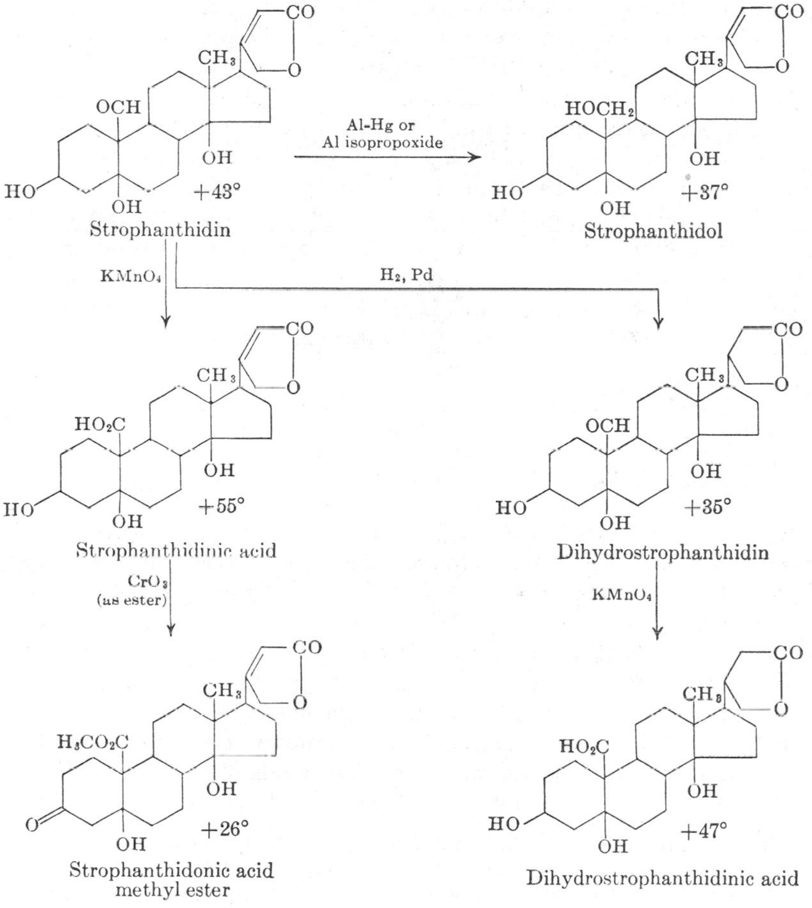

* The figures given in this and later formulations are $[\alpha]_D$ values.

dibenzoate.[7] Strophanthidol has been identified as the genin of cymarol, a cymaroside occurring in *S. kombé*. The carbonyl group of dihydrostrophanthidin is reducible with considerable difficulty by platinum-catalyzed

[6] Rabald and Kraus, *Z. physiol. Chem.*, **265**, 39 (1940).

[7] Blome, Katz and Reichstein, *Pharm. Acta Helv.*, **21**, 325 (1946).

hydrogenation.[8] The product is a dihydrostrophanthidol, m.p. 175°, 195°, $[\alpha]_D$ + 32°; hydrogenation (Pt) of strophanthidol leads to a different dihydride[6] (m.p. 208°, $[\alpha]_D$ + 35°), probably differing in the configuration at C_{20}.

Wolff-Kishner reduction[9] of dihydrostrophanthidin converts the aldehyde group into methyl and affords a product identical with the dihydro derivative of periplogenin.[10] A less direct correlation between strophanthidin and periplogenin had been established earlier (see below).

Lactone Ring. Since strophanthidin reduces Tollens' reagent in pyridine solution whereas dihydrostrophanthidin does not, the unsaturated lactone ring and not the aldehydic group must be responsible for the reducing action. Strophanthidin, but not dihydrostrophanthidin, exhibits a color reaction discovered by Legal (1883):[1] a pyridine solution of the genin and sodium nitroprusside acquires a deep red color on addition of a few drops of alkali.[2] The Legal test is characteristic of all the aglycones of the strophanthus-digitalis group. In model experiments with the angelica lactones I and II,[3] Jacobs[4] noted that the β,γ-unsaturated lactone I reacted

(I)	(II)	(III)
Positive Legal test	Negative	Negative

with nitroprusside as the cardiac aglycones react to give an immediate color, whereas the α,β-unsaturated lactone II developed a very faint color that deepened slowly, probably as the result of isomerization to I. When both α-hydrogen atoms of I were replaced by methyl (III) the test was negative. This evidence, coupled with a comparison[5] of the course of hydrogenation of the angelica lactones and of the aglycones and with considerations relative to the formation of isoaglycones under the influence of alkali, led to the formulation of the side chain as a β,γ-unsaturated lactone grouping. The formulation was accepted for some time, but was finally shown by Elderfield to be incorrect. A convincing piece of evidence that the aglycones

[8] Jacobs, J. Biol. Chem., **88**, 519 (1930); Jacobs and Bigelow, ibid., **99**, 528 (1932).

[9] Plattner, Segre and Ernst, Helv. Chim. Acta, **30**, 1432 (1947).

[10] Jacobs and A. Hoffmann, J. Biol. Chem., **79**, 519 (1928); Jacobs and Bigelow, ibid., **99**, 521 (1932).

[1] Hans Meyer, Analyse u. Konstitutionsermittelung, 6th Ed., p. 550 (1938). A reaction with alkaline picric acid suitable for colorimetry is described by W. Neumann, Z. physiol. Chem., **240**, 241 (1936).

[2] Jacobs and A. Hoffmann, J. Biol. Chem., **67**, 333 (1926).

[3] L. Wolff, Ann., **229**, 249 (1885).

[4] Jacobs, A. Hoffmann and Gustus, J. Biol. Chem., **70**, 1 (1926).

[5] Jacobs and Scott, J. Biol. Chem., **87**, 601 (1930); **93**, 139 (1931).

actually contain an α,β-unsaturated lactone ring is that they show absorption maxima close to 220 mμ,[6,7] indicative of conjugation. In absorption characteristics the aglycones correspond closely to ethyl crotonate. The angelica lactones are not reliable model compounds because they carry an alkyl substituent at the γ-rather than the β-position and because the lactonized alcoholic group is secondary rather than primary. Elderfield[6] synthesized a properly constituted model of the α,β-unsaturated structure, β-cyclohexyl-$\Delta^{\alpha,\beta}$-butenolide (a), and found it to be completely analogous to strophanthidin in behavior toward both nitroprusside and Tollen's reagent and in absorption spectrum. A study of the reaction of the model

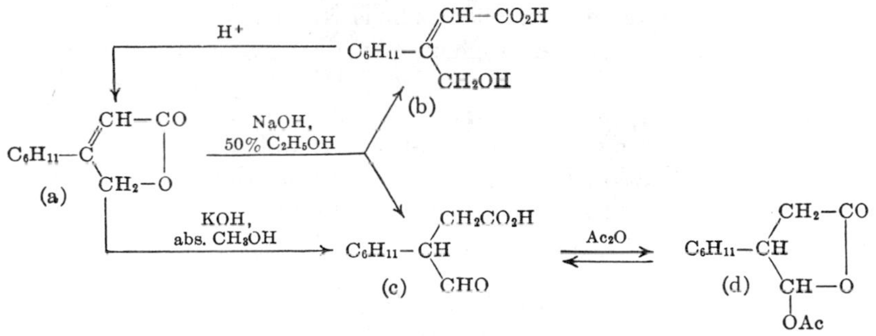

compound with alkali furnished information of value in the interpretation of the alkali isomerization of strophanthidin. Hydrolysis with alkali in aqueous ethanol proceeds in part to give the unsaturated hydroxy acid (b), which can be relactonized to (a). In addition, some of the aldehydic acid (c) is formed, and this substance is the sole product of the action of potassium hydroxide in absolute methanol. The transformation of (a) into (c) may proceed by isomerization to the β,γ-lactone and hydrolysis, but whatever the mechanism the reaction is irreversible, for lactonization of (c) with acetic anhydride does not lead to (a) but to the saturated lactone acetate (d).

Elderfield interpreted the transformation of strophanthidin into isostrophanthidin[8] as proceeding by a similar shift of the double bond to the β,γ-position followed by intramolecular addition of the C_{14}-hydroxyl group to the double bond. Isostrophanthidin is saturated and does not give the nitroprusside test. The isomerization is effected most efficiently by treatment of strophanthidin with methanolic sodium hydroxide for a brief period and dilution of the alkaline solution with water, when the product separates.

[6] Paist, Blout, Uhle and Elderfield, *J. Org. Chem.*, **6**, 273 (1941).

[7] Ruzicka, Plattner and Fürst, *Helv. Chim. Acta*, **25**, 79 (1942).

[8] Jacobs and Collins, *J. Biol. Chem.*, **61**, 387 (1924).

The original lactone ring thus does not seem to open in the course of the formation of the oxide bridge.

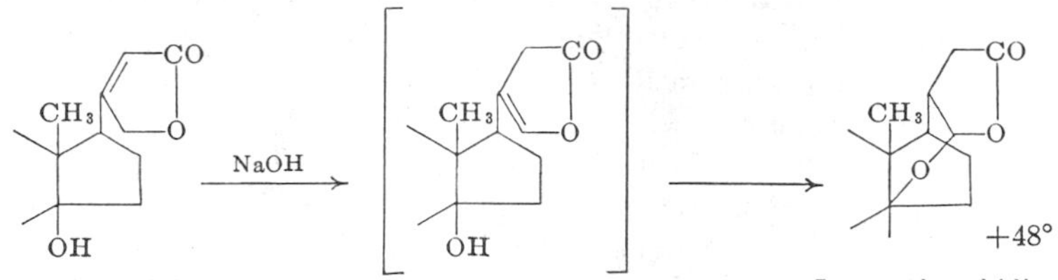

Strophanthidin   Isostrophanthidin

The transformation to isostrophanthidin is irreversible, for strophanthidin cannot be regenerated. Isostrophanthidin dissolves in alkali to give a solution that apparently contains the lactol IV, for oxidation with hypobromite affords the lactone acid V ($[\alpha]_D - 14°$).[9] Potassium permanganate attacks the C_{10}-aldehydic group of α-isostrophanthidic acid (V) to give α-isostrophanthic acid (VI $[\alpha]_D - 8°$); the lactone ring opens under the conditions of the experiment.[10] The same substance is obtained directly

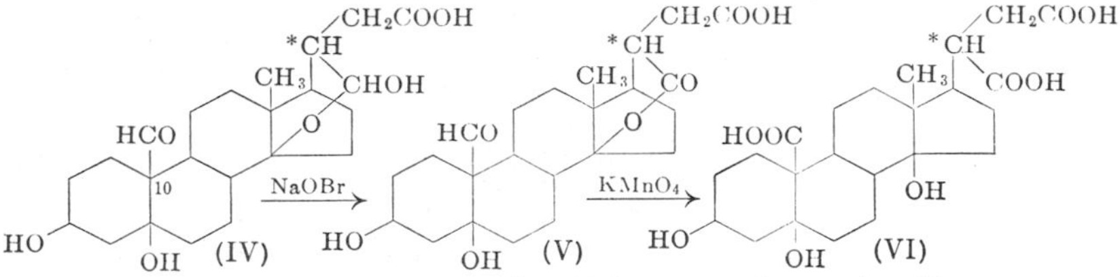

Isostrophanthidin α-Isostrophanthidic α-Isostrophanthic
acid (lactol form)   acid   acid

from isostrophanthidin by oxidation with potassium permanganate. The compounds of the iso series contain a center of asymmetry (*C) not present in the strophanthidin compounds and can exist in "α" - and "β"-modifications. Several pairs of C_{20}-epimers have been isolated; some, but not all, are partly interconvertible by alkali. The epimers differ in melting point but have nearly the same rotatory power (compare the two dihydrostrophanthidols cited above).

The presence in compounds of the iso series of a latent, cyclized aldehydic group was demonstrated by Jacobs[10] by first oxidizing the C_{10}-aldehyde group and then isomerizing the esterified product to α-isostrophanthidinic methyl ester, of structure analogous to IV except for the presence of a carbomethoxyl group at C_{10} instead of the aldehydic group. The corresponding dimethyl ester formed a crystalline semicarbazone.

[9] Jacobs and Collins, *J. Biol. Chem.*, **61**, 387 (1924); **65**, 491 (1925).
[10] Jacobs and Gustus, *J. Biol. Chem.*, **74**, 805, 811 (1927).

The formulation of the lactone ring as α,β-unsaturated at first seemed inconsistent with the general view, based upon an accumulation of results of Zerewitinoff determinations,[9,10,11] that the lactone ring is responsible for the liberation of approximately one mole of methane in this test. Elderfield[6] noted that the results are sometimes of dubious validity because of the great tenacity with which the aglycones retain solvent, and he presented evidence that an acetate group or a CH-group flanked by two double bonds liberates about 0.7 mole of methane. The model lactone (a) liberates 0.43 mole of methane, and Elderfield showed that the behavior of aglycones can be interpreted satisfactorily if the same amount of gas production is attributed to the unsaturated lactone ring.

The new formulation accounts adequately for the course of the oxidation of strophanthidinic acid (VII) by alkaline permanganate, first studied by Jacobs[12] and reinvestigated by Elderfield[13] The product, a keto-lactone

Chart 2. DEGRADATIONS WITH AND WITHOUT INVERSION AT C_{17}

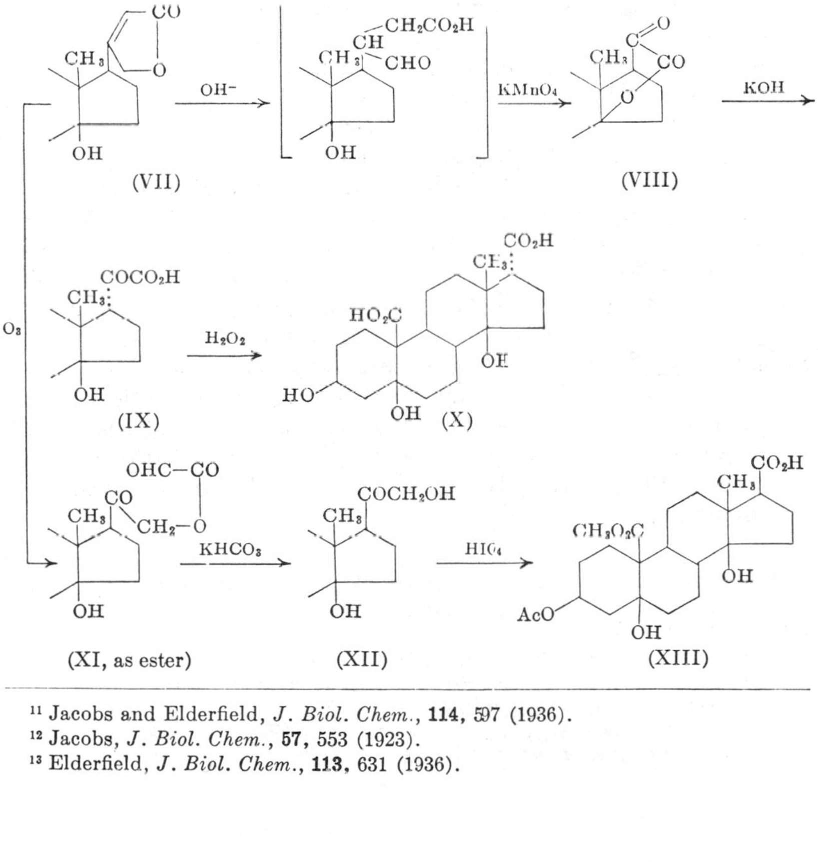

[11] Jacobs and Elderfield, *J. Biol. Chem.*, **114**, 597 (1936).
[12] Jacobs, *J. Biol. Chem.*, **57**, 553 (1923).
[13] Elderfield, *J. Biol. Chem.*, **113**, 631 (1936).

acid (VIII), presumably arises by oxidation of an intermediate aldehyde acid similar to (c) above. Opening of the lactone ring leads to a keto
acid that cannot be relactonized; this was degraded to the etio acid X.
Elderfield's suggestion that the failure of the keto acid IX to relactonize
is due to an inversion at C_{17} has been substantiated by Reichstein,[14] who
degraded strophanthidin by gentler methods and obtained a different etio
acid (XIII), in which the carboxyl group undoubtedly has the same orientation as the side chain of the aglycone itself.[15] This degradation involves
ozonization of the ester at $-80°$ (XI), hydrolysis to the ketol XII, and
periodic acid oxidation.

The 17-iso acid X has been converted into a Δ^4-3-ketone with the 10-
carboxyl and 14-hydroxyl group removed[16] and probably of the 14-iso
series[17] (no androgenic activity) and further[18] into 19-nordesoxycorticoster-
one and 19-norprogesterone. The latter two substances are noncrystalline
and probably consist of mixtures of stereoisomers. The configuration at
C_{10} is unknown; that at C_{17} is probably normal because the substances are
not isomerized by acid. The former is inactive, but 19-norprogesterone is
said to be about as potent as progesterone.[19]

Interrelation of Functional Groups. Some inferences regarding the relative locations of the different functional groups in strophanthidin followed
from observations made prior to elucidation of the skeletal structure,
although not all the early work can be interpreted with assurance even now.
The formation of iso compounds under the influence of alkali shows that
one of the tertiary hydroxyl groups is in the proximity of the lactone ring
and hence at C_8 or C_{14}. This is identified as the hydroxyl group most easily
eliminated on dehydration by the fact that treatment of strophanthidinic
ester (I, Chart 3) with alcoholic hydrochloric acid gives a monoanhydro
compound (II) that is incapable of forming an iso compound.[1] When the
secondary alcoholic group of II is oxidized to a keto group (III), the one
remaining tertiary hydroxyl group becomes labile and on gentle heating is
eliminated with the formation of IV. Thus in the original aglycone there is
in the β-position with respect to the secondary hydroxyl (C_3) a tertiary
group (C_5) different from the one (C_{14}) associated with the unsaturated
lactone ring.

[14] Buzas and Reichstein, *Helv. Chim. Acta*, **31**, 84 (1948).
[15] Reichstein names the free acid corresponding to XIII $3\beta,5\beta,14\beta$-trihydroxy-14-
iso-21-norpregnane-19,20-diacid; we prefer $3\beta,5\beta,14\beta$-trihydroxy-19-nor-5-isoandro-
stane-$10\beta,17\beta$-dicarboxylic acid.
[16] Butenandt and Gallagher, *Ber.*, **72**, 1866 (1939).
[17] Plattner, Heusser and Segre, *Helv. Chim. Acta*, **31**, 249 (1948).
[18] Ehrenstein, *J. Org. Chem.*, **9**, 435 (1944).
[19] W. M. Allen and Ehrenstein, *Science*, **100**, 251 (1944).
[1] Jacobs and Gustus, *J. Biol. Chem.*, **74**, 795 (1927).

Chart 3. ANHYDRO DERIVATIVES

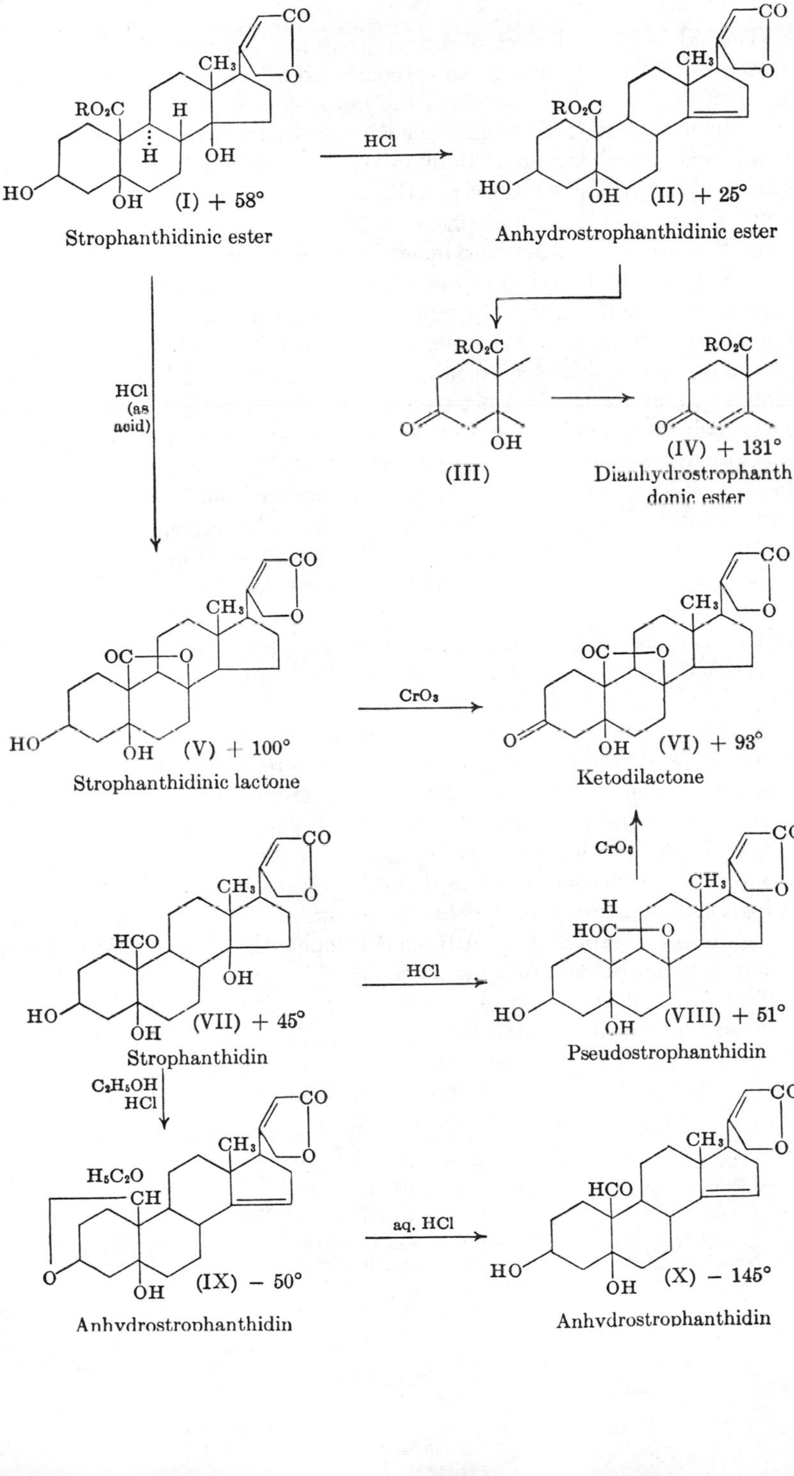

The aldehydic or derived carboxyl group at C_{10} forms a further point of reference. Strophanthidinic acid is converted by concentrated hydrochloric acid into a lactone (V) in which the newly formed ring is very stable.[2,3] Strophanthidin (VII) is transformed by acid isomerization into a related compound, pseudostrophanthidin (VIII). Oxidation of pseudostrophanthidin with permanganate[2] gives the corresponding ketone, but chromic acid[1] also attacks the lactol ring and gives a ketodilactone (VI) identical with that from V. This ketodilactone loses water readily and therefore still bears the hydroxyl group at C_5. Since pseudostrophanthidin forms no iso compound, the tertiary hydroxyl group originally at C_{14} must have combined with the carboxyl group of the acid and with the aldehydic group of the aglycone. The lactonization of strophanthidinic acid may involve simple elimination of water between the two β-oriented groups, but molecular models show that if the trans B/C junction is retained these groups are at a considerable distance from one another.[4] An inversion at C_8 is unlikely because this should be attended with increased levorotation, whereas small dextro shifts are observed. Thus the lactone and lactol rings are formulated in the chart as extending to position 8. Ring-formation presumably involves an unsaturated intermediate, but, since dehydration at C_{14} appears not to proceed by the unlikely path of cis elimination with the hydrogen at C_8 but to give the 14,15-anhydro derivative (II), the reaction probably proceeds through a small amount of the $\Delta^{8(14)}$-isomer present in equilibrium with the normal anhydro product.

A relation between the secondary hydroxyl group and the aldehydic group is established by the conversion of strophanthidin by hydrogen chloride in cold ethanol into the anhydro ethylal IX.[5] This substance forms neither an oxime nor a benzoate, but the hydrolysis product X is aldehydic and exhibits the characteristic test for the secondary hydroxyl group. The formation of the oxide bridge establishes the proximity of the two groups and shows that they have the same steric orientation (for further evidence, see Chapter X). Although strophanthidin has a 3β-hydroxyl group, it is not precipitated by digitonin.

Ring A. A degradation of strophanthidin first investigated by Jacobs and Gustus[6] afforded a specific though lengthy proof of the structure of Ring A. The starting material, anhydro-α-isostrophanthonic dimethyl ester (I, $[\alpha]_D + 74°$), was obtained by reactions similar to those described above. In this substance all the functional groups are modified or pro-

[2] Jacobs and Collins, *J. Biol. Chem.*, **65**, 491 (1925).
[3] Jacobs and Collins, *J. Biol. Chem.*, **63**, 123 (1925).
[4] Jacobs and Elderfield, *J. Biol. Chem.*, **108**, 497 (1935).
[5] Jacobs and Collins, *J. Biol. Chem.*, **59**, 713 (1924).
[6] Jacobs and Gustus, *J. Biol. Chem.*, **79**, 539 (1928).

tected except the α,β-unsaturated ketonic grouping, and the oxidative degradation resembles that of cholestenone; permanganate attacks the

(I)

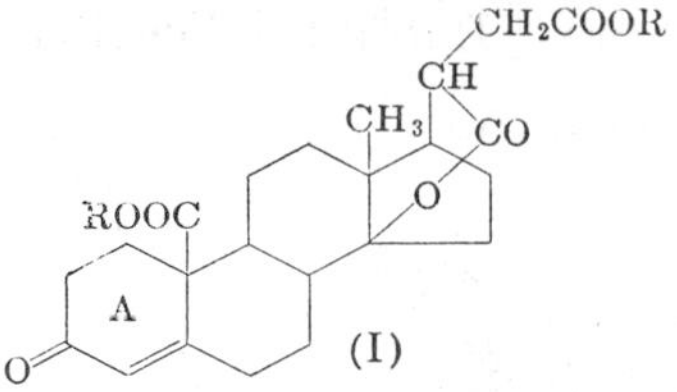

Anhydro-α-isostrophanthonic dimethyl ester

double bond and gives a keto acid (III) having one less carbon atom. Undephanthontriacid dimethyl ester (III) was recognized as a β-keto ester

(I) Anhydro-α-isostrophanthonic dimethyl ester → $KMnO_4$ → (II) → (III) Undephanthontriacid dimethyl ester → NaOH → (IV) Duodephanthondiacid → 2H → (V) Lactone

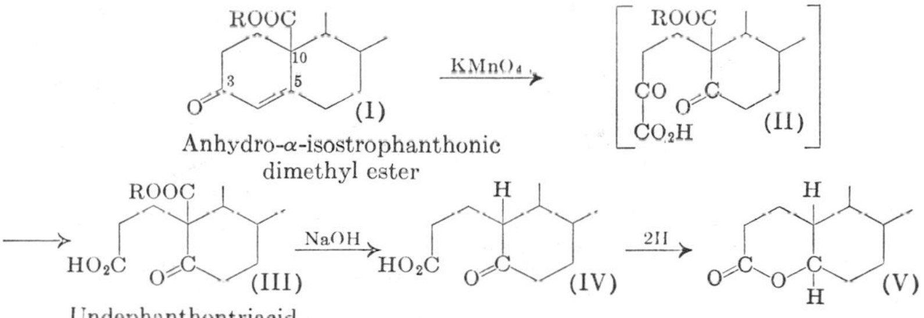

because hydrolysis with 0.1 *N* alkali resulted in decarboxylation (IV); the configuration at C_{10} is not known. The keto group in III and IV corresponds to the original point of attachment of the tertiary hydroxyl (C_5), which therefore is, in strophanthidin, β to the aldehydic group. Evidence cited in the preceeding section establishes that the secondary hydroxyl group (C_3) is β to the tertiary hydroxyl and either γ or δ with respect to the aldehydic group. The arrangements VI and VII both fulfill all these conditions

(VI)

(VII)

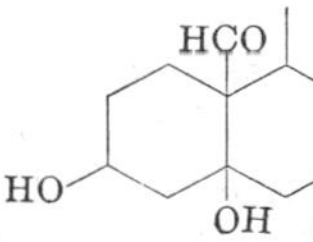

and account further for the ready lactonization of the hydroxy acid resulting on reduction of duodephanthondiacid (IV).

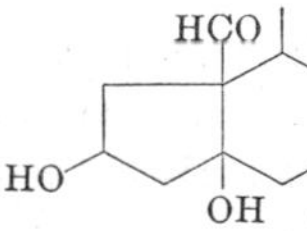

Windaus[7] had found that on opening of Ring A of a saturated 3-ketone of

[7] Windaus, K. Westphal and Stein, *Ber.*, **61**, 1847 (1928).

the gitoxigenin series the dibasic acid produced was converted into a ketone on pyrolysis. The conclusion from the Blanc rule that ring A is six-membered can be accepted as valid because of the following evidence that this is a terminal ring. Duodephanthondiacid (VIII) was degraded[8]

Chart 4. DEGRADATION TO DEPHANTHIC ACID

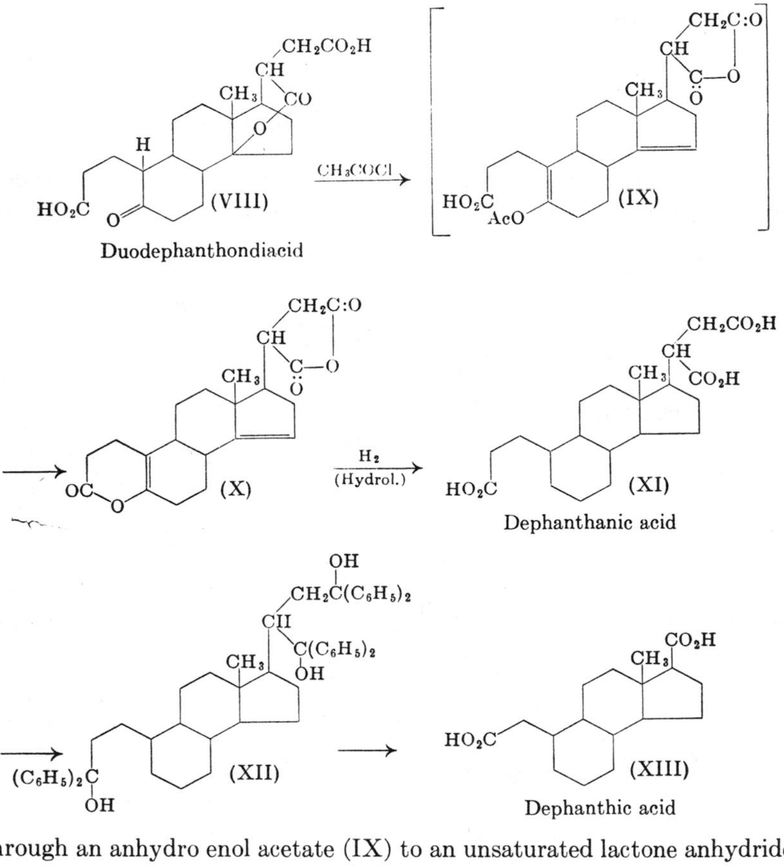

(VIII) Duodephanthondiacid

(IX)

(X)

(XI) Dephanthanic acid

(XII)

(XIII) Dephanthic acid

through an anhydro enol acetate (IX) to an unsaturated lactone anhydride (X). The lactone ring was cleaved on hydrogenation, and hydrolysis afforded a saturated tribasic acid (XI). When subjected to Barbier-Wieland degradation through the tritertiary carbinol (XII), dephanthanic acid gave a dibasic acid, dephanthic acid (XIII), having four less carbon atoms. Three of these must have come from the original lactone ring, and the

[8] Jacobs and Gustus, *J. Biol. Chem.*, **84**, 183 (1929); **92**, 323 (1931); Jacobs and Elderfield, *ibid.*, **102**, 237 (1933).

remaining one is then identified as originating from a methylene group in the original ring carrying the secondary hydroxyl group.   The degradation as a whole shows that ring A contains the three-carbon unit —CH$_2$CHOHCH$_2$— and therefore is a terminal ring.

Since in 1928 the similar oxidation of cholestenone was not understood, the changes occurring in these degradations were not all correctly interpreted in the original work.   An opportunity for rapid advancement of the problem was missed in the failure to take adequate account of the loss of a carbon atom in the first step in the degradation (III).   Unfortunately Jacobs gave more weight to the curious reaction described in the next section.

Trianhydrostrophanthidin.   Anhydrostrophanthidin is converted by alcoholic hydrochloric acid into a hemiacetal that on hydrolysis affords the strongly levorotatory dianhydrostrophanthidin (I).   On treatment with concentrated hydrochloric acid dianhydrostrophanthidin undergoes further dehydration and yields a trianhydrostrophanthidin[1] that lacks the proper-

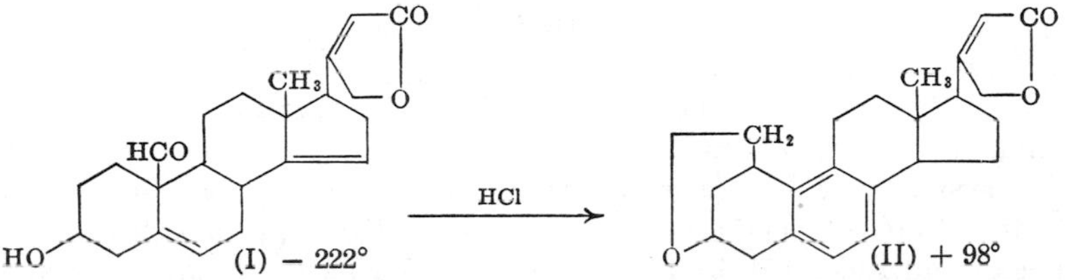

HCl →

(I) — 222°
Dianhydrostrophanthidin

(II) + 98°
Trianhydrostrophanthidin (?)

ties associated with either the carbonyl or the secondary hydroxyl group; these groups must have become joined together.   The three nuclear double bonds are resistant to hydrogenation, and the inference that they are present in a benzenoid ring was confirmed by determination of the absorption spectrum (λ_{max} 279 mμ).[2]   The observation[3] that trianhydrostrophanthidin can be oxidized with nitric acid to prehnitic acid (benzene-1,2,3,4-tetracarboxylic acid) is not evidence of the presence of a preformed benzenoid ring (see HNO$_3$ oxidations of abietic acid and of ergosterol) but shows that the aromatic system established as present by the other evidence is located in ring B.   The aldehydic group must have migrated, and both Tschesche and Knick[3] and Jacobs and Elderfield[1] assumed a migration to C$_1$ and formulated trianhydrostrophanthidin as in II.   Another possibility suggested in the first edition of this book is that the reaction proceeds by Wagner-

[1] Jacobs and Collins, *J. Biol. Chem.*, **63**, 123 (1925); Jacobs and Elderfield, *ibid.*, **108**, 693 (1935).
[2] Elderfield and Rothen, *J. Biol. Chem.*, **106**, 71 (1934).
[3] Tschesche and Knick, *Z. physiol. Chem.*, **229**, 233 (1934).

Meerwein rearrangement of the intermediate lactol Ia with resulting ring enlargement to III. There is no evidence to distinguish between formulas II and III.

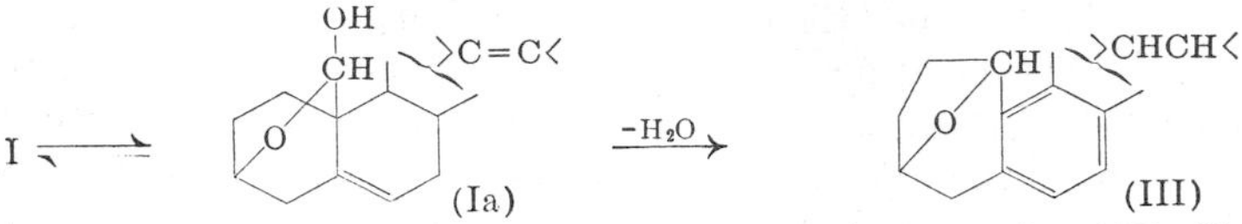

Trianhydrostrophanthidin (?)

The possibility of a rearrangement was not at first entertained. The ability of one ring to become aromatic without loss of the aldehydic carbon atom seemed to Jacobs to indicate that the aldehydic group does not occupy an angular position. This conclusion, however, was not consistent with the many instances of steric hindrance in reactions involving the aldehydic group and the corresponding carboxyl and carbalkoxyl groups. In investigations in the resin acid field, Ruzicka had similarly been led to disregard evidence pointing to the presence of a hindered, tertiary carboxyl group because of the results of a dehydration reaction later found to involve a molecular rearrangement.

Early Conception of the Ring System. The degradation of strophanthidin to duodephanthondiacid and dephanthic acid indicated that the ring system includes a terminal six-membered ring bearing a secondary hydroxyl group. The presence of a terminal five ring was established by Jacobs and Elderfield[4] by a degradation involving the opening of ring D. On oxidation of anhydrodihydrostrophanthidin (I, $[\alpha]_D$ + 48.5°) with permanganate in acetone solution only the aldehydic group is attacked, but when the oxidation is conducted in the presence of alkali the double bond is also attacked and the glycol acid II is formed. On oxidation of the ester of II with chromic acid the glycol linkage is cleaved with the opening of ring D and the production of the diketo acid III. On reduction of the two carbonyl groups by hydrogenation, the primary product lactonizes spontaneously (IV). The ease of lactone formation indicates a γ- or δ-relationship between one of the hydroxyl groups and the carboxyl group, and consequently the ring opened is five- and not six-membered. The oxidation of anhydrodihydrostrophanthidin takes a different course when conducted with permanganate in acetic acid solution; the aldehydic group is attacked as before but the product is an oxide and not a glycol.[5] The same oxide is formed by the action of perbenzoic acid, followed by permanganate oxidation of the aldehydic group. Jacobs and Elderfield[5] postulated that the

[4] Jacobs and Elderfield, *J. Biol. Chem.*, **97**, 727 (1932); **108**, 497 (1935). A similar degradation of gitoxigenin is reported by the same authors, *ibid.*, **96**, 357 (1932).

[5] Jacobs and Elderfield, *J. Biol. Chem.*, **113**, 611 (1936).

substance is the 8,14-oxide and assumed that the anhydrogenins consist of equilibrium mixtures of the 14,15- and 8,14-unsaturated forms. It seems more likely that the substance is a 14,15-α-oxide, formed from the evi-

Chart 5. CHARACTERIZATION OF RING D

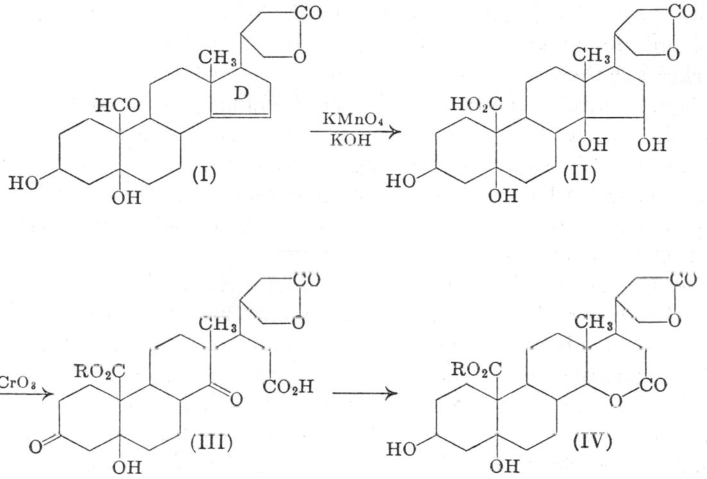

dently preponderant 14,15-anhydro derivative. The substance is stable to hydrogenation and in this respect is like known 14,15-α-oxides[6] and unlike the ditertiary oxide of apocholic acid.[7] The transformations described by Jacobs can be interpreted equally well on the basis of either structure.

From a consideration of the facts available at the time, Jacobs[8] tentatively suggested the partial formula V for strophanthidin. The status of

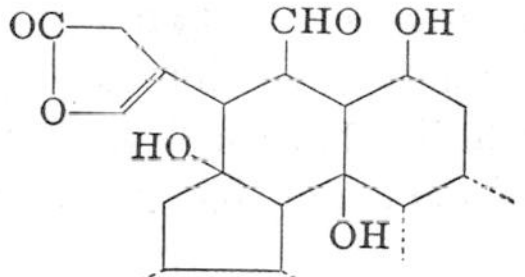

the problem resembled that of the sterol-bile acid work at the time of the Wieland-Windaus formulation (1928). A solution of the latter problem finally was achieved by application of the new experimental method of selenium dehydrogenation, and the same method proved of value in the investigation of the cardiac aglycones.

[6] Plattner, Ruzicka, Heusser and Meier, *Helv. Chim. Acta*, **29**, 2023 (1946).
[7] Plattner, Ruzicka and Holtermann, *Helv. Chim. Acta*, **28**, 1660 (1945).
[8] Jacobs and Elderfield, *J. Biol. Chem.*, **102**, 237 (1933).

Carbon Skeleton. Jacobs and Fleck[9] investigated the selenium dehydrogenation of strophanthidin in 1931, but the hydrocarbon isolated probably was not a single individual. Tschesche and Knick[10] succeeded in obtaining from the dehydrogenation of 30 g. of anhydrouzarigenin 0.1–.2 g. of a product fully identified as the Diels hydrocarbon, and Elderfield and Jacobs[11] isolated the same substance by the selenium dehydrogenation of strophanthidin at a controlled temperature (320–340°).

Tschesche[12] then degraded uzarigenin by nonpyrolytic reactions to etioallocholanic acid, and Jacobs and Elderfield[13] similarly degraded digitoxigenin to etiocholanic acid. Since neither series of transformations offered opportunity for inversion at C_5, the degradations established that uzarigenin and digitoxigenin belong to the cholestane and coprostane series, respectively, and showed that the skeletal structure of the side chain corresponds to that of a nor-bile acid.

Other Glycosides of Strophanthidin. The leaves and blossoms of lily of the valley (*Convallaria majalis*) yield a particularly potent cardiotonic principle, **convallatoxin.**[1] Tschesche and Haupt[2] established the formula $C_{29}H_{42}O_{10}$, identified the sugar component as rhamnose, and showed that the glycoside gives the Legal test, is isomerized by alkali, absorbs one mole of hydrogen rapidly (lactone ring), and is hydrogenated further only slowly and partially. The rhamnoside is resistant to acid hydrolysis and the product, isolated as the benzoate, proved to be a monoanhydrogenin. Tschesche and Haupt observed no reaction with ketonic reagents and proposed a formulation of the hypothetical genin with hydroxyl groups at the 3-, 5-, 8-, and 14-positions and with a presumably inert 9,11-double bond. An alternate interpretation was suggested in the second edition of this book: the aglycone contains an aldehydic group at C_{10} and probably is identical with strophanthidin. Fieser and Jacobsen[3] found that the glycoside on reaction with hydrogen chloride in methanol in the cold is converted into dianhydrostrophanthidin methylal, identical with a product of the methanolysis of strophanthidin described earlier by Jacobs.[4] Tschesche[5] contributed the confirming evidence that his anhydroaglycone benzoate is

[9] Jacobs and Fleck, *Science*, **73**, 133 (1931); *J. Biol. Chem.*, **97**, 57 (1932).
[10] Tschesche and Knick, *Z. physiol. Chem.*, **222**, 58 (1933).
[11] Elderfield and Jacobs, *Science*, **79**, 279 (1934); *J. Biol. Chem.*, **107**, 143 (1934).
[12] Tschesche, *Z. angew. Chem.*, **47**, 729 (1934); *Z. physiol. Chem.*, **229**, 219 (1934); *Ber.*, **68**, 7 (1935).
[13] Jacobs and Elderfield, *Science*, **80**, 434 (1934); *J. Biol. Chem.*, **108**, 497 (1935).
[1] W. Karrer, *Helv. Chim. Acta*, **12**, 506 (1929).
[2] Tschesche and Haupt, *Ber.*, **69**, 459 (1936).
[3] Fieser and Jacobsen, *J. Am. Chem. Soc.*, **59**, 2335 (1937).
[4] Jacobs and Collins, *J. Biol. Chem.*, **63**, 123 (1925).
[5] Tschesche, citation in Ref. 3.

identical with anhydrostrophanthidin benzoate, and Reichstein[6] later submitted convallatoxin to hydrolysis according to the Mannich procedure and succeeded in isolating the true aglycone, identified as strophanthidin. The glycoside also was shown capable of reaction with hydroxylamine.[6]

The seeds of lily of the valley contain no convallatoxin but a closely related glycoside, **convalloside**.[7] Hydrolysis with strophanthobiase converts convalloside into convallatoxin and glucose, and hence the structure is: strophanthidin-rhamnoside-glucoside.

Seeds of the wall flower (*Cheiranthus cheiri*) contain an active glycoside, **cheirotoxin**, m.p. 210°, $[\alpha]_D$ − 17°, composed of strophanthidin linked to glucose and a pentose or methylpentose.[8]

OTHER AGLYCONES OF THE STROPHANTHUS-DIGITALIS GROUP

Periplogenin. This aglycone[9] very probably corresponds in structure and configuration to strophanthidin except that it carries a methyl group at C_{10} instead of the aldehydic group. Correlation has been effected by Wolff-Kishner reduction of dihydrostrophanthidin, as noted above, and also by similar reduction of α-isostrophanthidic acid (Formula V, Lactone Ring) to a product identical with one resulting from the hypobromite oxidation of (saponified) periplogenin (α-isoperiplogenic acid).[10] The conditions of the Wolff-Kishner reaction do not preclude the possibility of a rearrangement.

17-Isostrophanthidin and 17-Isoperiplogenin. Since the strophanthobiase present in *S. kombé* seeds converts higher glycosides of strophanthidin into the cymaroside (cymarin) by hydrolytic cleavage of glucose units, Jacobs[1] sought to simplify the procedure for isolation of the rare sugar cymarose after eventual acid hydrolysis by first allowing the ground seeds to stand in water for some time. The product resulting from the incubation, however, was not cymarin but a physiologically inactive cymaroside ("allocymarin"), which on hydrolysis yields cymarose and a substance originally named allostrophanthidin and now known to be 17-isostrophanthidin (m.p. 262°, $[\alpha]_D$ + 37°). Katz and Reichstein[2] later isolated from the same source two inactive glycosides of the isomerized aglycone 17-isoperiplogenin (m.p. 250°, $[\alpha]_D$ + 41°): 17-isoemicymarin, $[\alpha]_D$ + 29°

[6] Reichstein and Katz, *Hundert Jahre Schweiz. Apoth.-Ver.*, 1843–1943, 521 (1943).

[7] Schmutz and Reichstein, *Pharm. Acta Helv.*, **22**, 359 (1947).

[8] Schwarz, Katz and Reichstein, *Pharm. Acta Helv.*, **21**, 250 (1946).

[9] Jacobs and A. Hoffmann, *J. Biol. Chem.*, **79**, 519 (1928).

[10] Jacobs, Elderfield, Grave and Wignall, *J. Biol. Chem.*, **91**, 617 (1931); Jacobs and Elderfield, *ibid.*, **91**, 625 (1931).

[1] Jacobs, *J. Biol. Chem.*, **88**, 519 (1930).

[2] Katz and Reichstein, *Pharm. Acta Helv.*, **19**, 231 (1944).

(digitaloside), and 17-isoperiplocymarin, $[\alpha]_D + 46°$ (cymaroside); together with the corresponding unisomerized, active glycosides emicymarin and periplocymarin. Emicymarin and 17-isoemicymarin had been isolated previously from *S. Eminii*.[3] The 17-isoglycosides are somewhat more dextrorotatory than the normal compounds. That the 17-isoaglycones give the Legal test and correspond in absorption spectra to the normal compounds but are not isomerized by alkali, suggested that they are inverted at either C_{14}[4] or C_{17}.[5] A fact that argues against isomerism at C_{14} is that periplogenin and its isomer form different trianhydro compounds.[3] Proof that the difference between the normal and isomerized compounds lies in the orientation of the side chain was presented by Speiser and Reichstein,[6] who degraded 17-isoperiplogenin (I) by the ozonization procedure

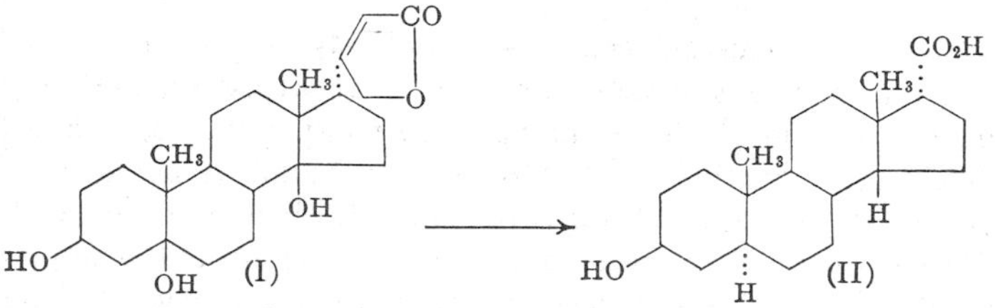

17-Isoperiplogenin

illustrated in Chart 2 to 3β-hydroxy-14-iso-17-isoetioallocholanic acid (II; see Chapter X). Emicymarin and 17-isoemicymarin are glycosides of the difficultly hydrolyzable type, but the genins were isolated without secondary change by the Mannich procedure of hydrolysis.[7]

Digoxigenin. Digoxigenin differs from periplogenin in having a secondary hydroxyl group at C_{12} in place of the tertiary hydroxyl at C_5 and a 3-hydroxyl group in the α-rather than β-orientation (Chart 6). The aglycone was characterized by Smith[1] as an unsaturated lactone (Legal test; dihydride) having a 14-hydroxyl group (iso compound with alkali) and two secondary hydroxyl groups (diacetate). The location and configuration of the latter groups were determined by Reichstein[2] by a procedure of oxidative degradation more efficient than the permanganate-hydrogen peroxide process employed in the case of strophanthidin (Chart 2,

[3] Jacobs and Bigelow, *J. Biol. Chem.*, **99**, 521 (1933); Lamb and S. Smith, *J. Chem. Soc.*, 442 (1936).
[4] E. Bloch and Elderfield, *J. Org. Chem.*, **4**, 289 (1939).
[5] Tschesche and Bohle, *Ber.*, **71**, 654, 1927 (1938).
[6] Speiser and Reichstein, *Experientia*, **3**, 323 (1947).
[7] Katz and Reichstein, *Helv. Chim. Acta*, **28**, 476 (1945).
[1] S. Smith, *J. Chem. Soc.*, 1305 (1935), and earlier papers.
[2] Steiger and Reichstein, *Helv. Chim. Acta*, **21**, 828 (1938).

above): the genin diacetate is treated with an equal weight of permanganate in neutral acetone solution and the acidic oxidation product separated from neutral starting material by extraction with soda and the recovered product reoxidized. Thus with six reoxidations, 2.7 g. of digoxigenin diacetate yielded 1.8 g. of the etio acid diacetate (II). After hydrolysis, treatment

Chart 6. DIGOXIGENIN

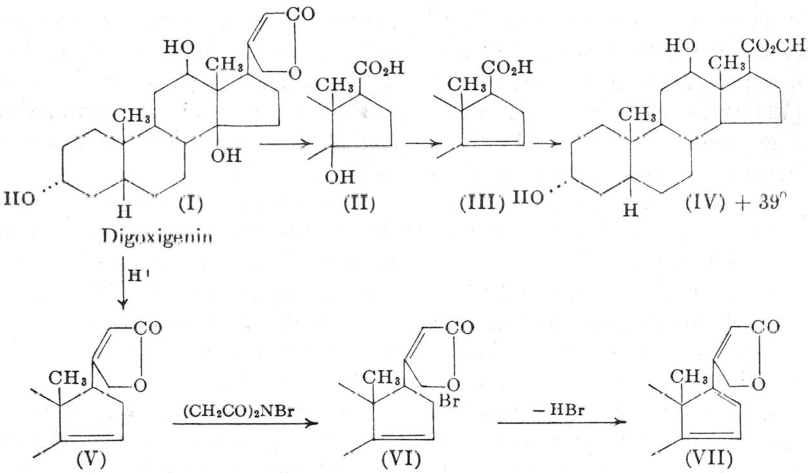

with dilute sulfuric acid in dioxane eliminated the 14-hydroxyl group to give the Δ^{14}-etiocholenic acid III and a small amount of a substance that is probably the $\Delta^{8(14)}$-isomer, since it does not absorb hydrogen under a variety of conditions. The main product III suffered ready hydrogenation and yielded a dihydroxyetiocholanic acid (ester, IV) that was unknown at the time but was very shortly identified by Mason and Hoehn[3] as $3\alpha,12\beta$-dihydroxyetiocholanic acid.

Both digoxigenin and the diacetate lose one hydroxyl group on treatment with dilute sulfuric acid in ethanol. The unacetylated product (35% yield) is known as "β"-anhydrodigoxigenin, m.p. 182°, $[\alpha]_{546} - 16°$Al; diacetate, m.p. 198.5°, $[\alpha]_D + 30°$ Chf.[4] Dehydration can also be effected with phosphorus oxychloride in pyridine in a sealed tube at 150° (65% yield). Other genins (digitoxigenin) are dehydrated by this reagent at room temperature and the reason for the resistance of digoxigenin is not apparent. Dehydration with concentrated hydrochloric acid[5] proceeds through an unstable

[3] Mason and Hoehn, *J. Am. Chem. Soc.*, **60**, 2824 (1938); **61**, 1614 (1939).
[4] Plattner and Heusser, *Helv. Chim. Acta*, **29**, 727 (1946).
[5] S. Smith, *J. Chem. Soc.*, 354 (1936).

chloride and affords the isomeric "α"-anhydrodigoxigenin, m.p. 192°, [α]₅₄₆ + 46° Al. Similar pairs of anhydroaglycones in other series have been variously designated; we shall define the "α"-isomer in each case as the one of higher dextrorotation produced by strong mineral acid. The newly introduced double bond of "β"-anhydrodigoxigenin (V) can be hydrogenated readily,[6] like that of the Δ¹⁴-stenols, and the 14,15-location was definitely established[4] by bromination of the diacetate with N-bromosuccinimide and elimination of hydrogen bromide. Bromination evidently occurs at the 16-position (VI), for the absorption maximum of the product is consistent with that expected for Δ¹⁴,¹⁶-dianhydrodigoxigenin diacetate (VII); m.p. 237°, [α]_D + 390° Chf., λ_max 332 mμ (log ε 4.25). "β"-Anhydrodigoxigenin oxide (m.p. 262°, [α]_D + 24° Chf) corresponds in resistance to hydrogenation to known 14,15-α-oxides.

Although the double bond in the "α"-anhydro compounds has been generally regarded as at the 8,14-position, this interpretation seems subject to question. The higher dextrorotation of the "α"-isomers has been cited as indicative of the Δ⁸⁽¹⁴⁾-structure on the ground that 3β-acetoxy-Δ⁸⁽¹⁴⁾-etioallocholanic acid methyl ester, [α]_D + 62°, bears a similar relationship to the Δ¹⁴-isomer, [α]_D + 30°.[7] However, in the A/B-cis series the situation is reversed: apocholic acid (Δ⁸⁽¹⁴⁾), [α]_D + 50°; Δ¹⁴-isomer, [α]_D + 68°; and the relationship of these substances to the Δ⁷-isomer does not correspond to that observed for the corresponding stenols. The behavior toward mineral acids and under hydrogenating conditions offers a more reliable guide, because in both the stenol and cholenic acid series the Δ⁸⁽¹⁴⁾-isomer is resistant to hydrogenation but capable of being isomerized by hydrochloric acid to a readily hydrogenated Δ¹⁴-isomer. An "α"-anhydro compound of the uzarigenin series is reported to be easily hydrogenated (see below), and Jacobs and Elderfield[8] found that "β"-anhydrodigitoxigenin is transformed by concentrated hydrochloric acid into the "α"-isomer. These relationships suggest that the "α"- like the "β"-anhydro compounds may be unsaturated at the 14,15-position[9] and inverted at a nearby center.

The diketone resulting from oxidation of the aglycone, digoxigenone (m.p. 265°, [α]₅₄₆ + 130°), has been observed to form only a monoxime and a monosemicarbazone, and hence the 12-carbonyl group appears to be hindered.

[6] Tschesche and Bohle, *Ber.*, **69**, 793 (1936).

[7] Plattner, Ruzicka, Heusser and Angliker, *Helv. Chim. Acta*, **30**, 1073 (1947).

[8] Jacobs and Elderfield, *J. Biol. Chem.*, **113**, 611 (1936).

[9] Position 16,17 is ruled out by the absence of selective ultraviolet absorption in the expected region (observation by Dr. S. Rajagopalan with a sample of "α"-anhydrodigitoxigenin kindly supplied by Dr. W. A. Jacobs).

Digitoxigenin. This genin[1] differs from periplogenin only in the absence

CHART 7. DIGITOXIGENIN

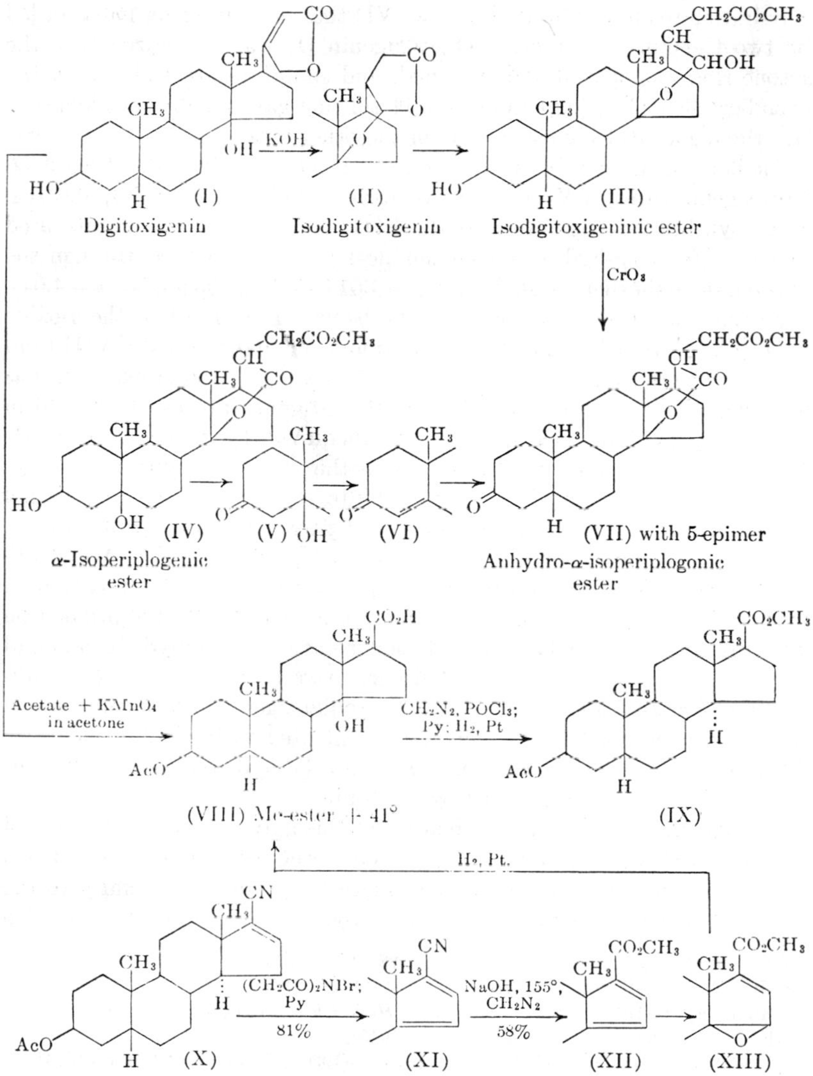
(I) Digitoxigenin
KOH
(II) Isodigitoxigenin
(III) Isodigitoxigeninic ester
CrO3
(IV) α-Isoperiplogenic ester
(V)
(VI)
(VII) with 5-epimer
Anhydro-α-isoperiplogonic ester
Acetate + KMnO4 in acetone
(VIII) Me-ester + 41°
CH2N2, POCl3; Py; H2, Pt
(IX)
H2, Pt.
(CH2CO)2NBr; Py
81%
NaOH, 155°, CH2N2
58%
(X)
(XI)
(XII)
(XIII)

[1] Early studies: Jacobs and Gustus, *J. Biol. Chem.*, **78,** 573 (1928); Windaus and Bandte, *Ber.*, **56,** 2001 (1923); Windaus and Stein, *Ber.*, **61,** 2436 (1928); S. Smith, *J. Chem. Soc.*, 2478 (1930); 1050 (1935).

of the tertiary hydroxyl at C_5, and the two series were related by elimination of this group from a suitable periplogenin derivative[2] (Chart 7). α-Isoperiplogenic ester (IV) was converted by oxidation (V) and selective dehydration to an unsaturated ketone (VI) that on hydrogenation afforded the two C_5-epimeric ketones. Digitoxigenin (I) was isomerized (II), the lactone ring was opened and esterified, and simultaneous oxidation of the secondary alcoholic group and of the lactol ring gave a substance identical with the higher-melting isomer VII of the other series.

Further evidence has been adduced more recently. Reichstein[3] degraded digitoxigenin through VIII to 3β-hydroxyetiocholanic acid (IX), and Ruzicka[4] synthesized the intermediate VIII as follows. The unsaturated nitrile X (from 3β-hydroxyetiocholanone-17[5]) was converted through the 15-bromide to the diene ester XII, $[\alpha]_D + 301$ Chf, λ_{max} 295 mμ (log $\epsilon = 4.04$). The oxide, obtained by the action of perbenzoic acid, must be the β-oxide XIII, $[\alpha]_D + 67°$ Chf, since hydrogenation leads to the etio acid VIII (and the 17-isomer: m.p. 203.5°, $[\alpha]_D - 11°$ Chf). Isodigitoxigenin has been degraded to etiocholanic acid[6] by the Grignard process illustrated in Chart 4 (Dephanthic Acid), and hence unequivocal evidence is available that the aglycone and isoaglycone have the same configuration at C_{17}.

Digitoxigenin on dehydration with dilute sulfuric acid in hot ethanol solution yields a mixture of "β"-anhydrodigitoxigenin, m.p. 202°, $[\alpha]_D - 13°$, and "α"-anhydrodigitoxigenin, m.p. 234°, $[\alpha]_D + 39°$.[7] Acetic anhydride-boron fluoride likewise yields a mixture,[3] but dehydration with phosphorus oxychloride in pyridine proceeds smoothly with the production of the "β"-isomer in good yield.[3] The levorotatory "β"-anhydro compound is formulated as a 14,15-unsaturated derivative because of its facile addition of hydrogen; as noted above (anhydrodigoxigenins), it is transformed to the dextrorotatory "α"-isomer by concentrated hydrochloric acid.[8]

Digitoxigenin and strophanthidin are both 3β-hydroxy compounds, but neither substance is precipitated by digitonin.

Gitoxigenin. The distinctive feature of this aglycone is the presence of a secondary hydroxyl group at C_{16}, as well as the usual hydroxyls at $C_3(\beta)$ and $C_{14}(\beta)$,[1] and the location of this functional group in proximity to the unsaturated lactone ring is reflected in a novel course of isomerization with

[2] Jacobs and Elderfield, *J. Biol. Chem.*, **92**, 313 (1931).

[3] Hunziker and Reichstein, *Helv. Chim. Acta*, **28**, 1472 (1945).

[4] Ruzicka, Plattner, Heusser and Meier, *Helv. Chim. Acta*, **30**, 1342 (1947).

[5] K. Meyer, *Helv. Chim. Acta*, **29**, 1580 (1946).

[6] Jacobs and Gustus, *J. Biol. Chem.*, **86**, 199 (1930); Jacobs and Elderfield, *ibid.*, **108**, 497 (1935).

[7] S. Smith, *J. Chem. Soc.*, 1050 (1935).

[8] Jacobs and Elderfield, *J. Biol. Chem.*, **113**, 611 (1936).

[1] Jacobs and Gustus, *J. Biol. Chem.*, **79**, 553 (1928); **82**, 403 (1929); **88**, 531 (1930).

alkali. Whereas the aglycone forms a dibenzoate and a diketone, isogitoxigenin forms only a monobenzoate and a monoketone, but readily
yields an anhydro derivative (loss of C_{14}-OH). The secondary hydroxyl

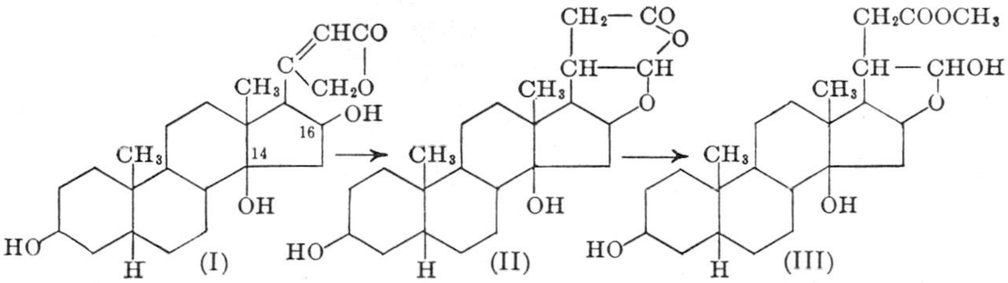

Gitoxigenin   Isogitoxigenin   Isogitoxigeninic ester

at C_{16} thus enters into cyclization with the lactone ring more readily than
the tertiary hydroxyl at C_{14} does (II). The difference is probably attributable to the size of the ring formed, for the new five-membered ring of isogitoxigenin is more stable than the corresponding six ring produced on
isomerization of the other aglycones. When the lactone ring of II is opened
by hydrolysis and esterification, the product III does not react with
carbonyl reagents and therefore is not in equilibrium with a hydroxy-
aldehyde form; the corresponding δ-lactols from the other aglycones display
aldehydic properties.

A relationship between the two hydroxyl functions in ring D is indicated
by the fact that the diketone V resulting from the oxidation of dihydrogitoxigenin (IV) loses water with such ease as to indicate that it is a β-hy-

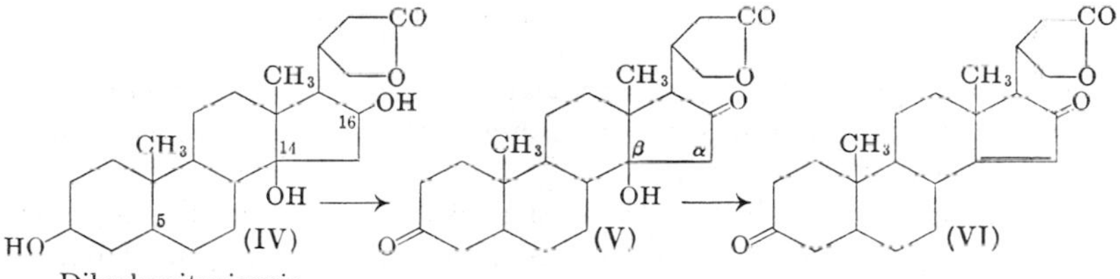

Dihydrogitoxigenin

droxy ketone.[2] That the tertiary hydroxyl eliminated is at C_{14} as in
structure V, and not at C_5, is established by the observation that oxidation
of gitoxigenin to the diketone gitoxigenone (VII) is accompanied by an
isomerization, for gitoxigenone no longer gives the Legal test or affords
an anhydro derivative. The lactone ring must have condensed with a
tertiary hydroxyl group at a nearby position, and the only available location
is at C_{14}. Interaction with the secondary hydroxyl at C_{16} ordinarily takes

[2] Jacobs and Elderfield, *J. Biol. Chem.*, **100,** 671 (1933).

precedence, but when this has been converted into a carbonyl group the
14-hydroxyl enters into the usual iso reaction.

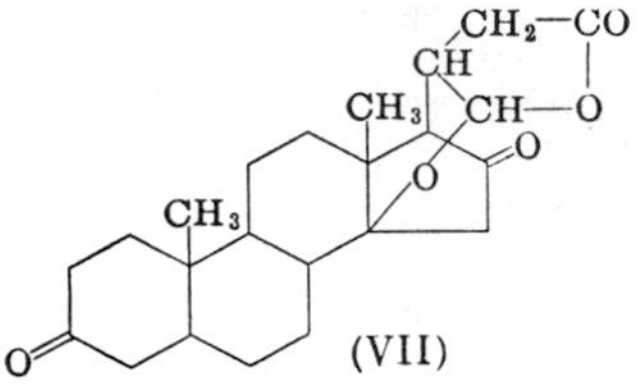

(VII)

Gitoxigenone

A further type of ring isomerization is responsible for the existence of
two dihydro derivatives of gitoxigenin.[1,2,3,4]   One of these, the "α"-form,
$[\alpha]_D + 42°$ Py, is represented by formula IV, above, and the structure is
established both by oxidation to V and by the preparation of the compound
from gitoxigenin diacetate.   The substance exhibits mutarotation owing
to the opening of the lactone ring and its closing in a different direction
(IV → VIII).   The structure of the "β"-form VIII, $[\alpha]_D - 55°$ Py, is

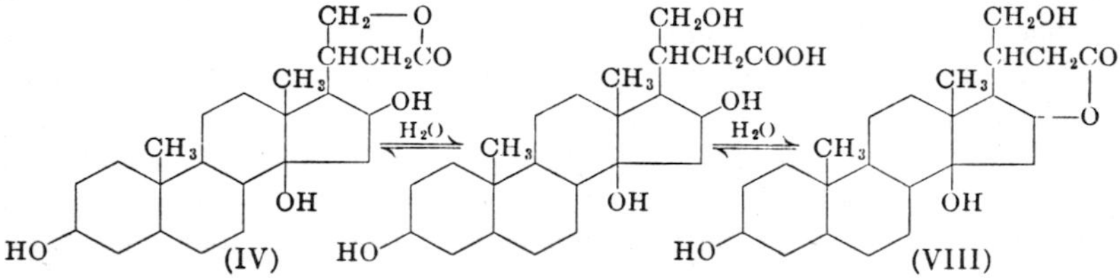

α-Form (dextro)   Dihydrogitoxigeninic acid   β-Form (levo)

established by oxidation to a keto acid ($C_{23}H_{32}O_6$), the carboxyl group of
which must come from a primary alcoholic group (the secondary group at
C_3 is oxidized at the same time).

A close approach to the correlation of gitoxigenin with the other aglycones
was made by Windaus,[5] who converted gitoxigenin through the dianhydro
compound to hexahydrodianhydrogitoxigenin, corresponding in composition to a similarly prepared tetrahydroanhydrodigitoxigenin.[6]   The two
substances, however, proved to be isomeric; the difference is maintained
in the corresponding ketones and the desoxylactones derived from them
by Clemmensen reduction.   The saturation of the multiple double bonds
in the anhydro compounds offers ample opportunity for stereoisomerism.

[3] Windaus, K. Westphal and Stein, *Ber.*, **61**, 1847 (1928).
[4] Cloetta, *Arch. exptl. Path. Pharmakol.*, **112**, 261 (1926).
[5] Windaus and Schwarte, *Ber.*, **58**, 1515 (1925).
[6] Windaus and Freese, *Ber.*, **58**, 2503 (1925).

The problem finally was solved by Jacobs and Gustus,[7] who succeeded in obtaining identical derivatives from the two genins by taking advantage of an isomerization to a new ("γ") stereochemical series under the influence of strong hydrochloric acid. Isogitoxigenic acid (IX) was converted through the 14-chloro compound into the anhydro derivative X; when

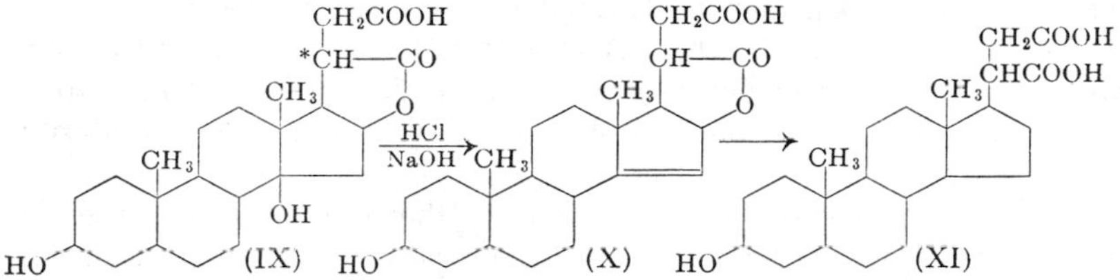

Isogitoxigenic acid   γ-Anhydro acid   γ-Digitoxanoldiacid

Isodigitoxigenic acid

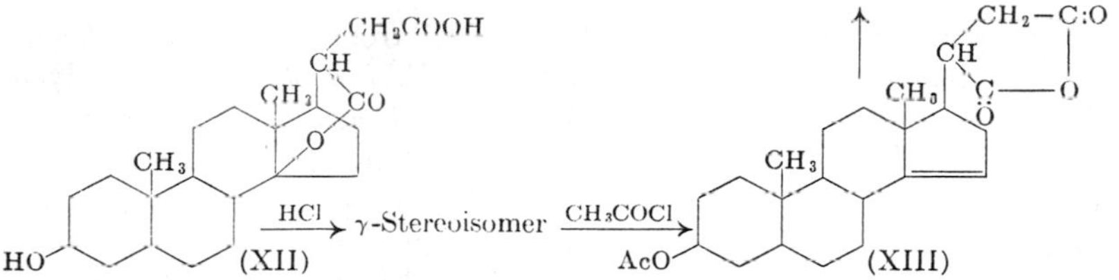

the ester of X was hydrogenated the lactone ring was cleaved simultaneously with saturation of the double bond and the product was the dibasic acid XI. This was identical with the corresponding acid of the digitoxigenin series obtained from XII by isomerization, conversion into the acetyl anhydroanhydride XIII, hydrogenation, and hydrolysis. Gitoxigenin therefore has the same carbon skeleton and 3β-hydroxyl group as the other aglycone.

Windaus[5] observed that gitoxigenin is converted by concentrated hydrochloric acid into a dianhydro derivative. More recently Kuno Meyer[8]

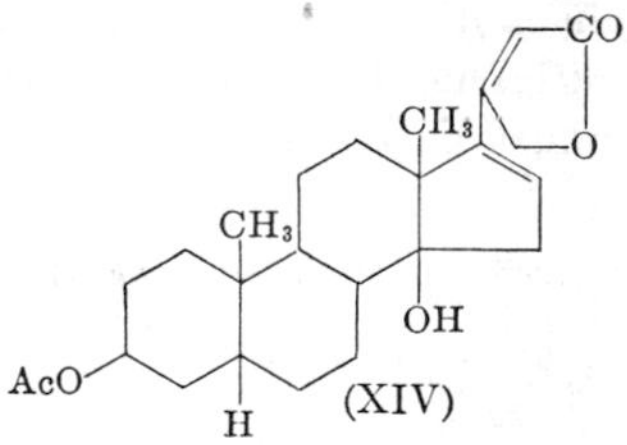

(XIV)
$[\alpha]_D + 83°$, λ_{max} 273mμ (4.4)

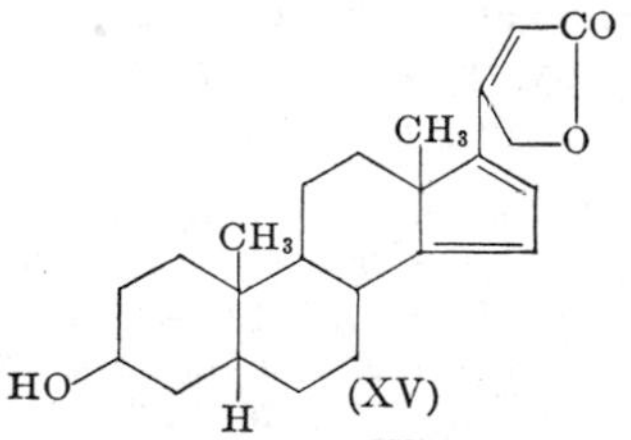

(XV)
$[\alpha]_D + 576°$, $\lambda_{max}^{CHCl_3}$ 337mμ

[7] Jacobs and Gustus, *J. Biol. Chem.*, **86**, 199 (1930).
[8] Kuno Meyer, *Helv. Chim. Acta*, **29**, 718 (1946).

found that chromatographic adsorption of the diacetate on alumina results in the elimination of the 16-acetoxyl group and formation of a monoanhydro compound of absorption spectrum indicative of conjugation of the double bond in ring D with that in the lactone ring, as in formula XIV. The preferential cleavage of the secondary alcoholic function instead of the tertiary group at C_{14} may be favored both by the tendency to form a conjugated system and by the fact of acetylation at the one position and not the other. The sequence of steps in the formation of dianhydrogitoxigenin is not known, but the structure XV follows from the absorption spectrum.[9]

Various isomeric etio acids encountered in the study of further degradations of gitoxigenin are described in Chapter X.[8,10] One of the acids has been further converted into 14-iso-17-isopregnane, m.p. 106°, $[\alpha]_D$ + 19° Chf.[11]

Oleandrin. Investigations reported in 1937 from three laboratories established that the cardiac-active principle of *Nerium oleander* is a 3-glycoside-16-acetyl derivative of gitoxigenin (I).[1,2,3] Controlled hydrolysis with dilute hydrochloric acid cleaves the glycosidic linkage with formation of oleandrigenin (III); the liberated sugar, oleandrose, $C_7H_{14}O_4$, $[\alpha]_D$ − 98°, has not been obtained crystalline but has been characterized as a methyl ether of a 2-desoxymethylpentose.[1,4] The aglycone is the 16-acetate of gitoxigenin and can be prepared by partial acetylation of gitoxigenin. The 16-acetoxyl group is subject to ready hydrolytic cleavage by dilute alkali; oleandrin can be saponified to the 16-desacetyl derivative IV. The acetyl group is eliminated as acetic acid with establishment of an anhydro linkage when either oleandrin or oleandrigenin is heated in vacuum at 250°. That the acetyl group is located at C_{16} rather than C_3 was established[2] by cautious oxidation of oleandrigenin to the corresponding ketone and dehydration with cold concentrated hydrochloric acid; the product was identical with dianhydrogitoxigenone. Hydrolysis of oleandrin with alcoholic hydrochloric acid affords dianhydrogitoxigenin (V),[5] at first regarded as a true aglycone ("digitaligenin"). Cautious hydrolysis of the glycoside with 5 percent sulfuric acid gives the same product and also a small amount of a substance that must be the 16-acetate of Δ^{14}-

[9] Tschesche, *Ber.*, **70**, 1554 (1937).

[10] Kuno Meyer, *Helv. Chim. Acta*, **29**, 1580, 1908 (1946); Plattner, Ruzicka, Heusser, Pataki and Meier, *ibid.*, **29**, 942, 949 (1946).

[11] Kuno Meyer, *Helv. Chim. Acta*, **30**, 2024 (1947).

[1] W. Neumann, *Ber.*, **70**, 1547 (1937).

[2] Tschesche, *Ber.*, **70**, 1554 (1937).

[3] Hesse, *Ber.*, **70**, 2264 (1937).

[4] Tschesche, Bohle and W. Newmann, *Ber.*, **71**, 1927 (1938).

[5] Windaus and Schwarte, *Ber.*, **58**, 1515 (1925).

Chart 8. OLEANDRIN

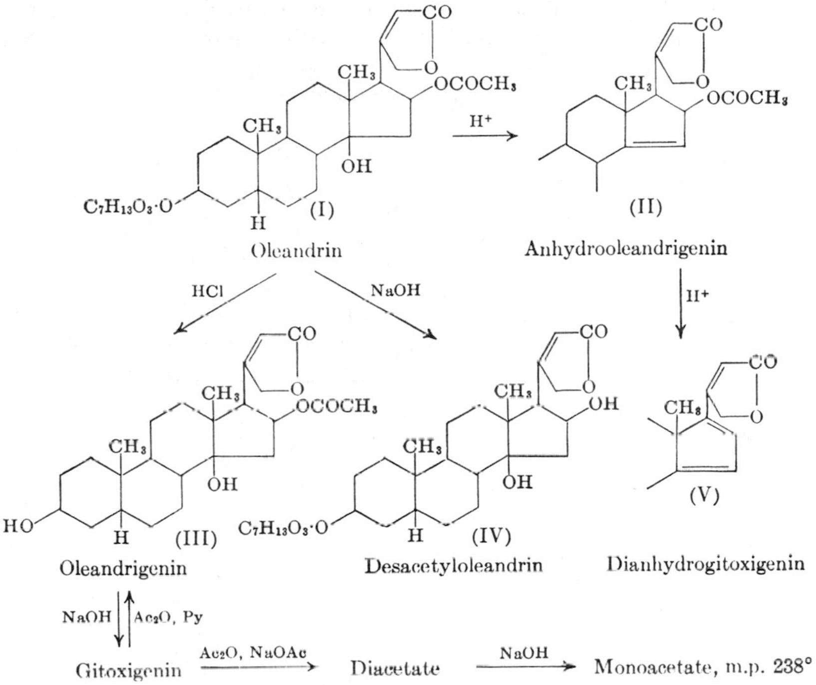

anhydrogitoxigenin, II. Partial saponification of gitoxigenin diacetate gives a monoacetate different from oleandrigenin; it may be the 3-acetate or the corresponding iso compound.

Adynerigenin and Neriantogenin. Adynerin and neriantin are physiologically inactive glycosides isolated in small amounts from oleander leaves. The structures of the genins have been investigated by Tschesche.[1] Tschesche effected a degradation of adynerigenin to tetrahydroanhydrodigitoxigenone (through II and IV, Chart 9), and hence the skeletal structure corresponds to that of genins of the digitalis group and one of two hydroxyl groups is at C_3; the other is placed at C_{14} because of the formation of an iso compound. Adynerigenin possesses a reducible double bond in the lactone ring and a nuclear double bond that is resistant to hydrogenation and therefore probably at position 8,9. Such a location would account for the ready formation of an anhydro compound, and the structure II assigned

[1] Tschesche and Bohle, *Ber.*, **71**, 654 (1938); Tschesche, Bohle and W. Neumann, *Ber.*, **71**, 1927 (1938).

to this substance is consistent with the absorption maximum (calcd. 244 mμ). On treatment with concentrated hydrochloric acid anhydro-adynerigenin is isomerized to a substance with an intense absorption band

Chart 9. ADYNERIGENIN

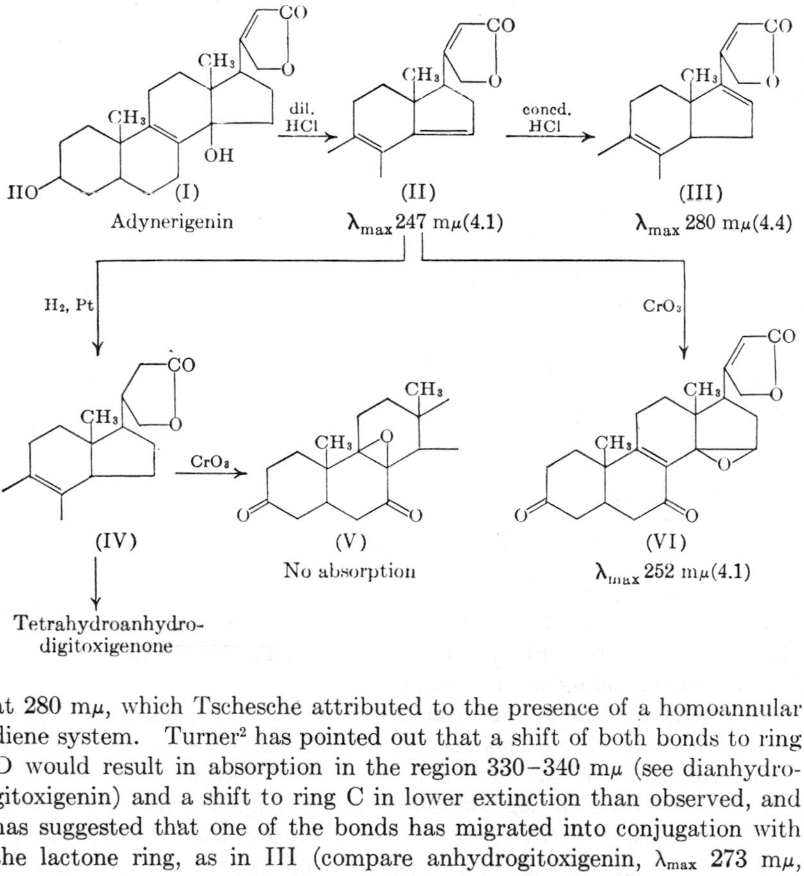

(I)
Adynerigenin

(II)
λ_{max} 247 mμ(4.1)

(III)
λ_{max} 280 mμ(4.4)

(IV)

Tetrahydroanhydro-
digitoxigenone

(V)
No absorption

(VI)
λ_{max} 252 mμ(4.1)

at 280 mμ, which Tschesche attributed to the presence of a homoannular diene system.   Turner[2] has pointed out that a shift of both bonds to ring D would result in absorption in the region 330–340 mμ (see dianhydro-gitoxigenin) and a shift to ring C in lower extinction than observed, and has suggested that one of the bonds has migrated into conjugation with the lactone ring, as in III (compare anhydrogitoxigenin, λ_{max} 273 mμ, log ϵ 4.4); thus it appears that the double bond at 14,15 migrates into conjugation with the lactone ring.   Whereas anhydroadynerigenin (II) absorbs only two moles of hydrogen, the rearranged product III absorbs three, perhaps through migration of the 8,9-double bond to the conjugated position 14,15 under the influence of the catalyst.[2]   No crystalline products of hydrogenation were isolated from III, but compound IV, the tetra-

[2] R. B. Turner, *Chem. Revs.*, **43**, 1 (1948).

hydride of II, was successfully reduced as the acetate by the known process of isomerization-hydrogenation[3]; hydrolysis of the product and oxidation at C_3 gave a ketolactone identical with tetrahydroanhydrodigitoxigenone.

Tschesche found that both anhydroadynerigenin (II) and its tetrahydride (IV) are oxidized by chromic acid to neutral substances that he regarded as resulting from severance of the 8,9-double bond with formation of two keto groups (the C_3 hydroxyl is oxidized at the same time). The structure suggested by Tschesche for the unsaturated compound is not consistent with the observed absorption maximum at 252 mμ, for the calculated value is 237 mμ. More likely the compounds are ketoxides of the structures V and VI (calcd. λ_{max} 249 mμ); the analysis of V conforms better to the revised formula $C_{23}H_{30}O_5$ than to $C_{23}H_{32}O_5$ and that for VI fits the alternate formulas about equally well.

Neriantogenin contains two acylable groups and two double bonds that are both easily reduced. It is converted by strong acid to a substance identified as dianhydrogitoxigenin, which is formed on similar treatment of either gitoxigenin or oleandrigenin (see Chart 8). Acetylation of neriantogenin gives a diacetate that is an isomer of 3,16-diacetoxy-Δ^{14}-anhydrogitoxigenin, prepared by acetylation of anhydrooleandrigenin (II, Chart 8). The two substances must be similar in structure, and it seems possible that neriantogenin differs in having an α-oriented hydroxyl at C_{16}. That the genin contains a reducible nuclear double bond probably at the 14,15-position suggests that a 14-hydroxyl group may have been eliminated in the course of the isolation. Although the glycoside appears to contain water of hydration not eliminated by drying in high vacuum, Tschesche considers the formula $C_{29}H_{42}O_9 \cdot 11/2 H_2O$ as established by the relation to the formulas of the genin ($C_{23}H_{32}O_4$) and the sugar (glucose, $C_6H_{12}O_6$) and by his observation that the glycoside absorbs two moles of hydrogen, corresponding to the two double bonds in the aglycone. This point requires confirmation.

Uzarin (Chart 10). The glycoside uzarin is a bioside containing glucose units and it is converted on drastic acid hydrolysis into a mixture of two anhydro compounds, here designated "β"-anhydrouzarigenin (chief product, m.p. 265°, $[\alpha]_D$ — 29.5°) and "α"-anhydrouzarigenin (m.p. 239°, $[\alpha]_D$ + 5°).[1] Uzarigenin itself is unknown. The hydroxyl group eliminated is evidently at C_{14}, since the remaining group is acylable and the glycoside forms an iso compound. According to Tschesche, the two anhydrouzarigenins are hydrogenated at about the same rate; the predominating "β"-isomer at least probably has the Δ^{14}-structure II (see Digoxigenin).

[3] Windaus, Linsert and Eckhardt, *Ann.*, **534**, 22 (1938).

[1] Windaus and Haack, *Ber.*, **63**, 1377 (1930); Tschesche, *Z. physiol. Chem.*, **222**, 50 (1933); Tschesche and Bohle, *Ber.*, **68**, 2252 (1935).

The degradation of this substance to etioallocholanic acid (see Carbon Skeleton) shows that uzarin, unlike all other known cardiac glycosides, has the A/B-trans configuration. This difference probably accounts for

Chart 10. UZARIN

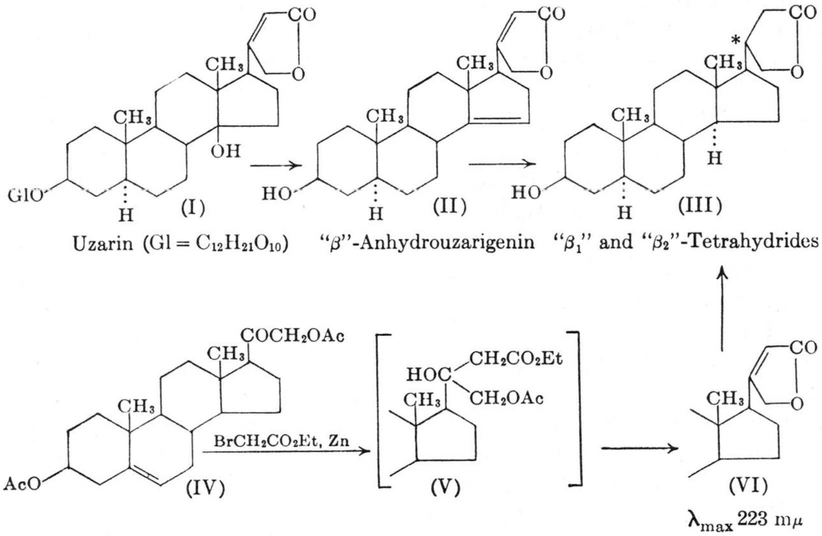

Uzarin (Gl = $C_{12}H_{21}O_{10}$)   "β"-Anhydrouzarigenin   "β_1" and "β_2"-Tetrahydrides

λ_{max} 223 mμ

the fact that "β"-anhydrouzarigenin is precipitated by digitonin, whereas strophanthidin, digitoxigenin, and gitoxigenin (all $C_3\beta$–OH) are not.

Tschesche effected a correlation with periplogenin as follows. "β"-Anhydrouzarigenin on hydrogenation yields two tetrahydrides (III) that are probably epimeric at C_{20} ("β_1", m.p. 217°, $[\alpha]_D$ + 11.4°; acetate, m.p. 248°, $[\alpha]_D$ + 3.9°; "β_2", m.p. 230°, $[\alpha]_D$ + 20°; acetate, m.p. 205°, $[\alpha]_D$ + 20°; the designations used here are the opposite of those employed by Tschesche). The two isomers were converted by oxidation to the ketones and these by Clemmensen reduction into the desoxylactones, and the "β_2"-desoxylactone proved to be identical with an octahydrotrianhydroperiplogenin that had been prepared by Jacobs and Bigelow.[2] The synthesis of isomers of the structure III was accomplished by the Swiss group[3] starting with pregnenolone acetate, which on reaction with lead tetraacetate afforded the ketol acetate IV. This on Reformatsky reaction with ethyl bromoacetate

[2] Jacobs and Bigelow, *J. Biol. Chem.*, **101**, 697 (1933).

[3] Ruzicka, Reichstein and Fürst, *Helv. Chim. Acta*, **24**, 76 (1941); Ruzicka, Plattner and Fürst, *ibid.*, **24**, 716 (1941); Ruzicka, Plattner, Fürst and Heusser, *ibid.*, **30**, 694 (1947).

afforded a carbinol (V) that underwent cyclization and dehydration with formation of the characteristic α,β-unsaturated lactone ring (VI). The doubly unsaturated product VI is not identical with either anhydrouzarigenin but isomeric with these substances. Hydrogenation of VI gave tetrahydrides that probably differ at C_{20}, since hydrogenation of a 5,6-double bond usually yields A/B-trans compounds exclusively.[4] The acetates of the synthetic compounds correspond closely in properties to the two tetrahydrides from "β"-anhydrouzarigenin: "β_1", m.p. 243°, $[\alpha]_D$ + 5.9°; "β_2", m.p. 204°, $[\alpha]_D$ + 19°. The difference in rotation is similar to that between known 20-normal and 20-iso compounds, and the relationship indicates that the slightly more dextrorotatory "β_2"-isomer must belong to the 20-normal series. The synthesis affords proof of the presence of the 3β-hydroxyl group.

Thevetin and Neriifolin. Thevetin was first isolated by Chen and Chen[1] as one of the poisonous principles of be-still nuts, the fruit of the plant

Chart 11. THEVETIN

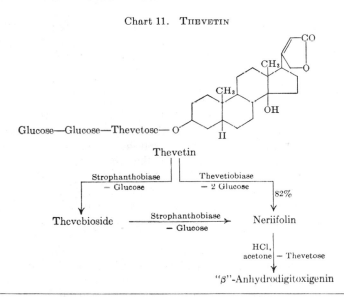

Thevetin

Thevebioside

Neriifolin

"β"-Anhydrodigitoxigenin

---

[4] Both A/B-trans and A/B-cis compounds are formed on hydrogenation of Δ^5-3β-acetoxyetiocholenic acid methyl ester [Steiger and Reichstein, *Helv. Chim. Acta*, **20**, 1040 (1937); Sorkin and Reichstein, *ibid.*, **29**, 1209 (1946)] and of Δ^5-androstene-3β-ol-17-one acetate [Reichstein and Lardon, *Helv. Chim. Acta*, **24**, 955 (1941); Wenner and Reichstein, *ibid.*, **27**, 24 (1944)]; but the A/B-trans product predominates. The absence of an extended side chain may be significant.

[1] K. K. Chen and A. L. Chen, *J. Pharmacol.*, **49**, 561 (1933); **51**, 23 (1934); *J. Biol. Chem.*, **105**, 231 (1934).

Thevetia neriifolia found in the Hawaiian Islands, South America, and India. An investigation by Tschesche[2] suggested that the aglycone is the 3α-epimer of digitoxigenin, but Helfenberger and Reichstein[3] have established that the genin is in fact identical with digitoxigenin. In thevetin this genin is linked to thevetose ($C_7H_{14}O_5$), a 6-desoxy-hexose 3-methyl ether isomeric with digitalose, and this in turn is linked to two molecules of glucose comprising a gentiobiose unit (Chart 11). Thevetose is a 2-hydroxy sugar and the linkage to the genin is cleaved with difficulty. Processes for the enzymatic hydrolysis of one and of two units of glucose are indicated in the chart; the end product neriifolin, which retains the thevetose unit, has been isolated from *Thevetia neriifolia* by Frèrejacque[4] and by Helfenberger and Reichstein.[3] Acetylneriifolin, isolated from the same source,[3,4] is hydrolyzed to neriifolin by potassium bicarbonate.[3] Elimination of the thevetose unit from neriifolin by the Mannich procedure was attended with loss of water and formation of "β"-anhydro-digitoxigenin.[3]

Antiarins. Two isomeric glycosides have been isolated from the latex of the upas tree *Antiaris toxicaria*, found chiefly in the Malayan archipelago. The gum was once used as an arrow poison. One form, "α"-antiarin, was encountered by Mulder in 1838; Kiliani[5] later (1896 – 1913) isolated "α"- and "β"-antiarin and developed techniques for purifying both isomers and for identifying them by the crystal form and the character of their hydrates; the melting points are not characteristic, and neither compound possesses significant optical activity. Many samples of latex contain only one of the antiarins. Kiliani found that both glycosides on hydrolysis yield the same aglycone derivative and that they differ only in the sugar residue; he identified the sugar derived from "β"-antiarin as L-rhamnose and characterized that from "α"-antiarin as a sirupy isomer designated antiarose. Kiliani also established the presence of a nuclear carbonyl group by the preparation of an oxime of "α"-antiarin and a semicarbazone of the aglycone derivative.

Tschesche and Haupt[6] later investigated samples obtained from Kiliani and by analyses and lactone titrations established that the antiarins have the formula $C_{29}H_{42}O_{11}$ and that the aglycone derivative is dianhydro-antiarigenin, $C_{23}H_{28}O_5$. This substance has one acylable hydroxyl group (monobenzoate), an unsaturated lactone ring (Legal test), a carbonyl group, an inert hydroxyl group, and two anhydro linkages that are not

[2] Tschesche, *Ber.*, **69**, 2368 (1936).

[3] Helfenberger and Reichstein, *Helv. Chim. Acta.* **31**, 1470 (1948).

[4] Frèrejacque, *Compt. rend.*, **221**, 645 (1945); **225**, 695 (1947).

[5] Kiliani, *Arch. Pharm.*, **234**, 438 (1896); *Ber.*, **43**, 3574 (1910); **46**, 667, 2179 (1913).

[6] Tschesche and Haupt, *Ber.*, **69**, 1377 (1936).

conjugated because there is no ultraviolet absorption in the region 230 – 280 mμ. Tschesche and Haupt suggested that antiarigenin may differ from strophanthidin only in the presence of an additional hydroxyl group (tertiary or hindered).

This conception was confirmed and extended by Reichstein[7] in an investigation conducted with 4.4 g. of material corresponding closely to Kiliani's description of "α"-antiarin. Hydrolysis by the Mannich pro-

Chart 12. "α"-ANTIARIN

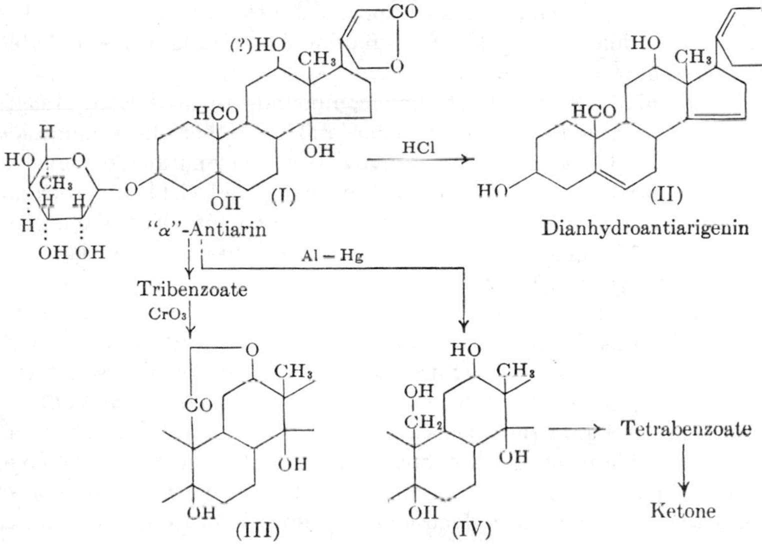

cedure afforded a small amount of nearly pure antiarigenin, m.p. 242°, $[\alpha]_D + 42°$; monobenzoate, m.p. 307°, $[\alpha]_D + 27°$, and sirupy antiarose, which was found to be identical with D-gulomethylose, the 5-epimer of L-rhamnose. The two antiarins therefore differ only in the configuration of one of the carbon atoms in the sugar unit. Reichstein found evidence in the absorption spectrum of "α"-antiarin for the presence of an α,β-unsaturated lactone ring (λ_{max} 217 mμ, log ε 4.1) and a carbonyl group (λ_{max} 305 mμ, log ε 1.8). Benzoylation of the glycoside gave a tribenzoate, in which the acyl groups are all in the sugar residue, and this on oxidation afforded a product that appears to be a lactone (III), formed by ring closure between a carboxyl group at C_{10} and a β-oriented hydroxyl group at a nearby position. Further evidence of the presence of an aldehydic group was

[7] Doebel, Schlittler and Reichstein, *Helv. Chim. Acta*, **31**, 688 (1948).

found in the reduction of "α"-antiarin to a substance having an additional acylable hydroxyl group, since it formed a tetrabenzoate: al-dihydro-"α"-antiarin (IV), m.p. 211°, λ_{max} 217 mμ, Legal test positive. The observation that the tetrabenzoate could be oxidized to a ketone shows that the non-acylable hydroxyl group involved in lactone formation is secondary. Reichstein considers the possible locations to be 11β, 12β, or 7β but notes that an 11β-hydroxyl could hardly withstand acid hydrolysis of the glycoside to dianhydroantiarigenin (II). The same objection can be raised to the placing of the group at C_7, adjacent to an anhydro linkage of II. A 12β-hydroxyl group should be stable under dehydrating conditions and is subject to some hindrance. The formulation shown thus seems probable but not certain.

Adonitoxigenin. Of two crystalline compounds isolated from *Adonis vernalis*, one appears to be the aglycone and the other the rhamnoside adonitoxin, of cardiac activity intermediate between cymarin and convallatoxin.[8] Adonitoxin, λ_{max} 218 mμ, forms an oxime and yields a carboxylic acid derivative on oxidation with chromic acid. Adonitoxigenin, obtained in poor yield by Mannich hydrolysis, appears to contain one tertiary and two secondary hydroxyl groups.[9]

Ouabagenin. The highly toxic glycoside ouabain was isolated by Arnaud[1] in 1888 as the active principle extracted by water from the bark and root of the ouabaio tree, long used by East African Somalis as an arrow poison. A sample of ouabaio wood secured by an explorer was found to yield as much as 3 g. of the glycoside per kilogram. Arnaud later[2] found the same glycoside in the seed of *Strophanthus gratus*, the inée (or onaye) used by the Pahouins as an arrow poison. The active principle, one of the most toxic of the cardiac glycosides, is known both as ouabain and as g-strophanthin.

The structure of ouabagenin presents an intriguing problem that is not yet solved. Ouabain is a difficultly hydrolyzable rhamnoside; isolation of the true genin was not accomplished until 1942, when Mannich and Siewert[3] applied the method of hydrolysis with hydrogen chloride and acetone, as noted in the introduction. Earlier studies of structure utilized the glycoside, for which Jacobs and Bigelow[4] established the formula $C_{29}H_{44}O_{12}$. Ouabain gives the Legal test, forms an iso compound and a dihydride that are both negative in the Legal test,[4] and reacts with sodium

[8] Rosenmund and Reichstein, *Pharm. Acta Helv.*, **17,** 176 (1942).
[9] Katz and Reichstein, *Pharm. Acta Helv.*, **22,** 437 (1947).
[1] Arnaud, *Compt. rend.*, **106,** 1011 (1888); **126,** 346, 1208, 1280, 1654, 1873 (1898).
[2] See footnote 1, ref. 3.
[3] Mannich and Siewert, *Ber.*, **75,** 737, 750 (1942).
[4] Jacobs and Bigelow, *J. Biol. Chem.*, **96,** 647 (1932); **101,** 15 (1933).

ethoxide in ethanol with opening of the lactone ring to form the crystalline sodium salt of ouabaic acid.[1] Arnaud[1] found that ouabain can be converted by the action of acetic anhydride and zinc chloride into a heptaacetylanhydroouabain (formula: $C_{43}H_{56}O_{18}$[4]). Three of the acetyl groups must be in the sugar residue, and the genin portion therefore contains four hydroxyl groups acylable under forcing conditions. Probably a tertiary hydroxyl group initially present at C_{14} is responsible for the iso reaction and is lost in the establishment of the anhydro linkage.[4] Mannich and Siewert[3] observed that acetylation of ouabain without addition of zinc chloride proceeds without formation of an anhydro linkage and gives a hexaacetate. Therefore the sugar residue is linked to a secondary alcoholic group, probably C_3, and the genin contains three other acylable hydroxyl groups, a 14-hydroxyl group, and a further tertiary hydroxyl capable of being acetylated under forcing conditions (possibly at C_5). Ouabagenin forms a monoacetonide that affords a diacetate, but it reacts to only a minor extent with lead tetraacetate.[3] The aglycone therefore contains four secondary (or primary) hydroxyl groups, two of which must bear the 1,3-relationship, and two tertiary hydroxyls, one of which is at C_{14}. The hydroxyl groups must all be nonadjacent. A minor product of the reaction of ouabain with hydrogen chloride in acetone is an anhydroouabagenin that yields the genin on hydration and that absorbs only one mole of hydrogen;[3] Mannich and Siewert suggest that the anhydro compound is an oxido derivative formed by loss of water between the two acylable hydroxyls involved in the formation of the acetonide.

In the earlier work Jacobs and Bigelow[4] conceived the idea of stabilizing the genin moiety by hydrogenation prior to hydrolysis. Heptaacetylanhydroouabain was converted into the tetrahydride and this was submitted to acetolysis with hydrochloric and acetic acids. A sugar-free reaction product was isolated and found, surprisingly, to be the acetate of a trianhydromonohydroxylactone of the formula $C_{22}H_{28}O_3$; the parent substance of the heptaacetate corresponds to $C_{23}H_{36}O_7$. Fieser and Newman[5] suggested that the carbon atom is lost through the elimination of formaldehyde from a hydroxymethyl group at C_{10} and found the absorption spectrum of the hydroxylactone (λ_{max} 270 mμ) to be indicative of the presence of a benzenoid ring. Both Tschesche[6] and Marker[7] noted that comparison with neoergosterol with respect to properties and behavior on dehydrogenation indicates that the degradation product is not similarly constituted (ring B aromatic) as suggested.[5] The simultaneous elimination of four

[5] Fieser and Newman, *J. Biol. Chem.*, **114**, 705 (1936); see also first edition of this book.

[6] Tschsche and Haupt, *Ber.*, **70**, 43 (1937).

[7] Marker and co-workers, *J. Am. Chem. Soc.*, **64**, 720 (1942).

hydroxyl groups is indicative of proximate locations, but the facts available do not permit full interpretation of the reaction.

Mannich and Siewert submitted ouabain to catalytic dehydrogenation (Pt, O_2) with the hope of converting the primary alcoholic group to an aldehydic group. Two isomeric dehydroouabains were obtained; they reduce Fehling's solution but do not give carbonyl derivatives and are regarded as lactols. These authors interpret the observations to date in terms of a provisional formulation for ouabagenin with hydroxyls at positions 1, 3, 5, 11, 14, and in the angular methyl group.

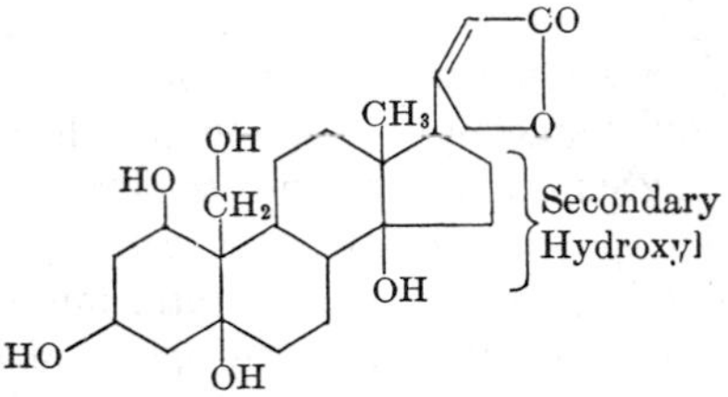

Ouabagenin (?)

Sarmentogenin. Jacobs and Heidelberger[1] characterized the aglycone from sarmentocymarin as an isomer of digoxigenin that likewise contains two acylable hydroxyl groups and a 14β-hydroxyl group (iso and anhydro compounds). They observed also that the product of oxidation, now recognized as a diketone[2] (sarmentogenone, m.p. 237°, $[\alpha]_D$ + 14°) forms only a monosemicarbazone; the diketone is different from digoxigenone.[2] Tschesche and Bohle[3] effected elimination of all three hydroxyl groups as follows: dehydration to two monoanhydro compounds; hydrogenation of one of these to a tetrahydride; oxidation to a diketone; Clemmensen reduction, which could not be pushed beyond reduction of the one normally reactive keto group (shown to be in ring A); catalytic hydrogenation of the inert keto group to an alcoholic group; dehydration and hydrogenation. The product was identical with the desoxylactone that had been obtained by similar degradations of digitoxigenin[4] and of digoxigenin.[5] At the time of this work digoxigenin was believed to have a hydroxyl group at C_{11}, and Tschesche and Bohle interpreted their observations on the assumption that sarmentogenin also has an 11-hydroxyl group and is the 9-isomer of digoxigenin. Later events showed that the somewhat hindered secondary hydroxyl group in digoxigenin is at C_{12} and not C_{11}, and hence the evi-

[1] Jacobs and Heidelberger, *J. Biol. Chem.*, **81**, 765 (1929).
[2] Katz and Reichstein, *Pharm. Acta Helv.*, **19**, 231 (1944).
[3] Tschesche and Bohle, *Ber.*, **69**, 2497 (1936).
[4] Windaus and Stein, *Ber.*, **61**, 2436 (1928).
[5] Tschesche and Bohle, *Ber.*, **69**, 793 (1936).

dence cited could be interpreted on the hypothesis that sarmentogenin has the normal configuration at C_9 and an 11α-hydroxyl group. An 11α-hydroxyl group is known to be acylable and an 11-keto group to be inert to most reagents; furthermore the alcohol that Tschesche and Bohle obtained by hydrogenation of the monoketo desoxylactone proved to be nonacylable, like the 11β-hydroxy cortical steroids that arise on hydrogenation of the 11-ketones.

Katz and Reichstein[2] observed that sarmentogenone and digoxigenone differ more in optical rotation than known 11- and 12-ketones, but Klyne[6] suggested that the apparent abnormality may arise from the 14-iso configuration or from the vicinal action of the unsaturated lactone ring. Tschesche and Bohle's desoxotetrahydroanhydrosarmentogenone presents neither of these interfering features of configuration or structure, and Klyne found that the molecular rotation differences for this substance and its transformation products correspond well with the values for analogous bile acid derivatives having an oxygen function at C_{11}.

Finally Katz,[7] in an investigation conducted with 320 mg. of sarmentogenin from 100 g. of a rare seed (possibly *Strophanthus sarmentosus*), secured unequivocal chemical evidence of the positions and orientations of the two secondary hydroxyl groups. Permanganate oxidation of sarmentogenin diacetate (I) yielded an etio acid (II) that was converted by

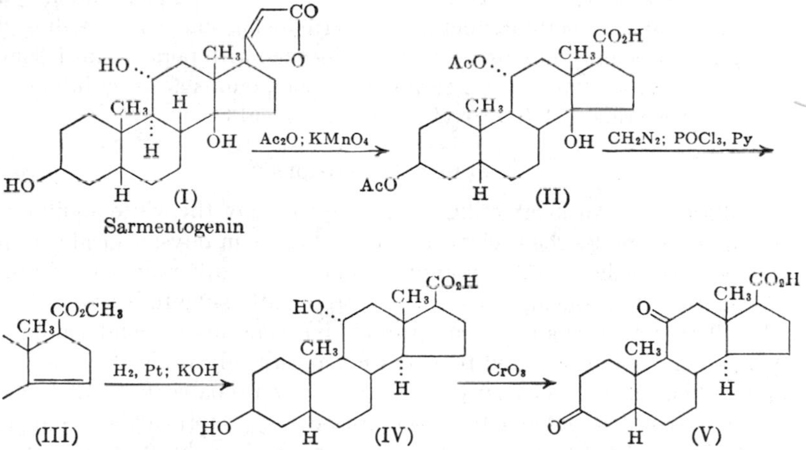

Sarmentogenin (I)

(II)

(III)

(IV)

(V)

elimination of the 14β-hydroxyl group and hydrogenation into a dihydroxy-etio acid (IV) of 14-normal configuration. This substance on oxidation

[6] Klyne, *Biochem. J.* (in press).
[7] Katz, *Helv. Chim. Acta*, **31**, 993 (1948).

gave a diketoetio acid (V) identical with that obtained by oxidation of $3\alpha,11\alpha$-dihydroxyetiocholanic acid.[8] Since the two dihydroxy acids are different but both contain two acylable hydroxyl groups, the acid from sarmentogenin must differ in the orientation of the 3-hydroxyl group. Sarmentogenin is thus a 3β-hydroxy compound, and it is another example of a cardogenin that is not precipitated by digitonin.

Calotropis Glycosides. Investigations by Hesse[9] of the African arrow poison of calotropis led to the isolation of calotropin from the leaves and stalks and of uscharin and calotoxin from the latex. The formulas and relationships between the three glycosides are indicated in the chart. Calo-

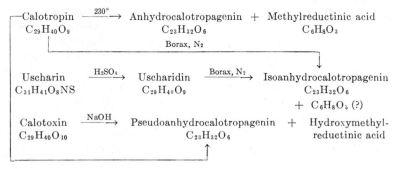

tropin cannot be hydrolyzed readily. Thermal splitting yields an anhydro derivative and a methylreductinic acid (reducing enediol); alkaline hydrolysis an isomeric anhydro derivative; cleavage with borax a third isomer. Hesse postulates that the two series of iso compounds arise by interaction of the lactone ring with hydroxyl groups at C_{14} and C_{16}.

SQUILL GLYCOSIDES

Scillaren A. Although scillaren A, a glycoside of the white squill *Scilla maritima*, resembles the typical cardiac glycosides in physiological activity, the aglycone scillaridin A (an anhydro derivative) differs in some features of structure from the aglycones of the strophanthus-digitalis group (Chart 13). The lactone ring is α,β-unsaturated but contains a second conjugated double bond and is enlarged to a six ring, and the glycoside also contains a double bond in the nucleus; the 5,6-location is probable but not certain. The glycoside does not give the Legal test but it does form an iso compound. Stoll published the first of a series of papers on the subject in 1933 after a

---

[8] W. P. Long, Marshall and Gallagher, *J. Biol. Chem.*, **165**, 197 (1946).

[9] Hesse and Reicheneder, *Ann.*, **526**, 252 (1936); Hesse, Reicheneder and Eysenbach, *ibid.*, **537**, 67 (1938).

ten-year period of investigation.[1] The analyses at first seemed to indicate the formula $C_{25}H_{32}O_3$ for the aglycone, but the differences in carbon and hydrogen content between this formula and $C_{24}H_{30}O_3$ are only 0.26 percent and 0.23 percent, respectively. The degradation of scillaridin A to two

Chart 13. SCILLAREN A AND SCILLARIDIN A

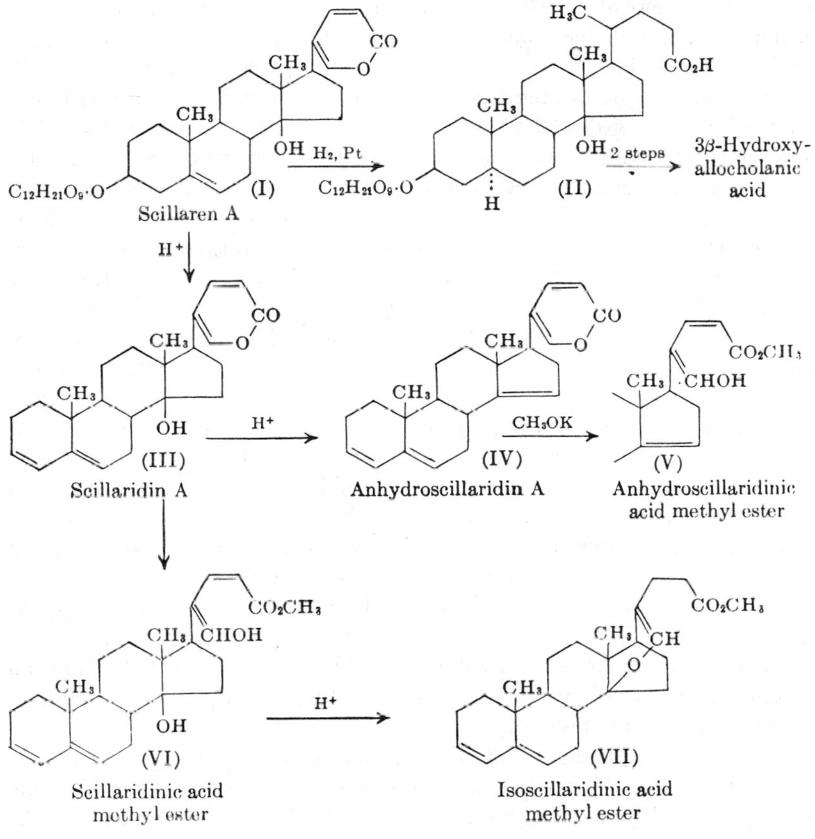

acids,[2] one of which proved to be identical with allocholanic acid, established correspondence in carbon content and skeletal structure to the bile acids, and determination of the molecular weights of the cholanic acids[3] with

[1] Stoll and collaborators, *Helv. Chim. Acta*, **16**, 703 (1933); **17**, 641, 1334 (1934); **18**, 82, 401 (1935); *Z. physiol. Chem.*, **222**, 24 (1933).
[2] Stoll, A. Hofmann and Helfenstein, *Helv. Chim. Acta*, **18**, 644 (1935).
[3] Stoll, A. Hofmann and Peyer, *Helv. Chem. Acta*, **18**, 1247 (1935).

an accuracy of 2–3 units by titration of large samples dispelled initial doubts that these are C_{24}-compounds.

Scillaren A is a bioside of the constitution: aglycone-rhamnose-glucose, for under the influence of either scillarenase (in squill) or strophanthobiase it is hydrolyzed to proscillaridin A, which is: aglycone-rhamnose.[1,4] The rhamnoside linkage is resistant to hydrolysis, but mild treatment with acid effects removal of the sugar residue by a process of cleavage, with introduction of a double bond. Thus scillaren A (I) is converted quantitatively into scillaridin A (III) by the action of 1 percent sulfuric acid in 50 percent methanol at the temperature of the steam bath. Stoll attributed the lability of the group at C_3 to the presence of a double bond at the 5,6-position and the consequent tendency to form a dienic system by an elimination reaction. Scillaridin A does not react with maleic anhydride and hence is not a homoannular diene, and Stoll suggests the $\Delta^{3,5}$-arrangement. The presence of such a grouping is not apparent from the absorption spectrum, for both scillaren A and scillaridin A show strong absorption at 300 mμ attributable to the lactone ring system and the latter compound shows no further band in the region of 235 mμ. This unexplained anomaly suggests that there is some error in either the data or the interpretation. Hydrogenation of both scillaren A and scillaridin A results in part in reductive fission of the unsaturated lactone ring with liberation of the bile acid side chain, as in hexahydroscillaren A acid (II). The saturation of the nuclear double bond eliminates the special lability of the bioside unit and its tendency to suffer cleavage. The saturated glycosidic acid II on treatment with acid suffers hydrolysis rather than cleavage.[4] The bioside residue was hydrolyzed by the action of 1 N hydrogen chloride in methanol at the reflux temperature and under these conditions the 14-hydroxyl group was also eliminated. The crude anhydro acid on hydrogenation afforded a product identified as 3β-hydroxyallocholanic acid, and this degradation establishes the position and orientation of the hydroxyl group originally linked to the bioside residue.

The doubly unsaturated lactone ring opens easily and stays open following methylation. Methyl alcoholic potassium hydroxide cleaves the ring of anhydroscillaridin A (IV) with esterification of the carboxyl group. The product V appears to be entirely enolic, for it is strongly acidic (titration), gives acyl derivatives, fails to form an oxime, semicarbazone, or phenylhydrazone, and can be methylated by the action of methanol and hydrogen chloride. On hydrolysis of V with alkali, followed by acidification, anhydroscillaridin A is regenerated. Scillaridin A itself reacts with methyl alcoholic potassium hydroxide in an analogous manner to form the enolic

[4] Stoll and Renz, *Helv. Chim. Acta,* **24,** 1380 (1941).

ester VI, which affords an ether-ester on reaction of freshly prepared material with diazomethane; alkaline hydrolysis of this substance affects only the ester group. The enol ester VI was not obtained as such in a fully pure condition, for on crystallization it lost water and yielded the iso compound VII. The oxide ring of the isoaglycone is more stable to hydrolysis than the oxide ring of the typical strophanthus-digitalis isoaglycones and resembles that of isogitoxigenin.

Scilliroside. The white and red variety of squill (sea onion) differ so little in morphology that they are not distinguished in botanical classification, but they differ markedly in the nature and physiological actions of the active principles. The red squill possesses high, specific toxicity for rats, and powder prepared from dried red squills is used widely as a rat poison, a use described by the Arabian Muhammed Elgâfaki early in the 13th century.

Scilliroside is the chief glycoside of the red variety of *Scilla maritima*; it is accompanied by scillaren A and scillaren F. Scilliroside is particularly lethal to rats and other rodents (median lethal dose, LD_{50}, for female rats, 0.4 mg./kg.; for male rats, 0.7 mg./kg.), whereas scillaren A from the white squill is almost inactive in this species (LD_{50} about 200 mg./kg.). The substance is a difficultly hydrolyzable glucoside and the genin has not been prepared. The chemistry of the glycoside has been investigated extensively by Stoll,[1] who has tentatively suggested the structure I (Chart 14). Scilliroside has the same ultraviolet absorption characteristics as scillaren A and similarly does not respond to the Legal test. On titration with alkali one mole of base is used for the opening of the lactone ring and a second for hydrolysis of a labile acetyl group (acetic acid was isolated as silver acetate). Methanolic potassium hydroxide removes the acetyl group and opens the lactone ring to give a potassium enolate, which on acidification is converted into an aldehyde-keto ester (IV), characterized by formation of a quinoxaline derivative (α-keto ester) and a hexaacetyl derivative (acetylation of both enolized carbonyl groups and of four hydroxyl groups in the sugar residue). The lactone ring is thus formulated as doubly unsaturated, like that of scillaren A, and with an acetoxyl group on the α-unsaturated carbon atom.

The acetyl group is also eliminated on catalytic hydrogenation, which proceeds with absorption of three moles of hydrogen and gives two tetrahydrides that probably are C_{20}-epimers. The presence of another double bond is indicated by the fact that the tetrahydrides, like scilliroside, form oxides with perbenzoic acid. The resistance to hydrogenation points to

[1] Stoll and Renz, *Helv. Chim. Acta*, **25**, 43, 377 (1942); Stoll, Renz and Helfenstein, *ibid.*, **26**, 648 (1943).

location of the double bond at either the 7,8- or 8,9-position (evidence mentioned below for the presence of a 14-hydroxyl group rules out the 8,14-position). In Stoll's formulation the bond is placed at 8,9.

Chart 14. SCILLIROSIDE; STOLL'S FORMULATION

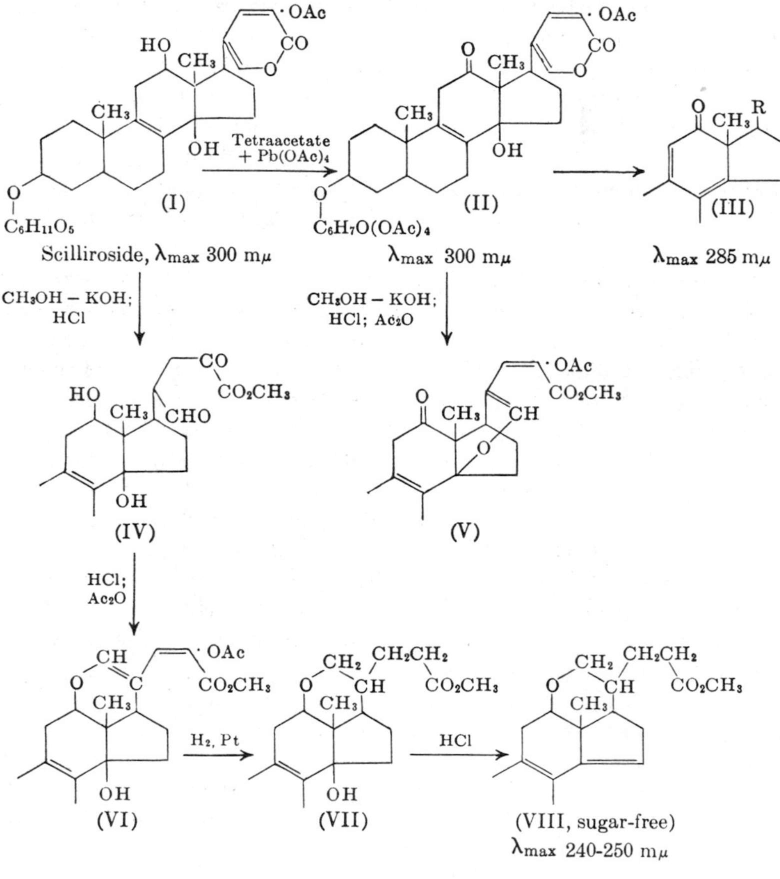

Scilliroside forms a tetraacetate; since the sugar unit contains four acylable groups, the acetyl residues evidently are all introduced into the sugar residue. Zerewitinoff determination shows two hydroxyl groups in scilliroside tetraacetate. One appears to be at C_{14}, but the other is a secondary group since scilliroside and the tetraacetate can be oxidized by either chromic acid or lead tetraacetate to ketones. The selective oxidation by lead tetraacetate of a secondary alcoholic group in preference to attack of the sugar moiety is an unusual process for which Stoll's formulation (Chart 14, I → II) affords no explanation. Since oxidation to the ketone results in no change in absorption spectrum, the carbonyl group is regarded as not conjugated with the nuclear double bond; the resistance of the secondary alcohol group to acetylation is attributed by Stoll to its location at C_{12}. The corresponding ketone reacts normally with semicarbazide. Although a keto group at C_{12} would not be close to either the nuclear double bond or the hydroxyl at C_{14}, conversion to the ketone influences the reactivity of both of these functions. Thus hydrogenation of the ketone II affords a lactone and the corresponding acid resulting from reductive fission of the lactone ring; both products are fully saturated and carry intact secondary and tertiary hydroxyls and the tetraacetoxyglucosido unit. Oxidation of the secondary hydroxyl group of scilliroside also renders the tertiary group at C_{14} more labile than before. The easily formed anhydro compound shows more intense absorption in the ultraviolet than scilliroside or the hydroxyketone (II), and the position of the maximum is shifted 15 mμ to shorter wave length. Stoll's formula III appears inconsistent with the maximum at 285 mμ, for the lactone ring absorbs at 300 mμ and the chromophoric grouping in ring C should absorb at still higher wave length.

The proximity of both the secondary and tertiary hydroxyl groups to the lactone ring is indicated by the following relationships. After the lactone ring of scilliroside has been opened with alkali (IV), treatment with acid effects ring closure to an iso compound (acetate, VI). The reaction was initially assumed to involve the aldehydic group and the tertiary hydroxyl at C_{14}. However, VI and the hydrogenated derivative VII have lost the property of undergoing smooth chromic acid oxidation and evidently lack the original secondary hydroxyl group, and the ready formation of an anhydro compound (VIII) indicates the presence of the tertiary hydroxyl instead. If the secondary hydroxyl is first oxidized, ring opening of the ketone (II) gives an aldehyde ester that on treatment with acid affords a different type of iso compound (V), formed by ring closure with the tertiary hydroxyl, which is thus located at C_{14}. The dehydration of VII is accomplished by brief refluxing with 0.5 N hydrogen chloride in methanol, and, surprisingly, is attended with hydrolysis of the sugar unit. The spectrum of the anhydro compound is consistent with the $\Delta^{8,14}$-structure, as in VIII (calcd. λ_{max} 244 mμ). A sugar-free product was also obtained by similar treatment of the saturated dihydroxy acid resulting from the reductive fission of dehydroscilliroside tetraacetate (II); the amorphous product, presumably the dihydroxyanhydro acid, was hydrogenated and then oxidized to an amorphous acid that formed a disemicarbazone, and hence the sugar is linked to a secondary hydroxyl group.

Stoll's formulation accounts adequately for many of the intricate relationships, but some points of inconsistency have been noted. An alternate formulation that accounts better for some of the observations is shown in Chart 14a. This assumes that the secondary hydroxyl group in scilliroside

Chart 14a. SCILLIROSIDE; ALTERNATE FORMULATION

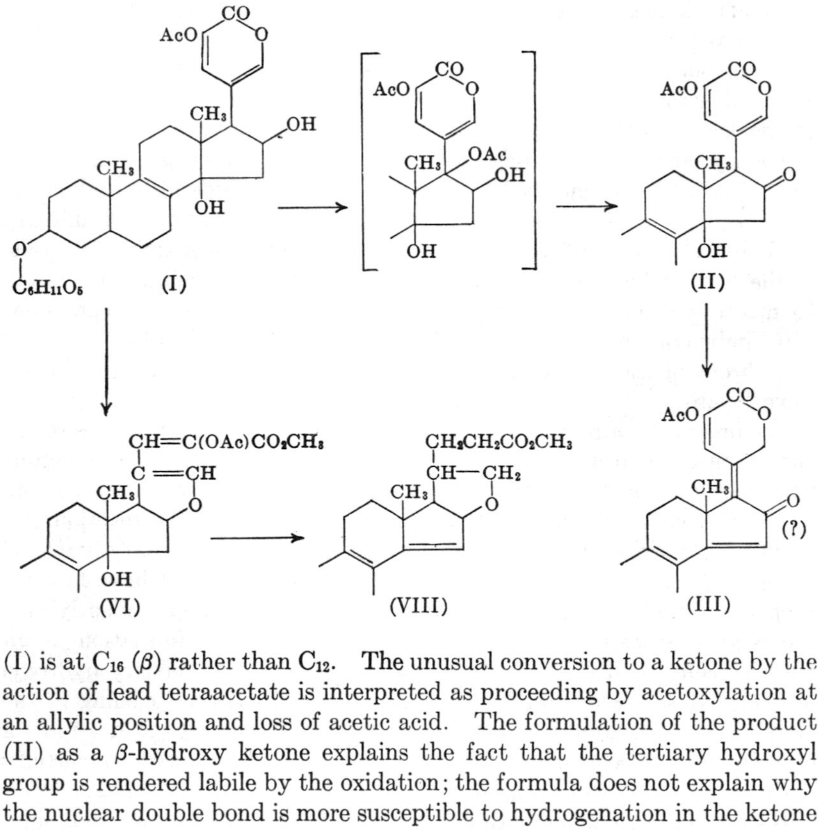

(I) is at C_{16} (β) rather than C_{12}. The unusual conversion to a ketone by the action of lead tetraacetate is interpreted as proceeding by acetoxylation at an allylic position and loss of acetic acid. The formulation of the product (II) as a β-hydroxy ketone explains the fact that the tertiary hydroxyl group is rendered labile by the oxidation; the formula does not explain why the nuclear double bond is more susceptible to hydrogenation in the ketone than it is in the alcohol. The shift in the absorption maximum attending formation of the anhydroketone (III) suggests that a change has occurred in the chromophoric system of the lactone ring. The data available do not suffice to indicate the nature of the change; indeed there is no evidence to show that the ketonic group is still present and has not condensed in some manner with the lactone ring. Possibly the 20,21-double bond migrates into conjugation with the 16-keto group as in III; the absorption characteristics of the complex cross-conjugated system cannot be estimated.

Hellebrin. This particularly active bioside of the Christmas rose (*Radix Hellebore niger*) was first isolated in a pure condition by W. Karrer,[1] who found that acid hydrolysis proceeds with considerable damage to the aglycone but affords glucose as one product. Hydrolysis by the Mannich procedure is unsuccessful because of lack of solubility in acetone.[2] Hydrolysis with strophanthobiase proceeds readily to give glucose and desglucohellebrin, which can then be hydrolyzed by the Mannich method to rhamnose and two isomeric aglycones, $C_{24}H_{32-34}O_6$; these probably contain two tertiary and one secondary hydroxyl group and a six-membered lactone ring. Hydrolysis of hellebrin by the Voss procedure ($CH_3OH-HCl$) yields a substance that contains a methoxyl group; probably hellebrin contains a C_{10}-aldehydic group and the product is a methylal derivative.[1] The presence of an aldehydic group is further indicated by the isolation of an oxime of hellebrin[2] and by the oxidation of desglucohellebrin triacetate to a carboxylic acid.[3] Hellebrin on acetylation yields only a heptaacetate, corresponding to the seven acylable groups in the bioside unit, and hence the genin moiety contains no acylable hydroxyl groups Of the six oxygen atoms of the aglycone, one is present in glycosidic linkage (presumably at C_3), one is aldehydic, two are in the lactone ring, and two are probably present as tertiary hydroxyl groups. One of the latter groups is probably at C_{14}, because treatment with potassium hydroxide in methanol leads to an inactive compound, isohellebrinic acid methyl ester. Evidence for the structure of the lactone ring is afforded by the fact that hellebrin, desglucohellebrin, and the two isomeric aglycones all show an absorption maximum at 300 mμ, corresponding to that of scillaren A.

SYNTHETIC APPROACH[4]

The production of pure cardiac-active glycosides by economical methods of partial or total synthesis is an attractive goal of future research. No natural representative of the group or physiologically active model compound has as yet been prepared by synthesis, but a start has been made in the development of methods for the construction of some of the characteristic groupings.

One method for the synthetic formation of the five-membered α,β-unsaturated ring, or β-substituted α,β-butenolide grouping, was developed by Elderfield[5] and by Ruzicka and associates[6] and employed by the latter

[1] W. Karrer, *Helv. Chim. Acta*, **26**, 1353 (1943).
[2] Schmutz, *Pharm. Acta Helv.*, **22**, 373 (1947).
[3] Buzas and Reichstein, *Helv. Chim. Acta*, **31**, 110 (1948).
[4] For a more detailed account see R. B. Turner, *Chem. Revs.*, **43**, 1 (1948).
[5] Fried, Linville and Elderfield, *J. Org. Chem.*, **7**, 362 (1942).
[6] Ruzicka, Reichstein and Fürst, *Helv. Chim. Acta*, **24**, 76 (1941).

for a synthesis of a tetrahydroanhydrouzarigenin illustrated above in Chart 10. As formulated again in Chart 15, this involves a Reformatsky condensation of ethyl bromoacetate with a 21-acetoxy-20-ketopregnane or allopregnane. In some instances both the β-hydroxylactone (II) and

Chart 15. SYNTHETIC CONSTRUCTION OF THE LACTONE RING

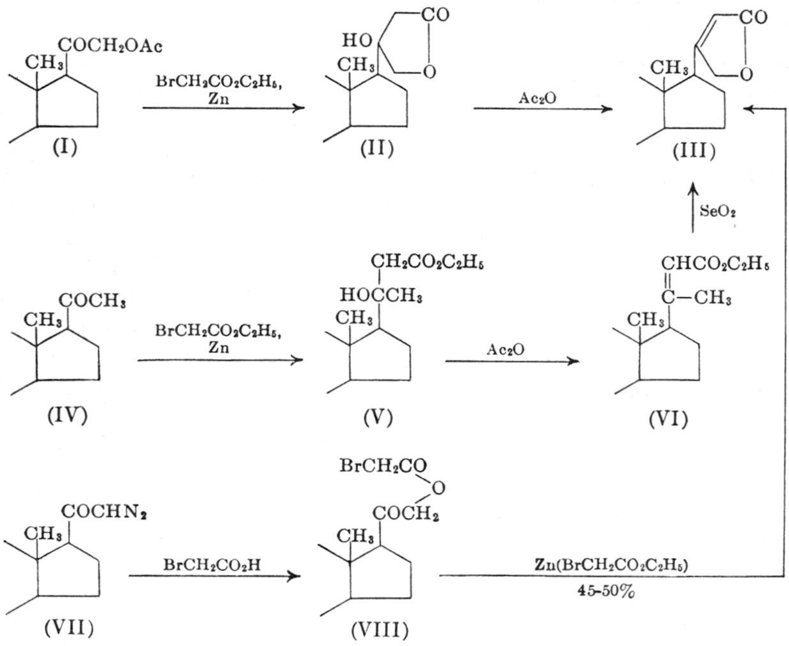

the unsaturated lactone (III) are obtained; dehydration of II proceeds mainly in the desired direction. Although the process has been used successfully in a number of instances, the butenolide is always accompanied by by-products and requires extensive purification. An alternate synthesis[7] in which dehydration can proceed in only one way starts with the condensation of ethyl bromoacetate with a methyl ketone (IV), which proceeds fairly satisfactorily. Dehydration of the hydroxy ester V followed by selenium dioxide oxidation of VI gives the butenolide, but the yield in the last step is not satisfactory. Treatment of the unsaturated ester VI with N-bromosuccinimide effects the desired ring closure but also results in the introduction of a double bond at the 16,17-position (λ_{max} 273 mμ).[8] An

[7] Torrey, Kuck and Elderfield, *J. Org. Chem.*, **6**, 289 (1941); Ruzicka, Plattner and Pataki, *Helv. Chim. Acta*, **25**, 425 (1942).

[8] Ruzicka, Plattner and Pataki, *Helv. Chim. Acta*, **28**, 1360 (1945).

apparently improved procedure described by Plattner and Heusser[9] involves condensation of a diazoketone (VII) with bromoacetic acid. The resulting bromo compound VIII does not yield the unsaturated lactone III on treatment with zinc alone but does so on the addition of ethyl bromoacetate.

A method for the introduction of a 14β-hydroxyl group through the 14,15-β-oxide is illustrated in Chart 7; the stereochemistry of the two types of 14,15-oxides and the derived products is discussed in Chapter X. The possibility of utilizing 5,6-oxides as a means for the introduction of the 5β-hydroxyl group characteristic of many of the potent cardiac-active principles has been explored without success, since on hydrogenation an α-oxide yields the 5α-hydroxy compound and a β-oxide yields the 6β-hydroxy compound. Δ[4]-Cholestenone-3, however, reacts with alkaline hydrogen peroxide to give the 4,5-β-oxide and this on hydrogenation is converted in part into coprostane-3α,5β-diol (m.p. 193°, $|\alpha|_D$ + 47° Chf; 3-acetate, m.p. 148°, $[\alpha]_D$ + 51° Chf).

TOAD POISONS[1]

The venom of the toad, known since antiquity and endowed with various legendary beliefs in the middle ages, has long been recognized as having significant medicinal qualities. For centuries the Chinese have employed a galenical preparation from the local toad (*Bufo bufo gargarizans*) known as Ch'an Su in China and as Senso in Japan. Hard, dark brown cakes of Ch'an Su are applied externally for treatment of toothache, sinusitus, and hemorrhages of the gums. Dried and powdered toad skin was commonly used as a remedy for dropsy until Withering introduced the use of the foxglove drug. Toad venom has a digitalis-like action on the heart and is highly lethal to mammals and to frogs, but not to toads (see next section).

The poisonous secretion is located in skin glands and can be obtained either from dried toad skins or from the living animal. The bulk of the venom is located in the parotid glands behind the eyes and can be removed by expression without damage to the toad and with subsequent regeneration of the glands. Apparently no use is made by the toad of its own poison, either in self-defense or in body functions, and the role of the venom is thus analogous to that of the active alkaloids and heart poisons of plants.

Early chemical studies of the constituents of toad venoms were undertaken by Faust and by Phisalix and Bertrand. The first isolation of an active principle was accomplished in 1911 by the American workers Abel

[9] Plattner and Heusser, *Helv. Chim. Acta*, **28**, 1044 (1945).

[10] Plattner, Heusser and Kulkarni, *Helv. Chim. Acta*, **31**, 1822 (1948).

[1] See reviews by Shoppee, *Ann. Rev. Biochem.*, **11**, 135 (1942); Behringer, *Die Chemie*, **56**, 83, 105 (1943).

and Macht,[2] who named the substance bufagin (L. *bufo*, toad), later changed to marinobufagin. The principal investigations of structure have been conducted by Wieland at the Freiburg and Munich laboratories. Pharmacological and chemical studies have also been carried out by H. Jensen at the Johns Hopkins University in collaboration with K. K. Chen of the Lilly Research Laboratories.

The skin secretions of toads have been found to contain the following substances: bufotoxins (conjugated genins), steroid genins (more specifically, bufogenins), bufotenines (bases), adrenaline, cholesterol, and occasionally ergosterol. Adrenaline has not always been detected but sometimes occurs in astonishingly large amounts. Abel and Macht isolated adrenaline in crystalline form along with marinobufagin from the venom of the large South American toad *Bufo marinus* in amount corresponding to a concentration of about 5 percent of the secretion. Adrenaline also has been isolated from Ch'an Su[3] and from the secretion of the tropical toad *B. arenarum*,[4] and its presence in other species of toads has been established by color tests and by blood pressure measurements on pithed cats.[5] It is surprising that the active pressor principle of the suprarenal glands occurs also in the skin glands of the toad; the amount stored in the parotid glands of a single Jamaican toad (*B. marinus*) is more than four times the amount present in a pair of human suprarenal glands.[6] The Chinese drug Ch'an Su contains, in addition to cardiotonic agents, this pressor substance of astringent and hemostatic properties.

The presence in the secretions of alkaloid-like organic bases other than adrenalin was indicated by the work of Phisalix and Bertrand,[7] who isolated a crude base that they named bufotenine. Handrovsky[8] prepared several crystalline salts, and Wieland[9] established the formula $C_{14}H_{18}O_2N_2$ for the base. Wieland obtained the substance from the common European toad *Bufo vulgaris* and isolated from the same source a second substance, bufotenidine, which proved to be the quaternary ammonium base of bufotenine. Ch'an Su contains bufotenidine[9] and a substance probably identical with bufotenine.[3]   On the basis of certain pharmacological observations,[10] Jensen

[2] J. J. Abel and Macht, *J. Am. Med. Assoc.*, **56**, 1531 (1911); *J. Pharm. Exp. Therap.*, **3**, 319 (1911).

[3] Jensen and K. K. Chen, *J. Biol. Chem.*, **82**, 397 (1929); **87**, 741 (1930).

[4] Deulofeu, *Z. physiol. Chem.*, **237**, 171 (1935).

[5] K. K. Chen and A. L. Chen, *J. Pharmacol.*, **49**, 526 (1933); see also earlier papers.

[6] K. K. Chen and A. L. Chen, *Arch. inter. pharmacodynamie*, **47**, 297 (1934).

[7] Phisalix and Bertrand, *Comp. rend. soc. biol.*, **45**, 477 (1893).

[8] Handrovsky, *Arch. exptl. Path. Pharmakol.*, **86**, 138 (1920).

[9] Wieland, Hesse and Mittasch, *Ber.*, **64**, 2099 (1931).

[10] Jensen and K. K. Chen, *Ber.*, **65**, 1310 (1932). A supposed series of "bufotenines" of different origin are identical with Wieland's bufotenine; Jensen and K. K. Chen, *J. Biol. Chem.*, **116**, 87 (1936).

and Chen correctly inferred that bufotenine is a derivative of tryptamine. Wieland[11] established the structures of bufotenine (I) and its betäin derivative (II) by synthesis. Bufotenine bears a striking resemblance to

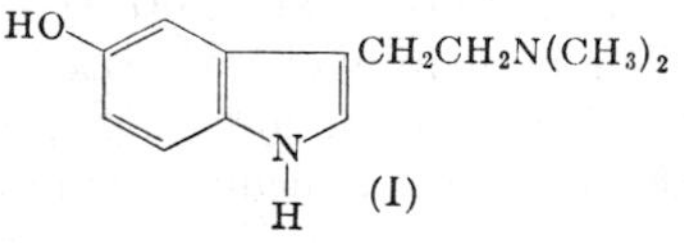

HO—[CH₂CH₂N(CH₃)₂ indole structure] (I) Bufotenine

Ō—[CH₂CH₂N⁺(CH₃)₃ indole structure] (II) Bufotenidine

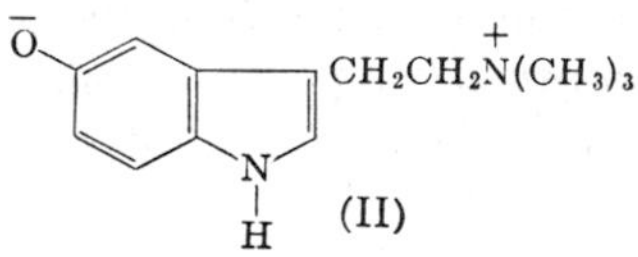

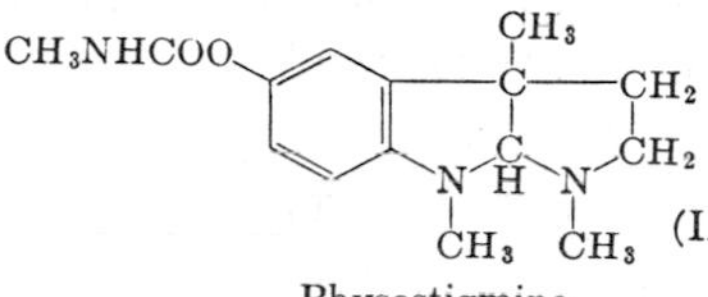

CH₃NHCOO—[physostigmine structure] (III)
Physostigmine

physostigmine (III), the principal alkaloid of calabar bean. Although many naturally occurring substances are derived from 6-hydroxyindole and may be synthesized in the cell from tyrosine, bufotenine and physostigmine are the only known natural derivatives of 5-hydroxyindole. Bufotenine has a pressor action similar to that of adrenaline but less pronounced. It produces a rise in blood pressure of pithed cats owing to both vasoconstriction and cardiac stimulation.

Two substances closely related to bufotenine and bufotenidine but devoid of pressor activity usually accompany these substances in various venoms. These are bufothionine (IV)[12] and dehydrobufotenine (V).[13] The structures were established by Wieland and Wieland.[14] Bufothionine (insoluble in acid or base, only slightly soluble in water) is hydrolyzed to dehydrobufotenine by dilute mineral acid; the dehydro compound V on

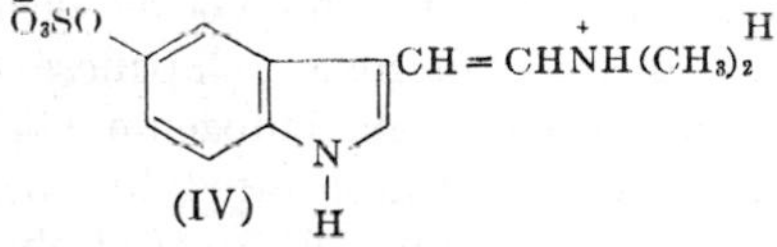

Ō₃SO—[CH=CHNH⁺(CH₃)₂ indole structure] (IV) Bufothionine

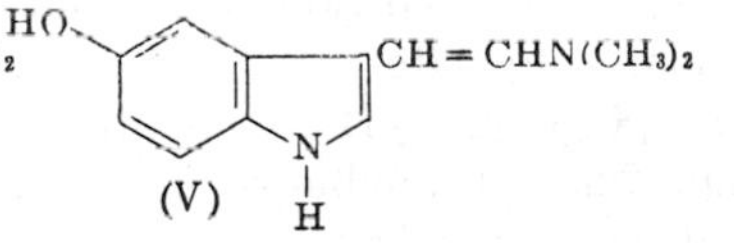

HO—[CH=CHN(CH₃)₂ indole structure] (V) Dehydrobufotenine

tures were established by Wieland and Wieland.[14] Bufothionine (insoluble in acid or base, only slightly soluble in water) is hydrolyzed to dehydrobufotenine by dilute mineral acid; the dehydro compound V on

[11] Wieland, Konz and Mittasch, *Ann.*, **513**, 1 (1934); see also Hoshino and Shimodaira, *ibid.*, **520**, 19 (1935).

[12] Wieland and Vocke, *Ann.*, **481**, 215 (1930); Wieland, Konz and Mittasch, *ibid.*, **513**, 1 (1934); Jensen, *J. Am. Chem. Soc.*, **57**, 1765 (1935); Jensen and K. K. Chen, *J. Biol. Chem.*, **116**, 87 (1936); Deulofeu and Duprat, *ibid.*, **153**, 459 (1944); Deulofeu and Berinzaghi, *J. Am. Chem. Soc.*, **68**, 1665 (1946).

[13] K. K. Chen and A. L. Chen, *J. Pharmacol.*, **49**, 1, 514 (1933); Deulofeu and coworkers, ref 12.

[14] H. Wieland and Th. Wieland, *Ann.*, **528**, 234 (1937).

hydrogenation yields bufotenine. The unsaturated side chain corresponds in structure to neurine, $CH_2\text{==}CHN(CH_3)_2$, a constituent of adrenal glands. **Cardiotonic Constituents.** Toad venoms contain both conjugates and the genins derived from them by enzymatic hydrolysis, and both types of compound are physiologically active. The most fully characterized conjugate is bufotoxin, isolated by Wieland and Alles[1] from *Bufo vulgaris*; the substance was later shown to contain one molecule of difficultly eliminated water of crystallization and to have the formula $C_{40}H_{60}O_{10}N_4 \cdot H_2O$.[2] Bufotoxin is the suberylarginine ester of the genin bufotalin and is probably hydrolyzed to some extent in the organism to the two intact components as follows:

$$\begin{array}{cc} CO_2H & NH_2 \\ | & | \\ C_{26}H_{35}O_5\text{---}O \cdot CO(CH_2)_6CONHCH(CH_2)_3NHC\text{==}NH \cdot H_2O & \rightarrow \end{array}$$

Bufotoxin, $C_{40}H_{60}O_{10}N_4 \cdot H_2O$

$$\begin{array}{ccc} & CO_2H & NH_2 \\ & | & | \\ C_{26}H_{36}O_6 \quad + \quad & HO_2C(CH_2)_6CONHCH(CH_2)_3NHC\text{==}NH \end{array}$$

Bufotalin   Suberylarginine

Under conditions of acid hydrolysis suberylarginine is split in whole or in part to suberic acid and arginine and bufotalin is converted into the dianhydro derivative bufotalien ($C_{24}H_{30}O_3$) as the result of cleavage of one molecule of water and one molecule of acetic acid. Bufotoxin is insoluble in water but more easily soluble in dilute than in absolute alcohol.

From the dried skins of Japanese toads Wieland and Vocke[3] isolated a similar conjugate, which they named gamabufotoxin, (Japanese *gama*, toad), $C_{38}H_{58}O_9N_4 \cdot H_2O$, m.p. 210°, and the genin, gamabufogenin, $C_{24}H_{34}O_5$, m.p. 263°. Gamabufogenin is converted by concentrated hydrochloric acid into anhydrogamabufogenin, $C_{24}H_{32}O_4$, m.p. 261°. Hydrolysis of gamabufogenin with 1 N hydrochloric acid gives suberic acid, arginine, and anhydrogamabufogenin; hydrolysis with 0.5 N hydrochloric acid affords an isomeric substance $C_{24}H_{32}O_4$, m.p. 204°, that is rearranged by concentrated hydrochloric acid to anhydrogamabufogenin, m.p. 261°.

Isolation. The processing of dried toad skins is usually accomplished by soaking the skins in dilute alcohol for several months, evaporating the extract in vacuum, and replacing the alcohol with water, when the genin and the bufotoxin precipitate and the basic constituents are retained in solution as salts. A single dried toad skin weighing about 15 g. yields 7 – 10 mg. of

[1] Wieland and Alles, *Ber.*, **55**, 1789 (1922).
[2] Wieland and Behringer, *Ann.*, **549**, 209 (1941).
[3] Wieland and Vocke, *Ann.*, **481**, 215 (1930).

genin. A more satisfactory method of obtaining venom from live toads for chemical investigation was introduced by Abel and Macht and used in the studies by Wieland at Freiburg and Munich.   A toad is held under an inverted bowl and the secretion contained in the pair of parotid glands behind the eyes is expressed with flat forceps; the stream of milky fluid is caught on the walls of the bowl and in cotton.   The animal is set free at the place of capture and suffers no injury.   A ten-day collection in the environs of Freiburg afforded venom from 27,000 common toads; no abundance of dead toads was observed after the collection, and the number captured was very nearly the same in two succeeding years.   In an improved procedure of isolation[4] the dried venom is extracted with chloroform and the extracted water-insoluble material is defatted with petroleum ether and adsorbed on alumina from acetone solution.   Development of the chromatogram with chloroform results in a fairly sharp separation of bufotalin and companion substances in different zones.   The secretion from 33,000 toads afforded 36 g. of bufotalin and 29 g. of companion substances.   In one of Wieland's investigations a comparison was made of the venoms of male and female toads, but no differences were observed in either output or composition.[2]   The average weight of dried secretion is 16 mg./toad for the male and 27 mg./toad for the female, and the female toad weighs about twice as much as the male.   The average amounts of components isolated, in mg./male toad, were: bufotalin, 0.55; companion poisons, 0.16; crude bufotoxin, 1.34; bufotenine, 0.05; bufotenidine, 0.07.   A single Jamaican toad yields about 260 mg. of dried venom.

Structure of Bufotalin.   A series of investigations of bufotalin conducted by Wieland [1-7] elucidated many features of the structure of this genin and led to the proposal of the specific formulation shown in Chart 16, but this contains some inconsistencies that have not been clarified.   The genin undoubtedly belongs to the class of the steroids, but this point has not been directly demonstrated.   Wieland and Hesse[7] investigated the selenium dehydrogenation of bufotalin and isolated chrysene, a product of rearrangement that sometimes results from high-temperature dehydrogenation of known steroids.   The more specific Diels hydrocarbon has been identified as a product of the dehydrogenation of a mixture of cinobufagin and cinobufotalin from Ch'an Su[8, 9] and of marinobufagin.[10]

The presence in bufotalin of the various functional groups indicated in

[4] Wieland, Hesse and Hüttel, *Ann.*, **524**, 203 (1936).
[5] Wieland and F. S. Weil, *Ber.*, **46**, 3315 (1913).
[6] Wieland, Hesse and Harry Meyer, *Ann.*, **493**, 272 (1932).
[7] Wieland and Hesse, *Ann.*, **517**, 22 (1935).
[8] Tschesche and Offe, *Ber.*, **68**, 1998 (1935).
[9] Jensen, *J. Am. Chem. Soc.*, **57**, 2733 (1935).
[10] Jensen, *J. Am. Chem. Soc.*, **59**, 767 (1937).

formula I has been fully demonstrated. The substance contains only one acylable hydroxyl group and on oxidation yields a monoketone, bufotalone (III). Two easily hydrogenated double bonds are evidently present in a

Chart 16. BUFOTALIN; WIELAND'S FORMULATION

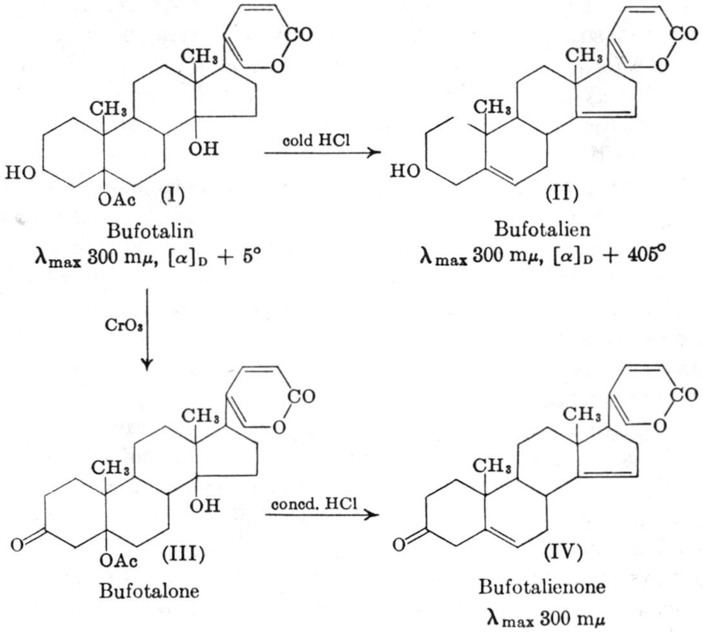

Bufotalin
λ_{max} 300 mμ, $[\alpha]_D + 5°$

Bufotalien
λ_{max} 300 mμ, $[\alpha]_D + 405°$

Bufotalone

Bufotalienone
λ_{max} 300 mμ

doubly unsaturated lactone ring corresponding to that of scillaridin A; bufotalin has the same type of absorption spectrum as this aglycone and similarly gives a negative Legal nitroprusside test; bufotalone forms an iso compound on reaction with very dilute alkali; ozonization of bufotalin acetate affords formic acid and glyoxylic acid.[7] The presence of a tertiary (nonacylable) hydroxyl group and of an acetoxyl group is indicated by analytical data showing that two such groups are eliminated in the conversion of bufotalin into bufotalien (II) by the action of cold concentrated hydrochloric acid.

Evidence of the location of the secondary hydroxyl group was obtained by Wieland and Behringer[2] by the degradation of two isomeric (C_{20}) hydroxybufotalanes, $[\alpha]_D + 56°$ and $+ 31°$, resulting from the hydrogenation of bufotalien. The lone hydroxyl group was eliminated by pyrolysis with boric anhydride, the two bufotalenes were hydroxylated with osmium tetroxide, and the glycols cleaved with lead tetraacetate to two dibasic acids. Both acids on pyrolysis yielded ketones, and hence the original ring must be six-membered and terminal, and the hydroxyl group is at position 1, 2, 3, or 4 in ring A; Wieland assumed that it is located as usual at position 3. That the acetoxyl group is tertiary was established[2] by a study of one of two isomeric (C_{20}) tetrahydrobufotalins, $[\alpha]_D + 28°$ and $+ 36°$. Treatment of the isomer of lower rotation with alkali opens the saturated lactone ring and removes the acetyl group by hydrolysis. When the resulting tetrahydroxy acid was heated at 150° the lactone ring closed with formation of a trihydroxy lactone (two forms), and this on oxidation gave a monoketone. If the acetylated group had been secondary, a diketone should have resulted.

The free tertiary hydroxyl group of bufotalin must be placed at C_{14} to account for the iso reaction, and the location of the tertiary acetoxyl group follows from the properties of the dianhydro compound, bufotalien (II). This substance does not differ in absorption spectrum from bufotalin and therefore the two anhydro linkages are not conjugated. One of these must be at the 14,15-position and the other at a nonconjugated position similarily accessible to hydrogenation, and the only possibility is the 5,6-position, since a 9,11-double bond is hydrogenated with difficulty. The acetoxyl group is thus located at position 5. Wieland and Behringer[2] found further that bufotoxin can be oxidized to a ketone and hence that the secondary hydroxyl group in ring A is not involved in the conjugation of the genin with suberylarginine, and they concluded that this residue is attached to the only other available group, namely the tertiary hydroxyl at C_{14}.

The evidence for the structure of the lactone ring and for the locations of hydroxyl functions in ring A, at C_5, and at C_{14} seems conclusive, but the specific formulation I is nevertheless subject to question. Wieland, Hesse and Meyer[6] effected degradation to a cholanic acid as follows: hydrogenation of bufotalien acetate resulted in part in the reductive fission of the unsaturated ring and gave as one product the acetate of a substance having the composition of a hydroxycholanic acid but different from any of the known isomers. Pyrolytic elimination of the hydroxyl group and hydrogenation gave a substance designated isobufocholanic acid, m.p. 179°, $[\alpha]_D + 50.5°$, because it proved to be different from cholanic acid, $[\alpha]_D + 21.7°$, allocholanic acid, $[\alpha]_D + 22.5°$, and bufocholanic acid, $[\alpha]_D - 20.3°$ (from the dihydroxy acid of toad bile). Wieland regarded isobufocholanic acid as the C_{20}-isomer of cholanic or allocholanic acid, but the known 20-iso nor and bisnor acids are slightly less dextrorotatory than the normal compounds rather than considerably more dextrorotatory. In another degradation,[2] hydrogenation of the two bufotalenes afforded two saturated lactones (bufotalanes), m.p. 155°, $[\alpha]_D + 56°$, and m.p. 133°, $[\alpha]_D + 37°$, neither of which was identical with octahydroscillaridin A (m.p. 183°).

Both degradations proceed through the intermediate bufotalien and should result in normal orientation at both C_5 and C_{14}. It thus appears that isobufocholanic acid and the bufotalanes must differ in configuration from the normal compounds at a center other than C_5, C_{14}, or C_{20}.

The strong dextrorotation of bufotalien ($+ 405°$) provides a clue to the nature of the isomerism. The structure II is closely analogous to that of dianhydrostrophanthidin, which is strongly levorotatory, $[\alpha]_D - 222°$. Wieland and Behringer[2] isolated as a companion substance a compound characterized as Δ^5-monoanhydrobufotalin, and this also exhibits abnormal dextrorotation: $[\alpha]_D + 79°$; compare cholesterol, $[\alpha]_D - 39°$. The possible sites for an inversion from the normal configurations are: C_8, C_9, C_{10}, C_{13}, and C_{17}. An inversion at C_8, C_{13}, or C_{17} would cause a shift to increased levo- rather than dextrorotation, but an inversion at either C_9 or C_{10} would lead to a change in the direction observed. Position 9, however, is too remote from either double bond of bufotalien to be subject to much exaltation, and an inversion at this point would hardly account for the difference in specific rotation of 627° between bufotalien and dianhydrostrophanthidin. Position 10 is subject to such exaltation, and in the case of ergosterol an inversion at this center is attended with a shift from levo- to dextrorotation amounting to 321°. Thus the present evidence seems to indicate that in bufotalin and isobufocholanic acid the angular methyl group at C_{10} is in the α-orientation.

Wieland recognized but discounted a different inconsistency in his formulation. Bufotalone (III) is readily converted by the action of concentrated hydrochloric acid into a dianhydro derivative (IV) that is not altered by aqueous acid or by hydrogen chloride in ether. If the keto group were at C_3, the double bond at C_5–C_6 would surely migrate to a position of conjugation, but bufotalienone exhibits absorption only at 300 mμ characteristic of the unsaturated ring and the spectrum contains no band at 235 mμ as expected for the α,β-unsaturated keto group. There is no ground for the supposition that strong absorption in one region of the spectrum can obstruct absorption in another; "α"-antiarin absorbs both at 305 mμ (carbonyl group) and at 217 mμ (lactone ring). It is equally improbable

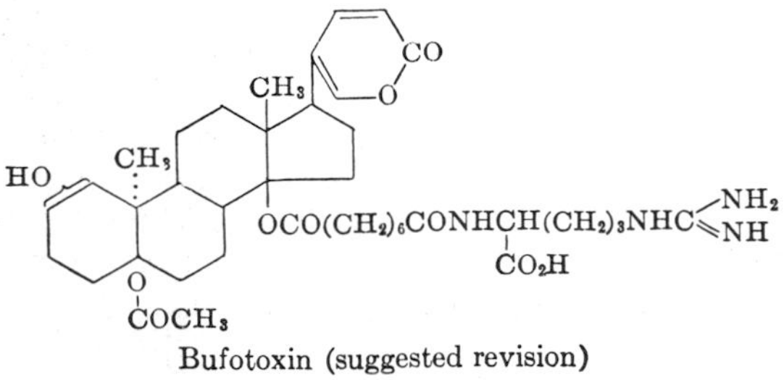

Bufotoxin (suggested revision)

that structure IV would not suffer bond migration. A more plausible interpretation is that the carbonyl group is not at C_3 but at one of the other positions permissible under existing evidence, namely C_1 or C_2. The suggested revisions in Wieland's conception of the structure of bufotoxin are shown in the formula.

Gamabufogenin, $C_{24}H_{34}O_5$, m.p. 263°, λ_{max} 300 mμ. This genin has been isolated from the skins of Japanese toads[1] (*Bufo vulgaris formosus*) and from Ch'an Su.[2] The composition is that of a desacetylbufotalin, but the two series are different. Gamabufogenin probably has the same doubly unsaturated lactone ring (absorption spectrum) and 14-hydroxyl group (formation of an iso compound). The presence of two secondary hydroxyl groups is indicated by the formation of a diacetate. The absorption of only two moles of hydrogen indicates that the nucleus is saturated. The genin is converted by reaction with concentrated hydrochloric acid into a monoanhydro compound.

Marinobufagin, $C_{24}H_{32}O_5$, m p 213°, $[\alpha]_D$ + 11°, λ_{max} 300 mμ. This genin first isolated by Abel and Macht as mentioned above, probably contains a doubly unsaturated lactone ring (spectrum, ozonization), a tertiary hydroxyl at C_{14} (iso compound), a hydroxymethyl group at C_{10} (liberation of formaldehyde; oxidation to an aldehyde), a second hydroxyl group that is tertiary (the genin forms a monoacetate, probably by reaction of the primary alcoholic group at C_{10}), and a nuclear double bond (absorption of three moles of hydrogen); when refluxed with dilute sulfuric acid in ethanol, the genin is converted into a dianhydro derivative.[3] Unfortunately, the various transformation products have not been characterized with respect to optical rotation and absorption in the ultraviolet.

Cinobufagin, $C_{26}H_{34}O_6$, m.p. 213°, λ_{max} 290 mμ. Early preparations from Ch'an Su of melting point 221 223°[4, 5, 6] have been shown by Kuwada and Kotake[7] to be separable by chromatography into a principal component, for which the name cinobufagin is retained, and a minor constituent named cinobufotalin. About 15 g. of the mixture, m.p. 223°, can be ob-

[1] Wieland and Vocke, *Ann.*, **481**, 215 (1930); Wieland, Hesse and Hüttel, *Ann.*, **524** 203 (1936).

[2] Kotake, *Ann.*, **465**, 11 (1928); *Sci. Papers Inst. Phys. Chem. Research*, **24**, 39 (1934); Kotake and Kubota, *ibid.*, **34**, 824 (1938); see also K. K. Chen, Jensen and A. L. Chen, *J. Pharmacol.*, **49**, 26 (1933).

[3] Jensen and E. A. Evans, Jr., *J. Biol. Chem.*, **104**, 307 (1934); Jensen, *J. Am. Chem. Soc.*, **59**, 767 (1937); Tschesche and Offe, *Ber.*, **69**, 2361 (1936); Deulofeu and Mendive, *Ann.*, **534**, 288 (1938).

[4] Jensen and K. K. Chen, *J. Biol. Chem.*, **87**, 741 (1930); Jensen, *Science*, **75**, 53 (1932).

[5] Kotake, *Ann.*, **465**, 1 (1928).

[6] Tschesche and Offe, *Ber.*, **68**, 1998 (1935).

[7] Kuwada and Kotake, *Sci. Papers Inst. Phys. Chem. Research*, **35**, 419 (1939).

tained from 2.5 kg. of Ch'an Su.[6] Cinobufagin contains a doubly unsaturated lactone ring, an acetoxyl group, a C_{14}-hydroxyl group (iso reaction), a free secondary hydroxyl group (monoketone, monoacetate), and a reducible double bond in the nucleus. According to Kuwada and Kotake[7] the acetyl group is attached to a secondary hydroxyl that is not acylable but capable of being oxidized to a keto group and regarded as probably located at C_{12}.

The companion substance cinobufotalin, $C_{26}H_{36}O_7$, m.p. 249°, λ_{max} 295 mμ, differs in composition from cinobufagin by the elements of water and it appears to contain one more secondary hydroxyl group (diacetate) and no nuclear double bond.

Other Genins. A few additional substances isolated from toad venoms

TABLE II., Other Toad Genins

GENIN	PROBABLE FORMULA	M.p.	SOURCE	PROPERTIES
Arenobufogenin[a]	$C_{24}H_{32}O_6$	252°	*B. arenarum*	
Arenobufagin[b, c]	$C_{24}H_{32}O_6$?	220,233°	*B. arenarum*	
Cinobufotalidin[d]	$C_{24}H_{34}O_6$	217°	Ch'an Su	Monoacet.; dianhydro cpd.
Bufalin[e]	$C_{24}H_{34}O_4$	235°	" "	Monoacet.
Pseudodesacetyl-bufotalin[f]	$C_{24}H_{34}O_5$	Amorph.	" "	
Bufotalidin[g]	$C_{24}H_{32}O_6$	230°	*B. vulgaris*	$[\alpha]_D \pm 0°$, λ_{max} 300 mμ
Bufotalinin[g]	$C_{24}H_{30}O_6$	Dec.	" "	$[\alpha]_D + 14°$, λ_{max} 300 mμ

[a] Wieland and Behringer, *Ann.*, **549**, 234 (1941).

[b] K. K. Chen, Jensen and A. L. Chen, *J. Pharmacol.*, **49**, 1 (1933); Jensen, *J. Am. Chem. Soc.*, **57**, 1765 (1935).

[c] Deulofeu, Duprat and Labriola, *Nature*, **145**, 671 (1940).

[d] Kondo and Ohno, *J. Pharm. Soc. Japan*, **58**, 235 (1938) [*Chem. Zentr.*, II, 1682 (1939)].

[e] Kotake and Kuwada, *Sci. Papers Inst. Phys. Chem. Research*, **36**, 106 (1939) [*Chem. Zentr.*, II, 1681 (1939)]; degradation to 3β-hydroxyetiocholanic acid, Kotake and Kuwada, *C. A.*, **41**, 6296 (1947).

[f] Kondo and Ohno, *J. Pharm. Soc. Japan*, **58**, 413 (1938); Ohno, *ibid.*, **60**, 559 (1940) [*C. A.*, **35**, 2902 (1941)].

[g] Wieland, Hesse and Hüttel, *Ann.*, **524**, 203 (1936).

are listed in Table II; except for bufalin, the characterization is only fragmentary.

Bufalin has recently been investigated by K. Meyer,[8] who reports the constants: m.p. 244°, $[\alpha]_D$ − 9° Chf; monoacetate, m.p. 247°, $[\alpha]_D$ − 6° Chf.

[8] Kuno Meyer, *Experientia*, **4**, 385 (1948).

Degradation of bufalin acetate with potassium permanganate in acetone gave 3β-acetoxy-14β-hydroxy-14-isoetiocholanic acid and 3β-acetoxy-14β-hydroxy-14-isopregnane-20-one-21-acid-(21→14)-lactone. Bufalin therefore corresponds in structure and configuration to digitoxigenin except that the lactone ring is six-membered as in scillaren A.

PHARMACOLOGICAL PROPERTIES

Plant extracts containing cardiac principles have been used for centuries as arrow poisons and ordeal drugs.[1] Therapeutic uses were known to some extent in the Middle Ages, but the introduction of digitalis (powdered leaves of *Digitalis purpurea*) into standard medical practice stems from a treatise (1785) by an English botanist and physician, William Withering, "An Account of the Foxglove and Some of its Medical Uses; with Practical Remarks on Dropsy and Other Diseases." At the time it was not known that the type of dropsy amenable to digitalis therapy is a secondary result of impaired cardiac function; the physiological effects of digitalis have become known only relatively recently, and the exact mode of action is still uncertain. One source of confusion is that digitalis elicits somewhat different responses depending upon the condition of the heart. Moreover normal cardiac function depends upon the maintenance of a delicate balance of many physiological actions. Recent studies of the action of the cardiac principles on the isolated heart-lung preparation (dog) have contributed to a better understanding of the activity of the cardiac glycosides. It is now certain that digitalis has a direct action on the heart muscle. Failure in the (isolated) heart, either spontaneous or drug-induced, is marked by an increase in atrial pressure, decrease (10–30%) in heart rate, and fall in cardiac minute volume output (heart rate × output per beat). Infusion with cardiac principles produces, after a slight delay, reduction of atrial pressure to normal, further decrease in heart rate, and an increase in the cardiac output to nearly normal levels. The increase in cardiac output, even though the rate is decreased, is accomplished by an increase in the output per stroke, owing to an increase in the force of systolic contraction in the diseased heart. As a consequence the ventricle empties more completely, and the heart can take care of an increased venous return. The decrease in pressure in the venous capillaries allows better resorption of extracellular fluid into the circulation and eventually into the kidneys. Thus digitalis has a diuretic effect, but only in edema due to cardiac failure. The ability of the glycosides to increase the force of contraction can be seen in the isolated papillary muscle of the heart; the effect forms the basis for one method of bioassay.

[1] Dragstedt, "Trial by Ordeal," *Quart. Bull. Northwestern Univ. Med. School* (1945).

The marked response of the heart muscle to digitalis is not shared by other muscles. Experiments designed to determine how much of the administered drug reaches the heart show that the relative amount of digitalis absorbed by the heart per unit of weight is about thirty-seven times the amount absorbed by the muscles and skin and about ten times the amount absorbed by the abdominal organs. The cardiac glycosides thus have a special affinity for the heart. Another peculiarity of the glycosides is that they do not act instantly, and that the action of at least some of the glycosides is partly or completely irreversible.

Infusion of the glycoside into the isolated heart-lung system beyond the point of therapeutic effect produces cardiac irregularities: increased heart rate, reduction in cardiac output, rise in atrial pressure, incoordination between ventricular and auricular contraction (irregularity dose). Further administration eventually leads to ventricular fibrillation (incoordinated contraction), the usual cause of death in cases of digitalis poisoning. The amount of drug causing ventricular fibrillation is known as the lethal dose. Toxic doses of digitalis also produce extracardiac symptoms: nausea, salivation, diarrhea, disturbance of vision, and muscular weakness.

The cardiac glycosides are invaluable for treatment of many types of congestive heart failure, and also find application in the therapy of auricular fibrillation (weak and rapid contraction).[2] The therapeutic effect in the latter case is due partly to the ability of the glycosides to block the muscular conduction system between the auricles and the ventricles and partly to their power to decrease the sensitivity of the ventricles to auricular impulses.

Since the glycosides are noncurative drugs, a patient usually requires the drug indefinitely. Only those drugs that are satisfactory for oral administration have application in long-range therapy. Intravenous administration is employed in emergencies for prompt initial digitalization. The estimation of initial and maintenance doses requires supervision by a clinical specialist. The drug has a cumulative effect, and digitalis is eliminated slowly at a rate that bears a definite relationship to the quantity of glycoside in the body. The high toxicity of the drugs constitutes a further hazard in digitalis therapy. The commonly used preparations consist of powdered leaves of *Digitalis purpurea* or of tinctures of the leaves, and the content of active principle varies greatly with the locality and age of the plants and with the season. The only available method of standardization is bioassay in cats or frogs with respect to toxicity, rather than therapeutic effective-

[2] Movitt, "Digitalis and Other Cardiotonic Drugs," Oxford University Press (1946); P. D. White, "Heart Disease," MacMillan (1944); Lendle, "Digitaliskörper und verwandte herzwirksame Glykoside," *Handbuch exper. Pharm.*, Ergänz. 1, J. Springer (1935).

ness. The results are expressed in terms of the lethal dose, or the amount of material in mg. per kg. of body weight required to kill the test animals. There is a marked species specificity; the rabbit is half as sensitive as the cat, the rat is one-sixtieth as sensitive, and the toad is practically immune. It is not certain that the therapeutic dose is proportional to the lethal dose or that the relative potencies of different cardiac glycosides correspond from one species to another. A practical goal of chemical research in this field is the production, by isolation or by partial or total synthesis, of a glycoside preparation that could be standardized on a weight basis, primarily by chemical characterization.

Physiological Activity. Early methods of bioassay employed both frogs and cats, but since the glycosides elicit somewhat different responses in amphibians and in mammals, cats are now used in the standard procedure now officially adopted in the U. S. Pharmacopocia. The drug is administered to the anesthetized animals intravenously rather than orally, since some of the glycosides are poorly absorbed from the gastrointestinal tract. A few drugs, oleandrin and digitoxin among others, are equally active by either route; the majority are more effective when given intravenously. Irritant qualities of most of the glycosides prohibit intramuscular administration. The activities reported in Table III were all determined by Chen[1] by a procedure[2] based upon that of Hatcher;[3] they are expressed in terms of the mean lethal doses (LD_{50}) in mg. per kg. body weight. Somewhat more accurate data can be obtained if the doses are based on heart weight rather than body weight. Since the glycosides vary considerably in molecular weight, the dosages expressed in micromoles rather than milligrams seem a better basis for comparison. These values are listed in the last column; they are subject to some reservation since some of the determinations were carried out with hydrated material of uncertain composition. Judged on a weight basis, cymarol would appear to be more active than k-strophanthin-β, whereas on a molar basis the two glycosides are eqully potent.

The effect on isolated heart muscle has been employed in a few instances as a criterion of potency, and the relative potencies determined in this way do not differ greatly from those found with the intact animal. Scillaren A and cerberin show somewhat greater activity in isolated muscle, whereas digilanide C is definitely less active. Factors of hydrolysis and extracardiac distribution may influence the results obtained with intact animals.

Farah has studied the activity of five glycosides in the isolated heart-

[1] K. K. Chen, *Ann. Rev. Physiol.*, **7**, 681 (1945).

[2] K. K. Chen and co-workers, *J. Am. Pharm. Assoc.*, **25**, 579 (1936); *J. Pharmacol.*, **74**, 223 (1942).

[3] Hatcher and Brody, *Am. J. Pharm.*, **82**, 360 (1910).

TABLE III. Activities in the Cat Assay (Chen)

SUBSTANCE (MOL. WT.)	MEAN LETHAL DOSE (LD$_{50}$)	
	mg./kg.	micromoles/ kg.
Strophanthidin Derivatives		
Convallatoxin (550.6)	0.074	0.13
Convalloside (739.8)	.215	.29
k-Strophanthoside (872.9)	.186	.21
k-Strophanthin-β (710.8)	.128	.18
Cymarin (548.6)	.110	.20
Cymarol (550.7)	.099	.18
Cymarylic acid, K-salt	8.73	
Cheirotoxin (766.8)	0.118	.15
Strophanthidin (418.5)	.325	.77
Strophanthidin-3β-d-glucoside (575.6)	.091	.16
tetraacetate (734.8)	1.166	1.6
Strophanthidin-3β-d-xyloside (581.6)	0.109	0.19
Strophanthidin-3β-l-arabinoside (545.6)	.094	.17
Strophanthidin-3-acetate (442.5)	.187	.42
Strophanthidin-3-propionate (456.5)	.257	.56
Strophanthidin-3-n-butyrate (470.5)	.426	.91
Strophanthidin-3-myristate (609.8)	.983	1.6
Strophanthidin-3-benzoate (504.6)	2.72	5.4
Periplogenin Derivatives		
Periplocin (696.8)	0.121	0.17
Periplocymarin (552.6)	.154	.28
Emicymarin (550.6)	.138	.25
Periplogenin (416.9)	.719	1.72
Periplogenin-β-d-glucoside	.125	
Digoxigenin Derivatives		
Digilanide C (1003)	0.233	0.23
Digoxin (780.9)	.231	.30
Digitoxigenin Derivatives		
Digilanide A (969.0)	0.361	0.37
Desacetyldigilanide A (927.1)	.469	.51
Digitoxin (764.5)	.325	.43
Thevetin (912.9)	.889	0.97
Thevebioside (714.8)	1.00	1.40
Acetylneriifolin = Cerberin (576.7)	0.147	0.25
Neriifolin (534.7)	.196	.36
Digitoxigenin (374.5)	.459	1.23

TABLE III.—*Continued*

SUBSTANCE (MOL. WT.)	MEAN LETHAL DOSE (LD₅₀)	
	mg./kg.	micromoles/kg.
Gitoxigenin Derivatives		
Digilanide B (1003)	0.388	0.39
Desacetyldigilanide B (943)	.548	.58
Gitoxin	Indeterminable	
Oleandrin (576.7)	.197	.34
Desacetyloleandrin (534.6)	.300	.56
Other Glycosides of the Strophanthus-Digitalis Type		
Uzarin (698.7)	4.57	6.5
"α"-Antiarin (566.6)	0.094	0.17
"β"-Antiarin (566.6)	.096	.17
Ouabain (648.7)	.116	.18
Sarmentocymarin (570.7)	.202	.35
Calotropin (532.6)	.111	.21
Uscharin (587.3)	.144	.01
Calotoxin (548.6)	.112	.20
Anhydrocalotropagenin (404.5)	2.57	6.3
Adonitoxin (550.6)	0.191	0.35
Sarmentoside A (577.6)	.112	.19
Adynerin	Inactive	
Neriantin	Inactive	
Diginin	Inactive	
Squill Glycosides		
Scillaren A (692.8)	0.146	0.21
Scillaridin A (366.4)	1.66	4.5
Hellebrin	about 0.1	
Desglucohellebrin (580.7)	0.086	0.15
Toad Venoms		
Bufotoxin (774.9)	0.292	0.38
Bufotalin (444.6)	.136	.31
Marinobufotoxin (712.8)	.417	.58
Marinobufagin (400.5)	.556	1.40
Gamabufotoxin (732.8)	.374	0.51
Gamabufogenin (402.5)	.101	.25
Arenobufotoxin (Chen-Jensen, 760.9)	.406	.53
Arenobufagin (Chen-Jensen, 430.5)	.092	.21

lung preparation (dog) and rates the glycosides on a molar basis of both therapeutic and toxic action in the following order of decreasing activity:[4] ouabain, digoxin, digitoxin, oleandrin, digilanide B. The order indicated by Chen's assays is: ouabain, oleandrin, digoxin, digitoxin, digilanide B. The discrepancies may be due to species differences. Thus the lethal dose of an extract of *S. kombé* seeds is about the same in dogs and cats, but digitoxin is much less active in dogs (3.27 mg./kg.) than in cats (0.4 mg./ kg.). Farah also finds that in the five drugs investigated the therapeutic dose is a fairly constant fraction of the lethal dose (12–19%) and that the irregularity dose is 61–63 percent of the lethal dose.

Since Chen's assays are the most extensive by any one investigator they form the basis for the following discussion of the relation of structure to pharmacological activity. Comparison of the molar activities of the different glycosides (last column) does not reveal any substantial generalizations. Among the glycosides derived from strophanthidin, convallatoxin (strophanthidin-3-rhamnoside) exhibits the highest molar potency, and this derivative of a 2-hydroxy sugar is almost twice as active as cymarin, a derivative of a 2-desoxy sugar. However, other 2-hydroxyglycosides of strophanthidin, for example, the synthetic *d*-xyloside, are about comparable in activity with cymarin. In the periplogenin series the 2-hydroxyglycoside emicymarin is intermediate in molar activity between the 2-desoxyglycosides periplocin and periplocymarin. Thus relative potency does not seem to depend upon the type of sugar and the consequent ease of hydrolytic fission of the sugar residue. The specific structure of the sugar residue seems to be of more importance than the type. From the limited comparisons that can be made it would appear that rhamnose intensifies activity (convallatoxin) somewhat more than the other sugars listed and that conjugation with thevetose results in particularly low activity (thevetin).

The aglycones strophanthidin, periplogenin, and digitoxigenin (also the anhydrogenin scillaridin A) are all distinctly less active, on a molar basis, than any of their known glycosidic derivatives. Acetylation of strophanthidin approximately doubles the molar potency but does not lead to activity comparable to that of the glycosidic derivatives; activity falls off with increasing size of the acyl group, and benzoylation results in a very decided drop in activity. Three of four comparisons of conjugated and unconjugated toad venoms indicate that the conjugation of a toad genin with suberylarginine results in some diminution of molar potency. The moderate activity of free strophanthidin is completely abolished by saturation of the lactone ring or conversion to the isoaglycone. A change from the

[4] Maresh and Farah, *J. Pharmacol.*, **90**, 304 (1947); Farah and Maresh, *ibid.*, **92**, 32 (1948).

α,β-unsaturated five-membered lactone ring of the plant glycosides to the doubly unsaturated 6-membered lactone ring characteristic of the squill glycosides and of the toad poisons has no appreciable effect on activity. Oxidation of the C_{10}-aldehyde group of cymarin has a very adverse effect, but reduction to an alcoholic function has no appreciable effect. The iso compounds produced by the action of alkali, and the 17-iso compounds, are all inactive. Thus the 14β-hydroxyl group and the normal orientation of the side chain are requisites for activity. The configuration at C_5 strikingly affects activity. Digitoxin and uzarin have different sugar residues (digitoxose; glucose), but this difference is overshadowed by the difference in configuration at C_5. Digitoxin (A/B cis) is a highly potent glycoside, whereas uzarin (A/B trans) has almost no cardiotonic activity. In view of these indications of structural and steric specificity, it is surprising that somewhat similar physiological responses are evoked by substances of unrelated structure (see erythrophleum alkaloids, veratrum alkaloids).

Chapter VIII
Steroid Saponins

Plant glycosides that have the distinctive property of forming a soapy lather in water are known as saponins. The plant heart poisons share this property but are classified separately because of their specific physiological action. Noncardiac-active saponin preparations from various plants have found some use as detergents (nonalkaline, not precipitated in hard water), medicinals (*Smilax* species), foaming agents in fire extinguishers, and fish poisons. Fish are dazed or killed by saponin introduced by maceration of a suitable plant in the water but are not rendered inedible, since the saponin is not toxic to humans when taken orally, probably because of nonabsorption from the intestines.

The sapogenins, the aglycones resulting on hydrolysis of the glycosidic saponins, have been divided into two distinct groups on the basis of dehydrogenation experiments: triterpenoid sapogenins, which yield chiefly naphthalene and picene derivatives; and steroid sapogenins, characterized by dehydrogenation to the Diels hydrocarbon. Since the triterpenoid sapogenins are related not to the perhydrophenanthrene derivatives that form the main theme of this book but to perhydropicene, the present survey is limited to the sapogenins of steroid structure.

Saponins. The presence of saponins along with cardiac glycosides in commercial preparations of digitalis from *D. purpurea* was recognized in 1875 by Schmiedeberg, who named the principal saponin component digitonin. Purer preparations were described in later investigations by Kiliani, but in 1913 Windaus and Schneckenburger[1] discovered the presence in a supposedly pure sample of digitonin of 10–20 percent of a second glycoside, which they named gitonin. Both glycosides can be crystallized from alcohol-water mixtures, and in each case the solubility passes through a minimum in going from absolute ethanol to 50 percent ethanol. Fortunately the concentrations of minimum solubility differ sufficiently to permit separation: gitonin is less soluble than digitonin in 95 percent ethanol but more soluble in 85 percent ethanol. Windaus[2] later discovered another method of separation based upon a difference in the rate of precipitation from aqueous solution by ether (as the etherate). On gradual

---

[1] Windaus and Schneckenburger, *Ber.*, **46**, 2628 (1913).
[2] Windaus, *Z. physiol. Chem.*, **150**, 205 (1925).

addition of ether to a 5 percent solution of crude digitonin in water, digitonin precipitates rapidly and gitonin more slowly.

The glycosidic part of digitonin is composed of five sugar units (2 glucose, 2 galactose, and 1 xylose) and that of gitonin is composed of four (Table I). The corresponding aglycones, digitogenin and gitogenin, are C_{27}-steroids having three and two hydroxyl groups, respectively. Windaus encountered degradation products other than those derived from digitonin and gitonin and suspected the presence in digitalis seeds of still other saponins. Although no other saponin has been isolated from this source, Jacobs and Fleck[3] isolated from the hydrolyzed extract of *D. purpurea* leaves a new aglycone, tigogenin, which has one less nuclear hydroxyl group than gitogenin. Tschesche[4] discovered the corresponding glycoside tigonin in extracts of *D. lanata* leaves; tigonin apparently is the only saponin present in the plant material and was isolated easily as the sparingly soluble cholesterol tigonide. Further saponins have since been isolated from plants other than those of the digitalis species, for example, from Californian soaproot, from Mexican sarsaparilla root, and from a number of Mexican plants of the lily family.

Digitonin, as well as the other steroid saponins, possesses the specific ability to effect hemolysis of red blood cells at high dilution; the addition of one part of digitonin to 168,000 parts of defibrinated human blood in physiological salt solution causes rapid destruction of the erythrocyte structure with liberation of hemoglobin. In 1901 Ransom[5] observed that the addition of cholesterol to a saponin solution destroys the hemolytic activity. This and other observations pointing to some form of combination between cholesterol and digitonin prompted an investigation by Windaus[6] in 1909 that resulted in the discovery of the sparingly soluble 1:1 complex cholesterol digitonide, which is devoid of hemolytic activity. The other steroid saponins form similar molecular compounds, but none has been found that surpasses digitonin for the precipitation of steroids of specific structure and configuration, including aglycones derived from the steroid saponins. Thus the solubility of cholesterol tigonide in 95 percent alcohol at 18° is 150 mg./100 cc.,[4] whereas that of cholesterol digitonide is only 14 mg./100 cc.[6]

Digitonin forms 1:1 molecular compounds with substances other than steroids, for example, with terpene alcohols, phenols, and thiophenols.[7] The saponin crystallizes from aqueous ethanol with water of crystallization

[3] Jacobs and Fleck, *J. Biol. Chem.*, **88**, 545 (1930).

[4] Tschesche, *Ber.*, **69**, 1665 (1936).

[5] Ransom, *Deut. med. Wochschr.*, **27**, 194 (1901).

[6] Windaus, *Ber.*, **42**, 238 (1909).

[7] Windaus and Weinhold, *Z. physiol. Chem.*, **126**, 299 (1923).

TABLE I. Saponins

SAPONIN, FORMULA	SOURCE	M.p.	$[\alpha]_D$	SAPOGENIN	SUGAR
Digitonin[a] $C_{56}H_{92}O_{29}$	D. purpurea, D. lanata	235°	−54° Al	Digitogenin $C_{27}H_{44}O_5$	2 Glucose 2 Galactose 1 Xylose
Gitonin[b] $C_{50}H_{82}O_{23}$	D. purpurea, D. germanicum	272°	−51° Py	Gitogenin $C_{27}H_{44}O_4$	3 Galactose 1 Pentose
Tigonin[c] $C_{56}H_{92}O_{27}$	D. lanata	260°		Tigogenin $C_{27}H_{44}O_3$	2 Glucose 2 Galactose 1 Xylose
Amolonin[d] $C_{63}H_{104}O_{31}$	Chlorogalum pomeridianum		−67.5° Di[e] −75.5° Py[e]	Tigogenin	3 Glucose 1 Galactose 2 Rhamnose
Sarsasaponin (Parillin)[f] $C_{45}H_{74}O_{17}$	Radix sarsaparillae, Yucca schottii	245°		Sarsasapogenin $C_{27}H_{44}O_3$	2 Glucose 1 Rhamnose
Dioscin[g] Dioscoreasapotoxin[g]	Dioscorea Tokoro Makino Dioscorea Tokoro Makino	288° 220°	−95° Al	Diosgenin $C_{27}H_{42}O_3$	Rhamnose? Glucose Rhamnose
Trillarin, $C_{39}H_{64}O_{13}$	Trillium erectum	200°		Diosgenin	2 Glucose
Trillin, $C_{33}H_{52}O_x$[h]	Trillium erectum	271°	−103°	Diosgenin	1 Glucose

[a] Schmiedeberg, Arch. exptl. Path. Pharmakol., **3**, 16 (1875); Kiliani, Ber., **24**, 339, 3951 (1891); **34**, 3561 (1901); **43**, 3562 (1910); **49**, 701 (1916); **51**, 1613 (1918); Száhlender, Arch. Pharm., **274**, 446 (1936).

[b] Kiliani, Ber., **49**, 701 (1916); **51**, 1613 (1918); Windaus and Schneckenburger, ibid., **46**, 2628 (1913).

[c] Tschesche, ibid., **69**, 1665 (1936).

[d] Jurs and Noller, J. Am. Chem. Soc., **58**, 1251 (1936).

[e] $[\alpha]_{546}$.

[f] van der Haar, Rec. trav. chim., **48**, 726 (1929).

[g] Tsukamoto and Ueno, J. Pharm. Soc. Japan, **56**, 802 (1936) [C. A., **32**, 7470 (1938].

[h] Grove, Jenkins and M. R. Thompson, J. Am. Pharm. Assoc., **27**, 457 (1938); Marker and Krueger, J. Am. Chem. Soc., **62**, 2548, 3349 (1940); Lieberman, Chang, Barusch and Noller, ibid., **64**, 2581 (1942).

rather than with alcohol, but it forms with amyl alcohol a 1:1 compound that has been employed for purification of digitonin; the glycoside is recovered after removal of the alcohol by steam distillation. Complexes are formed also with ether and with acetone. Racemic α-terpineol and ac-tetrahydro-β-naphthol have been resolved by virtue of the fact that the molecular compounds of levorotatory digitonin with the l-alcohols are less soluble than those with the d-alcohols.[8]

Empirical Formulas. The sapogenins are far more easily isolated in a pure form than the saponins; they are less alterable than the glycosides and more readily characterized by ordinary means of identification. Thus a number of sapogenins have been isolated whose glycosides are either unknown or only superficially characterized. The saponins are of such high molecular weight—digitonin, 1229; amolonin, 1357.5—that analyses alone are not definitive, and the empirical formulas assigned are inferred from the formulas assigned to the aglycones and from evidence available concerning the nature and relative proportion of the sugar units.

In a series of investigations conducted for the most part with his own hands in the years 1890–1918, Kiliani identified the sugars of the principal digitalis saponins and devised procedures for the oxidation of the corresponding sapogenins, particularly digitogenin, to a succession of acidic degradation products. Kiliani excelled in empirical experimentation but paid little attention to the technique and interpretation of analyses, and the formulas that he proposed for the acids were in many cases grossly in error. Windaus, who had completed work for the doctorate in 1899 with Kiliani at Freiburg on the subject of the cardiac glycosides and saponins of digitalis, in 1913 ascribed to gitogenin the formula $C_{26}H_{42}O_3$ on the basis of analyses including those of degradation products and of cholesterol gitonide.[1] Digitogenin and tigogenin, later correlated with gitogenin, were regarded in subsequent researches of Windaus as C_{26}-compounds. Power and Salway[2] similarly regarded sarsasapogenin as $C_{26}H_{42}O_3$, but in 1935 Simpson and Jacobs[3] concluded that the preponderance of analytical evidence favored revision to $C_{27}H_{44}O_3$.

The difficulty is that commonly encountered in the attempt to distinguish between homologs of molecular weights in the order of 350–450, where the differences in composition of alternate homologous formulas are only 0.06–0.3 percent carbon and 0.09–0.2 percent hydrogen. An expedient sometimes useful consists in the analysis of a derivative having a higher percentage of halogen, oxygen, or nitrogen than the parent substance, for example,

[8] Windaus, Klänhardt and Weinhold, *Z. physiol. Chem.*, **126**, 308 (1923).
[1] Windaus and Schneckenburger, *Ber.*, **46**, 2628 (1913).
[2] Power and Salway, *J. Chem. Soc.*, **105**, 201 (1914).
[3] J. C. E. Simpson and Jacobs, *J. Biol. Chem.*, **109**, 573 (1935).

an acetate dibromide,[4] a bromoacetate,[5] *p*-iodobenzoate,[6] or dinitrobenzo-ate,[5] for these derivatives show a greater spread in the carbon values for homologs (0.4–0.6% C), although the hydrogen percentages are but little affected. Another method is determination of the neutralization equiv-alent of an acidic substance or degradation product[7, 8] or the saponification equivalent of an acetate or benzoate[9, 10, 5] or of a series of homologous esters,[6] and if sufficiently large samples (0.5–1 g.) are employed it is pos-sible to determine the molecular weight with an accuracy of 2–3 units.[8, 10] The method of X-ray and crystallographic analysis sometimes furnishes a sufficiently precise value for the molecular weight to be decisive, for ex-ample, in the case of bufagin.[11]

The C_{27}- rather than the C_{26}-formulation was eventually established for most of the sapogenins by evidence of degradation rather than of analysis. In one instance, however, the formula was established by two direct com-bustion analyses of the natural product itself by the technique developed by Baxter and Hale[12] in a redetermination of the atomic weight of carbon. Liang and Noller[13] had isolated the new sapogenin chlorogenin, along with tigogenin, from Californian *Chlorogalum pomeridianum*, and had reported in all nineteen analyses (C-H, Br) of the sapogenin and its derivatives, in-cluding series of microanalyses by A. Schoeller and by M. Furter and seven determinations of saponification equivalents. From the results, Liang and Noller concluded that chlorogenin probably has the C_{26}-formula. However, the following analyses[14] of 1-g. samples by the precision method of Baxter and Hale show that the C_{27}-formula is correct.

CHLOROGENIN	C	H
Calcd. for $C_{26}H_{42}O_4$	74.58	10.12
$C_{27}H_{44}O_4$	74.956	10.250
Analysis No. 13	74.961	10.250
Analysis No. 14	74.987	10.254

[4] Reinitzer, *Monatsh.*, **9,** 421 (1888).

[5] Windaus, v. Werder and Gschaider, *Ber.*, **65,** 1006 (1932).

[6] Drake and Jacobsen, *J. Am. Chem. Soc.*, **57,** 1570 (1935).

[7] Windaus and Brunken, *Z. physiol. Chem.*, **140,** 47 (1924).

[8] Stoll, A. Hofmann and Peyer, *Helv. Chim. Acta*, **18,** 1247 (1935).

[9] K. A. Vesterberg and R. Vesterberg, *Ark. Kemi Mineral. Geol.*, **9,** No. 27, 1 (1926).

[10] Sandqvist and Gorton, *Ber.*, **63,** 1935 (1930); Sandqvist and Bengtsson, *ibid.*, **64,** 2167 (1931).

[11] Crowfoot, *Chemistry and Industry*, **54,** 568 (1935).

[12] Baxter and Hale, *J. Am. Chem. Soc.*, **58,** 510 (1936).

[13] Liang and Noller, *J. Am. Chem. Soc.*, **57,** 525 (1935).

[14] Fieser and Jacobsen, *J. Am. Chem. Soc.*, **58,** 943 (1936).

Analyses of sarsasapogenin similarly afforded fully decisive results:

SARSASAPOGENIN	C	H
Calcd. for $C_{26}H_{42}O_3$	77.56	10.51
$C_{27}H_{44}O_3$	77.835	10.644
Analysis No. 16	77.827	10.644
Analysis No. 17	77.822	10.641

These two samples were purified by C. R. Noller and by W. A. Jacobs, respectively, by ordinary methods. Samples of cholestanol and of dehydrodesoxycholic acid purified by R. P. Jacobsen also gave results in agreement with the theoretical values within about 0.02 percent for carbon and 0.01 percent for hydrogen and hence of sufficient accuracy to distinguish between $C_{26}H_{46}O$ and $C_{27}H_{48}O$, where the differences in composition are only 0.08 percent C and 0.07 percent H. The results of the precision analyses incidentally demonstrate that natural products of very high purity can be isolated from both plant and animal sources.

Skeletal Structure. The first suggestion of a relationship of the sapogenins to the sterols was an observation by Ruzicka and van Veen.[1] In the course of a study of the dehydrogenation of triterpenoid sapogenins, sarsasapogenin was submitted to dehydrogenation with selenium and was found to yield a fragrant ketone $C_8H_{16}O$ regarded as identical with methyl isohexyl ketone from cholesterol. In 1934 Jacobs and Simpson[2] reinvestigated the reaction and isolated a ketone whose semicarbazone melted several degrees lower than Ruzicka's preparation and appeared to be different from the semicarbazone of synthetic methyl isohexyl ketone.[3] The same ketone was obtained from gitogenin. A milder cleavage of the side chain was accomplished[2] by treatment of sarsasapogenin or gitogenin with hydrochloric and acetic acids, and in this case the volatile product was an unsaturated carbonyl compound, $C_8H_{14}O_3$. Although the identity of the various cleavage products remained unsettled, the observations all pointed to the presence in the sapogenins of a C_8-side chain. Jacobs and Simpson made the further important discovery that the mixtures resulting from the dehydrogenation of either sarsasapogenin or gitogenin contain the Diels hydrocarbon, and hence that these sapogenins possess the steroid ring system.

In 1935 Tschesche[4] established a correlation between tigogenin, gito-

---

[1] Ruzicka and van Veen, *Z. physiol. Chem.*, **184,** 69 (1929).

[2] Jacobs and J. C. E. Simpson, *J. Biol. Chem.*, **105,** 501 (1934).

[3] Jacobs and J. C. E. Simpson, *J. Am. Chem. Soc.*, **56,** 1424 (1934).

[4] Tschesche, *Ber.*, **68,** 1090 (1935).

genin, and digitogenin, which contain one, two, and three acylable hydroxyl groups, respectively, and which all contain two nonhydroxylic and apparently oxidic oxygen atoms. On mild chromic acid oxidation tigogenin was found to yield a dibasic acid identical with the product from gitogenin: gitogenic acid, $C_{27}H_{42}O_6$, m.p. 243°, $[\alpha]_D - 61°$ An.[5, 6, 7] The product of similar oxidation of digitogenin had been characterized as a keto dibasic acid: digitogenic acid, $C_{27}H_{40}O_7$, m.p. 210°, $[\alpha]_D - 67°$ (dil. alkali), oxime, mono and diesters.[8, 6] Tschesche found that digitogenic acid on Wolff-Kishner reduction affords gitogenic acid.

At this point Windaus[9] suggested the provisional formulation I for tigogenin (regarded as a C_{26}-compound), and Simpson and Jacobs[10] suggested formula II for sarsasapogenin. Shortly thereafter Tschesche and Hage-

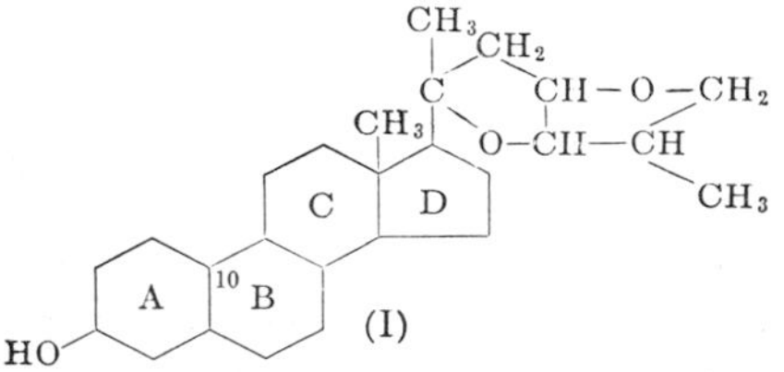

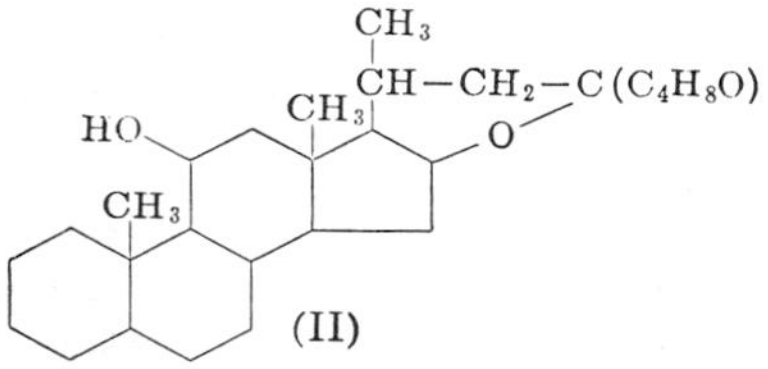

dorn[11] succeeded in degrading tigogenin to a product identified as etioallobilianic acid (Chart 1, VII). This work established the structure and configuration of the ring system and, coupled with the evidence for a C_8-side chain, strengthened the case for the C_{27}-formulation. The degradation also afforded a strong indication that the side chain includes a tetrahydrofurano ring fused to ring D, as in formula III. The chief product isolated on chromic acid oxidation of acetyl tigogenin is the acetyl derivative of a monobasic acid $C_{27}H_{42}O_5$ (tigogenoic acid), but a minor product proved to be the acetate of a C_{22}-hydroxylactone, formulated as IV. The deacetylated product was oxidized to a ketone and the ketonic oxygen removed by Clemmensen reduction (V). The lactone V is stable to cold alkali but reacts with phenylmagnesium bromide to give the diphenylcarbinol VI, which contains two active hydrogen atoms (Zerewitinoff). Dehydration of VI effects ring closure to a substance having the properties of a tetrahydrofuran derivative, which points to a 1:4 relationship between the two

[5] Windaus and Schneckenburger, *Ber.*, **46**, 2628 (1913).

[6] Windaus and Weil, *Z. physiol. Chem.*, **121**, 62 (1922).

[7] J. C. E. Simpson and Jacobs, *J. Biol. Chem.*, **110**, 565 (1935).

[8] Kiliani and Schweissinger, *Ber.*, **37**, 1215 (1904).

[9] Windaus, *Nachr. Ges. Wiss., Göttingen*, 89 (1935).

[10] J. C. E. Simpson and Jacobs, *J. Biol. Chem.*, **109**, 573 (1935).

[11] Tschesche and Hagedorn, *Ber.*, **68**, 1412 (1935).

hydroxyl groups. On oxidation of VI with chromic acid ring D is cleaved in two directions to give etioallobilianic acid (VII) and a monobasic lactone acid of composition and properties consistent with formula VIII.

Chart 1. DEGRADATION OF TIGOGENIN

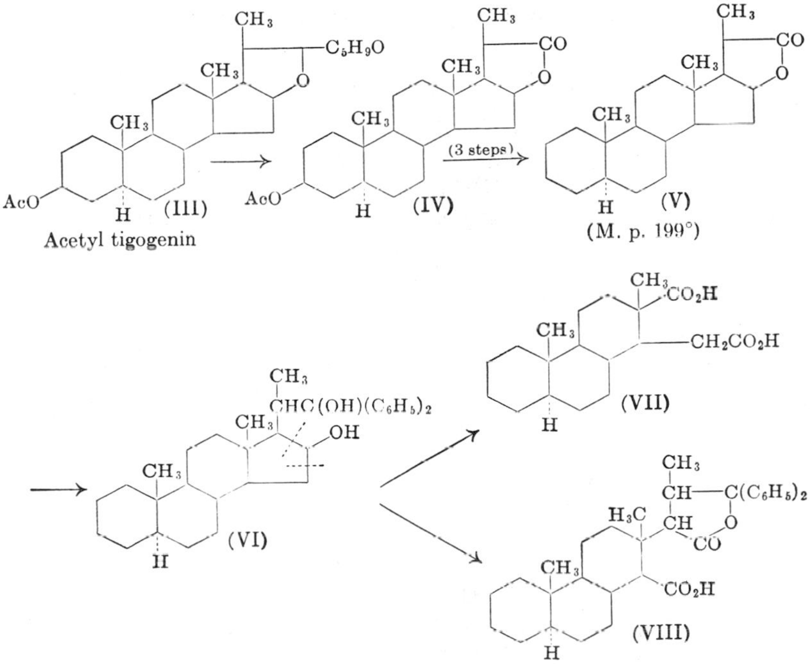

Acetyl tigogenin (III)

(IV) (3 steps)

(V) (M. p. 199°)

(VI)

(VII)

(VIII)

The same scheme of degradation was applied by Farmer and Kon[12] to sarsasapogenin; the results were analogous except that the final acidic degradation product proved to be etiobilianic acid. Sarsasapogenin thus belongs to the coprostane series, whereas tigogenin belongs to the cholestane series. Kon and co-workers also placed the nuclear hydroxyl group of sarsasapogenin at C_3 by dehydrogenating the methylcarbinol of sarsasapogenone to a hydrocarbon identified as 7-methyl-1,2-cyclopentenophenanthrene.[12, 13]

Side Chain. The spiroketal formulation I (Chart 2) for the terminal part of the sapogenin side chain was established by Marker in a series of investigations initially concerned particularly with the properties and transformations of sarsasapogenoic acid (II). This acid, which corre-

[12] Farmer and Kon, *J. Chem. Sob.*, 414 (1937).
[13] Kon and Woolman, *J. Chem. Soc.*, 794 (1939).

sponds to Tschesche's tigogenoic acid, had been obtained by Fieser and Jacobsen[1] by controlled chromic acid oxidation of sarsasapogenin acetate and had been found to undergo condensation in the presence of alkali to an anhydro compound (III) characterized as an α,β-unsaturated keto acid.

Chart 2. STRUCTURE OF THE SAPOGENIN SIDE CHAIN

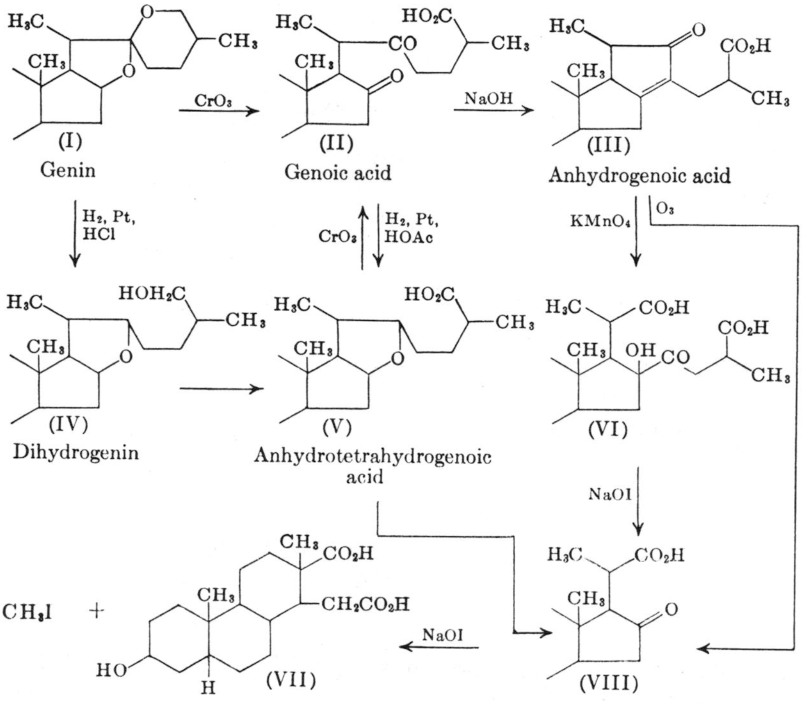

This substance on permanganate oxidation afforded a diacid initially regarded as $C_{27}H_{40}O_7$, and this on hypohalite oxidation gave iodoform and a substance tentatively regarded as a C_{25}- or C_{26}-acid.   Fieser and Jacobsen interpreted these and other transformations as supporting a perhydrodifuryl formulation of the sapogenin side chain suggested by Tschesche and Hagedorn,[2] but Marker showed this formulation to be wrong.   The diacid VI actually is $C_{27}H_{42}O_7$,[3a] and the final product of the hypohalite reaction

[1] Fieser and Jacobsen, *J. Am. Chem. Soc.*, **60**, (a) 28, (b) 2753, (c) 2761 (1938); see also (d) Fieser, Fry and R. N. Jones, *ibid.*, **61**, 1849 (1939).

[2] Tschesche and Hagedorn, *Ber.*, **68**, 1412, 2247 (1935).

[3] Marker and Rohrmann, *J. Am. Chem. Soc.*, (a) **61**, 2072 (1939); Marker and Shabica, *ibid.*, (b) **64**, 147 (1942); (c) **64**, 180 (1942).

is a C_{19}-acid identical with 3β-hydroxyetiobilianic acid (VII).[3c]   The formation of iodoform thus is not indicative of an aceto group in the compound oxidized.   Evidence supporting Marker's formula III for anhydrosarsasapogenoic acid was found in ozonization to the keto acid VIII; this on reduction with sodium and alcohol yielded the C_{22}-lactone (IV, Chart 1).[4] The unsaturated keto acid III is unreactive toward ketonic reagents, but can be reduced either catalytically or with sodium and amyl alcohol to a tetrahydride that readily lactonizes.[1b]   A lower-melting unsaturated keto acid, possibly the $\Delta^{17(20)}$-isomer, was isolated in small amounts.[3a]   The only conflicting evidence is that the anhydrogenoic acid shows an absorption maximum at shorter wave length than expected for the structure III (methyl ester acetate, λ_{max}^{alc} 243 mμ, log ϵ 4.13;[1d] calcd., λ_{max}^{alc} 254 mμ).   Marker's formulation of the diacid VI is based upon the chromic acid oxidation of this substance (as dimethyl ester acetate) to VIII.[3b]

In acetic acid solution sarsasapogenoic acid slowly absorbs two moles of hydrogen with loss of a molecule of water to form V.[1b,d]   Marker[5] found that the sapogenin itself can be hydrogenated in an acidic medium to a dihydride containing a newly formed, acylable hydroxyl group recognized as primary by oxidation to V.   The oxidation of V to sarsasapogenoic acid provides further evidence in support of Marker's formula II.[6]   Both carbonyl groups in this substance are hindered, but under forcing conditions (130°) dioximes can be obtained from both the acid[1b] and the methyl ester.[7]

The first indication of the sensitivity of the sapogenin side chain to acids was the observation of Jacobs and Simpson, cited above, of cleavage of the entire C_8-side chain on acetolysis.   The ready hydrogenation of sapogenins in the presence of acids (Chart 2) is one of several further instances of analogous reactions discovered by Marker.   One is an inversion at C_{22}, in which, according to Marker's conventional representation (Chart 3), a sapogenin (IX) is converted into an isosapogenin (X) by the action of alcoholic hydrochloric acid.[5]   On such treatment sarsasapogenin, $[\alpha]_D - 76.5°$, is converted into isosarsasapogenin, $[\alpha]_D - 69°$, identical with smilagenin, a constituent of Jamaican sarsaparilla (*Smilax ornata*).[5, 8]   Both the sapogenin and the isosapogenin are reducible by the Clemmensen method,[5] and they yield the same tetrahydrosapogenin (XI).   The reactions afford evidence of the presence of a latent carbonyl group; dihydrosarsasapogenin (IV, Chart 2) is unaffected by Clemmensen reduction.[5]   Some of the iso-

[4] Marker, Shabica and D. L. Turner, *J. Am. Chem. Soc.*, **63**, 2274 (1941).

[5] Marker and Rohrmann, *J. Am. Chem. Soc.*, **61**, 846 (1939).

[6] Marker and Rohrmann, *J. Am. Chem. Soc.*, **61**, 3477 (1939).

[7] Marker and Shabica, *J. Am. Chem. Soc.*, **64**, 721 (1942).

[8] Askew, Farmer and Kon, *J. Chem. Soc.*, 1399 (1936); Kon, Soper and Woolman, *ibid.*, 1201 (1939).

sapogenins isolated from plants may be artifacts formed during acid hydrolysis of the saponins. Marker[9] has speculated that the original glycoside synthesized by the plant may have an open side chain in which ring closure

Chart 3. Degradation to Pregnane Derivatives

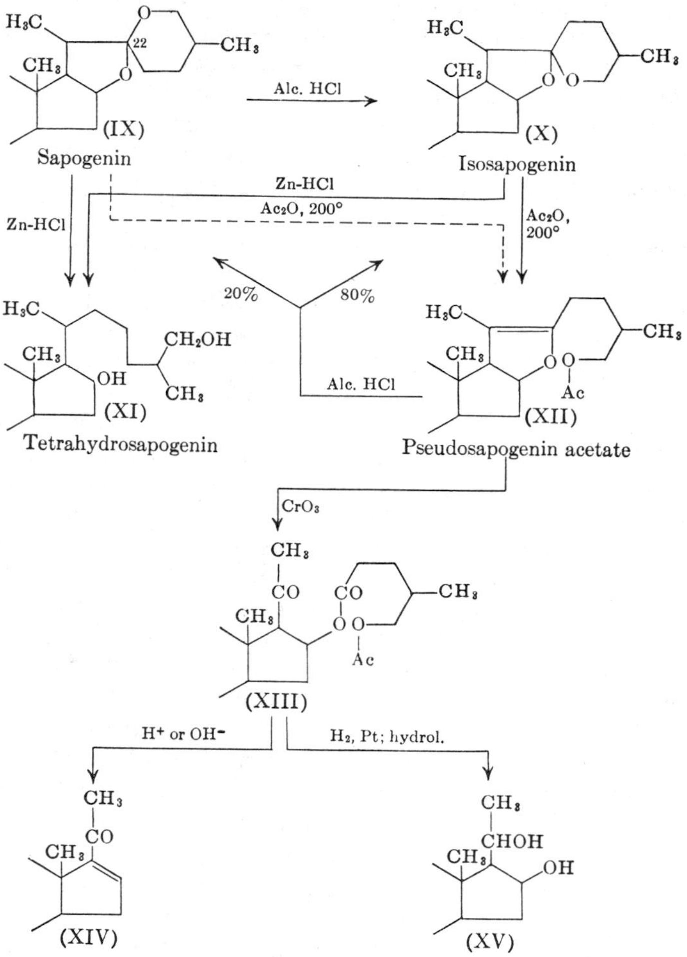

to the spiroketal structure is prevented by conjugation of the alcoholic functions at C_{16} or C_{26} with sugar units. If enzymatic hydrolysis of such

[9] Marker and co-workers, *J. Am. Chem. Soc.*, **69**, 2211 (1947); Marker and Lopez, *ibid.*, **69**, 2389 (1947).

units occurs in the plant, ring closure to a normal saponin may follow; if hydrolysis is effected by acids, the vigorous treatment necessary may lead to an iso compound.

Another form of isomerization is induced by treatment with acetic anhydride at 200°. Both sarsasapogenin[10] and the 22-iso compound smilagenin[11] yield the third isomer pseudosarsasapogenin, initially regarded as a diene[12] but more recently formulated as XII.[13] The structure XII is supported by the observed chromic acid oxidation to the ester XIII, which can be degraded further to the pregnane derivatives XIV and XV.[14] A degradation of tigogenin to an allopregnane-3β,20-diol afforded the first proof that the 3-hydroxyl group in the sapogenin has the β-orientation. Triols isomeric with those resulting from this degradation (XV) and probably differing from them in the configuration at C_{20} are formed on oxidation of the sapogenins with Caro's acid.[15] Still unexplained is the observation that dihydropseudosarsasapogenin differs from dihydrosarsasapogenin and is stated to yield different oxidation products.[16]

The pseudosapogenins can be recyclized by the action of mineral acid in the cold or at reflux temperature.[17] The isosapogenin is the chief product but is often accompanied by a small amount of the normal genin.[18] Thus a given pseudo compound reverts principally to the genin from which it was derived only if the latter has the 22-iso configuration. One exception is that pseudosarsasapogenin reverts to sarsasapogenin (22-normal) and not to smilagenin (22-iso); this is not a peculiarity associated with the A/B-cis configuration, for other pseudo compounds of the cholestane series on cyclization yield chiefly iso compounds.

Hormones from Sapogenins. Examples of a number of degradations to members of the pregnane and androstane series reported by Marker are summarized in Chart 4.[19] Diosgenin (I), one of the sapogenins isolated from the rhizomes of Mexican *dioscorea*, is converted to the pseudo derivative II and this is oxidized to the doubly unsaturated ketone III, which can be selectively hydrogenated to pregnenolone (VI) and further transformed

[10] Marker and Rohrmann, *J. Am. Chem. Soc.*, **61**, 3592 (1939); **62**, 518 (1940).

[11] Marker and co-workers, *J. Am. Chem. Soc.*, **62**, 648 (1940).

[12] Marker and co-workers, *J. Am. Chem. Soc.*, **62**, 2532 (1940).

[13] Marker and co-workers, *J. Am. Chem. Soc.*, **64**, 1655 (1942).

[14] Marker and co-workers, *J. Am. Chem. Soc.*, **62**, 518, 898, 2525 (1940); **63**, 774, 779 (1941).

[15] Marker and co-workers, *J. Am. Chem. Soc.*, **62**, 525, 2540 (1940); **63**, 772 (1941).

[16] Marker and co-workers, *J. Am. Chem. Soc.*, **62**, 521, 2532 (1940); **64**, 1655 (1942).

[17] Marker and co-workers, *J. Am. Chem. Soc.*, **62**, 896, 2525 (1940).

[18] Marker and Lopez, *J. Am. Chem. Soc.*, **69**, 2373 (1947).

[19] Marker, R. B. Wagner, Ulshafer, Wittbecker, Goldsmith and Ruof, *J. Am. Chem. Soc.*, **69**, 2172 (1947); Marker, *ibid.*, **69**, 2395 (1947).

into progesterone. Nologenin, a companion of diosgenin, is likewise convertible into pregnenolone by oxidation of the diacetate (IV) and Clemmensen reduction of the oxidation product (V). Sarsasapogenin (VII) has a saturated nucleus of the A/B-cis orientation and can be degraded to pregnanedione-3,20, also an intermediate to progesterone.

CHART 4. PROGESTERONE FROM SAPOGENINS

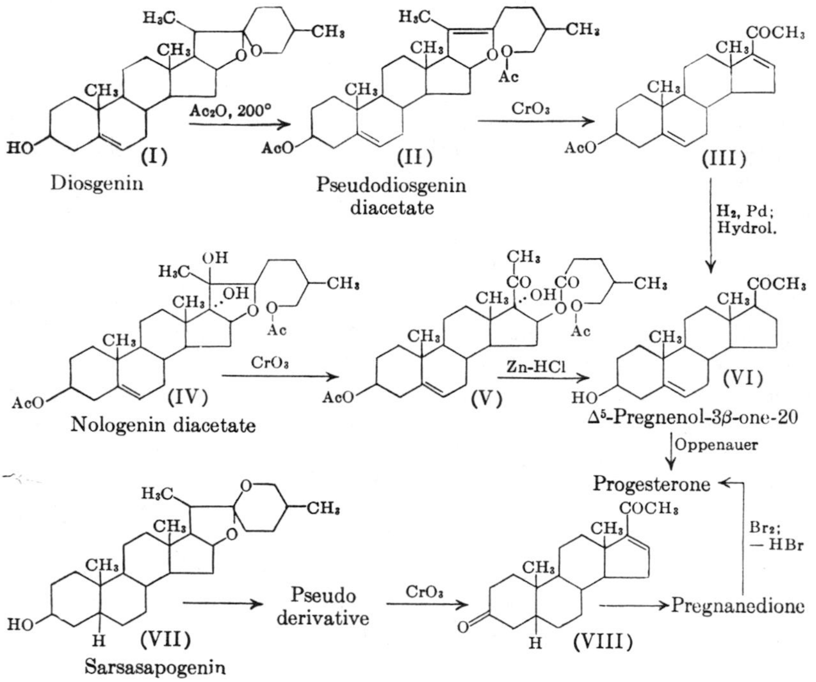

Variations in the Sapogenin Structure. The first six sapogenins listed in Table II all contain a lone nuclear hydroxyl group at C_3 in the β-orientation, as established for sarsasapogenin, tigogenin, and diosgenin by evidence cited above. The correlation of smilagenin with sarsasapogenin by the iso reaction has been mentioned. Tigogenin[1] was recognized as the 22-epimer of neotigogenin[2] by its formation on acid isomerization of the latter substance. The coprostane derivatives sarsasapogenin and smilagenin

[1] From *Digitalis purpurea*, Jacobs and Fleck, *J. Biol. Chem.*, **88**, 545 (1930). From *D. lanata*, Tschesche, *Ber.*, **69**, 1665 (1936). From *Chlorogalum pomeridianum*, Liang and Noller, *J. Am. Chem. Soc.*, **57**, 525 (1935); Jurs and Noller, *ibid.*, **58**, 1251 (1936).

[2] Goodson and Noller, *J. Am. Chem. Soc.*, **61**, 2420 (1939).

were further converted into neotigogenin and tigogenin (cholestane series) by standard sterol reactions.[3] Diosgenin[4] yields tigogenin on catalytic hydrogenation and also on Oppenauer oxidation followed by reduction with sodium and alcohol.[5] Marker transformed diosgenin into cholesterol[6]

TABLE II. Sapogenins

COMPOUND	C_{22}	A/B	SUBSTITUENTS	M.p.	$[\alpha]_D$
Sarsasapogenin	normal	cis	3β-OH	200°	$-76.5°$
Smilagenin	iso	cis	3β-OH	184°	$-69°$
Neotigogenin	normal	trans	3β-OH	203°	$-65°$
Tigogenin	iso	trans	3β-OH	204°	$-49°$
Yamogenin (Δ^5)	normal	—	3β-OH	201°	
Diosgenin (Δ^5)	iso	—	3β-OH	208°	$-129°$
Gitogenin	iso	trans	$2,3$-$(OH)_2$	272°	$-61°$
Chlorogenin	iso	trans	$3\beta,6\alpha$-$(OH)_2$	276°	$-46°$
Texogenin	normal	cis	$2,3$-$(OH)_2$	172°	
Samogenin	iso	cis	$2,3$-$(OH)_2$	212°	
Rockogenin	iso	trans	$3\beta,12(?)$-$(OH)_2$	220°	
Lilagenin (Δ^5)	normal	—	$2,3$-$(OH)_2$	246°	
Yuccagenin (Δ^5)	iso	—	$2,3$-$(OH)_2$	252°	
Botogenin (Δ^5)	iso	—	3β (OH), $12(?)$-CO	262°	
Digitogenin	iso	trans	$2,3,15(?)$-$(OH)_3$	283°	$-81°$
Hecogenin	iso	trans	3β-OH, $12(?)$-CO	268°	
Mexogenin	iso	cis	$2,3$-$(OH)_2$, $12(?)$-CO	246°	
Magogenin	iso	trans	$2,3,6$-$(OH)_3$	284°	
Agavogenin	iso	trans	$2,3,12(?)$-$(OH)_3$	242°	
Manogenin	iso	trans	$2,3$-$(OH)_2$, $12(?)$-CO	264°	
Kammogenin (Δ^5)	iso	—	$2,3$-$(OH)_2$, $12(?)$-CO	242°	
Cacogenin	iso	trans	$2,3,6$-$(OH)_3$, $12(?)$-CO	278°	

but isolated only one of the postulated[7] intermediates. Yamogenin[8] occurs with diosgenin and has been shown to be the 22-normal isomer of diosgenin. On Oppenauer oxidation and reduction with sodium and alcohol it affords neotigogenin.

Gitogenin, the first of the dihydroxy compounds listed in Table II, was isolated from *Digitalis purpurea* by Windaus and Brunken.[9] As mentioned

[3] Marker and co-workers, *J. Am. Chem. Soc.*, **62**, 647, 1162 (1940).

[4] From *Dioscorea Tokoro Makino*, Tsukamoto, Ueno and Ohta, *J. Pharm. Soc., Japan*, **56**, 135 (1936); **57**, 9 (1937). From *Trillium erectum*, Marker and co-workers, *J. Am. Chem. Soc.*, **62**, 2542, 2548 (1940).

[5] Marker, Tsukamoto and D. L. Turner, *J. Am. Chem. Soc.*, **62**, 2525 (1940).

[6] Marker and D. L. Turner, *J. Am. Chem. Soc.*, **63**, 767 (1941).

[7] Marker and co-workers, *J. Am. Chem. Soc.*, **69**, 2186 (1947).

[8] Marker and co-workers, *J. Am. Chem. Soc.*, **69**, 2184 (1947).

[9] Windaus and Brunken, *Z. physiol. Chem.*, **145**, 37 (1925).

above, the substance on oxidation affords a product, gitogenic acid, identical with the product of oxidation of the 3β-hydroxy compound tigogenin. Since the latter is of the A/B-trans type analogous to cholestanol the ring opening must occur between positions 2 and 3 and hence gitogenin is a 2,3-dihydroxy compound. Since it is inert to hydrochloric acid under the usual conditions of isomerization it presumably has the 22-iso configuration.

Chlorogenin, isolated by Liang and Noller,[10] is formulated as a $3\beta,6\alpha$-dihydroxy A/B-trans compound of the 22-iso series (stable to acid), as in formula IV, Chart 5, on the basis of the following transformations carried out by Marker.[11] When oxidized with chromic acid by the procedure ap-

Chart 5. Correlation of Diosgenin with other Genins

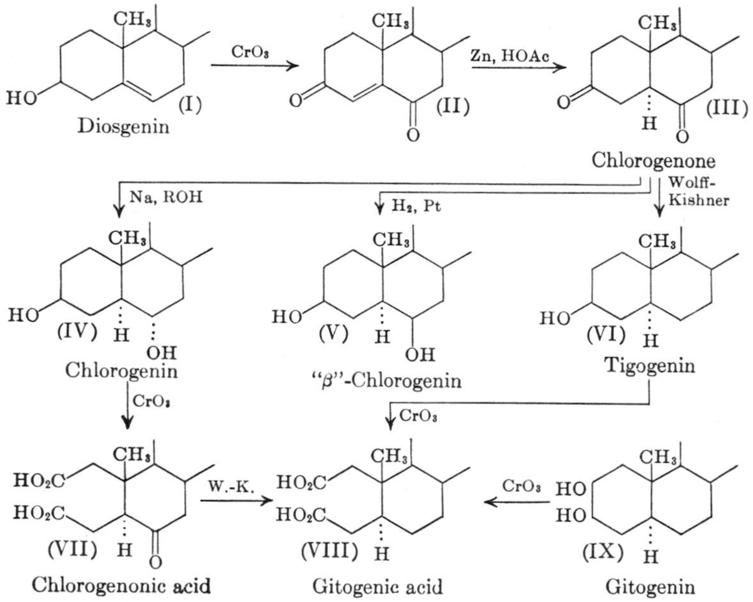

plied by Mauthner and Suida to cholesterol, diosgenin (I) similarly afforded the Δ^4-3,6-dione II, which on reduction yielded chlorogenone (III). Further transformations of this diketone are assumed to follow the same steric course as corresponding transformations of cholestane-3,6-dione. Reduction with sodium and alcohol gives natural chlorogenin, which is as-

[10] Liang and Noller, *J. Am. Chem. Soc.*, **57**, 525 (1935).

[11] Marker and co-workers, *J. Am. Chem. Soc.*, **62**, 2537, 3006, 3009 (1940); **64**, 221, 809 (1942).

signed the 3β,6α-orientation IV, whereas catalytic hydrogenation gives the 3β,6β-isomer V. By suitable treatment with chromic acid, chlorogenin can be oxidized to a ketodibasic acid, chlorogenonic acid (VII),[12] which on Wolff-Kishner reduction yields gitogenic acid (VIII), the initial product of chromic acid oxidation of both gitogenin (IX) and tigogenin (VI). The formation of tigogenin from chlorogenone (III) on Wolff-Kishner reduction corresponds to abnormal reductions of 3-ketosteroids observed by Dutcher and Wintersteiner;[13] for example, cholestanone yielded chiefly cholestanol. Chlorogenin was also transformed into tigogenin[11] by selective chromic acid oxidation to the 3-ol-6-one and Clemmensen reduction. Chlorogenonic acid, although formulated as having a carbonyl group adjacent to an asymmetric center carrying an enolizable hydrogen atom, is stable to the isomerizing action of alkali. The difference in behavior from that of the 6-ketone derived from hyodesoxycholic acid is attributed[11] to the fact that the substance has the stable A/B-trans configuration.

Marker reported that tigogenin, gitogenin, and chlorogenin are all precipitated by digitonin,[14] but Noller[15] found that the digitonides in this series have much higher solubilities than cholesterol digitonide and that a distinction between the 3α- and 3β-configuration can be made only by comparison of the solubility products of the two epimers.

The next six compounds listed in Table II were discovered by Marker in an investigation of the sapogenins of over 400 species of plants of the *Liliaceae, Dioscoreaceae,* and *Scrophulariaceae* families.[16] Texogenin is isomerized by mineral acid to samogenin, and hence these substances are regarded as normal and iso genins, respectively. Texogenin on chromic acid oxidation gives a dibasic acid analogous to gitogenic acid and hence is presumed to contain adjacent hydroxyl groups. One group is placed at C$_3$ because of digitonide formation and because the sapogenin is epimerized by the action of sodium ethoxide at 200°; according to Marker, the latter reaction is also indicative of the A/B-cis configuration. Rockogenin occurs in company with a hydroxyketosapogenin, hecogenin, formulated by Marker as a 3-hydroxy-12-keto isogenin. Both substances yield the same diketone on chromic acid oxidation (25°) and hecogenin on reduction (H$_2$, Pt; or Na, EtOH) yields rockogenin. Hecogenin on Wolff-Kishner reduction yields tigogenin. Marker suggests that one of the oxygen functions in these genins is located at C$_{12}$ for the following reasons: hecogenin reacts with difficulty with semicarbazide but more readily with 2,4-dinitrophenyl-

[12] Noller, *J. Am. Chem. Soc.,* **59,** 1092 (1937).
[13] Dutcher and Wintersteiner, *J. Am. Chem. Soc.,* **61,** 1992 (1939).
[14] Marker and Rohrmann, *J. Am. Chem. Soc.,* **61,** 946, 2724 (1939); **62,** 647 (1940).
[15] Noller, *J. Am. Chem. Soc.,* **61,** 2717 (1939).
[16] Marker and co-workers, *J. Am. Chem. Soc.,* **69,** 2167 (1947).

hydrazine; the corresponding hydroxyl group is acetylated only under drastic conditions; the 7-position for the carbonyl group is eliminated by comparison with synthetic 7-ketotigogenin, prepared from diosgenin acetate
by chromic acid oxidation followed by saturation of the 5,6-double bond.
Botogenin probably is 5,6-dehydrohecogenin.[17]　Mexogenin is a dihydroxy-
ketosapogenin that yields samogenin on Wolff-Kishner reduction; the
carbonyl group is regarded as being at C_{12} because of behavior analagous
to that of hecogenin.　Lilagenin and yuccagenin were related by the iso
reaction.　Yuccagenin yields gitogenin on catalytic hydrogenation and
the double bond was shown to occupy the same position as in diosgenin (5,
6) by a series of transformations leading in both cases to 7-ketogitogenic
acid.[18]　Yuccagenin occurs as a tetraglycoside, yucconin, which on catalytic
hydrogenation is reported to yield gitonin.[19]　Hydrolysis of yucconin
under mild conditions affords a triglycoside that appears to contain a newly
formed carbonyl group, presumably at C_{22}; this substance on hydrogenation and hydrolysis yields dihydroyuccagenin (reformation of ring E).
On the basis of these and other observations, Marker has advanced the
interesting hypothesis that in yucconin and gitonin the terminal ring F is
not closed, position 20 is hydroxylated, and sugar units are linked to the
oxygen functions at positions 2, 3, 20, and 26.[19]

　　The structure of digitogenin, the earliest known (Schmiedeberg, Kiliani)
and most extensively investigated of all the sapogenins, is still uncertain.
The relationship to gitogenin established by Tschesche (1935) by Wolff-
Kishner reduction of digitogenic acid to gitogenic acid, as noted above,
shows that two of the three secondary hydroxyl groups present are located
at positions 2 and 3.　Windaus and his associates made an extensive study
of the oxidative degradation of digitogenin and gitogenin and characterized
a number of transformation products.[20]　Tschesche and Hagedorn[21] later
reinvestigated the oxidative degradations, revised some of the empirical
formulas, and presented a rational interpretation of the data that seemed
to indicate that the third hydroxyl group of digitogenin is located at
C_6.[22]　The main piece of evidence was that the initial product of chromic
acid oxidation, digitogenic acid, characterized as a keto diacid, is isomerized
by alkali to digitoic acid[23] and hence must contain a carbonyl group adja-

[17] Marker and Lopez, J. Am. Chem Soc., **69**, 2397 (1947).

[18] Marker and Lopez, J. Am. Chem. Soc., **69**, 2401 (1947).

[19] Marker and Lopez, J. Am. Chem. Soc., **69**, 2389 (1947).

[20] Windaus and Willerding, Z. physiol. Chem., **143**, 33 (1925); Windaus and Linsert,
ibid., **147**, 275 (1925); Windaus and Shah, ibid., **151**, 86 (1926).

[21] Tschesche and Hagedorn, Ber., **69**, 797 (1936).

[22] For a summary, see Elsevier, **14**, 287 (1940).

[23] Kiliani and Windaus, Ber., **32**, 2201 (1899); Windaus and Weil, Z. physiol. Chem.,
121, 62 (1922).

cent to an asymmetric center bearing an enolizable hydrogen atom. However, chlorogenonic acid (VII, Chart 5) has the structure postulated for digitogenic acid but is different from this substance (or digitoic acid).[24] Marker[25] reduced digitogenic acid and digitoic acid (H_2, Pt, HOAc) and obtained in each case the same hydroxy diacid. This substance failed to lactonize, whereas 6-ketoalloisolithobilianic acid[26] and chlorogenonic acid[27] on similar reduction give hydroxy acids that immediately lactonize. The keto group of digitogenic acid therefore cannot be at C_6. The only available positions that would account for the isomerization to digitoic acid are 7, 11, and 15. Position 7 is unlikely[27] because digitogenic acid on permanganate oxidation yields a ketotricarboxylic acid (oxodigitogenic acid[20]) and not a tetracarboxylic acid as expected from the fission of the 6,7-linkage of a 7-ketone. Position 11 is improbable because there are no indications of hindrance of one of the three oxygen functions of digitogenin and its derivatives. Marker therefore suggests that the third hydroxyl group may be at C_{15}. This formulation does not afford a ready explanation of all the known transformations, but it cannot be said to be inconsistent with the known facts. Some of these are:[20, 21] decomposition of oxodigitogenic acid in boiling acetic acid with liberation of one mole of carbon dioxide, and in concentrated sulfuric acid with loss of 0.3 mole of carbon monoxide; conversion of oxodigitogenic acid into an enol lactone ester and into a pyro acid (loss of H_2O and 2 CO_2); permanganate oxidation of digitogenic acid or of oxodigitogenic acid to digitic acid ($C_{27}H_{40}O_{10}$, hydroxyketo triacid); chromic acid oxidation of digitogenic acid to a tetrabasic "acid A" ($C_{23}H_{32}O_8 \cdot H_2O^{21}$); decarboxylation of acid A to acid B ($C_{22}H_{32}O_8 \cdot H_2O$, tribasic[21]). Some of these transformations are particularly complicated because both the side chain and the nucleus may be attacked and a differentiation between the two is not possible from the available evidence.

Magogenin[28] is formulated as a 2,3,6-trihydroxy isogenin because it yields chlorogenonic acid on oxidation. Three isogenins regarded by Marker as having oxygen functions at positions 2, 3, and 12 are related as follows.[29] The ketone manogenin on Wolff-Kishner reduction gives gitogenin and on catalytic or sodium-alcohol reduction gives agavogenin. The carbonyl group has the same properties as that in hecogenin and is therefore tentatively placed at C_{12}. Kammogenin was correlated with manogenin, agavogenin, and yuccagenin, and assigned the structure of the 5,6-dehydro

[24] Noller and Lieberman, *J. Am. Chem. Soc.*, **63**, 2131 (1941).

[25] Marker, D. L. Turner and Ulshafer, *J. Am. Chem Soc.*, **64**, 1843 (1942).

[26] Windaus, *Ann.*, **447**, 233 (1926).

[27] Marker and co-workers, *J. Am. Chem. Soc.*, **69**, 2183 (1947).

[28] Marker, *J. Am. Chem. Soc.*, **69**, 2399 (1947).

[29] Marker and co-workers, *J. Am. Chem. Soc.*, **69**, 2167 (1947).

derivative of manogenin. Cacogenin[28] is regarded as 12-ketomagogenin. On chromic acid oxidation it gives hecogenic acid, also obtained from hecogenin and manogenin; on Wolff-Kishner reduction it is converted into magogenin.

The five substances listed in Chart 6 are not true plant products but are the result of the action of acid or alkali on the parent glycoside of Beth

Chart 6. 3β-HYDROXY-Δ^5-STEROIDS DERIVED FROM NOLONIN

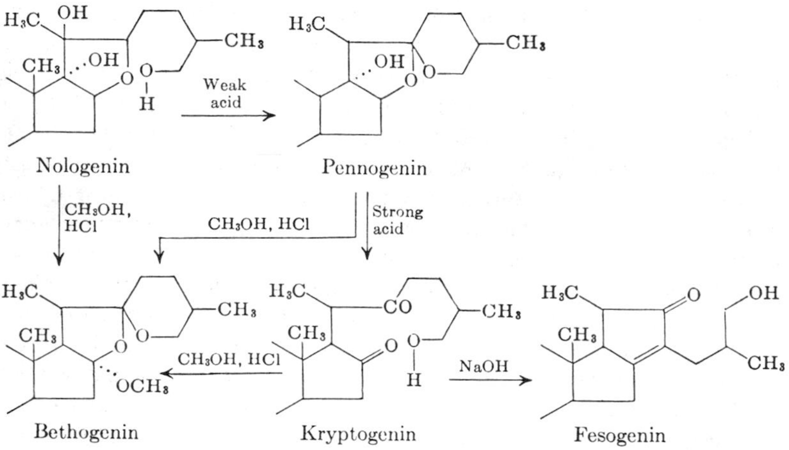

| Nologenin | Pennogenin |
| Bethogenin | Kryptogenin | Fesogenin |

root, nolonin, or its hydrolysis products.[30] Bethogenin was isolated from hydrolyzed Beth root by Noller[31] and the other substances were isolated by Marker.[30] Noller established that bethogenin forms a monoacetate, contains a methoxyl group, and does not form a pseudo compound. It yields a dioxime, but does not show ultraviolet absorption characteristic of a ketone. Treatment with hydrobromic acid gives a product that does have a spectrum indicative of the presence of an isolated carbonyl group (λ_{max} 285 mμ, log ϵ 1.77); the compound forms a dioxime and a diacetate. This substance (kryptogenin) was then isolated by Marker and shown to be reconvertible into bethogenin by the action of methanol and hydrogen chloride. Nologenin and pennogenin react similarly. Mild acid treatment of nologenin gives pennogenin, and stronger acid treatment affords kryptogenin. Kryptogenin is similar in structure to sarsasapogenoic acid and like this substance is cyclized by alkali to an unsaturated ketone, fesogenin. The saponin nolonin under various conditions of hydrolysis gives rise to all the substances listed in the chart.

[30] Marker and co-workers, *J. Am. Chem. Soc.*, **69**, 2167, 2386, 2395 (1947).
[31] Noller and co-workers, *J. Am. Chem. Soc.*, **64**, 2581 (1942); **65**, 1435 (1943).

Chapter IX
Steroid and Terpenoid Alkaloids

SOLANUM ALKALOIDS

A number of alkaloids and glycoalkaloids have been isolated from species of *Solanum*. The most fully characterized aglycones contain twenty-seven carbon atoms and one nitrogen atom. *S. tuberosicum* (potato) and *S. lycopersicum* (tomato) contain the glycoalkaloid solanine $(C_{45}H_{73}O_{15}N)$[1] and the corresponding aglycone solanidine $(C_{27}H_{43}ON)$.[2] Three isomeric aglycones of the formula $C_{27}H_{43}O_2N$, solasodine, solauricidine, and solangustidine, have been isolated from various other species of *Solanum*. The sugar part of the glycosides of solanidine, solasodine, and solauricidine consists of one unit each of glucose, galactose, and rhamnose and may well be identical in the three glycoalkaloids.[3] The trisaccharide residue has not been observed in substances other than those of the *Solanum* genus. In solanine the aglycone is linked to the glucose unit, for hydrolysis of the acetylated glycoside with hydrobromic acid in acetic acid solution gives the bromoacetyl derivative of a biose composed of galactose and rhamnose and an acetylated solanidine glucoside.[4] Solangustine $(C_{33}H_{53}O_7N)$, the glycoside of solangustidine, contains one unit of glucose.[5] In all instances hydrolysis is effected satisfactorily with mineral acid, for the aglycones are fully stable.

Solauricine and solauricidine, from *S. auriculatum*, correspond closely in physical and chemical properties to solasonine and solasodine but they are not identical with these substances.[6] Two related substances solanocapsine and solanocapsidine have been isolated from *S. pseudocapsicum*; the proposed formulas[7] $C_{26}H_{44}O_2N_2$ and $C_{26}H_{42}O_4N_2$ have been questioned by Rochelmeyer.[8]

[1] Briggs, Newbold and Stace, *J. Chem. Soc.*, 3 (1942).
[2] Schöpf and Herrmann, *Ber.*, **66**, 298 (1933).
[3] Briggs and Carroll, *J. Chem. Soc.*, 17 (1942).
[4] Zemplén and Gerecs, *Ber.*, **61**, 2294 (1928); Oddo and Caronna, *ibid.*, **67**, 446 (1934).
[5] Tutin and Clewer, *J. Chem. Soc.*, **105**, 559 (1914).
[6] Bell, Briggs and Carroll, *J. Chem. Soc.*, 12 (1942); Briggs and Carroll, *ibid.*, 17 (1942).
[7] Barger and Fraenkel-Conrat, *J. Chem. Soc.*, 1537 (1936).
[8] Rochelmeyer, *Arch. Pharm.*, **282**, 92 (1945).

TABLE I. Solanum Alkaloids

GLYCOSIDE	FORMULA	M.p.	$[\alpha]_D$	AGLYCONE	FORMULA	M.p.	$[\alpha]_D$
Solanine.........	$C_{45}H_{73}O_{15}N$		$-59°$ Py	Solanidine........	$C_{27}H_{43}ON$	219°	$-27°$ Chf
Solasonine........	$C_{45}H_{73}O_{16}N$	276°	$-69°$ Al	Solasodine.......	$C_{27}H_{43}O_2N$	202°	$-80°$ Al
Solauricine........	$C_{45}H_{73}O_{16}N$	270°		Solauricidine.....	$C_{27}H_{43}O_2N$	223°	$-90°$
Solangustine......	$C_{33}H_{53}O_7N$	235°		Solangustidine ...	$C_{27}H_{43}O_2N$		

Solanidine. The presence of the one oxygen atom as an alcoholic function was recognized from the formation of an acetate, m.p. 207°, $[\alpha]_D$ − 32.5°.[1, 2] Solanidine also forms an insoluble digitonide. It contains one double bond susceptible to hydrogenation.[1, 2] The empirical formula suggested a relation to the sterols, and this was established by the isolation of the Diels hydrocarbon (II) from the neutral fraction resulting on dehydrogenation with selenium.[3] The basic fraction contains pyridine[3] and

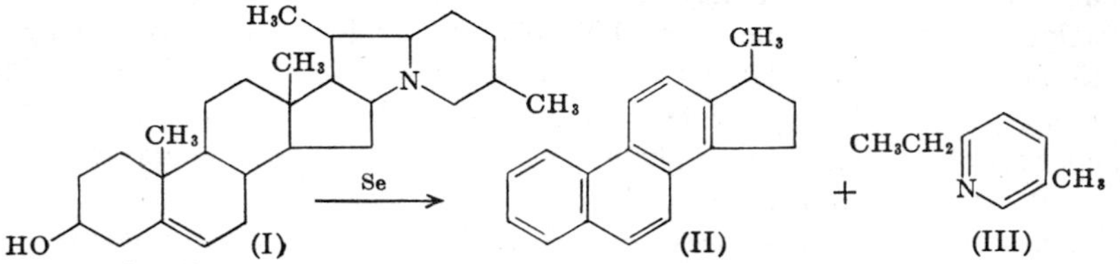

5-methyl-2-ethylpyridine[4, 5] (III), first obtained from cevine.[6] The identification of the latter degradation product provided a strong indication that the nitrogen atom, which is tertiary, occupies a bridgehead position in a terminal six-membered ring. Formula I, suggested in analogy with the sterols[4] and from results of the determination of the molecular dimensions by surface-film studies (7 × 7 × 18A°),[7] was established in a brilliant investigation by Uhle and Jacobs[8] that achieved an objective independently considered by Prelog,[2] namely the correlation of solanidine with sarsasapogenin. The diketo acid II (page 599) from oxidation of the sapogenin (as acetate) was converted into the dioxime III, and this on hydrogenation underwent ring closure to IV; in model experiments acetonylacetone dioxime was found

[1] Bergel and R. Wagner, *Ber.*, **66**, 1093 (1933).

[2] Prelog and Szpilfogel, *Helv. Chim. Acta*, **27**, 390 (1944).

[3] Soltys and Wallenfels, *Ber.*, **69**, 811 (1936).   Rochelmeyer, *Arch. Pharm.*, **274**, 543 (1936).

[4] Prelog and Szpilfogel, *Helv. Chim. Acta*, **25**, 1306 (1942).

[5] Craig and Jacobs, *Science*, **97**, 122 (1943).

[6] Jacobs and Craig, *J. Biol. Chem.*, **119**, 141 (1937); **120**, 447 (1937); **124**, 637 (1938).

[7] Rothen and Craig, *J. Am. Chem. Soc.*, **65**, 1102 (1943).

[8] Uhle and Jacobs, *J. Biol. Chem.*, **160**, 243 (1945).

to yield 2,5-dimethylpyrrolidine. The amino acid IV on pyrolysis yielded the lactam V, which was converted by hydrogenation into a substance (VI) identical with one of four C_3- and C_5-stereoisomeric derivatives of solanidine prepared by Prelog[2] in an investigation that established full correspondence between solanidine and cholesterol with respect to the nature and positions of the functional groups in rings A and B. These were prepared by the usual sterol reactions utilizing as a key intermediate the product of Oppenauer oxidation of solanidine, Δ^4-solanidene-3-one, m.p. 216.5°, $[\alpha]_D +$ 89°, λ_{max} 240 mμ.[2] Correspondence in optical activity between the solani-

Sarsasapogenin (I)   CrO₃ →   Sarsasapogenoic acid (II)   H₂NOH →

(III)   H₂, Pt 10% →   (IV)   145° →

(V)   H₂, Pt, HCl 41% →   (VI)

5-Isosolanidane-3β-ol
m.p. 218°, $[\alpha]_D + 27°$

dine and cholesterol series is shown by the data cited in Chapter X.

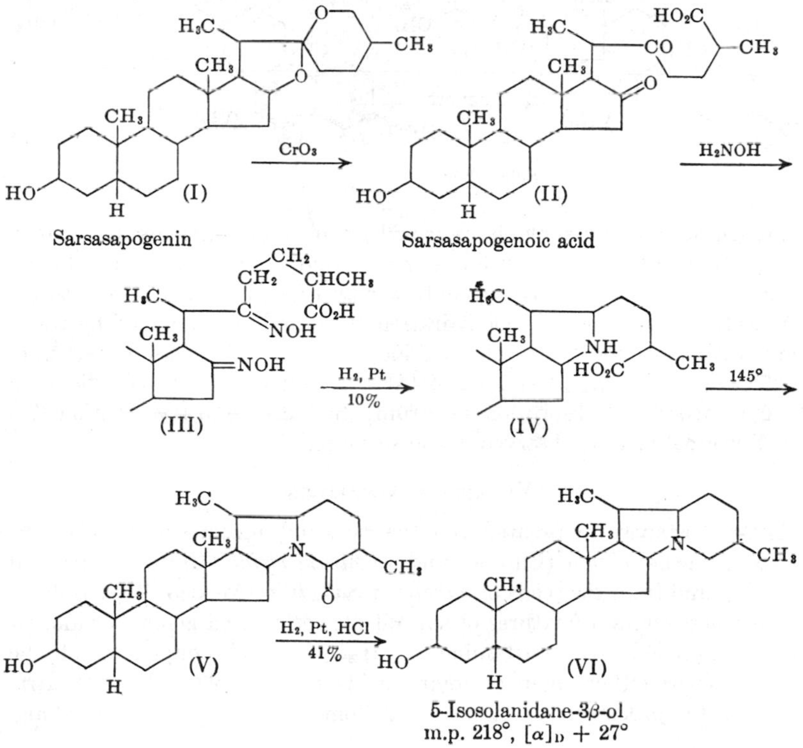

A glycosidic alkaloid demissine ($C_{50}H_{83}O_{20}N$, m.p. 305°, $[\alpha]_D - 20°$) isolated by Kuhn and Löw[9] from *S. demissum* was found to yield on acid hydrolysis an aglycone (demissidine, m.p. 218°, $[\alpha]_D + 21°$) identified as dihydrosolanidine (solanidane-3β-ol).

[9] Kuhn and Löw, *Ber.*, **80**, 406 (1947).

Solasonine and Solasodine. The glycosidic alkaloid solasonine has been isolated from the fruit of *Solanum aviculare* (Maori, "poro-poro"), *S. sodomaeum* (Dead Sea Apple), and *S. xanthocarpum*.[1, 2] The aglycone solasodine on selenium dehydrogenation affords the Diels hydrocarbon and pyrrole bases.[3] The formulation VII proposed by Briggs[4] and modified[5] to conform to the structure established for solanidine, is based upon the following considerations. Zerewitinoff determinations indicate two active

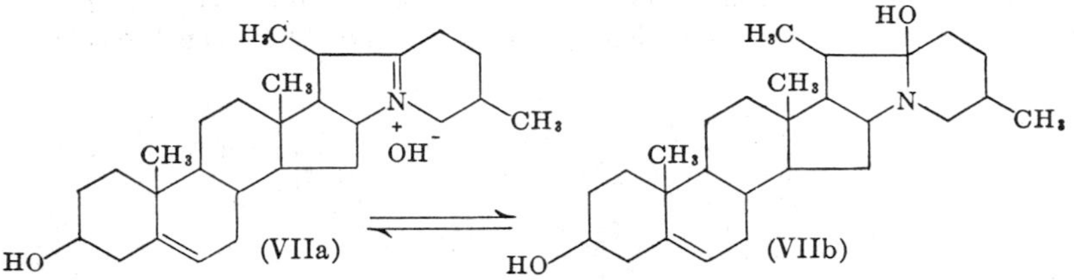

Solasodine

hydrogen atoms; one acylable hydroxyl group is present; the aglycone is precipitable with digitonin; the base resists hydrogenation in neutral alcoholic solution but suffers hydrogenation in acetic acid to dihydrosolasodine, m.p. 211.5°, $[\alpha]_D - 63.5°$. Dehydration of solasodine is effected by treatment with alcoholic hydrogen chloride; the product, solasodiene,[6] m.p. 170.5°, $[\alpha]_D - 87°$, λ_{max} 234.5 mμ (4.44), is formulated as the $\Delta^{3,5}$-diene on the evidence of the absorption spectrum; the increase in levorotation (7°) is not as great as that observed in the sterol series.

VERATRUM ALKALOIDS

These substances are isolated from the roots and rhizomes of the liliaceous plants *Veratrum album* (Europe) and *Veratrum viride* (United States and Canada), and from the seeds of *Veratrum Sabadilla* (Mexico, West Indies). The extracts contain mixtures of several nonconjugated genins, or alkamines, exemplified by veratramine ($C_{27}H_{39}O_2N$), and conjugates of the alkamines with either sugars or organic acids, for example, tiglic or veratric acid. In the processing of the material from *V. viride*, Jacobs and Craig[1]

[1] Bell and Briggs, *J. Chem. Soc.*, 1 (1942).
[2] Rochelmeyer, *Arch. Pharm.*, **275,** 336 (1937).
[3] Rochelmeyer, *Arch. Pharm.*, **274,** 543 (1936).
[4] Briggs, Newbold and Stace, *J. Chem. Soc.*, 3 (1942).
[5] Craig and Jacobs, *J. Biol. Chem.*, **149,** 451 (1943).
[6] Rochelmeyer, *Arch. Pharm.*, **277,** 329 (1939).
[1] Jacobs and Craig, *J. Biol. Chem.*, **155,** 565 (1944); **160,** 555 (1945).

took advantage of the fact that under the conditions used the basic alkamines are soluble in benzene whereas the glycosidic alkaloids are not. The alkamine fraction is thus easily removed by benzene extraction, and the isolation of jervine and veratramine is accomplished by crystallization of the sulfates followed by separation as the hydrochlorides (Saito, Ref. 19, below). The predominating base is jervine and the others isolated are rubijervine, isorubijervine, veratramine, germine, and an unnamed polyhydroxy secondary base $C_{27}H_{41}O_4N$ or $C_{27}H_{39}O_4N$, λ_{max}^{alc} 250 mμ (4.2), 360 mμ (1.85). Jervine is easily rearranged to isojervine on treatment with mineral acid. The residual plant material not extracted by benzene is extracted with alcohol, which removes a fraction containing the glycoalkaloid pseudojervine as the main component (20 g. from 6 kg. of plant material), accompanied by veratrosine. The majority of the ester alkaloids have been isolated from *V. album*, investigated extensively by Po-

TABLE II. Veratrum Alkaloids[a]

CONJUGATE	FORMULA	M.p.	$[\alpha]_D$	ALKAMINE	FORMULA	M.p.	$[\alpha]_D$	SUGAR OR ACID
Veratrosine	$C_{33}H_{49}O_7N$	dec.	−53°	Veratramine	$C_{27}H_{39}O_2N$	207°	−60°	Glucose
				Rubijervine	$C_{27}H_{43}O_2N$	242°	+19° Al	
				Isorubijervine	$C_{27}H_{43}O_2N$	237°	+ 6.5° Al	
Pseudojervine......	$C_{33}H_{49}O_8N$	305°	−133°	Jervine	$C_{27}H_{39}O_3N$	238°	−147° Al	Glucose
Germerine[b]	$C_{37}H_{59}O_{11}N$	195°	+10.8	Germine	$C_{27}H_{43}O_8N$	220°	+5 °	Methylethyl acetic and methylethylgly-colic acid
Cevadine[c]..	$C_{32}H_{49}O_9N$	201°	+12.5°	Cevine	$C_{27}H_{43}O_8N$	200°	−17.5° Al	Tiglic aid
Veratridine[d].....	$C_{36}H_{51}O_{11}N$		+8°	Cevine				Veratric acid
Protoveratrine[e].....	$C_{39}H_{61}O_{13}N$	276°	−0°	Protoverine	$C_{27}H_{43}O_9N$		−12° Py	Acetic, methylethyl-acetic, and methylethylgly-colic acid

[a] References are included only when they are not cited in the discussions of the individual compounds.
[b] Poethke, *Arch. Pharm.*, **275**, 357, 571 (1937).
[c] C. R. A. Wright and Luff, *J. Chem. Soc.*, **33**, 338 (1878); Freund and H. P. Schwarz, *Ber.*, **32**, 800 (1899); Macbeth and R. Robinson, *J. Chem. Soc.*, **121**, 1571 (1922).
[d] Blount, *J. Chem. Soc.*, 122 (1935).
[e] Salzberger, *Arch. Pharm.*, **228**, 462 (1890); Poethke, *ibid.*, **275**, 357, 571 (1937).

ethke.[2] The isolation of the conjugates themselves is difficult; isolation of the alkamines obtained on saponification of the mixture is usually simpler. The seven alkamines listed in Table II are C_{27}-compounds containing

[2] Poethke, *Arch. Pharm.*, **275**, 357, 571 (1937); **276**, 170 (1938).

one atom of nitrogen.   Jervine, veratramine, and the above base $C_{27}H_{41}O_4N$ are secondary amines and the others are tertiary.   A relationship to the solanum alkaloids was shown by the formulas established by Craig and Jacobs[3] and by the earlier identification of 5-methyl-2-ethylpyridine as a product of the selenium dehydrogenation of all of the alkamines.   The neutral fractions of the dehydrogenation mixtures were examined for the presence of the Diels hydrocarbon but this substance was in no instance found.   From rubijervine a hydrocarbon was isolated[4] that is isomeric with the Diels hydrocarbon and very similar to it in absorption spectrum and that appeared to correspond in physical constants to 1'-methyl-1,2-cyclopentenophenanthrene.[5]   1,2-Cyclopentenophenanthrene was the principal neutral product of the selenium dehydrogenation of isorubijervine.[6]   Fluorene derivatives and related substances are also formed in a number of the dehydrogenations.   Thus cevine yielded 4,5-benzohydrindene ($C_{13}H_{12}$) and substances of the formulas $C_{17}H_{16}$, $C_{18}H_{18}$, $C_{19}H_{20}$, and $C_{24}H_{30}$.[7]   A basic degradation product is cevanthridine, $C_{25}H_{27}N$,[8–10] of absorption spectrum indicative of a fluorene ring system.   The formation of derivatives of cyclopentenophenanthrene and of fluorene in the dehydrogenations, as well as the identical pyridine base obtained from solanidine, point to a sterol-like structure, and this conclusion is substantiated by surface-film measurements.[11]   That the Diels hydrocarbon apparently is not formed seemed to indicate some deviation from the usual sterol structure or configuration, but Sato and Jacobs[12] recently succeeded in removing one of the two hydroxyl groups of rubijervine and the product proved to be solanidine. A relationship to the sterols and to a second group of steroid alkaloids was thereby fully established.

Rubijervine, so named because it gives a red color in sulfuric acid, has been isolated from hydrolyzed fractions of *V. album*[13, 14] and directly from *V. viride* (Jacobs and Craig, Ref. 17, 1945).   A companion substance is

[3] Craig and Jacobs, *J. Biol. Chem.*, **149,** 451 (1943).

[4] Jacobs and Craig, *J. Biol. Chem.*, **148,** 41 (1943).

[5] Ruzicka, Ehmann, Goldberg and Hösli, *Helv. Chim. Acta*, **16,** 833 (1933).

[6] Jacobs and Craig, *J. Biol. Chem.*, **159,** 617 (1945).

[7] Craig, Jacobs and Lavin, *J. Biol. Chem.*, **139,** 277 (1941).

[8] Blount, *J. Chem. Soc.*, 122 (1935).

[9] Blount and Crowfoot, *J. Chem. Soc.*, 414 (1936).

[10] Craig and Jacobs, *J. Biol. Chem.*, **139,** 293 (1941).

[11] Rothen and Craig, *J. Am. Chem. Soc.*, **65,** 1102 (1943).

[12] Sato and Jacobs (unpublished work).   We are greatly indebted to Dr. W. A. Jacobs for informing us of this important new observation.

[13] C. R. A. Wright and Luff, *J. Chem. Soc.*, **35,** 405 (1879); Salzberger, *Arch. Pharm.*, **228,** 462 (1890); Poethke, *ibid.*, **276,** 170 (1938).

[14] Jacobs and Craig, *J. Biol. Chem.*, **148,** 41 (1943).

misleadingly named **isorubijervine,** for it is not formed by isomerization of rubijervine and has not been related to the substance; both substances are stable to acid. Rubijervine forms a diacetate that retains basic properties, and hence the alkamine is a tertiary base with two acylable hydroxyl groups. Both rubijervine and isorubijervine contain a double bond that can be hydrogenated in methanol containing an excess of acetic acid. Both substances are precipitated by digitonin, and in this respect they differ from the other veratrum alkamines.[15] From this evidence and from the observation that the substances yield α,β-unsaturated ketones on Oppenauer oxidation, Jacobs and Craig[16] concluded that the alkamines are 3β-hydroxy-Δ^5-stenols having an additional secondary hydroxyl group, and the more recent work of Sato and Jacobs[12] proves the correctness of the conclusion. Solanidine ($M_D - 107$ Chf) is levorotatory, and the additional hydroxyl group of rubijervine ($M_D + 79$ Al) produces a pronounced dextrorotatory shift ($\Delta^{OH} + 186$).

Jervine. Investigations of Jacobs and co workers[17] of the complex and perplexing chemistry of this alkaloid have established a number of interesting relationships between the various functional groups, some of which are summarized in the chart on page 604. Jervine ($C_{27}H_{39}O_3N$) contains two double bonds that appear to be isolated from one another; one is more easily hydrogenated (in alcohol), the other is hydrogenated with greater difficulty (in acetic acid). A carbonyl group present is inert to most reagents but is reducible with sodium and butanol. Jervine contains a secondary amino group and a secondary alcoholic group; it yields first an N-acetyl and then a diacetyl derivative. The nitrogen atom must occupy a position in the side chain corresponding to the nitrogen of solanidine but is not linked to ring D. The third oxygen is inert and probably oxidic. The isolation from the selenium dehydrogenation mixture of a phenolic substance that corresponds in composition to a hydroxy derivative of 5-methyl-2-ethylpyridine points to an association between the inert oxygen and the nitrogen-containing ring; among the possibilities considered by Jacobs and Huebner is an arrangement corresponding to the side ring structure of a steroid sapogenin but with one oxygen in the terminal ring replaced by the NH group.

Jervine shows intense absorption at 250 mμ, attributed by Jacobs and Sato to conjugation of the carbonyl group with the more easily reducible double bond, and has a second band of low intensity at 360 mμ (1.85).

[15] Craig and Jacobs, *J. Biol. Chem.*, **149,** 451 (1943).

[16] Jacobs and Craig, *J. Biol. Chem.*, **159,** 617 (1945).

[17] Jacobs, Craig and Lavin, *J. Biol. Chem.*, **141,** 51 (1941); Jacobs and Craig, *ibid.*, **148,** 51 (1943); **160,** 555 (1945); Jacobs and Huebner, *ibid.*, **170,** 635 (1947); Jacobs and Sato, *J. Biol. Chem.*, **175,** 57 (1948).

Evidence that the less reactive double bond is at C_5–C_6 and the hydroxyl group at C_3 is afforded by the results of various Oppenauer oxidations, two of which are shown in the chart.   Oxidation of jervine itself results in some

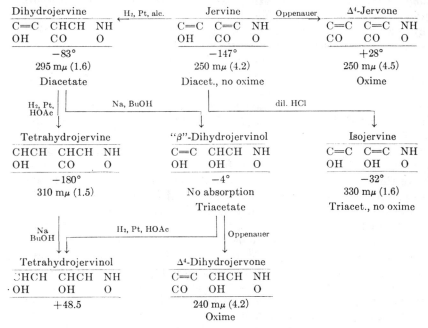

increased intensity of absorption at 250 mμ, but oxidation of "β"-dihydrojervinol produces absorption that did not before exist in the region characteristic of α,β-unsaturated ketones; the newly formed carbonyl group at C_3 possesses normal reactivity (oxime).   The changes in molecular rotation on acetylation and benzoylation of N-acetyljervine and on hydrogenation of dihydrojervine and of "β"-dihydrojervinol also correspond to those expected for a 3β-hydroxy-Δ^5-stenol structure.   Jacobs and Sato conclude that the inert carbonyl group is at C_{11} and the more easily reducible double bond in a position of conjugation at C_8–C_9.

The deductions of Jacobs and co-workers concerning the nuclear structure of jervine are expressed in formula I, which accords well with the observed absorption maximum at 250 mμ (calcd. for I, 249 mμ).   The representation of the side chain structure is a slight variant of one discussed but not formulated by these investigators.

The ready conversion of jervine into isojervine by dilute mineral acid is a remarkable reaction, for the ultraviolet absorption is considerably modified, a second acylable hydroxyl group is formed, and the double bonds are no longer hydrogenable except in a medium containing hydrochloric acid. This property seemed suggestive of the presence of a benzenoid ring, but

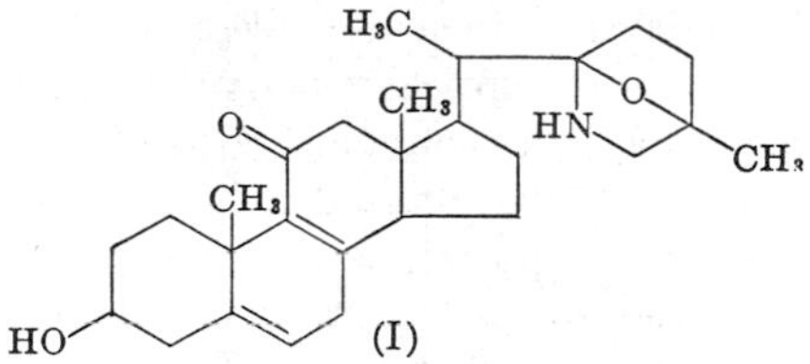

Jervine (?)

(I)

such a group is not clearly indicated by the spectrum. Jacobs and co-workers considered it doubtful that the new hydroxyl group arises from opening of the oxide ring, and hence an enolization of the ketonic group seems indicated.

Jervine is the alkamine of pseudojervine, but the acid used to effect hydrolysis of the glycoside causes isomerization of jervine to isojervine. When pseudojervine is first hydrogenated in a neutral medium and then hydrolyzed, the product is dihydrojervine, since this is stable to acids.

Veratramine is obtained along with glucose by hydrolysis of veratrosine with 2 percent aqueous hydrochloride at the reflux temperature;[18] it is very stable to acid. The substance was first isolated as such from *V. grandiflorum* Loes. fil.[19] Acetylation gives a triacetyl derivative that can be hydrolyzed with alcoholic alkali to N-acetylveratramine. Veratramine is thus a secondary amine and the two oxygen atoms are present as acylable hydroxyl groups. It contains one double bond susceptible to hydrogenation. Both veratramine and dihydroveratramine have an absorption maximum at 270 mμ, possibly an indication of an aromatic ring.[20]

Cevine, $C_{27}H_{43}O_8N$, is the product of either acid or alkaline hydrolysis of two different ester alkaloids. It is a tertiary amine with only two acylable hydroxyl groups, and it does not react with carbonyl reagents.[21] The remaining six oxygen atoms may all be present as tertiary hydroxyl groups.[21, 22] At least one oxygen atom must be associated with the nitrogen-containing ring because selenium dehydrogenation[23] affords two

[18] Jacobs and Craig, *J. Biol. Chem.*, **155,** 565 (1944).

[19] Saito, *Bull. Chem. Soc. Japan*, **15,** 22 (1940).

[20] Jacobs and Craig, *J. Biol. Chem.*, **160,** 555 (1945).

[21] Jacobs and Craig, *J. Biol. Chem.*, **119,** 141 (1937); **120,** 447 (1937); **124,** 659 (1938); Craig and Jacobs, *ibid.,* **148,** 57 (1943).

[22] Freund and A. Schwarz, *J. Prakt. Chem.*, **96,** 236 (1917).

[23] Blount, *J. Chem. Soc.*, 122 (1935); Craig and Jacobs, *J. Biol. Chem.*, **129,** 79 (1939); **139,** 293 (1941).

oxygen-containing bases, along with 5-methyl-2-ethylpyridine. Cevan-thridine, mentioned above, and cevanthrol ($C_{17}H_{16}O$), a tricyclic phenol, and various hydrocarbons are also formed. Chromic acid oxidation of cevine leads to a mixture of acids,[24] separated by fractionation of the methyl esters. One, an optically active hexanetetracarboxylic acid $C_{10}H_{14}O_8$ (11% yield), has been obtained also from germine. The acid forms a dianhydride on distillation and a ketomonoanhydride on pyrolysis. Two of the ester groups (especially one) of the tetramethyl ester are somewhat more resistant to hydrolysis than the others. Huebner and Jacobs[24] synthesized one of the possible structures, β,β'-dimethyl-β,β'-dicarboxyadipic acid, and found it to have entirely different properties.

Cevine is stable to hydrogenation with platinum catalyst but absorbs one mole of hydrogen in the presence of Raney nickel. Surprisingly, reduction can be accomplished with sodium and butanol and leads to a dihydro compound different from the product of nickel hydrogenation. Cevine can be isomerized with alkali to an iso base that is readily hydrogenated.

Possible representations of the interesting facts established by Jacobs and his associates are shown in formulas II and III for cevine and the hexanetetracarboxylic acid.

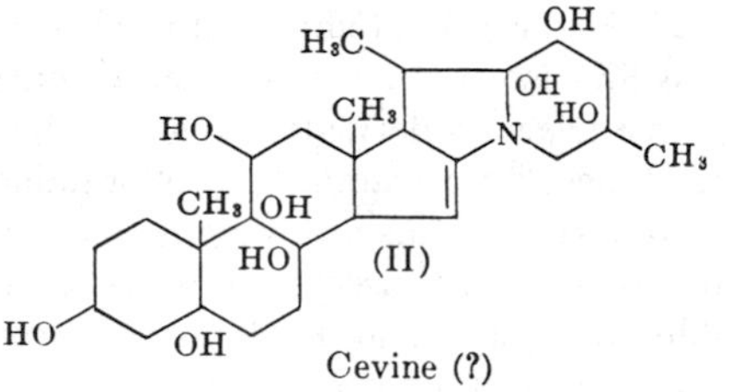

(II) Cevine (?)　　　(III) Acid $C_{10}H_{14}O_8$ (?)

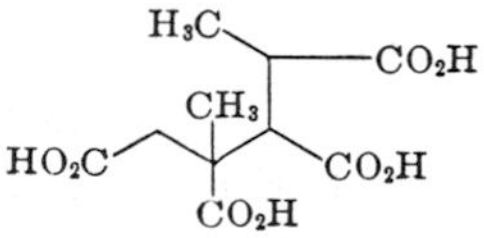

Germine. The alkaloid germerine (Poethke) is composed of germine esterified with one molecule each of methylethylacetic acid and methylethylglycolic acid. Partial hydrolysis removes the latter acid first and gives methylethylacetylgermine, identical with the alkaloid protoveratridine.[25] Germine is a tertiary base isomeric with cevine; the two substances evidently are closely related because they both yield the same degradation products: 5-methyl-2-ethylpyridine, cevanthridine, cevanthrol, and the hexanetetracarboxylic acid.[26]

Germine can be reduced with sodium and butanol but is resistant to platinum-hydrogenation. It is isomerized by alkali to isogermine, m.p.

[24] Craig and Jacobs, *J. Am. Chem. Soc.*, **61**, 2252 (1939); *J. Biol. Chem.*, **134**, 123, (1940); **141**, 253 (1941); Huebner and Jacobs, *ibid.*, **170**, 181 (1947).

[25] Salzberger, *Arch. Pharm.*, **228**, 462 (1890).

[26] Craig and Jacobs, *J. Biol. Chem.* **148**, 57 (1943)

260°, $[\alpha]_D$ − 47°, which is easily hydrogenated (Pt); the two dihydrides are different.[27] Isogermine forms a crystalline acetonide and hence two hydroxyl groups must bear the cis 1,2- or 1,3-relationship. Zerewitinoff diagnosis indicated the presence of eight hydroxyl groups in germine and six in the acetonide.[27] Jacobs and Sato have discussed the possibility that the natural polyhydroxylated bases germine and cevine are $\Delta^{8(14)}$-stenols and the iso-bases Δ^{14}-stenols.

Protoverine,[28] $C_{27}H_{43}O_9N$, has one oxygen atom more than cevine and germine, probably as an additional hydroxyl group, and closely resembles these substances in the nature of the dehydrogenation products and in properties: 9 active hydrogens; resistant to hydrogenation but reduced by sodium and butanol; acetonide; easily hydrogenated iso compound (with alkali).

Pharmacology.[29] The veratrum ester alkaloids decrease the rate of respiration, and the lethal effect of large doses is largely due to this action. Their action on the isolated heart muscle resembles that of the cardiac glycosides. The alkaloids also have an effect on the circulatory system, in small doses partly due to reflex vasodilatation and in large doses partly due to their ability to cause discharge of adrenaline. They also produce contraction of skeletal muscle. The alkaloids were used at one time as cardiac depressants, but they find little clinical use today. Comparative median lethal doses for some of the alkaloids are given in the Table. The

TABLE III. Intravenous Toxicity for Mice (Krayer)

	LD_{50}	
	mg./kg.	micromoles/kg.
Protoveratrine	0.048	0.06
Veratridine	.42	.63
Jervine	9.3	21.9
Rubijervine	70	170
Cevine	87	170
Germine	139	274
Protoverine	194	367

two ester alkaloids listed first are much more toxic than the alkamines; protoveratrine is 6000 times more potent than its alkamine, protoverine. Jervine is the most potent alkamine and the highly hydroxylated protoverine the least.

[27] Craig and Jacobs, *J. Biol. Chem.*, **149,** 451 (1943); Jacobs and Sato, *ibid.*, **175,** 57 (1948).

[28] Craig and Jacobs, *J. Biol. Chem.*, **143,** 427 (1942); Jacobs and Craig, *ibid.*, **149,** 271 (1943).

[29] See review by Krayer and Acheson, *Physiol. Rev.*, **26,** 383 (1946).

CONESSINE

Conessine ($C_{24}H_{40}N_2$, m.p. 125°, $[\alpha]_D$ — 1.9° Chf), a member of still another group of alkaloids, has recently been shown to be a steroid base. The alkaloid, isolated from the bark and seeds of the *Holarrhena* species (Indian "kurchi"),[1] has the feature uncommon among alkaloids or steroids of the absence of oxygen. It contains one double bond that is slowly saturated on hydrogenation in the presence of palladium (dihydride, m.p. 105°)[2] and that has been hydroxylated by reaction with potassium iodate (dihydroxyconessine, m.p. 295°, $[\alpha]_D$ + 12°).[3] Both nitrogen atoms are tertiary; one is present in a dimethylamino group and the other appears to bear one methyl group and to be a member of a ring. Hofmann degradation[2, 4] of conessine dimethylammonium dihydroxide yields apoconessine ($C_{23}H_{36}N$, m.p. 69°, 3 double bonds) with elimination of the original dimethylamino group and opening of the nitrogen-containing ring. The second nitrogen atom could not be eliminated by a further Hofmann reaction, but Emde degradation (reaction of the methochloride with sodium amalgam) conducted by Späth and Hromatka[2] afforded trimethylamine and a triply unsaturated hydrocarbon $C_{21}H_{30}$, m.p. 76°, $[\alpha]_D$ - 184° Py. Späth and Hromatka isolated an unidentified hexahydro derivative, m.p. 58°, $[\alpha]_D$ + 14.5°, but Haworth, McKenna, and Singh[5] isolated a second hydrocarbon identical with allopregnane.

Conessine and related alkaloids have found some use in India as remedies for amebic dysentery.

ERYTHROPHLEUM ALKALOIDS

The bark of trees of the genus *Erythrophleum* has been known for some time[1] to contain alkaloids possessing local anesthetic properties and digitalis-like activity.[2] Early workers[1, 3] assigned the name erythrophleine to amorphous preparations from *E. guineense* G. Don (African sassy or

¹ For early references to alkaloids of the group, see Henry, "Plant Alkaloids," Blakiston's Son and Co. (1939).

² Späth and Hromatka, *Ber.*, **63**, 126 (1930).

³ Giemsa and Halberhann, *Arch. Pharm.*, **256**, 201 (1918).

⁴ Kanga, Ayyar and Simonsen, *J. Chem. Soc.*, 2123 (1926).

⁵ R. D. Haworth, McKenna and N. Singh, *Nature*, **162**, 22 (1948).

¹ Gallois and Hardy, *Compt. rend.*, **80**, 1221 (1875); *J. Pharm. Chem.*, **24**, 25 (1876); *Bull. Soc. Chim.*, **26**, 39 (1876).

² K. K. Chen, A. L. Chen and R. C. Anderson, *J. Am. Pharm. Assoc.*, **25**, 579 (1936); K. K. Chen, Hargreaves and Winchester, *ibid.*, **27**, 9 (1938).

³ Harnack and Zabrocki, *Arch. exp. Path. Pharmakol.*, **15**, 403 (1882); Power and Salway, *Am. J. Pharm.*, **84**, 337 (1912); Cyril and Maplethorpe, *Pharm. J.*, **111**, 85 (1923).

redwater tree). In 1935 the Italian Dalma[4] isolated from the same species two crystalline alkaloids, cassaine and cassaidine.

Cassaine. This alkaloid is hydrolyzed by dilute mineral acid to cassaic acid and β-dimethylaminoethanol.[5] Alkaline hydrolysis gives the same aminoethanol but the acid fragment is an isomeric acid, allocassaic acid,

$$C_{24}H_{39}O_4N \xrightarrow{\;H_2O\;} C_{20}H_{30}O_4 + HOCH_2CH_2N(CH_3)_2$$

Cassaine   Cassaic acid
m.p. 142.5°,   m.p. 203°,
$[\alpha]_D - 103°$ $[\alpha]_D - 126°$

m.p. 224°, $[\alpha]_D + 82°$.[6] Cassaine and cassaic acid contain one carbonyl group, one secondary alcoholic group (oxidizable to a ketonic group[7]), and one double bond susceptible to hydrogenation; they both show intense absorption at 223 mμ (log ϵ 4.2), characteristic of α,β-unsaturated acids.[6] Allocassaic acid lacks characteristic absorption in the ultraviolet, and hence treatment with alkali probably causes migration of the double bond to a nonconjugated position.

The empirical formula and nature of the functional groups indicate that cassaic acid must be tricyclic, and degradation experiments point to a hydrophenanthrene structure. 1,7,8-Trimethylphenanthrene was first obtained on selenium dehydrogenation of dihydroxycassanic acid, obtained by reduction of the double bond and sodium-ethanol reduction of the keto group.[6] The result accounts for seventeen of the twenty carbon atoms; the three lost presumably are those of the carboxyl group and of two angular methyl groups. Blount, Openshaw and Todd[8] tentatively suggested the structure I, analogous to isoagathic acid and the triterpenoid sapogenins, and suggested that the 1,7,8-trimethylphenanthrene arises by retro-

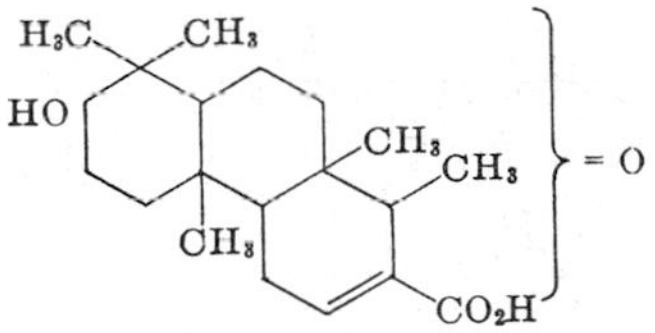

(I)

pinacol shift of methyl to the hydroxylated position. However, the same hydrocarbon has been obtained by the selenium dehydrogenation of cassanic acid, m.p. 224°, $[\alpha]_D + 3°$, in which the double bond is saturated and the

[4] Dalma, *Ann. chim. applicata*, **25**, 569 (1935).
[5] Faltis and Holzinger, *Ber.*, **72**, 1443 (1939).
[6] Ruzicka and Dalma, *Helv. Chim. Acta*, **22**, 1516 (1939).
[7] Dalma, *Helv. Chim. Acta*, **22**, 1497 (1939).
[8] Blount, Openshaw and Todd, *J. Chem. Soc.*, 286 (1940).

two oxygen functions are replaced by hydrogen.[9]   In an attempt to determine the position of the carboxyl group, Ruzicka and co-workers[10] converted this functional group of cassanic acid into an isopropyl group and submitted the resulting hydrocarbon to dehydrogenation. The product has the empirical formula of a trimethylisopropylphenanthrene but is not identical with the synthetic 1,2,8-trimethyl-7-isopropyl isomer predicted from formula I.

The second crystalline alkaloid isolated by Dalma, **cassaidine,** has since been shown[11] to be closely related to cassaine in composition, absorption spectrum, and behavior on hydrolysis:

$C_{24}H_{41}O_4N$ $\xrightarrow{H_2O}$ $C_{20}H_{32}O_4$ $+ HOCH_2CH_2N(CH_3)_2$
Cassaidine   Cassaidic acid
m.p. 139.5°,   m.p. 277°,
$[\alpha]-98°$ $[\alpha]-100°$

Cassaidic acid contains two hydroxyl groups.

Blount, Openshaw and Todd[8] investigated the amorphous erythrophleine obtained from E. Merck and Co. at Darmstadt and found it to consist essentially of a single alkaloid similar to the substances isolated by Dalma:

$C_{24}H_{39}O_5N$ $\xrightarrow{H_2O}$ $C_{21}H_{32}O_5$ $+ HOCH_2CH_2NHCH$
Erythrophleine   Erythrophleic acid
                              m.p. 218°,
                              $[\alpha]_D-40°$

Erythrophleic acid is readily esterifiable by the Fischer method; it contains one hydroxyl group, a methoxyl group, and a readily hydrogenated double bond conjugated with the carboxyl group: λ_{max} 221 mμ (4.2).   On selenium dehydrogenation it is converted in low yield into 1,7,8-trimethylphenanthrene.

In 1938 Dalma[12] reported the isolation from E. couminga of another crystalline principle named **coumingine,** that has been characterized as follows:[13]

$C_{29}H_{47}O_6N$ $\xrightarrow[(H_2SO_4)]{H_2O}$ $C_{25}H_{38}O_6$ $+ HOCH_2CH_2N(CH_3)_2$
Coumingine   Coumingic acid
m.p. 142°,   m.p. 200°,
$[\alpha]_D - 70°$ $[\alpha]_D - 81°$
max 225 mμ (4.3)   max 225 mμ

[9] Ruzicka, Dalma and W. E. Scott, *Helv. Chim. Acta,* **24,** 179E (1941).
[10] Ruzicka, Engel, Ronco and Berse, *Helv. Chim. Acta,* **28,** 1038 (1945).
[11] Ruzicka and Dalma, *Helv. Chim. Acta,* **23,** 753 (1940).
[12] Dalma, *Atti X Congr. Intern. Chim. Rome,* 1938.
[13] Ruzicka, Dalma and W. E. Scott, *Helv. Chim. Acta,* **24,** 63 (1941); Ruzicka, Dalma, Engel and W. E. Scott, *ibid.,* **24,** 1449 (1941).

Acid hydrolysis eliminates a molecule of β-dimethylaminoethanol and gives coumingic acid, a conjugate of cassaic acid and β-hydroxyisovaleric acid that is cleaved by alkali to these components. Since neither the original alkaloid nor coumingic acid possesses the free hydroxyl group present in cassaic acid, this group evidently is esterified with β-hydroxyisovaleric acid in the conjugates. A second, unnamed alkaloid from the same source is described thus:[14] $C_{25}H_{39-41}O_6N$, m.p. 151°, $[\alpha]_D - 47°$.

Pharmacology. The erythrophleum alkaloids have a digitalis-like action on the heart. In small doses they increase the work capacity; in larger doses they cause changes in heart rate and irregularities in rhythm. Table IV summarizes the mean lethal doses (cats)[2] and the minimal therapeutic doses (isolated heart-lung preparation, dog[15]) for four of the alkaloids.

TABLE IV. Toxicity and Therapeutic Activity

SUBSTANCE	LD$_{50}$ (CAT)	MINIMAL POSITIVE INOTROPIC EFFECT, MG./L. BLOOD
	mg./kg.	
Erythrophleine sulfate	0.364	0.54
Cassaine hydrochloride	1.111	.48
Norcassaidine hydrochloride[a]	0.684	.39
Coumingine hydrochloride	.128	.16

[a] $C_{23}H_{41}O_5N$; Dalma, *Ann. chim. applicata*, **25**, 569 (1935).

Coumingine is the most active of the compounds studied; it differs from cassaine only in that the nuclear hydroxyl group is esterified with β-hydroxyisovaleric acid, yet this conjugation has a marked effect on the activity. At least in the case of erythrophleine, esterification with β-methylaminoethanol is essential for cardiac activity, since erythrophleic acid is physiologically inactive. The N-alkyl-β-aminoethanols themselves elicit a positive inotropic response, but on a molar basis they possess only about 1/800 the potency of the erythrophleum alkaloids.[16]

ACONITE AND DELPHINIUM ALKALOIDS

Plants of the genus *Aconitum* (*Ranunculaceae* family) contain several groups of characteristic and probably related perhydropolycyclic monobasic alkaloids. Some of these are highly toxic and are composed of much less toxic hydroxylated basic genins known as alkamines esterified with one or two acids of simple type, for example, acetic, benzoic, veratric, or anthranilic

---

[14] Ruzicka, Plattner and Engel, *Experientia*, **1**, 160 (1945).
[15] Maling and Krayer, *J. Pharmacol.*, **86**, 66 (1946).
[16] Krayer, Farah and Uhle, *J. Pharmacol.*, **88**, 277 (1946).

acid. Thus the alkaloid aconitine is converted on hydrolysis into the alkamine aconine; the relationship between the two compounds and the nature of the functional groups are shown in the formulation:

$$C_{19}H_{19}(OH)_3(OCOCH_3)(OCOC_6H_5)(OCH_3)_4NC_2H_5 \xrightarrow{H_2O}$$

Aconitine, m.p. 198°, $[\alpha]+18°$

$$C_{19}H_{19}(OH)_5(OCH_3)_4NC_2H_5 \quad + \quad CH_3CO_2H + C_6H_5CO_2H$$

Aconine, m.p. 132°, $[\alpha]_D+23°$

TABLE V. Alkamines of *Aconitum* and *Delphinium* Species

ALKAMINE	FORMULA	STRUCTURE	PARENT TYPE	SOURCE
		A. Parent type: $C_nH_{2n-10}NR$		
Aconine[1]	$C_{25}N_{41}O_9N$	$C_{19}H_{19}(OH)_5(OCH_3)_4NC_2H_5$	$C_{19}H_{28}NC_2H_5$	*A. Napellus*
Talatisine[2]	$C_{20}H_{29}O_3N$	$C_{19}H_{23}(OH)_2NCH_3$, 1 C=C	$C_{19}H_{28}NCH_3$	*A. talassicum*
Talatisamine[2]	$C_{22}H_{35}O_4N$	$C_{19}H_{24}(OH)(OCH_3)_3NH$	$C_{19}H_{28}NH$	*A. talassicum*
Talatisidine[2]	$C_{23}H_{37}O_5N$	$C_{19}H_{23}(OH)_3(OCH_3)_2NC_2H_5$	$C_{19}H_{28}NC_2H_5$	*A. talassicum*
Isotalatisidine[2]	$C_{23}H_{37}O_5N$	$C_{19}H_{23}(OH)_3(OCH_3)_2NC_2H_5$	$C_{19}H_{28}NC_2H_5$	*A. talassicum*
Delphonine[3]	$C_{24}H_{39}O_7N$	$C_{19}H_{21}(OH)_3(OCH_3)_4NCH_3$	$C_{19}H_{28}NCH_3$	*D. staphisagria*
Napelline[4,5]	$C_{22}H_{33}O_3N$	$C_{20}H_{26}(OH)_3NC_2H_5$, 1 C=C	$C_{20}H_{30}NC_2H_5$	*A. Napellus*
Delphamine[6]	$C_{25}H_{41}O_7N$	$C_{20}H_{24}(OH)_4(OCH_3)_2NC_2H_5$	$C_{20}H_{30}NC_2H_5$	*D. species*
		B. Parent type: $C_nH_{2n-8}NR$		
Staphisine[7]	$C_{21}H_{31}ON^a$	$C_{20}H_{27}(OH)NCH_3$, 2 C=C	$C_{20}H_{32}NCH_3$	*D. staphisagria*
Heteratisine[8]	$C_{22}H_{33}O_5N$	$C_{18}H_{23}(OH)_2(OCH_3)(COO)NC_2H_5$	$C_{18}H_{26}(COO)$- NC_2H_5	*A. heterophyllum*
Atisine[9-12]	$C_{22}H_{33}O_2N$	$C_{20}H_{26}(OH)_2NC_2H_5$, 2 C=C	$C_{20}H_{32}NC_2H_5$	*A. heterophyllum*
		C. Unclassified		
Hetisine[8]	$C_{20}H_{27}O_3N$	$(OH)_3$, 1 C=C, tert. base		*A. heterophyllum*
Kobusine[13]	$C_{20}H_{27}O_2N$	$(OH)_2$, 2 C=C, tert. base		*A. sachalinense*

^{a} Or $C_{42}H_{60}ON_2$; see discussion.

[1] Freund and Beck, *Ber.*, **27**, 433 (1894).

[2] Konovalova and Orékhoff, *Bull. soc. chim.*, **7**, 95 (1940).

[3] Jacobs and Craig, *J. Biol. Chem.*, **127**, 361 (1939); **128**, 431 (1939); **136**, 303 (1940); Jacobs and Huebner, *ibid.*, **170**, 209 (1947).

[4] W. Freudenberg and E. F. Rogers, *J. Am. Chem. Soc.*, **59**, 2572 (1937).

[5] Craig and Jacobs, *J. Biol. Chem.*, **143**, 611 (1942).

[6] Rabinovich and Konovalova, *J. Gen. Chem. (U.S.S.R.)*, **12**, 321 (1942) [*C. A.*, **37**, 3097 (1943)].

[7] Jacobs and Craig, *J. Biol. Chem.*, **141**, 67 (1941).

[8] Jacobs and Craig, *J. Biol. Chem.*, **143**, 605 (1942); Jacobs and Huebner, *ibid.*, **170**, 189 (1947).

[9] A. Lawson and Topps, *J. Chem. Soc.*, 1640 (1937).

[10] Jacobs and Craig, *J. Biol. Chem.*, **143**, 589 (1942).

[11] Jacobs and Craig, *J. Biol. Chem.*, **147**, 567 (1943).

[12] Huebner and Jacobs, *J. Biol. Chem.*, **170**, 515 (1947); **174**, 1001 (1948).

[13] Suginome and Shimanouti, *Ann.*, **545**, 220 (1940).

Aconine is a tertiary base having five hydroxyl and four methoxyl groups; in the toxic alkaloid proper two of the hydroxyl groups are esterified with acetic and benzoic acid. Some of the many other known alkamines and alkaloids are listed in Tables V and VI; fuller references to the early literature are given in Henry's "Plant Alkaloids." The tables include representative related substances isolated from *Delphinium* species (*Ranunculaceae* family), or larkspurs. The larkspurs grow over wide areas of the western ranges of North America and constitute stock-poisoning plants. The alkaloids of the aconite and delphinium series are very similar in both pharmacological and chemical properties, and in one instance the same

TABLE VI. Aconite and Delphinium Alkaloids

ALKALOID		ALKAMINE		ACIDS	SOURCE
Name	Formula	Name	Formula		
Aconitine[1,14-10]	$C_{34}H_{47}O_{11}N$	Aconine	$C_{25}H_{41}O_9N$	Acetic, benzoic	*A. Napellus*
Jesaconitine[19]	$C_{35}H_{49}O_{12}N$	Aconine	$C_{25}H_{41}O_9N$	Acetic, p-anisic	*A. sachalinense*
Mesaconitine[20]	$C_{33}H_{45}O_{11}N$	Mesaconine	$C_{24}H_{39}O_9N$	Acetic, benzoic	*A. mandschuricum*
Hypaconitine[21]	$C_{31}H_{43}O_{10}N$	Hypaconine	$C_{24}H_{39}O_9N$	Acetic, benzoic	*A. senanense*
Indaconitine[22]	$C_{34}H_{47}O_{10}N$	Pseudaconine	$C_{25}H_{41}O_8N$	Acetic, benzoic	*A. chasmanthum*
Pseudaconitine[23]	$C_{36}H_{51}O_{12}N$	Pseudaconine	$C_{25}H_{41}O_8N$	Acetic, veratric	*A. deinorrhizum*
Bikhaconitine[24]	$C_{36}H_{51}O_{11}N$	Bikhaconine	$C_{25}H_{41}O_7N$	Acetic, veratric	*A. spicatum*
Delphinine[3]	$C_{34}H_{45}O_9N$	Delphonine	$C_{24}H_{39}O_7N$	Acetic, benzoic	*D. staphisagria*
Ajacine[25]	$C_{29}H_{40}O_7N_2$	Lycoctonine	$C_{20}H_{33}O_5N$	Acetic, anthranilic	*D. ajacis*
Methyllycaconitine[26]	$C_{32}H_{44}O_9N_2$	Lycoctonine	$C_{20}H_{33}O_5N$	Methylsuccinic, anthranilic	*D. elatum*
Condelphine[27]	$C_{31}H_{29}O_6N$	Isotalatisidine	$C_{31}H_{27}O_4N$	Acetic	*D. confusum*

[14] Dunstan and Carr, *J. Chem. Soc.*, **65**, 290 (1894).
[15] Schulze, *Arch. Pharm.*, **244**, 136, 165 (1906).
[16] Majima and Tamura, *Ann.*, **526**, 116 (1936).
[17] Jacobs and Elderfield, *J. Am. Chem. Soc.*, **58**, 1059 (1936).
[18] W. Freudenberg, *Ber.*, **69**, 1962 (1936).
[19] Majima and Morio, *Ber.*, **57**, 1472 (1924).
[20] Morio, *Ann.*, **476**, 181 (1929); Majima and Tamura, *ibid.*, **545**, 1 (1940).
[21] Majima and Morio, *Ann.*, **476**, 171 (1929).
[22] Dunstan and Andrews, *J. Chem. Soc.*, **87**, 1620 (1905).
[23] Henry and Sharp, *J. Chem. Soc.*, 1105 (1928).
[24] Dunstan and Andrews, *J. Chem. Soc.*, **87**, 1636 (1905).
[25] Goodson, *J. Chem. Soc.*, 108 (1944). Formula of lycoctonine: L. Marion and Manske, *Can. J. Res.*, **B24**, 1 (1946); L. Marion and O. E. Edwards, *J. Am. Chem. Soc.*, **69**, 2010 (1947). The latter paper reports the isolation of six new delphinium alkaloids.
[26] Goodson, *J. Chem. Soc.*, 139 (1943).
[27] Rabinovich and Konovalova, *J. Gen. Chem.* (*U.S.S.R.*), **12**, 321 (1942).

alkamine (isotalisidine) has been obtained from alkaloids of the two series.

The alkaloids and alkamines are difficult to purify and to analyze, and the empirical formulas are not yet fully secure. Aconine was generally thought to contain an N-methyl group until Jacobs and Elderfield[17] established that the group is ethyl by isolation of ethylamine as the principal volatile amine formed on fusion of aconine hydrochloride with potassium or barium hydroxide. They also decomposed aconine hydrochloride with hydrogen iodide by the usual analytical procedure and, after removal of methyl iodide coming from the methoxyl groups, isolated ethyl iodide as ethyltrimethylammonium iodide. Huebner and Jacobs[12] studied the behavior of the methoxyl-free alkaloid atisine and the product of its isomerization with alkali, isoatisine, and found that cleavage with hydrogen iodide afforded ethyl iodide together with a smaller quantity of methyl iodide. They report N-alkyl determinations for these and other alkaloids in which the values found for N-ethyl are notably below the calculated values but 20–30 times greater than the percentages found for N-methyl. Huebner and Jacobs regard the group that reacts as N-alkyl in aconine, napelline, heteratisine, and atisine as N-ethyl (or its equivalent) and that in delphonine and staphisine as N-methyl. They note, however, that in the first case the group may not be simply N-ethyl but that the tertiary nitrogen may be contained in two rings in such a way that the source of ethyl iodide is a two-carbon bridge. The ester alkaloids aconitine and mesaconitine appear to differ only in that the former has an N-ethyl and the latter an N-methyl group. Most of the bases are tertiary, but talatisamine is a secondary amine.

From a consideration of results of dehydrogenation experiments, Huebner and Jacobs* have suggested that staphisine may not have the formula $C_{21}H_{31}ON$ previously assigned but may be a dimolecular alkaloid:

$$2\,C_{21}H_{31}ON \;-\; H_2O \;=\; C_{42}H_{60}ON_2$$

The analytical results are in satisfactory agreement with either formula.

Table V lists the monomolecular empirical formulas, of which some or all may require revision in the light of the observation just mentioned. The partial structural formulas in the third column indicate the nature of the different functional groups identified. These are transcribed into formulas representing the possible parent types by substituting a hydrogen atom for each hydroxyl or methoxyl group and adding two hydrogen atoms for each nuclear double bond recognized as present either from the results of hydrogenation experiments or, in the case of staphisine, by absorption spectroscopy. Staphisine consumes only one mole of hydrogen but a maximum at 267 mμ indicates the presence of two conjugated double bonds in the

* See Ref. 36, below.

same ring.[28]   The striking fact emerges that the first six alkamines listed all correspond to the parent type $C_{19}H_{28}NR$ and the next two to the homologous type $C_{20}H_{30}NR$.   It is possible that the substances are all derived from the same parent compound $C_{19}H_{28}NR$ and that napelline and delphamine have an added methyl group.   If the failure of aconine and related compounds to absorb hydrogen is because the nucleus is fully saturated, then the structure must contain six rings.   However, the evidence pointing to an inert double bond in staphisine suggests that the alkamines of Group A have a similar inert double bond corresponding to a five-ring structure, and the further possibility exists that the structural unit contains two inert double bonds and only four rings (see below).   Staphisine, heteratisine, and atisine apparently belong to a second group (B) having either one double bond or one ring less than the members of the first group.   Heteratisine is a lactone, and since only nineteen carbon atoms, including that of the lactone group, are available for the nuclear structure, it is likely that the lactone carbon atom (a) corresponds to a methyl group in the other alkamines (b).

$$\underset{(\text{a})}{\overset{\displaystyle |\quad|}{\underset{\displaystyle \underset{}{\rule{0.8cm}{0.4pt}}\text{O}\underset{}{\rule{0.8cm}{0.4pt}}}{-\text{CHCHCHCO}}}} \qquad\qquad \underset{(\text{b})}{\overset{\displaystyle |\quad|}{\underset{\displaystyle \text{OH}}{-\text{CHCHCHCH}_3}}}$$

The parent substance of heteratisine, $C_{19}H_{30}NC_2H_5$, is the lower homolog of that of atisine.

The method of selenium dehydrogenation has given results that are complicated by the fact that some of the alkamines investigated contain only the fundamental C_{19}-unit while others bear one or two added methyl groups or an ethyl group (C_{20}–C_{21}-units).   Hetisine, atisine, napelline, and staphisine all yield abundant neutral fractions consisting of complex mixtures of phenanthrene hydrocarbons, of which the following have been identified:[29–36]

Hetisine[29] (C_{19}) → Pimanthrene (1,7-Dimethylphenanthrene)

[28] Jacobs and Craig, *J. Biol. Chem.*, **141,** 67 (1941); Craig, Michaelis, Granick and Jacobs, *ibid.*, **154,** 293 (1944).

[29] Jacobs and Huebner, *J. Biol. Chem.*, **170,** 189 (1947).

[30] A. Lawson and Topps, *J. Chem. Soc.*, 1640 (1937).

[31] Jacobs and Craig, *J. Biol. Chem.*, **143,** 589 (1942).

[32] Craig and Jacobs, *J. Biol. Chem.*, **152,** 651 (1944).

[33] Huebner and Jacobs, *J. Biol. Chem.*, **170,** 203 (1947).

[34] W. Freudenberg and E. F. Rogers, *Science*, **87,** 139 (1938).

[35] Craig and Jacobs, *J. Biol. Chem.*, **152,** 645 (1944).

[36] Huebner and Jacobs, *J. Biol. Chem.*, **169,** 211 (1947).

Atisine[30-33]   (C_{20}) → $\begin{cases} \text{1-Methylphenanthrene} \\ \text{1-Methyl-6-ethylphenanthrene} \end{cases}$

Napelline[5,34] (C_{20}) → $C_{17}H_{16}$ or $C_{18}H_{18}$

Staphisine[7,35,36] (C_{21}) → $\begin{cases} \text{Phenanthrene} \\ \text{Pimanthrene} \\ \text{3-Methylretene (1,3-Dimethyl-7-isopropylphenanthrene)} \end{cases}$

Huebner and Jacobs[12b] isolated 1,6-dimethylphenanthrene in place of 1-methyl-6-ethylphenanthrene on dehydrogenation of an acid oxidation product of isoatisine; evidently the oxidation involved that portion of the molecule that gave rise to the ethyl group in methylethylphenanthrene.

The formation of the phenanthrene homologs, particularly pimanthrene and 3-methylretene, suggested a relationship to the resin acids,[28] and hence the basic skeletal structure may be that of a desmethylditerpene. The formation of 1-methyl-6-ethylphenanthrene from atisine does not necessarily mean that the C_{19}-unit contains an ethyl group as such. The 3-methyl group of 3-methylretene obtained from staphisine may arise from an alkyl bridge forming the dimolecular alkaloid.

A hypothetical tetracyclic structure with two conjugated double bonds was discussed very tentatively by Jacobs and Craig[28] from evidence of absorption spectroscopy. Aconine, delphonine, heteratisine, and tetrahydroatisine all show strong absorption in the region 220–260 mμ (log ϵ 3.0–1.2), although the curves are without apparent maxima or minima. That the absorption is markedly reduced in acid solution was taken as an indication that the unsaturated system is associated with the nitrogen atom, which may account for the deviation from the usual type of diene absorption. N-Methylpyrrole showed similar uneventful absorption in the region investigated but the spectrum did not shift appreciably in acid solution. Aconine (pK 9.52) and delphonine (pK 10.02) are stronger bases than might be expected for unsaturated tertiary bases, but Adams and Mahan[37] found a series of cyclic vinyl tertiary amines to be unexpectedly strong bases of comparable order.

Jacobs and Craig found that, in contrast to the ready production of phenanthrene homologs from the four alkamines mentioned above, aconitine and delphinine in repeated attempts gave only minute amounts of material of a character unprofitable for study. With the idea that the divergence might be due to interference from the many oxygen functions (nine in aconitine, seven in delphinine), Jacobs and Huebner[38] effected a series of transformations of delphinine involving oxidation, pyrolysis, isomerization, and reduction that finally yielded a substance $C_{22}H_{33}O_6N$ in

---

[37] R. Adams and Mahan, *J. Am. Chem. Soc.*, **64**, 2588 (1942).

[38] Jacobs and Huebner, *J. Biol. Chem.*, **170**, 209 (1947).

which some of the original oxygen functions had been removed. This substance on selenium dehydrogenation yielded a hydrocarbon $C_{17}H_{24}$. The spectrum of this hydrocarbon is indicative of the presence of one benzenoid ring and the analysis and properties show that two alicyclic rings must be present. The hydrocarbon was in part recovered unchanged after prolonged heating with selenium at 325–340°, and Jacobs and Huebner suggested that it may be a bicyclopentenobenzene.

Aconitine forms a triacetate and aconine a pentaacetate, and hence the five free or acylated groups in the alkaloid are probably all primary or secondary. The acetyl group of aconitine is hydrolyzed by water under pressure or by dilute acids with the formation of benzoylaconine. General analogy would suggest that the four methoxyl groups of aconitine are probably primary or secondary.

An early known oxidation product of aconitine is the substance oxonitine, discovered by Carr.[39] Oxonitine, m.p. 282°, $[\alpha]_D$ − 45°, is formed along with acetaldehyde by oxidation of aconitine (NC_2N_5) with permanganate in acetone; and it is formed also by oxidation of mesaconitine (NCH_3). A plausible interpretation is that oxidation removes the N-alkyl group (ethyl as acetaldehyde) and converts the methylene group adjacent to nitrogen into the carbonyl group of a lactam.[17] Thus of the following formulas that have been proposed for oxonitine the third is the most likely: $C_{23}H_{29}O_9N$,[39] $C_{32}H_{43}O_{12}N$,[40, 41] $C_{32}H_{41}O_{12}N$,[16] $C_{33}H_{43}O_{12}N$.[42] Oxonitine is accompanied by a second neutral product, oxoaconitine ($C_{34}H_{45}O_{12}N$), which has a lactam structure[17, 42] and, in analogy with experience with delphinine,[3d] is a more normal oxo derivative formed without loss of carbon atoms from the alkaloid. Pyrolysis of the oxo derivatives with loss of acetic acid and introduction of a double bond is a reaction characteristic of this group.[3d, 43] A further oxidation product, first described by Lawson,[41] is aconitoline, formed on reaction with chromic acid. Jacobs and Craig[3d] revised the formula to $C_{33}H_{41}O_{10}N$ and showed that the substance results from oxidation of a secondary alcoholic group to a keto group and simultaneous loss of methanol.

Rogers and W. Freudenberg[44] obtained another interesting degradation product by distillation of crystalline aconitine with barium hydroxide; amorphous aconitine (Merck) afforded the same product in 2 percent yield. The substance is described as an autoxidizable green oil of the formula

[39] Carr, *J. Chem. Soc.*, **101**, 2241 (1912).
[40] Späth and Galinovsky, *Ber.*, **63**, 2994 (1930).
[41] A. Lawson, *J. Chem. Soc.*, 80 (1936).
[42] Jacobs, Elderfield and Craig, *J. Biol. Chem.*, **128**, 439 (1939).
[43] L. Marion and D. E. Edwards, *J. Am. Chem. Soc.*, **68**, 2565 (1946).
[44] E. F. Rogers and W. Freudenberg, *Ber.*, **70**, 349 (1937).

$C_{19}H_{24}O$ that appears to contain three nonconjugated double bonds (no absorption at 230–330 mμ). It contains three C-methyl groups, no methoxyl groups, one active hydrogen, no reactive carbonyl group, and it could not be acylated. Treatment with selenium eliminated the color without changing the composition. Rogers and Freudenberg regarded the substance as pentacyclic.

Pharmacology.[45] The *Aconitum* genus includes about sixty species of herbs, most of which contain the highly toxic ester alkaloids. Extracts from roots and leaves of aconite plants were used in ancient times as animal poisons and some of the species have common names associated with this use, for example, wolfsbane (wolf-killing) and leopardsbane. The data of Table VII illustrate the very high potency and the species specificity; the

TABLE VII. Toxicity of Two Ester Alkaloids (Chen)[46]

ANIMAL	METHOD OF ADMINISTRATION	LD$_{50}$ MG./KG.	
		Aconitine	Pseudaconitine
Mouse	Intravenous	0.32–.34	0.36
Rat	Intravenous	.14	.11
Rabbit	Intravenous	.04–.05	.03
Guinea pig	Subcutaneous	.06–.07	.02–.03

aconitines are more toxic to herbiverous animals (rabbit, guinea pig) than to carniverous animals (mouse, rat). The lethal dose for man is estimated to be about 5–6 mg. of aconitine.

The data of Table VIII show that loss of the acetyl group of aconitine reduces the toxicity considerably and that loss of both the acetyl and benzoyl groups renders the molecule practically nontoxic. The lethal dose usually kills the test animal within a few hours, but if the animal survives this period it recovers completely, probably as the result of detoxification by hydrolysis. Lycaconitine, in which the alkamine is esterified with

TABLE VIII. Comparison of Ester Alkaloids with an Alkamine (Munch[45])

COMPOUND	LD$_{50}$ MG./KG. (INTRAVENOUS)			
	Frog	Guinea pig	Rabbit	Cat
Aconitine	1.65	0.06–.12	0.08–.14	0.07–.13
Benzoylaconine	284	24–30	27	24
Aconine	1000–1750	275–300		400

[45] Swanson, Youngken, Zufall, Husa, Munch and Wolffe, "Aconitum," Am. Pharm. Assoc. Monograph No. 1, Washington, D. C. (1938).

[46] K. K. Chen, R. C. Anderson, and Robbins, *Quart. J. Pharmacol.*, **11,** 84 (1938).

succinic and anthranilic acid rather than with acetic and benzoic acid, is reported to be much less toxic than the other alkaloids (Munch[45]: LD_{50} 12 mg./kg. cat; 200–400 mg./kg. frog).

A preparation known as aconite was introduced clinically in 1762 for the treatment of gout, rheumatism, and intermittent fevers, and enjoyed considerable vogue as a circulatory depressant in spite of several cases of death due to overdosage or to use of deteriorated drug. Aconite was admitted to the first U. S. Pharmacopeia in 1820; the official form in the early editions was the dried leaves of *A. Napellus* (monkshood), in later revisions the roots of the same species.

A minute quantity of aconite applied to the tongue or lips causes an intense characteristic sensation of tingling, an effect sometimes used as a method of bioassay. Local application to the skin produces tingling followed by numbness and anesthesia of the sensory nerves. This action is the basis for the former use of aconite for the relief of neuralgia and toothache. The main systemic action is stimulation of the vagal centers with consequent slowing of the heart rate and decrease in blood pressure; the depressant action is counteracted by atropine and, to a lesser extent, by scopolamine. In recent years the therapeutic effects have been reexamined and all investigators agree that aconite is a dangerous drug of no significant clinical value. The drug was excluded from the 1942 revision of the U. S. Pharmacopeia.

Chapter X
Stereochemistry of the Steroids

BY RICHARD B. TURNER

Consideration of evidence for configurations at ring junctures and at certain other centers of asymmetry in the steroids has been deferred to this chapter so that correlation of data from various fields might be facilitated. The complexity of the problem is apparent from the fact that a relatively simple substance, desoxycholic acid, contains ten centers of asymmetry, and is therefore one of 1024 theoretically possible steric modifications. Solution of the main problems of stereochemistry constitutes an outstanding achievement and one that has required the concerted efforts of numerous investigators. Recent advances, particularly with regard to orientations at C_{12} and C_{17}, have necessitated revision of many early formulations. A great deal of the literature prior to 1946 must, accordingly, be reinterpreted.

NUCLEAR CONFIGURATION

A/B Ring Fusion. The perhydrocyclopentenophenanthrene ring system that composes the fundamental nuclear structure of the steroids contains six centers of asymmetry associated with the carbon atoms of the A/B, B/C, and C/D ring fusions. Although in this system sixty-four stereoisomeric forms are possible, all the naturally occurring saturated steroids thus far encountered, with the exception of the heart poisons and a few

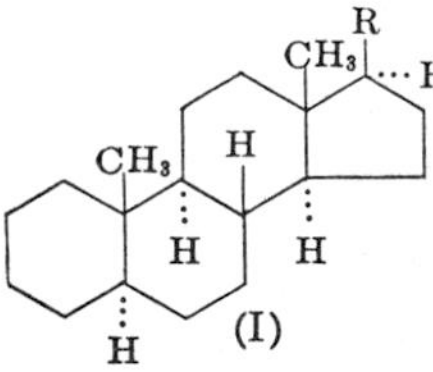

| | Allo series | | Normal series |

Androstane........	a) R = —H	Etiocholane
Allopregnane.....	b) R = —C_2H_5	Pregnane
Allocholanic acid.	c) R = —$CH(CH_3)CH_2CH_2CO_2H$	Cholanic acid
Cholestane........	d) R = —$CH(CH_3)CH_2CH_2CH_2CH(CH_3)_2$	Coprostane

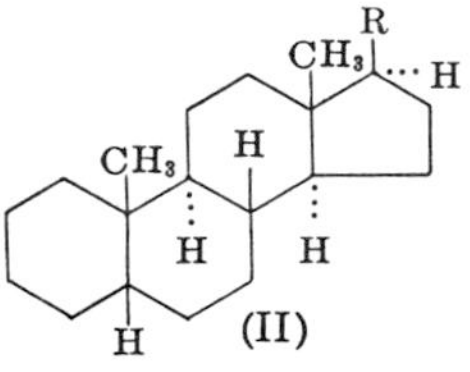

miscellaneous products, are related to one or the other of the C_5-isomers, androstane (Ia) and etiocholane (IIa). The nature of this isomerism was investigated at an early date in connection with the hydrocarbons cholestane (Id) and coprostane (IId) (Chapter III), and structures I and II are now firmly established by several independent lines of evidence.

The diketone III, obtained by careful oxidation of hyodesoxycholic acid, is easily converted by acids or bases into 3,6-diketoallocholanic acid (IV).[1]

(III)   (IV)

Isomerization of 3α-hydroxy-6-ketocholanic acid[2] and of 3,6-diketo-coprostane[3] to derivatives of the allo series has also been reported. These conversions are comparable to analogous transformations of simpler model substances. Hückel's classical study of the stereochemistry of the decalins[4] has established that cis α-decalone (V) is unstable with respect to the trans isomer (VI) and that conversion of the cis into the trans modification is

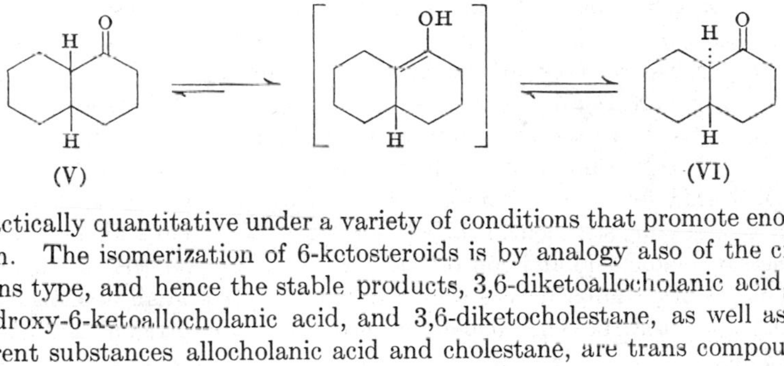

(V)   (VI)

practically quantitative under a variety of conditions that promote enoliza-tion. The isomerization of 6-ketosteroids is by analogy also of the cis to trans type, and hence the stable products, 3,6-diketoallocholanic acid, 3α-hydroxy-6-ketoallocholanic acid, and 3,6-diketocholestane, as well as the parent substances allocholanic acid and cholestane, are trans compounds; cholanic acid and coprostane therefore are A/B-cis derivatives.

Results of a study of the four lithobilianic acids VII, VIII, IX, and X substantiate this view. Windaus[1] observed that lithobilianic acid (VII) and allolithobilianic acid (VIII), when heated, decompose to the same pyroketone (XI), which in turn affords the desoxy compound XII by Clemmensen reduction. Clearly inversion at C_5 must occur during pyroly-

[1] Windaus, *Ann.*, **447**, 233 (1926).
[2] Wieland and Dane, *Z. physiol. Chem.*, **212**, 41 (1932).
[3] Prelog and Tagmann, *Helv. Chim. Acta*, **27**, 1880 (1944).
[4] Hückel and co-workers, *Ann.*, **441**, 1 (1925)

sis of one acid. The pyroketone (XI) is structurally related to α-hydrindanone, which incorporates the fusion of a five- to a six-membered ring,
and which, in contrast to α-decalone, exists preferentially as the cis isomer.[5]

CH₃   CH₃   CH₃   CH₃

HO₂C   HO₂C   HO₂C   HO₂C
HO₂C   HO₂C   HO₂C   HO₂C
     H   H   H   H
  (VII)   (VIII)   (IX)   (X)

CH₃   CH₃   CH₃   CH₃

     H   H   O   O
  (XI)   (XII)   (XIII)   (XIV)
     O H   H   H   H

Cis α-hydrindanone is, in fact, the only pure product that can be obtained
by cyclization of either cis or trans cyclohexane-1-carboxy-2-propionic acid.
The pyroketone (XI) and desoxy acid (XII) are presumably also cis
derivatives.

The hydrogen atom at C_5 in isolithobilianic acid (IX) and in isoallo-
lithobilianic acid (X) is not activated by a carboxyl group and these acids
undergo pyrolysis without inversion. Of the resulting pyroketones (XIII
and XIV) only XIII affords the desoxy acid XII on Clemmensen reduction. Cis structures are thus indicated for XIII and for isolithobilianic
acid (IX). Furthermore, since lithobilianic acid (VII) and isolithobilianic
acid (IX) are both derived from lithocholic acid, all three substances must
belong to the same stereochemical series. Lithocholic acid and the related
products, cholanic acid and coprostane,[6] are therefore A/B-cis derivatives.
Conclusions of a similar nature were reached by Lettré in an investigation
of analogous dicarboxylic acids obtained from coprostanol and from
cholestanol.[7]

Measurements of physical constants by Ruzicka, Furter, and Thomann[8]
reveal that cholestane has a slightly higher molecular refraction and a
slightly lower density than coprostane. The values are comparable to those

[5] Hückel, M. Sachs, Yantschulewitsch and Nerdel, *Ann.*, **518**, 155 (1935); *cf.*
Windaus, Hückel and Reverey, *Ber.*, **56**, 91 (1923); Hückel and H. Friedrich, *Ann.*,
451, 132 (1926); Linstead, *Ann. Repts.*, **32**, 310 (1935).

[6] Windaus and Neukirchen, *Ber.*, **52**, 1915 (1919); Wieland and Weyland, *Z. physiol.
Chem.*, **110**, 123 (1920).

[7] Lettré, *Z. physiol. Chem.*, **221**, 73 (1933).

[8] Ruzicka, Furter and Thomann, *Helv. Chim. Acta*, **16**, 327 (1933).

of cis and trans decalin[4] and of cis and trans β-decalone,[9] and confirm structures based on chemical evidence.

Clear proof for the cis arrangement of the A/B ring fusion in the bile acids has recently been advanced by Kendall and his associates[10] at the Mayo Clinic. When methyl 3α-hydroxy-12α-chloro-$\Delta^{9(11)}$-cholenate (XV) from desoxycholic acid[10, 11] is treated with pyridine, or when a chloroform solution is washed with water, the elements of hydrogen chloride are eliminated, and a product, for which the 3,9-epoxy structure XVI has been established, is isolated in nearly quantitative yield. The reaction is re-

(XV)   (XVI)

versible, for the chloro derivative (XV) is regenerated by treatment of XVI with anhydrous hydrogen chloride. Examination of a molecular model[12] of the epoxide shows that structure XVI is virtually unstrained. Models cannot be constructed with a trans fusion between rings A and B or with a β-oriented oxide bridge (see below).

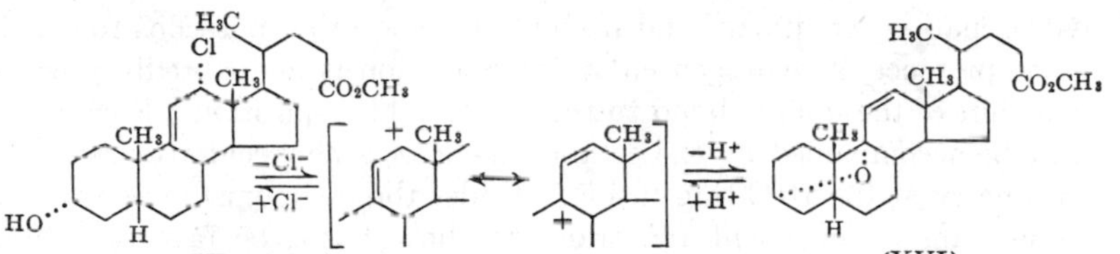

B/C Ring Fusion. Extensive X-ray diffraction studies of more than eighty steroids of a wide variety of types denote molecular dimensions of about $20 \times 7 \times 4$ Å (length $\times$ width $\times$ thickness).[1] These characteristics correspond to flat, lath-shaped molecules and are approximated only in models in which the B/C ring junction is trans.[2] The corresponding cis configuration is incompatible with the X-ray data, and examination of the structurally well-defined cis and trans hexahydrochrysenes[3] has shown that the trans hydrocarbon alone resembles the steroids.[4] A trans fusion be-

[9] Hückel, *Ann.*, **451,** 109 (1926).

[10] Mattox, R. B. Turner, L. L. Engel, B. McKenzie, McGuckin and Kendall, *J. Biol. Chem.*, **164,** 569 (1946).

[11] B. McKenzie, Mattox, L. L. Engel and Kendall, *J. Biol. Chem.*, **173,** 271 (1948).

[12] H. A. Stuart, *Z. physik. Chem.*, **B27,** 350 (1934).

[1] Bernal, *Nature*, **129,** 277 (1932); *Chem. and Ind.*, **51,** 466 (1932); *ibid.*, **52,** 11 (1933); Caglioti and Giacomello, *Gazz. chim. ital.*, **69,** 245 (1939); Giacomello, *ibid.*, **69,** 790 (1939); see especially Bernal, Crowfoot and Fankuchen, *Trans. Roy. Soc. (London)*, **A239,** 135 (1940); Carlisle and Crowfoot, *Proc. Roy. Soc.*, **A184,** 64 (1945); Crowfoot, *Vitamins and Hormones*, II, 409, Academic Press, New York (1944).

[2] Ruzicka and Thomann, *Helv. Chim. Acta*, **16,** 221 (1933).

[3] Ramage and R. Robinson, *Nature*, **131,** 205 (1933); *J. Chem. Soc.*, 607 (1933).

[4] Bernal, *Chem. and Ind.*, **52,** 288 (1933).

tween rings B and C is further indicated by the observation that 7,12-diketocholanic acid is not isomerized in hot alkaline solution,[5] as would be expected if the ring fusion were of the cis decalin type; 11-ketosteroids are also stable under these conditions.

Consideration of other facts lends support to the trans formulation. Of double bonds located at the 7,8-, 8,9-, 8,14-, and 14,15-positions only those at $C_{14}-C_{15}$ are ordinarily susceptible to catalytic hydrogenation. With platinum and warm acetic acid containing hydrogen chloride, however, it is possible to effect saturation of normally inert olefinic linkages.[6] In view of known shifts of double bonds from C_7-C_8 and C_8-C_9 to C_8-C_{14} under hydrogenation conditions,[7] and from C_8-C_{14} and other positions to $C_{14}-C_{15}$ in the presence of hydrogen chloride,[8] reduction is undoubtedly preceded by a shift of the double bond to the reactive 14,15-position. Such a shift must be accompanied by the establishment of a new center or centers of asymmetry at the B/C ring fusion. Under these circumstances the more stable trans arrangement (cf. trans decalin) should be favored. In all cases where this procedure has been employed, saturated products of the natural series have been obtained.

The trans fusion of rings B and C is apparently common to all naturally occurring steroids. Although a cis configuration has been suggested for the urane derivatives reported by Marker[9] as constituents of urine, evidence for such a structure is lacking. A synthetic product that apparently possesses the cis arrangement has been prepared by disproportionation of dihydroequilin on Raney nickel.[10] One of the two products is identical with dihydroequilenin; the other is isomeric with estradiol and is presumably an 8-iso compound.

C/D Ring Fusion. By a complicated series of degradations Wieland and his associates[1, 2] converted both desoxycholic acid and 12-ketocholanic acid

[5] Wieland and Wiedersheim, Z. physiol. Chem., **186**, 232 (1930).

[6] Windaus, Linsert and Eckhardt, Ann., **534**, 22 (1938); cf. Tschesche, Bohle and W. Neumann, Ber., **71**, 1927 (1938).

[7] Windaus and Langer, Ann., **508**, 105 (1934); Schenck, Buchholz and Wiese, Ber., **69**, 2696 (1936); Windaus and G. Zühlsdorff, Ann., **536**, 204 (1938); Wieland and Benend, ibid., **554**, 1 (1943); Stavely and Bollenback, J. Am. Chem. Soc., **65**, 1285, 1290, 1600 (1943).

[8] Reindel, Walter and Rauch, Ann., **452**, 34 (1927); Yamasaki, Z. physiol. Chem., **233**, 10 (1935); Laucht, ibid., **237**, 236 (1935); Plattner, Ruzicka and Holtermann, Helv. Chim. Acta, **28**, 1660 (1945); Wieland and Görnhardt, Ann., **557**, 248 (1947).

[9] Marker and co-workers, J. Am. Chem. Soc., **60**, 210, 1061, 1561 (1938).

[10] Serini and W. Logemann, Ber., **71**, 186 (1938); cf. Dirscherl and Hanusch, Z. physiol. Chem., **233**, 13 (1935); ibid., **236**, 131 (1935).

[1] Wieland and Schlichting, Z. physiol. Chem., **134**, 276 (1924); Wieland and Posternak, ibid., **197**, 17 (1931).

[2] Wieland and Dane, Z. physiol. Chem., **216**, 91 (1933).

into a tricarboxylic acid (I), in which the ring carboxyl groups are derived from carbon atoms 8 and 12 of ring C (Chapter III). Distillation of this product at 260° yields an anhydride (II), which on careful hydrolysis with

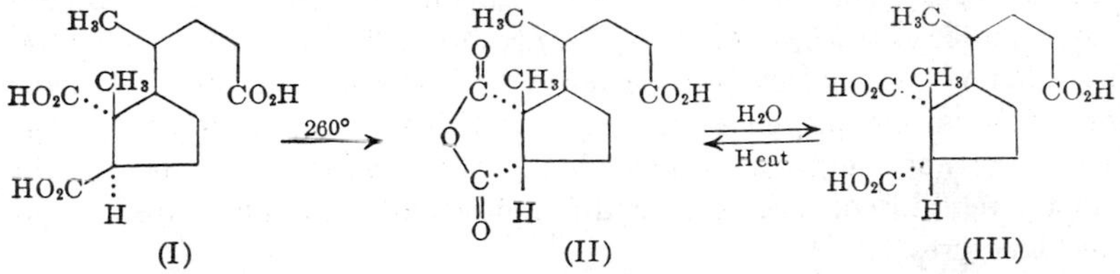

hot water furnishes a second tricarboxylic acid (III).[2] The anhydride (II) is reformed from III by distillation. The two acids (I and III) are clearly cis-trans isomers, and the cis configuration of III follows from the cis structure required by the anhydride (II).[3] The unrearranged isomer (I) is therefore trans, and a trans configuration is assigned to the C/D ring fusion of the bile acids.[2]

Objections to this conclusion raised by Peak[4] on the ground that inversions may occur in the degradative steps led Dimroth and Jonsson[5] at Göttingen to a further investigation of the problem. Vitamin-D₂ from ergosterol is oxidized by potassium permanganate under controlled conditions to a bicyclic ketone (IV) in which the carbonyl group adjoins the bridge head.[6] Irreversible isomerization of IV, induced by either acid or

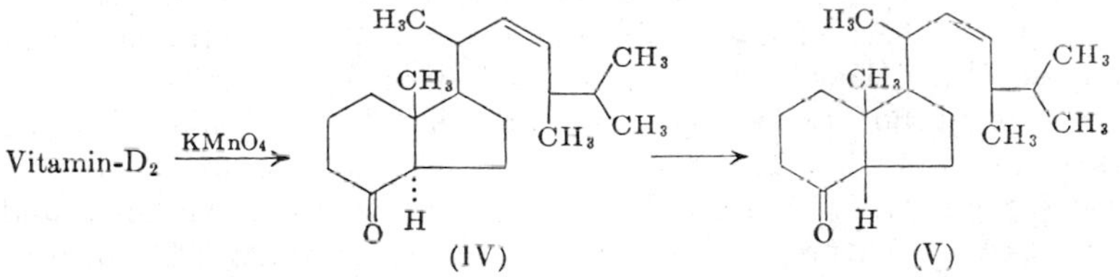

base,[5] affords an isomeric ketone (V) that has been characterized as a semicarbazone. In view of the greater stability of cis hydrindanone-4 as compared with the trans modification,[7,8] the configurations of the ketones (IV and V) are undoubtedly correctly assigned. The results agree with the conclusions of Wieland and Dane.[2]

---

[3] *cf.* Hückel, *Theoretische Grundlagen der Organischen Chemie*, 2nd ed., I, 68, Akademische Verlagsgesellschaft, Leipzig (1934).

[4] Peak, *Nature*, **140**, 280 (1937).

[5] K. Dimroth and Jonsson, *Ber.*, **74**, 520 (1941).

[6] Windaus and Grundmann, *Ann.*, **524**, 297 (1936).

[7] Hückel and Schnitzspahn, *Ann.*, **505**, 274 (1933).

[8] Hückel and Goth, *Ber.*, **67**, 2104 (1934); Hückel and Schlüter, *ibid.*, **67**, 2107 (1934).

Although the deductions cited above can be extended to the related steroid hormones, progesterone, testosterone, androsterone, the cortical hormones, and their derivatives, the configuration of the C/D ring fusion in the estrogenic hormones is not so well defined.[9]   This junction is generally regarded as trans, an inference that rests chiefly on analogy and on the conversion of androsterone into estradiol.[10]   However, since high-temperature pyrolysis is employed at one stage of this transformation, the possibility of rearrangement is not excluded.   X-ray data for estrone and estriol[11] unfortunately do not permit clear differentiation of the alternate cis and trans structures.

The probability that estrone, equilin and equilenin belong to the same stereochemical series[12] is indicated by the conversions of estrone and of equilin into 17-desoxoestrone,[13] of equilin into estrone,[13] and by the low-temperature dehydrogenation of equilin to equilenin.[14]   Analogous dehydrogenation of estrone[15] is accomplished only at high temperature (260°) and yields, not equilenin, but d-isoequilenin (IX), which possesses a 14-iso structure (Chapter IV).   The same product is obtained from equilin (VI) by isomerization with hydrochloric acid and dehydrogenation of the resulting isoequilin-A (VII).[16]   Because of the mild conditions employed for dehydrogenation (Pd, 80°), rearrangement in this step is unlikely, and inversion at C_{14} is assumed in the transformation of equilin into isoequilin-A.

Rearrangements at C_{13} are noted in the conversions of estrone (VIII) into lumiestrone (X)[15, 17] and of androsterone into lumiandrosterone[18] under the influence of monochromatic ($\lambda = 313$ mμ) ultraviolet light (Chapter IV).   Dehydrogenation of lumiestrone (X) significantly proceeds without further inversion and furnishes l-isoequilenin (XI), the enantiomorph of IX.   The diastereomers, IX and XI, are identical in melting point with the isoequilenins obtained by total synthesis, and, when mixed in equal proportions, yield a racemate (m.p. 222–223°) identical with synthetic dl-isoequilenin.[19]   The d- and l-isoequilenins hence are

[9] Shoppee, Nature, 160, 64 (1947).

[10] Inhoffen and G. Zühlsdorff, Ber., 74, 1911 (1941); Wilds and Djerassi, J. Am. Chem. Soc., 68, 2125 (1946).

[11] Bernal, Crowfoot and Fankuchen, Trans. Roy. Soc. (London), A239, 135 (1940).

[12] cf. Shoppee, Nature, 161, 207 (1948).

[13] Pearlman and Wintersteiner, J. Biol. Chem., 130, 35 (1939); ibid., 132, 605 (1940).

[14] Dirscherl and Hanusch, Z. physiol. Chem., 233, 13 (1935).

[15] Butenandt, A. Wolff and Karlson, Ber., 74, 1308 (1941).

[16] H. Hirschmann and Wintersteiner, J. Biol. Chem., 126, 737 (1938).

[17] Butenandt, W. Friedrich and Poschmann, Ber., 75, 1931 (1942); Butenandt and Poschmann, ibid., 77, 392 (1944).

[18] Butenandt and Poschmann, Ber., 77, 394 (1944).

[19] Bachmann, Cole and Wilds, J. Am. Chem. Soc., 62, 824 (1940).

either both cis or both trans, and it is evident that the inversions effected by hydrochloric acid, by high-temperature dehydrogenation, and by ultraviolet light all proceed in the same direction, *i.e.* cis to trans or trans to cis.

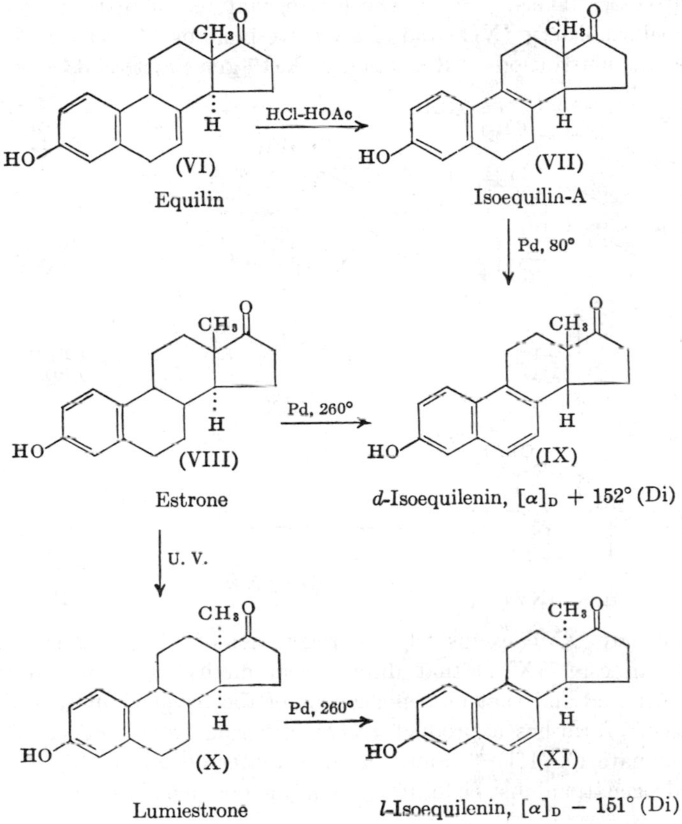

Since greater strain is associated with trans hydrindane than with the cis isomer,[20] the latter alternative is more attractive. The isoequilenins thus are probably cis compounds, and estrone, equilin, and equilenin belong to the normal C/D trans series.

The cardiac aglycones possess a β-oriented hydroxyl group at C_{14} (see below) and, unlike the sterols, bile acids, and steroid hormones, are C/D-cis derivatives. In addition to these substances and to the products noted above, several other steroids containing a cis C/D ring fusion have recently

[20] Hückel and H. Friedrich, *Ann.*, **451**, 132 (1926).

been obtained by synthesis. Although catalytic hydrogenation of Δ^{14}-compounds with normal, β-oriented side chains at C_{17} invariably results in restoration of the natural configuration at C_{14} (C/D trans), reduction of 17-iso-Δ^{14}-compounds and of $\Delta^{14,\ 16}$-dienes leads to the formation of 14-iso derivatives (C/D cis).[21, 22, 23] The hydrogenations of methyl 3β-acetoxy-Δ^{14}-etioallocholenate (XII) and of the corresponding C_{17}-isomer (XIV) can be cited as illustrations. Reduction of XII[24] gives methyl 3β-acetoxyetio-

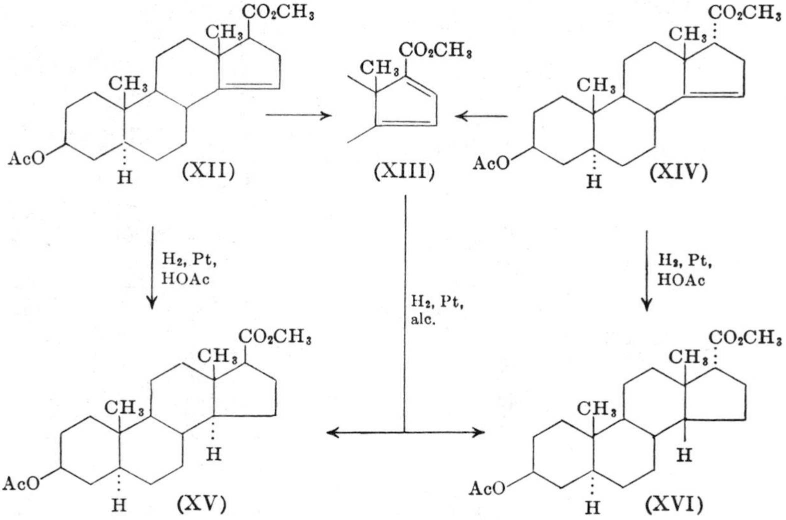

allocholanate (XV)[25] exclusively; hydrogenation of XIV, on the other hand, affords an ester (XVI) that differs from methyl 3β-acetoxy-17-isoetio-allocholanate[26] and that on replacement of the oxygen function at C_3 by hydrogen[27] furnishes a product (XIX) differing from methyl 17-isoetio-allocholanate (XVIII).[28] Since the new center of asymmetry introduced on hydrogenation must be located at C_{14}, the nonidentity of the compounds

[21] Kuno Meyer, *Helv. Chim. Acta*, **29**, 718, 1908 (1946).

[22] Ruzicka and co-workers, *Helv. Chim. Acta*, **29**, 942, 2023 (1946); *ibid.*, **30**, 395 (1947).

[23] Speiser and Reichstein, *Helv. Chim. Acta*, **30**, 2143 (1947).

[24] Plattner, Ruzicka, Heusser, Pataki and Kd. Meier, *Helv. Chim. Acta*, **29**, 942 (1946).

[25] Steiger and Reichstein, *Helv. Chim. Acta*, **20**, 1040 (1937).

[26] Sorkin and Reichstein, *Helv. Chim. Acta*, **29**, 1209 (1946).

[27] Plattner, Ruzicka, Heusser, Pataki and Kd. Meier, *Helv. Chim. Acta*, **29**, 949 (1946).

[28] von Euw and Reichstein, *Helv. Chim. Acta*, **27**, 1851 (1944).

in question is ascribed to a difference in spatial arrangement at this position. Corroborative evidence is provided by a study of the relative rates of hydrolysis of the esters XVII,[29] XVIII, and XIX. Heusser, Meier and

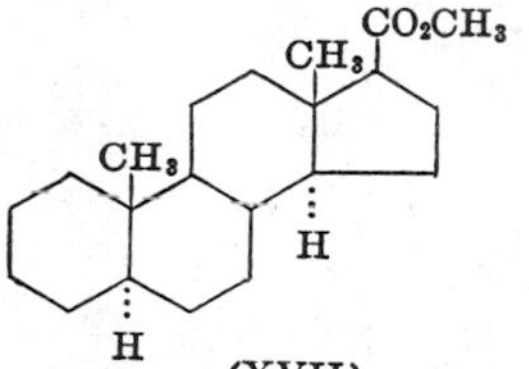

CO_2CH_3 CO_2CH_3 CO_2CH_3
CH_3 CH_3 CH_3
CH_3 CH_3 CH_3
H   H   H
H   H   H
(XVII) 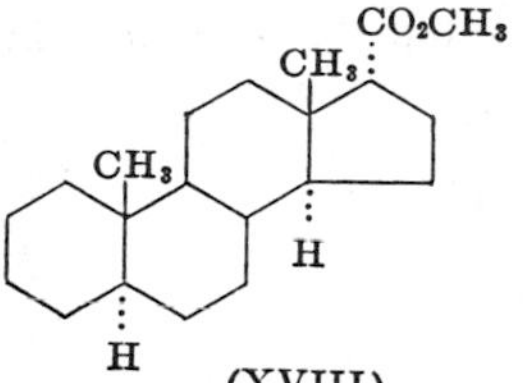   (XVIII) 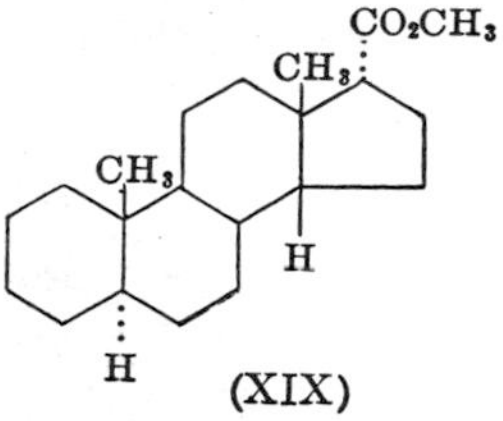   (XIX)

Ruzicka[30] predicted from inspection of models that, in terms of reactivity of the ester group, the 14-iso-17-iso compound (XIX) would resemble methyl etioallocholanate (XVII) rather than methyl 17-isoetioallocholanate (XVIII), which appears to be more strongly hindered. This hypothesis was tested experimentally by measurements of the percent of ester hydrolyzed in one hour under standardized conditions. The results for the three esters are as follows: XVII, 48.3 percent and 44.1 percent; XVIII, 17.8 percent; XIX, 48.6 percent. The fourth member of the series, methyl 14-isoetioallocholanate, is unknown, but according to the Swiss investigators would be more nearly comparable to XVII and to XIX than to XVIII.

Both Δ^{14}-esters XII and XIV, on treatment with N-bromosuccinimide, give the $\Delta^{14,16}$-dienic ester XIII, in which asymmetry at C_{17} is absent. Hydrogenation of the latter product[24] yields XV and XVI, but interestingly not the corresponding 14-normal-17-iso or 14-iso-17-normal derivatives. The results suggest a 1,4-cis addition of hydrogen at C_{14} and C_{17}.[31]

Configurations at Positions 8, 9, 10, and 14. From evidence cited above the A/B, B/C, and C/D ring fusions are rather well established as being trans, trans, trans, respectively, in compounds of the cholestane series, and cis, trans, trans, respectively, in derivatives of coprostane. These restrictions reduce the number of possible nuclear isomers in either series from sixty-four to eight. The eight forms differ in individual orientations of the three ring junctions, and correlation of the asymmetric centers at C_8 and C_9 with those at C_{10} and C_{14} is necessary for a complete description of the stereochemistry of the steroid nucleus.[1] The conventional practice

[29] Tschesche, Z. physiol. Chem., **229**, 219 (1934); Ber., **68**, 7 (1935).

[30] Heusser, Kd. Meier and Ruzicka, Helv. Chim. Acta, **29**, 1250 (1946).

[31] cf. Linstead, Doering, S. B. Davis, P. Levine and Whetstone, J. Am. Chem. Soc., **64**, 1985 (1942).

[1] cf. Cook, Nature, **134**, 758 (1934); Ruzicka, M. W. Goldberg and Wirz, Helv. Chim. Acta, **18**, 61 (1935).

of assigning the β-configuration to the angular methyl group at C_{10} as a point of reference limits the problem, in the case of androstane, to a choice among the four structures I, II, III, and IV; a distinction cannot as yet be made between these forms and the corresponding mirror images.

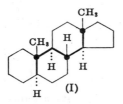

Trans, anti, trans, anti, trans

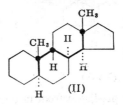

Trans, syn, trans, syn, trans

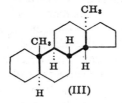

Trans, anti, trans, syn, trans

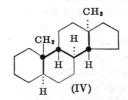

Trans, syn, trans, anti, trans

X-ray diffraction data, in addition to indicating flat structures for the steroids, further suggest that the hydrogen atom at C_9 is trans to the C_{10}-methyl group.[2] Available chemical evidence supports the X-ray work. The adrenal cortical hormones and numerous synthetic products that possess a β-oriented hydroxyl group[3] at C_{11} are dehydrated with ease by mineral acids, thionyl chloride, phosphorus oxychloride, and similar reagents and yield $\Delta^{9(11)}$-unsaturated products.[4] Only small amounts of the Δ^{11}-isomers are obtained. 11α-Hydroxy derivatives, on the other hand, are comparatively resistant to dehydration.[5] Inasmuch as elimination reactions of this type are greatly facilitated by a trans arrangement of the atoms or groups involved,[6] the 9-hydrogen and the 11-hydroxyl group are

[2] Bernal, Crowfoot and Fankuchen, *Trans. Roy. Soc. (London)*, **A239**, 164 (1940); Ruzicka, Furter and M. W. Goldberg, *Helv. Chim. Acta*, **21**, 498 (1938).

[3] Orientations of hydroxyl and halogen substituents pertinent to the following arguments are dealt with in subsequent sections.

[4] Shoppee, *J. Chem. Soc.*, 1134 (1946); Reich and Reichstein, *Helv. Chim. Acta*, **26**, 562 (1943); Lardon and Reichstein, *ibid.*, **26**, 586 (1943); *ibid.*, **28**, 1420 (1945); Seebeck and Reichstein, *ibid.*, **26**, 558 (1943).

[5] W. P. Long and Gallagher, *J. Biol. Chem.*, **162**, 517 (1946); *cf.* Shoppee and Reichstein, *Helv. Chim. Acta*, **26**, 1316 (1943).

[6] Vavon and Barbier, *Bull. soc. chim.*, **49**, 567 (1931); Hückel, Tappe and Legutke,

very probably trans in the easily dehydrated 11β-hydroxy compounds. The hydrogen atom at C_9 consequently is α-oriented and trans to the C_{10}-methyl group. Similar conclusions are drawn from the fact that methyl 3α-acetoxy-11β-bromo-12-ketocholanate (V) is converted into methyl

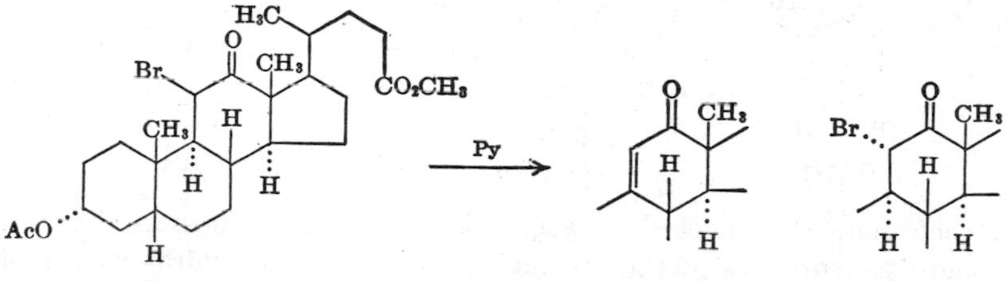

(V)   (VI)   (VII)

3α-acetoxy-12-keto-$\Delta^{9(11)}$-cholenate (VI) by boiling pyridine, whereas the epimeric 11α-bromo derivative (VII) is unaffected by such treatment.[7, 8]

In view of the trans arrangement deduced for the B/C ring junction, the hydrogen atom at C_8 must have the β-orientation. Confirmatory evidence for this point is also supplied by dehydration experiments. Cholic acid[9] and cholestanediol-$3\beta,7\alpha$,[10, 11] in which the 7-hydroxyl and 8-hydrogen are trans, are dehydrated without difficulty and yield Δ^7-derivatives accompanied by varying amounts of the Δ^8- or $\Delta^{8(14)}$-isomers. Cholestanediol-$3\beta,7\beta$, however, is relatively more stable than the 7α-hydroxy derivatives and, when treated (as the 3-monoacetate) with phosphorus oxychloride and pyridine, affords only a 7-chloro derivative.[11] Several 14β-hydroxy compounds have likewise been subjected to dehydration; the unsaturated products obtained from these substances possess a double bond at $C_{14}-C_{15}$ (trans elimination) rather than at the alternate 8,14-position (cis elimination).[12]

The orientations of the angular methyl groups at C_{10} and C_{13} can be correlated as follows. Methyl 3α-acetoxy-Δ^{11}-cholenate, on oxidation with

---

Ann., **543**, 191 (1940); C. C. Price and Karabinos, *J. Am. Chem. Soc.*, **62**, 1159 (1940). Cis elimination in the Tschugaeff dehydration has been observed by Hückel, Tappe and Legutke. This procedure apparently has not been employed in connection with stereochemical problems in the steroid series.

[7] Seebeck and Reichstein, *Helv. Chim. Acta*, **26**, 536 (1943); *cf.* Alther and Reichstein, *ibid.*, **26**, 492 (1943).

[8] Gallagher and W. P. Long, *J. Biol. Chem.*, **162**, 495 (1946).

[9] Boedecker, *Ber.*, **53**, 1852 (1920); Boedecker and Volk, *ibid.*, **54**, 2489 (1921); Wieland and Dane, *Z. physiol. Chem.*, **212**, 263 (1932).

[10] Wintersteiner and M. Moore, *J. Am. Chem. Soc.*, **65**, 1507 (1943).

[11] Fieser, Fieser and R. N. Chakravarti, unpublished results.

[12] Ruzicka and co-workers, *Helv. Chim. Acta*, **29**, 942, 2023 (1946).

perbenzoic acid, furnishes an oxide (VIII),[13, 14] which yields a bromohydrin (IX) on treatment with hydrobromic acid.[8] The bromohydrin (IX) is undoubtedly trans,[15] and since it affords methyl 3α-acetoxy-11β-bromo-12-

$$ \text{(VIII)} \quad \xrightarrow{\text{HBr}} \quad \text{(IX)} \quad \xrightarrow{\text{CrO}_3} \quad \text{(V)} $$

ketocholanate (V) on chromic acid oxidation, it must possess the 11β-bromo-12α-hydroxy structure as indicated. Catalytic hydrogenation of the oxide (VIII) in the presence of hydrochloric acid yields, after hydrolysis, desoxycholic acid.[14] The oxide (VIII), the bromohydrin (IX) and desoxycholic acid therefore possess the same configuration (α) at C_{12}. Since a trans arrangement of the 12-hydroxyl and 13-methyl groups in desoxycholic acid has been established with certainty (see below), the 13-methyl group must be β-oriented and cis to the angular methyl group at C_{10}. A trans relation of the hydrogen atoms at C_8 and C_{14} is inferred from this fact.

The evidence presented above indicates that configurations at successive centers of asymmetry in androstane are alternately α and β. The trans, anti, trans, anti, trans structure (I) is accordingly assigned to this steroid in agreement with Ruzicka's early formulations.[16]

Other Geometric Considerations. The positions in space assigned to atoms of the androstane ring system on the basis of detailed X-ray crystallographic analyses require that carbon atoms 2, 3, 5, 7, 8, and 10 lie in a plane (aa'bb' of Figure 1) with C_{15} located in the plane or very near it; carbon atoms 1, 9, 11, 13, and 14 are situated in a second plane (cc'dd') parallel to the first and separated from it by a distance of about 0.77 Å.[1] This arrangement is compatible with a trans, anti, trans, anti, trans structure and implies that, at least in the crystalline state, rings A, B, and C all possess the Sachse-Mohr[2] "chair" configuration. Construction of a model shows

[13] Press and Reichstein, *Helv. Chim. Acta*, **25**, 878 (1942).

[14] B. McKenzie, McGuckin and Kendall, *J. Biol. Chem.*, **162**, 555 (1946).

[15] R. Kuhn and Ebel, *Ber.*, **58**, 919 (1925); Böeseken, *Rec. trav. chim.*, **47**, 683 (1928); Bartlett, *J. Am. Chem. Soc.*, **57**, 224 (1935); C. E. Wilson and Lucas, *ibid.*, **58**, 2396 (1936); Winstein and Lucas, *ibid.*, **61**, 1576 (1939).

[16] Ruzicka and co-workers, *Helv. Chim. Acta*, **16**, 327 (1933); **17**, 1395, 1407 (1934).

[1] Shoppee, *J. Chem. Soc.*, 1138 (1946); *Ann. Repts.*, **43**, 200 (1946).

[2] Sachse, *Ber.*, **23**, 1363 (1890); *Z. physik. Chem.*, **10**, 203 (1892); Mohr, *J. prakt. Chem.*, **98**, 315 (1918); **103**, 316 (1921).

that rings B and C of androstane are locked in the rigid "chair" arrangement by trans fusions to rings A and D and that conversion of the B and C rings into "bed" forms leads to excessive deformation of bond angles.

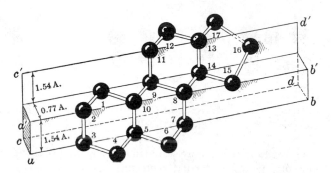

Fig. 1.—Androstane

Such a transformation in ring A, however, is apparently unrestricted. The energy difference between the "chair" and "bed" forms of cyclohexane has been variously estimated as 6–10 Kg. cal.[1, 3] owing to repulsions between opposed hydrogen atoms in the less stable "bed" structure.[4, 5] At equilibrium at room temperature cyclohexane should therefore exist predominantly as the "chair" modification, a conclusion that is supported by other lines of evidence.[6] Similar arguments applied to the case of androstane suggest that the "chair" form of ring A is also favored on energetic grounds.

The situation with respect to steroids of the A/B-cis series is less clear. Barton[7] has computed energy differences for the three forms of decalin shown on page 634 and deduced that the order of stability is a > b > c. His conclusions agree with thermal data for the cis and trans decalins[8] and with the electron-diffraction work of Bastiansen and Hassel,[9] which supports structure (b) for cis decalin. An arrangement of type (b) in steroids

[3] Kumler, *J. Am. Chem. Soc.*, **67**, 1904 (1945).

[4] *cf*. Spitzer and H. M. Huffmann, *J. Am. Chem. Soc.*, **69**, 211 (1947).

[5] A familiar example of this phenomenon is ethane, in which an energy differential of about 3 Kg. cal. favors the staggered over the opposed configuration. Eyring, *J. Am. Chem. Soc.*, **54**, 3191 (1932); Kemp and Pitzer, *J. Chem Phys.*, **4**, 749 (1936); *J. Am. Chem. Soc.*, **59**, 276 (1937); *cf*. Conn, Kistiakowsky and E. A. Smith, *ibid.*, **61**, 1868 (1939).

[6] Aston, Schumann, Fink and Doty, *J. Am. Chem. Soc.*, **63**, 2029 (1941).

[7] Barton, *J. Chem. Soc.*, 340 (1948).

[8] Hückel and co-workers, *Ann.*, **451**, 109 (1926).

[9] Bastiansen and Hassel, *Nature*, **157**, 765 (1946).

of the coprostane series, however, would result in L-shaped molecules,[1] rather than the flat structures demanded by X-ray crystallographic data.

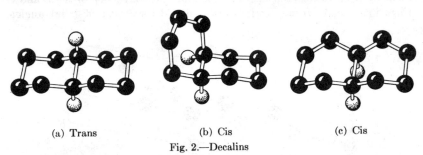

(a) Trans   (b) Cis   (c) Cis

Fig. 2.—Decalins

It is possible that form (b) is more stable in solution, and that the operation of intermolecular forces favors flat molecules (c) in the crystal. In this connection X-ray examination of Kendall's 3,9-epoxy derivatives (Figure 3), which can be regarded as modified Bastiansen-Hassel forms (ring A, "bed"; ring B, "chair"), would be of interest.

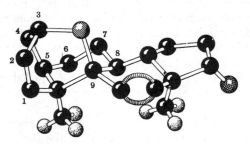

Fig. 3.—Δ^{11}-3,9-Epoxide

The energy barrier encountered in the "chair-bed-chair" conversion in cyclohexane does not greatly exceed 10 Kg. cal.[1] Since this value is small compared with activation energies of most chemical reactions and with energies that can be derived by thermal bombardment, independent existence of the forms discussed above is a remote possibility.[11]

Effects produced on molecular geometry can, however, be detected by dipole moment measurements. For example, the calculated moments for the "chair" and "bed" forms of cyclohexanedione-1,4 are, respectively, zero and 4.1 D. The value determined experimentally in benzene solu-

[10] cf. Ruzicka, Furter and M. W. Goldberg, Helv. Chim. Acta, 21, 498, plate II (1938).

[11] cf. Wightman, J. Chem. Soc., 1421 (1925); ibid., 2541 (1926).

tion, after correction for atomic polarization, is 1.2 D.[12] Simple calculations employing the squares of the dipole moments indicate that cyclohexanedione in benzene is an equilibrium mixture in which the "chair" form (carbonyl groups parallel and opposed) predominates to the extent of about ninety percent. Dipole moments of a large number of steroids have been measured by Kumler and co-workers,[3, 13] but quantitative interpretation of the results is unfortunately not possible at this time.

ORIENTATIONS OF SUBSTITUENT GROUPS

Position 3. Catalytic hydrogenation of cholestanone and of coprostanone in neutral solvents yields cholestanol (Ia) and epicoprostanol (IVa), respectively (p. 636). In acidic solution, epicholestanol (IIIa) and coprostanol (IIa) are obtained (Chapter III).

The four reduction products represent all possible modifications of the asymmetric centers at C_3 and C_5, and, on oxidative elimination of the side chain, furnish the corresponding 17-keto derivatives, epiandrosterone (Ib), 5-isoepiandrosterone (IIb), androsterone (IIIb), and 5-isoandrosterone (IVb).[1] Reichstein and Lardon[2] have further demonstrated that saturation of the ethylenic bond in dehydroepiandrosterone acetate (V) affords, in addition to epiandrosterone acetate, small amounts of 5-isoepiandrosterone acetate. The latter product is the first clear example of an A/B-cis derivative formed by hydrogenation of a Δ^5-compound. Identity of the orientations of the 3-hydroxyl groups in Ib and IIb, and thus in cholestanol, cholesterol and coprostanol, is hence established. Androsterone (IIIb) and 5-isoandrosterone (IVb) are related in a similar way, but belong to the opposite stereochemical series. The configurational correspondence of the bile acids and epicoprostanol (IVa) is indicated by the oxidation of lithocholic acid (VI) (as the acetate) to 5-isoandrosterone (IVb).[3]

Structures now accepted for these and related products were originally proposed by Ruzicka[1] on the basis of the von Auwers-Skita rule.[4] Ruzicka's inferences are supported by the discovery[5] that hydrolysis of the acetates of cholestanol (Ia) and of epicoprostanol (IVa) is more rapid than hydrolysis of the corresponding esters of coprostanol (IIa) and epi-

[12] C. G. Le Fèvre and R. J. W. Le Fèvre, *J. Chem. Soc.*, 1696 (1935).

[13] Kumler and Halverstadt, *J. Am. Chem. Soc.*, **64**, 1941 (1942); Kumler and Fohlen, *ibid.*, **67**, 437 (1945).

[1] Ruzicka and co-workers, *Helv. Chim. Acta*, **17**, 1395, 1407 (1934).

[2] Reichstein and Lardon, *Helv. Chim. Acta*, **24**, 955 (1941).

[3] Ruzicka and M. W. Goldberg, *Helv. Chim. Acta*, **18**, 668 (1935).

[4] von Auwers, *Ann.*, **420**, 91 (1920); Skita, *Ber.*, **53**, 1792 (1920).

[5] Ruzicka, Furter and M. W. Goldberg, *Helv. Chim. Acta*, **21**, 498 (1938); *cf.* Vavon and Jakubowicz, *Bull. soc. chim.* **53**, 581 (1933).

cholestanol (IIIa).   Inspection of models shows that the acetoxyl group
is less hindered in the two products in which this group is trans to the 5-
hydrogen (cholestanol and epicoprostanol) than in the two cis isomers

Chart 1.   CONFIGURATIONS AT C_3 AND C_5

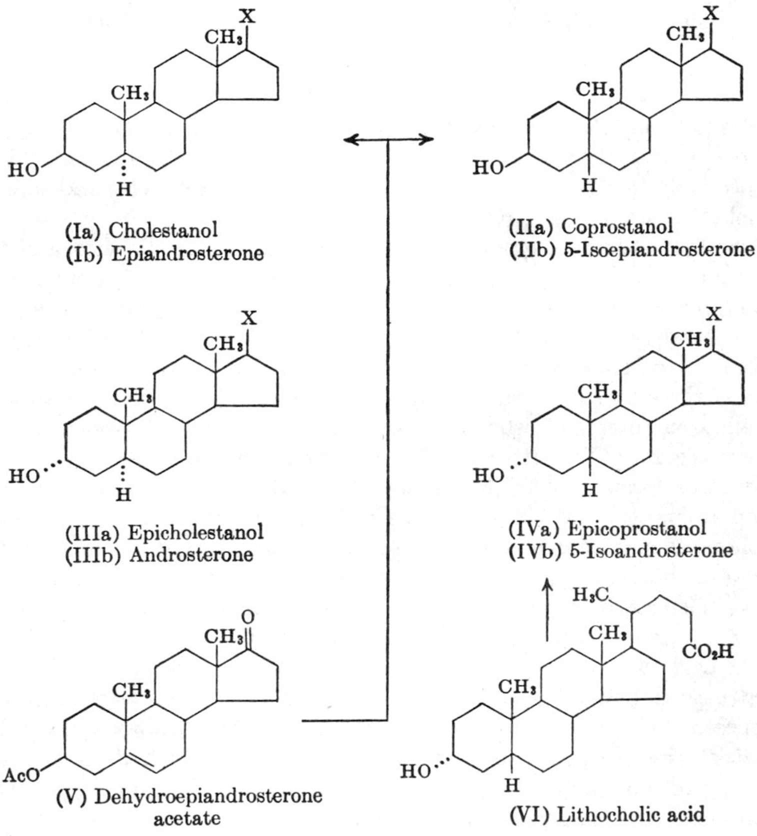

(Ia) Cholestanol
(Ib) Epiandrosterone

(IIa) Coprostanol
(IIb) 5-Isoepiandrosterone

(IIIa) Epicholestanol
(IIIb) Androsterone

(IVa) Epicoprostanol
(IVb) 5-Isoandrosterone

(V) Dehydroepiandrosterone
acetate

(VI) Lithocholic acid

(a) X, $-CHCH_2CH_2CH_2CH\diagdown\genfrac{}{}{0pt}{}{CH_3}{CH_3}$ with CH_3 above
(b) X, O =

(coprostanol and epicholestanol).   This observation also accounts for the
preponderance of the trans alcohols, cholestanol and epicoprostanol, in
equilibrium mixtures obtained by sodium alkoxide epimerization of epicholestanol and of coprostanol, respectively (Chapter III).   In each case
formation of the less hindered isomer is favored.

The first decisive evidence relating the 3-hydroxyl and 10-methyl groups was supplied by Kendall,[6] who demonstrated the reversible conversion of methyl 3α-hydroxy-12α-chloro-$Δ^{9(11)}$-cholenate, obtained from desoxycholic acid by reactions that do not involve the asymmetric center at C_3, into methyl 3,9-epoxy-$Δ^{11}$-cholenate (see above). The accepted mechanism of ether formation[7] excludes the possibility of inversion at C_3 during this transformation and since construction of a Stuart model is possible only when the oxide bridge is trans to the angular methyl group at C_{10}, the 3-hydroxyl group in desoxycholic acid must be α-oriented. Cholesterol and derived substances are therefore 3β-hydroxy compounds.

Other evidence for this point has recently been presented by the English chemist Shoppee.[8] Both 6- and 7-ketocholestanyl acetate (VII and IX), on bromination and subsequent oxidative hydrolysis (silver nitrate in pyridine) yield the α-diketone VIII. Mild saponification of VIII followed

Chart 2. CONFIGURATION AT C_3 IN CHOLESTEROL

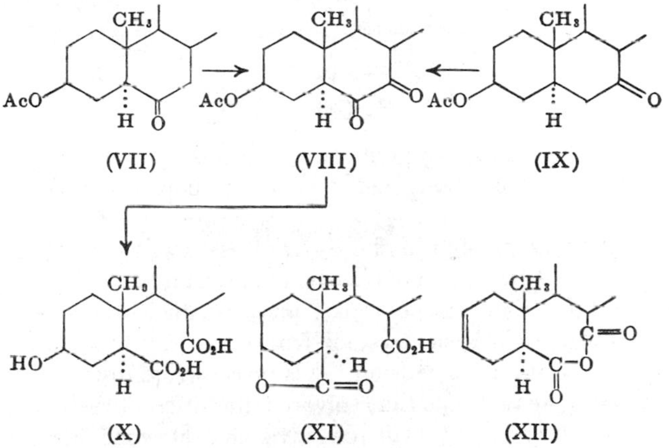

(VII)   (VIII)   (IX)

(X)   (XI)   (XII)

by oxidation with hydrogen peroxide furnishes the hydroxydicarboxylic acid X, first prepared by Windaus and Stein[9] in 1904, but by methods that obscured configurational relationships at C_3 (see below). When gently warmed with acetic anhydride, X affords a lactonic acid (XI),[8, 10] and,

[6] Mattox, R. B. Turner, L. L. Engel, B. McKenzie, McGuckin and Kendall, *J. Biol. Chem.*, **164**, 569 (1946).

[7] Kenyon and McNicol, *J. Chem. Soc.*, **123**, 14 (1923); Hughes, Ingold and Masterman, *ibid.*, 1197 (1937).

[8] Shoppee, *J. Chem. Soc.*, 1032 (1948).

[9] Windaus and G. Stein, *Ber.*, **37**, 3699 (1904).

[10] Lettré, *Ber.*, **68**, 766 (1935).

since the carboxyl group involved in lactone formation is β-oriented, the β-orientation of the 3-hydroxyl group is established.[11]   The C_3-epimer of X does not form a lactone, but yields instead an unsaturated anhydride (XII).[8]

Displacements at C_3.   An important group of steroid reactions includes displacements of hydroxyl and halogen substituents at C_3.   The stereochemical course of substitution is intimately associated with the reaction mechanism and has been studied extensively in simpler cases by Hughes, Ingold, and their collaborators in England.   Qualitative rules developed by these investigators[1] form the basis of the following discussion.

The normal steric outcome of nucleophilic bimolecular substitutions (S_N2) is inversion of configuration, because, owing to greater repulsive forces and higher electron density, the pyrimidal transition state I (retention of configuration) has higher energy than the linear transition state II (inversion), in which these effects are minimized.   Unimolecular substitutions

$$
\begin{array}{ccc}
R_1 \diagdown \;\; \diagup X & R_1 \;\; R_2 & R_1 \;\; R_2 \\
R_2 = C & X\text{----}C\text{----}Y & C^+ \quad Y^- \\
R_3 \diagup \;\; \diagdown Y & R_3 & R_3 \\
\text{(I)} & \text{(II)} & \text{(III)}
\end{array}
$$

(S_N1), on the other hand, can give rise to racemization, inversion, elimination, or retention of configuration depending upon a variety of circumstances.

The rate-determining step in the S_N1 process involves ionization of the $C-Y$ bond with the formation of a carbonium ion and an anionic fragment, Y^- (III).[2]   The carbon cation is flat and, if sufficiently long-lived, will yield a racemized product, since attack from either side is equally probable. In the event that attack on carbon takes place before dissociation is complete or involves the molecule that solvates the cation of the ion pair intermediate,[2] the steric result will be inversion of configuration.   Since stabilization of the carbonium ion can also be effected by ejection of a proton, elimination (E 1) often competes with the substitution reaction.

Displacements at centers adjacent to groups that can participate in the formation of cyclic intermediates (carboxylate ion, acetoxyl, halogen, etc.)

---

[11] *cf.* Alder and G. Stein, *Ann.*, **504, 229** (1933).

[1] Cowdrey, Hughes, Ingold, Masterman and A. D. Scott, *J. Chem. Soc.*, 1252 (1937); Dostrovsky, Hughes and Ingold, *ibid.*, 173 (1946); *cf.* Bateman, Church, Hughes, Ingold and Taher, *ibid.*, 1010 (1940).

[2] A somewhat more detailed formulation of the S_N1 reaction in terms of termolecular kinetics including the solvent has recently been proposed by Swain, *J. Am. Chem. Soc.*, **70,** 1119 (1948).

in general proceed without inversion. Solvolysis of the α-bromopropionate ion (IV)[3] and the conversion of trans 2-acetoxycyclohexyl-*p*-toluenesulfonate (VI) into trans 1,2-cyclohexanediol diacetate (VII) by

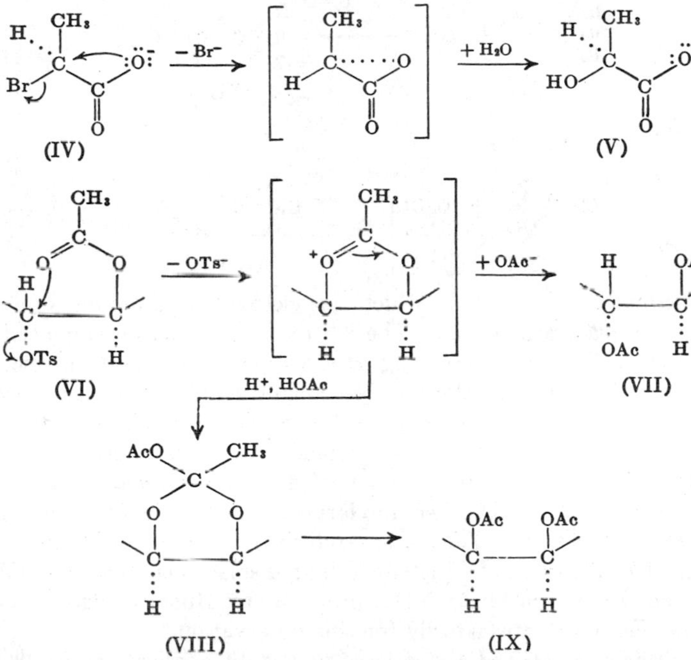

(IV) (V)

(VI) (VII)

(VIII) (IX)

acetate ion[4] are classic examples of this phenomenon, which has been examined in detail by Winstein and his associates.[5] The role of acetoxyl in the neighboring group effect is complicated by the fact that under certain conditions inverted products can also be obtained. Thus, in acidic solution in the absence of excess acetate ion, VI affords cis cyclohexanediol diacetate (IX), presumably by way of the orthodiacetate (VIII).[4, 6]

The S_N1 and S_N2 reactions can, of course, proceed simultaneously, and the results of substitution are not always clean-cut. In the absence of special structural features inversion predominates in both processes, the S_N1 reaction being variously accompanied by racemization and elimination.

[3] Cowdrey, Hughes and Ingold, *J. Chem. Soc.*, 1208 (1937).

[4] Winstein, Hess and Buckles, *J. Am. Chem. Soc.*, **64**, 2796 (1942).

[5] Winstein and Grunwald, *J. Am. Chem. Soc.*, **70**, 828 (1948); Grunwald and Winstein, *ibid.*, **70**, 841 (1948); see also other papers of this series.

[6] Winstein, Hanson and Grunwald, *J. Am. Chem. Soc.*, **70**, 812 (1948).

Substitution of halogen for hydroxyl is usually accomplished with the halides of phosphorus or sulfur. These reagents furnish ester halide intermediates (*cf.* X), which can rearrange intramolecularly (S_Ni) with retention

$$
\begin{array}{ccc}
\underset{R_3}{\overset{R_1}{\underset{\big|}{R_2}}}\!\!-\!C\!\!\overset{O}{\underset{Cl}{\diagdown}}\!\!S\!\rightarrow\!O & \xrightarrow{\ S_Ni\ } & \underset{R_3}{\overset{R_1}{\underset{\big|}{R_2}}}\!\!-\!C\!-\!Cl\ +\ SO_2 \\[2mm]
(X) & & (XI)
\end{array}
$$

$$+\ Cl^- \Big\downarrow S_N2$$

$$
\begin{array}{cc}
Cl\!-\!C\!\!\overset{R_1}{\underset{R_3}{\diagdown}}\!\!R_2\ +\ OSOCl^- & \quad \overset{H}{\underset{H_6C_5}{\diagup}}\!C\!\!-\!C\!\!\overset{O}{\underset{Br}{\diagdown}}\!\!H \\[2mm]
(XII) & (XIII)
\end{array}
$$

of configuration (X → XI) or which can yield inverted products (*cf.* XII) by direct displacement (S_N2). The S_Ni reaction is most pronounced with thionyl chloride, which, according to the capacity for electron release of R_1, R_2, and R_3, leads to retention of configuration.[7] Inversion, however, occurs with this reagent in polar solvents, for example, pyridine. An exception to the rule that inversion attends the use of phosphorus halides and the halogen acids is the reaction of hydrogen bromide with methylphenylcarbinol and with other alkylarylcarbinols at low temperature in the absence of solvent. The steric result in this case is predominantly retention of configuration.[8] Intramolecular displacement (S_Ni) in the hydrogen-bonded intermediate XIII, proposed by Hughes, Ingold, and coworkers,[1] accounts satisfactorily for this observation.

The principles outlined above have important applications to displacement reactions in the steroid series. When cholesterol (XIV) is treated with cold fuming nitric acid, a 6-nitro derivative (XV) is obtained that furnishes 6-ketocholestanol (XVI) on reduction with zinc and acetic acid.[9] Reaction of this product with phosphorus pentachloride affords the chloroketone XIX.[10] If, however, the order of reactions is reversed and cholesterol (XIV) is first converted into cholesteryl chloride (XVII), an epimeric chloro ketone (XVIII) is obtained. Both chloro ketones (XVIII and XIX) are susceptible to oxidative cleavage of ring B, and the resulting chlorodicarboxylic acids (XX and XXIII) yield hydroxy acids XXI and XXII, respectively, on alkaline hydrolysis.[10, 11] The hydroxy derivatives are

[7] *cf.* Shoppee, *J. Chem. Soc.*, 1138 (1946).

[8] P. A. Levene and Rothen, *J. Biol. Chem.*, **127**, 237 (1939).

[9] Mauthner and Suida, *Monatsh.*, **24**, 648 (1903); Windaus, "Über Cholesterin," *Habilitationsschrift*, Freiburg (1903).

[10] Windaus and G. Stein, *Ber.*, **37**, 3699 (1904).

[11] Windaus and von Staden, *Ber.*, **54**, 1059 (1921).

epimeric at C_3, for both are oxidized by chromic acid to the same 3-ketone; XXII is identical with compound X of Chart 2 and therefore has the same configuration (β) at C_3 as cholesterol. The interpretations of Hughes and

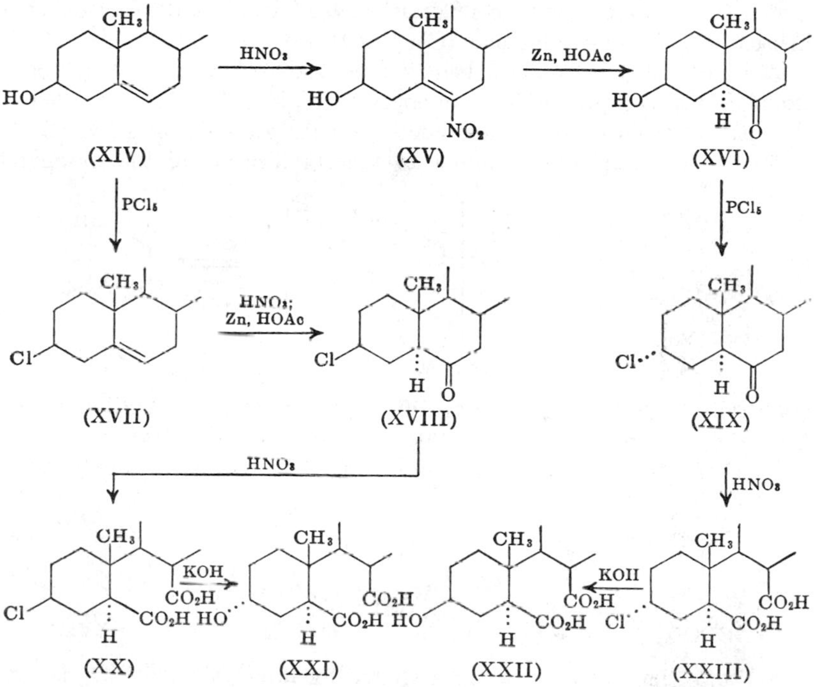

(XIV)   (XV)   (XVI)

(XVII)   (XVIII)   (XIX)

(XX)   (XXI)   (XXII)   (XXIII)

Ingold require Walden inversions in the reaction of XVI with phosphorus pentachloride and in the hydrolysis of XXIII, the net result being retention of configuration, as observed experimentally. The formation of a 3α-hydroxy compound (XXI) from cholesterol by the alternate route must involve only one inversion, which unquestionably occurs during hydrolysis of XX. The transformation of cholesterol (XIV) into cholesteryl chloride (XVII) is thus accomplished without inversion at C_3. Dodson and Riegel[12] have recently pointed out that the conversion of i-cholesteryl methyl ether into cholesteryl acetate[13] (acetic acid and sulfuric acid) on the one hand and into cholesteryl chloride (acetic acid and hydrogen chloride) on the other by strictly analogous procedures confirms the validity of this conclusion. The absence of inversion in the reaction of cholesterol with phosphorus

[12] Dodson and Riegel, *J. Org. Chem.*, **13,** 424 (1948).
[13] *cf.* McKennis, *J. Biol. Chem.*, **172,** 313 (1948).

pentachloride has further been noted in reactions of this substance with thionyl chloride[14] and with thionyl chloride in pyridine[15] and is paralleled by the similar behavior of stigmasterol, sitosterol, and dehydroepiandrosterone.[16, 17, 18] Retention of configuration also prevails in displacements of halogen in 3-halo-Δ⁵-compounds (Chapter III).

The apparently anomalous behavior of Δ⁵-derivatives is satisfactorily explained by the proposals of Shoppee[19] and of Winstein and Adams[20] that participation of the double bond through formation of a hybrid ion intermediate (XXIV), contributes to the stabilization of the pyrimidal

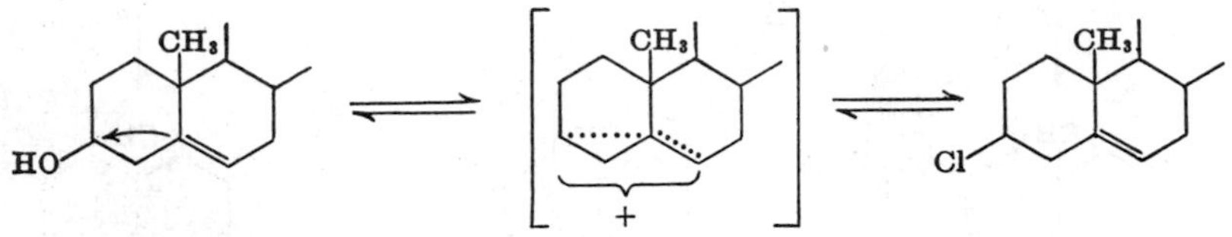

(XIV) (XXIV) (XVII)

transition state (neighboring group effect), which leads to retention of configuration. Of special interest in this connection is Marker's discovery that 7-ketocholesteryl chloride (XXV), in which polarization of the double bond

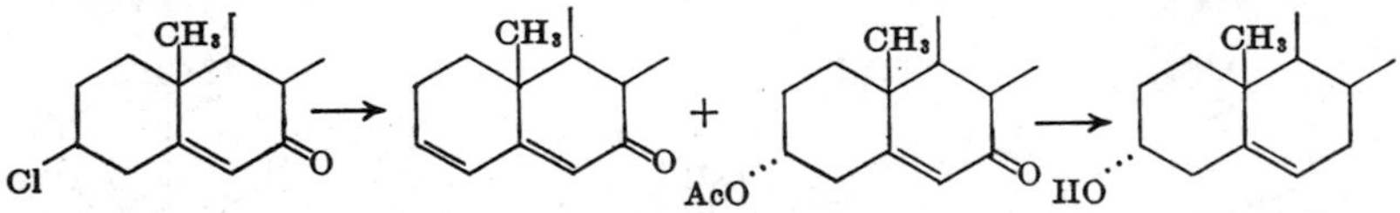

(XXV) (XXVI) (XXVII) (XXVIII)

is in a direction opposite to that required for interaction with C₃, is converted by acetate ion into 7-ketocholesterylene (XXVI) and an acetate (XXVII) that furnishes epicholesterol (XXVIII) on Wolff-Kishner reduction.[21]

The course of substitution reactions involving steroid *p*-toluenesulfonates is consistent with the observation of Kenyon and Phillips[22] that displace-

[14] Diels and Abderhalden, *Ber.*, **37**, 3092 (1904); Diels and Blumberg, *ibid.*, **44**, 2847 (1911).

[15] Daughenbaugh and Allison, *J. Am. Chem. Soc.*, **51**, 3665 (1929).

[16] Marker and Lawson, *J. Am. Chem. Soc.*, **59**, 2711 (1937).

[17] Wallis and Fernholz, *J. Am. Chem. Soc.*, **59**, 764 (1937).

[18] Butenandt, Dannenbaum, Hanisch and Kudszus, *Z. physiol. Chem.*, **237**, 57 (1935).

[19] Shoppee, *J. Chem. Soc.*, 1147 (1946).

[20] Winstein and Rowland Adams, *J. Am. Chem. Soc.*, **70**, 838 (1948).

[21] Marker, Kamm, Fleming, Popkin and Wittle, *J. Am. Chem. Soc.*, **59**, 619 (1937).

[22] Kenyon, Phillips and co-workers, *J. Chem. Soc.*, **123**, 44 (1923); **127**, 399, 2552 (1925); 1676 (1930); 1072, 1663 (1935).

ment of the p-toluenesulfonoxy group is accompanied by Walden inversion. Thus methyl 3β-p-toluenesulfonoxyetioallocholanate on treatment with sodium acetate in acetic acid affords, besides methyl Δ^3-etioallocholenate, about fifty percent of methyl 3α-acetoxyetioallocholanate.[23] Owing to participation of the double bond, cholesteryl p-toluenesulfonate under similar conditions yields cholesteryl acetate;[24] with aqueous acetone cholesterol is obtained.[25]

In contrast with the behavior of p-toluenesulfonates, sulfuric acid esters of steroid alcohols are cleaved without inversion. Sodium cholestanyl sulfate and sodium epicholestanyl sulfate on acid hydrolysis yield, respectively, cholestanol and epicholestanol; with silver acetate in acetic acid the corresponding acetates are formed.[26] Retention of configuration in these reactions indicates that attack is on sulfur rather than on oxygen, the carbon–oxygen bond in every case remaining intact.

Correlation of Configuration at C$_3$. Preparation by unambiguous methods of the bile acid derivatives listed in Table I (p. 644) provides a series of known reference compounds, which, in conjunction with the androstanolones (Chart 1) have been of great value in the determination of configurations in other steroids[1–11]. Both stigmastanyl acetate and ergostanyl acetate, for example, yield 3β-hydroxynorallocholanic acid (No. 12) on oxidation and hydrolysis and hence are 3β-hydroxy compounds. The degradations of lithocholic acid (No. 1) and of 3β-hydroxyallocholanic acid (No. 11) to 3α-hydroxypregnanone-20 and to 3β-hydroxyallopregnanone-20,[12] respectively, establish the structures of the latter products and make possible differentiation of the 3β-5-normal and 3α-5-iso ketones.[13]

[23] Plattner and Fürst, *Helv. Chim. Acta*, **26**, 2266 (1943).

[24] Beynon, Heilbron and Spring, *J. Chem. Soc.*, 907 (1936).

[25] W. Stoll, *Z. physiol. Chem.*, **207**, 147 (1932).

[26] Lieberman, Hariton and Fukushima, *J. Am. Chem. Soc.*, **70**, 1427 (1948).

[1] Reindel and Niederländer, *Ber.*, **68**, 1969 (1935).

[2] Sawlewicz and Reichstein, *Helv. Chim. Acta*, **20**, 949 (1937).

[3] Reindel and Niederländer, *Ber.*, **68**, 1243 (1935); Yamasaki and Kyogoku, *Z. physiol. Chem.*, **235**, 43 (1935).

[4] Reichstein and H. G. Fuchs, *Helv. Chim. Acta*, **23**, 658 (1940).

[5] Windaus and Hossfeld, *Z. physiol. Chem.*, **145**, 177 (1925).

[6] Wieland, Dane and Martius, *Z. physiol. Chem.*, **215**, 15 (1933).

[7] Dalmer, v. Werder, Honigmann and Heyns, *Ber.*, **68**, 1814 (1935).

[8] Fernholz and P. N. Chakravorty, *Ber.*, **67**, 2021 (1934).

[9] Dirscherl, *Z. physiol. Chem.*, **237**, 268 (1935).

[10] Fernholz, *Ann.*, **507**, 128 (1933).

[11] Steiger and Reichstein, *Helv. Chim. Acta*, **20**, 1040 (1937).

[12] Meystre and Miescher, *Helv. Chim. Acta*, **29**, 33 (1946).

[13] Marker, Kamm and Wittle, *J. Am. Chem. Soc.*, **59**, 1841 (1937); Butenandt and Mamoli, *Ber.*, **68**, 1847 (1935).

TABLE I

NO.	COMPOUND	M.p.	$[\alpha]_D$
1	3 α-Hydroxycholanic acid (lithocholic acid)	184–186°	+32° Al
2	3 α-Hydroxynorcholanic acid[1,2]	172–174°, 186–187°	—
3	3 α-Hydroxybisnorcholanic acid[1,2]	210–212°	—
4	3 α-Hydroxyetiocholanic acid[2]	273–275°	+50° Di
5	3 β-Hydroxycholanic acid[3]	176–177°	+25.9° Al
6	3 β-Hydroxyetiocholanic acid[4]	220–225°	—
7	3 α-Hydroxyallocholanic acid[5,6,7]	208°	+25.4° Al
8	3 α-Hydroxynorallocholanic acid[7]	205–207°	+21° Al
9	3 α-Hydroxybisnorallocholanic acid[7]	220°	+17° Al
10	3 α-Hydroxyetioallocholanic acid (acetate methyl ester)[7]	201–202°	+56° Chf
11	3 β-Hydroxyallocholanic acid[6,8]	218°	—
12	3 β-Hydroxynorallocholanic acid[8,9]	226°	+32° An
13	3 β-Hydroxybisnorallocholanic acid[10]	270°	—
14	3 β-Hydroxyetioallocholanic acid[11]	256–258°	—

Conclusive evidence for configurations of 3-hydroxyl groups in various cardiac aglycones is provided by the following conversions:[14] digitoxigenin into 3β-hydroxyetiocholanic acid,[15] digoxigenin into 3α,12β-dihydroxyetiocholanic (12-epietiodesoxycholic) acid,[16] sarmentogenin into methyl 3β,11α-dihydroxyetiocholanate,[17] gitoxigenin into methyl 3β-acetoxy-Δ[16]-etiocholenate,[18] scillaren A into 3β-hydroxyallocholanic acid,[19] periplogenin into methyl 3β-acetoxyetioallocholanate.[20] Recent work of Reichstein[21] suggests that the genin of thevetin is identical with digitoxigenin. The β-orientation of the 3-hydroxyl group in uzarigenin is established by correlations shown in Chart 10 of Chapter VII. Uzarigenin is the only aglycone recognized that possesses an A/B ring fusion of the trans decalin type. Conclusive evidence for this arrangement is furnished by degradation of anhydrouzarigenin to etioallocholanic acid.[22, 23]

[14] cf. R. B. Turner, Chem. Revs., 43, 1 (1948).

[15] Hunziker and Reichstein, Helv. Chim. Acta, 28, 1472 (1945).

[16] Steiger and Reichstein, Helv. Chim. Acta, 21, 828 (1938); Mason and Hoehn, J. Am. Chem. Soc., 60, 2824 (1938); ibid., 61, 1614 (1939).

[17] A. Katz, Helv. Chim. Acta, 31, 993 (1948).

[18] Kuno Meyer, Helv. Chim. Acta, 29, 1580 (1946).

[19] A. Stoll and Renz, Helv. Chim. Acta, 24, 1380 (1941).

[20] Speiser and Reichstein, Helv. Chim. Acta, 30, 2143 (1947).

[21] Helfenberger and Reichstein, Helv. Chim. Acta, 31, 1470, 2097 (1948).

[22] Tschesche, Angew. Chem., 47, 729 (1934); Z. physiol. Chem., 229, 219 (1934); Ber., 68, 7 (1935).

[23] The formation of allo derivatives from scillaren A and from periplogenin cannot

Assignment of the β-orientation to the 3-hydroxyl group of strophanthidin is based on the following observations. Strophanthidin (I) on treatment with alcoholic hydrogen chloride yields an anhydro derivative that

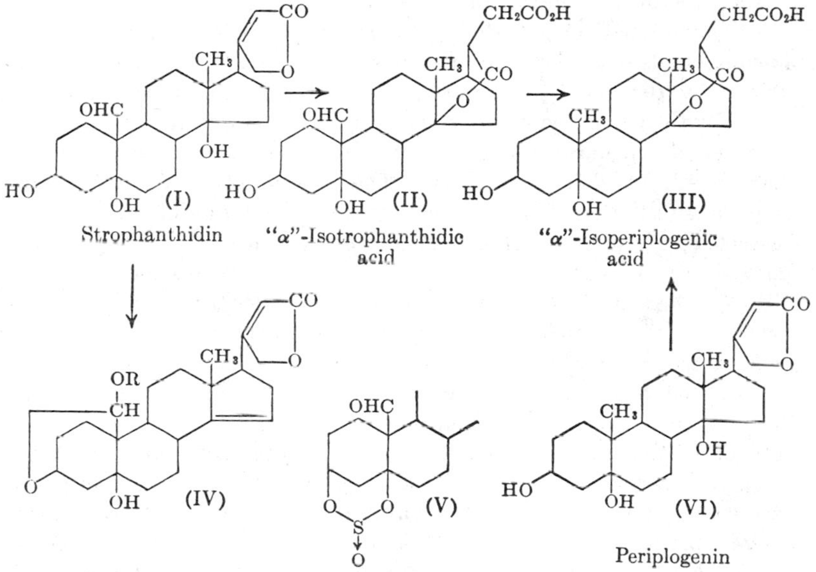

CO / CH₃ / OHC / OH / HO / OH (I)
Strophanthidin

→

CH₂CO₂H / CH₃ CO / O / OHC / HO / OH (II)
"α"-Isotrophanthidic acid

→

CH₂CO₂H / CH₃ CO / O / CH₃ / HO / OH (III)
"α"-Isoperiplogenic acid

↓

CO / CH₃ O / OR / CH / O / OH (IV)

OHC / O S O / O (V)

↑

CO / CH₃ O / CH₃ / OH / HO / OH (VI)
Periplogenin

contains an alkoxyl group but no longer possesses the aldehydic or secondary hydroxylic functions of the unaltered genin.[24] The cyclic lactol structure (IV) proposed for this product requires a cis relation between the 3-hydroxyl group and the angular aldehyde group at C_{10}. Correlation of configurations at C_3 and C_5 has been achieved by conversions of strophanthidin (I)[25] and of "α"-isostrophanthidic acid (II)[26] into cyclic sulfites of structure (V)[27] in the presence of thionyl chloride. The β-orientation of the 5-hydroxyl group is well established (see below) and, although the reversibility of these reactions has not been demonstrated, a β-orientation for the hydroxyl at C_3 is probable. Additional evidence is the transformation of

be construed as evidence for A/B trans junctions in these substances, since both contain a hydroxyl group at C_5 that is eliminated during degradation. Similar restrictions apply also to inferences regarding the C/D ring fusion in these and other aglycones.

[24] Jacobs and Collins, *J. Biol. Chem.*, **59**, 713 (1924).

[25] Plattner, Segre and O. Ernst, *Helv. Chim. Acta*, **30**, 1432 (1947); W. Lang, *Dissert.*, Zurich (1946).

[26] Jacobs, Elderfield, Grave and Wignall, *J. Biol. Chem.*, **91**, 617 (1931).

[27] A neutral carbonate of analogous structure has been obtained from a derivative of periplogenin by the action of phosgene and pyridine (reference 20).

strophanthidin (I) into "α"-isoperiplogenic acid (III) by Wolff-Kishner reduction of "α"-isostrophanthidic acid (II).[26] "α"-Isoperip genic acid is derived from periplogenin (VI),[28] the conversion of which into methyl 3β-acetoxyetioallocholanate has already been noted.

All the adrenal cortical steroids possessing a hydroxyl group at C_3 are 3β-compounds with the exception of substance C.[29] This fact is demonstrated by the conversion of substance A into 3β,17β-diacetoxyandrostane,[30] by the partial synthesis of substance K and other related compounds from dehydroepiandrosterone,[31] and by extensive correlations in this series that are discussed in Chapter V. The α-orientation of the 3-hydroxyl group in substance C is established by the degradation of this product to 3α-acetoxy-17α-hydroxy-11-ketoetioallocholanic acid.[32] All the saturated cortical principles thus far isolated are A/B trans derivatives.

A second group of 3β-hydroxy derivatives includes the steroid sapogenins, of which various representative members have been related to products of known structure. Sarsasapogenin, for example, has been converted by way of pseudosarsasapogenin[33] into 3β-hydroxy-Δ[16]-pregnenone-20 and 3β-hydroxypregnanone-20.[34] Direct oxidation of sarsasapogenin affords a 3-keto derivative, sarsasapogenone, which on hydrogenation (Pt, alcohol) yields episarsasapogenin,[35, 36] prepared also by treatment of sarsasapogenin with sodium amylate.[36] By transformations analogous to those described above, episarsasapogenin yields 3α-hydroxypregnanone-20 and pregnanediol-3α,20a, identical with the pregnanediol of urine.[37] Similar conversions have been effected with tigogenin[38] and with epitigogenin,[39] which yield, respectively, 3β- and 3α-hydroxyallopregnanone-20. Diosgenin under these conditions furnishes 3β-hydroxy-Δ[5]-pregnenone-20,[40] an important intermediate for the synthesis of progesterone.

The steroid alkaloid solanidine contains one hydroxyl group and one

[28] Jacobs and A. Hoffman, J. Biol. Chem., **79,** 519 (1928); cf. Jacobs and Elderfield, ibid., **91,** 625 (1931).

[29] von Euw and Reichstein, Helv. Chim. Acta, **30,** 205 (1947).

[30] Shoppee, Helv. Chim. Acta, **23,** 740 (1940).

[31] Serini, W. Logemann and W. Hildebrand, Ber., **72,** 391 (1939).

[32] von Euw and Reichstein, Helv. Chim. Acta, **25,** 988 (1942).

[33] Marker and Rohrmann, J. Am. Chem. Soc., **62,** 518 (1940).

[34] Marker and Rohrmann, J. Am. Chem. Soc., **62,** 521 (1940); Marker, Crooks and R. B. Wagner, ibid., **64,** 210 (1942).

[35] Askew, Farmer and Kon, J. Chem. Soc., 1399 (1936).

[36] Marker and Rohrmann, J. Am. Chem. Soc., **61,** 943 (1939).

[37] Marker, J. Am. Chem. Soc., **62,** 3350 (1940).

[38] Marker and Rohrmann, J. Am. Chem. Soc., **62,** 898 (1940).

[39] Marker, J. Am. Chem. Soc., **62,** 2621 (1940).

[40] Marker, Tsukamoto and D. L. Turner, J. Am. Chem. Soc., **62,** 2525 (1940); Marker and Krueger, ibid., **62,** 3349 (1940).

double bond, the disposition of which is assuredly that of cholesterol.[41] Solanidine (VII) on catalytic hydrogenation yields a saturated product, solanidanol (VIII), which is converted by treatment with chromic acid into a 3-keto derivative, solanidanone (IX). Hydrogenation of this substance

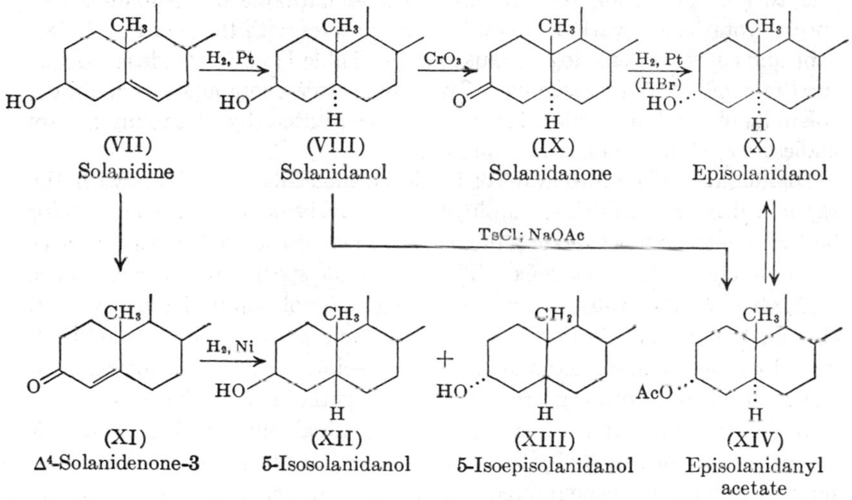

in the presence of mineral acid yields a 3α-hydroxy compound, episolanidanol (X), also obtained by treatment of solanidanyl p-toluenesulfonate with sodium acetate followed by saponification. The acetyl derivative (XIV) is identical with that obtained by acetylation of episolanidanol (X).

TABLE II[42]

SOLANIDINE SERIES	$[\alpha]_D$	CHOLESTEROL SERIES	$[\alpha]_D$
Solanidine (VII)	−27° ±4°	Cholesterol	−37°
Solanidine acetate	−32.5° ±2°	Cholesteryl acetate	−42.5°
Solanidanol (VIII)	+28.2° ±4°	Cholestanol	+28.4°
Solanidanyl acetate	+16.5° ±2°	Cholestanyl acetate	+17.7°
Solanidanone (IX)	+45.8° ±2°	Cholestanone	+40°
Episolanidanol (X)	+31.9° ±4°	Epicholestanol	+32.2°
Episolanidanyl acetate	+21.9° ±3°	Epicholestanyl acetate	—
Δ4-Solanidenone-3 (XI)	+89° ±1°	Δ4-Cholestenone-3	+88.6°
5-Isosolanidanol (XII)	+27.9° ±2°	Coprostanol	+28°
5-Isosolanidanyl acetate	+31.4° ±3°	Coprostanyl acetate	—
5-Isoepisolanidanol (XIII)	+34.5° ±3°	Epicoprostanol	+31°
5-Isoepisolanidanyl acetate	+45.2° ±3°	Epicoprostanyl acetate	+44°

[41] Prelog and Szpilfogel, *Helv. Chim. Acta*, **27**, 390 (1944).
[42] Citations to the original literature will be found in reference 41.

Solanidine undergoes the Oppenauer oxidation and yields an α,β-unsaturated ketone (XI) (λ_{max} 240 mμ, log ϵ 4.2), which on hydrogenation over a platinized Raney nickel catalyst affords 5-isosolanidanol (XII) and 5-isoepisolanidanol (XIII). These products are analogous to coprostanol and to epicoprostanol, respectively. The remarkable correspondence of specific rotations of various solanidane derivatives with those of the cholestane and coprostane analogs is illustrated in Table II and provides evidence for the configurations assigned. The 3β-hydroxy compounds (solanidine, solanidanol, and 5-isosolanidanol) are precipitated by digitonin as are cholesterol, cholestanol, and coprostanol.

Digitonides. The formation of insoluble molecular complexes with the saponin digitonin has been employed extensively in the past as a test for 3β-hydroxy steroids[1, 2] and as a means for the separation of these substances from closely related materials. The test is not specific for steroids, since a number of other substances[1, 3] including butanol, amyl alcohol, phenol, thiophenol, d- and l-α-terpineol, α-naphthol, ac-tetrahydro-β-naphthol, and chlorobromofluoromethane,[4] are also precipitated. The digitonides of these substances, however, are not so stable as those of the steroids.

In practice, numerous exceptions to the general rule that insoluble digitonides are formed by 3β-hydroxy derivatives but not by 3α-hydroxy compounds have been encountered. Thus 3β-hydroxy-Δ^5-17-isopregnenone-20,[5] 3β-hydroxyetioallocholanylmethyldiphenylethylene,[6] methyl 3β,5β, 14β-trihydroxyetiocholanate and methyl 3β,5β,14β-trihydroxy-17-isoetiocholanate,[7] methyl 3β-hydroxy-11α-acetoxyetiocholanate,[8] lumisterol and dihydrolumisterol,[9] and the cardiac aglycones gitoxigenin, digitoxigenin, sarmentogenin, and strophanthidin[10] are not precipitated. The introduction of substituent groups in the neighborhood of C_3 sometimes gives rise to products with anomalous properties; examples are cholesterol dibromide[11] and cholestanetriol.[2] Investigation of several synthetic 3β,17β-dihydroxy-17-iso derivatives reveals that these substances also are abnormal, though corresponding members of the 3β,17α-dihydroxy-17-normal series behave

[1] Windaus, *Ber.*, **42**, 238 (1909).

[2] Fernholz, *Z. physiol. Chem.*, **232**, 97 (1935).

[3] Windaus and Weinhold, *Z. physiol. Chem.*, **126**, 299 (1923).

[4] Berry and Sturtevant, *J. Am. Chem. Soc.*, **64**, 1599 (1942).

[5] Butenandt and G. Fleischer, *Ber.*, **70**, 96 (1937).

[6] Fernholz, *Z. physiol. Chem.*, **230**, 185 (1934).

[7] Speiser and Reichstein, *Helv. Chim. Acta*, **31**, 622 (1948).

[8] A. Katz, *Helv. Chim. Acta*, **30**, 883 (1947).

[9] K. Dimroth, *Ber.*, **69**, 1123 (1936).

[10] Tschesche and Bohle, *Ber.*, **68**, 2252 (1935); A. Katz, *Helv. Chim. Acta*, **31**, 993 (1948).

[11] R. Schönheimer, *Z. physiol. Chem.*, **192**, 77 (1930).

characteristically.[12] The test is inconclusive in its application to steroid sapogenins.[13]

Formation of insoluble digitonides from steroids that do not contain a hydroxyl group at C_3 has, unexpectedly, been observed in several instances. Cholesterylamine,[14] allopregnanedione-3,20,[15] cholestanone,[16] cholestenone,[17] 3-keto-17-benzoxyandrostane,[16] 3β-acetoxyallopregnanone-20[15] and one of the epimeric 2-hydroxycholestanes[18] can be cited. Estradiol-17β (m.p. 178°) and the corresponding 3-monobenzoate also afford insoluble digitonides,[19] whereas estradiol-17α(m.p. 223°),[19] 17-isoallopregnanedione-3,20,[15] 3β-acetoxy-17-isoallopregnanone-20,[15] and the 4-hydroxycholestanes,[20] elicit normal negative responses.

From a study of the solubility products of various digitonides, Noller[13] concluded that concentration is an important factor and determined that under certain conditions even epicholestanol, a 3α-hydroxy derivative, can be precipitated.

Although the formation of insoluble digitonides can frequently be interpreted as evidence for a 3β-hydroxy structure, it is clear that absence of this phenomenon is of little diagnostic value. The exceptions noted above show that great caution is required in evaluation of results obtained with this method.

Positions 5 and 6. The stereochemistry of the α- and β-cholesterol oxides and of various derived substances has been discussed in another connection in Chapter III. Special attention was called to the fact that catalytic hydrogenation of the α-oxide affords cholestanediol-3β,5α,[1] whereas reduction of the β-oxide yields cholestanediol-3β,6β and products of hydrogenolysis, but not a 5β-hydroxy derivative. The preparation and configuration of 5-hydroxy steroids is of considerable interest in connection with the synthesis of cardiac genins that possess a hydroxyl group at this position.

The spatial arrangement at C_5 in strophanthidin was established in 1936 by Jacobs and Elderfield.[2] Saturation of the lactone double bond furnishes

---

[12] Reichstein and Gätzi, *Helv. Chim. Acta*, **21**, 1185 (1938).

[13] Noller, *J. Am. Chem. Soc.*, **61**, 2717 (1939).

[14] Windaus and Adamla, *Ber.*, **44**, 3055 (1911).

[15] Butenandt and Mamoli, *Ber.*, **68**, 1847 (1935).

[16] Velluz, Petit and Pesez, *Bull. soc. chim.*, 558 (1946).

[17] Haslewood, *Biochem. J.*, **41**, 639 (1947).

[18] Ruzicka, Plattner and Furrer, *Helv. Chim. Acta*, **27**, 524 (1944).

[19] Wintersteiner, *J. Am. Chem. Soc.*, **59**, 765 (1937).

[20] Tschesche and Hagedorn, *Ber.*, **68**, 2251 (1935).

[1] Excellent evidence for the structure of this compound is the conversion of the 5-monoacetate into epicholesterol by the action of p-toluenesulfonyl chloride and pyridine (Chapter III; see also Plattner, Fürst, Koller and W. Lang, *Helv. Chim. Acta*, **31**, 1455 (1948)).

[2] Jacobs and Elderfield, *J. Biol. Chem.* **113**, 625 (1936).

dihydrostrophanthidin (I), which on treatment with potassium cyanide yields a mixture of epimeric cyanohydrins (IIa and IIb). The cyanohydrin mixture was not resolved but on direct acid hydrolysis afforded two crystalline homolactones (IIIa and IIIb). These products are epimeric at C_{19}

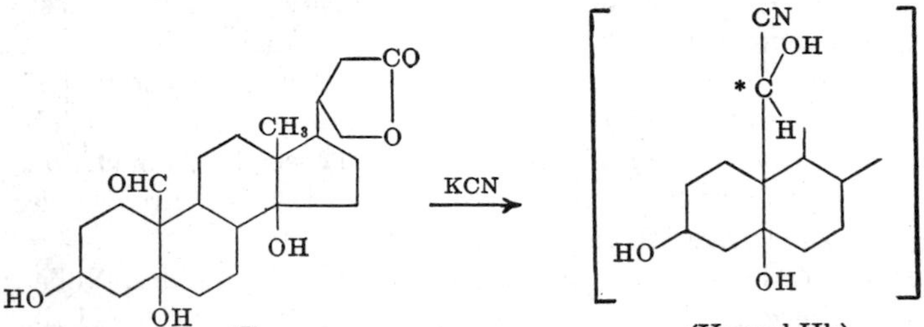

(I)
Dihydrostrophanthidin

(IIa and IIb)

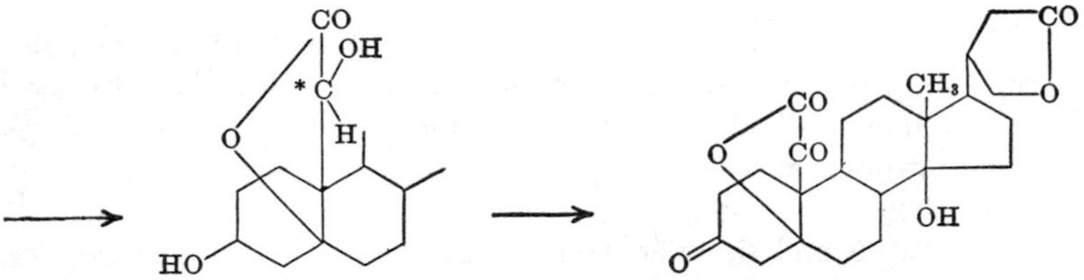

(IIIa and IIIb)

(IV)

as shown by oxidation of both substances to the same diketohomolactone (IV). The β-configuration of the angular aldehyde group is known from the conversion of strophanthidin into "α"-isoperiplogenic acid (see above), related to digitoxigenin and to the bile acids,[3] and a β-orientation is therefore assigned to the 5-hydroxyl group of this genin.

The investigations of Plattner, Segre and Ernst[4] establish a similar arrangement at C_5 in periplogenin. Elimination of the 14-hydroxyl group from dihydroperiplogenin (V), followed by saturation of the resulting double bond, furnishes a dihydroxy derivative (VI) that differs from an isomeric synthetic product (VIII) of known structure, obtained by hydrogenation of a 5,6-α-oxide.[4, 5] The difference persists in the 3-keto derivatives VII and IX, which, however, on dehydration yield the same unsaturated ketone (X). Corresponding products of the synthetic and natural series therefore differ only in configuration at C_5, which is α in the former and consequently β in the latter.

[3] Jacobs and Gustus, *J. Biol. Chem.*, **86**, 199 (1930); Jacobs and Elderfield, *ibid.*, **92**, 313 (1931); *ibid.*, **108**, 497 (1935); *cf.* Hunziker and Reichstein, *Helv. Chim. Acta*, **28**, 1472 (1945).

[4] Plattner, Segre and O. Ernst, *Helv. Chim. Acta*, **30**, 1432 (1947).

[5] Ruzicka, Plattner, Heusser and O. Ernst, *Helv. Chim. Acta*, **29**, 248 (1946).

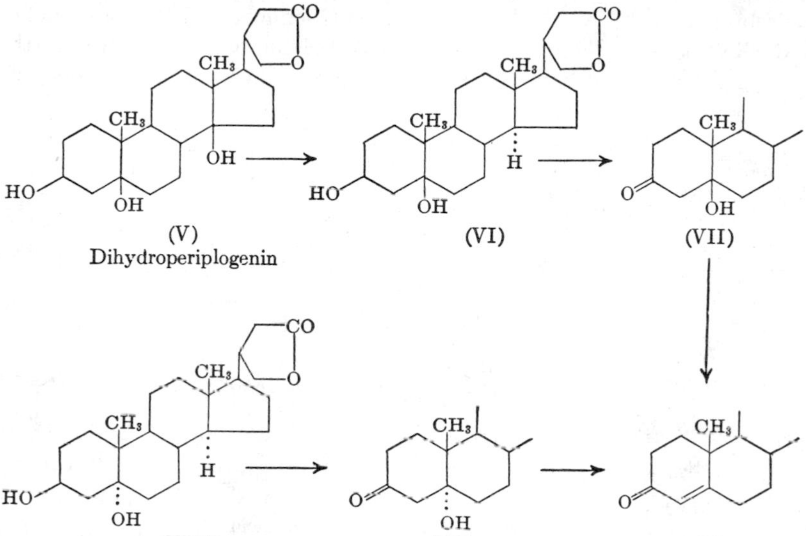

Hydrogenation of 5,6-epoxycholestane[6] and of 4,5-epoxycholestane[7] has been investigated as a route to 5β-hydroxy derivatives.[8] Both oxides yield a mixture of products, from which a 5-hydroxy compound can be isolated. The configuration of this substance, however, remains in doubt, because of uncertainties regarding the structures of the parent oxides. A recently reported preparation of coprostane-3α,5β-diol is described on page 561.

By reductions of 3α- and 3β-hydroxy-6-ketocholanic acid (XI, XIII, p. 652), Tukamoto[9] obtained the four possible 3,6-dihydroxycholanic acids (XIV, XV, XVI, and XVII), of which XV and XVI[10] have been isolated from hog bile. Oxidative degradation of 3β,6β-diacetoxycoprostane[11] affords 3β,6β-dihydroxycholanic acid (m.p. 250°),[12] which corresponds to acid XVII but not to Kimura's acid (XVI). Kimura's acid is, therefore, by inference 3β,6α-dihydroxycholanic acid. Furthermore, since Oppenauer oxidation of hyodesoxycholic acid (XV) furnishes a 3-keto-6-hydroxy acid XII,[13, 14] convertible into Kimura's acid (XVI) by hydrogenation in the presence of

[6] Ruzicka, Furter and Thomann, *Helv. Chim. Acta*, **16**, 332 (1933).
[7] Heilbron, W. Shaw and Spring, *Rec. trav. chim.*, **57**, 529 (1938).
[8] Plattner, Petrzilka and W. Lang, *Helv. Chim. Acta*, **27**, 513 (1944).
[9] Tukamoto, *J. Biochem. Japan*, **32**, 451, 467 (1940).
[10] Kimura, *Z. physiol. Chem.*, **248**, 280 (1937).
[11] Prelog and Tagmann, *Helv. Chim. Acta*, **27**, 1880 (1944); see Chapter III.
[12] J. S. Moffatt, *J. Chem. Soc.*, 812 (1947).
[13] Gallagher and Xenos, *J. Biol. Chem.*, **165**, 365 (1946).
[14] *cf.* Hoehn, Linsk and R. B. Moffett, *J. Am. Chem. Soc.*, **68**, 1855 (1946).

hydrobromic acid,[15] XV and XVI must be C_3-epimers. Hyodesoxycholic acid (XV) is accordingly $3\alpha,6\alpha$-dihydroxycholanic acid, and the fourth acid (m.p. 208°) must have the $3\alpha,6\beta$-structure (XIV). The cis fusion of

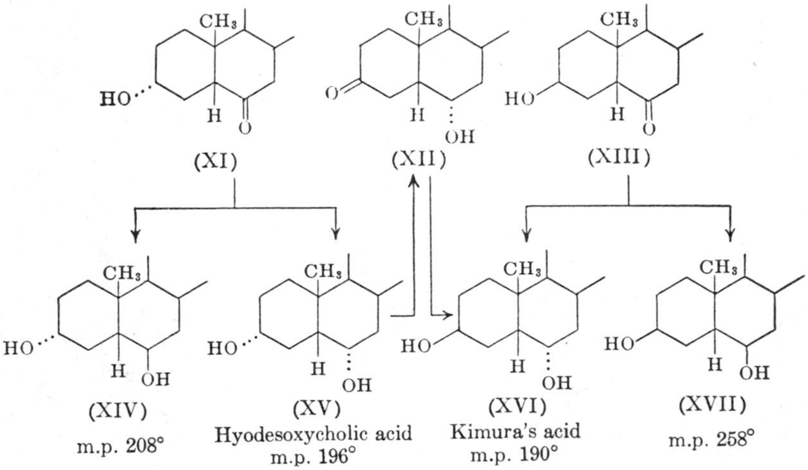

rings A and B in hyodesoxycholic acid is well established,[16] and although Windaus[17] has observed inversion at C_5 accompanying hydrogenation of dehydrohyodesoxycholic acid, the possibility that either XVI or XVII can belong to the allo series is excluded by the proved relationships of these acids to hyodesoxycholic acid and to coprostanediol-$3\beta,6\beta$. Oxidation of XIV as the 3-monoacetate yields methyl 3α-acetoxy-6-keto-cholanate,[15] identical with the acetyl methyl ester of XI; XIV therefore also belongs to the A/B-cis series.

Examination of models shows that, although hindrance of the hydroxyl groups in XIV is well differentiated, the difference in hindrance of these groups in hyodesoxycholic acid (XV) is slight.[18] These observations account for the poor yields of 6-monoacetate obtained by partial saponification of hyodesoxycholic acid diacetate.[13, 14]

In 3-dehydrohyodesoxycholic acid (XII) the 6-hydroxyl group and tertiary hydrogen at C_5 are trans. Elimination is thus facilitated and treatment of the p-toluenesulfonate methyl ester of XII with collidine gives methyl 3-keto-Δ^4-cholenate in good yield.[13] Of special interest is the conversion of cholestanediol-$3\beta,6\beta$ dimesylate into cholesteryl acetate by the

[15] R. B. Moffett and Hoehn, J. Am. Chem. Soc., 69, 1995 (1947).
[16] Windaus and Bohne, Ann., 433, 278 (1923).
[17] Windaus, Ann., 447, 233 (1926).
[18] cf. Plattner and W. Lang, Helv. Chim. Acta, 27, 1872 (1944).

action of silver acetate.[19] This reaction likewise involves trans elimination, which clearly precedes substitution, for otherwise epicholesteryl acetate would be obtained. Methyl 3β,6-dimethanesulfonoxy-12α-acetoxyetioallocholanate similarly yields methyl 3β,12α-diacetoxy-Δ^5-etiocholenate with retention of configuration, but the 3,6-epimer, methyl 3α,6-dimethanesulfonoxy-12α-acetoxyetiocholanate, which furnishes the same product, undergoes inversion at C_3.[20] Shoppee[21] has suggested that in the latter case the order of events is substitution followed by elimination and that the results indicate 6β-structures for both dimesylates; the steric outcome can then be explained by differences in the ease of cis and trans elimination. The apposite reaction of epicholesteryl mesylate with silver acetate has apparently not been investigated.

The steroid sapogenin, chlorogenin, contains hydroxyl groups at C_3 and C_6;[22, 23] on oxidation there is obtained a diketo derivative, chlorogenone, that is recovered unchanged after treatment with acid and that is reconverted into chlorogenin by sodium-alcohol reduction.[23] These facts indicate an A/B-trans ring junction for this sapogenin. Inasmuch as analogous reduction of 3,6-cholestanedione yields cholestanediol-3β,6α,[23, 24] the 3β, 6α-structure assigned to chlorogenin is probably correct.

Position 7. By oxidation with sodium hypobromite chenodesoxycholic acid (I) is converted in part into a lactonic acid (II). Alkaline hydrolysis of II affords the hydroxy tricarboxylic acid (III), which is rapidly relac-

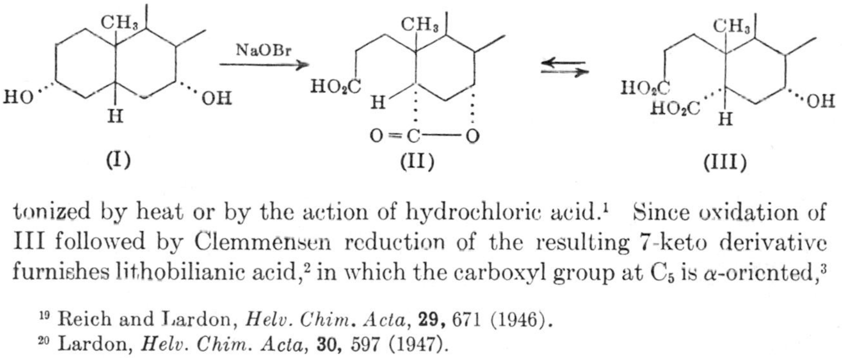

tonized by heat or by the action of hydrochloric acid.[1] Since oxidation of III followed by Clemmensen reduction of the resulting 7-keto derivative furnishes lithobilianic acid,[2] in which the carboxyl group at C_5 is α-oriented,[3]

[19] Reich and Lardon, *Helv. Chim. Acta*, **29**, 671 (1946).
[20] Lardon, *Helv. Chim. Acta*, **30**, 597 (1947).
[21] Shoppee, *J. Chem. Soc.*, 1043 (1948).
[22] Marker and Rohrmann, *J. Am. Chem. Soc.*, **61**, 946 (1939).
[23] Marker, E. M. Jones and D. L. Turner, *J. Am. Chem. Soc.*, **62**, 2537 (1940).
[24] cf. Windaus, *Ber.*, **50**, 136 (1917); Windaus and Lüders, *Z. physiol. Chem.*, **115**, 257 (1921) and references 18 and 19.
[1] Windaus and van Schoor, *Z. physiol. Chem.*, **148**, 225 (1925); *ibid.*, **157**, 181(1926).
[2] Windaus, Bohne and Schwarzkopf, *Z. physiol. Chem.*, **140**, 177 (1924).
[3] Iwasaki, *Z. physiol. Chem.*, **244**, 181 (1936).

the α-orientation of the 7-hydroxyl group is well established.[4] Cholic acid, which has been converted into chenodesoxycholic acid[5] and, by another route, into the lactonic acid II,[6] is also a 7α-hydroxy derivative. A third product, ursodesoxycholic acid, is epimeric with chenodesoxycholic acid at C_7[3] and thus has the β-configuration at this position. Hypobromite oxidation of ursodesoxycholic acid affords a hydroxytricarboxylic acid that is acetylated by treatment with hot acetic anhydride but that does not yield a lactone.

Positions 11 and 12. Steroids possessing substituent groups at C_{11}, at C_{12}, or at both positions are important intermediates for the synthesis of cortical hormones (Chapter V). Stuart models show that, although no exceptional properties are associated with the 11α-position, substituents at the 11β-position are subject to marked steric hindrance. This criterion provides the basis for assignment of configurations to compounds substituted in ring C.

When methyl 3α-acetoxy-Δ¹¹-cholenate (I) is treated with hypobromous acid, a bromohydrin is obtained that yields the oxide II when treated with alkali or when filtered through a column of alumina.[1] An epimeric oxide (IV) results from the reaction of I with perbenzoic acid.[2, 3] Both oxides are

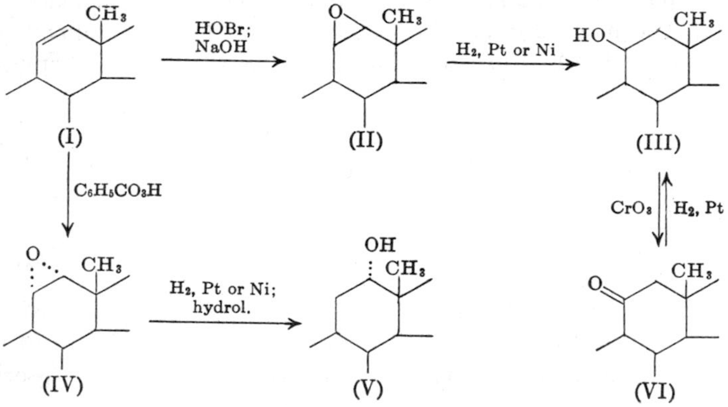

Desoxycholic acid

---

[4] Lettré, *Ber.*, **68**, 766 (1935).

[5] Kawai, *Z. physiol. Chem.*, **214**, 71 (1933); Plattner and Heusser, *Helv. Chim. Acta*, **27**, 748 (1944).

[6] Pringsheim, *Ber.*, **48**, 1324 (1915); Wieland and Fukelman, *Z. physiol. Chem.*, **130**, 144 (1923); Borsche and R. Frank, *Ber.*, **59**, 1748 (1926).

[1] Ott and Reichstein, *Helv. Chim. Acta*, **26**, 1799 (1943); *cf.* Reich and Reichstein, *ibid.*, **26**, 562 (1943).

[2] Press and Reichstein, *Helv. Chim. Acta*, **25**, 878 (1942); B. McKenzie, McGuckin and Kendall, *J. Biol. Chem.*, **162**, 555 (1946).

[3] Gallagher and W. P. Long, *J. Biol. Chem.*, **162**, 495 (1946).

cleaved on hydrogenation; IV, after hydrolysis, yields desoxycholic acid (V),[2] whereas II furnishes an 11-hydroxy derivative (III).[1] The latter product is resistant to acetylation[4] and is therefore assigned an 11β-structure.[5] The oxide II is hence the β-isomer, and oxide IV and desoxycholic acid (V) belong to the α-series.

Chromic acid oxidation of III affords methyl 3α-acetoxy-11-ketocholanate (VI), which, though unreactive toward the usual ketone reagents, can be hydrogenated catalytically (Pt, HOAc). Reduction proceeds slowly and yields III as the sole product.[4] Preferential adsorption of the unhindered α-face of III on the catalyst surface with addition of hydrogen on this side may account for the stereospecificity.[6] The situation with respect to reduction of 12-keto derivatives is somewhat more involved, for the 12-position is hindered both by the angular methyl group at C_{13} and by the 17-methine group. Mixtures of epimers are usually obtained in this case. Koechlin and Reichstein[7] have observed that hydrogenations in acetic acid with a platinum catalyst afford principally 12α-hydroxy compounds (desoxycholic acid series), whereas the chief products of hydrogenation in alkaline solution (Raney nickel) are 12β-hydroxy derivatives.[7, 8] Partial hydrogenation of methyl 3α-hydroxy-12-keto-$\Delta^{9(11)}$-cholenate with platinum oxide in ethanol-acetic acid solution, however, yields a mixture of methyl 3,12-dihydroxy-$\Delta^{9(11)}$-cholenates, in which the ratio of the 12α- to the 12β-isomer is about one to four.[9]

Further correlation of configurations in ring C has been achieved by Gallagher and Long.[10] Bromination of methyl 3α-acetoxy-12-ketocholanate (VII, p. 656) yields epimeric 11-bromo derivatives (VIII and IX), of which VIII is formed in very small amounts.[10, 11] On steric grounds this compound should be the hindered 11β-bromide, the major product (IX) being the unhindered 11α-isomer. Evidence supporting these assumptions is as follows. Both bromo ketones (VIII and IX) are hydrolyzed by aqueous alcoholic alkali and yield, respectively, hydroxy ketones XI and XII, though at markedly different rates.[10] Conversion of VIII into XI is accomplished in less than three hours, whereas transformation of IX into XII under the same conditions is incomplete even after twenty hours. The

[4] Lardon and Reichstein, *Helv. Chim. Acta*, **26,** 586 (1943).

[5] The epimeric 11α-hydroxy compound is easily acetylated (see below).

[6] *cf.* Linstead, Doering, S. B. Davis, P. Levine and Whetstone, *J. Am. Chem. Soc.*, **64,** 1985 (1942).

[7] Koechlin and Reichstein, *Helv. Chim. Acta*, **25,** 918 (1942).

[8] Sorkin and Reichstein, *Helv. Chim. Acta*, **26,** 2097 (1943); Wenner and Reichstein *Helv. Chim. Acta*, **27,** 965 (1944).

[9] B. McKenzie, Mattox and Kendall, *J. Biol. Chem.* (in press).

[10] Gallagher and W. P. Long, *J. Biol. Chem.*, **162,** 521 (1946).

[11] Seebeck and Reichstein, *Helv. Chim. Acta*, **26,** 536 (1943).

results are consistent with current views of S_N2 substitution (see above). Hydrolysis of the 11β-bromo ketone (VIII) involves attack by hydroxyl ion on the unhindered α-side of carbon 11 and is comparatively fast.

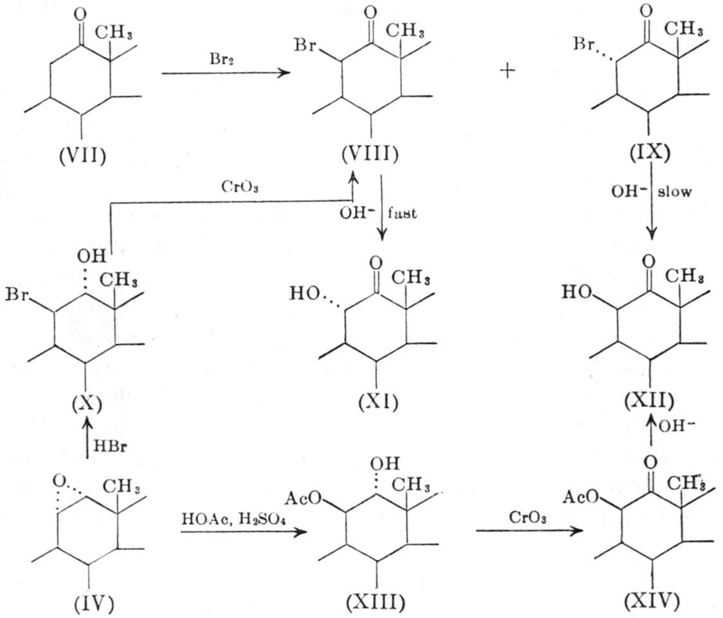

Hydrolysis of IX, on the other hand, requires approach of the reagent to C_{11} on the strongly hindered β-side with resultant diminution in rate. Walden inversion must occur in both processes, and, significantly, only the 11α-hydroxy ketone (XI), derived from the 11β-bromide (VIII), affords an 11-acetyl derivative.[10, 12] Conversion of the α-oxide (IV) into a bromohydrin (X) and thence into the bromo ketone (VIII) has already been noted (see above). By entirely analogous reactions IV is converted by sulfuric acid and acetic acid into an 11-acetoxy-12-hydroxy compound (XIII),[3] which affords the 12-keto derivative (XIV) on chromic acid oxidation.[13] The acetoxyl group of XIII is hydrolyzed only with difficulty and is therefore presumably β-oriented. Hydrolysis of XIV is accomplished somewhat more easily,[13] the product being 3α,11β-dihydroxy-12-ketocholanic acid (XII).

Both XI and XII undergo Wolff-Kishner reduction and yield, in addition to variable amounts of lithocholic and Δ[11]-lithocholenic acids, about thirty

[12] Gallagher and Hollander, *J. Biol. Chem.*, **162**, 533 (1946).
[13] W. P. Long and Gallagher, *J. Biol. Chem.*, **162**, 511 (1946).

percent of $3\alpha,11\alpha$-dihydroxycholanic acid.[10, 12, 13] This substance forms a 3,11-diacetate with ease and is otherwise distinguished from $3\alpha,11\beta$-dihydroxycholanic acid (III) by resistance to dehydration. Both epimers furnish the same 11-keto derivative on oxidation. The inversion at C_{11} that accompanies reduction of XII is explained by tautomerism in the intermediate hydrazone (Chapter V);[10] an alternate mechanism involves epimerization of the hydroxyl group under the influence of sodium ethoxide.[14] In any case the less hindered α-structure is favored.

Since all the natural cortical hormones containing a hydroxyl group at C_{11} exhibit properties resembling those of compounds of the 11β- but not of the 11α-series (resistance to acetylation and ease of dehydration), the cortical steroids are clearly 11β-hydroxy compounds.[15] The point is further clarified by the partial synthesis of corticosterone, in which introduction of the hydroxyl group at C_{11} is effected by hydrogenation of an 11-keto derivative.[16] In all known cases this reduction gives rise to a β-oriented hydroxyl group at C_{11}.

On treatment with hot alkali, XI and XII undergo rearrangement[17, 18] and furnish the Marker-Lawson acid,[19] for which structure XV is now established. The Marker-Lawson acid does not form a hydrazone,[20] but

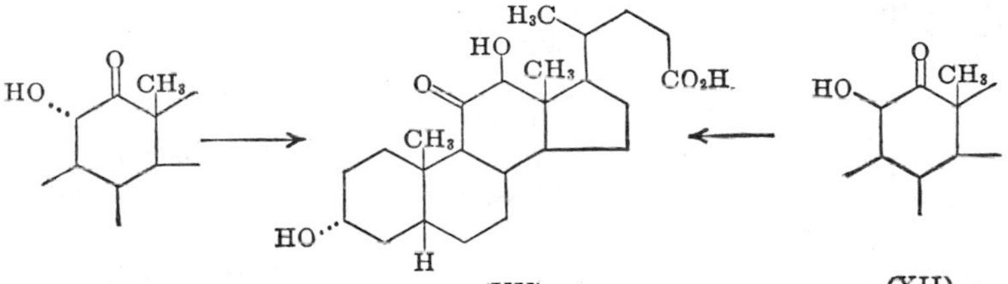

(XI) (XV) (XII)

Marker-Lawson acid

under the conditions of the Wolff-Kishner reaction yields the 3,11,12-trihydroxy acids listed in Table III. Structures assigned to these products are based on the following observations. Treatment of methyl 3α-acetoxy-Δ^{11}-cholenate (I) with osmium tetroxide followed by hydrolysis of the resulting osmic ester furnishes a trihydroxy compound identical with acid 1.

[14] *cf.* Hückel and Naab, *Ber.*, **64**, 2137 (1931); Doering and Aschner, unpublished results.

[15] von Euw and Reichstein, *Helv. Chim. Acta*, **30**, 205 (1947).

[16] von Euw, Lardon and Reichstein, *Helv. Chim. Acta*, **27**, 821, 1287 (1944).

[17] Gallagher, *J. Biol. Chem.*, **162**, 539 (1946).

[18] *cf.* Lobry de Bruyn and van Eckenstein, *Rec. trav. chim.*, **15**, 92 (1896).

[19] Marker and Lawson, *J. Am. Chem. Soc.*, **60**, 1134 (1938).

[20] Longwell and Wintersteiner, *J. Am. Chem. Soc.*, **62**, 200 (1940).

This product must be one of the 11,12-cis isomers, and since it is readily converted into a 3,11,12-triacetate, an $11\alpha,12\alpha$-configuration is probable. Acid 4 is identical with the product obtained from methyl $3\alpha,11\beta$-diacetoxy-12α-hydroxycholanate (XIII) by drastic hydrolysis[17] and is therefore the

TABLE III

NO.	COMPOUND	M.p.	$[\alpha]_D$
1	$3\alpha,11\alpha,12\alpha$-trihydroxycholanic acid[10,17,21]	173–175°	+31° Al
2	$3\alpha,11\alpha,12\beta$-trihydroxycholanic acid[17,21]	164–166°	+45° Al
3	$3\alpha,11\beta,12\beta$-trihydroxycholanic acid[21]	177°	+43° Al
4	$3\alpha,11\beta,12\alpha$-trihydroxycholanic acid[3,17]	147–149°	+54° Al

$11\beta,12\alpha$-isomer. Of the two remaining substances, acid 2 yields a triacetate when heated with acetic anhydride and pyridine.[17] At room temperature a 3,11-diacetate is obtained[21] that on esterification and oxidation affords methyl $3\alpha,11\alpha$-diacetoxy-12-ketocholanate, derived also from XI. Acid 2 is thus $3\alpha,11\alpha,12\beta$-trihydroxycholanic acid and the corresponding $3\alpha,11\beta,12\beta$-structure is, by exclusion, assigned to acid 3. The latter compound yields a 3,12-diacetyl methyl ester, but under no circumstances can acetylation be effected at C_{11}. Oxidation of the diacetate furnishes the diacetyl methyl ester of the Marker-Lawson acid (XV),[21] which is hence $3\alpha,12\beta$-dihydroxy-11-ketocholanic acid.

Preferential formation of a 12β-hydroxy derivative (XV) in the rearrangements of XI and of XII implies less hindrance of a 12β- than of a 12α-substituent. From a study of the relative rates of saponification of epimeric 12-acetates, Koechlin and Reichstein[7] also reached this conclusion. The comparative difficulty with which the 12α-acetates undergo hydrolysis is paralleled by the similar behavior of 17α-acetates, which are less reactive than the 17β-epimers (Chapter IV). These observations suggest that hindrance of the 12α-position by the 17-methine group, and of the 17α-position by the 12-methylene group, is of greater significance than shielding effects of the angular methyl at C_{13} on the corresponding 12β- and 17β-positions.[22]

[21] Wintersteiner, M. Moore and K. Reinhardt, J. Biol. Chem., 162, 707 (1946).

[22] The length of the side chain at C_{17} is a further complicating factor, for the rates of hydrolysis of 12α-acetates increase in the pregnanone-20 and etio acid series (reference 7).

The order of hindrance of substituents at positions 11 and 12, indicated by differential rates of hydrolysis and of acetylation, is $11\alpha < 12\beta < 12\alpha < 11\beta$. This sequence is determined by reactions that occur at oxygen rather than at carbon and is not necessarily valid for the region immediately surrounding C_{11} and C_{12}, *i.e.* at the limits of van der Waals' radius. Additions and substitutions at these positions sometimes lead to the formation of apparently anomalous products. Thus treatment of methyl 3α-acetoxy-Δ^{11}-cholenate (I) with hypobromous acid yields an 11β-hydroxy-12α-bromo derivative (XVI)[1]; bromination[23] of I furnishes a trans[24] dibromide that

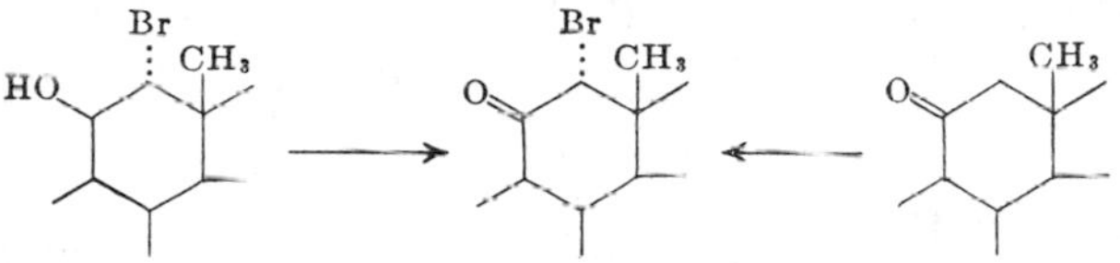

(XVI)   (XVII)   (VI)

is likewise assigned an 11β,12α-configuration.[25] On the basis of the scheme presented above this configuration is the more hindered of the two trans structures (11β,12α and 11α,12β). Whether bromohydrin formation proceeds through a bromonium ion intermediate[24] or by a termolecular mechanism,[26] it is clear from the formation of an 11β-hydroxy derivative (XVI) that attack by water must occur on the β-side. Since polarization effects are negligible, approach to the 11β-position is apparently less hindered than that to the 12β-position. A second inconsistency appears in the bromination of methyl 3α-acetoxy-11-ketocholanate (VI), which yields a 12α-bromo derivative (XVII), identical with that obtained by oxidation of the bromohydrin (XVI). In view of the 12β-structure established for the Marker-Lawson acid (XV) a β-orientation for bromine would have been predicted.

In the course of work directed toward the synthesis of dehydrocorticosterone (Chapter V), Kendall and his associates[27] investigated several 12-substituted-9,11-unsaturated steroids. Probable configurations have recently been assigned to a number of these substances.[25] When 11β,12α-dibromolithocholic acid is treated with aqueous alkali,[28] both bromine

[23] L. L. Engel, Mattox, B. McKenzie, McGuckin and Kendall, *J. Biol. Chem.*, **162**, 565 (1946).

[24] Hammett, *Physical Organic Chemistry*, 147, McGraw-Hill, New York (1940).

[25] Mattox, R. B. Turner, B. McKenzie, L. L. Engel and Kendall, *J. Biol. Chem.*, **173**, 283 (1948).

[26] Nozaki and Ogg, *J. Am. Chem. Soc.*, **64**, 697, 704, 709 (1942).

[27] Kendall and co-workers, *J. Biol. Chem.*, **162**, 571 (1946); *ibid.*, **164**, 569 (1946).

[28] *cf.* Sarett, *J. Biol. Chem.*, **162**, 591 (1946).

atoms are lost, and a 12-hydroxy-$\Delta^{9(11)}$-compound (XIX) is formed. The same product (3-acetate methyl ester) is obtained in small amounts by the reaction of methyl 3α-acetoxy-11β-bromo-12α-hydroxycholanate (X) with silver acetate.[13] Inversion at C_{12} in the latter transformation is unlikely,

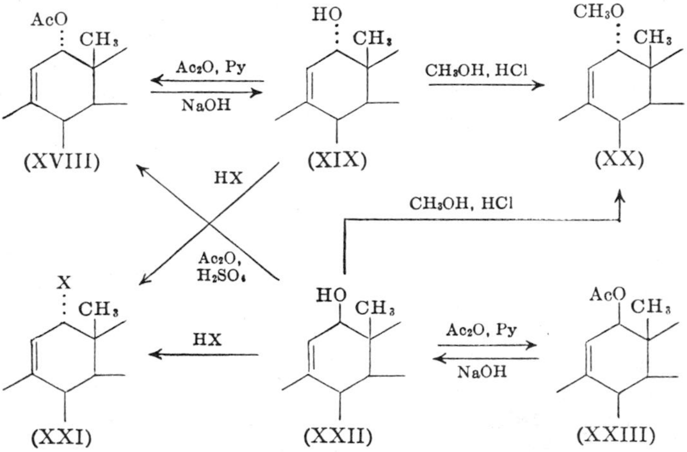

and an α-orientation is therefore assigned to the 12-hydroxyl group of (XIX). Acetylation with acetic anhydride and pyridine, or with acetic anhydride and sulfuric acid, affords an acetate XVIII, from which the starting material is regenerated by saponification. The acetoxyl group of XVIII is thus also α-oriented. Similar transformations have been carried out with the epimeric 12β-hydroxy derivative (XXII), obtained by catalytic hydrogenation of 3α-hydroxy-12-keto-$\Delta^{9(11)}$-cholenic acid. In this case, however, inversion attends acetylation with acetic anhydride and sulfuric acid, and the 12α-acetate (XVIII) is isolated as the sole product. The base-catalyzed reaction proceeds normally and gives the expected 12β-acetyl derivative (XXIII). Both XIX and XXII furnish the same methyl ether (XX) when treated with methanolic hydrogen chloride and the same 12-halo derivatives (XXI) in the presence of halogen acids. The acid-catalyzed reactions clearly involve substitution rather than esterification, the 12α-position being favored.[29] The steric results are consistent with the formation of methyl 3α-acetoxy-11-keto-12α-bromocholanate (XVII)

[29] Support for the 12α-structure proposed for the methoxy derivative (XX) is provided by the formation of this substance from 3α-hydroxy-$11\beta,12\alpha$-dibromocholanic acid and sodium methoxide. The parallel reaction with sodium hydroxide, as noted above, furnishes $3\alpha,12\alpha$-dihydroxy-$\Delta^{9(11)}$-cholenic acid. Specific rotations of epimeric pairs in this series are consistent with the proposed structures (*cf.* Chapter III).

from methyl 3α-acetoxy-11-ketocholanate (VI), but do not agree with predictions based on rates of acetylation and of hydrolysis in the saturated series. The effect produced on the stereochemistry of ring C by introduction of a double bond at the 9,11-position may be a contributing factor.

Although methyl 3α-acetoxy-Δ¹¹-cholenate (I) yields only one dibromide, two crystalline dibromides (XXIV and XXVI) are obtained in the bromination of methyl 3,9-epoxy-Δ¹¹-cholenate (XXV). These products are

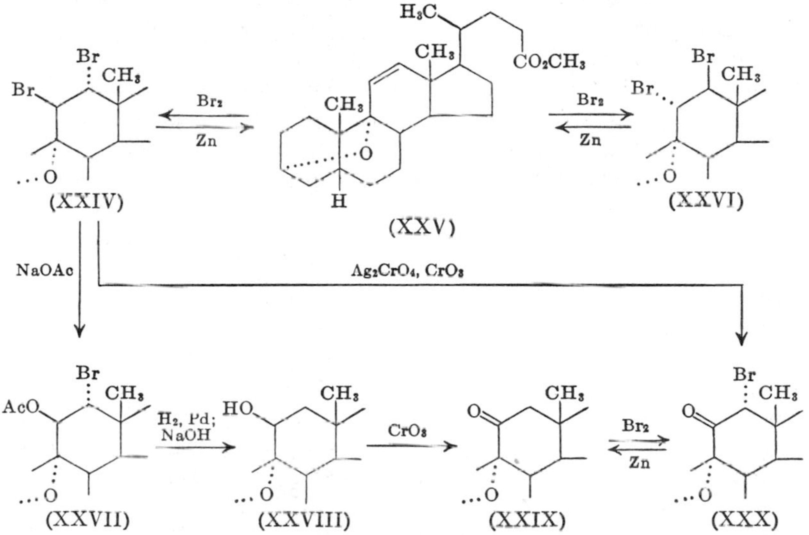

presumably trans, and both are converted into the starting material by treatment with zinc dust. Selective replacement of one bromine in XXVI is not possible, but can be effected in good yield and with a variety of reagents in the case of XXIV. Substitution of acetoxyl for bromine, for example, is accomplished in eighty-five percent yield by the use of sodium acetate in acetic acid. The product (XXVII) affords an oxide with alkali and is therefore trans in accordance with predictions based on the neighboring group theory (see above). An epimeric oxide is obtained by the action of perbenzoic acid on XXV.

The structure assigned to XXVII is supported by the following evidence. Reductive debromination yields an 11-acetoxy compound that is hydrolyzed only with difficulty. The resulting alcohol (XXVIII) cannot be acetylated and does not react with phosphorus pentachloride. Although the epimeric 11-hydroxy compound is not available for comparison, the properties of XXVIII suggest that it is the 11β-derivative. Models do not show appreciable hindrance of the 11α-position by the oxide bridge. Oxidation of XXVIII furnishes the corresponding ketone (XXIX), which is readily converted into a monobromo derivative (XXX). The latter substance is obtained also from XXIV (95% yield) by treatment with a mixture of silver chromate and chromic acid. Further transformations of these products are described in Chapter V.

The cardiac aglycone, digoxigenin, possesses a 12-hydroxyl group, for which a β-orientation is indicated by the conversion of digoxigenin into 12-epietiodesoxycholic acid.[30] Sarmentogenin is an 11α-hydroxy derivative as shown by the recent degradation of this substance to methyl 3β,11α-dihydroxyetiocholanate.[31]

Position 14. The cardiac aglycones are unique in the possession of a hydroxyl group at the tertiary position C_{14}. The configuration at this center is deduced from the following observations. In the presence of cold methanolic potassium hydroxide, digitoxigenin undergoes irreversible isomerization to isodigitoxigenin (Chapter VII). This reaction is characteristic of the other aglycones as well as of the parent glycosides. The bridged bicyclic system of the isogenin can be formed only if the 14-hydroxyl group and lactone side chain of digitoxigenin are cis or if inversion at C_{14} or at C_{17} occurs during isomerization. Although such a change at C_{14} is unlikely, shift of the lactone double bond to the β,γ-position (C_{17}:C_{20}) under the influence of alkali might lead to inversion at C_{17}. By reactions not involving this center of asymmetry, digitoxigenin and isodigitoxigenin have been degraded, respectively, to 3β-hydroxyetiocholanic acid[1] and to etiocholanic acid,[2] in which β-configurations at C_{17} are certain (see below). The identity of digitoxigenin and isodigitoxigenin with respect to the configuration (β) of the side chain excludes the possibility of inversion in the formation of the latter product and establishes a β-orientation for the 14-hydroxyl group.

Additional evidence has been presented by Buzas and Reichstein.[3] Strophanthidinic acid (I) on hydrolysis followed by permanganate oxidation yields a keto lactone (II),[4] also formed from I by ozonization, hydrolysis and periodate oxidation[3] (Chapter VII). A product of analogous struc-

[30] Steiger and Reichstein, *Helv. Chim. Acta*, **21**, 828 (1938); Mason and Hoehn, *J. Am. Chem. Soc.*, **60**, 2824 (1938); *ibid.*, **61**, 1614 (1939).

[31] A. Katz, *Helv. Chim. Acta*, **31**, 993 (1948); *cf.* W. Klyne, *Biochem. J.*, **43**, xi (1948).

[1] Hunziker and Reichstein, *Experientia*, **1**, 90 (1945); *Helv. Chim. Acta*, **28**, 1472 (1945).

[2] Jacobs and Gustus, *J. Biol. Chem.*, **86**, 199 (1930); Jacobs and Elderfield, *ibid.*, **108**, 497 (1935).

[3] Buzas and Reichstein, *Helv. Chim. Acta*, **31**, 84 (1948).

[4] Jacobs, *J. Biol. Chem.*, **57**, 553 (1923); Elderfield, *ibid.*, **113**, 631 (1936); Butenandt and Gallagher, *Ber.*, **72**, 1866 (1939); Ehrenstein, *J. Org. Chem.*, **9**, 435 (1944).

ture is obtained from digitoxigenin by the latter procedure.[1] Hydrolysis of the keto lactone (II) is accompanied by inversion at C_{17}, for the resulting keto acid (III) cannot be relactonized. Oxidation of III with hydrogen

Chart 3. RELATIVE CONFIGURATIONS AT C_{14} AND C_{17}

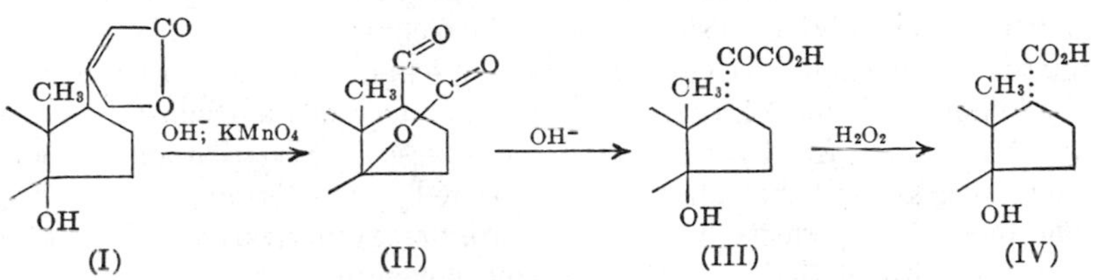

pcroxide furnishes an etio acid (IV) that differs from an epimeric acid obtained from I under conditions that make rearrangement improbable, and IV is accordingly assigned a 17α-configuration. The keto lactone (II) and strophanthidinic acid (I) are thus $14\beta,17\beta$-compounds.

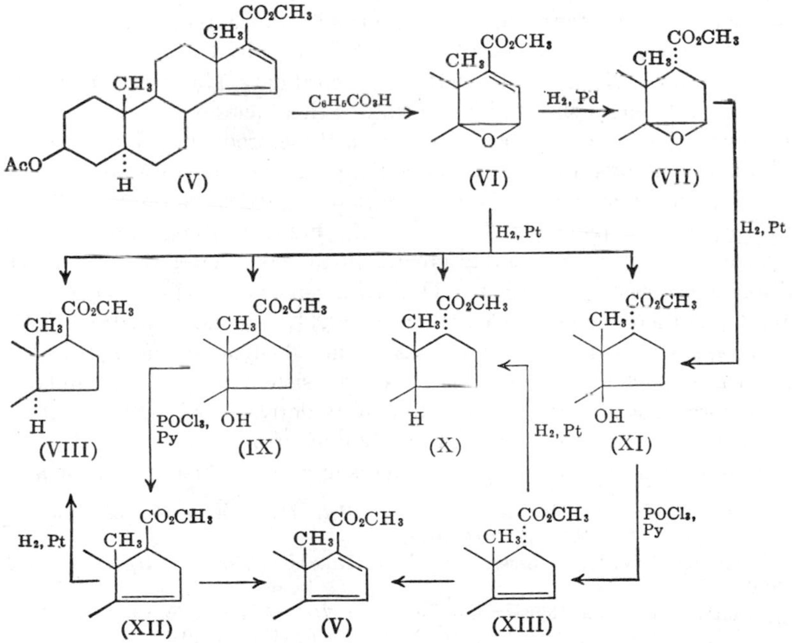

Final proof for this arrangement is supplied by the synthetic work of Ruzicka and his collaborators. When methyl 3β-acetoxy-$\Delta^{14,16}$-etioallocholadienate (V) (λ_{max} 292 mμ, log ϵ 4.2) reacts with perbenzoic acid, one mole of peracid is consumed, and an oxide (VI) is produced,[5] the structure of which is indicated by an ultraviolet absorption maximum at 233 mμ (log ϵ 3.86) characteristic of an α,β-unsaturated ester. Hydrogenation of VI in alcohol with a palladium catalyst affords a saturated epoxy ester (VII). When platinum is substituted for palladium, cleavage of the oxide ring occurs in addition to saturation of the olefinic linkage.[6] The resulting mixture is amenable to chromatographic separation and furnishes four crystalline products, VIII, IX, X, and XI. Two of these substances, IX and XI, contain free hydroxyl groups that resist acetylation and chromic acid oxidation and that are therefore located at the tertiary position C_{14}. The remaining products, VIII and X, are desoxy derivatives, VIII being identical with methyl 3β-acetoxyetioallocholanate.

Since IX and XI are derived from the same oxide (VI), they undoubtedly possess the same configuration at C_{14}. The nonidentity of these substances must therefore be ascribed to a difference in configuration at C_{17}. Both products are dehydrated by phosphorus oxychloride in pyridine and yield, respectively, the epimeric unsaturated esters XII and XIII. The latter substances are converted by treatment with N-bromosuccinimide into the same dienic ester V, in which asymmetry at C_{17} is absent. Assignment of the double bonds in XII and XIII to the 14,15-position is based on the fact that both substances are easily reduced. Since hydrogenation of XII furnishes the known 17β-ester VIII, both XII and IX must also belong to the 17β-series; X, XI, and XIII are accordingly 17α-compounds. The marked differences observed in the ease with which dehydration occurs in IX and in XI serve further to distinguish these products. Whereas in XI elimination is quantitative at room temperature, dehydration of IX requires higher temperature.[7] Examination of models of the four possible hydroxy esters, epimeric at C_{14} and at C_{17}, indicates that hindrance of the hydroxyl group is considerably greater in the cis isomers than in the corresponding trans derivatives. The arrangement of substituents at C_{14} and C_{17} is therefore cis in IX and trans in XI, and the 14-hydroxyl group hence is β-oriented in both products. The Δ^{14}-structures assigned to the unsaturated esters (XII and XIII) are consistent with this formulation, since formation of the corresponding $\Delta^{8(14)}$-derivatives would require cis elimination. No lactone has been obtained from the free acid of IX. The formation of a five-membered ring is apparently blocked[8] by the angu-

[5] Ruzicka, Plattner, Heusser and Pataki, Helv. Chim. Acta, 29, 936 (1946). cf. Swern, J. Am. Chem. Soc., 69, 1692 (1947).

[6] Plattner, Ruzicka, Heusser, Pataki and Kd. Meier, Helv. Chim. Acta, 29, 942 (1946).

[7] Plattner, Ruzicka, Heusser and Kd. Meier, Helv. Chim. Acta, 29, 2023 (1946).

[8] cf. Ehrenstein and A. R. Johnson, J. Org. Chem., 11, 823 (1946).

lar methyl group at C_{13} as in the analogous case of 12-epietiodesoxycholic acid (see below).

The synthetic methods described above have been extended to the preparation of various other 14β-hydroxy derivatives[9] and correlation with the natural genins has been achieved by conversion of methyl 3β-acetoxy-14β,15β-epoxy-Δ16-etiocholenate into methyl 3β-acetoxy-14β-hydroxyetiocholanate[10] (see Chart 7, Chapter VII), identical with an oxidation product of digitoxigenin acetate.[1]

In all cases that have been investigated, the reaction of Δ14, 16-dienes with perbenzoic acid yields 14,15-oxides of the β-series. α-Oxides are, however, the sole products of reactions of peracids with Δ14-monounsaturated compounds.[7] For example, XIII with monoperphthalic acid furnishes an oxide (XIV) that differs from VII and that is not subject to cleavage by

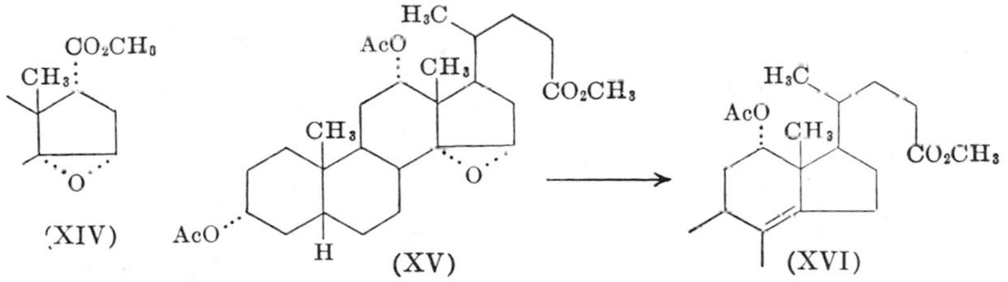

hydrogenation. The oxide obtained from XII is likewise resistant to hydrogenation. Reduction can be effected with the oxide XV, derived from methyl Δ14-desoxycholate diacetate,[11] but the only crystalline product is diacetylapocholic acid methyl ester (XVI).[12]

Position 17. Various interconversions described in previous chapters establish that carbon side chains at C_{17} occupy the same spatial position in all naturally occurring steroids. The natural configuration at this center is important for biological activity, for products with the inverted 17-iso arrangement, 17-isoprogesterone,[1] 17-isodesoxycorticosterone[2] and the "alloglycosides" of the heart poison group[3] are physiologically inactive.

[9] Plattner, Ruzicka, Heusser and Anglıker, *Helv. Chim. Acta*, **30**, 385, 395 (1947).

[10] Ruzicka, Plattner, Heusser and Kd. Meier, *Helv. Chim. Acta*, **30**, 1342 (1947).

[11] Boedecker and Volk, *Ber.*, **54**, 2489 (1921); Yamasaki, *Z. physiol. Chem.*, **233**, 10 (1935).

[12] Plattner, Ruzicka and Holtermann, *Helv. Chim. Acta*, **28**, 1660 (1945).

[1] Butenandt, Schmidt-Thomé and H. Paul, *Ber.*, **72**, 1112 (1939).

[2] Shoppee, *Helv. Chim. Acta*, **23**, 925 (1940).

[3] Jacobs, *J. Biol. Chem.*, **88**, 519 (1930); Jacobs and Bigelow, *ibid.*, **99**, 521 (1933); I. D. Lamb and S. Smith, *J. Chem. Soc.*, 442 (1936); Katz and Reichstein, *Pharm. Acta Helv.*, **19**, 231 (1944).

Detailed X-ray diffraction data, notably those for cholesteryl iodide,[3a] indicate a 17β-configuration in steroids of natural origin. Conclusive evidence is provided by the work of Sorkin and Reichstein.[4] Treatment of methyl etiodesoxycholate (I) with sodium methoxide affords an equilibrium mixture from which about fifteen percent of methyl 17-isoetiodesoxycholate (II) can be isolated. Equilibration of methyl 12-epietiodesoxycholate

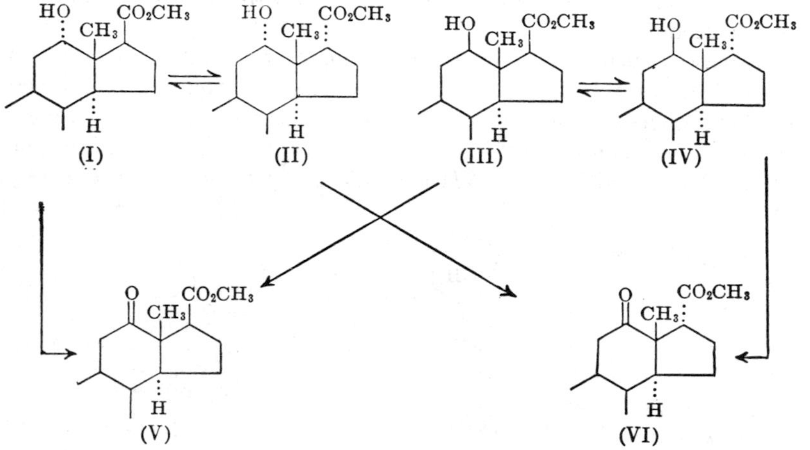

(III) similarly yields small amounts of methyl 12-epi-17-isoetiodesoxycholate (IV).[5] Structural relationships among the four products are indicated by the conversion of I and III into methyl 3,12-diketoetiocholanate (V) and of II and IV into methyl 3,12-diketo-17-isoetiocholanate (VI).

Hydrolysis of esters I, II, III, and IV yields the corresponding free acids, of which only the acid derived from II furnishes a lactone. The lactone can be reconverted into ester II, which is accordingly the less hindered (12α,17α) of the two cis isomers. Etiodesoxycholic acid and 12-epietiodesoxycholic acid (*cf.* III) are therefore 17β-derivatives. The failure of lactone formation in 12-epietiodesoxycholic acid is clearly the result of hindrance by the angular methyl group. A lactone (VIII) can be obtained, although with considerable difficulty from 12-epibisnordesoxycholic

---

[3a] Carlisle and Crowfoot, *Proc. Roy. Soc.*, **A184**, 64 (1945).

[4] Sorkin and Reichstein, *Helv. Chim. Acta*, **29**, 1218 (1946).

[5] The preponderance of 17-normal products at equilibrium contrasts with the behavior of keto lactone II of Chart 3, which is converted by base into a keto acid of the 17-iso series. The difference is perhaps a reflection of hindrance between cis substituents at C_{14} and C_{17}.

acid (VII),[6] and an oxide of structure X has been isolated among the dehydration products of the diphenylcarbinol IX.[7] The corresponding 12-epimers do not participate in these reactions.

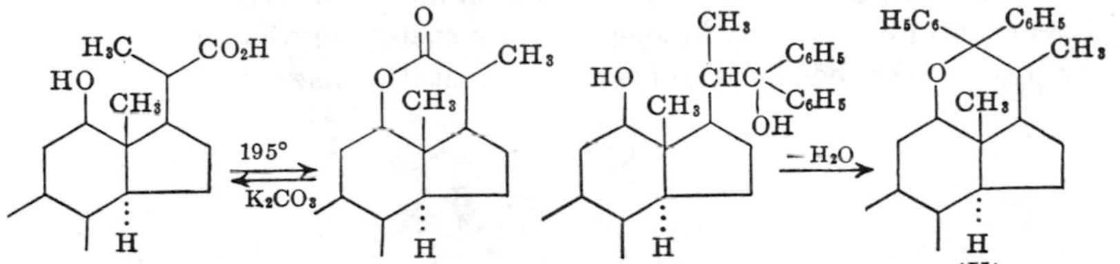

Of special interest are the inactive glycosides allocymarin, alloemicymarin and alloperiplocymarin, isolated from plant material after prolonged storage.[3] These substances furnish aglycones, allostrophanthidin and alloperiplogenin, that are isomeric with strophanthidin and with periplogenin, respectively. Isomerization in the plant is apparently effected by enzymes, for Lamb and Smith[3] obtained alloemicymarin from pure emicymarin by treatment of the latter with a crude extract of the seeds of *Strophanthus Eminii*. Allostrophanthidin, in contrast with strophanthidin, does not furnish an isogenin with alkali, and Tschesche and Bohle[8] have observed the failure of alloemicymarin to form an iso compound under similar conditions. The allogenins thus apparently differ from their normal counterparts in a trans arrangement of the 14-hydroxyl group and lactone side chain. This conclusion was verified by Speiser and Reichstein,[9] who degraded alloperiplogenin to an etio acid of the 17-iso series.

The orientation of 17-hydroxyl substituents and configuration at various side chain centers are discussed in previous chapters (III, IV and V).

STEREOCHEMISTRY AND SYNTHESIS

Recent progress in the final and most difficult phase of steroid chemistry, that of total synthesis, offers hope that successful completion of this problem may soon be realized. Syntheses of equilenin (two asymmetric centers) and of estrone (four asymmetric centers) have already been accomplished through the brilliant work of Bachmann, Cole, and Wilds and of Anner and Miescher. Although the difficulties besetting total synthesis of a saturated steroid, which, with a minimum of six asymmetric centers, is

---

[6] Sorkin and Reichstein, *Helv. Chim. Acta*, **27**, 1631 (1944).

[7] Sorkin and Reichstein, *Helv. Chim. Acta*, **28**, 875 (1945).

[8] Tschesche and Bohle, *Ber.*, **71**, 654 (1938).

[9] Speiser and Reichstein, *Helv. Chim. Acta*, **30**, 2143 (1947).

capable of at least sixty-four stereochemical modifications, are formidable, a path toward this goal is now provided by the notable researches of Cornforth and Robinson.[1]

Among the neutral oxidation products of methyl desoxycholate diacetate is an unsaturated acetoxy ketone (I), the structure of which was established by Reich.[2]   A product (III) of similar constitution has been obtained by the

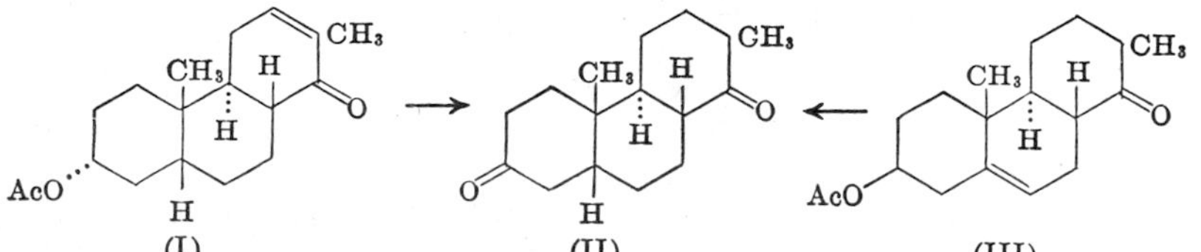

CH₃   CH₃   H   H   O   AcO   H   (I)   →   CH₃   CH₃   H   H   O   O   H   (II)   ←   CH₃   CH₃   H   H   O   AcO   (III)

oxidation of cholesteryl acetate dibromide.[3]   By suitable transformations both substances yield the saturated diketo derivative II, which Robinson has now synthesized from 1,6-dimethoxynaphthalene (Chart 4).

Reduction of 1,6-dimethoxynaphthalene (IV) with sodium and alcohol furnishes 5-methoxy-2-tetralone (V), which on methylation affords 1-methyl-5-methoxy-2-tetralone (VI).   This product is converted into the α,β-unsaturated ketone VII by treatment with diethylaminobutanone methiodide.[4]   Hydrogenation of VII in neutral alcoholic solution yields a dihydro derivative (VIII), to which the A/B cis structure is assigned by analogy to the reductions of cholestenone[5] and of 2-keto-10-methyl-$\Delta^{1(9)}$-octalin.[4, 6]   By further hydrogenation with platinum in acetic acid a diol (IX) is obtained in which a cis relation of methyl and secondary alcoholic groups is probable.[7]   Partial acetylation of IX can be effected without esterification of the hindered phenolic hydroxyl group, and successive hydrogenation, oxidation, and saponification afford a mixture of racemic hydroxy ketones (XIa and XIb) that are separable by crystallization of the hydrogen succinates.   Resolution of the resulting racemates provides four optically pure compounds; m.p. 120.5–121.5°, $[\alpha]_D \pm 38.5°$ ($\pm 2°$) and m.p. 113–114° (hemihydrates), $[\alpha]_D \pm 10°$ ($\pm 0.5°$).   Although hydrogenation

[1] J. W. Cornforth and R. Robinson, *J. Chem. Soc.*, 676 (1946); *Nature*, **160,** 737 (1947).

[2] Reich, *Helv. Chim. Acta*, **28,** 892 (1945); cf. Reich and Reichstein, *ibid.*, **26,** 2102 (1943).

[3] Köster and W. Logemann, *Ber.*, **73,** 299 (1940).

[4] du Feu, McQuillin and R. Robinson, *J. Chem. Soc.*, 53 (1937).

[5] Grasshof, *Z. physiol. Chem.*, **223,** 249 (1934).

[6] Linstead, Millidge and Walpole, *J. Chem. Soc.*, 1140 (1937); Burnop and Linstead, *ibid.*, 720 (1940).

[7] cf. Grasshof, *Z. physiol. Chem.*, **225,** 197 (1934).

of the benzenoid ring probably results in B/C cis products, conversion into trans forms should accompany alkaline hydrolysis;[8] XIa and XIb thus represent the two possible trans fusions of rings B and C.   Formylation,

Chart 4.   SYNTHESIS OF TRICYCLIC KETONE DERIVED FROM NATURAL STEROIDS

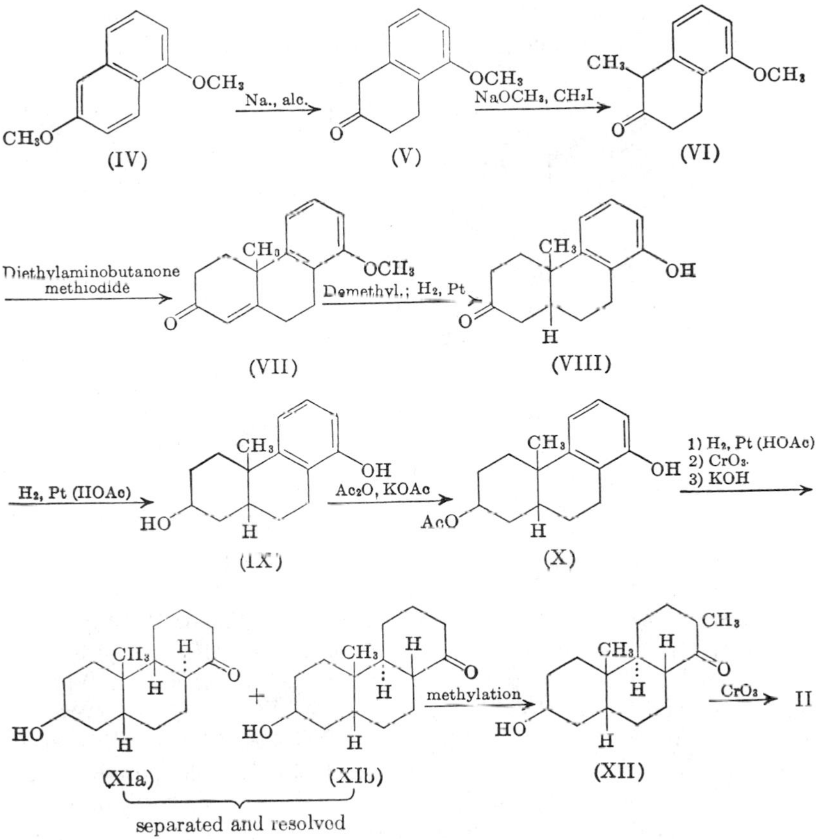

methylation, and hydrolysis[9] furnish the corresponding methyl hydroxy ketones (cf. XII), which are converted by oxidation into the 3,14-diketones (steroid numbering).   One of the latter synthetic substances is identical with II from natural sources.   Addition of ring D by standard procedures should present no insurmountable difficulties and, if successful, will lead the way to total synthesis of various saturated steroid derivatives.

[8] Hückel, *Ann.*, **441**, 1 (1925).
[9] Sen and Mondal, *J. Ind. Chem. Soc.*, **5**, 609 (1928).

Limitation of isomers in Robinson's synthesis is accomplished by the expedients of (a), directed hydrogenation and (b), cis-trans isomerization of a substituted α-decalone.   The stereospecificity of the Diels-Alder reaction[10] likewise lends itself to this end and diene additions have been employed in projected syntheses by a number of investigators.   A further attr active approach that has apparently not been explored is based upon isomerization and hydrogenation of nuclear unsaturated derivatives.   Windaus and

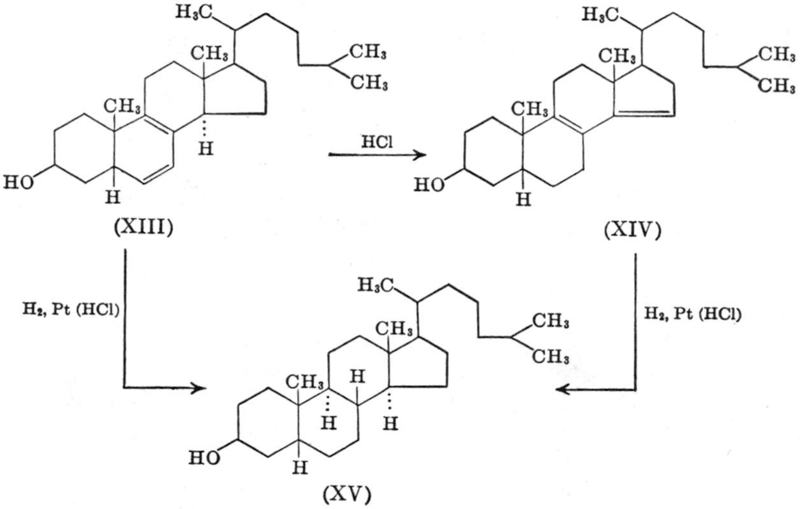

(XIII)   (XIV)

(XV)

Zühlsdorff[11] have demonstrated that forced hydrogenation of $\Delta^{6,8}$-coprostadienol-3 (XIII) or of the isomerization product XIV[12] affords coprostanol (XV).   Similar transformations have been observed with methyl $\Delta^{8,11}$-lithocholadienate and with methyl $\Delta^{8,14}$-lithocholadienate, both of which are reduced to methyl lithocholate; hydrogenation of Δ^{7}-, Δ^{8}-, $\Delta^{8(14)}$-, or $\Delta^{9(11)}$- compounds in the presence of hydrochloric acid also furnishes products of natural configuration.[13]   Synthesis of intermediates of type XIV, in which the presence of a diene system reduces the number of asymmetries by three would therefore be of considerable interest.

[10] Alder and G. Stein, *Angew. Chem.*, **50**, 510 (1937).

[11] Windaus and G. Zühlsdorff, *Ann.*, **536**, 204 (1938); *cf.* Windaus, Linsert and Eckhardt, *ibid.*, **534**, 22 (1938).

[12] *cf.* Barton, *J. Chem. Soc.*, **512**, 1116 (1946).

[13] R. B. Turner and Kendall, unpublished results.

Author Index

SUBJECT INDEX

The principal references to physical constants are identified by an asterisk. Ester and acyl derivatives are listed only by the name of the parent acid or alcohol.